Sally Nelson
~~E16~~ Halifax Hall
OB11

Sally Nelson
~~E16~~ Halifax Hall

Textbook of Physiology

BDS

GEORGE H. BELL

B.Sc., M.D. (Glasg.), F.R.C.P. (Glasg.), F.R.S.E.

Emeritus Professor of Physiology in the University of Dundee;
Honorary Fellow of the Accadèmia Anatomico-Chirurgica of Perugia

DONALD EMSLIE-SMITH

M.D. (Aberd.), F.R.C.P., F.R.C.P. (Edin.)

Reader in Medicine in the University of Dundee; Honorary Consultant
Physician, the Royal Infirmary and Ninewells Hospital, Dundee

COLIN R. PATERSON

M.A., D.M., B.Sc. (Oxon.), M.R.C.Path.

Senior Lecturer in Biochemical Medicine in the University of Dundee;
Honorary Consultant to the Tayside Area Health Board

Textbook of Physiology

BDS

GEORGE H. BELL
DONALD EMSLIE-SMITH
COLIN R. PATERSON

Tenth Edition

CHURCHILL LIVINGSTONE
EDINBURGH LONDON AND NEW YORK   1980

CHURCHILL LIVINGSTONE
Medical Division of the Longman Group Limited

Distributed in the United States of America by Churchill Livingstone Inc.,
19 West 44th Street, New York, N.Y. 10036, and by associated companies,
branches and representatives throughout the world.

First Edition (Textbook of Physiology and Biochemistry)   1950
Second Edition   1953
Third Edition   1956
Fourth Edition   1959
Spanish Edition   1959
Italian Edition   1959
Fifth Edition   1961
Sixth Edition   1965
   ELBS Edition first published   1965
Seventh Edition   1968
   ELBS Edition of Seventh Edition   1970
Eighth Edition   1972
   ELBS Edition of Eighth Edition   1972
Ninth Edition   1976
   ELBS Edition of Ninth Edition   1976
Italian Edition   1979
Tenth Edition (Textbook of Physiology)   1980
   ELBS Edition of Tenth Edition   1980

ISBN 0 443 02152 X

Bell, George Howard
   Textbook of physiology. – 10th ed.
   1. Human physiology
   I. Title   II. Emslie-Smith, Donald
   III. Paterson, Colin Ralston   IV. Textbook of
   physiology
   612   QP34.5   80-40036

Printed and bound in Great Britain by
William Clowes (Beccles) Limited, Beccles and London

Contributors

Dr Marjorie Allison, Department of Medicine, University of Glasgow (Chapter 15).

Dr B. L. Andrew, Department of Physiology, University of Dundee (Chapter 21).

Mr K. Baxby, Department of Surgery, University of Dundee (Chapter 29).

Professor E. L. Blair, Department of Physiology, University of Newcastle upon Tyne (Chapter 4).

Miss Margaret Browning, Department of Biochemical Medicine, University of Dundee (Chapters 28, 29).

Professor F. I. Caird, Department of Geriatric Medicine, University of Glasgow (Chapter 31).

Dr Sheila Callender, Nuffield Department of Clinical Medicine, University of Oxford (Chapter 8).

Dr C. Cameron, Scottish National Blood Transfusion Service (Chapter 9).

Professor M. de Burgh Daly, Department of Physiology, St Bartholomew's Hospital Medical School (Chapter 13).

Dr J. S. Davison, Department of Physiology, University of Dundee (Chapters 3,5).

Professor G. S. Dawes, Nuffield Institute for Medical Research, Oxford (Chapter 29).

Professor J. V. G. A. Durnin, Department of Physiology, University of Glasgow (Chapter 2).

Dr M. J. W. Faed, Department of Pathology, University of Dundee (Chapter 32).

Dr Constance Forsyth, Department of Child Health, University of Dundee (Chapter 30).

Dr H. B. Goodall, Department of Pathology, University of Dundee (Chapter 8).

Dr D. M. Green, Department of Bacteriology, University of Dundee (Chapter 9).

Professor F. F. Hellier, Department of Dermatology, University of Leeds (Chapter 17).

Mr C. G. Henderson, Department of Pharmacology and Therapeutics, University of Dundee (Chapter 25).

Professor A. Iggo, Department of Veterinary Physiology, Royal (Dick) School of Veterinary Studies, University of Edinburgh (Chapter 22).

Dr T. E. Isles, Department of Biochemical Medicine, University of Dundee (Chapter 6).

Professor W. R. Keatinge, Department of Physiology, London Hospital Medical College (Chapter 26).

Professor R. D. Keynes, Physiological Laboratory, University of Cambridge (Chapter 20).

Dr J. A. R. Lenman, Department of Medicine, University of Dundee (Chapters 19, 21, 23, 24).

Dr D. M. Lewis, Department of Physiology, University of Bristol (Chapter 21).

Dr A. G. D. Maran, Ear, Nose and Throat Department, Edinburgh Royal Infirmary (Chapter 23).

Dr J. A. Mills, Department of Obstetrics and Gynaecology, University of Dundee (Chapter 29).

Dr P. E. G. Mitchell, Department of Biochemical Medicine, University of Dundee (Chapter 9).

Dr G. Nicholson, Department of Medicine, University of Dundee (Chapter 7).

Dr Maureen Palmer, Department of Physiology, Queen Elizabeth College, London (Chapter 5).

Professor W. W. Park, Department of Pathology, University of Dundee (Chapter 9).

Dr J. M. Patrick, Department of Physiology, University of Nottingham (Chapters 13, 14).

Dr T. D. M. Roberts, Department of Physiology, University of Glasgow (Chapter 23).

Dr J. G. Robson, Physiological Laboratory, University of Cambridge (Chapter 27).

Professor I. C. Roddie, Department of Physiology, The Queen's University of Belfast (Chapters 11, 12).

Professor P. Sleight, Department of Cardiology, University of Oxford (Chapter 10).

Dr P. J. Stoward, Department of Anatomy, University of Dundee (Chapter 1).

Dr A. S. Todd, Department of Pathology, University of Dundee (Chapter 8).

Dr D. Vérel, Sheffield Cardiothoracic Unit (Chapter 10).

Dr D. B. Walsh, Department of Biochemical Medicine, University of Dundee (Chapter 16).

Dr I. C. Whitfield, Neurocommunications Research Unit, University of Birmingham (Chapter 27).

Dr K. G. Wormsley, Department of Pharmacology and Therapeutics, University of Dundee (Chapter 5).

Preface to the tenth edition

The tenth edition of a textbook is, for its authors and editors at least, a special one, presenting an opportunity to make changes greater than the usual revision and re-writing necessary between successive editions. Thirty years ago, when the first edition of BDS was written, there were few university departments of biochemistry for the instruction of medical students, and few appropriate textbooks of biochemistry were available for them. Now the position is very different, and most students of physiology are taught biochemistry as a separate subject. Accordingly in this edition the physiology and biochemistry components of the previous edition have been separated. We have not hesitated however to include in this textbook biochemical information essential to the understanding of physiological events.

This edition of BDS is, like its predecessors, addressed to medical, dental and science students of physiology, both undergraduate and postgraduate. All the chapters have been revised and some have been completely re-written. Throughout, we have tried to indicate the relevance of the basic physiology to the practice of clinical medicine.

We owe a great debt to our contributors. Some are responsible for virtually whole chapters, others have made much smaller, but valuable, contributions to the chapters whose numbers are linked to their names. We are grateful, too, for their remarkable tolerance of our editorial activities.

We should like to express our gratitude to Mrs Mina Geekie and Mrs Sheena Moreland for their skilled secretarial work, to Miss Mary Benstead who has prepared many new illustrations for this edition, to Mrs Elizabeth Donnelly for help with the illustrations and to the staff of the Dundee University Library for their assistance.

We acknowledge the help and encouragement of members of the staff of Churchill Livingstone.

Dundee, 1980 G.H.B.
D.E-S.
C.R.P.

Contents

1 Introduction

The term *physiology* refers to the functioning of a living organism or its parts. The workings of a plant or animal are explained partly by its structure but mainly by physics and chemistry. In this textbook we are not concerned specifically with biochemistry but chemical details will be discussed where necessary. A complete description of all events in the human body is not yet possible and sometimes we have to depend on experimental data derived from other mammals or even from bacteria. However, we cannot assume that what is true of other animals is also true for man.

Physiological Processes

In the more complex animals such as birds and mammals, the first characteristics of life that come to mind are warmth and movement. If a non-hibernating animal is still and cold it is assumed to be dead. By taking in food and oxidizing it an animal obtains energy which is used to produce heat or movement. The energy is obtained by the breakdown of body constituents by a process known as *catabolism*. The energy obtained by these catabolic processes may also be used for *anabolic* or synthetic processes such as those necessary for growth. Since both processes occur side by side it is convenient to use the word *metabolism* when referring to the total chemical changes occurring in the cell or in the body. So long as metabolic processes continue, however slowly, the cell is alive; their arrest is death. Since these chemical processes are under the control of enzymes the cells can move or grow only within certain limits of temperature. If the temperature is too high the enzymes are destroyed, while at low temperatures enzymic reactions are retarded and finally cease.

Living material is *organized*, that is, it has a definite structure. Moreover, particular functions, such as movement or secretion or conduction, are carried out by cells or organs whose structure is peculiarly fitted to these purposes. For a cell to survive there must be *integration* of function within it. In multicellular organisms there must be *co-ordination* of the activities of various cells, either by chemical messengers (*hormones*) or by a system of *nerves*.

Growth is a characteristic feature of living material. Growth of a single cell, however, cannot go on indefinitely because, as the cell increases in volume, its surface through which oxygen and food materials are admitted becomes so far removed from its centre that its supply of essential material is endangered. Before this stage is reached the cell divides into two daughter cells, a process known as *reproduction*.

Because a cell does not live in isolation, and can only obtain its food from outside, it must be capable of *reacting* to changes in its environment. Such changes are called *stimuli*. If a stimulus increases the rate of chemical changes in the cell it is said to *excite*; if it decreases the metabolic rate it is said to *depress* or *inhibit*.

Homeostasis. Living organisms possess two properties which at first sight seem to conflict. These are best described under the headings of *adaptation* and *homeostasis*. Simple forms of life can survive over a wide range of temperature and can adapt themselves to changes in their environment and to the foodstuffs available. Indeed, if they could not do so they would soon die. The study of adaptation forms a large part of the subject of physiology, for the cells of the body can adjust themselves to a wide variety of changes. On the other hand, many physiological reactions are directed towards preserving a constant physical and chemical internal environment. All the cells in the body except those on the surface are provided with a fluid environment of relatively constant temperature, hydrogen ion concentration and osmotic pressure. This permits many bodily activities to be carried out under optimum conditions. Small changes in the composition of the extra-cellular fluid produce reactions which quickly restore the internal environment to its original state. The maintenance of a constant environment for the cells is known as homeostasis.

The first requirement for homeostasis is a detector of deviation from the standard conditions; the appropriate regulator must then be 'instructed' to reduce the deviation. The new state of affairs is continuously assessed by the detector and the regulator is given fresh instructions. In other words the activity of the regulating device is constantly modified on the basis of information fed to it from the detector: such systems are termed 'feed-back' or 'control' mechanisms. Sensory receptors in muscles and joints send information to the central nervous system about length of muscles and angle of joints and movement and posture are regulated; cells sensitive to osmotic changes in the blood regulate the loss of water from the body; receptors in blood vessels detect changes in blood pressure and allow appropriate adjustments in the output of the heart and the calibre of the blood vessels. In many cases, however, the detecting mechanism has still to be discovered.

Our knowledge of the properties and functions of living cells is incomplete but we know that the laws of conservation of matter and energy apply to the animal body just as certainly as they apply to non-living material. Investigation of living matter is largely a matter of observation supplemented by the methods of physics and chemistry. Thus we may measure pressures and potentials, make chemical analyses, or trace the pathways of radioactive substances through the body. The results of these observations are correlated, interpreted in the light of previous knowledge, and used as evidence for or against a particular hypothesis.

Thus the study of physiology may be of great practical importance in leading to methods for the diagnosis and treatment of disease. At one time the organic basis for a patient's symptoms could be established only at post-mortem examination. The trend today, however, is to study the living patient in order to understand the way in which normal physiological and biochemical processes have broken down, for diseases are increasingly regarded as disordered physiological or biochemical processes which the homeostatic mechanisms have been unable to correct.

The bodily activities depend so closely on one another that

the workings of one part of the system cannot be comprehended without an understanding of the functioning of the whole. For example, in thinking of the activities of the heart we have to bear in mind the influence of the peripheral blood vessels, of the central nervous system, of respiration and of the chemical changes occurring in cardiac muscle. Our subject may, therefore, be likened to a circle: it is difficult to know where to enter it to begin our study, for it is only when we have completed the circle that we can fully understand it. For this reason we need to consider briefly the subject as a whole before beginning a more detailed description of its various parts.

Outline of Human Physiology

The source of all the energy required by the body for carrying out muscular activity, for respiration, for the beating of the heart and the working of the nervous system, is the food. This consists mainly of proteins, fats and carbohydrates which are oxidized in the tissues. In addition to sources of energy the food must contain inorganic substances which are necessary for example to provide material for the formation of blood and bone and to make good the loss of salts in the excreta. The food must also supply certain substances which the body cannot synthesize, such as vitamins and essential amino acids. Since fluid is lost continuously by way of the kidneys as well as by the skin and lungs, water must be drunk to make good this loss. When food is swallowed it reaches the stomach and small intestine, where it is broken down by enzymes into substances of simpler chemical constitution which are absorbed through the lining of the small intestine into the blood and distributed throughout the body.

Respiration. The oxygen required for combustion of the foodstuffs reaches the blood through the lungs. During breathing the chest expands and air flows into the lungs which are richly supplied with capillary blood vessels. Oxygen diffuses readily through the very thin walls of the capillaries and becomes attached to the haemoglobin contained in the red cells in which it is distributed throughout the body by the circulation. The carbon dioxide produced in combustion in the tissues is taken up by the blood and carried to the lungs where it escapes from the blood and is breathed out. By-products of oxidation not needed by the body reach the kidneys in the blood and are excreted into the urine.

Circulation. The heart is a two-sided muscular pump which drives the blood along the blood vessels. The left side pumps blood to the heart muscle itself, to the skeletal muscles, the brain and other organs (Fig. 1.1) The blood from these parts returns to the right heart which sends the blood to the lungs where oxygen is taken up and carbon dioxide is eliminated. The oxygenated blood then returns to the left side of the heart and is pumped out to the tissues. The blood is conveyed away from the heart at a fairly high pressure in thick-walled tubes, the arteries. These vessels branch repeatedly and become smaller in diameter, with thinner and thinner walls. In the tissues the smallest blood vessels, the capillaries, are bounded by a single layer of cells through which gases, water, or chemical substances of small molecular size move easily. The blood is drained away from the tissues at low pressure in the veins, wide vessels with relatively thin walls.

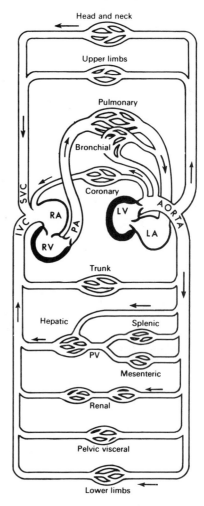

Fig. 1.1   Diagram to show the heart and circulation displayed as two ('left' and 'right') hearts and two circulations (systemic and pulmonary) arranged in series. Various important divisions of the systemic circulation are also indicated. Blood flows from arteries through capillary beds to veins. The renal circulation has two capillary beds, glomerular and tubular. PV=portal vein.

William Harvey's great discovery of the circulation of the blood is the basis of modern physiology. Harvey's work was important in a wider sense: the methods he used were essentially those of modern science—verifiable experiments yielding qualitative and quantitative data and the subsequent use of the data to develop a hypothesis. He observed, for example, that the arterial pulse occurred a very short time after the contraction of the heart and concluded that the one was responsible for the other. He noted that when an artery was cut the blood gushed out from the end nearer to the heart; the force of the gush was increased at each contraction of the ventricles. Once the blood had reached the great arteries it could not flow back into the heart because of the semilunar valves. The flow of blood in the arteries must therefore be from the heart. Similarly he made observations which indicated that blood flowed back to the heart in the veins. One of these is shown in Figure 1.2. He showed, as well, that the amount of blood ejected by a ventricle beating at its usual rate is much greater during half an hour than the total blood volume. Only a circulation could explain his findings.

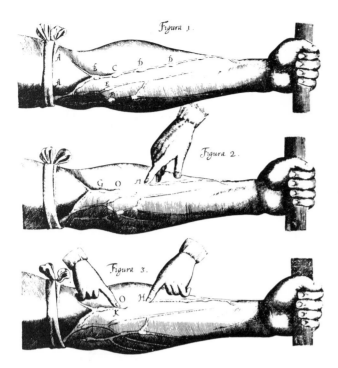

Fig. 1.2 Illustrations from Harvey's *De motu cordis* (1628). If a bandage is put around the arm tight enough to obstruct the superficial veins (but not the arteries) the veins swell. Valves can be seen as dilatations at intervals along the veins (Figura 1). If blood is milked backwards along a vein from O to H (Figura 2) none flows back through the valve at O. If then the vein is allowed to refill and the finger put back at H, blood can be milked through the valve at O but none flows back through the valve. The section H to O can be repeatedly refilled from H and emptied through O. It is clear therefore that blood in the veins can only move from the periphery toward the heart and must be derived from arterial blood.

Co-ordination. The skeletal muscles are the main effector tissues. By their contractions the position of the bones is altered during motion and respiration and speech are made possible. The highly complex movements of the limbs in walking, and of the tongue in speech, are co-ordinated by the central nervous system, consisting of the brain and spinal cord. Nerves called *efferent* or *motor* nerves leave this system and pass to all the structures of the body and control muscular movement as well as the secretion of some of the glands, the heart beat and the calibre of the blood vessels. Central control is, however, valueless unless the centre has full information about events in the body and around it. This information is conveyed to the central nervous system by the *sensory* or *afferent* nerves which carry impulses from the eye, the ear, the skin, the muscles and joints, and the heart, the lungs and the intestines. The sensory nerves are much more numerous than the motor nerves. Although many of the activities occurring in the central nervous system are exceedingly complex, relatively few rise to consciousness. We are quite unaware, for example, of the muscular adjustments needed to maintain balance or to move our eyes so that images of the external world are kept fixed on the retinae. These adjustments are called *reflex* and the pathways involved, namely sensory nerves, central nervous system and motor nerves, are called *reflex arcs*.

In addition to the rapidly acting co-ordinating mechanism of the nervous system the body possesses a chemical (*humoral*) system which operates more slowly. For example, during the digestion of food a chemical substance (*hormone*) called secretin is produced in the mucous membrane of the duodenum, is absorbed into the blood and carried to the pancreas which responds by pouring out its digestive juices.

Reproduction. Under this heading, we consider the processes necessary for the maintenance of the species. The male cells, the *spermatozoa*, are produced in the testes and when deposited in the female genital tract one of them may fertilize an *ovum* produced in the ovary. This sets off a series of complicated changes, mainly under hormonal control, to provide for the nutrition of the fertilized cell in the uterus. At the end of pregnancy the muscular wall of the uterus contracts, the fetus is delivered and then acquires oxygen directly, by breathing air into its lungs, instead of indirectly through the *placenta*.

The Composition of Living Tissues

In addition to a large amount of water, the living body contains protein which is the main nitrogenous constituent of all living material, a variable amount of fatty material known collectively as lipid, a small amount of carbohydrate, mainly glycogen and carbohydrate-protein complexes, and mineral salts. In man the relative proportions of these constituents, especially fat and carbohydrate, vary greatly from one person to another, and in the one individual at different times in his life, according to his nutrition. Nevertheless, the composition of the human body may be represented roughly as shown in Table 1.3.

Table 1.3 Approximate composition of a man weighing 70 kg (154 lb)

	Percentage	kg
Water	70	49
Fat	15	10·5
Protein	12	8·4
Carbohydrate	0·5	0·35
Minerals	2·5	1·75
	100	70

The considerable variations in total body water between one person and another are the result of differences in fat content since the amount of water in the fat-free parts of the body is remarkably constant. In very fat people the body water may be no more than 40 per cent of the total body weight. In the fetus the relative proportion of water in the body is much higher, for example 94 per cent at the third month of fetal life.

Most tissues contain more than 70 per cent water. Exceptions are adipose tissue (50 per cent), bone (30 per cent) and teeth (5 per cent). Table 1.4 shows that by far the greatest amount of water is to be found in muscle which accounts for the largest part of the body mass.

In its capacity as a solvent, water plays a fundamental role in cellular reactions. A very large number of substances are soluble in water; other substances such as fats can be carried in

Table 1.4 Percentage of the total body water which is found in the various tissues and organs

Muscle	50·8	Brain	2·7
Skeleton	12·5	Lungs	2·4
Skin	6·6	Fatty tissue	2·3
Blood	4·7	Kidneys	0·6
Intestine	3·2	Spleen	0·4
Liver	2·8	Rest of body	11·0
			100·0

Table 1.5 Composition of the human body (per cent by weight)

Oxygen	65	Chlorine	0·15
Carbon	18	Magnesium	0·05
Hydrogen	10	Iron	0·004
Nitrogen	3	Iodine	0·00004
Calcium	1·5	Copper	
Phosphorus	1·0	Manganese	
Potassium	0·35	Zinc	traces
Sulphur	0·25	Fluorine	
Sodium	0·15	Molybdenum, etc.	

fine emulsions or be rendered water-soluble in other ways, for example by combining with proteins. Some other properties of water are also important. The high heat capacity of water and its high latent heat of evaporation both contribute to the control of body temperature (Chap. 26).

Normally a large amount of water is lost from the body daily and a corresponding amount is taken in, so that water balance is maintained. The amount of water gained and lost by an adult man engaged in a sedentary occupation in a temperate climate is about 2.5 litres per day.

The elements of the human body are shown in Table 1.5.

The most abundant are carbon, oxygen and hydrogen, but minerals such as calcium and phosphorus are also plentiful. Other minerals such as iodine and iron are present only in small quantities. Nevertheless their presence in the diet is of great nutritional importance (pp. 32 to 34).

THE CELL

A schematic diagram of a 'typical' animal cell is shown in Figure 1.6. The cell is surrounded (or limited) by a cell

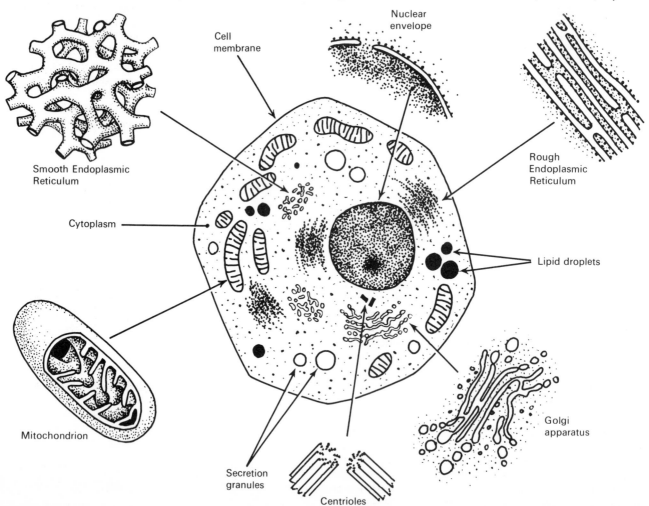

Fig. 1.6 The composition of a typical cell. The organelles as seen by electron microscopy are shown in greater detail around the outside. The interpretation of appearances shown by the electron microscope remains controversial but the appearances shown are those most widely accepted. (*After* W. Bloom & D. W. Fawcett (1975) *Textbook of Histology*. 10th edition. Philadelphia: Saunders.)

membrane or *plasma membrane*. All cells except red cells contain a nucleus; the rest of the cell contents is known as cytoplasm which consists of a number of other organelles embedded in a liquid cell sap or *cytosol*. The cytosol contains a number of enzymes and also the low molecular weight transfer RNA.

Membranes. The plasma membrane and also the bounding membranes of the nucleus and other organelles have many features in common. All contain both phospholipids and proteins; the lipids have their hydrophilic 'heads' outermost and their hydrophobic fatty acid chains pointed toward the interior of the membrane (Fig. 1.7).

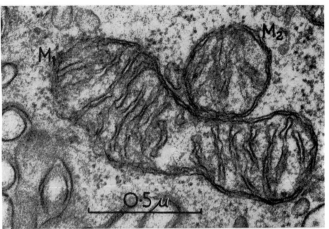

Fig. 1.8 Mitochondria in longitudinal section (M_1) and in cross section M_2 lying close to the surface membrane of the cell. (*By courtesy of P. G. Toner and G. M. Wyburn.*)

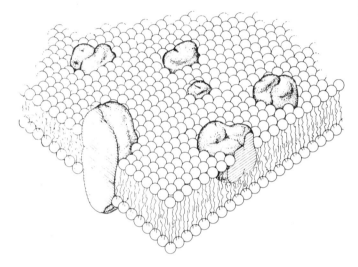

Fig. 1.7 A model to show current views of membrane structure. Irregularly shaped proteins float randomly in a lipid 'sea'. It seems likely that the proportion of protein varies greatly between membranes in different sites. (*After* P. Chapnick (1973) The skin of our cells. *The Sciences*, April 1973, 20–24.)

The ease with which a molecule can cross a membrane depends partly on its size but to a greater extent on its solubility in lipids. Thus membranes are usually impermeable to large molecules such as proteins and also to small ions, but permeable to water and small uncharged molecules like urea. Membranes are selective with regard to water-soluble substances such as sugars and amino acids. They are transported by carrier proteins which are highly specific and capable, for example, of carrying D-glucose but not L-glucose. Apart from carrier proteins the plasma membrane has special proteins which are receptors for hormones and proteins to express the person's immunological identity such as the blood group antigens on red cells and the histocompatibility antigens on other cells (Chap. 9).

The membranes surrounding subcellular organelles also have a selective permeability and enclose discrete compartments, each with its own complement of enzymes, substrates and co-factors. This arrangement ensures that different metabolic processes within the cell proceed optimally. For example, the ideal conditions for fatty acid synthesis are not the same as for fatty acid breakdown; the former takes place in the cytosol while the latter occurs within the inner membrane of mitochondria.

Because lipids are electrical insulators there may be

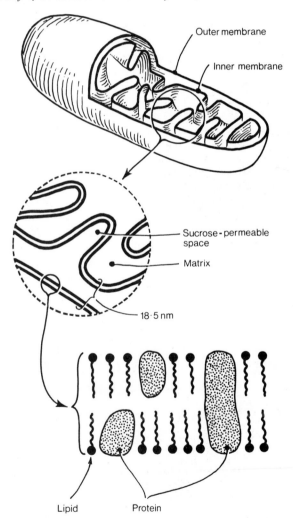

Fig. 1.9 Sketch of mitochondrion to show the double wall. The inner membrane, which is folded to give the cristae, separates the outer *sucrose permeable space* from the inner *matrix*. The bottom diagram shows an enlarged view of the double membrane which, like the cell membrane, consists of lipids and proteins. The proteins of the inner membrane include the enzymes of the electron transport system.

considerable differences in electrical voltage across a membrane.

The organelles. The *nucleus* contains a mesh-work of densely staining DNA, the chromatin of the histologist. Before a cell divides, the chromatin condenses to form the *chromosomes* which contain almost all the DNA of the cell. The nucleus is surrounded by a double membrane pierced at intervals by pores, and contains one or more dense, spherical bodies termed *nucleoli* which are rich in RNA and are the sites of synthesis of the ribosomal RNA responsible for protein synthesis.

Surrounding the nucleus is the *cytoplasm* in which are found various organelles such as secretion granules, lysosomes and mitochondria (Fig. 1.8). Each *mitochondrion* is bounded by a double membrane, the inner layer of which is folded to produce the *cristae* which divide the interior into compartments. Each membrane consists of a lipid bilayer containing proteins (Fig. 1.9). The mitochondria (of which there are about 400 in a liver cell) contain the enzymes responsible for oxidative phosphorylation, and are the site of the production of high energy compounds (such as adenosine triphosphate, ATP) in the cell. They have been termed the 'power houses of the cell'. But probably an equally important function of mitochondria is the regulation of the calcium concentration within the cell by the uptake and release of calcium ions. Thus the activity and metabolism of many cells, especially cardiac cells, are regulated to some extent by their mitochondria.

The cytoplasm also contains a complex meshwork of canals and vesicles known as the *endoplasmic reticulum* (Fig. 1.10) with membranes about 5 nm thick. Two kinds of endoplasmic reticulum can be distinguished under the electron microscope, rough endoplasmic reticulum (RER) and smooth endoplasmic reticulum (SER). These tubules appear to form a series of canals leading from the exterior of the cell to the nucleus. The SER contains enzymes responsible for metabolic pathways such as those for the detoxication of foreign substances and for the synthesis of hormones and glycoproteins. In the RER the surface of the tubules and vesicles is studded with small round electron-dense particles (diameter 10 to 20 nm) known as *ribosomes*. These consist of about equal amounts of protein

and RNA and, together with transfer RNA, messenger RNA, activated amino acids, enzymes and other factors, are responsible for protein synthesis. Ribosomes also occur free in the cytoplasm, unattached to reticular membranes. Indeed, in some cells (intestinal epithelium, tumour cells) the endoplasmic reticulum is scanty and most of the ribosomes are unattached. During the mechanical disruption of cells, the endoplasmic reticulum also is disrupted and, after isolation by differential centrifugation, is obtained in the form of fragments of membrane, each bearing some ribosomes. These fragments of membrane are known as *microsomes* (diameter 60 to 150 nm) and the ribosomes may be released from them by a suitable surface active agent such as sodium deoxycholate. The ribosomes may then be purified and analysed.

The cytoplasm of most cells also contains small organelles known as *lysosomes* (formerly known as microbodies) which are essentially little sacks of hydrolytic enzymes which can break down large molecules. The enzymes include peptidases (cathepsins) which break down proteins, ribonuclease, deoxyribonuclease, β-glucuronidase and acid phosphatase. These enzymes are thought to be responsible for the dissolution of damaged or dead cells during the process of autolysis. They also play an important role in the phagocytes, the cells which ingest and destroy foreign particles such as bacteria (Chap. 9). Peroxisomes are small organelles which contain catalase and take up hydrogen peroxide.

Some cells contain a *Golgi apparatus* which is concerned with the packaging of proteins produced by the RER before their excretion from the cell. It is generally thought that the Golgi apparatus is continuous with the RER and also with other organelles, particularly lysosomes.

Also in the cytoplasm are microfilaments and microtubules which are 25 nm in diameter and have walls consisting mainly of very fine helical filaments of the protein 6-*S* tubulin. The microtubules (Fig. 1.11) are concerned with movements of the cell and also movements of organelles within the cell; they

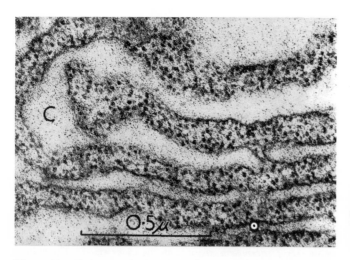

Fig. 1.10 Cisternae of granular endoplasmic reticulum showing cavities (C) bounded by membranes. Ribosomes are attached to the outer, or cytoplasmic, surfaces of the cisternae and also lie free in the cytoplasm. (*By courtesy of P. G. Toner and G. M. Wyburn.*)

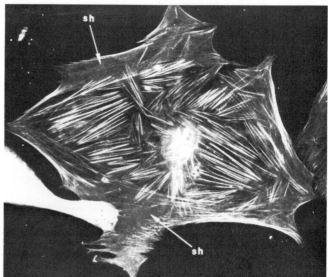

Fig. 1.11 Fibroblast from human skin with immunofluorescent staining to show actin in microfilaments. **sh** indicates sheath-like structures whose function is unknown. From Lazardides, E. (1975) *Journal of Cell Biology*, **65**, 549–561.

form the spindle of the mitotic apparatus which draws apart the chromosomes in anaphase during cell division.

Coated vesicles (60 to 110 nm) found in many cells transport cell membrane from one place to another in the form of small bags inside the cell. The crystalline coat of these vesicles is of a protein called *clathrin* in the form of an open polyhedral lattice. In nerve cells the coated vesicles recycle the membrane used to carry packets of transmitter substance. In oocytes the vesicles gather up pieces of yolk protein.

It is easy to get the idea from a histological section that cells are fixed immobile structures but immuno-fluorescence methods have shown that many cells as well as muscle cells contain filaments of the muscle proteins actin, myosin and tropomyosin. Both microfilaments and microtubules are likely to be involved in normal cell movement.

REFERENCES

Barrow G M 1974 Physical chemistry for the life sciences. McGraw Hill, New York

Brooks C McC, Cranefield P F (eds) 1959 The historical development of physiological thought. Haffner, New York

Dyson R D 1978 Cell biology: A molecular approach, 2nd edn. Allyn and Bacon, Boston and London

Hall T S 1976 History of general physiology 600 BC to AD 1900. University of Chicago Press

Hodgkin A, Huxley A, Feldberg W S, Rushton W A H, Gregory R A and McCance R A 1977 The pursuit of nature. Informal essays of the history of physiology. University Press, Cambridge

Junqueira L C, Carneiro J and Cantopoulos 1977 Basic histology, 2nd edn. Lange, Los Altos, CA

Lancet 1978 Malfunctioning microtubules. Lancet 1: 697–698

Medawar P B, Medawar J S 1977 The life science. Harper and Row, New York

Novikoff A B, Holtzman E 1976 Cells and organelles. 2nd edn. Holt, Rinehart and Winston, New York

Riggs D S 1971 Control theory and physiological feedback mechanisms. Churchill Livingstone, Edinburgh

Roberts F 1971 Medical terms: their origin and construction. Heinemann, London

Robinson J R 1974 A prelude to physiology. Blackwell, Oxford

Roddie I C, Wallace W F M 1975 The physiology of disease. Lloyd-Luke, London

Sheilds R 1976 Mini-muscles make cells move. New Scientist 489–491

Weissman G E, Claiborne R (eds) 1975 Cell membranes: biochemistry, cell biology and pathology. Freeman, Reading

Young J Z 1974 An introduction to the study of man. Oxford University Press, Oxford

2 Food, Energy and Nutrition

The food we eat is composed of animal and plant tissues or products derived from them. Its oxidation provides the energy needed for the maintenance of body temperature, for muscular activity including that of the heart and for metabolism including synthetic processes. In addition, food provides materials which cannot be synthesized in the body.

THE COMPOSITION OF FOODS

Milk

The human infant starts life on a diet consisting solely of milk. Human and cow's milk differ in composition and average values are given in Table 2.1. Cow's milk varies with the season, the breed of the cow and its feeding. Artificial milks used for infant feeding often differ markedly from human milk.

Table 2.1 Composition of human and cow's milk per 100 g

	Human milk	Fresh summer cow's milk
Energy value	289 kJ	272 kJ
Water	87·1 g	87·6 g
Protein	1·3 g	3·3 g
Casein: whey proteins	1:3	4:1
Fat	4·1 g	3·8 g
Carbohydrate (lactose)	7·2 g	4·7 g
Calcium	34 mg	120 mg
Iron	70 μg	50 μg
Phosphorus	14 mg	95 mg
Sodium	14 mg	50 mg
Potassium	58 mg	150 mg
Citrate	80 mg	150 mg
Retinol and carotene	35 and 22 μg	35 and 22 μg
Thiamin	20 μg	40 μg
Riboflavin	30 μg	190 μg
Niacin	220 μg	80 μg
Ascorbic acid	3·7 mg	2 mg
Vitamin D sulphate	0·9 μg	0·03 μg

This and the subsequent food tables are derived from *McCance and Widdowson's The Composition of Foods* 4th edition (1978) by Paul, A. A. & Southgate, D. A. T. London: H.M.S.O.

The chief proteins of milk are casein and the whey proteins, α-lactalbumin and β-lactoglobulin. Casein, a phosphoprotein, occurs as calcium caseinate. When acid is added to milk casein is rendered insoluble and the milk curdles. Milk goes 'sour' and curdles if kept at room temperature because bacteria in it multiply and produce lactic acid. When milk comes into contact with the enzymes rennin or pepsin *coagulation* or *clotting* occurs and a clot of calcium caseinate separates. On standing the clot contracts, expressing a clear fluid known as whey. The clot retains all the milk fat.

Milk is an excellent source of protein, calcium and phosphorus but it is deficient in iron. However, infants are born with a store of iron sufficient to prevent anaemia unless the period of suckling is more than about four months.

Milk is an important source of vitamins A and D and riboflavin; it is a poor source of vitamins C and K. Human breast milk contains sufficient vitamin D as water-soluble vitamin D sulphate to meet the needs of the young infant. Breast-fed infants rarely suffer from rickets.

Raw milk is perishable because it provides an ideal substrate for the growth of micro-organisms. Freshly drawn milk may contain bacteria, some of them pathogens, and it may be further infected during handling before reaching the dairy or factory. Thus to ensure that a bacteriologically safe product of good keeping quality is delivered to the consumer it is necessary to destroy the pathogens by appropriate heat treatment and to reduce the population of the other bacteria. Most milk destined for the liquid market is pasteurized by the high temperature short time (HTST) process in which it is heated to 71 to 73°C for not less than 15 seconds. Pasteurized milk should contain no pathogenic micro-organisms and the content of other micro-organisms should be so low that the milk will remain fresh for several days if kept cool. Pasteurization has little effect on the nutritional value of milk, the only significant change being a loss of about one-quarter of the vitamin C.

For longer term storage milk is sterilized by being heated to 130 to 150°C for one second and filled aseptically into cartons. The resulting product, ultra heat treated (UHT) milk, has suffered little loss of nutritive value and keeps for up to six months without refrigeration.

Dried milk. In the preparation of dried milk, water is removed either by spray-drying or by roller-drying. The resulting product is of high nutritive value but it cannot be stored for very long periods since the fat tends to be oxidized and become rancid. Dried skim milk is a valuable source of protein and calcium but it is, of course, almost free from fat and the fat-soluble vitamins A and D.

Condensed milk. This is prepared by removing part of the water in a vacuum. The concentrate is then sterilized at a high temperature in tins (*evaporated milk*), or it is treated with sugar (about 40 per cent) to prevent the growth of bacteria (*sweetened condensed milk*).

Cream and butter. In the preparation of *cream* the fat is separated from milk either by gentle centrifugation or by allowing it to rise to the surface. Cream contains a high proportion (40 to 50 per cent) of fat. Milk from which the cream has been removed is known as *skim milk*.

Table 2.2 Composition of dairy produce per 100 g

	Protein g	Fat g	Carbo-hydrate g	kJ	Calcium mg	Iron mg
Cow's milk, whole	3·3	3·8	4·7	272	120	0·05
Cow's milk, skimmed	3·4	0·1	5·0	142	130	0·05
Butter	0·4	82	0·0	3041	15	0·16
Margarine vitaminized	0·1	81	0·1	3000	4	0·3
Cheese, cheddar type	26	33·5	0·0	1682	800	0·4

When cream is submitted to prolonged shaking (churning) the fat globules coalesce to form a solid mass of *butter* which is, like cream, an important source of the fat-soluble vitamins, especially vitamin A. It contains 65 per cent saturated fats. The residual fluid, known as buttermilk, has a composition similar to that of skim milk and is a rich source of protein, lactose and the inorganic salts of milk.

Cheese. This is made by coagulating the proteins of milk with rennet (an enzyme preparation from calf stomach) at 30°C. Most of the fat is included in the coagulated mass which is pressed out and allowed to 'ripen' under the influence of bacteria. The characteristic texture and taste of the finished cheese depends on the particular bacteria and moulds involved in the ripening process. During the ripening process tyramine may be formed from tyrosine; some varieties may contain more than 0·5 mg of tyramine per g. Cheese is a good source of protein, fat, and mineral elements such as calcium.

Margarine

Margarine is prepared from blends of vegetable oils and animal fats. The mixture after hydrogenation acquires a consistency similar to that of butter. Soft margarines contain 25 to 50 per cent of polyunsaturated fatty acids. Butter has only 2 per cent. Vitamins A and D are added to margarine in Britain.

Meat, Fish and Eggs

Meat is essentially skeletal muscle (Table 2.3). When fresh meat is allowed to hang glycogen disappears and acids such as lactic acid are produced which tend to soften the muscle fibres and make the meat more tender.

Other parts of animals usually described as offal are used for food. Liver and kidney are both rich in nucleoprotein and contain less fat than most meat. Liver is rich in vitamin A and in iron. 'Sweetbreads' (pancreas and thymus) are rich in nucleoprotein.

Fish is an important source of animal protein (Table 2.3). White fish such as cod, haddock and plaice contain only a small proportion (less than 2 per cent) of fat but fat fish, herring, mackerel and salmon, contain 5 to 18 per cent of fat and can provide useful amounts of the fat-soluble vitamins A and D.

Eggs are a good source of proteins, vitamins and minerals. One average egg (6·25 g) supplies 327 kJ, 6·4 g protein, 5·9 g fat, 30 mg calcium, 1·6 mg iron (all of which is available), 80 μg retinol, 1 μg vitamin D, 0·06 mg thiamin and about 260 mg riboflavin.

Meat substitutes, mostly based on soya beans, have recently become available. Their amino acid content is different from that of beef. The methionine content is low but is compensated by a higher content of cystine. These soya products contain little fat.

Cereals

The main constituents of cereals (and therefore flour) are starch (about 70 per cent), water (about 15 per cent) and protein (about 11 per cent) (Table 2.4). The amount of fat varies widely (0·5 to 8 per cent) from one cereal to another, being particularly high in oatmeal. The inorganic matter, about 2 per cent, consists chiefly of calcium, phosphorus and iron.

The endosperm in the centre of the wheat grain (Fig. 2.5) is mainly starch with some protein, but the outer layer of the endosperm contains the important proteins glutelin and gliadin as well as minerals and nicotinic acid. The germ is particularly rich in vitamins of the B group.

Table 2.3 Composition of meat, fish and eggs per 100 g edible portion

	Protein g	Fat g	Carbo-hydrate g	kJ	Calcium mg	Iron mg
Beef, sirloin, roast, lean only	27·6	9·1	0·0	806	10	2·1
Lamb leg, roast, lean only	29·4	8·1	0·0	800	8	2·7
Bacon back, fried, lean and fat	24·9	40·6	0·0	1926	13	1·3
Liver, calf, fried	26·9	13·2	7·3	1063	15	7·5
Cod, grilled	20·8	1·3	0·0	402	10	0·4
Haddock, smoked, steamed	23·3	0·9	0·0	429	58	1·0
Herring, fried	23·1	15·1	1·5	975	39	1·0
Eggs, whole, fresh	12·3	10·9	0·0	612	52	2·0

Table 2.4   Composition of some cereal products per 100 g

	Protein g	Fat g	Carbo-hydrate g	kJ	Calcium mg	Iron mg
Bread, brown	8·9	2·2	44·7	948	100	2·5
Bread, white	7·8	1·7	49·7	991	100	1·7
Flour, fortified 72 per cent extraction for making white bread	11·3	1·2	74·8	1433	140	2·2
Oatmeal, raw	12·4	8·7	72·8	1698	55	4·1
Biscuits, water	10·8	12·5	75·8	1859	120	1·6
Rice, polished, boiled	2·2	0·3	29·6	522	1	0·2

In the process of milling the degree of extraction, that is, the percentage of the whole grain retained in the flour, can be varied widely. 'Wholemeal' (92 per cent extraction) or flour of 100 per cent extraction contains a large proportion of indigestible fibrous matter. When the extraction is less than 80 per cent the loss in minerals and vitamins is considerable.

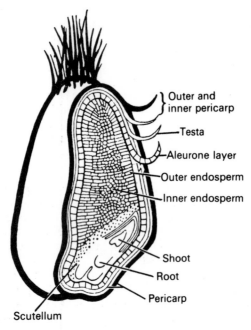

Fig. 2.5   Longitudinal section through a grain of wheat. (*From* R. A. McCance (1946) *Lancet*, **i**, 77.)

White flour (72 per cent extraction) has the advantage of good keeping qualities but much of the minerals, vitamins and proteins have been removed with the bran and embryo. In Britain white flour is therefore fortified with calcium, iron and thiamin.

'Brown bread' is usually made from white flour to which a proportion of bran has been added. It has a higher vitamin content than has white bread, has more flavour and contains more fibre (p. 21).

Bread. When wheat flour is kneaded with water a sticky mass of dough is formed by promotion of disulphide bond interchange in soluble proteins. Traditionally the dough is made to rise by the action of yeast on the starch in the dough but now rapid mechanical agitation is applied to produce the same effect. During baking the starch grains are ruptured and some of the starch is converted into soluble starch and dextrins; caramelized products are formed in the crust. When bread is toasted it loses water, it is caramelized further and the starch on the surface is largely converted into degradation products which give toast its brown colour. The composition of bread is given in Table 2.4.

Gluten is the mixture of proteins, mainly gliadins and glutelins, present in wheat, barley and rye and the flours made from these cereals produce a dough on the addition of water. Cornflour (wheat starch), oatmeal and flour made from maize contain less gluten and therefore can be made into bread only with difficulty. The intestinal mucosa of patients with coeliac disease is damaged by the α-gliadin of wheat but its mode of action is not fully understood.

Fruit and Vegetables

Most green vegetables contain much indigestible fibrous material. They are good sources of minerals and of ascorbic acid and carotene, the precursor of vitamin A (Table 2.6).

Potatoes contain mainly starch in the form of granules which swell up and burst on cooking. Potatoes are traditionally described as 'fattening' but since they contain 80 per cent water they are low in energy value compared with many other carbohydrate foods; removal of boiled potatoes from the diet leads only to a modest reduction in the energy intake. Potatoes provide about one quarter of the ascorbic acid intake, a small amount of good quality protein, and useful amounts of iron and fluorine. If cooked in fat the energy value goes up about three fold (see Table 2.6).

The pulses (beans, peas, lentils) are good sources of protein (20 to 25 per cent in the dried state). In the fresh form but not when dried they supply ascorbic acid and carotene.

Most fruits are of little nutritive value except as sources of ascorbic acid. When ripe they contain varying amounts of sugar; the banana is unique in supplying starch as well.

Sugar manufactured from cane or sugar beet is almost pure sucrose. Since it contains no vitamins or minerals it is said to provide 'empty' calories. Recently, because of its relative cheapness, large quantities of *isoglucose* have been used in some kinds of food processing in which liquid sugar is needed. It is a mixture of glucose and fructose formed by the action of the enzyme isomerase on glucose derived from the starch of maize.

Chocolate and cocoa have a relatively high protein, fat and carbohydrate content and have thus a high energy value, but the energy value of tea and coffee depends entirely on the

Table 2.6   Composition of some fruits and vegetables (edible portion per 100 g)

	Protein g	Fat g	Carbo- hydrate g	kJ	Calcium mg	Iron mg
Apples, eating	0·3	0·0	11·9	196	4	0·3
Bananas	1·1	0·3	19·2	337	7	0·4
Oranges (flesh only)	0·8	0·0	8·5	150	41	0·3
Tomatoes	0·9	0·0	2·8	60	13	0·4
Raisins (dried)	1·1	0·0	64·4	1049	61	1·6
Peanuts, fresh	24·3	49	8·6	2364	61	2·0
Beans, broad, boiled	4·1	0·6	7·1	206	21	1·0
Carrots, old, boiled	0·6	0·0	4·3	79	37	0·4
Peas, fresh, boiled	5·0	0·4	7·7	223	13	1·2
Potatoes, new, boiled	1·6	0·1	18·3	324	5	0·4
Potatoes, chips (deep fat fried)	3·8	10·9	37·3	1065	14	0·9
Cabbage, winter, boiled	1·7	0·0	2·3	66	38	0·4

Table 2.7   Composition of miscellaneous foodstuffs per 100 g or per 100 ml

	Protein g	Fat g	Carbo- hydrate g	kJ	Calcium mg	Iron mg
Honey	0·6	4·6	74·4	1201	8	0·2
Chocolate (milk)	8·4	30·3	59·4	2214	220	1·6
Cocoa, powder	18·5	21·7	11·5	1301	130	10·5
Jams	0·6	0	69·0	1114	24	1·5
Beer, 3·1 per cent alcohol, draught bitter	0·3	0	2·3	132	11	0·01
Coffee, ground, roasted	10·4	15·4	28·5	1203	130	4·1

added sugar and milk. A cup of tea or coffee contains 100 to 150 mg of the stimulant caffeine. Cocoa is a valuable source of iron (Table 2.7).

Alcohol

Ethanol (ethyl alcohol) has a potential energy of 29 kJ/g. It is absorbed quickly from the intestine, especially if accompanied by a carbonated fluid such as soda water. It is oxidized in the liver and the energy released there is enough to meet most of its energy needs so that other nutrients are little used by the liver during oxidation. The enzyme responsible, alcohol dehydrogenase, converts ethanol to acetaldehyde; this in turn is oxidized to acetic acid which enters the metabolic pool as acetyl-CoA.

Ethanol diffuses rapidly into the brain where it has a depressant action; deep coma occurs when the blood alcohol is 90 mmol/l. After an alcoholic drink the blood level falls only slowly—about 3 mmol/l per hour. Only 150 mmol (7 g) can be metabolized per hour, the limiting factor being the availability of NAD (Fig. 2.8).

Alcoholic drinks lower the blood glucose level by inhibiting hepatic glucogenesis and by potentiating the insulin-releasing properties of glucose and glucose-releasing foods. Healthy persons drinking large quantities of gin and tonic develop hypoglycaemia $2\frac{1}{2}$ to 4 hours later and may then suffer discomfort and impairment of critical judgement. The consumption of large quantities of carbohydrate cannot, for the reasons just given, prevent the onset of hypoglycaemia. Small amounts of alcohol (say, 3 per cent of the intake) are excreted in the urine and breath. This fact underlies the breathalyser test used by the police. It is important to note that methanol (methyl alcohol) is highly toxic since it is metabolized to formic acid.

Beer is made by fermentation with yeast of a solution of sugars and other nutrients derived from a carbohydrate source, usually barley in Europe, but many other cereals are used. Since yeast cannot break down carbohydrate material larger than trisaccharides, the cereal is allowed to germinate in the complex process of malting to produce hydrolytic enzymes which break down starch and other polymers.

Beer contains, in addition to 4 to 6 per cent of alcohol, a little

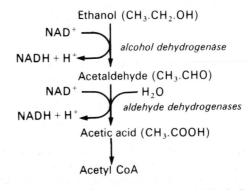

Fig. 2.8   Pathway for the oxidation of ethanol ('alcohol').

carbohydrate and significant amounts of calcium and of members of the vitamin B group derived chiefly from the yeast used in its fermentation. Spirits contain about 40 per cent alcohol, fortified wines (such as sherry and port) 20 per cent and ordinary wines 10 to 15 per cent alcohol.

EFFECTS OF COOKING AND FREEZING

Cooking. The chemical composition of food may be considerably altered in the process of cooking. Cooking renders most foodstuffs more palatable and digestible and destroys bacteria. The most obvious effect of cooking is the coagulation of protein such as occurs during the boiling of an egg. When meat is cooked water is lost, soluble protein is coagulated and collagen is converted to gelatin. At the same time the fibres shrink and become softer and looser so that the meat is easier to chew.

When meat is boiled the soluble constituents, such as inorganic salts, gelatin and extractives (soluble organic substances responsible for flavour) are lost. Loss of soluble materials is much less during roasting and baking, and less still during grilling and frying, in which the heat is usually applied for a short time and the surface rapidly sealed by the heat. During cooking the starch granules of cereals and potatoes swell up and burst and in this form they are more easily digested; cooking loosens the cellulose framework of vegetables.

Cooking has little effect on any of the vitamins except thiamin and ascorbic acid. Thiamin is destroyed by heat and does not survive the temperature used for example in the baking of biscuits. It is, however, not destroyed in the baking of bread unless sodium bicarbonate is used. As much as 60 per cent of the ascorbic acid content of foods may be lost during cooking because (a) it is destroyed by the enzyme ascorbic acid oxidase liberated from damaged cells during the preparation of vegetables, (b) it is very soluble and thus is easily dissolved out by the water in which vegetables are cooked, and (c) part of it is destroyed by heat, especially in an alkaline medium. Vegetables should therefore be prepared immediately before they are to be used and cooked for as short a time as possible in the minimum of water.

Freezing. Freezing is a very useful method of storing food, especially meat and vegetables. When meat is being frozen it first cools to below the freezing point (*supercooling stage*) and then crystals of ice begin to form. While this continues the temperature of the food remains near the freezing point until most of the water within the food has become ice (*freezing stage*). Thereafter the temperature falls to the storage temperature (*post-cooling stage*). The rate of freezing is important. The disruption of the cells is considerably greater

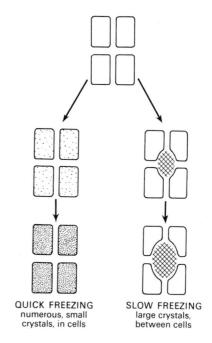

QUICK FREEZING
numerous, small
crystals, in cells

SLOW FREEZING
large crystals,
between cells

Fig. 2.9 Differences between slow freezing and rapid freezing in the size of ice crystal formed and therefore the extent to which cells are damaged. (*After* D. J. Cook (1974) *British Nutrition Foundation Bulletin,* 11, 39.)

with slow freezing than with quick freezing because much larger crystals are formed (Fig. 2.9). During the freezing stage the organic and inorganic constituents are concentrated in a diminishing volume of unfrozen water and this concentration may cause changes in the nutritional value of the food. For example the level of vitamin C falls in many vegetables to between 10 and 50 per cent of the initial value during freezing and thawing. This is attributed to the increased concentration of both vitamin C and copper compounds (which catalyse its oxidation) between the crystals at this stage. Other water soluble vitamins are less affected.

During prolonged storage of frozen foods slow oxidation of fats may lead to rancidity and destruction of vitamin A and vitamin E. Oxidation may be minimized by reducing the oxygen content within the package, for example by packaging in nitrogen or in a vacuum or by the use of antioxidants. During storage the ATP of meat is rapidly converted to inosine 5-phosphate which is said to improve its flavour. The usual temperature for the storage of frozen foods is —18°C. Lower temperatures allow more prolonged storage, but at —18°C storage of fresh meat is satisfactory for three to six months while vegetables and cooked meat may be stored for 12 months or more.

ENERGY REQUIREMENTS AND EXPENDITURE

The potential energy of a foodstuff can be determined by measuring the amount of heat produced when the foodstuff is burned in a *bomb calorimeter*. The 'bomb' is a strong cylindrical steel vessel which can resist very high internal pressures. A weighed amount of the foodstuff is placed in the bomb which is then filled with oxygen under pressure. The foodstuff is ignited electrically and the amount of heat produced by oxidation is calculated from the rise in temperature of the known volume of water surrounding the bomb and the water equivalent of the calorimeter.

The unit of heat used in nutrition was until recently the kilocalorie (kcal) or Calorie. However, with the introduction of S.I. units it is now usual to use joules (J) as a measure of heat. One kilocalorie is equal to 4184 J, or 4·184 kJ; 1 MJ (megajoule) $=10^6$ J. One joule per second is one watt (W).

The energy derived from the complete combustion of the usual mixture of carbohydrates in human foodstuffs has been found to be 17 kJ per g. The value for fat is 39 kJ per g. In the bomb carbohydrates and fats are oxidized to carbon dioxide and water just as they are in the body. In the bomb protein is oxidized to carbon dioxide, water, and oxides of nitrogen and other elements but in the body it is incompletely oxidized, part being excreted as urea which has an appreciable energy value. When the potential energy of the urea excreted is subtracted from the figure for the complete oxidation (23 kJ per g) a physiological value of 17 kJ per g is obtained for protein.

METHODS FOR ESTIMATING ENERGY OUTPUT

Direct Calorimetry

To determine energy expenditure by direct calorimetry the subject is placed in a calorimeter, a small room with heavily insulated walls. The heat generated by the subject is taken up by water pumped through a series of pipes which pass through the calorimeter. By multiplying the difference in temperature between the ingoing and outgoing water by the volume of water flowing his heat output can be obtained; the oxygen consumption can be read on a meter. By its use Atwater showed many years ago that over several days energy expenditure balances energy intake within 1 per cent or so. He also showed that measurements by direct calorimetry agreed well with measurements by indirect calorimetry which is much more convenient and relatively cheap, and very nearly as accurate.

More recently the gradient calorimeter has come into use, particularly for measuring directly the heat output of domestic animals. A system of thermocouples is used to measure the difference in temperature, and hence the heat flow, across the walls of an insulated box large enough to house the animal.

Indirect Calorimetry

In indirect methods the heat output of the subject is calculated from his oxygen consumption. Because the relationship between oxygen consumption and heat production depends on the type of food being oxidized, we must briefly consider the *respiratory quotient* (R.Q.) which is by definition the *volume* of carbon dioxide produced divided by the *volume* of oxygen used in the same time.

The oxidation of carbohydrate can be represented by the equation

$$C_6H_{12}O_6 + 6O_2 = 6CO_2 + 6H_2O + heat$$

The respiratory quotient is 6/6, that is 1·0. Oxidation of the fat triolein is represented by the equation

$$C_{57}H_{104}O_6 + 80O_2 = 57CO_2 + 52H_2O + O + heat$$

Its R.Q. is 57/80 or 0·71; the R.Q. of human fat is 0·72. The R.Q. for an average protein is 0·80. A subject on an ordinary mixed diet containing carbohydrate, fat and protein has an R.Q. of the order of 0·85. In other words the R.Q. gives a clue to the type of food being oxidized at any given time if we assume that the carbon dioxide collected and measured is derived solely from the oxygen taken into the body during the same period.

The calorific values of oxygen used by the body in the combustion of mixtures of fat and carbohydrate for different levels of the R.Q. are shown in Figure 2.10.

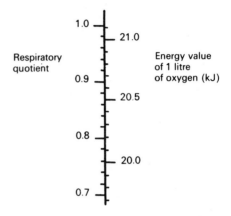

Fig. 2.10 A nomogram from which may be read off the energy value of a litre of oxygen (at s.t.p.) at non-protein R.Q.s from 0·7 to 1·0.

The R.Q. can lie outside the limits 0·7 to 1·0. When carbohydrate is transformed into fat the non-protein R.Q. is greater than 1, since carbon dioxide is produced and oxygen is not used.

$$13C_6H_{12}O_6 \rightarrow C_{55}H_{104}O_6 + 23CO_2 + 26H_2O.$$

In one experiment overfeeding of thin men with carbohydrate gave a respiratory quotient as high as 1.3. Conversely when fat is being transformed to carbohydrate in excess of that being oxidized, the R.Q. is less than 0·7 because oxygen is used up without a corresponding production of carbon dioxide.

Closed circuit methods. The subject is kept in an airtight chamber through which a continuous circulation of air is maintained by a rotary blower. Oxygen is added through a meter to make good the oxygen used in metabolism; the water in the expired air is caught in a sulphuric acid trap in the ventilation circuit; the carbon dioxide is caught in a soda-lime trap and is estimated by weighing or by a chemical method.

The subject remains within the chamber for a period of several hours; since his oxygen consumption and carbon dioxide output are measured his R.Q. can be calculated. Protein metabolism can be estimated by measuring the nitrogen content of the urine excreted during the time of the experiment.

Simpler methods have been evolved for clinical use. The Benedict-Roth spirometer (Fig. 2.11) consists of a gasholder (spirometer bell) which is filled with oxygen. As the oxygen is used up by the subject the level of the gasholder falls and from the record of its movements on the rotating drum the amount of oxygen consumed in a given period can be measured. Because the expired carbon dioxide is not measured, the R.Q.

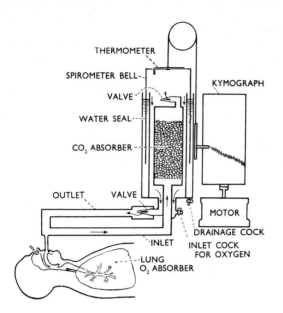

cannot be calculated but an arbitrary value of 0·8 is usually assumed. At this R.Q. the calorific value of oxygen is 20·2 kJ per litre, and by multiplying this value by the number of litres of oxygen consumed the energy output during the experimental period is obtained with an error of no clinical importance (Fig. 2.12).

Open circuit method. In the open circuit method the subject's nose is closed by a clip and he breathes through a mouthpiece fitted with valves so that he inspires atmospheric air and expires through a wide tube into a rubberized canvas or polythene bag (Douglas bag) of capacity 100 or 200 litres (Fig. 2.13). The volume of the air in the bag is measured with a gas meter.

For the calculation of the metabolic rate in the Douglas bag method it is necessary to find only (1) the volume of the expired air and (2) the percentage of oxygen in the expired air. For the usual range of protein intake, that is where protein contributes 10 to 15 per cent of the total energy, Weir has shown that the energy value of a litre of expired air is $0·209$ (O_i—O_e) kJ where O_i is the percentage of oxygen in the inspired air (normally 20·9) and O_e is the percentage of oxygen in the expired air. The following example illustrates the method.

The subject breathed into a Douglas bag for 10 minutes. The volume of the expired air was 80·3 litres at 16·8°C and 750 mm Hg atmospheric pressure, equivalent to 73·2 litres at s.t.p.d. The expired air contained 16·9 per cent oxygen. From Weir's formula the energy value of a litre of this expired air is 0·209 (20·9–16·9) or 0·84 kJ. The energy output was therefore 73·2×0·84=61·5 kJ in 10 minutes or 369 kJ per hour. The subject weighed 50 kg and his height was 163 cm; his surface

Fig. 2.11 Diagram of recording spirometer. The subject wears a nose-clip and breathes through a mouthpiece which is connected to the apparatus by two tubes. He breathes in oxygen through the inspiratory valve and breathes out into the carbon dioxide absorber and then, through the expiratory valve, into the spirometer bell. A pump may be introduced in place of the valves shown in the diagram to ease the circulation of air through the carbon dioxide absorber. The amount of oxygen used is recorded on the revolving drum by the pen attached to the counterweight. (Diagram by J. B. de V. Weir.)

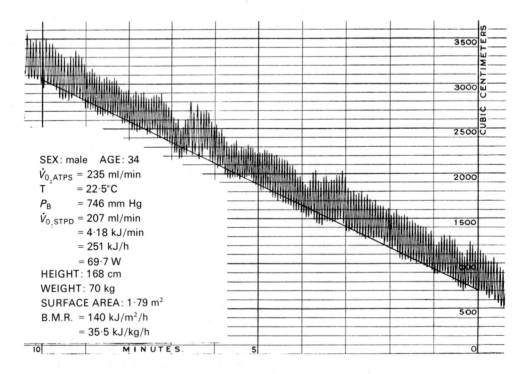

SEX: male   AGE: 34
$\dot{V}_{O_2,ATPS}$ = 235 ml/min
T   = 22·5°C
P_B = 746 mm Hg
$\dot{V}_{O_2,STPD}$ = 207 ml/min
        = 4·18 kJ/min
        = 251 kJ/h
        = 69·7 W
HEIGHT: 168 cm
WEIGHT: 70 kg
SURFACE AREA: 1·79 m²
B.M.R. = 140 kJ/m²/h
        = 35·5 kJ/kg/h

Fig. 2.12 Chart of oxygen consumption and data for the estimation of B.M.R. obtained with the apparatus shown in Figure 2.11 $\dot{V}_{O_2}$=rate of oxygen consumption; ATPS=atmospheric temperature and pressure saturated with water vapour; STPD=standard temperature and pressure, dry; P_B=barometric pressure. The calculations are explained in the text. Note that as the spirometer bell falls the writing lever rises; the zero time on this chart is on the right and the graph must be read from right to left.

Fig. 2.13 The subject is wearing a 100 litre capacity Douglas bag which is partly filled with expired air. The cylindrical box attached to the mouth-piece contains valves so arranged that the subject breathes in atmospheric air and breathes out through the corrugated tubing into the bag.

area obtained from the formula on this page was $1.52 \, m^2$ and his metabolic rate was therefore $369 \div 1.52 = 243 \, kJ$ per m^2 per hour $= 68 \, W$ per m^2.

Because of its limited capacity the Douglas bag can be used for only 2 or 3 minutes if the subject is carrying out strenuous activity. It is often more convenient to use the Max-Planck respirometer. This apparatus, weighing less than $4 \, kg$, is a small accurately built gas meter. It measures directly the volume of expired air and at the same time diverts a small fraction (0.3 or 0.6 per cent) of the air into a rubber bag for subsequent analysis. The energy expenditure can be calculated from Weir's formula.

So many figures for the energy expenditure during different kinds of activity are now tabulated in the literature that reasonably accurate estimates (as distinct from laborious measurements) of the energy expended in different jobs can be made by an observer, equipped with stop-watch, paper and pencil who records the duration of each kind of activity.

BASAL METABOLIC RATE

The output of energy and the rate of oxygen consumption depend on many factors including body size, muscular activity, the nature and amount of food eaten, changes in environmental and body temperature, thyroid activity and emotional excitement. To reduce the influence of these factors to a minimum and allow a valid comparison of the metabolism of one individual with that of another, it is desirable to measure the metabolism under basal conditions. It is well known, however, that it is difficult, especially for an untrained subject, to achieve the necessary mental and physical relaxation. The oxygen consumption measured in the morning while the subject is lying relaxed and warm in bed 12 to 15 h after the last meal, gives the *basal metabolism*. A certain amount of energy

must continually be produced to maintain essential processes such as the beating of the heart, the breathing and the maintenance of the body temperature.

The heat production of animals of various sizes is closely correlated with the surface area of the body but not with the body weight (Table 2.14). Small animals have a greater surface area per unit of weight than large ones and therefore a relatively greater surface from which heat can be lost. These observations led to the convention established many years ago by which the basal metabolism of large and small persons was standardized by referring it to the surface area of the body. The basal metabolic rate (BMR) is expressed as kJ per m^2 per hour.

Table 2.14 Energy expenditure by different species

	Weight (kg)	kJ/day Per kg	Per m^2 surface
Pig	128.0	80	4510
Man	64.3	134	4360
Dog	15.2	216	4347
Goose	3.5	279	4046
Fowl	2.0	297	3946
Mouse	0.018	2736	4971

The surface area of the body was determined directly by Du Bois by clothing his subjects in thin, wax-impregnated garments. The formula giving the best fit to his data is:

$$S = W^{0.425} \times H^{0.725} \times 0.007184$$

where S is the surface area in m^2, W is the nude weight in kg, H is the height in cm. In practice S is usually determined by the use of standard tables and nomograms based on this formula. The surface area of an adult man is of the order of $1.8 \, m^2$. Because of the scatter of the data it is likely that the value obtained from the formula for any one person deviates appreciably from his true value and that the error in estimation of surface area may be greater than that in estimating oxygen consumption.

The *basal metabolic rate* (BMR) is usually expressed as a percentage of the standard value of a subject of the same sex and age. Variations within the range from 85 to 115 per cent or, as it is usually expressed, minus 15 to plus 15 per cent are accepted as being within normal limits. Occasionally healthy persons deviate more than 20 per cent above or below the standard. The test has therefore little diagnostic value.

Figures 2.15 and 2.16 show how the BMR and total energy requirements vary with age.

For a man the average BMR is about $167 \, kJ/m^2/h$ ($46 \, W/m^2$) and for a woman about $150 \, kJ/m^2/h$ ($42 \, W/m^2$). The lower figures for women are probably due to the greater fat content of the female body.

In babies there is a small range of environmental temperature, namely $36°$ to $38°$ in the newborn, $32°$ to $37°$ at 1 week, in which the metabolic rate at rest is at a minimum. In this range the basal oxygen consumption of newborn infants is about $4.8 \, ml/min/kg$. On the second day it is about $6.6 \, ml/min/kg$. By the seventh day the oxygen consumption reaches $7 \, ml/min/kg$ and remains about $7.2 \, ml/min/kg$ for

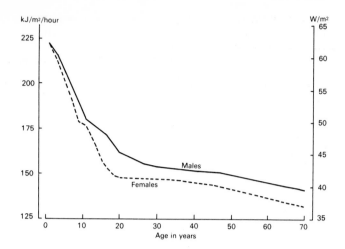

Fig. 2.15 Mean figures for basal metabolic rate in kJ/m²/hour or W/m² from the age of 1 year.

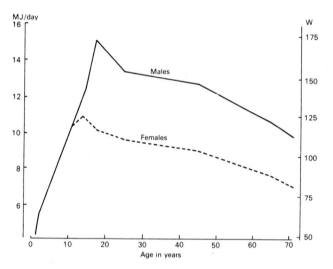

Fig. 2.16 The total daily energy requirement for basal metabolism from 1 year onwards. (Data for this figure and for Figure 2.15 derived from A Fleisch (1951) *Helvetica medica Acta,* **18**, 23–44 and S. Davidson & R. Passmore (1966) *Human Nutrition and Dietetics.* 3rd edition. Edinburgh: Livingstone.)

the first 18 months. The total energy to be supplied in the food is 500 kJ/kg in the first 3 months gradually decreasing to 420 kJ/kg at the end of the first year.

Adipose tissue, having a rich blood supply, is not metabolically inert but it contributes relatively little to the metabolic rate. The oxygen uptake of a person at rest is probably mostly due to the activity of the non-fatty tissues or fat-free mass, FFM. The fat-free mass has a density of $1100\,9\mathrm{kg.m^{-3}}$ but the density of the whole body is less because fatty tissue has a lower density ($900\,\mathrm{kg.m^{-3}}$) than the other tissues of the body. A thin man has a density of the order of $1075\,\mathrm{kg.m^{-3}}$ a plump man about $1046\,\mathrm{kg.m^{-3}}$. Density is measured by weighing the subject in air and then, after maximum expiration, by weighing him in water during complete submersion, due allowance being made for the residual volume of air in the lungs (Chap. 13). From the figure for density the FFM can be calculated. Passmore measured the

Table 2.17

Students	Resting oxygen consumption	
	ml per m² per min	ml per kg lean body mass per min
24 men	141	4·22
25 women	115	4·31

(*From* M. G. MacMillan, C. M. Reid, D. Stirling & R. Passmore (1965) *Lancet,* i, 728–729.)

resting oxygen consumption of 49 medical students (Table 2.17) and found that although there was a significant sex difference in oxygen consumption referred to surface area, the difference in oxygen consumption per kg of lean body mass was not significant. This method is obviously unsuitable for routine use but it has been shown that skinfold thickness measured by suitable callipers gives a fairly good indication of body fat and FFM. The correlation coefficient of skin fold thickness with body density is usually between 0·7 and 0·9. A triceps skinfold thickness of 20 mm for men and 23 mm for women are probably good cut-off points for obesity: these correspond to body fats of about 28 per cent for men and 34 per cent for women.

Specific dynamic action (SDA). After food is absorbed the metabolic activities of the body are stimulated and heat production increases. Thus a person whose metabolism under basal conditions is 7·1 MJ/day actually needs more than 7·1 MJ of food to maintain himself in equilibrium. The metabolism of 7·1 MJ of food raises his energy output to about 7·9 MJ. This increase in metabolism is termed the *specific dynamic action.*

The mechanical efficiency of the human body. The efficiency of a steam engine, or an internal combustion engine, is given by the ratio of the useful work done to the total potential energy (PE) of the fuel used. Thus

$$\text{efficiency} = \frac{\text{useful work}}{\text{PE of fuel}} = \frac{\text{useful work}}{\text{useful work} + \text{heat}}$$

The difference between the total potential energy and the useful work appears as heat. The efficiency of the petrol engine is of the order of 25 per cent.

In man the situation is different since metabolism must continue even at complete rest when no external work is done. In these circumstances the efficiency is obviously zero. Values approaching the true efficiency can be obtained if a very large mass of muscles is brought into action. In such experiments the subject pedals a stationary bicycle connected to an ergometer to measure the external work; the oxygen consumption is measured at the same time to find the potential energy of the fuel used. The gross efficiency in such experiments is of the order of 10 to 20 per cent when care is taken to avoid, or correct for, an oxygen debt (Chap. 21).

Energy Expenditure

Food provides energy for three main purposes. First it is required to maintain basal bodily activities such as heart beat, breathing, muscle tone and body temperature. A man weighing 70 kg has an energy output for basal purposes of 318 kJ/h or 7·7 MJ per day.

Additional food, 1·5 to 2·0 MJ per day, is needed to cover the expenditure of energy in everyday activities, such as sitting, standing, walking and dressing; a further allowance, depending on the nature of the occupation, has to be made for work carried out. Men engaged in hard muscular work may expend as much as 1·6 MJ/h.

Such simple calculations have been found to be misleading for three main reasons. First, the energy expenditure varies considerably from minute to minute in any particular job—few people work steadily at a given rate for an hour. Secondly, even within one sort of job, say domestic work or light engineering, the work varies from sedentary to heavy. Thirdly, very high expenditure cannot be kept up for long. The average man doing physical work for 8 h a day is not likely to show evidence of fatigue if the intensity of the work and the length of the rest pauses are adjusted to give an average energy expenditure of less than 21 kJ/min. This is equivalent to walking on the level at 3·8 miles per hour (6 km/h). If he works twice as hard, he must have rest pauses equal to the actual working time. If we allow 2·1 MJ for sleep and 5·9 MJ as energy expenditure off

Table 2.18 Energy output and intake of a clerk over 1 week (Ian C., age 29, ht. 165 cm, wt. 66 kg.)

Activity	Total time spent hr min		kJ/min	Total MJ
In bed	54	4	4·7	15·4
Daytime dozing	1	43	5·7	0·6
Recreational and off work:				
Light sedentary activities	31	14	6·2	11·8
Washing, shaving, dressing	3	18	12·5	2·5
Light domestic work	7	14	12·5	5·4
Walking	8	35	27·6	14·2
Gardening	2	48	20·1	3·4
Standing activities	6	45	6·5	2·6
Watching football	2	10	8·4	1·1
Total recreational and off work	62	32		41·0
Working:				
Sitting activities	22	22	6·9	9·2
Standing activities	25	27	7·9	12·4
Walking	1	22	27·6	2·3
Total working	49	41		23·9
Grand total	168			80·8
Daily average	24			11·5
Food intake (daily av. determined by diet survey)				11·0

(*From* R. C. Garry, R. Passmore, G. M. Warnock & J. V. A. Durnin (1955) Studies on expenditure of energy and consumption of food by miners and clerks. *Medical Research Council Special Report, 289.* London: H.M.S.O.)

Table 2.19 Energy output and intake of a coal miner over 1 week (John H., age 32, ht. 175 cm, wt. 67 kg.)

Activity	Total time spent hr min		kJ/min	Total MJ
In bed	58	30	4·4	15·4
Recreational and off work:				
Light sedentary activities	38	37	6·6	15·4
Washing, shaving, dressing	5	3	13·8	4·2
Walking	15		20·5	18·5
Standing	2	16	7·5	1·0
Cycling	2	25	27·6	4·0
Gardening	2		20·9	2·5
Total recreational and off work	65	21		45·6
Working:				
Loading	12	6	26·4	19·1
Hewing	1	14	28·0	2·1
Timbering	6	51	23·8	9·8
Walking	6	43	28·0	11·3
Standing	2	6	7·5	1·0
Sitting	15	9	7·0	6·4
Total working	44	9		50·0
Grand total	168			110·7
Daily average	24			15·8
Food intake (daily av. determined by diet survey)				16·7

(*From Garry et al.* as in Table 2.18.)

duty, the total energy expenditure (including 10 MJ for 8 h of work) for this upper limit activity is of the order of 18 MJ/day. This is much less than was at one time given as the daily requirements for blacksmiths or lumbermen but even these strong men must have rest pauses which bring down their average requirements in spite of their high peak performance.

Tables 2.18 and 2.19 show the results of investigations of energy expenditure in a sedentary worker and in a heavy manual worker. To assess the requirements accurately, detailed minute to minute diaries of their activities were kept for a complete week because omission of weekend activities gives a false impression of the average needs. About one-third of the day is spent asleep. The amount of muscular movement in sleep varies from person to person, but it is considerable and no one sleeps like the proverbial log. On average the energy requirement is at the basal level—for an adult man 5·4 kJ/min. The performance of personal necessities, such as dressing and undressing, requires in different people 10 to 17 kJ/min. An average adult walking on the level at 2 miles per hour (3 km/h) needs 12 kJ per minute; at 4 miles per hour (6·5 km/h) he requires 24 kJ per minute. Walking up an incline of 15 per cent at 2 miles per hour (3 km/h) requires 25 kJ/min. Mental 'work', for example adding or multiplying figures, has no significant effect on metabolism. Light indoor recreations may require up to 17 kJ/min while hard exercise may involve 84 kJ. Domestic work varies between 8 and 33 kJ/min. Typing requires about 5·9 kJ/min. Christensen's gradings of severity for different forms of work are generally accepted:

Unduly heavy	over 2·5 litres oxygen per min	= 850 W
Very heavy	over 2·0 litres oxygen per min	= 680 W
Heavy	over 1·5 litres oxygen per min	= 510 W
Moderate	over 1·0 litres oxygen per min	= 340 W
Light	over 0·5 litres oxygen per min	= 170 W

His observations on Swedish ironworkers led him to point out that in a hot environment grading by oxygen uptake does not measure the real stress on the subject. Pulse rate then becomes a better indicator of stress and the above gradings would correspond to pulse rates of: over 175, 150 to 175, 120 to 150, 100 to 125 and 75 to 100 respectively.

HUNGER AND APPETITE

Hunger is usually taken to mean the sensation of emptiness resulting from abstinence from food. On the other hand appetite is thought of as the desire for food or the pleasure in taking food.

Many people report that their body weight remains constant over many years and conclude that the body possesses some mechanism which adjusts the intake of food so that it balances the energy output. Detailed investigations have shown however that body weight fluctuates quite considerably. A survey in Wales showed that middle aged and elderly subjects may gain or lose 5 kg during a five year period. Since however the weight changes, in spite of considerable day to day variation in intake, are slow it is difficult to avoid the conclusion that there is a control mechanism even if it is not always very effective. Overfeeding experiments show that some men gain weight more readily than others. Individuals therefore vary in the efficiency with which they use food energy. The conversion of surplus energy to heat rather than to fat (so-called inefficient utilization) is called 'dietary induced thermogenesis'. However there is no general agreement as to the extent which appetite contributes to the maintenance of a nearly constant body weight.

The sensation of hunger may be associated with gastric contractions. However, after complete vagotomy the sensation of hunger is modified but does not disappear; even after surgical removal of large portions of the stomach patients feel hungry much as other people do. Insulin administered in sufficient dose to produce a marked hypoglycaemia gives rise to a sensation of hunger even after denervation of the stomach. Hunger decreases and even disappears during complete starvation perhaps because of the onset of ketosis (p. 93).

Experiments on rats, cats and monkeys have shown that food intake is controlled by the hypothalamus; bilateral damage to the ventromedial nuclei of the hypothalamus causes obesity but bilateral lesions placed more laterally abolish hunger and the animals die of starvation. Whether the ventromedial nuclei should be regarded as 'satiety centres' and the lateral areas as 'feeding centres' remains controversial because damage to these areas causes changes in behaviour which might well affect feeding. The origin and nature of the signals to the hypothalamus are unknown; a blood-borne factor related to fat may be responsible. The increase in metabolism due to specific dynamic action may be related to satiety especially as the increase is greater in subjects grossly overfed.

Since the body's store of carbohydrate is small it is reasonable to ask if the cause of hunger is to be found in carbohydrate metabolism and in particular in the level of blood sugar. A sensation of hunger is present when the blood sugar is markedly lowered by the administration of insulin but in hungry, healthy, fasting persons the blood sugar is always in the normal range. Furthermore many middle-aged patients with diabetes mellitus have excellent appetites despite prolonged elevation of the blood glucose level.

2DG (2-deoxy-D-glucose), a non-metabolizable analogue of glucose, blocks transport into the cells and inactivates certain enzymes involved in the oxidation of glucose. After intravenous infusion of 2DG the blood sugar rises but the subject becomes hungry presumably because of the fall in intracellular glucose.

It is often said that exercise increases appetite and this must be true since the body weight of active people and animals usually remains constant. Various surveys of healthy persons with normal body weight in the range 45 to 80 kg show that heavier individuals have only a slightly greater energy intake than lighter ones. This may seem rather surprising since extra body weight requires greater energy expenditure at rest or during exercise. However, heavy people are usually less active than lighter ones.

Fat persons have a shorter expectation of life than thin persons and have a greater incidence of cardiovascular and other diseases. Although the immediate cause of increase in weight is an excess of food intake over energy output, it is only a part of the story. Genetic factors are shown by the finding that the body weights and skinfold thickness of identical twins are closer than those of non-identical twins even when the former are separated and reared in different environments. Hormonal influences are shown by the tendency of some women to put on weight with each pregnancy. It is possible that some metabolic pathways and the methods of disposal of energy may be different in the obese; it is likely that some individuals remain slim because they possess 'wasteful' metabolic pathways.

THE 'NORMAL' DIET

The daily energy requirements can be derived from carbohydrates, fats and proteins in a wide variety of proportions. Although it is theoretically possible to replace a given amount of one foodstuff by an isocaloric amount of another, such a process is limited by considerations mentioned later. A diet containing 400 g carbohydrate, 100 g fat and 100 g protein provides 12·4 MJ. Most diets contain a large proportion of carbohydrate because foods containing it are abundant and cheap. Wasted food—plate waste, left-overs, spilled food, sour milk, stale bread, spoiled fruit—amounts to 5 or 6 per cent of potentially edible food.

Protein Requirements

The growing child requires an adequate supply of protein to provide the amino acids out of which new tissue protein is constructed; the adult requires protein to make good tissue lost by wear and tear, to build up new tissue protein after a wasting illness, and to supply amino acids essential for the synthesis of enzymes and certain hormones.

The proteins of the tissues of the body are continuously being broken down into their constituent amino acids, most of which are used to build up new protein molecules. This turnover of proteins in an adult is of the order of 400 g per day.

The nutritional value of any particular protein depends upon the nature of its constituent amino acids and their relative proportions. Some amino acids are readily synthesized from ammonia and simple carbon compounds; their presence in the diet is therefore not essential. Other amino acids cannot be synthesized by the tissues and must be supplied in the diet. These are known as the *essential amino acids* and have been defined as 'not synthesized by the animal organism out of the materials ordinarily available at a speed commensurate with normal growth'. For example lysine and threonine must be supplied in the diet. In some cases a particular grouping, or nucleus, may be all that is necessary to allow the body to form a complete amino acid. For example, histidine is an essential amino acid but the body can complete its synthesis if the imidazole ring is supplied in the form of imidazole pyruvic acid, the oxo acid corresponding to histidine. In such a case the indispensable unit appears to be the carbon chain, the amino group being introduced by the body as required. Indeed, all the essential amino acids except lysine and threonine take part in the reversible transfer of amino groups from amino acids to oxo acids.

The distinction between the essential and the non-essential amino acids is not precise. The amino acid glycine is readily synthesized by the tissues of the growing chick but its glycine requirements are so great that the rate of utilization exceeds the rate of synthesis and glycine becomes one of the essential amino acids in its diet. It should also be noted that if certain essential amino acids are present in suboptimal amounts the deficiency in the diet may be made good by others not normally regarded as essential.

Thus the essential amino acid methionine may be converted to cystine in the body and used in reactions involving cystine. Although cystine cannot be transformed to methionine its presence in the diet releases dietary methionine for other purposes. To take another example, the tissues can synthesize tyrosine from phenylalanine but not phenylalanine from tyrosine. Phenylalanine is therefore an essential amino acid while tyrosine is not, but the addition of tyrosine to a diet containing suboptimal amounts of phenylalanine may prevent the appearance of deficiency symptoms.

The amino acid requirements of the young animal or child differ in some respects from those of the adult. In the absence of certain amino acids from the diet growth may be retarded. For example when young rats were fed an otherwise adequate

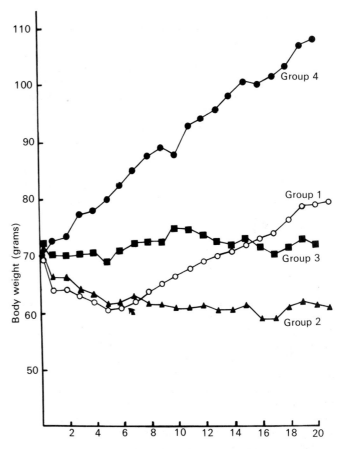

Fig. 2.20 An experiment by H. N. Munro to show the effect of adding lysine and tryptophan to a zein diet fed to young rats. The rats in Group 2 were fed on a diet containing 15 per cent zein as sole source of protein. They did not grow and tended to lose weight. The rats in Group 1 were similarly fed, but lysine and tryptophan were added at the point indicated by the arrow. Good growth then occurred. The rats in Group 3 were pair-fed with those in Group 2 on a diet containing 15 per cent casein in place of zein, that is they were given only that amount of food which the rats in Group 2 ate spontaneously. They showed poor growth, but they did not lose weight. The rats in Group 4 received the casein diet in the same amounts as those in Group 3, but they were allowed to eat as much as they wanted of a non-protein diet as well. They grew very well. It is clear that while addition of the missing amino acids improves the deficient diet, the animals on the deficient diet have a poor appetite and this tends to aggravate their condition.

diet in which the sole protein was zein from maize, which is deficient in tryptophan and lysine, they not only ceased to grow but lost weight. When tryptophan was added the fall in weight was arrested and when both tryptophan and lysine were given normal growth was resumed. Tryptophan and lysine are therefore essential amino acids for the growing rat (Fig. 2.20).

The amino acid requirements of the adult human being are not easily determined, but when certain amino acids are missing from an otherwise adequate diet, the output of nitrogen in urine and faeces exceeds the intake (Fig. 2.21). This negative nitrogen balance (p. 20) can be made positive by the addition of the appropriate amino acid to the diet.

The amino acids essential for the maintenance of nitrogen balance in adult man are lysine, tryptophan, phenylalanine, leucine, isoleucine, threonine, methionine and valine. About 1 g of each is the minimum daily requirement. Histidine and arginine are apparently not essential for nitrogen equilibrium in man but their lack may have adverse effects. Thus the absence of arginine from the diet is followed by a reduction in the number of spermatozoa in the seminal fluid. The remaining amino acids (alanine, aspartic acid, cystine, glutamic acid, glycine, hydroxyproline, serine and tyrosine) are not essential for man.

The dietary value of any protein thus depends upon its content of essential amino acids. A protein such as lactalbumin containing all the essential amino acids ('biologically complete') is clearly nutritionally superior to zein of maize, which is deficient in tryptophan and lysine, or to gelatin which is deficient in tryptophan. Proteins are said to have a high biological value if they supply all the essential amino acids in approximately optimal proportions and are able to maintain nitrogen balance even if they are the sole source of nitrogen in the diet. Most animal proteins with the notable exception of gelatin fall into this category. Most plant proteins are of low biological value because they are deficient in one or more of the essential amino acids.

The distinction between these two types of protein, however, is seldom of practical importance for man does not normally eat a diet containing a single protein. In a mixed diet the lack of particular amino acids in one protein is made up by their presence in others. Plant proteins are of great importance to the diet in many developing countries. Pulses and beans are important sources of protein; examples are *dal* in India and kidney beans in Latin America. These contain only small amounts of methionine but this lack can be made up from the protein of potatoes or cereals whose lack of lysine is compensated at the same time.

Attempts have been made to assess the minimum protein requirement by nitrogen balance requirements. On any given diet, there are three possible results: (1) nitrogen output may exceed intake: the subject is then in negative balance; (2) output may be less than intake, in which case he is storing nitrogenous compounds and is said to be in positive balance; (3) nitrogen intake may be just adequate to offset excretion and the subject is then in nitrogenous equilibrium. Equilibrium is reached at a wide range of protein intake but below a certain level it cannot occur for the following reasons. If a human subject is given a diet of adequate energy value but containing no protein, the output of nitrogenous compounds in the urine is reduced to the equivalent of 2 to 3 g of nitrogen per day (Fig. 2.21). This so called endogenous output of nitrogen is of course derived from the breakdown of tissue protein. The obligatory loss in the faeces is about 1 g nitrogen per day. Loss of skin cells, hair, nails and sweat causes a further loss of over 1 g of nitrogen per day. In women 2 or 3 g nitrogen are lost at each menstrual bleeding. Some infections cause large and prolonged loss of urinary nitrogen.

Figure 2.21 also shows that measurement of the urinary nitrogen in a balance experiment can give a measure of the biological value of different proteins in man or in experimental animals. The biological values of some foodstuffs are given in Figure 2.22.

Another measure of the nutritional value of proteins is the *chemical score*. This is obtained by calculating the proportion of each essential amino acid in a foodstuff as a percentage of

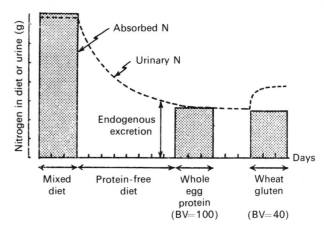

Fig. 2.21 The urinary nitrogen output of a human subject on a protein-free diet gradually falls to a fairly constant level, the so-called 'endogenous output', representing obligatory loss of body protein. If the subject is now fed with whole egg protein, equivalent in amount to the loss of body protein, the urinary nitrogen output does not increase above the endogenous level; this indicates that the egg protein has been fully utilized by the body. Whole egg protein thus has a biological value (BV) of 100. Biological value is defined as the ratio

$$\frac{\text{Dietary nitrogen retained}}{\text{Dietary nitrogen absorbed}} \times 100$$

If wheat gluten is fed in similar quantity, the urinary nitrogen output rises because this protein is poorly utilized, having a biological value of 40. (H. N. Munro & J. B. Allison (1964) in Mammalian Protein Metabolism, ed H. N. Munro Vol. 1. New York: Academic Press.)

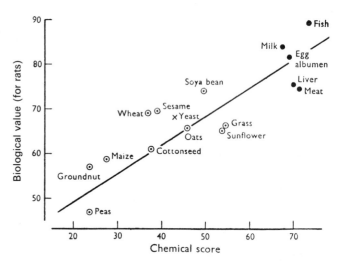

Fig. 2.22 Correlation diagram of the biological value and chemical score of five animal (⊙) and ten vegetable (●) materials and yeast (×). (*From* K. J. Carpenter (1951) *British Journal of Nutrition* 5, 243.)

the proportion of the same amino acid in whole egg protein which is selected as a 'reference protein'. The lowest percentage obtained is used as the chemical score since the limiting amino acid is held to determine the value of the whole protein. Figure 2.22 shows the chemical score of various proteins plotted against their biological value for rats obtained by nitrogen balance experiments. The two methods of evaluation correlate well. A diet containing fat and carbohydrates as well as protein produces nitrogenous equilibrium at a lower level of nitrogen intake than does a diet of protein only. Carbohydrate and fat are therefore said to have a *protein-sparing action*. If his energy requirements are met, man can adjust to wide variations in protein intake. In western countries between 10 and 15 per cent of the total energy intake is in the form of protein, of which about 60 per cent is animal protein. Some races eat more protein than this without any apparent deleterious or beneficial effect.

The popular impression that men engaged in hard physical work require more protein and consequently need to eat more meat than those engaged in sedentary occupations has no scientific support. The fuel used in muscular work is carbohydrate and fat, not protein, and the increased energy needs of the manual worker can generally be met out of an increased consumption of carbohydrate and fat. But the man who is habitually engaged in hard physical work is generally larger, better developed and heavier than his sedentary colleague and his protein requirements are presumably greater.

Protein deficiency. The body does not possess a store of protein but if the dietary intake is inadequate the proteins in the tissues break down into amino acids which may help to maintain the protein in essential tissues. The loss of protein is not critical until the body weight falls by 25 per cent; in an average man with (initially) normal amounts of adipose tissue this occurs after two months of total starvation. Protein is lost from different organs at different rates. The liver loses protein rapidly and prolonged protein deficiency can cause the death of large numbers of liver cells (liver necrosis). The kidney is less rapidly depleted of protein than the liver, and the loss of protein from skeletal muscle is much slower and less severe. Some organs, for example the eye, may actually continue to grow during protein depletion. Furthermore, a skin wound heals quite rapidly in a protein-deficient animal, though the process is less rapid than in the case of a well-fed animal. Malignant tumours also continue to grow in animals given protein-free diets. Since enzymes are protein in nature, it would be expected that they would be affected by severe protein deficiency. The effect varies from enzyme to enzyme; thus liver phosphatase is little changed whereas xanthine oxidase almost disappears from the liver.

Protein lack causes a considerable reduction in the plasma albumin level which, unlike the other manifestations of protein deficiency, can easily be measured. Since the colloid osmotic pressure of the plasma falls the subject may develop oedema (Chap. 16).

Severe protein malnutrition, called *kwashiorkor*, affects millions of young children in Asia, Africa and Latin America. It occurs in infants after weaning when instead of their mothers' milk they are given a mainly carbohydrate diet. Many of these children also have an inadequate energy intake and the disorder is known as protein-energy malnutrition. The affected child stops growing, loses weight and becomes listless, apathetic and peevish. The skin and hair become depigmented; the body becomes oedematous. The fundamental defect is a lack of amino acids and thus impairment of protein synthesis. The serum albumin concentration falls and pathological changes are found in the liver and pancreas. The children can be cured by giving them protein-containing foods but if not treated the condition is often fatal.

A physical injury, such as a fracture of bone or a surgical operation, is immediately followed by a period of negative nitrogen balance which reaches its maximum about a week after the injury. Since the urinary loss of nitrogen (mainly urea) is paralleled by that of sulphate and phosphate these substances must be derived from the breakdown of muscle. The hormonal changes responsible for the metabolic events are very complex; presumably sympathetic activity is greatly increased.

Fat Requirements

The fat of the diet is important not only on account of its high energy value but because it is the vehicle for the fat-soluble vitamins A, D, E and K, and contains the essential fatty acids, *linoleic acid* and *linolenic acid*. These unsaturated fatty acids cannot be synthesized by the tissues. Essential fatty acid deficiency is uncommon in man but has been described in patients with impaired absorption after resection of large parts of the intestine.

Provided that the supply of fat-soluble vitamins and essential fatty acids is adequate, fat itself is not an essential constituent of the diet. The fat content of human diets varies widely according to climate, race and dietary custom. In Western countries the fat intake per day is about 80 to 150 g per head, or about 35 to 40 per cent of the total energy intake. In tropical countries much less fat is eaten, 15 per cent or less of the total energy. A diet lacking in fat, if it supplies adequate energy, tends to be bulky.

Carbohydrate Requirements

The proportion of carbohydrate in the diet varies widely. In western countries less than 50 per cent of the energy intake may come from carbohydrate. Since carbohydrate foods derived from cereals are generally cheap they tend to form a large proportion of the diet in developing countries.

It is of course desirable to eat sufficient carbohydrate to prevent ketosis (p. 93) but the amount required for this purpose is low and is in practice always exceeded unless a ketogenic diet is devised deliberately.

Fibre Requirements

Insoluble material, such as cellulose or bran, has been long described as roughage and was regarded simply as a stimulant of the muscle of the large bowel (p. 83). The term fibre, as now used, includes bran and a heterogeneous collection of other materials relatively resistant to digestion such as pectin, guar gum and similar gel-forming polysaccharides, cellulose, lignin and cutin. In 1970 Burkitt found that rural populations in Africa who had a high fibre intake were remarkably free from many of the diseases of the intestinal tract and vascular system commonly found in city dwellers. The extent to which a diet low in fibre contributes to the causation of these diseases remains to be decided.

Table 2.23   Recommended daily intakes of nutrients

Age	Body weight kg	Energy MJ	Protein (a) g	Vitamin A (b) µg	Vitamin D µg	Thiamin mg	Ribo-flavin mg	Niacin mg	Folic acid µg	Vitamin B$_{12}$ µg	Ascorbic acid mg	Calcium g	Iron (c) mg
Children													
<1	7·3	3·4	14	300	10·0	0·3	0·5	5·4	60	0·3	20	0·5-0·6	5-10
1-3	13·4	5·7	16	250	10·0	0·5	0·8	9·0	100	0·9	20	0·4-0·5	5-10
4-6	20·2	7·6	20	300	10·0	0·7	1·1	12·1	100	1·5	20	0·4-0·5	5-10
7-9	28·1	9·2	25	400	2·5	0·9	1·3	14·5	100	1·5	20	0·4-0·5	5-10
Male adolescents													
10-12	36·9	10·9	30	575	2·5	1·0	1·6	17·2	100	2·0	20	0·6-0·7	5-10
13-15	51·3	12·1	37	725	2·5	1·2	1·7	19·1	200	2·0	30	0·6-0·7	9-18
16-19	62·9	12·8	38	750	2·5	1·2	1·8	20·3	200	2·0	30	0·5-0·6	5-9
Female adolescents													
10-12	38·0	9·8	29	575	2·5	0·9	1·4	15·5	100	2·0	20	0·6-0·7	5-10
13-15	49·9	10·4	31	725	2·5	1·0	1·5	16·4	200	2·0	30	0·6-0·7	12-24
16-19	54·4	9·7	30	750	2·5	0·9	1·4	15·2	200	2·0	30	0·5-0·6	14-28
Adult man (moderately active)	65·0	12·6	37	750	2·5	1·2	1·8	19·8	200	2·0	30	0·4-0·5	5-9
Adult woman (moderately active)	55·0	9·2	29	750	2·5	0·9	1·3	14·5	200	2·0	30	0·4-0·5	14-28
Pregnancy (later half)		+1·5	38	750	10·0	+0·1	+0·2	+2·3	400	3·0	50	1·0-1·2	(d)
Lactation (first 6 months)		+2·3	46	1200	10·0	+0·2	+0·4	+3·7	300	2·5	50	1·0-1·2	(d)

From various official reports of FAO/WHO expert groups collected together by R. Passmore, B. M. Q. Nicol and M. Narayana Rao (1974) *Handbook of Human Nutritional Requirements* Geneva: World Health Organisation. Reproduced by permission.

Footnotes:

(a) Expressed as egg or milk protein.

(b) Expressed as retinol.

(c) On each line the lower value applies when over 25 per cent of the energy in the diet comes from animal foods; the higher value when animal foods represent less than 10 per cent of energy.

(d) For women whose iron stores are adequate at the commencement of pregnancy iron requirements are the same as for non-pregnant women. Supplementary iron is probably needed by women who begin their pregnancy with iron depletion.

The Effects of Starvation

When the body is deprived of food it calls first on its stores of carbohydrate and fat for the provision of energy. Stores of carbohydrate—glycogen in liver and muscle—are never great and are soon exhausted but, in the well nourished subject, fat stores may be sufficient, if activity is reduced, to supply the needs of the body for several weeks. When fat is being metabolized in large amount, ketosis results and the urine may contain large amounts of ketone bodies. Long before, the reserves of non-nitrogenous fuel are exhausted, the tissue proteins begin to be broken down to provide energy. The skeletal, cardiac and visceral muscle all atrophy but the brain does not. When the fat stores are exhausted protein is the sole source of energy. Thus, while nitrogen excretion is low in the early stages of starvation, it rises sharply after the exhaustion of carbohydrate and fat stores, when the tissue proteins are being drawn upon. Death is preceded by a rise in nitrogen excretion.

THE VITAMINS

It was first realized at the beginning of the present century that disease in laboratory animals and in man could be produced by a diet adequate in energy but deficient in certain other respects. The idea of accessory food factors (now called vitamins) is strikingly illustrated by a series of experiments carried out by Hopkins between 1906 and 1912 (Fig. 2.24). He showed that young rats fed on diets consisting of purified casein, starch, sucrose, lard and inorganic salts ceased to grow and then became ill and died. If the purified diet was supplemented with a small daily allowance of milk, no more than 4 per cent of the total food eaten, the health of the animals was restored and they began to grow again.

The vitamins, organic substances of known structure and low molecular weight, are essential components in metabolic processes. In their absence a 'biochemical lesion' develops which may be accompanied by structural changes in various tissues. The amount that has to be ingested to maintain health is different for each vitamin but is usually quite small. The *daily requirement* for any one vitamin depends on a number of factors and may be increased during growth, pregnancy and lactation. Although the vitamins are described below one by one it should be appreciated that diets in poor communities are often deficient in several vitamins.

Vitamin A (Retinol)

Both forms of vitamin A, retinol and dehydroretinol, are lipid-soluble, unsaturated alcohols (Fig. 2.25). Plants, the ultimate source of all vitamin A-active substances, do not contain the vitamin but animals eating the plants convert the carotenes into vitamin A within the intestinal mucosa. The carotenes are widely distributed in vegetables and fruits especially in the greener or most highly coloured parts. Red palm oil, the traditional cooking oil in many parts of west and central Africa, is a particularly good source. In developing countries most of the vitamin A in the diet comes from vegetable sources while in Western countries animal and vegetable sources contribute equally to the dietary intake of the vitamin. The estimated daily requirements are given in Table 2.23.

The most widely used foods containing significant amounts of vitamin A are liver, eggs, milk, butter and vitaminized margarine (Table 2.26). The vitamin A content of eggs and dairy produce depends on the diet of the fowl or cow and thus on the season. Most of the vitamin A in animal tissues is in the form of esters.

Vitamin A is readily oxidized in the presence of molecular oxygen to biologically inactive compounds, but in an inert atmosphere it is quite stable to heat. Most foodstuffs retain their vitamin A content if they are stored under conditions in which oxygen is excluded. Vitamin A is slowly destroyed in fats and oils, even at room temperature, especially if the fat becomes rancid. The frying of food in deep fat results in considerable loss of vitamin A, not only in the fat but also in material cooked in it. The cooking of vegetables usually reduces their carotene content only to a slight extent.

Vitamin A is absorbed after first being incorporated into micelles in the presence of bile salts (p. 73). At this stage the vitamin A esters are hydrolysed by pancreatic esterases. Within the mucosal cell vitamin A is again esterified, mainly with palmitate, and transported via the lymphatic vessels and the thoracic duct to the liver which is the principal site of its storage. The liver of a healthy adult contains sufficient vitamin A to last many months. Bile salts are also needed for carotene

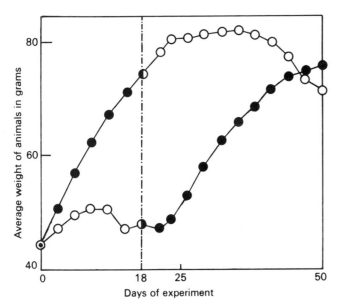

Fig. 2.24 An experiment of Hopkins illustrating the concept of accessory food factors. 'Lower curve (up to 18th day) eight male rats upon pure dietary; upper curve eight similar rats taking 3 ml of milk each day. On the 18th day, marked by vertical dotted line, the milk was transferred from one set to the other.' (F. G. Hopkins (1912), *Journal of Physiology*, 44, 425.)

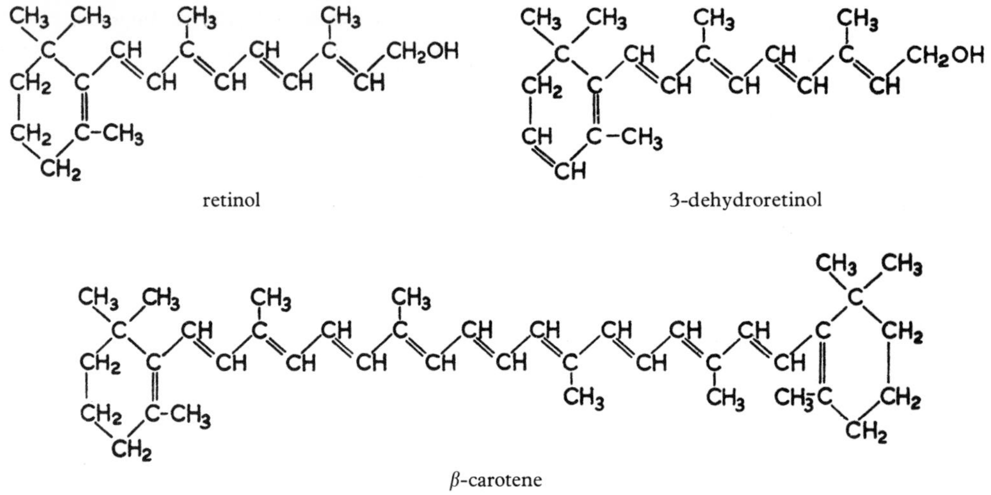

Fig. 2.25 Structures of the two forms of vitamin A and of carotene.

absorption. Within the mucosal cell much of the absorbed carotene is converted to vitamin A while the remainder is absorbed unchanged. Some carotene is stored in adipose tissue. In the plasma vitamin A and carotene are carried by albumin and lipoproteins, respectively. In health the concentration of vitamin A in the plasma is 200 to 500 $\mu g/l$; that of carotenoids is 200 to 2000 $\mu g/l$.

Vitamin A deficiency may be the result of an inadequate intake or of defective absorption, as in obstructive jaundice. Dietary deficiency of vitamin A causes *xerophthalmia*, a major cause of blindness in hundreds of thousands of children in developing countries. Since visual purple (Chap. 27) is derived from retinol, it is easy to understand that vitamin A deficiency causes atrophy of the rods and cones of the retina and other retinal abnormalities. The patient's first symptom is usually night-blindness; at this stage the disorder is reversible. Later there is progressive dryness (*xerosis*) of the cornea; this is reversible in the early stages, but eventually irreversible corneal scarring and *keratomalacia* (softening and destruction of the cornea) ensues. At the same time there may be changes in other epithelia including *follicular hyperkeratosis* (rough dry skin).

An excessive intake of vitamin A leads to toxic effects such as drowsiness, headache and vomiting. In addition there may be skin changes, loss of hair, anaemia, bone resorption and hypercalcaemia.

Thiamin

Thiamin (vitamin B$_1$) is water-soluble and consists of a pyrimidine and a thiazole ring system joined by a methylene bridge. In acid solution it withstands prolonged heating at 120°C but in alkaline solution it is rapidly destroyed. Under ordinary conditions thiamin is not oxidized by atmospheric oxygen.

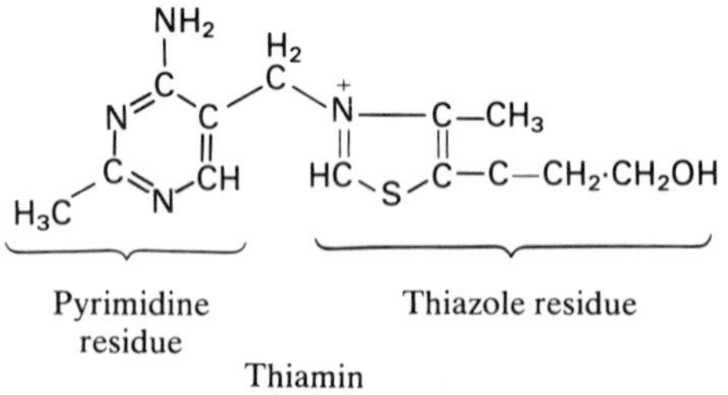

Table 2.26 Vitamin A potency of foods

	Retinol equivalent* μg per 100 g		
Animal sources			
Halibut-liver oil	1 000 000	to	12 000 000
Cod-liver oil	10 000	to	100 000
Fatty fish, e.g. herring and sardines	30	to	200
White fish, e.g. cod and plaice		trace	
Ox liver	3000	to	13 000
Beef (lean)	10	to	20
Cow's milk (varies with season)	20	to	50
Human milk	70	to	200
Butter	700	to	2000
Cheese	300	to	1000
Margarine (fortified)	800	to	1000
Eggs	200	to	400
Vegetable sources			
Red palm oil	up	to	10 000
Carrots	1000	to	2000
Spinach	800	to	1500

*Values are expressed in terms of retinol. Carotene has a lower potency than vitamin A; 6 μg carotene can be regarded as equivalent to 1 μg retinol in man.

The physiological actions of thiamin are due to its pyrophosphoric ester, co-carboxylase (thiamin pyrophosphate, TPP). TPP is a coenzyme in the enzyme systems needed for the decarboxylation of α-keto acids such as pyruvic acid.

When thiamin is lacking, pyruvic acid cannot be metabolized and so it accumulates in the fluids and tissues of the body. The estimation of the pyruvate level in the blood may be helpful in detecting thiamin deficiency but it is not specific

Fig. 2.27 A patient with 'dry' beri-beri suffering from wrist-drop, foot-drop and marked wasting of the lower extremities. (*Courtesy of B. S. Platt.*)

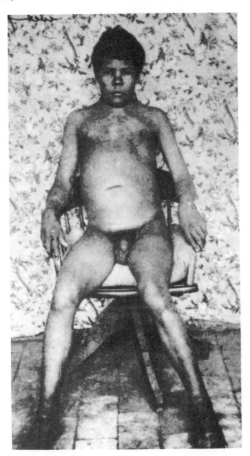

Fig. 2.28 A case of beri-beri with extensive oedema. 'Wet' beri-beri (*Courtesy of Wellcome Museum of Medical Science.*)

Table 2.29 Thiamin in foods (mg per 100 g)

Wheat (germ)	2·5 to 5·6
Flour, wholemeal	0·35 to 0·4
85 per cent extraction	0·30 to 0·4
70 per cent extraction (white)	0·05
Oatmeal	0·5
Yeast	1·8 to 3·0
Milk	0·04 to 0·06
Eggs	0·1 to 0·15
Beef and mutton	0·05 to 0·1
Pulses	0·5 to 0·9
Rice, polished	0·02 to 0·04
Rice, whole	0·1

since the pyruvate level may be raised in other conditions.

Prolonged deficiency of thiamin in man results in the disorder known among rice eating peoples as *beri-beri* (Fig. 2.27). This condition, still common in many parts of the world, is occasionally seen in Britain in chronic alcoholics living on a very poor diet. It is characterized by: (a) polyneuropathy, that is to say peripheral nerve destruction leading to muscle weakness and atrophy and disturbances of sensation; (b) enlargement of the heart, generalized vasodilatation and cardiac failure causing oedema (Fig. 2.28). 'Wet' beri-beri often improves within hours of injecting thiamin.

Thiamin is present in many plants; particularly high concentrations are found in seeds such as pulses and nuts and in the outer coats of grains (Table 2.29). Polished rice, because it has lost its husk, contains little thiamin. Similarly white flour contains little thiamin unless fortified. Wholemeal flour, however, contains 350 to 400 μg per 100 g and is therefore a relatively good source. The vitamin is widely distributed in animal tissues and the lean parts of meat, especially pork, may be important dietary sources. Yeast and yeast extracts contain very large amounts of thiamin and many bacteria are capable of synthesizing it. Although high temperatures and an alkaline medium favour destruction of the vitamin, losses during the cooking of food are not large.

The blood contains some 5 to 11 μg of thiamin per 100 ml, almost entirely in the form of TPP. The body stores very little thiamin—about 25 mg—principally in the heart, brain, liver and kidney.

The recommended thiamin intake is of the order of 1 mg per day but the amount should be increased if the intake of carbohydrate increases. Diets consisting mainly of polished rice supply much less and continued subsistence on such a diet produces beri-beri.

Riboflavin

In 1932 Warburg and Christian isolated from yeast a 'yellow enzyme' which they later showed could be separated into a protein component and a coloured substance neither of which was active without the other. The yellow compound proved to be riboflavin phosphate.

In the living cell riboflavin is converted into riboflavin phosphate or into flavin-adenine dinucleotide (FAD), both of which combine with proteins to form the *flavo-proteins* that act as hydrogen carriers in biological oxidation systems.

riboflavin

Riboflavin is absorbed from the upper alimentary tract. Its blood level is about 100 nmol/l, mainly combined as FAD and riboflavin phosphate. High concentrations of the vitamin are found in the liver, heart and kidneys which retain relatively large amounts even when the body is seriously depleted. Riboflavin is eliminated in the urine as the pigment, uroflavin.

Deficiency of riboflavin (*ariboflavinosis*) has been produced experimentally in man. The skin becomes rough and scaly; the pink parts of the lips are bright red, swollen and cracked (*cheilosis*); and the tissues at the corners of the lips are swollen and fissured (*angular stomatitis*). The tongue is sometimes tender and magenta in colour. In minor degrees of riboflavin deficiency, microscopic examination of the patient's eyes with a slit-lamp shows that the transparent cornea is invaded by minute blood vessels.

Riboflavin is widely distributed in foods; it is synthesized by plants and occurs particularly in germinating seeds and young growing green plants. Peas, beans, grains and yeast are the most important plant sources. Animal sources are milk, egg yolk, liver, kidney and heart muscle. The riboflavin found in most plant and animal tissues, as well as in yeast, is present mainly in the combined form but in milk the greater part is in the free state (Table 2.30).

Table 2.30 Riboflavin in foods (mg per 100 g)

Yeast	5·0	Cheese	0·50
Wheat	0·18 to 0·25	Egg	0·4
Pulses	0·15 to 0·3	Meat	0·25
Milk	0·15 to 0·20	Liver	3·0

The vitamin is relatively stable in acid solution in the dark. Ordinary cooking causes little destruction of riboflavin although some is lost by extraction in the cooking water. Considerable loss of riboflavin occurs in milk exposed to bright sunlight.

The recommended daily allowance of riboflavin is 1·5 to 1·8 mg per day but a more generous intake is advised in pregnancy.

Niacin

The term 'niacin' includes nicotinic acid and nicotinamide. Nicotinic acid has been known to chemists for more than a hundred years but the discovery that it is the factor preventing pellagra was made only in 1937. The beneficial effects produced by the administration of nicotinic acid to human patients or to dogs or pigs suffering from deficiency are due to its conversion into the amide which is then converted into

nicotinic acid   nicotinamide

nicotinamide adenine dinucleotide (NAD) and nicotinamide adenine dinucleotide phosphate (NADP). Additional nicotinic acid is provided by its synthesis from tryptophan by the intestinal flora and probably by the tissues. In man about 60 mg of tryptophan can replace 1 mg of nicotinic acid in the food.

Niacin is a very stable vitamin; it is not destroyed by heat, light or alkali. Losses in cooking are small although some is extracted into the cooking water.

Pellagra (Fig. 2.31), the disorder which is relieved by the administration of niacin, affected millions of people in the southern United States of America between 1900 and 1940. Extreme poverty made these people dependent on maize and molasses. Improvement in the diet during the 1930s led to a decline in the incidence of the disease and to its virtual disappearance in 1942.

Pellagra is now uncommon but is still found in communities subsisting principally on maize. Maize diets consumed by people who suffered from pellagra often contained more niacin than did the poor rice diets of groups of people who did

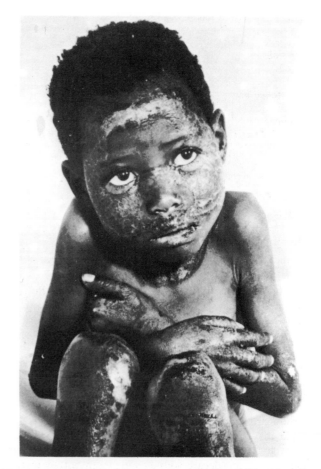

Fig. 2.31 Ulcerative lesions in the skin of a child with pellagra. (*Courtesy of J. G. Prinsloo.*)

not suffer from pellagra. This apparent anomaly is due to the fact that niacin in maize is present in a bound form, niacytin, which is not broken down in the alimentary canal. Niacytin can, however, be broken down by alkalis.

Pellagra begins with a prolonged period of general ill-health, characterized by irritability, depression, loss of weight and strength and lack of appetite. The patient often develops diarrhoea which accelerates the loss of weight and strength. About the same time the skin becomes reddened and later roughened and scaly, especially on the exposed parts of the body normally subjected to the action of light and heat. Redness and soreness of the mouth, with swelling and redness of the tongue, further increase the patient's difficulties and a vicious circle occurs, in which the more severe the deficiency the more difficult it becomes for the patient to eat a curative diet and the more rapidly the disorder progresses. Patients eventually develop dementia. Most of these symptoms can be rapidly corrected by the administration of nicotinic acid. Nearly all patients with pellagra, however, have signs of other vitamin deficiencies.

In the combined form of NAD and NADP, nicotinic acid is widely distributed in animal tissues. Liver, kidney and muscle are the best animal sources. About $50\ \mu mol/l$ is found in blood. Yeast and the outer parts of grain are good sources of the vitamin (Table 2.32), but the valuable part of the grain is almost completely removed as bran in the milling process.

Table 2.32 Niacin in foods (mg per 100 g)

Barley, whole	5·5	
Maize, whole	2·0	
Rice, brown	4·6	
milled (polished)	1·6	
Oatmeal, rolled oats	0·9	
Wheat, whole	2·8	to 5·0
Flour, white	0·6	to 0·8
85 per cent extraction	0·15	to 0·20
Bran	30	to 35
Yeast, dry	10	to 50
Liver, fresh	10	to 27
Kidney	6	to 10
Fresh meat	3	to 10
Cow's milk	0·1	to 0·5
Fish	3	to 8

The daily requirement of nicotinic acid is probably of the order of 12 mg per day but usually a higher intake, up to 20 mg per day, is recommended. In spite of its chemical relationship to nicotine, nicotinic acid is non-toxic even in large doses. Nicotine has no curative value in pellagra.

Pyridoxine (Vitamin B₆)

Pyridoxine is the name given to a group of naturally occurring derivatives of pyridine. The principal members of the group are pyridoxol, pyridoxal and pyridoxamine. It is probable that pyridoxol and pyridoxamine are converted to pyridoxal in the tissues. Pyridoxal phosphate acts as coenzyme for some amino acid decarboxylases and for aminotransferases. Pyridoxal phosphate catalyses the synthesis of tryptophan from indole and serine and is necessary for the conversion of

pyridoxol

pyridoxamine

pyridoxal

tryptophan to nicotinic acid. It is also required in the haem synthetic pathway.

The daily requirement for pyridoxine is probably 0·2 to 1·0 mg; 2 mg/day gives a good margin of safety. The vitamin is widely distributed in both animal and vegetable foods. Lack of pyridoxine in the diet of some animals produces skin changes, anaemia or convulsions but deficiency very rarely if ever occurs in man since he is supplied with pyridoxine by the activity of his intestinal bacteria. Isoniazid (isonicotinic acid hydrazide), used in the treatment of tuberculosis, has occasionally produced a peripheral neuropathy which has been ascribed to competition with pyridoxine.

Pantothenic Acid

This substance is usually regarded as a vitamin but there is no good evidence that its lack causes disease in man. Various changes have been found in experimental deficiencies in rats and dogs. It is widely distributed in food and its importance lies in the fact that it is built up in the living cell into coenzyme A which has an essential role in the metabolism of fat and carbohydrate. The structure of pantothenic acid is

$$HO.CH_2-\underset{\underset{CH_3}{|}}{\overset{\overset{CH_3}{|}}{C}}-CH(OH).CO.NH.CH_2.CH_2.COOH$$

Biotin

Biotin has the structure

It acts as coenzyme in the fixation of carbon dioxide in carboxylation reactions such as the conversion of pyruvic acid to oxaloacetic acid

$$CO_2 + CH_3.CO.COOH \rightleftharpoons HOOC.CH_2.CO.COOH$$

or the carboxylation of acetyl-coenzyme A to form malonyl-coenzyme A in fatty acid synthesis.

Biotin is found in yeasts and in liver and kidney. Since it is made by intestinal bacteria deficiency is most unlikely to occur except when these bacteria are suppressed or when the diet contains an excess of avidin, a protein in egg white, which binds biotin in the intestine and prevents its absorption.

Folacin

The term *folacin* is used to describe folic acid and related compounds. Folic acid itself, pteroylglutamic acid, has a pterin nucleus linked to *p*-aminobenzoic acid to form pteroic acid which is, in turn, linked to a glutamic acid residue.

pterin residue

p-aminobenzoic acid residue

glutamic acid residue

Folic acid (pteroyl-monoglutamic acid)

The best food sources of folic acid are fresh green vegetables and liver. In plant and animal tissues folic acid mostly occurs in the form of *polyglutamates* with one to seven glutamic acid residues attached to each molecule. Folic acid, synthesized by bacteria in the large intestine, is of little nutritional value since folic acid is absorbed mainly in the jejunum.

Dietary folic acid in the polyglutamate form is broken down in the intestine to the monoglutamate which is absorbed into the mucosal cell. There it is converted to 5-methyl tetrahydrofolic acid (methyl THF), the principal form of folate in the blood.

Once it has entered a cell methyl-THF is converted into THF by a reaction involving methylcobalamin (p. 29). THF acts as a coenzyme capable of carrying one-carbon units. For example, it can accept the β-carbon of serine to give 5,10-methylene THF. This is a particularly important substance because it is responsible for the methylation of the pyrimidine ring to give thymine needed for DNA synthesis. THF is also involved in the synthesis of purines and in the formation of serine and histidine.

Folic acid thus plays an essential role in cellular metabolism. Its deficiency causes a disturbance of DNA synthesis which is revealed mainly by a disturbance of red cell formation in the bone marrow (*megaloblastic anaemia*, Chap. 8) and sometimes mental disturbances. Non-pregnant adults need about 200 μg folic acid daily, and dietary lack is the most important cause of deficiency. More is required in pregnancy when megaloblastic anaemia is liable to occur; routine prophylaxis with 400 μg folic acid daily, usually administered with iron, has largely eliminated this. Folic acid deficiency also occurs as a result of intestinal malabsorption, and after treatment with various drugs such as those used in epilepsy.

Vitamin B_{12}

In 1926 it was found that *pernicious anaemia*, a relentlessly progressive disorder with anaemia and neurological defects, could be relieved by the administration of liver. Because there is no animal model of pernicious anaemia patients in relapse had to be used for assays of liver extracts. The vitamin was not isolated until 1948.

The term vitamin B_{12} is used to describe a number of *cobalamin* compounds, complex molecules which consist of two main parts, a nucleotide, and a corrin ring. The two parts are set at right angles to each other with a cobalt atom at the centre of the corrin ring (Fig. 2.33).

Three cobalamins are important in man. 5'-deoxyadenosyl-

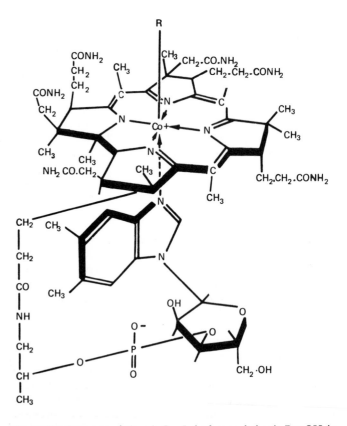

Fig. 2.33 Structure of vitamin B_{12}. In hydroxocobalamin R = OH, in methylcobalamin R = CH$_3$ and in 5-deoxyadenosyl cobalamin R = a deoxyadenosyl group. (*After* I. Chanarin (1969) *The Megaloblastic Anaemias*. Oxford: Blackwell.)

cobalamin is the major form of vitamin B_{12} in normal human and animal tissues and thus probably in the diet. Methylcobalamin is the principal form of vitamin B_{12} in the plasma. Both are rapidly converted to hydroxocobalamin in the presence of light. In the treatment of pernicious anaemia hydroxocobalamin is injected intramuscularly usually at monthly intervals. In the body it is converted to the tissue forms of vitamin B_{12}.

Man depends almost entirely on his diet for his supply of vitamin B_{12} which is present in small amounts in all foods of animal origin. The daily requirement is about $2\,\mu g$ and normal diets throughout the world contain 5 to $30\,\mu g$ daily. Dietary deficiency of vitamin B_{12} is not uncommon in very strict vegetarians (*vegans*) who do not eat eggs or milk products.

Vitamin B_{12} is passively absorbed in the jejunum and ileum but less than one per cent of an oral dose is absorbed in this way. Much more important physiologically is an active transport mechanism involving *intrinsic factor* and specific absorption sites in the ileum. Intrinsic factor is a glycoprotein, secreted into the stomach by the parietal cells. One molecule of intrinsic factor (IF) binds one molecule of vitamin B_{12} and the IF-B_{12} complex is actively taken up by mucosal cells in the lower ileum. It is not yet clear whether the intrinsic factor enters the mucosal cells; it does not accompany the vitamin B_{12} into the portal blood.

Vitamin B_{12} deficiency can be caused by diseases of the ileum or by lack of intrinsic factor. The latter can result from total gastrectomy or from atrophy of the gastric parietal cells, which is the cause of classical pernicious anaemia. Vitamin B_{12} absorption is assessed by measurements of plasma vitamin B_{12} levels and by the *Schilling test*. In this test the patient is given a large dose of unlabelled vitamin B_{12} by intramuscular injection to saturate the tissues and then a small oral dose (less than $1\,\mu g$) of vitamin B_{12} labelled with radioactive cobalt. The amount of labelled vitamin appearing in the urine gives an indication of the efficiency of vitamin B_{12} absorption.

Methylcobalamin in the plasma is bound to two carrier proteins, transcobalamin I and II. The plasma level of vitamin B_{12} is between 250 and 1000 ng/l. Vitamin B_{12} is stored in the liver which may contain 1 to 2 mg. After total gastrectomy, with consequent loss of the source of intrinsic factor, this store delays the onset of the symptoms of vitamin B_{12} deficiency for one or two years.

5′-deoxyadenosyl-cobalamin in mammals is a coenzyme in the isomerization of methylmalonyl CoA to succinyl CoA. The excretion of methymalonic acid in the urine is greatly increased in vitamin B_{12} deficiency. Methylcobalamin is responsible, with folic acid, for the methylation of homocysteine to methionine. This reaction is important in folic acid metabolism so that vitamin B_{12} deficiency, like folic acid deficiency, causes megaloblastic anaemia.

The principal features of vitamin B_{12} deficiency are megaloblastic anaemia (Chap. 8), soreness of the tongue, mental changes and peripheral neuropathy. Often the posterior and lateral columns of the spinal cord are damaged. The damage to the central nervous system may be permanent but the anaemia responds rapidly to treatment with hydroxocobalamin. Patients suffering from pernicious anaemia require maintenance treatment with hydroxocobalamin indefinitely. Since this is stored in the liver injections, usually of $1000\,\mu g$, are given monthly.

Vitamin C (Ascorbic Acid)

Scurvy was at one time a common disorder in seamen on long voyages and many died until Lind proved in 1747 that it could be prevented and cured by eating fresh fruit or vegetables. The antiscorbutic vitamin ascorbic acid was isolated in 1928.

L-ascorbic acid   L-dehydroascorbic acid

Ascorbic acid possesses an asymmetrical carbon atom (C) but only the L-compounds are biologically active. Ascorbic acid is a powerful reducing agent, giving up two hydrogen atoms to become dehydroascorbic acid. This oxidation is reversible in the body. Ascorbic acid may, however, be irreversibly oxidized beyond the stage of dehydroascorbic acid to diketogulonic acid and oxalic acid.

Ascorbic acid is synthesized from glucose by certain moulds, fungi, all the higher plants and by most mammals. However, the guinea pig, primates and man lack the enzyme necessary for the final step in the synthesis of ascorbic acid, and these species develop scurvy if the diet is deficient.

The precise role of ascorbic acid *in vivo* remains uncertain. Lack of the vitamin *in vitro* leads to defects in the hydroxylation of peptides containing lysine and proline and thus in a reduction in collagen synthesis. Ascorbic acid is necessary for the synthesis of L-dopa from tyrosine.

Ascorbic acid is present in all body fluids and tissues. Particularly high concentrations are found in the adrenal gland, the pituitary, corpus luteum and thymus. Normally blood plasma contains from 30 to $100\,\mu mol/l$, but values below $30\,\mu mol/l$ may be found over a long time in an individual who shows no sign of ill-health. Ascorbic acid appears in the urine when the concentration in the plasma exceeds about $60\,\mu mol/l$. The total amount of ascorbic acid in the body of a man replete with the vitamin is about 30 mmol (5g). In the blood much of the vitamin C is found in the platelets and leucocytes. Assays of leucocyte ascorbic acid are useful in the diagnosis of deficiency; normal values are 1 to 2 mmol/kg. In subjects depleted of ascorbic acid the ascorbic acid content of the leucocytes and platelets falls progressively over several months to reach very low values 3 to 6 weeks before signs of scurvy appear.

Ascorbic acid is found in nearly all fruits and vegetables, especially rich sources being rose hips, blackcurrants, green vegetables and citrus fruits (Table 2.34). Although potatoes contain smaller amounts they are an important dietary source especially when they are new. The ascorbic acid content of potatoes and vegetables diminishes gradually if they are stored and much more rapidly when they are cooked.

Deficiency of ascorbic acid leads to defective formation of the collagen fibres of connective tissue. Since the laying-down of new connective tissue is essential to the healing of wounds, this process is retarded in man and in guinea-pigs made

Table 2.34 Approximate content of ascorbic acid in some foods (mg per 100 g)

Rose hip syrup	150 to 200
Blackcurrant syrup	60
Leafy vegetables (fresh)	50
Eggs, meat, milk	Trace
Citrus fruits	25 to 60
Tomato	20
Peas (dried)	0
Peas (sprouting)	20 to 50
Potatoes (uncooked)	10 to 30
Potatoes (boiled)	5 to 15

deficient in ascorbic acid. Formation of bone is also abnormal because of the abnormal collagen formation. The teeth of guinea-pigs made deficient in ascorbic acid become soft and spongy but they are quickly restored to normal by the administration of ascorbic acid. There is no good evidence, however, that ascorbic acid is essential for healthy teeth in man.

The main features of scurvy are swollen bleeding gums, and bleeding into the skin and deeper tissues. In young children there is bleeding under the periosteum of the bones and into the joints. The bleeding has been attributed to deficiencies of the intercellular cement substance between the endothelial cells of capillaries. Scurvy is rapidly and completely cured by giving ascorbic acid.

A daily intake of about 10 mg is sufficient to prevent scurvy. Most people in Britain take more than 20 mg/day. To provide a margin of safety 30 mg has been suggested as a desirable daily intake although with this dose the body is by no means saturated.

Vitamin D (Calciferol)

Rickets, a disorder of children characterized by stunted growth and bowing of the limbs (Fig. 2.35) has been known for hundreds of years but it was recognized as a deficiency disease only in 1918. Adults may have a corresponding deficiency disease, known as osteomalacia. Both disorders can be prevented or cured either by administration of vitamin D or by exposure to ultraviolet light.

The name vitamin D has been applied to a number of chemically similar heat-stable compounds, the most important being vitamin D_2 (ergocalciferol) and vitamin D_3 (cholecalciferol). Ergocalciferol does not occur naturally but is produced artificially by the ultraviolet irradiation of a plant sterol, ergosterol. Cholecalciferol, the naturally occurring antirachitic compound of animals, is produced in man by the irradiation of a provitamin, 7-dehydrocholesterol (Fig. 2.36) present in his skin.

Vitamin D is found in a limited number of foods (Table 2.37) but fish livers are by far the richest source. Cod liver oil has been used as a household remedy for a hundred years. The vitamin D content of eggs and butter is very variable and depends on the diet and exposure to sunlight of the hens and cows. Ergocalciferol is added to margarine during manufacture. Powdered milk for infants is usually fortified by the addition of the vitamin. In the United States and some other countries vitamin D is added to all milk.

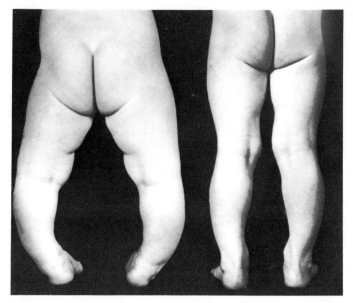

Fig. 2.35 Infantile rickets before treatment and 2 years later after vitamin D therapy. (*By courtesy of* I. D. G. Richards, E. M. Sweet & G. C. Arneil (1968) *Lancet*, i, 803.)

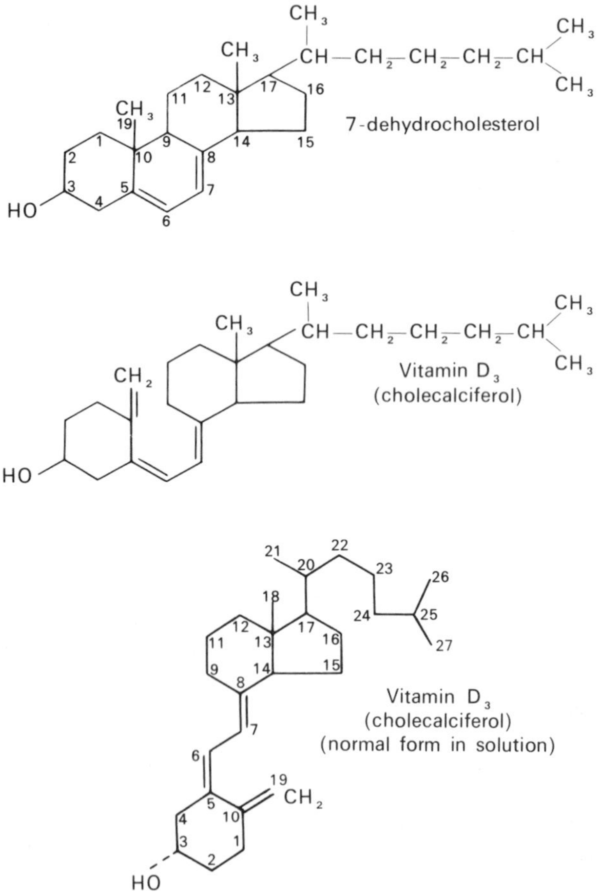

Fig. 2.36 Structures of 7-dehydrocholesterol and vitamin D_3 (cholecalciferol). The lower structure represents the ('elongated') form which vitamin D takes in solution and in crystals. Vitamin D_2 (ergocalciferol) differs from vitamin D_3 only in the structure of the side chain: it has a double bond at C22-23 and an additional methyl group (C28) at C24.

Table 2.37 Vitamin D in foods (per 100 g)

Tunny-liver oil	2 mg to 6 mg
Halibut-liver oil	0·5 to 10 mg
Cod-liver oil	50 to 700 μg
Fat fish, e.g. herring	5 to 50 μg
Ox liver	1 μg
Egg yolk	4 to 10 μg
Butter	0·2 to 2 μg
Cow's milk	trace to 0·2 μg
Meat, white fish (e.g. cod)	trace

Vitamin D is relatively stable so that losses during the storage, cooking, canning or drying of food are probably small.

Vitamin D is absorbed in the upper half of the small intestine in the presence of bile salts. Vitamin D and its metabolites are found in the plasma bound to an α-globulin. Adipose tissue and muscle are the most important sites of storage. Vitamin D stores in man may be sufficient to postpone signs of vitamin D deficiency for several years.

Both vitamin D_2 and vitamin D_3 are hydroxylated in the liver to give 25-hydroxy derivatives. A further hydroxylation takes place in the kidney to yield either the very active 1,25-dihydroxycholecalciferol (1,25-DHCC) or the relatively inactive metabolite 24,25-dihydroxycholecalciferol (24,25-DHCC).

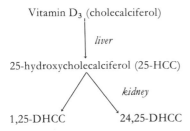

Vitamin D_3 (cholecalciferol)

liver

25-hydroxycholecalciferol (25-HCC)

kidney

1,25-DHCC   24,25-DHCC

1,25-DHCC appears to act as a hormone since its output by the kidney is governed in part by the plasma calcium operating through parathyroid hormone (Chap. 18). It operates at the cell nucleus by influencing the transcription of messenger RNA and the formation of calcium transport proteins. 1,25-DHCC seems to act directly on bone, muscle and kidney as well as on the intestine. Its role is discussed further in Chapter 18.

The ill-effects of deficiency of vitamin D seem to be due to the limitation of the output of 1,25-DHCC. Clinical disorders similar to osteomalacia and rickets occur when the renal 1-hydroxylase activity is impaired as in chronic renal failure.

Vitamin D deficiency occurs whenever there is *both* dietary deficiency and lack of exposure to sunlight. Rickets and osteomalacia remain common diseases in some parts of the world, notably North Africa, the Middle East and parts of the Indian subcontinent. In Britain vitamin D deficiency is found particularly in Asian immigrants and in house-bound elderly women. Osteomalacia also occurs in disorders which impair the absorption of vitamin D: in coeliac disease, in obstructive jaundice, and after partial gastrectomy.

In both rickets and osteomalacia there is inadequate deposition of calcium salts in newly formed bone matrix. In babies with rickets ossification is retarded or ceases but the cartilage cells of the epiphyseal plate continue to grow, producing swellings adjacent to joints and to the costal

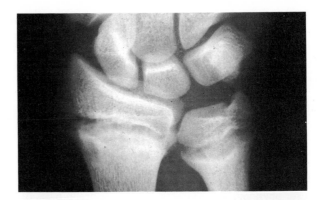

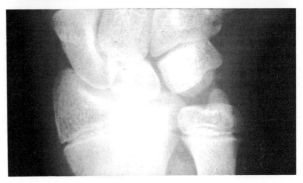

Fig. 2.38 A: Radiological appearance of the right wrist in an adolescent with rickets. Note the widened, irregular epiphyses. B: The same wrist after treatment; the epiphyses are now normal.

cartilages ('rickety rosary'). Since cartilage is transparent to X-rays, radiographs of rickets are easily recognized (Fig. 2.38). The process of bone remodelling, which normally maintains the shape of the bones, is abnormal and the bones tend to bend Fig. 2.35). Deformities of the pelvis in girls may lead subsequently to difficulties in childbirth.

Infants and young children require some 10 to 18 μg of vitamin D per day. It is important to note that the toxic effects of hypercalcaemia may be produced by higher doses—as little as 50 μg per day in some infants. The vitamin D requirement for adults is about 2·5 μg daily.

Vitamin E

Vitamin E is the generic name given to a number of lipid soluble compounds, the most active of which is α-tocopherol.

$$CH_3-C\overset{\overset{\displaystyle CH_3}{|}}{\underset{\underset{\displaystyle CH_3}{|}}{C}}\ \ \overset{\overset{\displaystyle CH_3}{|}}{\underset{\underset{\displaystyle CH_2}{|}}{C}}-\left[-(CH_2)_3-\overset{\overset{\displaystyle CH_3}{|}}{CH}-\right]_3-CH_3$$

α-Tocopherol

Vitamin E behaves as a biological antioxidant; this effect is particularly evident in the protection from oxidation of polyunsaturated fatty acids, vitamin A and carotene. The biochemical role of vitamin E is not yet clear; deficiency of vitamin E in experimental animals has been shown to result in testicular degeneration and fetal death, but there is no evidence of a deficiency disease in adult man due to dietary lack. Vitamin E is widely distributed in food. Patients with intestinal malabsorption have low blood levels of vitamin E and abnormalities of the red blood cells. Premature infants may have a haemolytic anaemia which responds to small doses of vitamin E.

Vitamin K

At least two forms of this fat-soluble vitamin are found in nature: phylloquinone (vitamin K_1) in the green parts of the plants, and menaquinone (vitamin K_2) synthesized by intestinal bacteria.

The best natural sources of vitamin K are the dark green parts of plants. The bacterial flora in the human intestine can synthesize menaquinone and probably for this reason deficiency symptoms have not been produced in healthy human subjects solely as the result of diets lacking in the vitamin.

Vitamin K_1

Vitamin K_2

However vitamin K deficiency with bleeding can occur after surgical operations in patients taking little food and also taking antibiotics which suppress the intestinal flora.

In vitamin K deficiency blood clotting is impaired as a result of a reduction in the amounts of prothrombin and factors VII, IX and X in the blood (Chap. 8). The impaired coagulability of the blood may cause haemorrhage.

Vitamin K is fat-soluble and its absorption from the alimentary tract depends upon bile salts. In obstructive jaundice the amount of bile salt reaching the intestine is much reduced and vitamin K is not absorbed in adequate amounts. Similarly in other disorders in which fat absorption is impaired, vitamin K deficiency may arise and a tendency to bleeding may result. Very little vitamin K is stored in the body so that depletion can occur rapidly. In *haemorrhagic disease of the newborn* bleeding from the gastrointestinal tract in the first few days of life results from deficiency of prothrombin and factors VIII, IX and X. It is quickly corrected by treatment with vitamin K and is now prevented by the routine administration of vitamin K_1.

MINERALS

The metabolism of calcium and phosphorus is discussed in Chapter 18. Iron metabolism is covered in Chapter 8 and iodine metabolism in Chapter 28. This section is concerned with other minerals.

Magnesium. The adult human body contains about 25 g (1000 mmol) of magnesium, about half being in the bones and half in the cells. The cells contain 15 to 20 mmol/l where it is an essential component of many enzymes, and an essential co-factor in all reactions involving ATP. Magnesium is also essential for the stability of intracellular organelles such as ribosomes and mitochondria. The plasma contains only 0·7 to 1·0 mmol/l; about 55 per cent is ionized. The urinary excretion is usually 3·3 to 4·9 mmol per day; the amount depends on the intake which is ordinarily between 8 and 17 mmol per day.

The minimum daily requirement of magnesium is about 10 mmol (250 mg) for an adult but simple dietary deficiency is unknown in man since green vegetables and cereals contain large amounts of magnesium. Magnesium depletion may occur, however, in patients with excessive intestinal losses due to diarrhoea or after extensive removal of gut. If the serum level falls, epileptic fits, tetany and muscular weakness are seen; these disturbances may in fact be due to an accompanying hypocalcaemia.

In renal failure, both the total body magnesium and the plasma magnesium level rise and contribute to the toxic effects of renal failure such as drowsiness, impaired muscular co-ordination and slurred speech.

Copper. A normal adult has about 100 mg (1·6 mmol) of copper in his body. Any excess of copper that is absorbed is removed from the blood by the liver cells and excreted in the bile. The copper content of plasma is normally 13 to 24 μmol/l and most of this is bound to *caeruloplasmin*, an α_2-globulin. The urinary excretion of copper is 0·2 to 0·8 μmol per day.

Copper is an essential element. Its most important role is as a component of cytochrome oxidase which is involved in the final step for the reduction of molecular oxygen. It is also a component of the copper protein enzymes: tyrosinase, ascorbic acid oxidase, monoamine oxidase, lysyl oxidase (essential for the synthesis of collagen and elastin) and enzymes concerned with phospholipid synthesis.

Copper deficiency is not known in adults but in infants an anaemia may occur which responds to treatment with copper and iron. Copper excess occurs in *Wilson's disease* (hepato-lenticular degeneration) in which caeruloplasmin is deficient and copper is deposited in the brain, liver and other tissues including the cornea.

Zinc. Zinc is an essential element in man; the body contains 2 to 3 g. It is a component of at least 80 enzymes, including carbonic anhydrase (the first metalloenzyme to be identified). Others are carboxypeptidase, alcohol dehydrogenase, alkaline phosphatase and retinene reductase. Zinc plays a part in non-enzymic free radical reactions; for example, it protects against iron-catalysed free radical damage.

Good sources of zinc are herrings, eggs, nuts, beef and liver but most foods contain significant amounts. About 5 to 6 mg per day is required but the diet usually contains much more. Only one-third of the ingested zinc is absorbed, the remainder escapes in the faeces. The plasma level of zinc, about 15 mol/l, remains remarkably constant in health.

Zinc deficiency may occur when the diet contains large quantities of cereal rich in phytic acid which interferes with the absorption of zinc. Growth and sexual development may be greatly delayed (Fig. 2.39). Malnourished children have a low concentration of zinc in their tissues and atrophy of the thymus with impairment of cell-mediated immunity which can be reversed by administration of zinc.

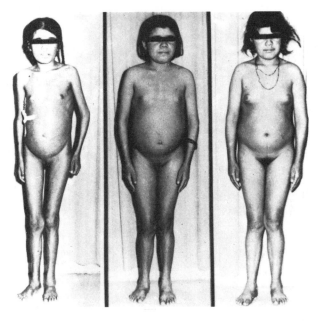

Fig. 2.39 Zinc deficiency in a 19-year-old Iranian girl. She had been admitted to hospital with severe malnutrition 1 month before the first photograph was taken. After 6 months on a good diet she gained weight (from 27 to 41 kg) but there was little gain in height or in sexual development. Her plasma zinc had risen from 4·4 to 11·9 μmol/l. For a further 6 months zinc sulphate (120 mg daily) was given; her first menstrual period began 33 days after the beginning of the zinc therapy and in the 6-month period there was other evidence of sexual development such as growth of the breasts. She also gained 9 cm in height. Her plasma zinc level rose further to 16·5 μmol/l. *Courtesy of* J. A. Halsted (1972) *American Journal of Medicine, 53,* 277).

Manganese. The human adult contains about 20 mg (360 μmol) of manganese; the daily intake is about 5 mg (90 μmol), mainly derived from cereals and tea. Plasma contains 45 nmol/l carried by a β-globulin, *transmanganin*; whole blood contains about 220 nmol/l. Manganese is accumulated in mitochondria and seems to be essential for their function. In addition manganese forms part of the enzymes arginase and pyruvate carboxylase and is an essential co-factor in the function of many other enzymes. No deficiency disease has been recognized in man.

Cobalt. The body contains about 80 μg (1·4 μmol) of cobalt in vitamin B_{12}. Deficiency of cobalt causes a wasting disease of

animals, and a few cases of cobalt-deficiency anaemia have now been recognized in man. Cobalt poisoning has been described after the consumption of beer containing cobalt; it caused liver damage and cardiac failure which was often fatal.

Chromium. Trivalent chromium was first recognized as essential in mammals in 1955 when its deficiency was shown to impair glucose tolerance in rats. In man chromium deficiency may contribute to the impaired glucose tolerance in maturity-onset diabetes and in protein-energy malnutrition. Hexavalent chromium has no known biological function and cannot be converted to trivalent chromium in the body.

Fluorine. Fluorine is present in animal soft tissues in amounts ranging from 0·2 to 1·5 mg per 100 g of the dry material. Bones and teeth contain larger amounts (20 to 30 mg per 100 g ash). A small proportion of fluoride appears to be important for the stability of crystals of hydroxyapatite in calcified tissues.

The optimal intake of fluoride appears to be between 1·0 and 2·0 mg daily. Drinking water is the principal source of fluoride but other sources are sea food and tea (one cup provides about 0·2 mg). In areas where the drinking water contains less than 1 mg/l fluoride the incidence of dental caries is substantially higher than in areas with 1 mg/l or more in the water.

In areas where the water contains fluoride at a concentration greater than 4 mg/l, the enamel of the teeth may show patches of brown pigmentation but they are still resistant to caries. In some parts of India a high intake of fluoride is associated with severe and sometimes crippling bone changes, but in other areas with water of a similar composition the same problem does not arise. The reason for these differences is not yet known.

Other essential elements. Molybdenum is a component of the enzyme xanthine oxidase, important in purine breakdown. Selenium is essential as a constituent of glutathione peroxidase of red cells. In neither case has a deficiency disease been identified in man. Other elements shown to be essential in minute quantities in mammals include nickel, vanadium, silicon and tin.

Some Non-Essential Minerals

Strontium. The body contains about 350 mg of strontium in the skeleton where its distribution is like that of calcium. Strontium has no known physiological function but it is of possible clinical importance because ^{90}Sr, produced as a result of atomic fission, is radioactive. This isotope has a long half-life (25 years) and accumulates in the skeleton. Fortunately the amount of ^{90}Sr in human bone has declined since a peak figure was reached in 1964.

Lead. The estimated weekly intake of lead in Britain is about 1 mg. This amount is not a health hazard. However, higher intakes occur in soft water districts where the domestic pipes are made of lead. Fumes from the combustion of lead-containing petrol may also add to the body burden. Lead accumulates within the skeleton and displaces calcium from the hydroxyapatite structure. High intakes of lead are thought to be a cause of mental deficiency in children.

Cadmium. Cadmium is present in traces in many foodstuffs but the average intake is so low that there is no nutritional hazard. Cadmium intoxication occurs in coppersmiths and also in workers making Ni/Cd batteries. This causes renal and intestinal damage and may lead to hypertension.

Mercury. Most food-stuffs, notably fish, contain small quantities of mercury but very little is absorbed by the intestine. Mercury vapour from spilled mercury is absorbed through the lungs. Mercurial compounds used as fungicides may contaminate food-stuffs.

REFERENCES

General

Abelson P H (ed) 1975 Food: politics, economics, nutrition and research. Washington: American Association for the Advancement of Science. Academic Press, London

Antia F P 1974 Clinical dietetics and nutrition, 2nd edn. Oxford University Press, Delhi

Canosa C A (ed) 1975 Nutrition, growth and development. Karger, Basel

Christie A B, Christie M C 1977 Food hygiene and food hazard. Faber, London

Davidson S, Passmore R, Brock J F, Truswell A S 1975 Human nutrition and dietetics, 6th edn. Churchill Livingstone, Edinburgh

Dickerson J W T, Lee H A (eds) 1978 Nutrition in the clinical management of disease. Arnold, London

King M H, King F M A, Morley D C, Burgess H J L, Burgess A P 1972 Nutrition for developing countries. Oxford University Press, Nairobi

Jarrett R J 1979 Nutrition and Disease. Croom Helm, London

Jelliffe D B, Jelliffe E F P 1978 Human milk in the modern world. University Press, Oxford

McLaren D S (ed) 1976 Nutrition in the community. Wiley, London

McLaren D S, Burman D (eds) 1976 Textbook of paediatric nutrition. Churchill Livingstone, Edinburgh

Nutrition Foundation 1974 Nutrition misinformation and food faddism. Nutrition Reviews, 32: suppl 1

Oddy D J, Miller D S 1976 (eds) The making of the modern British diet. Croom Helm, London

Palmer S, Ekvall S (eds) 1978 Pediatric nutrition in development disorders. Thomas, Springfield

Stanway P, Stanway A 1978 Breast is best. Pan, London

Food Composition

Bender A E 1977 Food processing and nutrition. Academic Press, London

Cook D J 1974 The nutritional value of frozen foods. British Nutrition Foundation Bulletin 11: 39–51, 12: 42–56

Lieber C S 1977 Metabolism of ethanol. In: C S Lieber (ed) Metabolic aspects of alcoholism. MTP, Lancaster p. 1–50

Paul A A, Southgate D A T 1977 McCance & Widdowson's The composition of foods. HMSO, London

Webb M (ed) 1975 Chemicals in food and environment. British Medical Bulletin 31: No 3

Energy Balance

Bennett J R, Baddeley M 1976 Obesity. British Medical Journal 2: 1052–1055

Durnin J V G A, Passmore R 1967 Energy, work and leisure. Heinemann, London

Garrow J S 1978 Energy balance and obesity in man. 2nd edn. Elsevier, Amsterdam

Heaton K W 1973 Food fibre as an obstacle to energy intake. Lancet ii: 1418–1421

James W P T, Trayhurn P 1976 An integrated view of the metabolic and genetic basis for obesity. Lancet ii: 770–773

McHardy, G J R, Stirling D, Passmore R 1967 Basic techniques in human metabolism and respiration. Blackwell, Oxford

Payne P R, Dugdale A E 1977 Mechanisms for the control of body-weight. Lancet i: 583–586

Dietary Requirements

Alleyne G A O, Hay R W, Picou D I, Stanfield J P, Whitehead R G 1977 Protein–energy malnutrition. Arnold, London

Burkitt D P 1973 Epidemiology of large bowel diseases. In: Taylor S (ed) Recent advances in surgery, no 8. Churchill Livingstone, Edinburgh, p 257–274

Clark H E 1978 Cereal-based diets to meet protein requirements of adult man. World review of nutrition and dietetics 32: 27–48

Keys A, Brozek J, Henschel A, Michelson O, Taylor H L 1950 The biology of human starvation. Oxford University Press

Passmore R, Nicol B M Q, Narayana Rao M 1974 Handbook of human nutritional requirements. World Health Organisation, Geneva

Scott H W, Dean R H, Shull H J, Gluck F W 1976 Metabolic complications of jejunoileal bypass for morbid obesity. Annual Review of Medicine 27: 397–405

Vitamins

Ansell J E, Kumar R, Deykin D 1977 The spectrum of vitamin K deficiency. Journal of the American Medical Association 237: 40–42

Chanarin I 1978 Folates, cobalamins and their interrelationship in man. In: Marks V, Hales C N (ed) Essays in medical biochemistry 3. Biochemical Society, Colchester

Chatterjee I B 1978 Ascorbic acid metabolism. World Review of Nutrition and Dietetics 30: 69–87

De Luca H F (ed) 1978 The fat-soluble vitamins. Plenum, New York

Hoffbrand A V 1975 Disturbances of folate absorption and metabolism. In: Lant A F (ed) Advanced medicine symposium 11. p 164–175

Lawson D E M (ed) 1978 Vitamin D. Academic Press, New York

Lewin S 1976 Vitamin C. Academic Press, New York

Oomen H A P C 1974 Vitamin A deficiency, xerophthalmia and blindness. Nutrition Reviews 32: 161–166

Pereira S M, Begum A 1976 Vitamin A deficiency in Indian children. World Review of Nutrition and Dietetics 24: 1976 192–218

Rogers A F 1974 The death of Chief Petty Officer Evans. Practitioner 212: 570–580

Sebrell W H, Harris R S 1967–1970 The vitamins, 2nd edn. Academic Press, New York

REFERENCES

Minerals

Aikawa J K 1978 Biochemistry and physiology of magnesium. World Review of Nutrition and Dietetics 28: 112–142

Brewer G J, Prasad A S 1977 Zinc metabolism: current aspects in health and disease. Alan R. Liss, New York

Burch R E, Sullivan J F (eds) 1976 Symposium on trace elements. Medical Clinics of North America 60: 653–852

Chesters J K 1978 Biochemical function of zinc in animals. World Review of Nutrition and Dietetics 32:135–164

Davies G N 1974 Cost and benefit of fluoride in the prevention of dental caries. WHO, Geneva

Davies I J T 1972 The clinical significance of the essential biological metals. Heinemann, London

Delves H T 1977 The clinical value of trace metal measurements. In: Marks V, Hales C N (eds) Essays in medical biochemistry, 2nd edn. Biochemical Society, Colchester

Leach R M, Lilburn M S 1978 Manganese metabolism and its function. World Review of Nutrition and Dietetics 32: 123–134

Massry S G, Seelig M S 1977 Hypomagnesemia and hypermagnesemia. Clinical Nephrology 7: 147–153

Prasad A S (ed) 1976 Trace elements in human nutrition and disease, vol I. Academic Press, New York and London

Prasad A S 1978 Trace elements and iron in human metabolism. Plenum, New York

Prasad A S, Oberleas D 1976 Trace elements in human health and disease. Vol I: Zinc and copper. Vol II: Essential and toxic elements. Academic Press, New York

Underwood E J 1977 Trace elements in human and animal nutrition, 4th edn. Academic Press, New York

Vernon W B, Wacker W E C 1978 Magnesium metabolism. In: Alberti K G M M (ed) Recent advances in clinical biochemistry 1. Churchill Livingstone, Edinburgh, p 39–71

3 Mouth, Oesophagus and Swallowing

The oral cavity and tongue are covered by a stratified squamous epithelium richly supplied with pain, tactile and temperature nerve endings; in addition the tongue has taste buds distributed over its surface. If, when food enters the mouth, the impulses from these nerve endings and those in the olfactory area indicate that the food is acceptable, mastication prepares it for swallowing. Chewing breaks up the solid parts of the food and at the same time increases the salivary secretion and mixes up the food with it to make a bolus suitable for swallowing. Mastication may increase slightly the digestibility of some foodstuffs, but no advantage seems to accrue from prolonged mastication.

THE SALIVARY GLANDS

Saliva is produced by three pairs of salivary glands, the parotids, the submandibulars and the sublinguals, together with numerous small salivary glands scattered over the oral mucosa. Their ducts all open into the buccal cavity, and so the saliva is described as an *external secretion* and the glands as *exocrine*.

Composition and Functions of Saliva

The composition and physical properties of saliva in the mouth are summarized in Table 3.1. The saliva in the mouth differs in several respects from the secretion produced by the secreting cells of the glands, not only because the saliva in the mouth is a mixture of several secretions but also because the secretions are modified during their passage through the salivary ducts and further altered in the mouth itself.

Table 3.1 Saliva-composition and properties

Volume	750 ml/day (submandibular 70%; parotid 25%; sublingual 5%)
pH	6·2–7·4 (depending on flow rate)
Specific gravity	1002–1010 (usually 1003)
Inorganic constituents	calcium: 1·5 mmol/l ⎫ precipitate phosphorus: 5·5 mmol/l ⎬ as calculus at ⎭ low pH. sodium (flow rate dependent see Fig. 3.5) chloride (flow rate dependent see Fig. 3.5) bicarbonate (flow rate dependent see Fig. 3.5) potassium: 20 mmol/l
Organic constituents	amylase (optimum pH 6·8); kallikrein; mucin; lysozyme; carbonic anhydrase; amino acids; urea; citrate; glycoproteins with same specificity as red blood cell antigens of ABO, Lewis and SD groups; squamous cells from buccal lining; disintegrating leucocytes and gland cells; micro-organisms

A particularly important function of saliva is to cleanse and protect the teeth and the oral epithelium by washing away food particles and buccal cell debris and by keeping the delicate buccal epithelium moist. Since the time available for the action of amylase on starch in the mouth is short it may be that its main use is in dislodging food debris from between the teeth. The enzyme lysozyme helps to reduce bacterial activity. When the flow of saliva is reduced, as in fever, the lips, teeth and mouth become coated with cell debris which, unless removed mechanically, can become infected. Degeneration of the buccal epithelium is characteristic of xerostomia, a condition in which there is little or no production of saliva.

Other functions of saliva include lubricating and moistening the food to assist swallowing, facilitating the movements of the tongue and lips to aid rapid speech, dissolving sapid substances so enabling them to stimulate the taste buds, neutralizing and buffering actions, which not only help to prevent a fall in oral pH by bacterial action but also help to neutralize gastric acid during the interdigestive period, and digestion of starch by salivary amylase. This digestion may continue for a time in the stomach since the centre of a swallowed bolus of food may remain for some time at a pH suitable for the action of amylase even though the pH in the stomach is too low for the digestion of starch.

Histological Structure

The salivary glands are compound racemose glands, the glandular cells being arranged in acini each of which consists of a single layer of cells around a central cavity into which the cells discharge their secretions (Figs. 3.2 and 3.3). In man this acinus or secretory end-piece may be entirely mucous (secreting mucoproteins) as in the sublingual, or entirely serous (secreting enzymes) as in the parotid, or mixed as in the submaxillary gland (Fig. 3.2). Small intercalated ducts from a number of adjacent acini, usually surrounded by myoepithelial cells, join together to form striated ducts lined by tall cells whose basal membranes have numerous infoldings which produce the characteristic striated appearance. These ducts drain into larger excretory ducts which in turn connect with a large collecting duct which opens into the mouth (Fig. 3.3).

Innervation

The salivary glands are supplied by both parasympathetic and sympathetic nerves (Fig. 3.4). The secretory end-pieces always have a parasympathetic innervation and also, in most cases, a sympathetic innervation. Each acinus may be supplied by several fibres but it is not necessary for each cell to be directly innervated since the acinar cells are electrically coupled and thus the influence of each nerve ending spreads to adjacent cells.

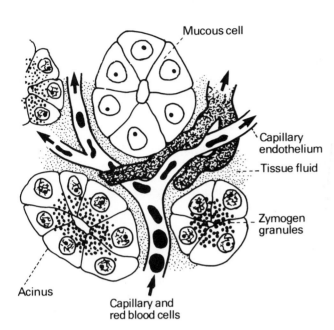

Fig. 3.2 This diagram shows the relation between the blood vessels and secreting cells of a salivary gland. The blood vessels bring fluid which passes through the capillary endothelium to the tissue fluid. From these it passes into the periphery of the cells of the acinus. Excess of tissue fluid is drained off in the lymphatics (dark stipple).

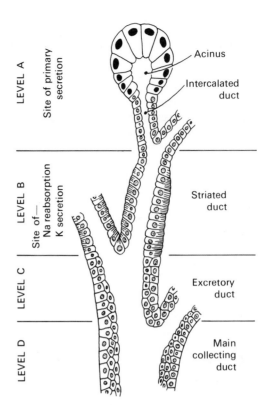

Fig. 3.3 Much simplified diagram of an acinus and ducts of a salivary gland.

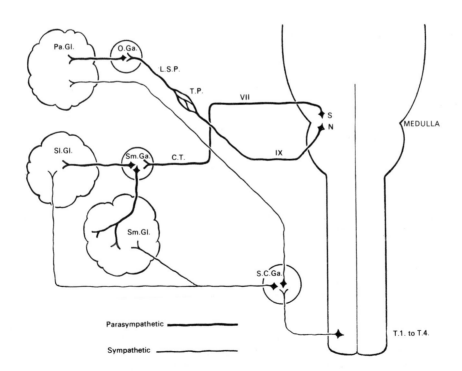

Fig. 3.4 The nerve supply to the salivary glands. Pa.Gl., parotid gland. Sl.Gl., sublingual gland. Sm.Gl., submandibular gland. O.Ga., otic ganglion. S.C.Ga., superior cervical ganglion. Sm.Ga., submandibular ganglion. L.S.P., lesser superficial petrosal nerve. T.P., tympanic plexus. C.T., chorda tympani. VII, facial nerve. IX, glossopharyngeal nerve. SN, salivary nuclei. T.1. to T.4., first to fourth thoracic segments of the spinal cord.

The myoepithelial cells lie close to the acinar cells in the secretory end-piece and, being in close contact with the intra-acinar nerve endings, they probably receive the same pattern of innervation as the acinar cells. When activated they increase duct pressure and therefore salivary flow. The striated duct cells of the cat submandibular gland appear to have a dual sympathetic and parasympathetic innervation since membrane potential changes are seen after stimulation of either of these nerves. This innervation may not be direct. The nerve endings may terminate near acinar cells and the action of the transmitters may pass to the duct cells by electrical coupling. The blood vessels receive a sympathetic constrictor innervation and a parasympathetic dilator innervation. The transmitter at the parasympathetic junctions is acetylcholine and at the sympathetic endings is noradrenaline.

Control of Salivary Secretion and Blood Flow

Stimulation of the parasympathetic nerves causes much salivary secretion and an associated vasodilatation. Electrical stimulation of the sympathetic nerves also stimulates salivary secretion though that is more difficult to demonstrate and, because of the accompanying vasoconstriction, it may be transient. Whereas it is generally accepted that the parasympathetic nerves provide the efferent pathway for 'natural' and conditioned reflex control of salivary secretion, the role of the sympathetic nerves remains obscure, even though in some species the sympathetic nerves may provide the greater part of the acinar cell innervation.

Reflex salivation is normally evoked by the food in the mouth stimulating taste buds and by impulses from sensory nerves in the teeth, muscles and oral epithelium in response to masticatory movements. Stimuli acting on the 'sour' taste buds appear to be most potent. However, even chewing paraffin wax can stimulate a salivary flow of up to 250 ml per hr from a resting level of 2 to 10 ml per hr. Receptors in the oesophagus can detect a bolus which might lodge there and, besides initiating peristalsis, can induce salivary secretion. It is possible to condition salivary secretion in man, though it is not clear whether the so-called mouth-watering at the thought, sight or smell of food is a conditioned reflex (Chap. 24) or merely an awareness of saliva already in the mouth.

Salivary secretion is reduced in conditions that lead to tissue dehydration. Exercise and emotional stress also depress salivary secretion perhaps, in part, as a result of a reduction in salivary blood flow.

The vasodilatation that accompanies parasympathetic nerve stimulation seems to be mediated by more than one mechanism. The first of these involves the enzyme kallikrein which is produced by the salivary glands. It not only appears in the saliva but also in the interstitial fluid. This enzyme acts on specific plasma proteins (kininogens) to split off kinins which are powerful vasodilators. The best known of these is bradykinin.

It seems probable that there is another mechanism for vasodilatation mediated by parasympathetic fibres which may be both cholinergic and non-cholinergic. The non-cholinergic transmitter is not known but it may be the polypeptide *vasoactive intestinal polypeptide* (VIP). The receptors for cholinergic vasodilatation are unusual in that they are not blocked by atropine but are blocked by botulinum toxin.

The microcirculation of the secretory end-pieces lies in parallel with that of the duct system and is controlled separately.

The control of the duct system. Little is known about the control of the duct system. Both parasympathetic and sympathetic nerves can cause membrane potential changes in striated duct cells. Sympathetic nerve stimulation mediated by α-adrenoreceptors can alter Na^+ and K^+ transport in the excretory duct.

Cellular Secretory Mechanisms

Protein secretion. The salivary glands synthesize and secrete many proteins including the enzymes amylase and kallikrein as well as glycoproteins.

Amino acids are taken up across the basal membranes of the acinar cells. Within the rough endoplasmic reticulum they are brought together in the synthesis of the various proteins which are then transported to the Golgi complex and finally stored in the secretory granules. Following stimulation of the cell the proteins are transported across the luminal membrane. Amylase, and possibly the other proteins such as mucoprotein, are transported by exocytosis. In exocytosis the membrane of the vesicle containing the zymogen granules fuses with the plasma membrane. The membranes then rupture releasing the contents of the vesicle into the lumen. During stimulation of the glands the cells are virtually depleted of secretory granules but they reappear several hours after stimulation ceases.

Fluid and electrolyte secretion. Fluid secretion occurs principally in the secretory end-pieces and this *primary secretion* closely resembles an ultrafiltrate of plasma. The rate of secretion, but not its composition, depends upon the intensity of stimulation. The ducts do not appear to secrete fluid but they are not mere conduits. They reabsorb much NaCl but very little water. Secretion of K^+ and HCO_3^- occurs mainly in the striated ducts. Na^+-K^+ pumps (Na^+-K^+ activated ATPase) are present in greater concentration in the basal membrane of the cells of the striated ducts than anywhere else in the salivary glands and actively transport these two ions in much the same way as in the kidney tubule (Chap. 15). HCO_3^- (or H^+) is also actively transported but Cl^- moves passively along its electrochemical gradient.

Thus the ducts greatly modify the primary secretion. The degree of modification depends upon the rate of flow, the faster the flow the smaller the changes resulting from the passage of the fluid along the duct (Fig. 3.5).

Activation of Secretion

The primary secretion is formed by active transport processes requiring energy and is not simply an ultrafiltrate even though it closely resembles one in composition. The activation of these transport mechanisms is summarized in Figure 3.6.

The neurotransmitters (first messengers), acetylcholine and noradrenaline, interact with specific receptors on the outside of the cell membrane and produce marked changes in the concentration of free Ca^{2+} in the cytoplasm. This in turn causes an increase in the conductance of the plasma membrane and an influx of external Ca^{2+} which raises the level of free Ca^{2+} in the cytoplasm still further. The free cytoplasmic Ca^{2+} acts as the

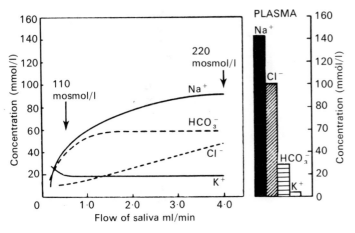

Fig. 3.5 Human parotid saliva produced by parasympathomimetic stimulation. Plasma has an osmotic pressure of 310 mosmol/l. (*After Thaysen (1954) American Journal of Physiology, 178, 155–159.*)

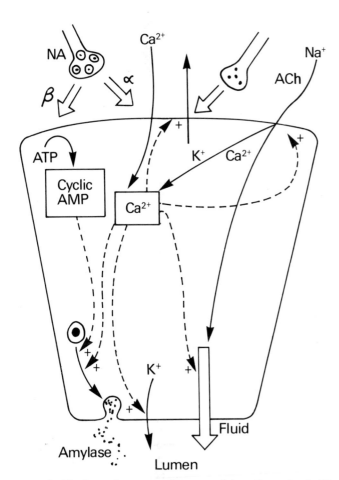

Fig. 3.6 The 'second messenger' systems of the salivary glands. The dotted lines show the intracellular sites of action of the two 'second messenger' systems, Ca^{2+}, and cAMP. The sites of action of these messengers are (a) the plasma membrane to increase conductance, (b) exocytosis of enzymes, (c) secretion of fluid and electrolytes. These systems are activated by the neurotransmitters acetylcholine (ACh) and noradrenaline (NA). The latter may act on either α or β receptors. Ionic movements across the membranes are shown by solid lines. (*After O. H. Petersen.*)

intracellular 'second messenger' and is responsible for activating several mechanisms. (a) The increased membrane conductance (described above) not only allows in more Ca^{2+} but also an inflow of Na^+ causing depolarization of the cell. The Na^+ inflow may in turn lead to the release of membrane-bound calcium but its importance is to make sodium available for the activation of fluid and electrolyte secretion. The increase in conductance also enhances the movement of potassium out of the cell into the lumen of the acinus as well as into the interstitial fluid. (b) The intracellular Ca^{2+} can directly stimulate fluid and electrolyte secretion and exocytosis of enzymes. (c) The breakdown of GTP to cyclic GMP is stimulated by free intracellular Ca^{2+}. The role of cyclic GMP is, however, uncertain.

Excitation of β-adrenoceptors causes very minor changes in membrane potential and therefore does not trigger these mechanisms significantly. β-adrenoceptor activation, however, activates the membrane-bound enzyme, adenyl cyclase, which produces cyclic AMP from ATP. The cAMP acts as the 'second messenger' and triggers the exocytosis of enzymes.

THE OESOPHAGUS

The oesophagus is a tube about 25 cm long and about 2 cm in diameter joining the pharynx to the cardiac orifice of the stomach (the cardia). The stratified squamous epithelium lining the buccal cavity is continued through the pharynx down into the oesophagus. The lowest 2 cm or so of the oesophagus, the 'abdominal segment', lying in the abdominal cavity between the diaphragm and the cardia, is normally lined with gastric mucosa and is covered by peritoneum. In the undistended state the mucosa of the oesophagus is thrown into longitudinal folds which disappear when it is distended. The submucous coat contains mucous glands. Outside this there is a muscular layer (circular fibres internally and longitudinal externally) chiefly striated in the upper third, but consisting almost entirely of smooth muscle fibres in the lower third; both striated and smooth muscle fibres are found in the middle third. The oesophagus, like the rest of the alimentary canal, has a well-developed intrinsic innervation. Extrinsic nerves pass to the oesophagus in the vagus and sympathetic nerves.

SWALLOWING

This complex process which occupies only a few seconds may be divided into three stages; the first buccal, the second pharyngeal and the third oesophageal. Only the first is under voluntary control.

Buccal Phase

The mouth is closed and the bolus, collected on the upper surface of the tongue, is forced through the oropharyngeal isthmus by an upward and backward movement of the tongue caused mainly by the contraction of the mylohyoid and styloglossus muscles. At the same time the soft palate rises and approaches the posterior pharyngeal wall which is brought forward to close off the nasopharynx. Respiration is reflexly inhibited. The larynx begins to rise as the bolus passes over the back of the tongue. From this moment the process of deglutition is involuntary.

Pharyngeal Phase

Since the pharynx communicates with both oesophagus and trachea, the movements occurring in the next stage are designed to allow the bolus to enter the oesophagus while avoiding the air passages. The tongue moves back like a piston towards the posterior pharyngeal wall and forces the bolus back against the epiglottis which arrests it for a short time and then becomes folded to form a cowl-like hood over the laryngeal orifice. The entrance to the larynx is closed by the sphincteric action of the girdle of muscles surrounding it. The food passes over the lateral edges of the epiglottis in two streams into the part of the pharynx immediately posterior to the larynx and then on into the oesophagus. At this moment the cricopharyngeus (the lowest fibres of the inferior constrictor), which forms the upper oesophageal sphincter, relaxes for about one second. The cricopharyngeal sphincter is easy to recognize because it produces at rest a band of high pressure, about 50 to 80 mm Hg above atmospheric pressure. On swallowing it opens and the pressure falls briefly to atmospheric levels. After about 1 second the sphincter contracts with a rise in pressure above the resting levels. This contraction, which is part of the peristaltic wave initiated in the pharynx, progresses down the oesophagus as the primary peristaltic wave (Figs. 3.7 and 3.8). When the bolus is safely past the cricopharyngeus, the larynx drops to its original position, the vocal folds open and the epiglottis quickly resumes its initial position. The cricopharyngeal sphincter then contracts. This is the end of the second stage. If a number of swallowing movements are made in rapid succession the soft palate and epiglottis do not return to their resting positions until the series is completed. The epiglottis can be removed without any harmful effect on swallowing.

During the first stage of swallowing the lips and jaws are normally closed. If the lips are not closed swallowing becomes difficult; but if the jaws cannot be closed swallowing is nearly impossible. During dental operations, when the jaws must be kept open, saliva accumulates in the mouth and has to be removed by suction. Breathing is reflexly arrested, no matter the actual phase of respiration, during the act of swallowing. During this respiratory inhibition the larynx is drawn upwards—without this movement swallowing is very difficult or even impossible. Swallowing, however, can be carried out after the whole of the larynx has been removed to eradicate malignant disease.

Oesophageal Phase

The oesophagus at rest is relaxed but closed above and below by sphincters. The upper sphincter, the cricopharyngeal sphincter, is a thick muscular band about 2 to 3 cm long. The lower sphincter cannot be defined anatomically. However, since the intragastric pressure is usually higher than the intra-oesophageal pressure it is clear that there must be an effective barrier between the lower oesophagus and the cardia. It is now

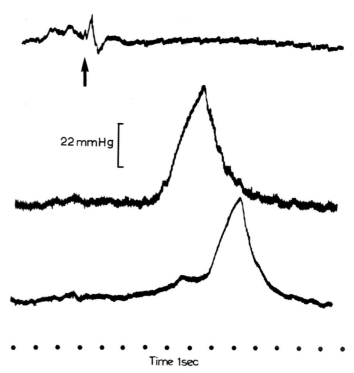

Fig. 3.7 Peristalsis in oesophagus. Upper trace is a pneumographic record which detects laryngeal movements during swallowing. Middle and lower traces—pressure recordings from mid-oesophagus, recorded with perfused open-tipped catheters. After initiation of a swallow (at the arrow) a peristaltic wave passes down the oesophagus causing a rise in pressure which is detected by the two pressure-sensitive catheters. Since the tips of the two catheters are separated by 5 cm the difference in the time of arrival (about 1·3 sec) of the propulsive wave at the pressure sensing orifices enables the speed of propagation of the wave to be calculated, about 4 cm per sec. (*By courtesy of J. S. Davison.*)

generally accepted that there is a functional sphincter in the distal oesophagus rather than some passive mechanical barrier as was previously supposed. Oesophageal activity can be observed radiologically by a 'barium swallow' but in more detail by pressure recording. This is normally performed with open-tip catheters continuously perfused with fluid from a pump during the recording period and connected to pressure sensitive transducers.

At rest the intra-oesophageal pressure is a true index of intrathoracic pressure; it varies with respiration, showing a fall with inspiration and a rise with expiration. It is frequently used by respiratory physiologists as a convenient measure of intrathoracic pressure. After a swallow a single peristaltic wave of contraction moves down the oesophagus and can be recorded as a rise of pressure as it passes the open tip of a tube. The wave passes down at a rate of 2 to 4 cm per sec, (Fig. 3.7) being faster in the lower half of the oesophagus. The peak of the wave is usually above 40 mm Hg pressure but there is considerable individual variation. In the erect position swallowed liquids pass quickly down the oesophagus under the influence of gravity and may enter the stomach well in advance of the peristaltic wave. More solid food forms a bolus which is actively pushed down by peristalsis. Secondary peristaltic waves arise from the stimulation of the oesophagus by

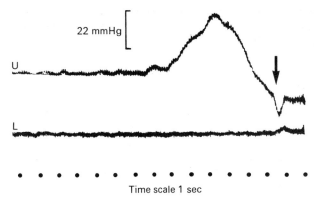

Time scale 1 sec

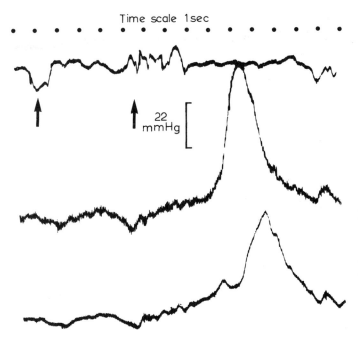

Time scale 1sec

22 mmHg

Fig. 3.8 Traces as in previous figure. A propulsive wave is not initiated after the first swallow if a second swallow (second arrow) occurs too soon after the previous one. Note how, in this circumstance, a second swallow is achieved only with considerable difficulty. (*By courtesy of J. S. Davison.*)

Fig. 3.9 Pressure traces recorded as the pressure-sensing catheters are withdrawn from the stomach through the lower oesophageal sphincter at a speed of 5 mm per sec. The catheters were continuously perfused throughout the withdrawal period. As the upper catheter U passes through the sphincter it detects a zone of high pressure. On passing into the oesophagus the pressure drops to a level below that in the stomach. When the subject inspires after the catheter is in the oesophagus (arrow) there is a negative pressure swing whereas the lower catheter L, still in the stomach, detects a smaller positive swing caused by descent of the diaphragm. (*By courtesy of J. Allen and J. S. Davison.*)

distension and serve to move sticky lumps of food or refluxed material back into the stomach.

The lower oesophageal sphincter. The lower oesophageal sphincter (LOS) can be located as a zone of high pressure when the pressure-sensing catheter is withdrawn slowly at a known speed from the stomach into the oesophagus. The high pressure zone, 2 to 6 cm in length, has an intraluminal pressure of 15 to 40 mm Hg above intragastric pressure (Fig. 3.9). This LOS however is not a static barrier; it can vary its tone in a number of different situations.

During swallowing the LOS seems to relax and to remain so until the peristaltic wave has passed over it. While the remainder of the oesophagus relaxes after the peristaltic wave is over, the LOS remains closed. This relaxation during deglutition has not been measured reliably since the LOS changes its position relative to the pressure-sensing catheter during swallowing.

The period of relaxation of the LOS seems to be prolonged by repetitive swallowing, prolonged distension of the body of the oesophagus or abnormal repetitive oesophageal contractions (diffuse oesophageal spasm). Relaxation also occurs in vomiting.

The neural control of the sphincter is poorly understood. The sphincter has cholinergic excitatory nerves but the extrinsic excitatory nerve supply is principally noradrenergic, passing to the sphincter by non-vagal pathways. The vagal

efferent fibres are predominantly, if not entirely, inhibitory.

The LOS is highly sensitive to the hormone gastrin whose primary action is to stimulate gastric acid secretion (p. 58). It has been suggested that this sensitivity to gastrin provides at least one of the means of maintaining sphincter tone and of increasing this tone after a meal. Protein digestion products which are highly effective in releasing gastrin from the pyloric antrum also raise sphincter tone when placed in the stomach. Although this is an attractive theory crucial supporting evidence is lacking.

Low sphincter pressures predispose to reflux of gastric contents into the oesophagus and the well-known symptom of 'heartburn'. Prolonged exposure of the oesophageal mucosa to gastric contents, as in congenital or hereditary sphincter incompetence, leads to erosion of the mucosa with accompanying chest pain (reflux oesophagitis). It is common clinical teaching that gastric reflux also occurs with a hiatus hernia, not because of loss of sphincter function, but because the necessary supporting function of the diaphragm is lacking. Recent findings, however, have challenged this assumption. Another disorder of the LOS is the uncommon condition 'achalasia' characterized by high resting sphincter pressures (100 mm Hg or more) and failure of relaxation on swallowing. The intrinsic innervation of the sphincter is destroyed in this condition and the muscle shows a marked hypersensitivity to gastrin and other humoral stimuli. It is possible that this is a form of denervation hypersensitivity and the enhanced response to blood gastrin levels or other circulating substances accounts for the high resting sphincter tone.

REFERENCES

Bosma J F 1967 Symposium on oral sensation and perception. Charles C Thomas, Springfield, Illinois
Burgen A S V, Emmelin N G 1961 Physiology of the salivary glands. Arnold, London
Code C F (ed) 1968 Handbook of physiology. Section 6: Alimentary Canal, vol IV: American Physiological Society, Motility, Washington

Cohen S, Harris L D 1972 The lower esophageal sphincter. Gastroenterology 63: 1066–1073
Davison J S 1977 Relaxation of the lower oesophageal sphincter during swallowing. Digestion 15: 73–76
Jenkins G N 1970 The physiology of the mouth. 3rd edn revised. Blackwell, Oxford
Payne W S, Olsen A M 1974 The esophagus. Henry Kimpton, London
Petersen O H 1978 Salivary glands – Physiological aspects. In: Recheigl M Jr (ed) Handbook of nutrition and food. CRC Press, Cleveland
Schneyer L H, Schneyer Charlotte A (eds) 1967 Secretory mechanism of salivary glands. Academic Press, London

4 The Stomach

The major functions of the stomach in man can be summarized under four heads. (1) By storing food temporarily and controlling its entry into the small intestine it spreads out the time during which food is presented to the digestive and absorptive processes of the upper small intestine. In this way the time spent in the actual ingestion of food is conveniently reduced. (2) It liquefies the ingested food and passes it on to the small intestine in a quantity and form suitable for small intestinal function. (3) It reduces the risk of swallowed noxious agents entering the small intestine. (4) The gastric mucosa produces hydrochloric acid and pepsin, intrinsic factor and a number of hormones.

GASTRIC MUSCLE AND GASTRIC MOTILITY

The musculature is responsible for the stomach's action as a reservoir and for the mixing and onward propulsion of the chyme. The word chyme is used to describe food that has undergone partial digestion so that it is semifluid.

Muscular structure and innervation. The muscular coat covers the whole of the stomach and is composed of four layers (Fig. 4.1):

1. An external longitudinal layer (immediately under the serosa) part of which is continuous with the longtitudinal fibres of the oesophagus.

2. A circular layer (continuous with the circular layers of the oesophageal muscle) which increases in thickness in the antrum and pylorus.

3. In the proximal portion only, a well-developed oblique layer lying inside the circular layer.

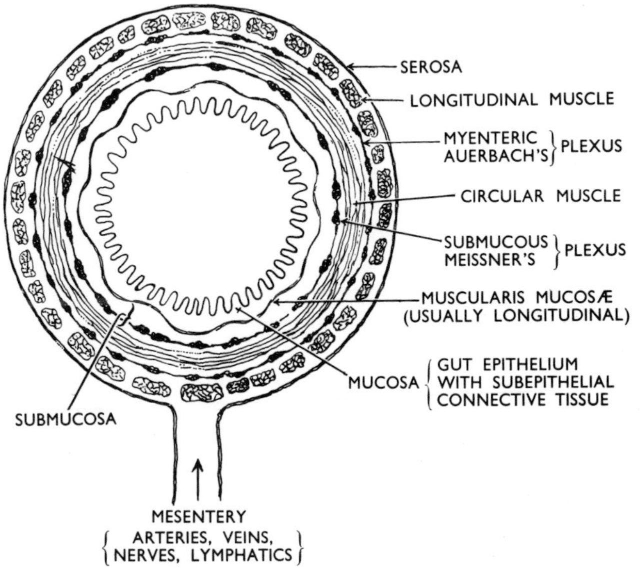

4. A thin layer of muscle (muscularis mucosae) in the mucous coat.

The stomach is innervated by the terminal branches of the right and left vagi (parasympathetic) and also by sympathetic fibres from the coeliac plexus. It is generally accepted that the parasympathetic nerves relay in the two nerve plexuses within the stomach, the myenteric plexus lying between the two main muscle coats and the submucous plexus lying in the submucosa (Fig. 4.1). The sympathetic nerves which supply the stomach are postganglionic.

Extracellular and intracellular recording techniques reveal a regular 'basal electrical rhythm' (BER) a 'pace-setter potential' (Fig. 4.2a) that is propagated aborally to the pylorus at the rate of about three per minute in man. The pace-setter is not precisely located and may shift but normally originates on the proximal greater curvature and spreads by direct electrical conduction from cell to cell. Extrinsic innervation appears to influence the BER so that vagotomy results in a decreased velocity and a temporary period of disorganization of the BER. In the presence of contractile activity the BER is followed by a second non-propagated electrical component (Fig. 4.2b) on which a burst of action potentials may be superimposed. It seems that the BER produces some change essential for inducing a second potential and contraction and is responsible for the frequency and co-ordination of contractile activity. Acetylcholine appears to be important for the production of second potentials, action potentials and contraction; catecholamines reduce the state of excitability.

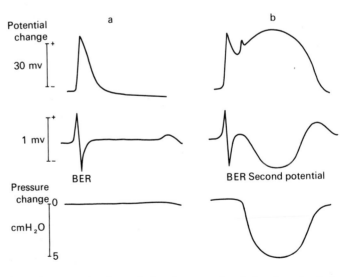

Fig. 4.2 Postulated correlations between electrical and mechanical events in the pyloric antrum. *Top row*, intracellular recordings. *Middle row*, extracellular recordings. *Bottom row*, intraluminal pressure. a: Inactive muscle. b: Active muscle, in which the whole complex lasts 8 to 12 sec. The time scale in a and b is the same. (*After* Daniel, E. E. (1965) *Gastroenterology*, **49**, 411).

Fig. 4.1 A simplified plan of the main features of the wall of the intestinal tract.

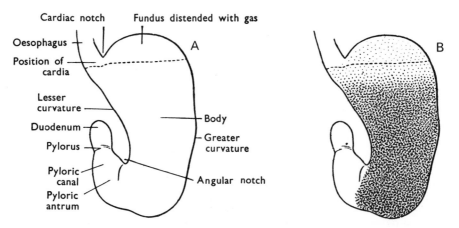

Fig. 4.3   An outline of the full stomach to show the names of the various parts. The dotted line represents the level to which a large barium meal fills the stomach. The shaded area of the diagram on the right indicates the density of distribution of oxyntic cells according to Berger. There are almost none in the antrum and relatively few in the fundus.

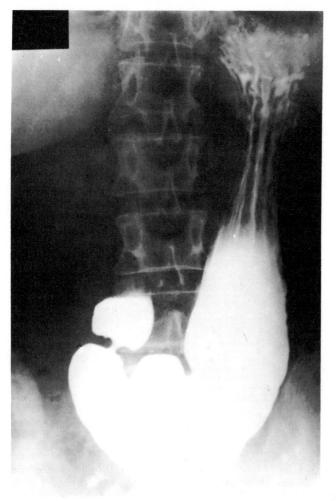

Fig. 4.4   Radiograph of stomach after a barium meal. Patient erect.

Reservoir Function of the Stomach

The shape of a full stomach is illustrated in Fig. 4.3A. The outline of the human stomach can be observed by X-rays after the administration of a meal containing barium which is opaque to X-rays (Fig. 4.4). The shape and position of the normal stomach vary considerably according to the posture of the subject, the skeletal build, the tone of the abdominal wall and the state of adjacent viscera. When the stomach of an animal has been outlined with silver-wire sutures which can be seen on an X-ray photograph, it has been found that the lesser curvature remains nearly constant in position and contour whereas the greater curvature of the body and fundus increase markedly in length as the organ distends.

As food enters the stomach and fills it, the smooth muscle fibres increase in length so that between peristaltic contractions the intragastric pressure remains nearly constant at low values not very different from those found in the empty stomach (<5 mm Hg or <68 mm H_2O). The intragastric pressure remains low unless the stomach becomes very large.

The low pressure at which the stomach holds its contents can in part be explained on physical grounds. Laplace's law states that the transmural pressure P, across the wall of a cylinder is directly proportional to the tension in its walls, T, and is inversely proportional to its radius, R, so that $P = T/R$. Therefore although the tension in the wall of the stomach increases as it fills, the transmural pressure alters relatively little because its radius is also increasing. The stomach is often said to undergo *receptive relaxation* as it fills but this explanation of the low pressure in the full stomach would not be justified if Laplace's law alone explained these low pressures. When, however, smooth muscle is held in a constant state of stretch for some time its tension decreases; further, impulses in the vagus nerve probably cause muscular relaxation in the filling stomach. Relaxation as well as contraction of gastric muscle can be induced by appropriate stimulation of efferent fibres in the vagus and splanchnic nerves. This has been illustrated in animal experiments in

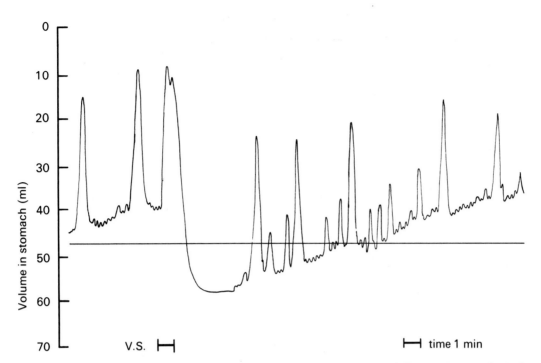

Fig. 4.5 Illustrating changes of intragastric volume at constant intragastric pressure (50 mm H_2O) in the anaesthetized cat with its pylorus occluded. After 60 seconds stimulation of the peripheral end of the cut vagus nerve in the thorax (VS) there is an initial decrease in 'background' volume lasting 1 to 2 minutes, followed by a more prolonged period during which the 'background' volume is increased. Superimposed on these 'background' changes are additional short-lived alterations in volume caused by waves of contraction.

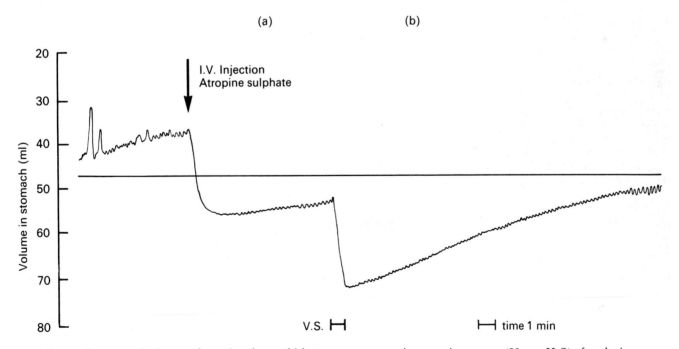

Fig. 4.6 (a) Illustrating the increased gastric volume which occurs at constant intragastric pressure (50 mm H_2O) after the intravenous administration of atropine sulphate. (The experimental conditions were the same as those described in Figure 4.5.) Atropine also abolishes 'spontaneous' contractility. (b) Illustrating that the relaxation of gastric musculature which follows vagal stimulation (VS) occurs in the atropinized animal. The stimulus was the same as that used in the experiment illustrated in Figure 4.5. Note the absence of contraction in response to vagal stimulation after atropine and the immediate onset of relaxation.

which the peripheral end of the cut vagus nerve is stimulated in the lower thorax while intragastric pressure is maintained constant and the volume of the gastric contents is recorded (Fig. 4.5). In these circumstances it is assumed that the external pressure on the stomach is constant and therefore the transmural pressure is constant so that a decrease in volume of the gastric contents indicates that contraction is the predominant response in the gastric muscle whereas an increase in volume indicates that the predominant effect is relaxation. Stimulation of the splanchnic nerves also causes gastric relaxation. Some of the tone of the gastric musculature undoubtedly originates from intrinsic cholinergic mechanisms, probably the nerve plexuses in the stomach wall. In experimental animals with the vagus and splanchnic nerves to the stomach divided and the transmural pressure held constant, an increase of intragastric volume follows the administration of atropine (Fig. 4.6a).

The relaxation of gastric muscle which accompanies vagal and splanchnic stimulation can be shown to be confined to the proximal part of the stomach and not to occur in the antrum. Relaxation caused by splanchnic stimulation is probably due to the release of noradrenaline and is abolished by sympathetic blocking agents such as guanethidine. The chemical transmitter released from the vagal nerve endings to cause gastric relaxation has not been identified and relaxation following vagal stimulation is not prevented by either atropine (Fig. 4.6b) or guanethidine. Compounds which contain purine bases have however been shown to cause relaxation of gastrointestinal smooth muscle and on the assumption that such compounds may be the elusive transmitter the nerve fibres are sometimes referred to as purinergic fibres. More recently evidence has been presented to suggest that 'vasoactive intestinal polypeptide' (VIP) (p. 69) may be the neurohumoral transmitter responsible for gastric receptive relaxation. Large numbers of biologically active peptides have now been isolated from central and peripheral nervous tissue. Many of these peptides have been shown to be associated with the autonomic innervation of the gut so that it is currently generally believed that peptide neurotransmitters have an important part to play in the nervous control of gastrointestinal function.

The physiological stimuli responsible for originating gastric relaxation are incompletely investigated but experiments on cats and dogs show that stimulation of the central end of one cut vagus immediately above the diaphragm causes gastric relaxation. Experiments on dogs show that swallowing is accompanied by relaxation in the fundus of the stomach and gastric relaxation after a meal is reduced if the meal is passed directly into the stomach through a fistula (an artificial opening into the stomach through the abdominal wall). Relaxation of the body and fundus of the stomach also occurs during vomiting (p. 64).

Mixing and Propulsive Movements of the Stomach

Peristaltic movements can be observed on X-ray examination when the stomach contains a suspension of barium. These are seen as waves which begin in the body of the stomach and travel towards the pylorus as shallow indentations becoming deeper in the pyloric antrum where they may

be so marked as to appear to bisect the organ. As a rule from one to three such waves can be seen at a time. They have also been observed directly in a few human subjects who, because of a stricture of the oesophagus or because of damage to the abdominal wall, have acquired a gastric fistula. Wolf and Wolff made many such observations on their subject Tom.

The stomach has an autonomous peristaltic rhythm which can be modified by vagal stimulation. Gastric motility is decreased after bilateral vagotomy in man. In animals, perfusion of the stomach with acetylcholine increases its motility and putting eserine (which interferes with the action of choline esterase) into Tom's stomach produced very marked and vigorous contractions. Atropine (which blocks the action of acetylcholine) stops gastric contractions for a long time both in animals and man.

The peristaltic movements in the upper two-thirds of the stomach are relatively weak but are much more intense over the more muscular pyloric antrum. Only a few of the peristaltic waves which originate near the cardia proceed along the antrum but when they do they may be sufficiently strong to produce a localized obliteration of its lumen. The peristaltic movements in the upper two-thirds of the stomach serve to mix the gastric secretions with the surface of the food bolus and to 'milk' the chyme into the pyloric antrum. The pyloric antrum and pylorus can be regarded as a peristaltic pump which moves fluid from the stomach to the duodenum. The fact that the pylorus is narrow means that only suitably liquified chyme is able to pass through. In contrast to the gastro-oesophageal junction, the pylorus is usually relaxed. It closes only as the peristaltic wave passes over it. While each wave of peristalsis in the antrum moves a small spurt of chyme forward into the duodenum it also squeezes a considerable amount backwards into the stomach so that antral peristalsis also mixes and macerates the gastric contents. Because the pylorus is normally open duodenal contents can regurgitate into the stomach from the duodenum whenever appropriate pressure gradients develop.

Control of Gastric Emptying

The intensity of peristalsis of the gastroduodenal pump and duodenal resistance to the transfer of the gastric contents both affect the rate at which the stomach empties. The action of the gastroduodenal pump is in its turn modified by the volume of the gastric contents and the composition of the chyme being transferred to the duodenum.

The effect of the volume of the gastric contents on the rate of gastric emptying can be studied by means of a special liquid meal. Despite wide variations in the original volume of the liquid meal introduced into the stomach under standardized conditions there is a linear relationship between the square root of the volume of the meal remaining in the stomach and the passage of time (Fig. 4.7). This relationship may depend on alterations in tension in the wall of the stomach. The tension is proportional to the radius of the stomach (Law of Laplace) and the radius of a cylinder varies with the square root of its volume.

Tension could act directly on the gastric muscle or could alter reflexly the number of impulses travelling in the efferent vagus and splanchnic nerves to the stomach. The finding that

possibly VIP (handwritten margin note)

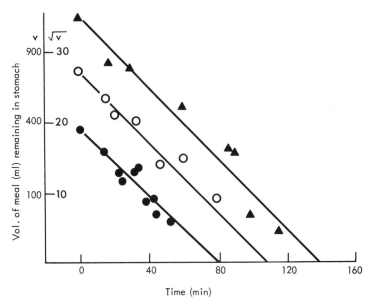

Fig. 4.7 Illustrating the relationship between the volume of a standard liquid meal remaining in the stomach and the passage of time, in a single human subject. The initial volumes of the meals introduced into the stomach were ▲ 1250 ml, ○ 750 ml and ● 330 ml. (*Redrawn from* A. Hopkins (1966) *Journal of Physiology*, **182**, 144–149.)

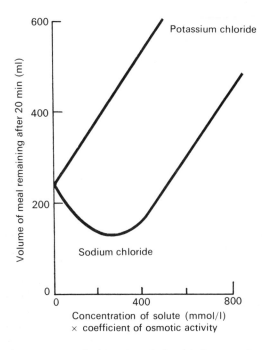

Fig. 4.8 Diagram showing the relationship between the volume of 750 ml test 'meals' of two different solutes and of water remaining in the stomach after 20 minutes and the effect of varying concentrations of the solutes in the meals. The volume remaining at zero concentration on the abscissa represents the effect of water alone. (*From* J. N. Hunt (1961) *Gastroenterology*, **41**, 49–51.)

distension of the stomach causes an increase in the frequency of impulses travelling in afferent fibres of the vagus suggests that there are tension receptors in the stomach wall.

Distension of the stomach causes it to contract and inhibits electrical and motor activity in the duodenum through an efferent nervous pathway which is probably adrenergic. Such reciprocal effects of gastric distension on the stomach and duodenum have the advantage of aiding the onward propulsion of chyme; unless the tension in the wall of the narrower duodenum is less than that in the stomach, with its larger diameter, intraduodenal pressure will be greater than intragastric pressure (Law of Laplace). The force of the gastroduodenal pump is decreased and gastric emptying time is greatly prolonged after bilateral vagotomy which is often performed to reduce gastric acid secretion in man. To avoid gastric stasis the operation is usually combined with measures designed to decrease the normal resistance at the pylorus. The muscle in the region of the pylorus may be incised, *pyloroplasty*, or a connexion may be made between the pre-pyloric region of the stomach and the upper small intestine, a *gastroenterostomy*, to by-pass the pylorus.

The composition of the gastric contents affects the rate of gastric emptying. A number of feedback mechanisms from the duodenum influence the rate of gastric emptying according to the nature of the chyme delivered from the stomach.

Effect of osmolality of duodenal contents. The effects on the rate of gastric emptying when water and two different solutes are introduced into the stomach are illustrated in Figure 4.8. Hunt has suggested that these and similar observations could be explained by the presence of osmoreceptors in the walls of the duodenum and jejunum which exert a control over those factors which modify the strength of the gastroduodenal pump. It is assumed that the membrane of the osmoreceptor has permeability characteristics like those of the red blood cell but unlike the red cell the osmoreceptor is not disrupted by increased intracellular volume. It is presumed that the osmoreceptor alters in size according to the tonicity of the duodenal contents. Hunt believes that when relatively large volumes of solute are placed in the stomach and their rate of emptying is studied over short periods the composition of the instilled fluid is a reasonable indication of the nature of the solute reaching the duodenum despite dilution by the gastric and intestinal secretions. The moderate degree of osmoreceptor distension which is presumed to occur when water alone is ingested results in a moderate inhibition of gastroduodenal emptying ('b' in Fig. 4.9; 240 ml remaining in the stomach after 20 min, at zero concentration of solute, Fig. 4.8). When the receptor becomes smaller than this there is increased inhibition of gastric emptying ('c' in Fig. 4.9): this occurs at all concentrations of KCl which does not penetrate the osmoreceptor membrane. That is water leaves the osmoreceptor at all concentrations of KCl and so the inhibition of gastric emptying is always greater than that which occurs with water alone (Fig. 4.8). Amino acids, glucose, and potassium chloride solutions of the same osmolal concentration are equally effective in slowing gastric emptying. When the osmoreceptor becomes larger than the size attained with water alone there is less inhibition of gastric emptying ('a' in Fig. 4.9). This occurs with NaCl concentrations less than approximately 500 mmol/l. (Fig. 4.8). It is believed that there is a limited facilitated diffusion or active transport of NaCl into

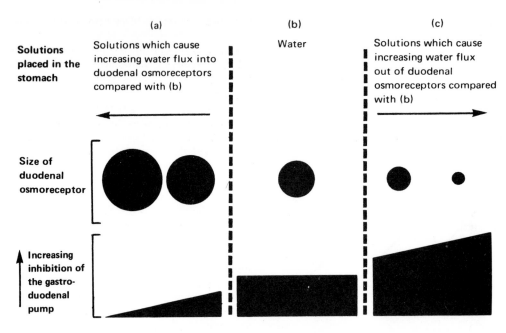

Fig. 4.9 A diagrammatic representation of the duodenal osmoreceptor hypothesis in the control of gastric emptying.

the osmoreceptor: as the NaCl concentration increases from zero to approximately 300 mmol/l increasing amounts of NaCl enter the cell and these are accompanied by water so that more water enters the cell than in the presence of water alone. At concentrations of NaCl above 300 mmol/l however the membrane behaves towards NaCl as it does towards KCl and so the facilitated transfer of NaCl becomes less and less effective in causing distension of the receptor because the entry of water into the receptor is opposed by the increasing external concentration of NaCl. If the external NaCl concentration continues to increase a point is reached (approximately 500 mmol/l, Fig. 4.8) when the osmotic effect of the internal

and external concentrations of NaCl balance one another and the net flux of water across the cell membrane is the same as in the presence of water alone. If the NaCl concentration is increased still further then relatively more water will leave the cell than in the presence of water alone and so there is increased inhibition of gastric emptying (Fig. 4.8).

When the stomach is filled with fluids known not to reduce the rate of emptying by the osmoreceptor mechanism, gravity has, at least during the first 20 min, a significant effect on the rate of gastric emptying. In the head-down position the rate of emptying of such solutions is 80 per cent of that which occurs in the head-up position. With meals of similar concentration

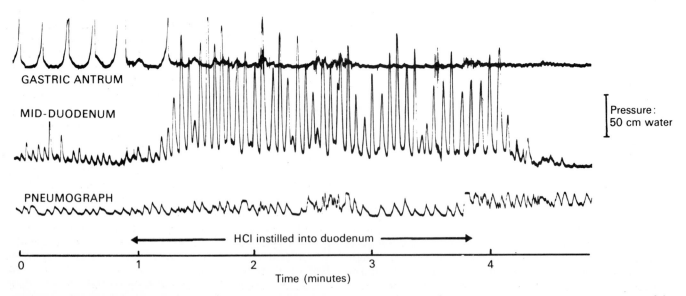

Fig. 4.10 Effect of the instillation of acid (HCl 100 mmol/l at 6 ml/min) into the duodenum on motor activity of the gastric antrum and the duodenum in a fasting dog. (Brink, M., Schlegel, J. F. & Code, C. F. (1965) *Gut, 6*, 163–171).

which markedly reduce the rate of emptying by their osmotic effect, the rate of emptying is the same in the head-up position and in the head-down position.

It is believed that the osmoreceptors are in the duodenum rather than in the stomach. Starch and glucose meals of equal carbohydrate concentration, placed in the stomach through a tube, empty at similar rates. It is therefore assumed that starch can exert its effect on emptying only after it has been hydrolysed in the upper small intestine and that the same is true for protein.

Effect of acid entering the duodenum. The presence of acid in the duodenum reduces gastric motility, increases duodenal motility (Fig. 4.10) (and presumably therefore duodenal resistance) and delays the rate of gastric emptying. When citrate solutions of similar osmolarity but different pH are placed in the stomach in man, more acid solutions leave less rapidly (Fig. 4.11). In these experiments a constant amount of

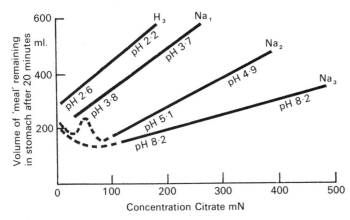

Fig. 4.11   The influence of salts of citric acid on gastric emptying. H₃, citric acid; Na₁, dihydrogen monosodium citrate; Na₂, monohydrogen disodium citrate; Na₃, trisodium citrate. The volume of the 'meal' instilled was 750 ml in each instance. (*From* J. N. Hunt & M. T. Knox (1961) *Journal of Physiology*, 163, 34–45.)

acid titratable to pH 6·5 is delivered to the duodenum in unit time and the duodenum appears to have a receptor that responds quantitatively to acids. Little is known about the nature of these receptors in the upper small intestine.

The rate of gastric emptying must depend not only on the rate of delivery of acid into the duodenum but also on the neutralizing capacity of the duodenal contents. The presence of acid in the duodenum increases the buffering capacity of the duodenal contents because it increases the secretions of the pancreas (p. 68) and of Brunner's glands (p. 73), both of which contain bicarbonate.

Effect of the products of digestion of fat. The presence of emulsified fat in the duodenum decreases gastric motility and the rate of gastric emptying. It is unlikely that even in its most finely divided state fat could exert its effect through the osmoreceptor mechanism. The salts of the longer fatty acids (with 12 to 18 C atoms) are considerably more effective in slowing gastric emptying than those of the smaller fatty acids with 2 to 10 C atoms. The reason for this is uncertain but it may be significant that the shorter chain fatty acids are esterified to a very small extent only in the mucosa of the small intestine and are absorbed into the portal vein whereas the longer chain

fatty acids are esterified in the mucosa and pass mainly into the lymphatics.

Effect of duodenal distension. There is evidence that duodenal receptors respond to distension and that distension causes inhibition of electrical and motor activity in the pyloric antrum.

Duodenal stimulation affects gastric motility by both nervous and humoral mechanisms which may act separately or in combination. In some instances vago-vagal reflexes have been identified; in others local enterogastric reflexes are involved whose pathway may pass through the coeliac ganglion. A polypeptide which stimulates gastric motor activity in dogs has been extracted from the duodenal mucosa of pigs and its amino acid sequence determined. It remains to be determined whether this polypeptide which has been named *motilin* (molecular weight 2700) is concerned in the physiological control of gastric emptying. Since inhibitory effects can be demonstrated in denervated and transplanted gastric pouches (p. 54) they can in part at least be explained by a humoral mechanism. An inhibitory humoral agent 'enterogastrone' has been postulated but it has not been identified with certainty. Secretin (p. 67), cholecystokinin-pancreozymin (CCK-PZ) (p. 68) and gastric inhibitory polypeptide (GIP) have all been shown to have some enterogastrone-like activity. *Gastric inhibitory polypeptide* (molecular weight 5105), as extracted from the mucosa of the small intestine, has 43 amino acid residues and is structurally similar to glucagon and secretin. It has been identified by immunofluorescence techniques in cells of the duodenum and jejunum distinct from the S-cell (secretin) and the EG-cell (enteroglucagon).

Other factors. Observation of the human stomach through gastric fistulae has shown that the emotional state of the subject has a great influence on emptying time and motility. In a state of fear, food may remain in the stomach for 12 hours or more whereas excitement may reduce emptying time.

GASTRIC MUCOSA AND GASTRIC SECRETION

Mucosal structure and growth. The gastric mucosa consists of simple branched tubular glands packed tightly together and arranged perpendicularly to the surface. Groups of glands, usually four, open into gastric pits which in turn open on to the mucosal surface. In the mucosa of the distal part of the stomach in man (the pyloric area) the glands are lined by mucous secreting cells only. In the mucosa of the remainder of the stomach the glands are lined not only with mucous cells but also with parietal (oxyntic) cells (Fig. 4.3B) and peptic (chief or zymogen) cells. The different cell types are arranged as illustrated in Figure 4.12. The glands are described as having three parts, base, neck and isthmus. The neck region has irregularly-shaped mucous cells with basal nuclei and most of the parietal cells. A few parietal cells are also found in the isthmus and basal regions. Peptic cells (zymogen cells with granular cytoplasm) are present in the base of the glands. Special staining techniques reveal a few scattered argentaffin cells in the basal region. The gastric pits and the mucosal surface throughout the stomach are lined with characteristic mucus-laden, columnar epithelial cells with oval basal nuclei.

The mucosal structure is the outcome of a dynamic

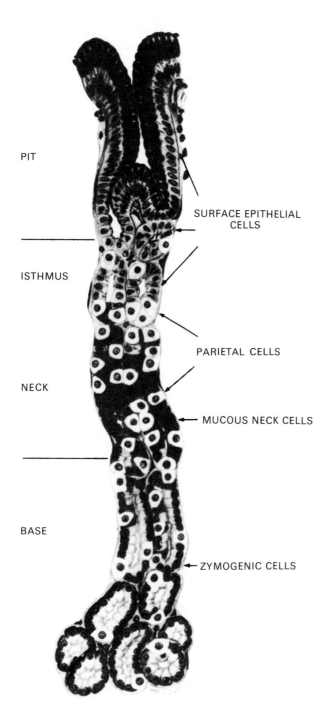

PIT

SURFACE EPITHELIAL
CELLS

ISTHMUS

PARIETAL CELLS

NECK

MUCOUS NECK CELLS

BASE

ZYMOGENIC CELLS

Fig. 4.12 A drawing of a section of the body of the stomach of a monkey. Mucus and nuclei are shown in black. (*From* A. W. Ham. *Textbook of Histology*. 5th edition. Preparation by C. P. Leblond. Figs. 24–28, p. 683.)

equilibrium between mucosal cell production and destruction. These cells are produced by cellular division probably from a common 'mother' cell in the mucous neck cell region. From this region gradually maturing cells pass up to the surface or down into the glands. The process of cell renewal has been studied by the use of tritiated thymidine. The cells take 2 to 3 days to migrate from the neck region to the surface; the oldest surface cells are extruded into the gastric lumen and are digested. Estimation of the DNA content of gastric washings shows that in normal people about half a million cells are lost per minute. The cells which pass down into the glands give rise to the parietal and peptic cells; they are probably destroyed eventually in the base of the glands.

The mechanisms controlling cell proliferation are not fully understood but they are known to be influenced by hormones such as growth hormone and dietary factors affecting somatic growth. Mucosal growth may also be influenced by nervous stimulation and by trophic effects of gastrointestinal hormones such as gastrin.

Gastric Secretions

Mucus and bicarbonate secretion. Mucus secreted by the surface cells of the stomach (Fig. 4.12) protects the gastric mucosa against physical and chemical damage. The mucus gel adheres to the stomach wall and provides a protective layer over which the chyme can move with minimal mechanical damage to the underlying mucosal cells. This mucus barrier also protects the underlying cells from digestion by the gastric juice. The HCl which diffuses through the mucus gel is neutralized within the gel layer by bicarbonate secreted from the mucosa, possibly from the same cells that secrete the mucus; the higher pH in the mucus layer also inhibits the action of pepsin (p. 55). Although mucus lines the whole of the mucosal surface, including the gastric pits, it does not line the gastric glands and it is as yet unexplained how the glands are protected from the mixture of acid and pepsin they are assumed to contain.

Mucus is a high molecular weight glycoprotein in which the carbohydrate–protein ratio is many times greater than for most other glycoproteins secreted by the gastrointestinal tract. Gastric mucus is composed of polymers of subunits each with a protein backbone to which are attached a large number of carbohydrate side chains. In ABO blood group 'secretors' (p. 131) the terminal sugar residues of the gastric mucus are the same as those that determine the specificity of the ABO blood groups on the red cell surface (p. 131); in the case of blood group A this is *N*-acetylgalactosamine and in blood group B it is galactose. About a quarter of the protein backbone of each subunit is however non-glycosylated and the gastric mucus molecule comprises four subunits joined by disulphide bridges at their non-glycosylated regions. Although the carbohydrate covering protects the underlying protein from proteolysis the polymer can be split into its water-soluble subunits at the non-glycosylated region by proteolytic enzymes such as pepsin and trypsin and by chemicals that break disulphide bonds.

The visco-gelatinous character of gastric mucus depends on the presence of glycoprotein in the polymeric form (subunits at the same concentration do not have this property) so that

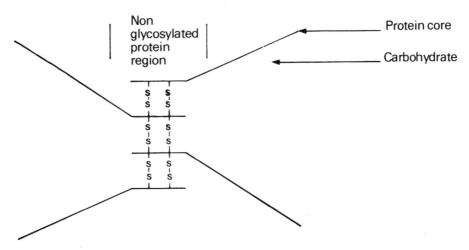

enzymes and chemicals which split the mucus into its glycoprotein subunits also destroy the physico-chemical properties responsible for its physiological function. The surface of the mucus layer in contact with the gastric chyme is no doubt continually being solublized by pepsin and replaced from beneath by newly secreted mucus. The ability of the gastric mucosa to renew the surface cells as they complete their life cycle must clearly be important for the provision of a normal mucous barrier. The mucus must also be formed at a suitable rate because strong non-covalent intermolecular interactions between the polymers are necessary for gel formation to occur and these interactions increase as the

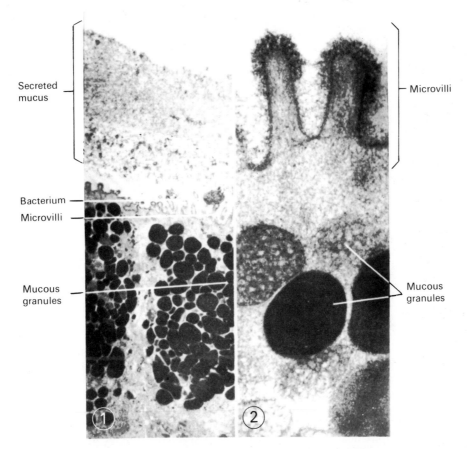

Fig. 4.13 (1) A low-power electron micrograph of the apical parts of two surface mucous cells from the luminal surface of human gastric mucosa. A thick layer of secreted mucus occupies most of the upper half of the illustration. The apical surfaces of the cells are separated from the mucus by a clear space containing a section through a bacterium (arrow). Projecting into the lumen are a few short microvilli with a fuzzy surface. Most of the apical cytoplasm is filled with dense mucous granules (×5000). (2) A high magnification of human surface mucous cell microvilli and mucous granules. The trilaminar plasma membrane has a prominent surface coat of fine filamentous material. Mucous granules of varying density are found in the apical cytoplasm (×43 000). (From S. Ito (1967). *Gastric Secretion, Mechanisms and Control*, pp. 3–24. Oxford: Pergamon.)

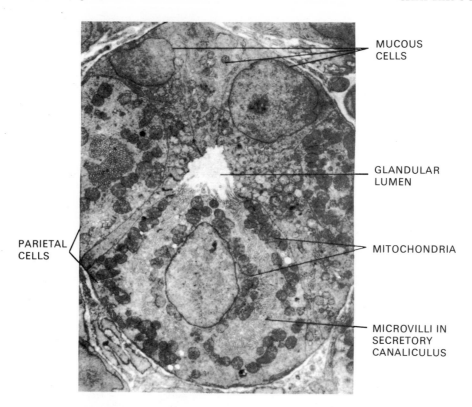

MUCOUS
CELLS

GLANDULAR
LUMEN

PARIETAL
CELLS

MITOCHONDRIA

MICROVILLI IN
SECRETORY
CANALICULUS

Fig. 4.14A A low-power electronmicrograph of a transverse section through the neck region of a bat gastric gland. The specimen was obtained when the tissue was secreting acid. The section passes through a large parietal cell and parts of two others: note the numerous microvilli in the secretory canaliculi and the numerous large mitochondria around the nucleus and in the peripheral cytoplasm. Several mucous cells containing a few mucous granules surround the glandular lumen ($\times$ 4300). (*From* S. Ito (1967) *Gastric Secretion, Mechanisms and Control.* pp. 3–24. Oxford: Pergamon.)

glycoprotein concentration increases. The production of mucus with the correct structure at suitable rates must be genetically determined and specific glycosyltransferase enzymes are for example necessary to catalyse the step-wise addition of sugar residues during glycoprotein synthesis. Drugs such as salicylates interfere with the ability to synthesize mucus.

The physiological control of mucus secretion is not fully understood but the rate of mucus secretion is increased by mechanical and chemical irritation of the mucosa and by acid in the lumen of the stomach. It is also increased by vagal and sympathetic stimulation. In dogs its secretion seems to be reduced during starvation but it rapidly returns to normal when feeding begins again.

Intrinsic factor. Intrinsic factor (p. 29) originates in the parietal cell region of the glandular mucosa of the stomach. When mucosal sections are incubated with labelled vitamin B_{12} ($^{57}CoB_{12}$), autoradiographs show radioactivity localized to this region of the gastric mucosa. Gastric intrinsic factor is probably not normally absorbed from the gut but in abnormal circumstances cellular damage may result in its entry into the circulation with the subsequent formation of antibodies. The injection of stimulants of gastric acid secretion increases the rate of secretion of intrinsic factor; the quantity of intrinsic factor normally secreted is considerably in excess of that required for the complete absorption of the vitamin B_{12} in the diet.

Acid secretion. The gastric juice contains hydrochloric acid secreted apparently by the parietal cells (Figs. 4.12 and 4.14). Acid secretion occurs only from the glandular region of the body and fundus of the stomach which contains parietal cells (Fig. 4.3B). The electron-microscope shows that these cells have large numbers of mitochondria and during acid secretion possess a massive canalicular system packed with microvilli; this suggests that they are well adapted for the secretion of large volumes of fluid. At rest the parietal cell cytoplasm contains relatively few, small canaliculi with few villi but has an extensive cytoplasmic smooth membrane system of tubular and vesicular components (tubulovesicles) (Fig. 4.14B). On stimulation of acid secretion the tubulovesicles migrate to become incorporated in the canalicular surface so that the proliferating microtubular and canalicular system becomes a predominant feature of the cell structure (Figs. 4.14 A and C). The microfilaments which are not seen at the magnifications in Figure 4.14 appear to orientate themselves in a form of cytoskeleton within the microvilli. When the cell returns to its resting state the surfaces of the microvilli are thought to be recycled back into cytoplasmic tubulovesicles and the microfilaments again become disorientated.

Histochemical studies of biopsy specimens of gastric mucosa reveal intense concentrations of the flavoprotein enzymes and of cytochrome oxidase in the parietal cells (Fig. 4.15). These enzymes are presumably important for the production of the

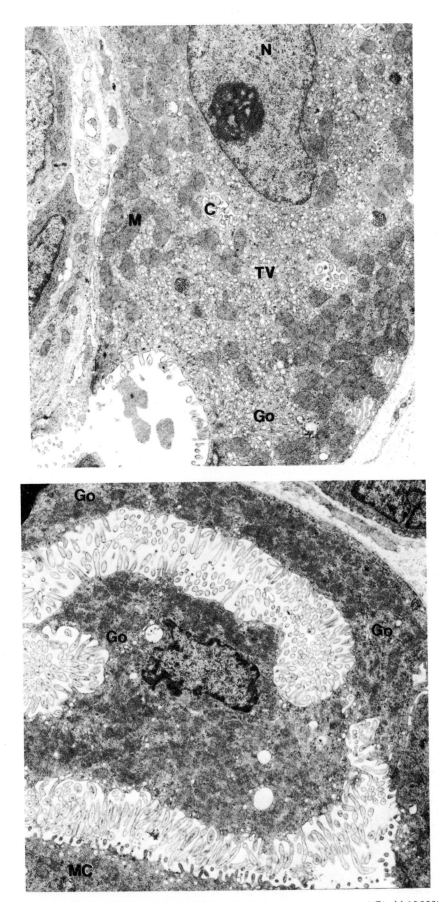

Fig. 4.14B and C. Electronmicrographs of portions of parietal cells in a non-secretory state ((B), × 10000) and following histamine stimulation ((C), × 9600). In B, note the extensive cytoplasmic tubulovesicles (TV) and the relative paucity of canaliculi (C). In Fig. 4.14C note the tubulovesicles replaced by an extensive canalicular system filled with microvilli seen in longtitudinal and transverse section (N, nucleus; M, mitochondria; Go, Golgi complexes). (*From* T. E. Forte, T. E. Machen & J. G. Forte (1977) *Gastroenterology,* **73**, 941–955).

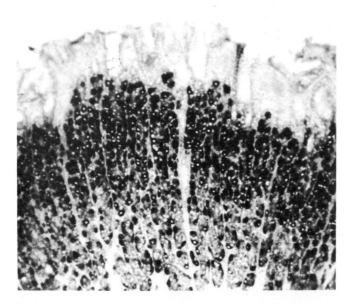

Fig. 4.15 Low-power photomicrograph of monkey stomach. Cytochrome oxidase reaction (*black granules*). Parietal cells are stained strongly and peripheral epithelium and chief cells give a trace reaction. This is a black stain and the appearance is similar for all oxidative enzymes, succinate dehydrogenase, reduced nicotinamide adenine dinucleotide, and nicotinamide adenine dinucleotide phosphate dehydrogenases ($\times$ 100). (*From* M. H. Floch, S. V. Noorden & H. M. Spiro (1967) *Gastroenterology*, **52**, 230–238.)

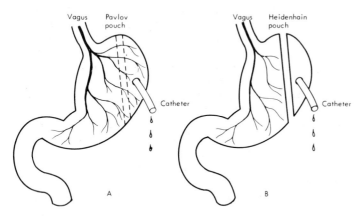

Fig. 4.16 A diagram of two commonly used types of gastric pouch. A. *A Pavlov (vagally innervated) pouch*. This is constructed by sewing the opposing mucosal surfaces together beneath the muscular layer in the region indicated by the two dotted lines. The nerve and blood supply to the pouch which reaches the mucosa through the muscular coat, is preserved intact. Note the vagal innervation of the pouch. B. *A Heidenhain (vagally denervated) pouch*. This is constructed by completely severing the mucosa and muscle of the stomach in the region indicated by the two solid lines. Separate whole stomach and body pouches are created. The sympathetic nerves and blood supply continue to reach the Heidenhain pouch along the greater curvature but the vagal innervation which normally spreads to this region from the lesser curvature is severed.

large amounts of energy necessary to elaborate a concentrated acid solution.

Uncontaminated parietal cell secretion has not yet been obtained because gastric juice is, of course, a mixture of secretions from a variety of cell types. However, maximal stimulation of the mucosa might be expected to yield a concentration of acid in the juice closely approximating to that secreted by the parietal cell. Such secretion can be collected in man by continuous suction through a tube passed from the nose or mouth through the oesophagus into the stomach; contamination by swallowed saliva may be prevented by simultaneous aspiration of saliva through another tube placed in the mouth. In animals it is possible to obtain samples of juice secreted by the parietal cell glandular region of the stomach without contamination by secretion from the mucosa of the pyloric gland area by isolating a pouch of mucosa of the body of the stomach as illustrated in Figure 4.16. The secretion of the parietal glands in man appears to have a chloride content of about 170 mmol/l and a hydrogen ion concentration of about 155 mmol/l. The other cations are sodium, potassium, calcium and magnesium, of which potassium is the most abundant at a concentration of about 10 mmol/l.

The hydrogen ion concentration of parietal cell secretion is therefore a million times greater than that found in plasma. The energy required for the secretion of hydrogen ions against this concentration gradient is derived mainly from aerobic oxidation. The energy-rich phosphate compounds produced by these mechanisms are of great importance. If they are rendered unavailable by dinitrophenol, cell respiration continues but acid secretion is inhibited. Since both at rest and during acid secretion the mucosal surface of the body of the stomach is electronegative to the serosal surface, secretion of chloride must take place against an electrical gradient as well as against a concentration gradient (from 107 mmol/l in the intracellular fluid to 170 mmol/l in the canaliculus). Movement of chloride ions across the mucosa, like the movement of hydrogen ions, requires an active transport mechanism (Fig. 4.17). The existence of the hydrogen ion pump can be demonstrated if the chloride potential is first abolished by replacing the chloride in the bathing medium of isolated mucosa with sulphate, to which the mucosal cells are impermeable. If the mucosa is now stimulated to secrete acid, the mucosal surface becomes electropositive with respect to the serosa as the action of the hydrogen ion pump is unmasked.

The details of these pumps, as with all biological pumps, are incompletely understood. The immediate source of the H^+ could be from an oxidation-reduction mechanism with electron carriers providing H^+ from substrate H atoms or it could be from oxidative metabolism by transduction of the chemical energy of ATP. A unique K^+–ATPase, dependent on Mg^{2+} and stimulated by K^+, is believed to be associated with H^+ secretion by oxyntic tubulovesicular membranes. This K^+–ATPase is distinct from the more usual $(Na^+ + K^+)$–ATPase which also occurs in oxyntic cells and its activity, unlike that of $(Na^+ + K^+)$–ATPase, is not depressed by the enzyme inhibitor ouabaine. Uncontrolled accumulation within the parietal cell of the OH^- ions produced during the formation and secretion of hydrogen ions would result in a rise of intracellular pH sufficient to interfere with cell metabolism and with acid secretion. The accumulation of OH^- ions is prevented by combination with H_2CO_3, which is also in

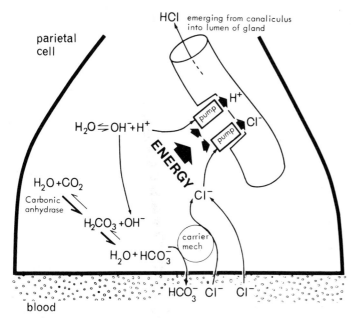

Fig. 4.17 Simplified scheme to illustrate current views on the method of production of hydrochloric acid by the parietal cell of the stomach.

abundant supply, to form HCO_3^-; the supply of H_2CO_3 is facilitated by the enzyme carbonic anhydrase which is present in high concentration in the parietal cell. The bicarbonate ions are transported into the blood (Fig. 4.17) so that the blood leaving the stomach during acid secretion shows an increase in pH. This is presumably responsible for the postprandial 'alkaline tide', that is the slight increase in plasma and urine pH which occurs after meals. The chloride required for the formation of HCl enters the parietal cell from the extracellular fluid. This chloride diffuses down a concentration gradient but its entry into the cell is in part facilitated by a carrier mechanism and coupled to the transport of bicarbonate out of the cell (Fig. 4.17).

Enzyme secretion. The only gastric enzymes of any consequence in digestion are the pepsins. The gastric pepsins are a complex of several enzymes each with its own distinct chemical characteristics; at least seven have been detected electrophoretically and four of these (so-called pepsins 1, 2, 3 and 5) have been isolated and purified in sufficient quantities to allow their functional characterization. These enzymes are formed by the action of acid and of pepsin itself on corresponding inactive precursors, *pepsinogens*, secreted by the gastric mucosa. The pepsinogens arise from the mucous neck and chief cells in the oxyntic gland mucosa (Fig. 4.12) and from cells in the pyloric antral glands and Brunner's glands. After prolonged stimulation of pepsin secretion the number of granules in the peptic cells is decreased.

The pepsins are unusual enzymes in that their pH optima are in the range 1·5 to 3·5. Pepsin breaks the polypeptide chain at several specific peptide bonds; the most susceptible bonds involve tyrosine or phenylalanine (see below). Pepsins 1, 2 and 3 have similar primary bond specificities which differ from those of pepsin 5 but the rates of bond cleavage are slower for pepsin 1 and 2 than for pepsin 3. The pepsins act on proteins to produce short peptide chains with N-terminal amino acids which have a lipophilic side-chain. These amino acids bound to

peptide chains or liberated from them by mucosal N-terminal end peptidases in the intestinal mucosa appear particularly effective in the stimulation of pancreatic enzymes, possibly by causing the release of the hormone CCK-PZ (p. 67).

Line of cleavage

Phenylalanine

After complete removal of the human stomach, digestion of proteins in the intestine proceeds quite well in spite of the absence of preliminary digestion. Pepsin also has the property of clotting milk.

The physiological significance of the different forms of pepsin is at present unknown but pepsin 1 secretion may be increased in patients with peptic ulcer. Normal human plasma contains all the pepsinogens in small quantities but urine appears to contain only those which in the stomach are limited to the body and fundus (uropepsinogens). There is some evidence that the concentration of certain of the pepsinogens in the serum is related to the chief cell mass (compare parietal cell mass, p. 64).

Control of Gastric Secretion

The secretion of gastric juice is controlled by a variety of mechanisms, nervous and chemical, both excitatory and inhibitory, which are integrated during the process of digestion in a complex manner not yet completely understood.

Nervous excitation. Stimulation of the peripheral end of a cut vagus nerve is followed by the secretion of acid, mucus and pepsin. The importance of the vagus nerves for gastric secretion was demonstrated by Pavlov's experiments on dogs in which the oesophagus was cut in the neck and the two ends made to open separately on the surface of the skin (oesophagostomy). Food which was chewed and swallowed was diverted to the exterior and did not enter the stomach (sham feeding) but gastric juice was secreted provided that the vagi were intact. The sight and smell of food alone was found to initiate a flow of gastric juice (psychic or appetite juice) when the vagi were intact but not when they were cut. This phase of gastric secretion does not appear to be as important in man as it is in the dog. These initial stages of stimulation are described as the *cephalic phase* of gastric secretion.

Reflex stimulation of gastric secretion is not, however, limited to these reflexes alone and the presence of food in the stomach and upper small intestine as well as distension in these regions stimulates gastric secretion by nervous reflexes whose afferent and efferent nerve fibres are in the vagus.

The excitatory effect of vagal stimulation occurs mainly by a direct stimulation of the secretory cells but partly by an indirect stimulation of these cells consequent upon the liberation of a hormone *gastrin*, a polypeptide from the mucosa of the pyloric

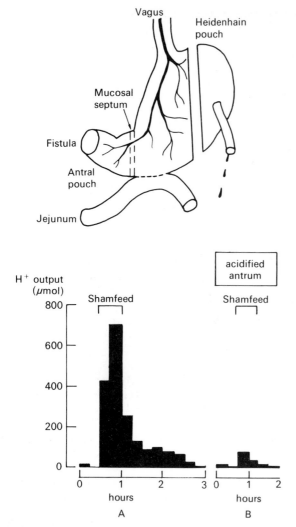

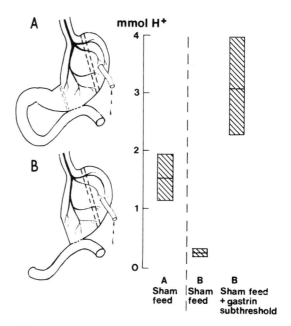

Fig. 4.19 Comparison of the acid secretory responses from Pavlov pouches in five dogs in which the pyloric antrum and duodenum were excluded from gastrointestinal continuity (A) and from the same dogs after the pyloric antrum and first part of the duodenum had been excised (B). The mean acid output is indicated by the mid-line of the hatched area which includes ± 1 s.e. of these mean values. (Based on data from L. Olbe (1964) *Acta physiologica scandinavica*, **62**, 169–175.)

Fig. 4.18A and B. (A) Response of Heidenhain pouch to sham feeding in a dog with an isolated vagally innervated pouch of the pyloric antrum. (B) Response of Heidenhain pouch to the same sham feeding stimulus as in A but with the antral pouch irrigated with HCl 100 mmol/l. (Adapted from Maung Pe Thein and B. Schofield (1959). *Journal of Physiology*, **148**, 291–305.)

antrum and from the upper upper small intestine. The release of gastrin in response to vagal stimulation has been demonstrated in dogs by the finding that vagally denervated pouches (Heidenhain pouches) of gastric body mucosa show an increase of acid secretion in response to sham feeding (Fig. 4.18A). This acid secretion occurs even when complete denervation of the 'body' pouch is ensured by transplanting it into the body wall where it acquires an entirely new blood supply. Vagal denervation of the antrum abolishes this response as does the intravenous administration of a drug like hexamethonium which blocks transmission at ganglionic synapses in the autonomic nervous system.

Chemical excitation. The presence of certain food materials, especially meat extracts, within the pyloric antrum provokes acid secretion even in the absence of vagal innervation of the antrum; this is part of the so-called *gastric phase* of gastric secretion. These materials cause the liberation of gastrin from the mucosa of the pyloric antrum into the blood

which carries it to the glands of the mucosa of the body of the stomach.

Unequivocal proof of the existence of an antral hormone which stimulates acid secretion was first provided by experiments in dogs which showed that distension of a denervated pouch of the pyloric antrum in the absence of food caused secretion of acid from a denervated or transplanted pouch of the body of the stomach.

Cytochemical and ultrastructural studies and associated immunohistochemical studies with gastrin antibodies have revealed gastrin containing cells (G cells) in the surface epithelium of the mid-zone of the pyloric glands and in the mucosa of the small intestine in a number of species including man. These cells contain numerous basal granules and on their apical surface microvilli protrude into the gut lumen (Fig. 4.20). The G cells belong to a group of endocrine polypeptide cells which possess cytochemical characteristics described as APUD (amine precursor uptake and decarboxylation). There is now good evidence that all the APUD cells, which include other endocrine cells of the gut, have a common neuroectodermal origin developmentally and are part of a widespread 'diffuse neuroendocrine system'. In addition to gastrin a number of other peptides (somatostatin, enkephalin, bombesin, substance P and vasoactive intestinal polypeptide) have been identified in the antrum by immunohistochemical techniques. All appear to be located in neural axons as well as in endocrine cells.

The neurotransmitter responsible for the vagal release of gastrin in man has not been identified with certainty but it does not appear to be acetylcholine and may be one of the other

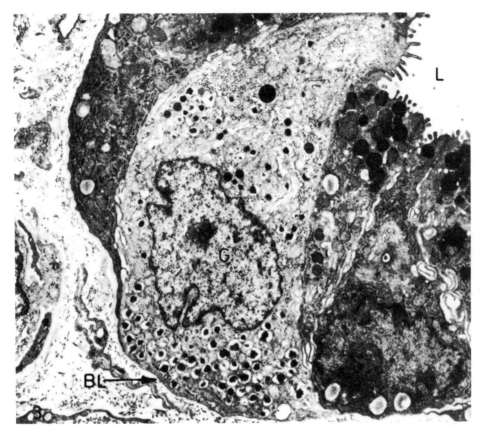

Fig. 4.20 A low-power electron micrograph of a G cell in the pyloric gland epithelium of the cat. Gastrin (G cell) (G). Basal lamina (BL). Lumen (L). (G. Vassallo, E. Solcia & C. Capella (1969) *Zeitschrift für Zellforschung und mikroskopische Anatomie*, 98, 337.)

peptides found in the pyloric antrum. Bombesin (p. 70), for example, is known to stimulate the release of antral gastrin. It is probable that chemical stimuli in the lumen of the pyloric antrum directly stimulate the G cell by way of its microvillous surface.

The gastric glands can also be excited from the intestine by the products of digestion and by distension. When a dog with its oesophagus anastomosed to the second part of the duodenum is fed, secretion occurs in an isolated vagotomized stomach or in a transplanted pouch of body mucosa. This represents part of the so-called *intestinal phase* of gastric secretion and is possibly in part due to a gastrin-releasing peptide such as bombesin (p. 70) passing from the intestinal mucosa to the pyloric antrum and in part to the direct release of gastrin from the mucosa of the upper small intestine. Some patients with peptic ulcer treated by excision of the pyloric antrum and anastomosis of the remaining gastric stump to the duodenum still have a significant increase in serum gastrin concentration after feeding.

Gastrin has been isolated from the antral mucosa of a number of species including man and is now known to exist in several forms (see below) but the form first isolated by Gregory and Tracy consists of seventeen amino acid residues (a heptadecapeptide) and in each species it occurs in two slightly different forms which they named gastrins I and II (sometimes described as G-17-I and G-17-II, or Little Gastrin I and Little Gastrin II, respectively). The physiological actions of the endogenously liberated hormone are very similar to the responses which follow the injection of these peptides. Human

gastrin 17-I isolated from the antral mucosa in man has a molecular weight of 2114 and the following structure:

*Glu-Gly-Pro-Trp-Leu-Glu-Glu-Glu-Glu-Glu-Ala-Tyr-Gly-

Trp-Met-Asp-Phe.NH$_2$

Human gastrin 17-II differs in that tyrosine is replaced by tyrosine-*O*-sulphate. This difference in structure has led to a preference for the abbreviations hG-17-NS and hG-17-S respectively to describe these peptides. The compositions of pig, sheep and dog gastrins differ slightly from one another and from human gastrin in amino acid content. Both termini of the polypeptide molecule are blocked; the N-terminal residue (indicated by the asterisk) is pyroglutamyl (pyrrolidone carboxyl)

$$H_2C{-\!\!-}CH_2$$
$$O{=}C\underset{\underset{H}{|}}{\diagdown}{N}{\diagup}CH{-}C{-}$$

and as in a number of other biologically active polypeptides there is no free C-terminal carboxyl group, since the chain ends with an amide (see secretin, pancreozymin and vasopressin). While the C-terminal residue of secretin is valine.NH$_2$ and of vasopressin is glycine.NH$_2$, both gastrin and pancreozymin end with phenylalanine.NH$_2$. Removal of the C-terminal amide causes complete biological inactivation of gastrin.

These gastrins have been synthesized by Kenner and his co-workers and it has been found that all of the physiological actions of the total molecule are possessed by the C-terminal tetrapeptide (indicated above in heavy type) which appears to be the 'active centre' of the molecule. Pentagastrin, a synthetic analogue containing five amino acids (the C-terminal tetrapeptide of gastrin with β-alanine added at the N-terminus) is used in medicine for testing the secretory capacity of the stomach (p. 63).

Pure gastrin injected intravenously has many actions on the gastrointestinal tract. In addition to its effect on the secretion of acid it stimulates the secretion of pepsin and intrinsic factor by the stomach, secretion of Brunner's glands and of succus entericus, secretion of water, bicarbonate and enzymes by the pancreas and the secretion of hepatic bile and bicarbonate. Gastrin also increases the tone of the musculature of the lower oesophageal sphincter, the stomach and small intestine; it stimulates cell division and growth of gastric and duodenal mucosa and of the pancreas and it stimulates the release of insulin and calcitonin. The other gastrointestinal hormones, secretin and pancreozymin (p. 68), when injected intravenously, also have more than one action on gastrointestinal function. The physiological significance of these multiple effects observed after the injection of large doses of exogenous hormone is uncertain but many hormones which are similar in chemical structure show an overlap in their biological effects. The old idea that each gastrointestinal hormone has a single action on one target tissue is no longer tenable.

The concentration of gastrin in plasma is normally too low to be detected by bioassay. Radioimmunoassay (Chap. 9) has shown that the mean serum gastrin concentration in normal fasting subjects is equivalent to less than 30 pg synthetic hG-17-NS/ml. A significant increase in the immunoreactive gastrin concentration in plasma has been detected after meals in man (Fig. 4.21).

Gel filtration and electrophoresis reveal that immunoreactive gastrin in plasma and in the gastrointestinal mucosa exists in a number of molecular forms in addition to the G-17-NS and G-17-S ('little' gastrins) already referred to (p. 57). There are two gastrins, 'big' gastrins, containing 34 amino acid residues, which consist of an N-terminal pentadecapeptide linked through two lysine residues to G-17; in G-34-NS the G-17 has a non-sulphated tyrosine residue and in G-34-S the G-17 has a sulphated tyrosine residue. When G-34 is digested with trypsin it breaks the polypeptide chain at the lysine residues. Two forms of gastrin smaller than G-17 consist of the C-terminal residues of the two forms of G-17 (G-14-Ns and G-14-S or 'mini' gastrins). Two forms of gastrin larger than G-34 have also been described, a 'big, big' gastrin (BBG) which in serum at least may be an artefact, and 'component I' (CI) which is intermediate in size between BBG and G-34. These two forms have not yet been characterized chemically but when digested with trypsin they also give rise to G-17 (Fig. 4.22). An inactive N-terminal 1–13 portion of G-17 has been identified in plasma and gastrointestinal mucosa so that the active C-terminal tetrapeptide amide G-4 may eventually prove to have a physiological role.

The significance of the different forms of gastrin is uncertain but many peptide hormones occur in blood and tissues in more than one form. For example, the large form of insulin is a precursor which gives rise to active insulin when the polypeptide chain is broken by enzymes found in the beta cells of the pancreatic islets (p. 88). Like the smaller form of insulin, the smaller forms of gastrin have a much greater biological activity. Caution is required, however, in pursuing this analogy of gastrin and insulin too far because, whereas proinsulin is essentially inactive and circulates in only small amounts, G-34 has about 25 per cent of the acid stimulating activity of G-17 (on a molar basis) and there is a high ratio of G-34 to G-17 in plasma after meals. The larger gastrins have however a longer half-life in the circulation than the smaller

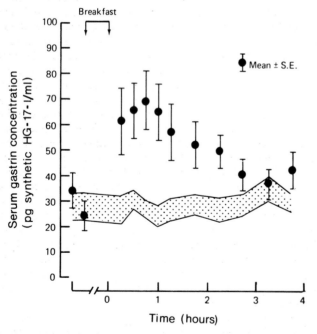

Fig. 4.21 Changes in serum gastrin concentration in 13 normal subjects after a breakfast of orange juice, two boiled eggs, two slices of buttered toast with marmalade and coffee. The meal took between 12 and 20 min to consume and the end of the meal is indicated as time 0. The results are expressed as mean values ± 1 standard error and the stippled area represents ± 1 standard error about the mean values for serum gastrin concentration during a morning fast by the same subjects. (*Courtesy of* E. L. Blair, E. R. Grund, J. D. Reed & D. J. Sanders.)

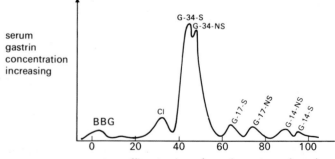

Fig. 4.22 The various forms of immunoreactive gastrins in serum. The meaning of BBG, CI, etc. is explained in the text. (*Based on the data of* Yalow & Berson (1972) *Biochemical & Biophysical Research Communications,* 48, 391–395; and Rehfeld and his colleagues (1973) *Gut,* 14, 369–373 and 856–860; (1974) *Gut,* 15, 102–111.)

gastrins and more G-17 than G-34 is released by feeding. It remains to be determined whether the different molecular forms of gastrin have different relative potencies on other target tissues.

During digestion there is in the dog undoubted interdependence of the nervous and chemical factors which control gastric acid secretion; these are not simply additive in their effects, they potentiate one another. The acid secretory response to sham-feeding a dog with a Pavlov pouch can be markedly reduced if the gastrin bearing areas of the stomach and small intestine are removed. This response can be restored by giving, simultaneously with the sham-feed, subthreshold doses of gastrin (doses of gastrin which by themselves are ineffective in stimulating gastric acid secretion) (Fig. 4.19). Furthermore, the response to injected gastrin can be shown to be considerably greater if the stomach is innervated by the vagus nerve even under conditions of basal vagal activity (Fig. 4.23). It seems that in man the acid secretory response to vagal stimulation is much less dependent on the simultaneous release of gastrin from the pyloric antrum and duodenum and acid secretion in response to sham feeding is only slightly decreased by removal of the main gastrin bearing areas of the pyloric antrum and duodenal bulb.

Additional nervous mechanisms in the wall of the stomach. Local cholinergic mechanisms within the wall of the body of the stomach, independently of vagal stimulation, also potentiate responses to gastrin stimulation in the dog. The rate of acid production in a vagally denervated secreting pouch in response to a given dose of gastrin is considerably increased

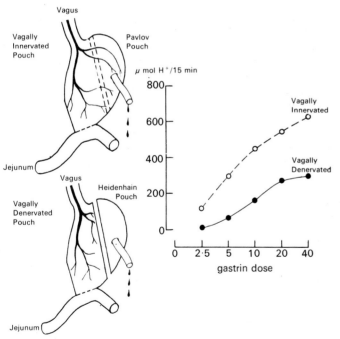

Fig. 4.23 Comparison of acid secretory responses to graded doses of gastrin from vagally innervated (Pavlov) pouches and vagally denervated (Heidenhain) pouches of gastric body mucosa in the same four dogs after their pyloric antra had been excised. The mean results only are illustrated but the responses from the innervated pouches were significantly greater than those from the denervated pouches at all dose levels of gastrin. (*Adapted from* A. Andersson & M. I. Grossman (1965) *Gastroenterology*, **48**, 449–462.)

by distension of the pouch (Fig. 4.24). This effect can be prevented by atropine.

The excitatory mechanisms which result in gastric secretion are summarized in Figure 4.25. Stress must be included as a cephalic influence on gastric acid secretion because there is no doubt that emotional factors modify gastric secretion. In the subject Tom, who had a gastric fistula, emotions of aggression and hostility were associated with increased acid secretion. In the absence of recognizable stimuli the human stomach secretes acid at low rates (basal secretion) and this secretory rate decreases during the sleeping hours and is minimal about 2 a.m. Stimulation of the anterior hypothalamus in monkeys increases gastric secretion provided that the vagus nerves are intact. It is not surprising that anticholinergic drugs markedly reduce the normal acid secretory responses in digestion and that they reduce the responses in both nervous and chemical phases of stimulation. It must now be clear why vagotomy is effective in reducing gastric acid secretion. It is for this reason that vagotomy is frequently carried out in patients who suffer from ulcers of the stomach or duodenum.

Many attempts have been made to implicate histamine in the physiological control of the secretion of acid in the stomach. For over 50 years it has been known that histamine has a powerful stimulatory effect on gastric acid secretion, and until pure preparations of gastrin became available histamine was the most powerful known stimulant of acid secretion. Recently, the hypothesis has been advanced that histamine receptors can be classified as H_1 (antagonized by conventional antihistamine drugs such as mepyramine) and H_2 (antagonized by a new group of drugs of which burimamide, metiamide and cimetidine are examples). The stimulation of gastric acid secretion by histamine is not prevented by blockade of H_1-receptors but is prevented by the drugs which are assumed to block H_2-receptors which are found also on atrial muscle of the guinea pig and uterine muscle of the rat. These H_2-receptor blocking drugs can inhibit gastric acid secretion in response to pentagastrin, cholinergic and food stimulation. If the action of these drugs on acid secretion should eventually prove to be due entirely to a histamine blocking action and not to some other effect, as yet unrecognized, it will be proper to conclude that histamine plays a role in the production of acid secretion by all these stimuli. This role could be either as the final common mediator in parietal cell stimulation or as a factor that influences the responsiveness of the parietal cell to other stimulants. Histamine is ubiquitous in the body and it may be of fundamental importance in all metabolically active tissues. In the rat, mobilization of gastric mucosal histamine has been demonstrated on excitation of acid secretion by gastrin, vagal and food stimulation but it has not as yet proved possible convincingly to demonstrate such mobilization of histamine in other species (Fig. 4.26).

The factors controlling pepsin secretion are less well defined than those known to control acid secretion. Pepsin secretion results from vagal stimulation and from the intravenous injection of large doses of gastrin and secretin. In man, vagotomy reduces pepsin production but the spontaneous output of pepsin remains substantial.

Inhibition of gastric secretion. Gastric acid secretion is controlled not only by the stimulatory mechanisms just described but also by inhibitory mechanisms, both nervous and hormonal.

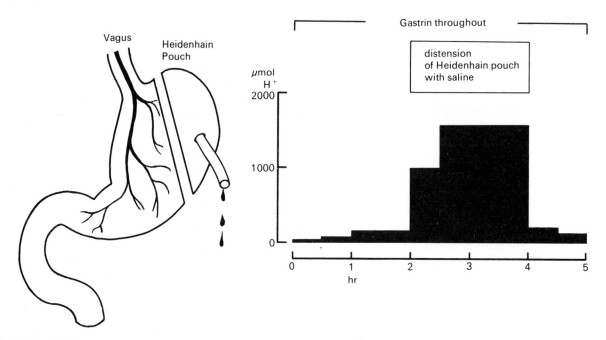

Fig. 4.24 The effect on gastric secretion in the dog of distending a denervated pouch of the stomach. (*Adapted from* M. I. Grossman (1961) *Gastroenterology*, 41, 385–390.)

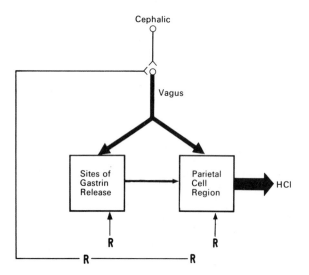

Fig. 4.25 The physiological excitatory mechanisms which cause gastric acid secretion. **R** represents receptor mechanisms within the walls of the stomach and upper small intestine.

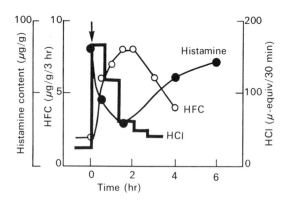

Fig. 4.26 The relationship in the rat between alterations in gastric acid secretion and alterations in the histamine content and histamine forming capacity (HFC) of the gastric mucosa following the injection of gastrin (injected at the arrow). HFC is expressed as the amount of ^{14}C-histamine formed when the mucosa is incubated with ^{14}C-histidine. (*Adapted from* G. Kahlson, E. Rosengren, D. Svahn & R. Thimberg (1964) *Journal of Physiology*, 174, 400–416.)

In the subject Tom, who had a gastric fistula, emotions of sadness and fear and sensations of nausea were associated with decreased acid secretion. There is no experimental evidence that efferent vagal stimulation can inhibit gastric acid secretion even when the stimulatory effects are blocked with atropine. It is likely that this kind of inhibition is brought about simply by a reduction of the normal tonic vagal stimulation.

There is no doubt that mechanisms capable of inhibiting acid secretion can be activated by large concentrations of H^+ in the pyloric antrum and by large concentrations of H^+, fatty acids or osmotically active particles in the duodenum. While some if not all of these inhibitory mechanisms have a neural component they may also act in the absence of vagal or sympathetic innervation of the secreting mucosa. The inhibitory effects of high H^+ concentrations are the most thoroughly investigated. Fluid at low pH bathing the pyloric antrum or duodenum suppresses the acid secretion of vagally denervated or transplanted pouches of gastric mucosa secreting in response to sham feeding (Fig. 4.18B). The acid secretory response to meat extract in the antrum is similarly decreased if the pH of the meat extract is reduced below 2·5 (Fig. 4.27).

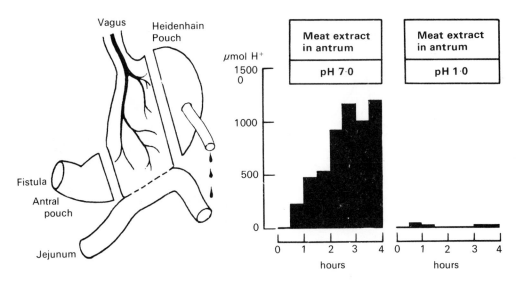

Fig. 4.27 The effect on gastric acid secretion from a Heidenhain pouch (dog) of placing meat extract at pH 7·0 and pH 1·0 in a denervated pyloric antrum. (*Adapted from* E. H. Longhi, H. B. Greenlee, J. L. Bravo, J. D. Guerro & L. R. Dragstedt (1957) *American Journal of Physiology,* **191**, 64–70.)

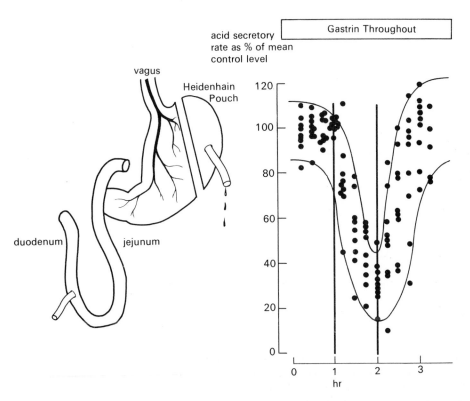

Fig. 4.28 Inhibitory effect of the installation of HCl into the duodenum on gastrin-stimulated acid secretion from Heidenhain pouches (three dogs). The dogs each had a pylorojejunostomy and a cannula was placed in the duodenum. During the 1-h period of acid instillation the duodenal contents were at approximately pH 2. The control intraduodenal pH was between 7 and 8. The mean H⁺ secretory output from the pouches/15 min during the hour immediately preceding duodenal acid infusion is taken as 100 per cent and all the 15-min rates of H⁺ output are expressed as a percentage of this mean value. (*Adapted from* S. Andersson (1960) *Acta physiologica scandinavica,* **50**, 105–111.)

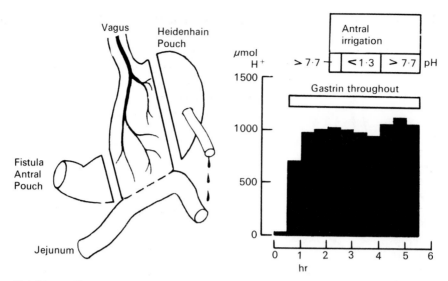

Fig. 4.29 The absence of inhibitory effect on gastrin stimulated acid secretion from a Heidenhain pouch (dog) of placing meat extract at pH 7·0 and pH 1·0 in a denervated pyloric antrum. (*Adapted from* E. H. Longhi, H. B. Greenlee, J. L. Bravo, J. D. Guerro & L. R. Dragstedt (1957) *American Journal of Physiology*, **191**, 64–70.)

This chemical 'brake' to acid secretion could be the result of a decrease in the rate of release of gastrin either by a direct inhibition within the stimulated mucosa or by the entry into the circulation of a humoral inhibitor of gastrin release. It might on the other hand result from the release into the blood of an inhibitory 'chemical messenger' (chalone) which inhibits parietal cell activity. It is thought that in the pyloric antrum acid inhibits the release of gastrin but that in the small intestine a chalone is released (Figs. 4.28 and 4.29).

Many attempts have been made to identify the chalone or chalones released from the mucosa of the small intestine. Injections of secretin (p. 68), cholecystokinin-pancreozymin (p. 68), gastric inhibitory polypeptide (p. 49) somatostatin (p. 89) and vasoactive intestinal polypeptide (p. 69) can be shown to lead to inhibition of gastrin-stimulated acid secretion and all have from time to time been invoked as the intestinal chalone. Some of these peptides also inhibit gastrin release. Within 5 min of a single intravenous injection of secretin (p. 69) in man, the duodenal pH rises to 7·4 or higher; the secretion of bicarbonate by the pancreas is undoubtedly an important cause of the rise in pH, but clearly a reduction of gastric acid secretion would reinforce this. An additional candidate chalone, bulbogastrone, is believed to be present in duodenal bulb mucosa and, although it has not yet been identified chemically, it is different from secretin and cholecystokinin-pancreozymin in its actions. Injection of certain prostaglandins can lead to a reduction of gastric acid secretion in man and prostaglandin-like substances can be extracted from the gastrointestinal mucosa, but there is no clear understanding at present about the physiological significance of the prostaglandins. It is uncertain how far, if at all, these humoral agents relate to the postulated entero-gastrone (p. 49) but acid in the small intestine does inhibit the rate of gastric emptying (p. 49) in addition to inhibiting gastric acid secretion. It may be that under physiological conditions these inhibitory effects are the result of the combined action of a number of humoral agents. The evidence for interplay between the various gastrointestinal hormones

(see CCK-PZ and secretin, Chap. 5) is only one of the factors that makes it difficult to elucidate their true physiological roles; in addition there is the complication created by the interplay of the autonomic nervous system with these hormones and the difficulty of measuring many of these hormones in the circulation.

It is uncertain to what extent these inhibitory mechanisms operate during digestion. Raised concentrations of gastrin are, however, found in the plasma in many cases of pernicious anaemia where, because gastric atrophy leads to achlorhydria, there is increased gastrin release from the pyloric antrum. Ingestion of acid by these patients results in a reduction in plasma gastrin concentrations. The threshold values of intraluminal pH which produce these effects vary widely and there are technical difficulties in following pH changes within the gastrointestinal tract during digestion. It is thought that these inhibitory mechanisms operate at intraluminal pH values below 2·5; however, intraluminal pH is not necessarily the same as that at the mucosal surface where it is assumed the receptors lie. The pH of the gastrointestinal contents can be determined by aspirating small samples through a tube but this procedure has obvious limitations. Studies have also been made with glass electrodes threaded into the gastrointestinal tract and with free radio-telemetering capsules whose transmission frequency is related to the pH.

During fasting the pH in the second and third parts of the duodenum is usually above 6·0. However, in the first part of the duodenum and in the pyloric antrum the pH is much lower and it probably remains below pH 2·0 in the pyloric antrum during fasting. It is likely therefore that normally the rate of gastrin release from the pyloric antrum is low except in the hour or so after a meal when the antral pH rises owing to the buffering effect of the meal. If acid chyme is unable to reach the pyloric antrum the secretion of acid by the stomach increases considerably; this situation may be brought about in man if the body of the stomach is joined to the jejunum (gastrojejuno-stomy) so that the pyloric antrum and duodenum are excluded from the main stream of acid chyme; the resulting increase of acid secretion may lead to ulceration of the intestinal mucosa.

Emulsified fat lying in the small intestine beyond the duodenum not only inhibits gastric emptying (p. 49) but also inhibits gastrin and histamine-stimulated gastric acid secretion. Both nervous and humoral mechanisms are probably involved but they are as yet incompletely elucidated. The nature of the chalone or chalones responsible for the enterogastrone-like effect caused by fat in the small intestine is also uncertain as are the mediators of the inhibitory effects of acid in the small intestine. Radioimmunoassay reveals that the plasma concentration of gastric inhibitory polypeptide (p. 49) increases in response to the fat and carbohydrate content of a meal, and this evidence together with the effects of the injection of this polypeptide have led to the suggestion that it is a physiological chalone.

A substance with enterogastrone-like characteristics has been isolated from urine and has been named urogastrone. Urogastrone is a polypeptide with a molecular weight of about 4000. It is not excreted enterogastrone because its output in dogs is not decreased by resection of their small intestine, and some workers believe it to be a gonadotrophin.

Blood Flow through the Gastric Mucosa

It is likely that mucosal blood flow and secretion in the stomach are closely related and that the blood flow is disturbed in disease processes in the stomach. However, little is known about the control of the gastric mucosal circulation. The mucosa possesses extensive arterial anastomoses; consequently interruption of flow even in a major gastric blood vessel is unlikely to affect the mucosal flow significantly. The flow of blood through the mucosal capillaries must depend to an important extent on the state of the numerous submucosal arteriovenous anastomoses as well as on the arterial perfusion pressure and flows. Sympathetic stimulation and vasoconstrictor drugs may interfere with mucosal blood flow sufficiently to depress secretion.

Changes in mucosal blood flow may be assessed very roughly from the colour of the mucosa if it can be seen through a gastric fistula. The basic lipid-soluble drugs amidopyrine and ^{14}C aniline can be used in the quantitative measurement of mucosal blood flow in animals; more recently the technique of ^{99}technetium clearance has been used to measure gastric mucosal blood flow in man. Acidic lipid-soluble drugs remain in the undissociated state in the acid of the stomach lumen and are rapidly absorbed whereas basic drugs like amidopyrine and aniline are completely ionized and are absorbed very slowly. In blood, however, these drugs are not ionized at the pH of blood so that as they circulate through the gastric mucosa they diffuse rapidly and completely into the acid gastric lumen where they are trapped and ionized. If, therefore, amidopyrine or ^{14}C aniline is injected to maintain a constant plasma concentration and if at the same time the rate of gastric excretion of these drugs is measured the rate of flow in the gastric mucosa can be calculated. Mucosal blood flow probably accounts for more than 50 per cent of the total gastric blood flow. Extremely rapid rates of blood flow may occur in the gastric mucosa as in other secretory tissues and values thirty times the secretory rate may occur during maximal secretion produced by histamine.

ABSORPTION FROM THE STOMACH

Reference has already been made to the absorption of lipid-soluble substances. Their rapid absorption in the undissociated form is the result of the mucosal cell membranes behaving as though they are complexes of lipid and protein. There is a continuous flux of water and water soluble substances across the water permeable pores of the gastric mucosa but normally their net rate of absorption from the lumen is small.

TESTS OF GASTRIC SECRETION

Tests of gastric function are used to show the lack of acid secretion characteristic of pernicious anaemia (p. 64) as well as the excessive secretion found in some patients with duodenal ulcers and all patients with the *Zollinger-Ellison syndrome*. The latter is a disorder characterized by recurrent peptic ulcers and caused by a pancreatic tumour which secretes large amounts of gastrin.

In these investigations a radio-opaque tube is passed into the stomach and manoeuvred so that the secretions can be collected. The volume of each sample is measured and the 'acid content' determined by titration with NaOH to pH 7·4.

Basal acid output (BAO). The basal acid output may be measured either with a 12-hr (overnight) collection or with a 1-hr collection. Normal people produce up to 60 ml of secretion with up to 4 mmol H^+ per hour. This measurement is particularly useful for the diagnosis of the Zollinger-Ellison

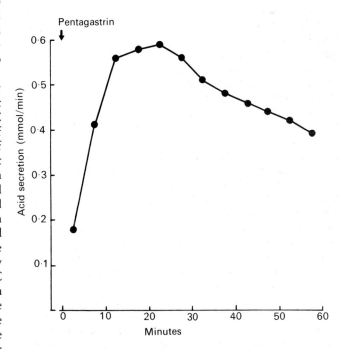

Fig. 4.30 Mean response to intramuscular pentagastrin (in a dose of 6 μg per kg) in 100 tests. The peak acid output for most subjects occurs during the period from 10 min to 30 min after the injection. (Johnston, D. & Jepson, K. (1967) *Lancet*, ii, 585–588.)

syndrome in which the stomach is secreting maximally or near maximally even at rest (more than 200 ml/hr and 15 to 50 mmol/hr).

Peak acid output after pentagastrin (PAOPG). A variety of substances has been used to stimulate acid secretion by the stomach. Until recently histamine was widely used for this purpose but, although some side effects could be suppressed with an antihistamine drug, the *augmented histamine test* was often unpleasant for the patient. Histamine has now been superseded by *pentagastrin* (p. 58) a peptide containing four of the amino acids from the sequence found in gastrin. After the intramuscular injection of pentagastrin the output of hydrogen ion increases to a maximum at 10 to 15 min and remains maximal for a further 20 min in most people (Fig. 4.30).

The values for peak acid output obtained by this test are very similar to those obtained by an augmented histamine test. The test gives reproducible results in any individual and is probably correlated with the mass of parietal cells (Fig. 4.31). Young adult males have a peak acid output of 10 to 40 mmol/hr while lower values are found in females and in the elderly. Patients with pernicious anaemia have no acid secretion even after pentagastrin; abnormally high values are found in about half of a group of patients with duodenal ulcers. Patients with gastric ulcers generally have normal values for peak acid output.

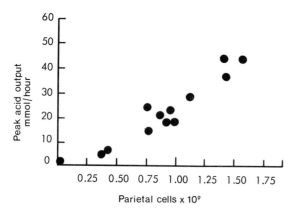

Fig. 4.31 The relationship between the number of parietal cells in human gastric mucosa and the peak acid output in response to histamine stimulation. The parietal cells were counted in the mucosa removed at operation from patients with gastroduodenal diseases. The peak output of this excised mucosa was assumed to be the difference between the peak output of acid secreted by the patients before and after operation. (*Adapted from* W. I. Card & I. N. Marks (1960) *Clinical Science*, 19, 147–163.)

Peak acid output after insulin (PAOI). Hypoglycaemia normally stimulates acid production by the stomach and this effect is mediated by the vagus nerve. In some patients peptic ulcers are treated by cutting the vagus (*vagotomy*) and the success of the operation can be assessed by giving insulin, in a dose of about 15 units intravenously, to cause hypoglycaemia. The test is valid only if the blood glucose falls below 2·8 mmol/l; patients with an intact vagus have a marked increase in acid output which is not seen after a successful vagotomy.

THE PROTECTIVE FUNCTION OF THE STOMACH

The strong acid and pepsin secreted by the stomach destroys or limits the growth of ingested micro-organisms. Thus, after gastrectomy, development of an abnormal bacterial flora in the lumen of the small intestine, together with the removal of the source of intrinsic factor (p. 52) may lead to deficient absorption of vitamin B_{12} and so cause anaemia. Similar changes may occur in pernicious anaemia when the acid, pepsin and intrinsic factor-secreting region of the gastric mucosa becomes atrophied.

Vomiting. Vomiting, by emptying the stomach and upper small intestine, limits the possibility of damage from ingested noxious agents by preventing their access to the major absorptive region of the alimentary tract.

Vomiting may be initiated by mucosal irritation or abnormal distension of the gastrointestinal tract or gall-bladder or it may result from a great variety of causes, such as feelings of disgust or pain, or from abnormal stimulation of the labyrinths or their central nervous pathways, as in sea-sickness. Vomiting may be induced by irritating the back of a person's throat or by making him drink warm salt-and-water or mustard-and-water. Such preparations are called *emetics*. The afferent impulses from the gastric mucosa are probably carried by the parasympathetic and also the sympathetic nerves to an *emetic centre* situated in the lateral reticular formation of the central nervous system. The *emetic centre* is stimulated also by impulses from higher centres and from near-by brain-stem nuclei and vomiting excited by visual and labyrinthine stimuli can be explained in this way.

In the cat there is a bilateral *trigger zone* in the reticular formation of the medulla; electrical stimulation of this area produces vomiting and ablation abolishes the emetic effect of apomorphine. Drugs such as phenothiazines inhibit only the *trigger zone* and do not suppress vomiting due to direct stimulation of the *emetic centre*. Drugs such as atropine and its derivatives on the other hand inhibit the *emetic centre* and can ameliorate many forms of vomiting.

Vomiting is usually accompanied by nausea and preceded by retching, in which the stomach is periodically compressed by a series of more or less violent contractions of the diaphragm and abdominal muscles. At the same time there are autonomic disturbances such as pallor, slowing of the heart rate, sweating and excessive salivation. The act of vomiting is brought about by a complex series of movements of the respiratory and abdominal muscles. Vomiting can be produced after complete motor and sensory denervation of the stomach and intestine in animals and even after the replacement of the stomach by a rubber bag.

X-ray observations in man show that the stomach contracts at the angular notch and that the contents of the pyloric antrum are forced into the relaxed body and fundus. A deep inspiration is taken and the glottis closes; the soft palate rises and prevents vomitus entering the nose. A sharp increase in intra-abdominal pressure, brought about by a violent contraction of the abdominal muscles, forces the gastric contents through the relaxed cardia and along the oesophagus into the mouth. In an unconscious subject the glottis may not close completely and vomited material may be inhaled into the lungs. Prolonged vomiting may endanger life because of the loss of fluid, hydrogen ion, sodium, chloride and potassium.

REFERENCES

Allen A 1978 Structure of gastrointestinal mucus glycoproteins and the viscous and gel-forming properties of mucus. British Medical Bulletin 34: 28–33

Beck J C (ed) 1976 Polypeptide hormones, molecular and cellular aspects. Ciba foundation symposium 41: Elsevier Excerpta Medica, North Holland, Amsterdam

Blair E L 1974 Control of gastric emptying and acidity. In: Linden J R (ed) Recent advances in physiology. Churchill Livingstone, London, pp. 279–339

Bloom S R (ed) 1978 Gut hormones. Churchill Livingstone, Edinburgh

Burn-Murdoch R A, Fisher Margaret A, Hunt J N 1978 The slowing of gastric emptying by proteins in test meals. Journal of Physiology 274: 477–485

Bynum T E, Jacobsen E D 1971 Blood flow and gastrointestinal function. Gastroenterology 60: 325–335

Code C F (ed) 1967 Handbook of physiology. Section 6, Alimentary canal; vol II, secretion. American Physiological Society, Washington D C

Garner A, Flemström G 1978 Gastric HCO_3^- secretion in the guinea pig. American Journal of Physiology, 234b, E535–E541

Glass G B J (ed) 1979 Gastrointestinal hormones. Raven Press, New York

Hunt J N, Know M T 1968 Regulation of gastric emptying. In: Code C F (ed) Handbook of physiology. Section 6, Alimentary canal; vol IV, Motility. American Physiological Society, Washington D C

Johnson L R 1971 Control of gastric secretion: no room for histamine. Gastroenterology 61: 106–118

Johnson L R 1976 The trophic actions of gastrointestinal hormones. Gastroenterology 70: 278–288

Rehfeld J F, Amdrup E (eds) 1979 Gastrins and the vagus. Report of a conference. Academic Press, London

Roberts N B, Taylor W H 1978 The preparation and purification of individual human pepsins by using diethylaminoethyl-cellulose. Biochemical Journal 169: 607–615

Roberts N B, Taylor W H 1979 Action of human pepsins 1, 2, 3 and 5 on the oxidized B-chain of insulin. Biochemical Journal 179: 183–190

Soll A H, Walsh V H 1979 Regulation of gastric acid secretion. Annual Review of Physiology 41: 35–53

Thompson J C (ed) 1975 Gastrointestinal hormones. University of Texas Press, Austin and London

Wolf S 1965 The stomach. Oxford University Press, New York

Wolf S, Wolff H G 1943 Human gastric function. Oxford University Press, New York

Wood C J, Simkins M A (eds) 1973 International symposium on H_2-receptor antagonists. Smith, Kline and French Ltd, Welwyn Garden City

5 Digestion and Absorption in the Intestine

After leaving the stomach food enters the small intestine where its components are broken down by digestive enzymes. The most important source of these is the pancreas.

Throughout embryonic development, the endocrine and exocrine elements of the pancreas are closely intermingled but differentiation of the different cell types occurs at a very early stage. The islet cells may be derived from the neural crest; the exocrine cells are derived from diverticula of the primitive gut. Ultimately, the cells with endocrine function are found in clumps (interalveolar cell islets or islets of Langerhans) interspersed throughout the much greater mass of the cells which produce the exocrine secretions.

THE PANCREAS

The external (exocrine) secretions of the pancreas contain the important digestive enzymes which catalyse the hydrolysis of food materials. The cells which secrete the enzymes are arranged in acini around small ducts. The acinar cells contain much rough-surfaced endoplasmic reticulum and large zymogen granules and have microvilli on their apical (ductular) surfaces. The small ducts drain eventually into the main pancreatic duct which opens into the duodenum.

The pancreatic enzymes, formed on the ribosomes of the rough-surfaced endoplasmic reticulum of the acinar cells, pass into the cisternal spaces from which vesicles containing the enzymes bud off to reach the Golgi region of the cells. The vesicles coalesce and grow to become mature zymogen granules containing the concentrated secretory proteins. During the process of secretion the membranous sacs of the zymogen granules fuse with the apical cell membrane and the granular contents are extruded from the cell (exocytosis). Pancreatic juice contains much sodium bicarbonate, produced mainly by the centroacinar cells and duct cells, which provides a buffered solution of optimal pH for the activity of the pancreatic enzymes.

Electrolytes. Much of the information about the electrolytes of pancreatic juice has been obtained from animal experiments but uncontaminated human pancreatic juice can now be obtained by introducing small collecting tubes into the pancreatic duct under direct vision through a duodenoscope.

The electrolytes of pancreatic juice are mainly sodium, bicarbonate and chloride, with much smaller amounts of potassium and calcium. The concentrations of sodium and potassium in the juice are usually fairly constant while small, but regular, increases in the concentration of calcium occur with increases in the concentration of enzymes. The concentrations of the two main anions—bicarbonate and chloride—vary widely in a reciprocal fashion, so that the sum of the concentrations of the two anions remains constant. The probable explanation of this phenomenon is that the primary secretion of the electrolyte-producing cells of the pancreatic ducts consists mainly of sodium bicarbonate and that at low rates of flow bicarbonate exchanges with chloride across the ductal epithelium.

In pancreatic disease both enzyme and bicarbonate secretion are impaired but bicarbonate output is usually more severely affected than the enzyme output.

Enzymes. The proteases secreted by the pancreas include trypsinogens, chymotrypsinogens, procarboxypeptidases and proelastase. All have remarkably similar amino acid compositions with a serine residue at the enzymically active centre and all are secreted as inactive zymogens. Trypsinogen, with 229 amino acids in known sequence, is converted into the active proteolytic trypsin by the loss of a small N-terminal peptide chain of six amino acids under the influence of the enzyme enteropeptidase (enterokinase). This enzyme originates in the microvillous brush border membrane of the duodenal mucosal cells and is released into the duodenal lumen during digestion, probably by the action of bile salts. Trypsin subsequently activates chymotrypsinogen and proelastase by a more elaborate multistage process involving peptide bond cleavage. The optimal pH for trypsin activity is 7·8.

Proteases hydrolyse the peptide bonds of proteins to produce shorter peptide chains and amino acids. The individual proteases tend to be selective in the type of peptide bond which is hydrolysed. (Fig. 5.1). Starch and related polysaccharides, which form about two-thirds of the carbohydrate of the food, are hydrolysed at $\alpha1,4$-glucosidic bonds by pancreatic amylase. The resultant end-products, maltose, maltotriose and α-dextrins, are further split to glucose during

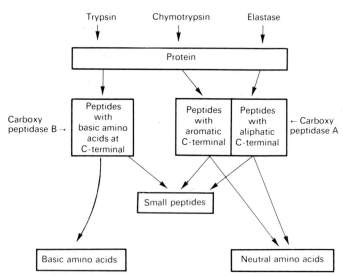

Fig. 5.1 Interrelationships of the endopeptidases and exopeptidases. Carboxypeptidase B hydrolyses the C-terminal peptide bonds of the end-products of trypsin digestion. Carboxypeptidase B breaks the C-terminal peptide bonds of the end-products of chymotrypsin and elastase digestion. (Beck, I. T. (1973) The role of pancreatic enzymes in digestion. *The Americal Journal of Clinical Nutrition*, 26, 311–325.)

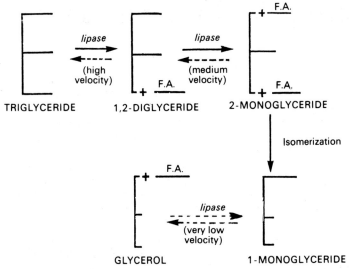

Fig. 5.2 Schematic representation of the hydrolysis of long chain triglycerides by pancreatic lipase. Because of the relative speeds of the various reactions the main products of triglyceride lipolysis are monoglycerides and fatty acids. F. A. = fatty acid. (*After* A. M. Dawson (1967). *British Medical Bulletin*, 23, 247.)

absorption into the villous cells of the small intestine by the enzymes of the microvillous membrane. Similarly disaccharides, such as sucrose and lactose, which make up about one-third of the diet are hydrolysed in the brush border to monosaccharides during transport in the intestinal cells. Celluloses and hemicelluloses are not digested in the human intestine and consequently are exreted unchanged.

The neutral, long chain fats in food are hydrolysed by pancreatic lipase to fatty acids, di- and mono-glycerides and glycerol (Fig. 5.2). Pancreatic lipase, in the presence of the enzyme co-lipase and calcium and bile salts, acts especially at the lipid-water interphase on the surface of fat drops formed from dietary fat under the influence of bile salts in the lumen of the upper small intestine. Co-lipase counteracts the inhibition of lipase by bile salts.

Ribo- and deoxyribo-nucleases secreted by the pancreas break down the nucleic acids of the food to nucleotides.

The pancreatic enzymes act best in a neutral or mildly alkaline solution. Exposure to acid gastric juice rapidly and irreversibly inactivates amylase and lipase; trypsin is rapidly destroyed by pepsin in acid solution. The bicarbonate secreted by the pancreas is therefore very important for the satisfactory functioning of the pancreatic enzymes, both by buffering the acid and by inactivating the pepsin of gastric juice which has passed into the duodenum.

The pancreatic enzymes are all concentrated in the zymogen granules of the pancreatic acinar cells and are secreted together. However the relative proportions of the individual enzymes in pancreatic juice are not constant but may be influenced by the composition of the diet, the rate of secretion of pancreatic juice and by disease processes affecting the pancreas. Not all the pancreatic enzymes are equally susceptible to changes in the diet. Oral administration of starch, fructose or glucose and raised insulin levels all serve to raise the concentration of amylase in rat pancreatic juice. High protein diets have very little effect on the concentration of

proteases in the pancreatic juice. The mechanism by which the pancreas can alter the proportion of the various enzymes in the juice is not known.

After discharge into the duodenum the pancreatic enzymes are partly adsorbed on to the glycocalyx of the cells lining the small intestine. In spite of cellular adsorption a marked loss of enzyme activity occurs during transit through the small intestine. Amylase and lipase are destroyed by the proteases. Trypsin is more labile than chymotrypsin in the intestine and, although the pancreas secretes more trypsin than chymotrypsin, much more chymotrypsin is excreted in the faeces. Indeed, the faecal content of chymotrypsin is used as an index of the ability of the pancreas to secrete enzymes.

Stimulants of pancreatic exocrine secretion. The most powerful stimulants of the pancreatic exocrine cells are the gastrointestinal hormones secretin and cholecystokinin-pancreozymin (CCK-PZ) and the neurotransmitter acetylcholine.

Secretin is a polypeptide composed of 27 amino acids with a cyclic secondary structure. Immunofluorescence tests have shown secretin-producing cells in the crypts of the duodenal mucosa of the dog. The whole molecule is required for its stimulant action. Secretin stimulates principally the secretion of electrolytes and water from the pancreas and is only a weak stimulant of the secretion of enzymes.

Pancreozymin is a polypeptide containing 33 amino acids which stimulates the secretion of pancreatic enzymes. Pancreozymin has been shown to be identical with the polypeptide cholecystokinin which brings about contraction of the gallbladder. The hormone is therefore referred to as cholecystokinin-pancreozymin (CCK-PZ). The five C-terminal amino acids of CCK-PZ are identical with those of gastrin and hence these two hormones share a number of stimulant properties. The tyrosine-*O*-sulphate residue in CCK-PZ is essential for its cholecystokinetic action; it is found also in human gastrin II.

The CCK-producing cells have been identified in the human duodenum and jejunum by highly specific immunofluorescence methods. They are pear-shaped granular cells with apical processes reaching into the intestinal lumen lying among the columnar cells covering the mucosa.

The pancreatic exocrine cells are also stimulated by acetylcholine and neural influences seem to be very important for satisfactory pancreatic exocrine function. Electrical stimulation of the vagus induces pancreatic secretion containing enzymes, the amount depending on the animal species. The pancreas of the pig is the most dependent on vagal stimulation while the human pancreas is less dependent since vagotomy reduces only slightly the pancreatic responsiveness to direct stimulation with hormones.

STIMULUS-SECRETION COUPLING

In the pancreatic cells, as in other secreting cells, a 'second messenger' is involved in the sequence of events between the stimulation of the cell and its response of secretion. The intracellular events thought to occur after excitation by the main stimulants of pancreatic secretion, namely secretin, CCK-PZ and ACh, are shown schematically in Figure 5.3. All three secretagogues are shown here acting on the same cell. However secretin acts principally on centroacinar and duct cells to cause release of water and electrolytes while ACh and

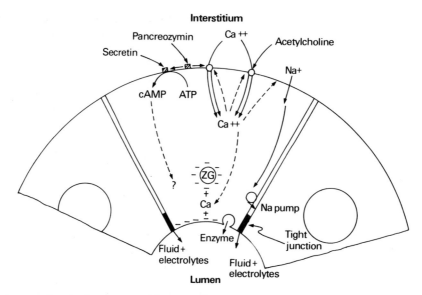

Fig. 5.3 Stimulus–secretion coupling in the pancreas. Two second messenger systems may be involved. Pancreozymin and acetylcholine operate by increasing free cytoplasmic calcium which then activates the secretory mechanisms by several pathways shown $\cdots\rightarrow$ Pancreozymin also utilizes another second messenger system which it shares with secretin. This is cAMP which activates fluid secretion by a mechanism (as yet unknown) indicated by $\cdots\rightarrow$? ZG, vesicle containing zymogen granules. (*After* I. Schultz and K. J. Ullrich.)

CCK-PZ act mainly on acinar cells causing release of enzymes. Activation of receptors by secretin causes the release of membrane-bound adenyl cyclase which catalyses the breakdown of ATP to cAMP. This then activates the intracellular secretory mechanism by a process which may vary from one species to another. Pancreozymin too can operate through this mechanism but, together with ACh, it can also activate another second messenger system dependent on Ca^{2+}. Activation of membrane receptors causes an increase in free intracellular Ca^{2+} by release of membrane bound Ca^{2+} which in turn increases the membrane conductance. this allows more Ca^{2+} to enter the cell from outside. The Ca^{2+} then stimulates directly the release of zymogen granules. The increased membrane conductance also allows Na^+ to pass into the cell which activates sodium pumps in the baso-lateral membrane of the cell. When these pumps are activated they extrude the Na^+ which then passes into the lumen of the gland through the tight junctions taking water with it.

Control of pancreatic secretion. The cephalic phase of pancreatic stimulation results from seeing, smelling and tasting food. Reflexes arise in various cranial nerves and impulses from the vagal nuclei result both in direct vagal excitation of the pancreatic secretory cells by local release of acetylcholine and indirect excitation through a further, double mechanism. First vagal impulses release gastrin from the antral mucosa, and gastrin then stimulates the pancreatic exocrine cells (in dogs, but not in man). Secondly, interaction between direct vagal excitation and vagally released gastrin (p. 60) on the gastric parietal cells promotes the secretion of acid which acts as a stimulant of the release of secretin and CCK-PZ from the small intestinal mucosa. The net result of 'cephalic' stimuli is the secretion of both electrolytes and enzymes by the pancreas.

The gastric phase of pancreatic stimulation has been well documented in dogs, but not yet in man. Distension of the stomach elicits both long (vago-vagal) and local reflexes which

activate the pancreas both directly and indirectly as in the cephalic phase. Similarly, the chemical stimulus of food materials in the antrum elicits neural reflexes, particularly through local nerve nets, resulting both in local release of gastrin and in more distant neural activity.

The intestinal phase of pancreatic stimulation is elicited by distension and, chemically, by acid and food materials in the lumen of the small intestine. This phase depends especially on the release of secretin and CCK-PZ from the mucosa of the small intestine. The magnitude of the pancreatic response to acid is related to the total amount of acid which enters the small intestine and depends on the length of small intestine (duodenum and jejunum) exposed to contents more acid than pH 4·5. Amino acids and fatty acids release mainly CCK-PZ from the small intestine. Only the L-forms of the essential amino acids (especially phenylalanine, valine, methionine and tryptophan in man) are capable of evoking a pancreatic response from the small intestine.

The purgative action of magnesium sulphate and other salts, formerly thought to be an osmotic effect, may be at least partly due to release of CCK-PZ which has a motor effect on the intestine.

The release of the small intestinal hormones in response to intraluminal stimuli appears to be mediated by neural reflexes, since vagotomy, atropine and local anaesthetics markedly decrease the pancreatic response to the intraluminal stimuli, while not greatly affecting the direct response of the pancreas to the hormones of the small intestine.

Neurohormonal and interhormonal interactions have also been shown to be largely responsible for the secretory stimulation of the pancreatic exocrine cells. In addition to the potentiation of the stimulant effect of secretin by vagal impulses, a small dose of secretin greatly increases the stimulant effect of CCK-PZ on both pancreatic secretion of electrolytes and enzymes (Fig. 5.4). The potentiation occurs in physiological circumstances, since the introduction of amino

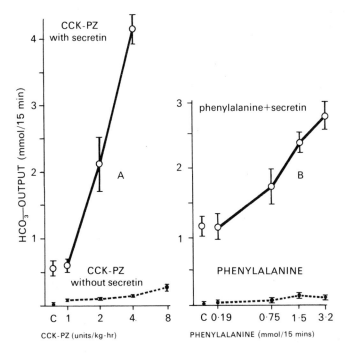

Fig. 5.4 A. Pancreatic bicarbonate responses to exogenous porcine CCK-PZ alone or CCK-PZ plus 1·0 unit/kg per hour of secretin (four observations in two dogs). In this figure responses to 8 units/kg per hour of CCK-PZ alone were obtained in separate experiments (four observations in two dogs). Note that secretin greatly augments the bicarbonate stimulating effect of CCK-PZ and that CCK-PZ increases the stimulating effect of secretin. **B.** Pancreatic bicarbonate outputs in response to phenylalanine alone or phenylalanine plus 1·0 unit/kg per hour of secretin (four observations in two dogs). Note that phenylalanine increases the bicarbonate-stimulating effect of secretin and vice versa. C in both diagrams is Control. (J. H. Meyer, L. J. Spingola & M. I. Grossman (1971). *American Journal of Physiology* **221**, 742.)

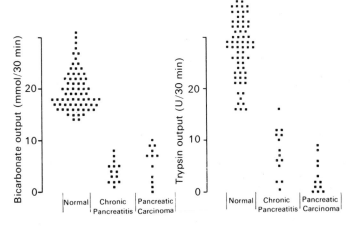

Fig. 5.5 A tube was passed down the oesophagus and into the duodenum to aspirate the duodenal contents for estimation of bicarbonate and trypsin. Each point represents the response of one individual to stimulation with an intravenous infusion of secretin plus cholecystokinin-pancreozymin. The pancreas has been severely damaged in the patients with chronic pancreatitis and pancreatic carcinoma. (K. G. Wormsley (1970) *British Journal of Clinical Practice*, **24**, 271.)

acids into the small intestine greatly increases the pancreatic response to small doses of secretin (Fig. 5.4). Similarly, the pancreatic response to secretin liberated by acid in the small intestine is potentiated by endogenous CCK-PZ liberated in response to L-amino acids in the small intestine.

Tests of pancreatic function. Tests of pancreatic function are used to confirm the clinical diagnosis of pancreatic disease, to define prognosis—that is, how the patient and his disease are likely to fare over a period of time—and to guide treatment. Pancreatic disease presents clinically as pain, which indicates inflammation of the gland, and by failure of normal endocrine and exocrine function.

The principal tests of pancreatic function indicate either what the pancreas can do (tests of exocrine secretory capacity) or what the pancreas does do (in response to small intestinal stimulation). Both types of test require intubation of the duodenum and aspiration of the duodenal contents. In tests of exocrine secretory capacity the pancreas is stimulated directly by intravenously administered secretin and CCK-PZ, in quantities sufficient to elicit maximal output of bicarbonate and pancreatic enzymes. A low output suggests that the exocrine secretory cells of the pancreas are diseased or have been destroyed (Fig. 5.5). Tests involving indirect stimulation of the pancreas from the small intestine depend on measuring the response to meals, or to acid or amino acid solutions, introduced into the small intestine. The magnitude of the indirect response is normally as great as that to direct stimulation of the pancreas but is reduced if the pancreas is diseased or if the small intestine does not release normal amounts of hormones as in coeliac disease.

CANDIDATE (PUTATIVE) HORMONES OF THE GUT

The earlier parts of this chapter have described the well-established nervous and hormonal mechanisms regulating gastrointestinal activity. Recently a large number of polypeptides with powerful actions on gastrointestinal function has been extracted from almost all regions of the gut. Although the physiological status of these substances remains uncertain it is possible that they act as hormones or, in some cases, as neurotransmitters or modulators (that is as substances which regulate the release of primary transmitters).

One group of peptides, homologous with secretin, includes gastric inhibitory peptide (GIP), vasoactive intestinal peptide (VIP) and glucagon. GIP is found in the duodenum and jejunum and may be released by fat and hexoses. Its actions include inhibition of gastric secretion and stimulation of intestinal secretion and insulin release. The ability to release insulin in the presence of glucose is believed to be of physiological significance and the hormone is therefore often referred to as Glucose-dependent Insulin-releasing Polypeptide. VIP is found throughout the gastrointestinal tract, not only in endocrine-like cells but also in intramural nerves. It may have a dual function as a hormone and as a transmitter or modulator. It is released by vagal stimulation but the physiological stimuli for its release are not known. It has the same actions as GIP but in addition it stimulates pancreatic HCO_3^- secretion and glycogenolysis. Glucagon-like immunoreactivity is found throughout the gastrointestinal tract. This *entero*glucagon is released by hexoses and fat in the intestine and stimulates glycogenolysis.

Other active peptides, unrelated to any of the established hormones, have been found. Motilin, from the duodenum and jejunum, is a potent stimulant of gastric and intestinal motility. It can be released by alkali in the intestine but the physiological significance of this is unclear. Chymodenin, also found in the upper intestine, stimulates the secretion of chymotrypsinogen but the mechanism of its release is unknown. However its ability to stimulate the release of this specific enzyme may explain how the pancreas can vary the enzyme composition of its secretion in response to changes in the diet. Another peptide, bombesin, is a powerful stimulant of pancreatic enzymes. It is unrelated to gastrin or CCK-PZ and must therefore act on different receptors.

Recently a hormone, pancreatic polypeptide (PP), has been isolated from cells scattered through the head of the pancreas; its plasma concentration is raised after taking food. PP appears to oppose the activity of CCK; it reduces the output of trypsin. PP is raised when there are tumours in the pancreatic endocrine tissue and since PP is relatively easy to measure, its estimation may well be an aid to early diagnosis of such conditions.

Finally an important group of compounds, the enkephalins and endorphins, localized in the intrinsic nerve plexuses, are widely distributed throughout the gastrointestinal tract. Because of their possible role in the mechanism of pain most studies have concentrated on their actions of the brain. However in the gut they appear to function as neuromodulators, regulating the release of acetylcholine and possibly noradrenaline.

The established hormones, namely gastrin, secretin and CCK-PZ, have many biological actions other than those already described. They are listed in Table 5.6 with the actions generally accepted as physiological. Their other actions are not yet accepted as having physiological significance.

Table 5.6 Biological actions of the established gastrointestinal hormones

Action	Hormone		
	Gastrin	CCK-PZ	Secretin
Acid secretion	S√	S	I
Gastric emptying	I	I√	I√
Pancreatic bicarbonate secretion	S	S√	S√
Pancreatic enzyme secretion	S√	S√	S√
Biliary secretion	S	S√	S√
Gall-bladder contraction	S	S√	S
Gastric motility	S	S	I
Intestinal motility	S	S	I
Insulin release	S	S	S
Gastrointestinal mucosal growth	S√	S*	I

S: stimulates   I: inhibits   √: physiological or potentially physiological   S*: stimulates pancreatic growth

THE SMALL INTESTINE

The movements of the small intestine mix the digestive juices with the chyme and expose the greatest possible surface area of the intestine to the chyme so that absorption may be maximal.

Peristalsis, as seen in the oesophagus, does occur in the small intestine but peristaltic activity is intermittent and interspersed with non-propulsive contractions. Even during fasting, intermittent bursts of peristaltic-like activity occur in empty segments of intestine. These are referred to as *migrating myoelectrical complexes* and their function is to clear the bowel of remnants of chyme. Lack of this activity leads to bacterial overgrowth.

Apart from peristalsis, movements of the small intestine are of two kinds. First the intestinal muscle has an intrinsic basic electrical rhythm which arises from a pace-maker in the duodenum just above the entry of the bile and pancreatic ducts. Recordings in animals show a gradient of electrical activity; waves are propagated down the intestine from the duodenum, the rate in the duodenum being 12 to 16 per min decreasing to 6 to 8 per min in the ileum. If the small intestine is cut across the rate below the level of the transection falls to 8 per min. If a loop of intestine is cut in two places, then reversed and sewn up in continuity, the intestinal contents are held up although the lumen remains patent.

This basic electrical rhythm produces rhythmic segmentation movements: annular constrictions form temporary intestinal segments 1 to 2 cm long; these constrictions are replaced by others so that the segments are divided, reformed, redivided and so on. These movements are not related to the autonomic nerve supply since nerve section does not affect them, neither are they related to the intrinsic nerve supply since they continue even after atropinization, and are therefore said to be myogenic. Each muscular contraction is accompanied by spike potentials superimposed on a slow wave.

Larger movements which shunt chyme up and down a length of intestine of 15 to 20 cm are known as pendular movements. These movements are not affected by autonomic section but they are reduced by atropinization and they are therefore presumably controlled by cholinergic arcs. The pendular movements cause an increase of blood flow to the mucosa which should enhance the removal of absorbed materials.

Although the myogenic electrical activity of the smooth muscle provides the basis for all intestinal movements, they can be modified and regulated by nervous and hormonal mechanisms. In general cholinergic nerves excite activity and adrenergic nerves inhibit activity. A third group of non-adrenergic, non-cholinergic nerves in the gut wall inhibits motility. They are believed to be 'purinergic', that is they may utilize ATP or a related substance as their transmitter. Other transmitter substances or neural modulators (substances which regulate transmitter release) occur in the intrinsic nerve networks but their role in local control is as yet uncertain. They include 5-HT, enkephalins and endorphins, dopamine and vasoactive intestinal peptide (VIP). Hormones such as gastrin and secretin affect motility as do a wide range of gastrointestinal peptides of uncertain hormonal status such as motilin. Again their physiological role is uncertain.

In man intestinal transit is usually studied by observing the passage of a radio-opaque barium meal through the gut. The barium suspension is propelled into the duodenum by gastric contractions and is then shuttled to and fro by segmenting activity so that the meal is rapidly spread out over a large area of mucosa. The time of transit from stomach to ileocaecal valve is normally about 3 hours but there is great individual variation. The rate of transit slows distally in the small intestine. The transit time is influenced by the rate of gastric emptying so that fast emptying produces fast transit. Intestinal activity increases after eating and speeds the transit of barium already present in the small intestine.

The length of the intestine (mouth to anus) after death is usually given as 7 m but it may be as little as 4 or as much as 8 m. The length in life is about 4.5 m but a narrow rubber tube 2·5 m long can be passed from mouth to anus in a living man as if the intestine had gathers on it like accordion pleating. The great increase in length of the intestine which occurs after death is due to loss of tone.

The ileocolic junction. A short segment, about 4 cm long in man, acts as a sphincter and a band of raised intraluminal pressure has been found in this position but not as constantly as in other sphincters. Inspection through the opened caecum shows that the lips of the ileocaecal valve remain closed unless the ileum is discharging its contents. *In vitro* muscle from this region contracts under the effect of acetylcholine and α-adrenergic stimulation but relaxes to β-adrenergic stimulation. The ileocaecal sphincter also responds to polypeptide hormones; it is contracted by secretin but relaxed by gastrin. It is interesting to note that these hormones have diametrically opposite actions on the lower oesophageal sphincter. However, when the colon is filled with a barium enema reflux into the ileum is common.

The Intestinal Villi

The surface of the mucous membrane of the small intestine possesses about 5 million projections or villi each about 1 mm

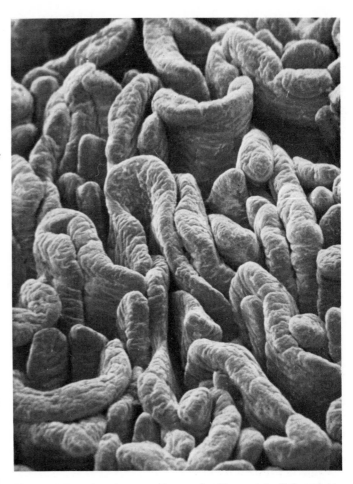

Fig. 5.8 Scanning electron micrograph of human small intestinal villi (×72). (*By courtesy of K. G. Carr and P. G. Toner.*)

long (Figs. 5.7 and 5.8) at a density of 20 to 40 per mm² of mucosa. The columnar cells covering the villi are known as enterocytes. Each villus contains an arteriole and a venule, with their communicating capillary plexus, and also a blind-ended lymphatic vessel or lacteal. Arterio-venous anastomoses occur in the gastric mucosa but are not found in the small intestine. The surface area of the small intestine is increased a further 30-fold due to the presence of microvilli on the free surface of the enterocytes. In man each enterocyte has about 1000 minute processes or microvilli, from 0·9 to 1·3 μm in height and with a maximum width of 0·12 μm, which project into the intestinal lumen. Many simple tubular glands (intestinal glands or crypts of Lieberkuhn) open into the spaces between adjacent villi. The stroma lying below the mucosa contains numerous leucocytes; in the ileum they are collected in aggregated lymph follicles (Peyer's patches).

The total blood supply of the cat intestine is 20 to 40 ml/min/100 g but this may be increased to 200 to 300 ml/min/100 g on maximal dilatation. The veins ultimately open into the portal vein going to the liver. In man about 1·4 litres of blood flow through this vein per minute; during absorption of a meal the flow increases by about one-third.

Blood passing through the minute vessels of the intestine is brought into close proximity to the fluid in the intestine over an area estimated to be 10 m². The fenestrated capillaries in the villi permit a very rapid exchange of absorbed materials. A

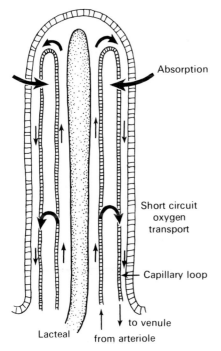

Fig. 5.7 Principles of the countercurrent exchange in the 'hair-pin' capillary loops in the villus of the small intestine. (After Lundgren, 1967.)

countercurrent exchange system in each villus allows only about 15 per cent of the intestinal blood supply to be equilibrated with the absorbed materials in the upper part of the villus although 70 per cent of the intestinal blood supply actually reaches the mucosa (Fig. 5.7). Small molecules absorbed through the epithelium pass into the descending limb of the capillary loop and cross by diffusion into the nearby ascending limb of the capillary loop. In this way a high concentration of these molecules is built up in the distal end of the villus so that they only slowly reach the venous effluent. In other words, the entrance of rapidly absorbed food materials into the circulation is slowed down. At the base of the villus oxygen leaves the ascending limb of the capillary loop and crosses over by diffusion to the descending loop so that the P_{O_2} at the tip of the villus is relatively low.

During digestion and absorption the villi contract fairly quickly at irregular intervals and relax slowly. These contractions are brought about by smooth muscle fibres derived from the muscularis mucosae which pass into the villi to be attached to the lacteals. Contraction of these fibres probably helps to pump lymph into the lacteals of the submucosa and eventually into the thoracic duct, which discharges into the large veins in the neck at the junction of the left internal jugular and subclavian veins. The flow of lymph in the thoracic duct is about 1 to 2 ml per min between meals but may be increased 5

to 10 times during digestion and absorption of a meal.

The tips of the villi undergo constant abrasion and were it not for rapid cell renewal they would gradually be reduced in length. The fast cell turnover may be a consequence of the countercurrent exchange. The oxygen tension at the tip of the villus is probably lower than that at the base; the low P_{O_2} at its tip may limit the life of the cell (Fig. 5.7). From observations of human biopsy material and from measurements of the DNA content of the intestinal lumen it has been estimated that 50 to 200 g of the human gastrointestinal mucosa are renewed daily. The fastest rate of renewal occurs in the ileum; total cell renewal takes 5 to 7 days. With such a rapid rate of renewal the intestinal epithelium is particularly susceptible to factors affecting mitosis. Normally the mitotic rate is approximately equal to the extrusion rate and the length of the villi remains constant. Ionizing radiation and cytotoxic drugs, for example colchicine, inhibit mitosis and as a result the mucosa is flattened as cell extrusion continues. Starvation and protein depletion markedly slow the mitotic cycle and cause thinning of the mucosa and sometimes flattening. In coeliac disease the villi become stunted and the crypts elongated so that the ratio villus:crypt length is 1:2 instead of the 4:1 of the normal intestine.

Three types of cells are present in the intestinal glands: (a) columnar cells, undifferentiated whilst in the crypts, become

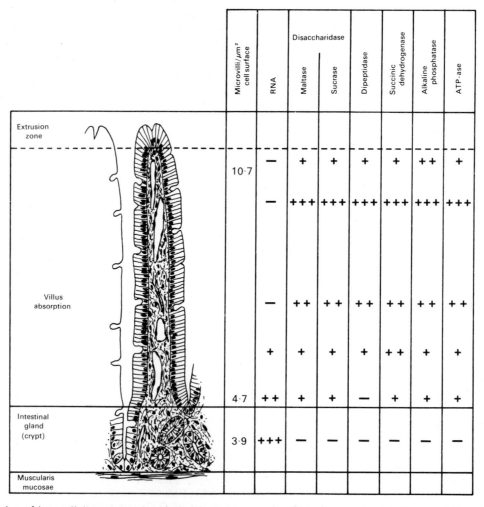

| | Microvilli/μm^2 cell surface | RNA | Disaccharidase | | Dipeptidase | Succinic dehydrogenase | Alkaline phosphatase | ATP-ase |
			Maltase	Sucrase				
Extrusion zone								
	10·7	—	+	+	+	+	+ +	+
		—	+ + +	+ + +	+ + +	+ + +	+ + +	+ + +
Villus absorption		—	+ +	+ +	+ +	+ +	+ +	+ +
		+	+	+	+	+ +	+	+
	4·7	+ +	+	+	—	+	+	+
Intestinal gland (crypt)	3·9	+ + +	—	—	—	—	—	—
Muscularis mucosae								

Fig. 5.9   Distribution of intracellular enzymes in relation to position on the villus. (*By courtesy of Maureen Palmer.*)

capable of absorption during their upward migration, (b) goblet cells, which produce mucus while they are in the crypts but extrude mucus as they migrate upwards, (c) Paneth cells, confined to the crypts, appear to secrete glycoprotein; their function is still unknown. Numerous endocrine cells are scattered throughout the small intestine.

As the columnar cells migrate from the crypt on to the villus their enzymes, and thus their function, become differentiated (Fig. 5.9). In the crypts the cells have a high concentration of RNA and a predominantly basophilic cytoplasm. The RNA is probably associated with the production of the enzymes which appear during the migration of the cell. In the proximal third of the villus much of the RNA has disappeared from the cell. The activities of all the cellular enzymes reach a maximal concentration in the distal part of the villus (Fig. 5.9).

The enzymes can be shown by histochemical methods to be located in the brush border of the cell and quantitative determination of the enzyme activity of isolated brush borders is now possible. Electron microscopy shows that the microvilli are surrounded by a glycocalyx, a polysaccharide-protein complex, whose importance may be due to its property of adsorbing the pancreatic enzymes. Within the glycocalyx and bound to the microvillous membrane is a large number of particles which appear to be 'packets' of enzymes. Some of these enzymes are closely associated with the transport system and thus impart a kinetic advantage for absorption to the substances hydrolysed.

The enzymes of the brush border are altered by changes in diet, especially by changes in the proportions of ingested disaccharides. In human subjects fed a high sucrose or a high maltose diet, an increase in the concentrations of enzymes in the brush border occurs within 2 to 5 days. Within 24 hours changes are found in the intracellular glycolytic enzymes. It is suggested that dietary sugars act immediately on enzyme synthesis within the metabolic pool of the cells and also on synthesis of enzymes on the brush border of the cells being differentiated in the intestinal glands. The time taken for the changes to become apparent, namely 2 to 5 days, corresponds to the time taken by a cell to migrate from the intestinal gland up to the villus. Stimulation of the synthesis of lactase in the brush border does not occur even after four weeks of lactose feeding. The protein content of the diet does not seem to affect the concentration of peptide-splitting enzymes in the brush border but a diet deficient in protein may cause a fall in the concentration of all enzymes.

The Intestinal Juice (Succus Entericus)

Two distinct types of glands are found in the small intestine: (1) the duodenal (Brunner's) glands, found only in the submucosa of the duodenum, which produce a protective alkaline secretion containing mucus but no enzymes; (2) the intestinal glands (Fig. 5.9), present throughout the small intestine, which secrete mucus and a few enzymes. The intestinal juice, or succus entericus, produced by the intestinal glands has a pH of about 7·6 and an electrolyte composition similar to that of extracellular fluid. The only enzyme of importance in the succus entericus is enteropeptidase (enterokinase) derived from the microvillous membrane; it converts trypsinogen to trypsin (p. 66). A rare inborn error of metabolism causing deficiency of enteropeptidase results in

Table 5.10 Composition of intestinal juice (succus entericus) (pH 6·5 to 7·6)

Organic constituents 0·6 per cent	Enteropeptidase (enterokinase)
	Amylase
	Mucin
	Nucleases
	Traces of disaccharidases, e.g. maltase, lactase, sucrase
	Traces of dipeptidases and aminopeptidases
	Traces of lipase, esterases, phosphatases
	Intracellular enzymes released by shedding of mucosal cells
Inorganic constituents 1·0 per cent	Na^+ Ca^{2+} K^+ Mg^{2+} Cl^- HCO_3^- HPO_4^{2-}

very severe impairment of protein digestion. Other enzymes found in minute amounts in the succus entericus are derived from villus cells shed into the lumen; the enzymes normally act within the enterocytes.

Digestive changes in the small intestine. The chyme entering the duodenum from the stomach is a mixture of coarsely emulsified fat, protein (together with protein derivatives produced by the action of pepsin) and carbohydrates. The bicarbonate of the pancreatic juice raises the pH of the intestinal juice to 6·5 or 7·6. The proteins of the chyme are hydrolysed to tri- and di-peptides. The carbohydrates are hydrolysed to disaccharides. The human intestinal enzymes have little effect on cellulose. Fats are hydrolysed by pancreatic lipase (Fig. 5.2) and under the influence of bile salts are dispersed as small particles or micelles (Fig. 5.11).

Control of the secretion of the small intestine. The

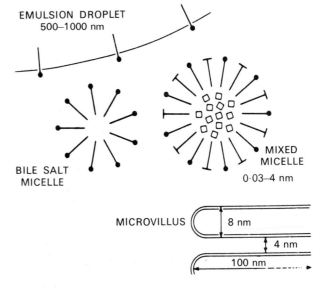

SURFACE EFFECTS OF BILE SALTS

Fig. 5.11 Relative size of emulsion, micelle, and small gut brush border. Note that when a bile salt micelle has been converted into a mixed micelle with, for example, an unsaturated monoglyceride, then non-polar sterols and saturated fatty acids can be more freely solubilized. (A. M. Dawson (1968) *Fourth Symposium on Advanced Medicine*, ed. O. Wrong, p. 258. London: Pitman.)

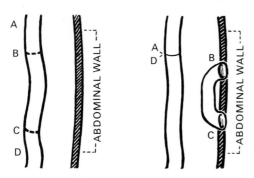

Fig. 5.12 Thiry-Vella fistula. An isolated loop of intestine is made by cutting the gut at two places, B and C, and then restoring the continuity at AD. The loop BC is then made to open on the abdominal wall.

secretory processes can be studied in animals by means of Thiry-Vella fistulae (Fig. 5.12) or by using blind-ending pouches of small lengths of intestine.

In most animals feeding, particularly of fatty foods such as cream or egg yolk, causes secretion from the duodenal glands both in innervated and denervated pouches. Stimulation of the vagus nerves in the neck of a decerebrate cat causes secretion but since the response to feeding is identical whether the pouches used are innervated or denervated the vagus probably plays only a minor role.

Electrolytes and water pass continuously across the mucosa of the small intestine (Chap. 16). When there is a net accumulation of fluid in the lumen, secretion is said to have occurred. Secretion of water and electrolytes occurs most strikingly under the influence of the toxin produced by the organism which causes cholera. Hormones such as gastrin, cholecystokinin, secretin and prostaglandin increase fluid and electrolyte content of the ileum but it is not clear whether this reflects increased secretion or impaired absorption. Vasoactive intestinal peptide (VIP) causes a marked increase in secretion and endocrine tumours of the small intestine, which produce increased amounts of VIP, cause watery diarrhoea. The splanchnic nerves may exert an inhibitory effect on the secretion of intestinal juice, since a denervated loop at first secretes more juice than an innervated loop, perhaps due to the vasodilatation which follows splanchnic section. Stimulation of the vagus gives inconsistent results but injection of eserine or pilocarpine causes the secretion of succus entericus. Nausea induced by the injection of apomorphine causes a very large secretion from a Thiry-Vella loop; this effect is abolished by atropine or by vagal section.

Absorption from the Small Intestine

The site of absorption in the small intestine depends upon the relationship between the rate of transit and the rate of absorption. Despite the fact that transit through the jejunum is much faster than that through the ileum a rapidly absorbed substance can be cleared completely from the jejunal lumen. More slowly absorbed materials are absorbed more distally in the ileum (Fig. 5.13).

The site of absorption also depends on whether the substance is transferred by an active transport mechanism or by diffusion. Active transport implies that substances are absorbed through the intestinal mucosa against a concentration gradient. The rate of active transport is reduced by metabolic inhibitors because the processes require energy. The absorption due to active transport is usually rapid and therefore occurs in the jejunum. Passive absorption is due to diffusion through the intestinal mucosa in the same direction as the concentration gradient. Diffusion does not require metabolic energy, although a carrier may be involved; metabolic inhibitors do not reduce the rate of transfer. Where absorption is passive, the site of absorption depends upon the rate of transit through the intestine and the luminal concentration of the substance to be transferred. Some hormones affect the ability of the gut to absorb nutrients. In the diabetic rat glucose and amino acid transport is enhanced because of stimulation of the Na^+ pump at the basolateral membranes. CCK enhances blood and lymph flow and a high-lipid meal, which in turn causes release of CCK, enhances lymph flow and also uptake of peptides.

Substances which are actively transported require a special carrier mechanism and therefore the site of absorption is limited to the site of the carrier. For this reason, vitamin B_{12} and bile salts are absorbed specifically in the terminal ileum.

Absorption of water and food materials occurs most actively in the upper part of the small intestine where the structure of the mucous membrane is specially adapted for the purpose. Substances absorbed across the villous mucosa pass through (1) the outer or free border of the epithelial cell, (2) the body of the cell itself, and (3) the lateral border of the cell before they reach the venule or lacteal. Some sugars (for example glucose) and essential amino acids are transported into the cell from the lumen of the gut by an inward-acting carrier at the microvillous membrane, and then move passively down the concentration gradient into the blood. Sodium ions are needed for the uptake of amino acids and glucose and the sodium is then actively pumped out of the cell. Small particles may be taken up by the intestinal cells by pinocytosis. The lymphatic system transports most of the water absorbed by the intestinal mucosa.

In health the absorption of foodstuffs is virtually complete during passage through the small intestine. After a mixed meal all of the carbohydrate, about 95 per cent of the fat and 90 per cent of the protein are absorbed.

In the colon absorption is confined to water and substances of low molecular weight such as glucose, inorganic salts and perhaps short chain fatty acids. It is impossible to maintain metabolic equilibrium by introducing into the colon fluids containing protein and fat since they cannot be absorbed by the colonic mucous membrane.

At least one third of the intestine can be excised and, provided that the continuity is restored, no permanent harm ensues; but removal of more than 50 per cent reduces absorption. A few patients have survived with less than 25 per cent of their intestine. Loss of the ileum is more serious than loss of the jejunum because active reabsorption of bile salts occurs only in the ileum. After a massive resection of the small intestine the absorption of fat is grossly reduced, whereas that of amino acids and carbohydrates is only slightly diminished. The fat soluble vitamins and calcium are poorly absorbed. Surgical resection of the ileum and part of the colon may be necessary for the treatment of diseased bowel. It is often followed by diarrhoea, the severity of which depends on

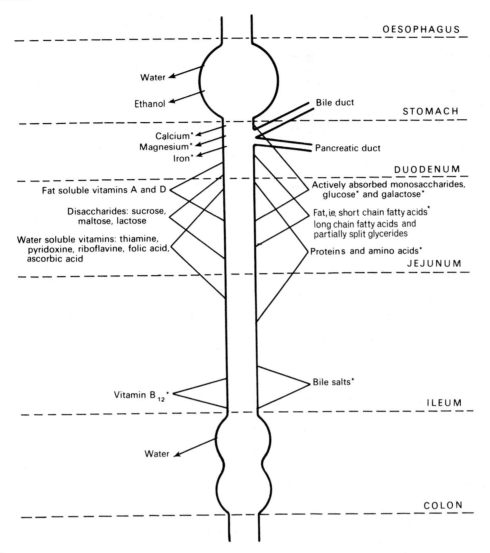

Fig. 5.13 Known sites of absorption in the alimentary canal, partly derived from a diagram by C. C. Booth (1968). *Handbook of Physiology* Section 6, Vol. III, 1524.
*Indicates substances known to be actively transported. Passively absorbed substances begin to be transferred in the duodenum but their movement relies on the maintenance of a concentration gradient. Bile salts are absorbed passively along the whole of the intestine by ionic and non-ionic diffusion. Calcium is absorbed from all parts of the small intestine, but especially the duodenum.

the amount of colon removed. The diarrhoea may be caused by unabsorbed bile salts, by the increased amount of fat reaching the colon, or simply by the increase in water and electrolytes which the reduced colon is not able to absorb.

When a large portion of the small intestine of the rat is removed the remainder increases in weight per unit length owing to the increased thickness of the mucosa and the muscle coats. The number of epithelial cells per villus increases because of an increase in the mitotic rate; the villi increase in length since the rate of cell extrusion remains constant. The increased cell renewal reduces the age of the villous cells and the enzyme activity, particularly of disaccharidases, is reduced. Nevertheless, glucose absorption does improve probably because of the increase in the number of absorbing cells, although each cell may have a reduced capacity for glucose transport. In man there is no evidence that the rate of mitosis is altered, although during recovery from massive resection the capacity to absorb glucose increases considerably and fat

absorption eventually improves.

The nervous system appears to have little influence on absorption. After vagotomy in man intestinal absorption of monosaccharides and of electrolytes soon returns to pre-operative values. The faecal excretion of fat is often increased after vagotomy but the increase may be due to defective digestion rather than to changes in absorption.

The absorption of carbohydrate. After digestion by pancreatic amylase, dietary carbohydrates are found in the small intestine mainly as the disaccharide maltose, together with sucrose and lactose which are present as such in the food. The disaccharides are further digested to monosaccharides during transfer across the microvillous membrane.

Monosaccharides are seldom found in food but their transport has been intensively investigated. In the small intestine glucose and galactose are transported much more rapidly than fructose, mannose and pentoses although all have nearly the same molecular weight. Metabolic inhibitors reduce the rate of transport of glucose and galactose across the small intestinal mucosa but the transfer of the more slowly absorbed sugars is unaffected, presumably because an active transport mechanism operates for glucose and galactose but not for the slowly absorbed sugars.

Sugars which are actively transported have several chemical features in common. First, they all have a six-membered ring. Secondly they all have one or more carbon atoms attached to carbon 5. Thirdly they have a hydroxyl group at carbon 2 with the same stereoconfiguration as occurs in D-glucose (Fig. 5.14).

Glucose is absorbed very rapidly and completely even from a very dilute solution by two independent mechanisms, diffusion and active transport. Active transport is explained by supposing that the brush border possesses a sodium-dependent carrier, specific for the configuration of Figure 5.14, which transports sugars across the membrane in either direction in the presence of sodium ions. The carrier is not energy-dependent; by the interaction of the sodium-dependent sugar carrier and the sodium pump, actively transported sugars

are concentrated within the cell without any sugar leaking back into the lumen.

The dependence of the active transport of glucose upon the presence of sodium ions has been demonstrated in isolated loops of rat intestine by replacing the sodium of the bathing medium by lithium. In these circumstances the rate of glucose transfer is markedly reduced (Fig. 5.15). Drugs such as strophanthin and ouabain which inhibit active ion transport (sodium pump) also inhibit active transport of sugars. Substances preventing the liberation of metabolic energy, such as dinitrophenol, also inhibit active transport of sugars. Phloridzin, a glycoside, inhibits glucose transport by competing for the carrier site at the brush border (Fig. 5.16).

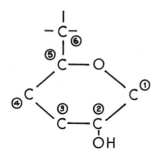

Fig. 5.14 Structural formula of the monosaccharides which are actively transported by the mucosa of the small intestine.

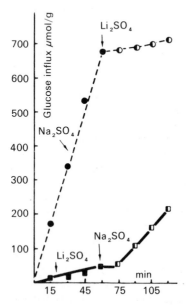

Fig. 5.15 Effect of Na$^+$ on absorption *in vivo*. Glucose influx in μmol/g dry tissue from small intestine of rat perfused *in situ* with isosmotic solution of either Na$_2$SO$_4$ or Li$_2$SO$_4$. The composition of the perfusate was changed as shown in the diagram at 60 min in each case. (T. Z. Csaky & L. Zollicoffer (1960) *American Journal of Physiology*, 198, 1056–1058.)

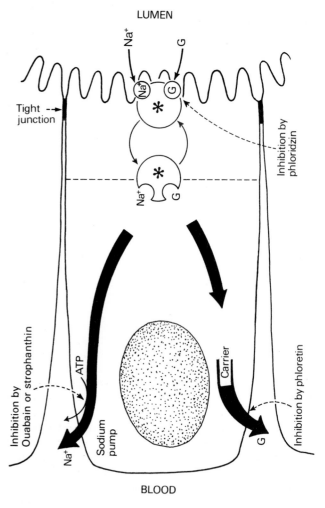

Fig. 5.16 Scheme showing the co-transport of sodium and glucose by the intestinal epithelium. Sodium (Na) and glucose (G) are transported together across the luminal membrane by a carrier mechanism located in the membrane. This membrane event is shown above the dotted line. From the cytoplasm (below the dotted line) sodium and glucose are transported across the basolateral membrane into the intercellular space and from there pass into the blood. Sodium is transported actively by the sodium pump. Glucose moves by facilitated diffusion, using some carrier system. The various transport processes at luminal or basolateral membranes can be blocked by specific blocking agents as shown. The epithelial cells are connected by tight junctions and transport processes are accompanied by changes in electrical potential between the lumen and the blood. (*By courtesy of Maureen Palmer and J. S. Davison.*)

Glucose is transported at a greater rate than galactose because, although they share a carrier site, glucose has a greater affinity for the carrier than galactose. Active transport of sugars is characterized by generation of a potential difference across the epithelial cells, probably due to the presence of an electrogenic pump. Recent work suggests that this pump is located at the serosal side of the cell. Measurements of potential difference across the mucosal border did not change whether the cells were transporting or not but that across the serosal border increased by a factor of two during active transport (Fig. 5.16). This increase can be eliminated by ouabain or strophanthin, drugs which block the Na^+ pump.

The reason for the success of the oral administration of isotonic solutions containing glucose, NaCl, $NaHCO_3$ and KCl in the treatment of cholera and other diarrhoeal diseases is obvious from the findings just described. In epidemics large numbers of dehydrated patients can be simply and effectively treated orally and intravenous replacement of fluid, with all its complications, may be required less often. (See also p. 76.)

Fructose absorption is passive, that is, it cannot be absorbed against a concentration gradient and the presence of inhibitors does not affect the rate of transfer. However, the rate of absorption of fructose is more rapid than can be explained by passive diffusion alone and in some species fructose is converted to glucose or lactate within the mucosal cells so that a steep concentration gradient is maintained. Fructose has been infused into the jejunum of human subjects undergoing laparotomy and subsequent analysis of mesenteric blood for glucose and fructose has shown that between 20 and 50 per cent of fructose is converted to glucose. The conversion probably involves glucose-6-phosphatase and alkaline phosphatase which are found in the brush border of the intestine. The conversion to glucose is not essential since subjects with hereditary malabsorption of glucose and galactose who lack the active hexose carrier mechanism absorb fructose at a normal rate although the rate of absorption of glucose is very much reduced and the conversion of fructose to glucose does not take place.

Hydrolysis of disaccharides to the constituent monosaccharides occurs at the brush border by 'membrane-bound' disaccharidases. The disaccharides are trapped in the glycocalyx and come to lie very close to the enzyme. Once hydrolysis has occurred the constituent monosaccharides are very close to the transport sites and are therefore rapidly absorbed. It is likely that the enzymes and carriers are so orientated spatially that hydrolysis and subsequent absorption are sequential events. The disaccharidases are highly specific, there being three types of maltase, one of which attacks sucrose (sucrase), and two forms of lactase. All the disaccharidases are developed at the time of birth but in most species after weaning there appears to be regression of lactase activity which cannot be prevented by maintaining the animal on a high lactose diet. The decline in people of North European ancestry is slower than that in other ethnic groups and the ability to digest lactose in adulthood appears to be transmitted as an autosomal dominant and it has been concluded that this represents a mutated gene or polymorphism.

Deficiency, either inherited or acquired, of a disaccharidase can lead to malabsorption of the corresponding sugar. In turn this may cause diarrhoea owing to bacterial breakdown of the unabsorbed sugar to lactic and other acids. Lactase deficiency is not uncommon and exclusion of milk from the diet of these patients may completely relieve diarrhoea. Deficiency of a specific disaccharidase is tested clinically by giving a test dose of the specific disaccharide to a patient and observing whether diarrhoea develops. When a disaccharidase is present, the blood glucose rises after the test dose but remains unchanged in its absence. Quantitative estimates of enzyme activity of intestinal mucosa may be made by the technique of peroral biopsy.

Carbohydrates are absorbed in the proximal part of the small intestine and both monosaccharides and disaccharides have completely disappeared from the lumen by the time the meal reaches the ileum. However, since resection of the jejunum does not impair the absorption of glucose and galactose, the specific carrier systems for the actively absorbed sugars must be present throughout the small intestine. Disaccharidase activity is greatest in the jejunum and diminishes throughout the ileum.

The absorption of amino acids. The protein of food is digested in the stomach and intestine to peptides and amino acids. In addition nitrogenous material passed into the intestine, partly as proteins in the gastrointestinal secretions (approximately 140 g per day) and partly as desquamated epithelial cells (approximately 25 g per day) undergoes digestion. In health approximately 90 per cent of the ingested and endogenous protein is absorbed. Both digestion and absorption are very rapid in man since $^{15}NH_3$ appears rapidly in the urine with a peak at one hour after the ingestion of either ^{15}N-labelled protein or ^{15}N-labelled hydrolysate.

Most of the naturally occurring amino acids are L-isomers. L-amino acids are transported against concentration gradients by carrier mechanisms while D-amino acids are absorbed passively much more slowly.

Active transport of amino acids is sodium-dependent. Experiments with everted sacs of golden hamster intestine have shown that replacement of the sodium of the bathing fluid by lithium or potassium reduces the rate of transfer of L-tryptophan. However, if the chloride is replaced by sulphate the rate of transfer is not altered. Transport of L-amino acids is oxygen dependent and in the absence of oxygen the rate of absorption is reduced to that of the D-isomers.

All the neutral L-amino acids, including L-histidine, are actively transported. Experiments with mixtures of neutral amino acids have shown that they compete with each other for transport because they share a common carrier system. Transport of neutral amino acids is unaffected by basic or acidic amino acids. A second carrier mechanism is shared by the basic amino acids, lysine, ornithine, arginine and cystine. Some neutral amino acids can inhibit basic amino acid transport; for example, L-methionine can inhibit arginine transport. A third carrier mechanism is available for the dicarboxylic acids, glutamic acid and aspartic acid. A fourth carrier transports the amino acids proline, hydroxyproline and glycine.

Absorption of polypeptides. The disappearance of polypeptides from jejunal loops of the dog is faster than can be accounted for by intraluminal enzymatic activity. After feeding dipeptides there is a great increase of amino acids in the portal blood but no trace of dipeptides. It is thought, therefore, that dipeptides are hydrolysed by dipeptidases within the epithelial cells during the absorptive process. The constituent amino acids are then transferred to the mucosal cells. Amino acids, for

Table 5.17 Rate of absorption of glycine, methionine and their peptides

Substance absorbed	Concentration mmol/litre	Absorption μmol/ cm/10 min
Methionine	100	2·42
Dimethionine	100	3·42
		μmol/cm/5 min
Glycine	267	4·24
Diglycine	267	6·88
Triglycine	267	6·63

Methionine data J. L. Craft, R. F. Crampton, M. T. Lis & D. M. Matthews (1969). *Journal of Physiology*, 200, 111P.

Glycine data, D. M. Matthews *et al.* (1968). *Clinical Science* 35, 415.

example glycine and methionine, are absorbed more rapidly when presented to the gut as the di- or tripeptide than as the free amino acids (Table 5.17). This is also true of the dipeptide carnosine, which is β-alanyl-L-histidine. Dipeptidase activities develop in the microvillous brush border fairly late in fetal life and reach full activity at birth. Breast-fed animals then show a fall in dipeptidase activity followed by a rise to a new steady level. The fall is probably due to inhibition by colostrum since artificially fed animals do not show such reduction in dipeptidase activity. Dipeptidases are very susceptible to the quantity of protein in the diet; for example in the rat after 10 days on a low protein diet the aminopeptidase activity is greatly reduced.

It has long been accepted that small amounts of large protein molecules pass across the intestinal mucosa into the circulation. Such a process is necessary to explain the immunization produced by oral administration of antigens. Recent experiments in rats suggest that the transmucosal passage of intact protein molecules is quite considerable and large enough to be of nutritional significance.

The absorption of fat. The main bulk of the dietary fat of man, some 70 g per day, consists of triglycerides with mixed long chain fatty acids of which 95 per cent are absorbed. From 0·5 to 1·0 g of cholesterol is ingested daily but only 20 to 50 per cent of this is absorbed. The secretions and movements of the stomach cause the fat to enter the intestine as a coarse suspension but there appears to be no hydrolysis of fat in the stomach and it is doubtful if gastric juice contains any lipase. During digestion the triglycerides and other fats must be rendered water-soluble so that they can enter the intestinal cells.

In the duodenum triglycerides are emulsified by bile salts and they can then undergo lipolysis under the influence of pancreatic lipase. Bile salts are not essential for the action of pancreatic lipase; in fact at the pH optimum for lipase, the rate of hydrolysis of triglyceride is greater in the absence than in the presence of bile salts, but bile salts are essential for the uptake and subsequent transport of cholesterol into the cells. However, lipolysis is very sensitive to pH and the finely adjusted secretion of bicarbonate in pancreatic juice is of great importance. Lipase acts specifically at the interface between the fat globule and water and hydrolyses the triglyceride (Fig. 5.2) at the two primary positions, producing fatty acids and monoglycerides. Under the influence of the salts and monoglycerides the emulsion of fat is broken down into water-soluble micelles which are aggregates of molecules containing both water-soluble polar groups (hydroxyl and carboxyl) and fat-soluble hydrocarbon chains (long chain fatty acid mono-glycerides). The molecules orientate themselves so that the water-soluble hydrophilic groups face outwards and the fat-soluble (hydrophobic) groups form the interior of the aggregate. The micelles are stable water-soluble structures which can dissolve other water insoluble (hydrophobic) compounds in their interior (Fig. 5.11). Substances made soluble in this manner include fatty acids, cholesterol and fat soluble vitamins.

After lipolysis the mixed micelles are ready to enter the cell. It has been demonstrated in man by a perfusion technique that the different components of a mixed micelle disappear from the perfusate at different rates. This suggests that the micellar aggregates are not absorbed intact. The mixed micelles are taken up intact by the brush border by a passive process and the bile salts participate in the transport of fat across the luminal margin of the cell. Since the bile salts are not completely absorbed in the jejunum, where the bulk of the fat is absorbed, the bile salts are probably expelled from the cell into the intestinal lumen to be absorbed by an active process in the terminal ileum. Once absorbed the bile salts are returned to the liver by the portal blood to be re-excreted in the bile (p. 101). The entero-hepatic circulation is very efficient and the whole bile salt pool is recirculated about six times in 24 hours with a total loss of only about 5 per cent.

The mixed micelle penetrates the membrane of the cell either by dissolving in the membrane or by a process of pinocytosis. The latter mode of entry is suggested by electron micrographs which have shown cytoplasmic vesicles containing fat after ingestion of fat. Once the fat is inside the cell it is transported to the smooth endoplasmic reticulum where triglyceride is resynthesized. The triglycerides are rendered water-soluble as chylomicrons with a covering of lipoprotein. The covering of the triglyceride with a protein coat is a definite synthetic step rather than a non-specific adsorption of protein on to the triglyceride. In patients with the rare condition of abetalipoproteinaemia, characterized by absence of plasma β-lipoproteins, ingestion of fat is not followed by an increase in the chylomicron count in the blood. If the intestinal cells are examined it can be shown that they are full of fat but, because of the inability to manufacture the protein coat, the fats cannot pass into the lacteals.

The chylomicrons pass out of the cells into the lacteals, from which they pass into the thoracic duct and the systemic circulation. Fatty acids with chains longer than 14 carbon atoms are transported as triglycerides in the chylomicrons. Short chain fatty acids are absorbed very rapidly from the lumen of the intestine directly into the portal blood stream. Micelles do not seem to be formed. The entry of these short chain substances is sodium-dependent and can take place against a concentration gradient by a process of active transport.

Fat digestion and absorption are assessed in man by collecting the faeces over a period of 3 or 5 days and measuring the amount of fat excreted. Normal subjects excrete less than 5 g of fat per day, not all of which is residue from the dietary fat since a considerable amount of endogenous fat, about 25 g, is added from bile and desquamated cells during intestinal transit. Excessive excretion of fat in the faeces (steatorrhoea) indicates either maldigestion due to deficient secretion of pancreatic lipase or bile salts (p. 101) or to defective absorption resulting from disease of the small intestinal mucosa. In disease steatorrhoea usually appears as a result of both factors. In coeliac disease sensitivity to gluten in cereals causes mucosal damage and the villi disappear particularly in the upper small intestine. The condition can be greatly improved and the villi can regrow if gluten is withheld. The abnormal mucosa is not only inefficient in absorbing material but also it secretes fluid. This dilutes the enzymes in the intestine which are already deficient as a result of a secretory defect of the pancreas. Bile salt secretion is also impaired.

Similarly the short gut syndrome and even pancreatitis are mixed syndromes involving maldigestion and malabsorption.

THE LARGE INTESTINE

The calibre of the large intestine is greater than that of the small, the transverse measurement being greatest at the caecum and becoming narrower towards the rectum. The longitudinal muscle is gathered into three longitudinal strands (taeniae coli) which, since they are shorter than the other coats, produce puckering (Fig. 5.18). The capacity of the large bowel in man, as measured by a contrast enema, ranges from 0·9 to 1·8 litres. The mucous coat is smooth without villi. The mucosal glands are 0·07 mm long and closely packed and are composed largely of mucus-secreting goblet cells. As in the small intestine, the epithelium is in a state of continuous renewal, migration and loss, the turnover time being 1 to 2

days. Lymph nodes are present in the proximal part of the colon and especially in the vermiform appendix. The transition from the columnar epithelium of the rectum to the stratified squamous epithelium of the anal canal is not sharply defined but it usually occurs just above the anal valves. The rectum, about 13 cm long, is sensitive to stretch but not to tactile or thermal stimuli. The anal canal is sensitive to tactile, thermal and painful stimuli but localization is poor.

Movements of the Large Intestine

The caecum and colon usually fill with chyme from the small intestine when food is eaten as the result of a peristaltic wave in the small intestine accompanied by a relaxation of the ileocolic sphincter. A barium meal usually enters the caecum about 4 hours after it has been taken and soon after this the meal quickly fills the ascending and transverse colon. On average a barium meal reaches the hepatic flexure of the colon in 6 hours, the splenic flexure in 9 hours and the pelvic colon in 12 hours; three-quarters of a barium meal are expelled in 72 hours, the remainder escaping in the succeeding 4 or 5 days. Normal food residues probably pass more slowly than the barium meal. Individual and day-to-day variations in the rate of passage of residues through the intestinal tract are quite large.

Colonic motor activity may be propulsive or non-propulsive. The non-propulsive mode predominates and consists of segmental, non-peristaltic contractions which produce localized elevations of colonic intraluminal pressure. These

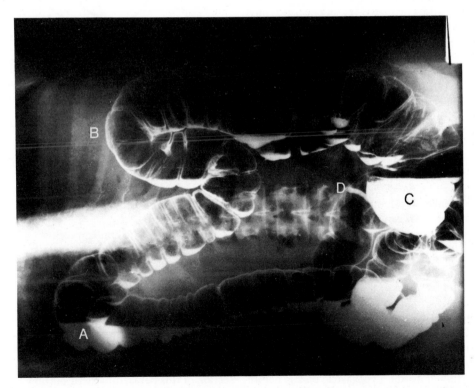

Fig. 5.18 The normal colon demonstrated by a 'double contrast' radiological technique in which a barium emulsion and carbon dioxide are introduced into the bowel and the patient is rotated so that the emulsion outlines the mucosal surface of the colon. For this picture the patient was lying on his left side, so the level surfaces of pools of barium emulsion are horizontal. The picture is also viewed from behind, so A marks the splenic flexure, B the hepatic flexure, C the caecum and D the appendix. Haustration caused by muscular contraction is clearly shown. (*By courtesy of G. F. A. Howie.*)

pressure waves occur at the rate of 2 to 3 per min, their average amplitude being approximately 30cm H_2O in the proximal, and 50cm H_2O in the distal, colon. Segmental pressure activity is increased by ingestion of food and by cholinergic stimuli but is unaffected by gastrin; it diminishes during sleep. Although normal segmental motor activity occurs for about 50 per cent of recording time, it is unperceived by the subject. On the other hand excessive segmentation may cause abdominal pain. Segmental contractions probably delay rather than accelerate the transit of colonic contents. Segmental activity tends to be high in constipated and low in diarrhoeal patients: there is, however, an overlap between the two groups. Gross thickening of colonic muscle in the sigmoid region is a common finding in the older population in the Western countries. This abnormality is accompanied by colonic pressure waves of high amplitude and by the formation of numerous mucosal diverticula which may become inflamed (diverticultis). (See also p. 84.)

Propulsion of faeces is brought about by mass action or mass peristalsis, consisting of a ring of muscular contraction which passes for a variable distance along the colon. The haustral folds disappear momentarily ahead of the peristaltic contraction, only to reform behind it. The frequency of mass movements increases after meals and during somatic activity. If haustration of the colon is destroyed by disease (for example ulcerative colitis), distal resistance to the flow of faeces is diminished with resultant fast transit time, diminished water absorption and diarrhoea.

Certain laxatives (senna, bisacodyl) act by stimulating the propulsive activity of the colon. Studies on patients whose colon has been brought to the surface of the abdominal wall as a surgical fistula (colostomy) suggest that these substances activate mucosal receptors. The propulsive activity is probably mediated through the myenteric nerve plexus, and the plexus can be damaged by prolonged use of high doses of these drugs. The habitual use of certain purgatives may also cause a considerable loss of electrolytes, especially potassium, and cause hypokalaemia.

Nerve supply of colon and rectum. Fibres from the vagus nerves reach the proximal colon; section of the vagi leads to degeneration of nerve fibres in the proximal, but not in the distal colon. The outflow from the spinal cord to the distal colon in man is shown in Figure 5.19. The thoracolumbar sympathetic outflow leaves the lumbar sympathetic chains, forming plexuses on the aorta, and passes eventually in the mesentery to the colon as the inferior mesenteric nerves. The presacral nerve is in fact a nerve plexus, the superior hypogastic plexus, formed by an extension of the aortic plexus together with branches from the lumbar sympathetic trunks. Below it is continued as two narrow plexiform strands, the right and left hypogastric nerves, which in turn become continuous with the corresponding inferior hypogastric or pelvic plexus. The main sacral (parasympathetic) outflow in man (pelvic splanchnic nerves) comes from the second, third and fourth sacral nerves and joins the hypogastric plexus. The parasympathetic outflow joins the hypogastric plexus before arriving at the rectum and internal sphincter. The striated muscle of the external sphincter is supplied by the pudendal nerve (Figs. 5.19 and 5.20). This muscle is bilaterally innervated since section of one pudendal nerve does not affect its reflex behaviour. Stimulation of the perianal skin in man

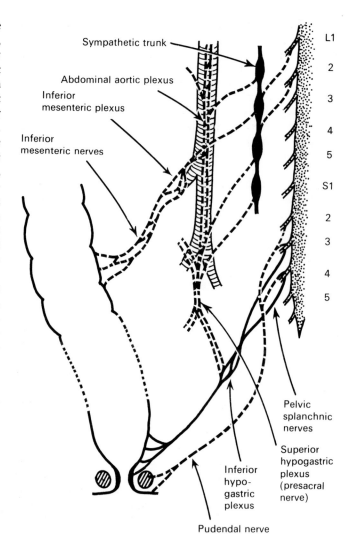

Fig. 5.19   The nervous outflow to the distal colon in man (*After* R. C. Garry (1934) *Physiological Reviews,* 14, 107).

causes a contraction of the external sphincter (anal reflex). Afferent impulses pass in the pudendal nerves to S2 and S3 segments of the cord and efferent impulses pass out in the pudendal nerves. This reflex is of importance in maintaining faecal continence.

Stimulation of the lumbar outflow (sympathetic efferent) in the cat inhibits the colon and contracts the anal sphincter. When it is cut, or when the cord is anaesthetized, the colon is more active and the internal anal sphincter relaxes. Transection of the spinal cord in man by trauma or disease is also followed by hyperactivity of the pelvic colon. On the other hand bilateral removal of the lumbar chains seems to have no long-term effects on the motility of the colon. Stimulation of the pelvic nerves in the cat causes contraction of the colon and inhibition of the smooth muscle of the anal sphincter. After section of this parasympathetic outflow the movements of the distal colon become weak and the internal anal sphincter contracts. The parasympathetic pathway has a long latent period (about 100 msec in the cat) and is therefore a multisynaptic pathway. Occasionally the parasympathetic outflow has an inhibitory effect on the colon.

Labels in figure: Sympathetic trunk; Abdominal aortic plexus; Inferior mesenteric plexus; Inferior mesenteric nerves; L1, 2, 3, 4, 5, S1, 2, 3, 4, 5; Pelvic splanchnic nerves; Superior hypogastric plexus (presacral nerve); Inferior hypogastric plexus; Pudendal nerve

Defaecation. Throughout the greater part of its length the intestinal tract shows a large degree of autonomy. Co-ordinated movements continue after complete destruction of the spinal cord. At its caudal extremity, however, the gut comes directly under control of the nervous system. If the lumbo-sacral region of the cord is destroyed the anal sphincters, the internal sphincter of smooth muscle and the external sphincter of striped muscle, are patulous and the caudal portion of the large intestine is paralysed. In time there may be some return of activity and the internal sphincter may recover tone. The caudal region of the gut may thus eventually recover its autonomy. In those conditions faecal matter may be expelled at intervals but the patient is unaware of it and can exert no voluntary control.

If the spinal cord is transected above the sacral region of the cord the condition of the gut, so long as spinal shock persists, resembles that seen after destruction of the sacral region of the cord. Subsequently, when the spinal shock has passed off, reflex defaecation is established. Expulsion of faecal matter may be complete but the patient is unaware of the act and is unable to exert any voluntary control over it.

The reflex pathways subserving defaecation are shown in Figure 5.20. Stimulation of the distal colon in the cat by friction or distension causes contraction of the colon through the pelvic splanchnic nerve and relaxation, through the pelvic splanchnic and pudendal nerves, of the internal and external sphincters respectively. When the faeces pass through the sphincter these contractions and relaxations are reinforced by reflexes involving afferents and efferents in both pelvic splanchnic and pudendal nerves. A continuous inflow of impulses passes along the pelvic nerves in the cat; if these nerves are cut the external sphincter closes more firmly and distension of the colon no longer causes it to relax. The anal sphincter is normally closed and remains so in man even if he is deeply anaesthetized. The afferent impulses which reflexly

maintain the tone of the external sphincter probably arise in the muscle spindles in the muscle and enter the cord mainly by the dorsal root of the second sacral segment (Fig. 5.20).

Defaecation is a complex act involving not only contraction of the rectum and distal portion of the colon with inhibition of both internal and external sphincters but also contraction of the diaphragm and of the muscles of the abdominal wall which are, of course, under voluntary control. The levator ani muscles in the pelvic floor aid defaecation by pulling up the anal canal over the faecal mass. During defaecation the pressure in the rectum may rise as high as 200 mm Hg with violent expulsive efforts. Such high intra-abdominal pressures have important effects on the circulation, especially on the venous return to the heart.

Massive peristaltic contractions in the transverse and descending colon drive the contents onwards and the subject may experience a sensation of fullness in the rectum and a desire to defaecate. Such a peristaltic movement frequently follows the eating of a meal. This response is the basis of the usual habit of defaecating after a meal, often after breakfast. However, the time of defaecation depends not only on the sensation of fullness of the rectum but also on habit and the opportunities available according to the occupation of the individual. Reflex defaecation occurs soon after birth: the social skill of defaecation is gradually acquired in the first two years of life. Defaecation does not occur *in utero* unless the fetus is distressed.

A survey in 1965 of 1500 healthy persons showed that two-thirds defaecated between 5 and 7 times per week and about one-quarter about twice a day. The range three bowel actions per week to three per day included 99 per cent of the group. If the act of defaecation is postponed, either by voluntary contraction of the external sphincter of the anus or by resisting the call to defaecate, the sensation of fullness rapidly fades. In this fashion the habit of constipation may be acquired.

Small radio-opaque discs administered with meals are distributed over long segments of colon and if a different size of disc is given with each meal they are often found to be out of chronological order. A great deal of mixing must occur in the colon. No particular distribution or change of distribution of the discs can be correlated with the desire to defaecate; quite often there is no urge to defaecate even when the rectum contains faeces. The length of colon emptied at defaecation varies considerably; in some subjects the whole of the left side is evacuated while in others even the rectum is not completely emptied. Purgatives in full doses may cause the large bowel to empty completely and two or three days may elapse before the distal colon becomes filled with faeces and the defaecation reflex is elicited once more.

Distension of the lower colon in man by means of a balloon produces a sensation of colic in the abdomen. The nerve impulses pass into the spinal cord along the sympathetic pathways. Distension of the rectum, however, produces a desire to pass flatus or faeces and a reflex contraction of the external sphincter, the afferent pathway being in the pelvic nerves (Fig. 5.20). The rectum is able to distinguish between flatus and faeces probably because flatus produces less distension. When these sensations rise to consciousness a voluntary decision is made as to whether the contraction of the external sphincter, initially reflex, should be maintained or relaxed. The external sphincter shows continuous electrical

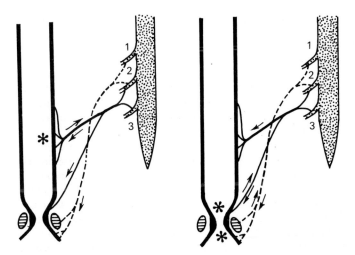

Fig. 5.20 Diagram of the supposed course of the nerve impulses in defaecation. The sacral cord of the cat: continuous line, the pelvic nerve; interrupted line, the pudendal nerve; *the point of stimulation by friction or distension. The afferent impulses reach the cord by way of the dorsal roots; the efferent impulses leave by the ventral roots. (*After* R. C. Garry (1933) *Transactions of the Royal Medico-Chirurgical Society of Glasgow* in *Glasgow Medical Journal*, **28**, 9, Fig. 6.)

activity. When the rectum is distended by a balloon, at first the electrical activity increases along with the sensation of distension; then the electrical activity declines as the sphincter relaxes. All the factors maintaining rectal continence are not yet known but it is generally agreed that the external sphincter allows a voluntary emergency control effective up to a minute; the internal sphincter apposes the sides of the anal canal which allows some mechanism (perhaps a flutter valve) to maintain continence.

Absorption and Secretion in the Large Intestine

About 1000 ml of chyme pass from the small intestine through the ileocolic valve into the caecum each day. An ileostomy is a surgically created opening through the abdominal wall into the ileum. In healthy subjects with well-established ileostomies about 60 mmol of sodium and about 4 mmol of potassium are lost per day together with 1·5 g of nitrogen and 2 or 3 g of fat. The volume of the chyme is much reduced during its stay in the colon by absorption mainly in the caecum and ascending colon of about 850 ml of water. The retention of this water is of importance for the maintenance of fluid equilibrium but the absorption of water in the small intestine, about 7 litres per day, is very much greater. Persistent diarrhoea, that is the passage of frequent watery stools, leads ultimately to loss of water and electrolytes, especially potassium and bicarbonate and may, especially in infants, be quickly fatal. Faecal fluid in man contains much potassium which is probably mostly actively secreted. Sodium chloride is readily absorbed from the colon but chloride ions are more rapidly absorbed than sodium ions—a fact of some importance if the ureters are transplanted into the colon because a diseased urinary bladder has been removed. Some amino acids, aspirin, short chain fatty acids and some steroids are also well absorbed but protein, fat, sugars and calcium are not. Large amounts of electrolytes, especially potassium, can be removed from the body by introducing ion exchange resins into the distal colon. The use of enemas consisting of tap water or soap and water may lead to excessive water absorption and water intoxication. Some of the absorptive power attributed to the colon may, in fact, be due to the passage of the chyme back through the ileocolic valve into the lower ileum.

An isolated loop of colon secretes a small amount of mucus which is produced by the goblet cells; mechanical stimulation produces a small quantity of watery secretion with practically no enzymic activity. The mucus lubricates the faeces and neutralizes acids formed in them. The pH of the contents of the colon is about 8. If one pelvic splanchnic nerve is cut, stimulation of either the peripheral or the central end produces secretion of mucus in the large intestine. The former is a direct effect, the second a reflex effect. Secretion can also be obtained by injection of vagomimetic drugs such as pilocarpine and can be prevented by atropine.

The Bacteria of the Intestine

The intestine of the newborn child is bacteriologically sterile and the material excreted from it is a semi-fluid greenish mass known as *meconium*. It remains sterile for a few days only; thereafter the intestine is invaded and colonized by ingested bacteria. It is well known that the large intestine has a high bacterial content but the small intestine also has a substantial flora. This is now recognized as a useful symbiosis and not merely a contamination.

In healthy subjects the acid in the stomach acts as a barrier against a massive invasion by organisms derived from food and water or from the mouth. However, bacteria are constantly invading the small intestine from above. The organisms that flourish in the small intestine are mutually selected; their biochemical performance matches the local conditions. Some live in the lumen but it is thought that the major site is in the intestinal mucus. By adhering to the intestinal mucosa they hold a position against the flow of fluid and the propulsive action of the gut; they probably increase and decrease in numbers with meals. The fluid of the small intestine contains about 10^3 to 10^5 organisms per ml. In the upper small intestine the flora is mainly streptococci, staphylococci, lactobacilli and fungi; in the lower small intestine rather more organisms are found and they are similar to those in the colon.

If an intestinal cul-de-sac (blind loop) is created in a patient, for example in the course of an operation to relieve obstruction, he is liable some time later to develop steatorrhoea (the passage of fatty stools) and anaemia. His small intestine harbours numerous bacteria which hydrolyse conjugated bile acids; the free acids so liberated have a toxic effect on the mucosa and do not promote the formation of micelles necessary for the absorption of fat (p. 73). The steatorrhoea is more pronounced the greater the number of bacteria. The anaemia is explained by the competition between the host and the bacteria for vitamin B_{12}.

Many intestinal bacteria can synthesize nutritionally useful substances but it is uncertain whether the amounts formed are significant. It is generally held that in man vitamin K is principally derived from intestinal bacteria. The role of intestinal bacteria has been helped by the study of germ-free animals (gnotobiotics) which develop in much the same way as conventionally reared ones except that rodents develop an enormous caecum which may be ten times the normal size. In the germ-free animal the villi are slender, the total surface area is reduced and cell turnover is slowed so that cells take 4 days to reach the top of the villus instead of 2. The number of lymphocytes and plasma cells in the intestinal wall is also reduced and the submucosal connective tissue is thinner. Mucus accumulates so that it seems likely that bacteria normally degrade it. In germ-free animals rather more protein than usual appears in the faeces. It may be that some protein is utilized by the intestinal bacteria of the normal animal or that its bacteria enhance the absorption of protein. Obviously some aspects of small intestinal structure and function are determined by the normal flora. A stable gut flora clearly contributes to normal function of the intestine provided that the challenge of the bacterial load can be resisted. The mucosa does secrete some immunoglobulins, most important of which is IgA synthesized by the cells of the lamina propria. Germ-free animals have practically no lamina propria.

In spite of its small molecular size urea passes only slowly from the circulation into the lumen of the colon but when it enters the lumen it is immediately broken down to ammonia by urease produced by non-sporing aerobic organisms lying on the mucosa and is quickly reabsorbed. About 7 g urea is degraded per day and the process is so efficient that normally no urea is found in the faeces. Most of the ammonia in the body is produced in the colon. After reabsorption it is partly changed back to urea in the liver.

Certain products of bacterial metabolism are normally absorbed and excreted in the urine; they are phenol, cresol, indole, skatole and pyrocatechol. The level of indole excretion in the urine is used as an index of small intestinal bacterial activity in man.

Blood from the intestine passes to the liver which acts as a filter to remove bacterial, viral and other antigens. The Kupffer cells seem to degrade and render harmless the antigens rather than process them for antibody formation.

Colonic bacteria are predominantly bacteroides and bifido-bacteria but lactobacilli and streptococci are also present. They bring about fermentation of carbohydrates with the production of carbon dioxide and hydrogen sulphide and also combustible gases such as hydrogen and methane; flatus contains very little oxygen. More than half of the gas found in the colon is, however, derived from the atmospheric air which can pass surprisingly quickly down the alimentary canal; air which was swallowed has been seen by X-rays to reach the caecum in 14 min and to be passed as flatus in 30 min. About 50 per cent of the flatus is nitrogen derived mainly from air; a small amount of nitrogen diffuses out of the blood vessels of the intestinal mucosa into the lumen. Even the gas which accumulates behind an intestinal obstruction is derived mainly from the air. Normally part of the gaseous content of the colon is absorbed and is excreted in the lungs and the remainder, about 500 ml per day, is passed per rectum as flatus. The composition of flatus is extremely variable depending on the micro-organisms and the food eaten. A diet containing large amounts of baked beans may increase the output of flatus 10 times. Lactose in some susceptible persons may be the source of excess flatus. Since the volume of the gas in the stomach and intestines doubles at 5 km (16 000 ft) it is easy to see that pain due to distension may occur in a sudden rise to a high altitude.

The activity of the intestinal bacteria can be approximately assessed by the ^{14}C-glycocholic acid breath test. This bile acid is given by mouth and is deconjugated by the intestinal bacteria. The ^{14}C-glycine so released is converted to ^{14}CO$_2$ which is exhaled. The amount of ^{14}CO$_2$ in the breath is related to the amount of bacterial deconjugation.

The Faeces

Meconium, the first stool passed in the first day of life, is viscid and odourless. It contains mainly carbohydrate substances. Meconium is derived from amniotic fluid which the fetus has swallowed. Its greenish-black colour is due to bile. About 36 hours after birth the contents of the large intestine have become solid or semi-solid and are known as faeces.

An adult produces 80 to 200 g of faeces, but on a European diet it is usually about 100 g. The surface is usually slightly alkaline (pH 7·0 to 7·5). The colour is due to *stercobilin* derived from bile pigment, but in disease the colour may be greatly changed, for example to black (melaena) in the presence of altered blood or to clay colour in the absence of bile.

In steatorrhea the stool is pale because the pigment is decolorized by the intestinal bacteria. The faecal odour is due mainly to indole and skatole and to gases produced by the fermentation of carbohydrates.

The water content of faeces varies from 60 to 80 per cent according to the length of time that they are retained in the colon, but the wet weight of the faeces is quite unaffected by the drinking of large quantities of water. In health, on a normal diet, the proportion of the faecal mass attributable to undigested or unabsorbed foodstuffs is small. The faeces consist chiefly of the residues of bile and other intestinal secretions, mucus, leucocytes and desquamated epithelium together with enormous numbers of bacteria. Faeces continue to be formed during starvation; though smaller in quantity their composition remains essentially unaltered. This shows clearly that the faeces are produced chiefly within the intestinal tract and are not simply the unabsorbed residues of foodstuffs. In health and in the absence of diarrhoea the energy value of the faeces is from 3 to 8 per cent of the total energy intake. The composition of faeces is as follows:

1. Inorganic material accounts for 10 to 20 per cent of the total solid and consists mainly of calcium and phosphates.

2. Nitrogenous material containing between 1 and 2 g N per day. On a protein-free diet the faecal N is about 1 g and even in starvation it lies between 0·1 and 0·8 g per day. Normal persons given protein or protein hydrolysate labelled with ^{15}N excrete in their faeces, in the course of the following three days, nitrogenous material with a much lower ^{15}N content than that of the food. These results can only be explained by assuming that non-dietary sources such as gastric juice, pancreatic juice, desquamated cells and bacteria contribute much of the faecal N. In gross disease of the pancreas with defective secretion of trypsin the faeces often contain more than the normal amount of nitrogen.

3. Most of the fatty material extractable by ether arises from sources other than dietary fat. The amount of fat in the faeces can be increased by taking a diet containing large amounts of fat but with an ordinary intake of some 50 to 100 g per day the faecal fat content is less than 5 g and some 10 to 20 per cent of the total solids consists of fatty acids (so-called 'split' fat), neutral fats, phospholipids and sterols. The neutral fat in faeces consists largely of fat derived from cellular debris and from bacteria. The sterols in faeces consist of cholesterol, coprosterol, produced by the bacterial reduction of cholesterol, derivatives of bile acids and of plant sterols (phytosterols) which are not normally absorbed.

4. Undigested material. A variable proportion of the faecal solids consists of cellulose and other undigested food residues such as the seeds and skins of fruit.

The composition of the faeces is not dependent on the constituents of the diet but when the food contains much insoluble material (fibre or roughage) the bulk of the intestinal contents is greater and intestinal peristalsis is stimulated so that transit time is reduced. Volatile fatty acids, products of bacterial metabolism of the fibre, may have a cathartic effect. These factors all result in reduced absorption of water. Tests in which the subjects swallowed radio-opaque pellets (about the size of rice grains) showed that the transit time on a European diet was 40 to 70 hours, whereas on an unrefined diet it was about 35 hours and faecal bulk was increased about four-fold. Dietary fibre has long been recognized as an important part of the diet but interest revived in 1972 when Burkitt claimed on the basis of epidemiological data that populations on a fibre-deficient diet had a higher incidence of colonic cancer, coronary disease and other illnesses than populations eating high-fibre diets. About the same time came the finding that addition of bran to the diet was beneficial in diverticulitis of the colon which had hitherto been treated with fibre-free diets. Bran particles of less than 1 mm have little effect on transit time; coarser particles, probably because of their water holding properties, decrease transit time. The term 'dietary fibre'

comprises a heterogeneous collection of items such as lignin, cellulose, pectins, gums, bran and pentose-containing polysaccharides. The faecal weight is best correlated with the pentose-containing polysaccharides but variation in normal subjects is considerable. The amount of fibre in Western diets has been much reduced during the last 100 years because of reduction in cereal fibre; nowadays the chief sources are fruit and vegetables. The claim that many of the diseases of civilization are caused, directly or indirectly, by low fibre diets has still to be substantiated.

REFERENCES

Asquith P (ed) 1978 Immunology of the gastrointestinal tract. Churchill Livingstone, Edinburgh

Beck I, Sinclair D (eds) 1971 The exocrine pancreas. Churchill, London

Berk J E (ed) 1968 Gastrointestinal gas. Annals of the New York Academy of Sciences 150: 1–190

Bloom S R (ed) 1978 Gut hormones. Churchill Livingstone, Edinburgh

Bonfils S (ed) 1974 Endocrine secreting tumours of the GI tract. Clinics in Gastroenterology 3: no 3

Booth C C 1970 Enterocyte in coeliac disease. British Medical Journal iii: 725–731; and iv: 14–17

Bouchier I A D 1976 Recent advances in gastroenterology 3. Churchill Livingstone, Edinburgh

Burkitt D P, Walker A R P, Painter N S 1972 Effect of dietary fibre on stools and transit-times and its role in the causation of disease. British Medical Journal ii: 1408–1412

Burland W L, Samuel P D (eds) 1971 Transport across the intestine. Churchill Livingstone, Edinburgh

Burnstock G 1975 Purinergic transmission. In: Iversen L, Snyder S (eds) Handbook of psychopharmacology. Plenum Press, New York, vol 5

Case R M, Goebell H (eds) 1976 Stimulus-secretion coupling in the gastrointestinal tract. MTP Press, Lancaster

Crane R K (ed) 1977 Gastrointestinal physiology II. International Review of Physiology, vol 12

Creamer B 1974 The small intestine. Heinemann, London

Csáky T Z (ed) 1975 Intestinal absorption and malabsorption. Raven Press, New York

Dawson A M (ed) 1971 Intestinal absorption and its derangements. Supplement, Journal of Clinical Pathology. British Medical Association, London

Demling L, Ottenjann R 1971 Gastrointestinal motility. Springer Verlag, Stuttgart

Drasar B S, Hill M J 1974 Human intestinal flora. Academic Press, London and New York

Eastwood M A, Fisher N, Greenwood C T, Hutchinson J B 1974 Perspectives on the bran hypothesis. Lancet i: 1029–1033

Friedman M H F (ed) 1975 Functions of the stomach and intestine. University Park Press, Baltimore

Gray G M, Cooper H L 1971 Protein digestion and absorption. Gastroenterology 61: 535–544

Grossman M I and 17 other authors 1974 Candidate hormones of the gut. Gastroenterology 67: 730–755

Harper A A 1968 Hormonal control of pancreatic secretion. In: Handbook of physiology. Section 6, Alimentary canal, vol II, p 969–995

Jacobson E D, Shanbour L L (eds) 1974 Gastrointestinal physiology. Butterworth, London

McColl I, Sladen G E (eds) 1975 Intestinal absorption in man. Academic Press, London

McMinn R M H 1974 The human gut. Oxford University Press

Magee D F (ed) 1974 Gastrointestinal physiology. Medical Clinics of North America 58: 1163–1555

Matthews D M 1975 Intestinal absorption of peptides. Physiological Reviews 55: 537–608

Matthews D M, Payne J W (eds) 1975 Peptide transport in protein nutrition. Frontiers of Biology 37. Elsevier, Holland

Munro H N (ed) 1967 The role of the gastrointestinal tract in protein metabolism. Blackwell, Oxford

Rindi G, Ventura U 1972 Thiamin intestinal transport. Physiological Reviews 52: 821–827

Schuster M M 1975 The riddle of the sphincters. Gastroenterology 69: 249–262

Skinner F A, Carr J G (eds) 1974 The normal microbial flora of man. Academic Press, London and New York

Smyth D H (ed) 1974 Intestinal absorption. Plenum Press, London

Truelove S C, Goodman M S (eds) 1975 Topics in gastroenterology. Blackwell, Oxford

Truelove S C 1966 Movements of the large intestine. Physiological Reviews 46: 457–512

Wormsley K G 1972 Tests of pancreatic function. Clinics in Gastroenterology 1: 27–51

6 Control of Metabolism

For most of the world's population carbohydrate is much the most important source of energy in the diet. This is a consequence of the fact that cereals, which are chiefly starch, yield up to six times more energy per acre than cattle. Consequently in developing countries, carbohydrates provide up to 90 per cent of the energy intake. The principal carbohydrates in the diet are starch, sucrose and, particularly for infants, lactose. A typical western diet yields approximately 100g glucose, 20g galactose and 80g fructose over a 24-hour period. Fructose and galactose can be oxidized or else converted to glucose or glycogen.

The supply of carbohydrate in the diet is intermittent. Mechanisms are therefore needed for the prevention of undue fluctuations in the plasma levels of glucose. In particular, methods for the storage of carbohydrate are needed. This is done in two ways. A limited amount of carbohydrate can be stored in the form of glycogen in the liver and in muscles.

Liver glycogen can be broken down again to free glucose which is available to all the tissues by way of the blood stream. Muscle glycogen does not give rise to glucose directly but may provide substrates for the process of gluconeogenesis (Fig. 6.1). Alternatively, circulating glucose can be taken up by the adipose tissue and converted to triglycerides. The fuel reserves contained in the adipose tissue are very much larger than those stored in the form of glycogen in liver and muscle. An average man might have the equivalent of 800kJ in glycogen in his liver and another 1700kJ in his muscles, whereas the triglycerides of his adipose tissue might well amount to 400000 kJ.

The manner in which glucose and glycogen are metabolized varies from tissue to tissue but the major metabolic patterns are as follows:

1. Complete oxidation to CO_2 and water by way of the glycolytic pathway and the citric acid cycle. This yields approximately 36 molecules of ATP per molecule of glucose or 6 molecules of ATP per molecule of oxygen. This is the main pathway used in nervous tissue.

2. Anaerobic conversion to lactate, for example in tissues which lack either mitochondria or an adequate oxygen supply. This yields only 2 molecules of ATP (3 if the glucose is in the form of glycogen) but the lactate can be oxidized to provide energy in other tissues.

3. Complete oxidation to carbon dioxide and water by the pentose phosphate pathway. This is sufficient to reduce 12 molecules of NADP per molecule of glucose. It is important in adipose tissue, for example, where large quantities of $NADPH_2$ are required for the synthesis of fatty acids.

Energy Sources of Tissues

All cells and tissues require energy and all or almost all use carbohydrate to some degree. Some organs are of particular importance: brain, skeletal muscle, heart muscle, liver, kidney and the red and white blood cells. Each uses carbohydrate in a different and characteristic manner. The simplest pattern is that found in nervous tissue.

The brain. The brain has a constant requirement for energy at the rate of approximately 1700kJ per day, or about 25 per cent of the energy requirement of a normal resting adult. It is met almost entirely by the conversion of approximately 120g glucose per day to carbon dioxide and water. This requirement is remarkably constant. It is unaffected by intellectual exertion or by sleep. It is maintained even when the level of glucose in the blood is moderately depressed. Interruption of the supply of oxygen or of glucose, for even a brief period, results in irreversible brain damage.

Erythrocytes and leucocytes. These provide an interesting contrast. Their energy requirements are constant yet small even though their total mass (2·5 kg) far exceeds that of the brain. They are met by the conversion to lactate of about 36g glucose per day.

Muscle. Skeletal muscle, unlike nervous tissue and erythrocytes, has a variable requirement for energy. At rest its circulation is sluggish and its metabolic rate is low. It is likely but not yet certain that resting muscle depends largely on the oxidation of fat rather than carbohydrate. Though its total mass in a 75 kg man may well amount to about 25 or 30 kg, its glucose requirement in the resting state is probably less than 30g per day. Mild exertion does not greatly change this pattern; the energy output of muscles as a whole increases but it is still supported mainly by the oxidation of fatty acids and their derivatives.

Vigorous exercise brings about a marked change. The mechanical output of the muscles can increase as much as 64-fold. This is accompanied by a great increase in blood supply which provides the muscle mitochondria with an increased supply of oxygen. The enormously increased energy output is met not by accelerating the existing process of fatty acid oxidation but by switching to the oxidation of carbohydrate. Some of this carbohydrate is derived from the blood since exertion increases the passage of glucose from the blood into muscle cells. The major reserve of carbohydrate in the body is, however, the muscles' own store of glycogen. The extent of this store is difficult to measure since different muscles have different concentrations of glycogen but it appears to support 60 to 90 min of very hard physical exertion, for example, long distance running. When this reserve is used up the blood sugar concentration declines steeply. This decline is accompanied by a sense of fatigue, although the muscles continue to maintain a high energy output at the expense once again of fatty acids rather than glucose. Relief of fatigue can be obtained by administration of a quite small amount of glucose which has the effect of raising the blood sugar while the muscles continue to depend on their supply of fatty acids.

Muscle thus possesses the capacity for prolonged exertion whether it is supplied with carbohydrate or with fat. The yield of ATP per molecule of oxygen is slightly higher for carbohydrate than for fat. An important advantage of carbohydrate as a fuel is that anaerobic glycolysis can be an important source of energy especially in brief periods of very vigorous exertion when the supply of oxygen is inadequate. The extent of this extraordinary activity is limited because the production of ATP by glycolysis is accompanied by the liberation of large amounts of lactic acid (Fig. 6.1). The upper limit of sustained exertion is set by the ability of the muscles to maintain the oxidation of fat or carbohydrate and by the ability of the heart and lungs to maintain the supply of oxygen (Chap. 21).

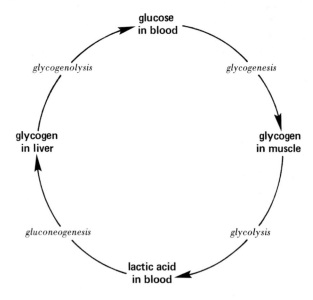

Fig. 6.1 The Cori cycle. In vigorous muscular exercise muscle glycogen is broken down anaerobically to lactic acid which diffuses out into the blood. The liver can convert this back to glycogen by 'reverse glycolysis'. In turn liver glycogen can break down to free glucose which is carried by the blood to the muscles and can be used to replenish muscle glycogen.

The liver. Unlike the tissues considered so far, the liver is important in carbohydrate metabolism chiefly because of functions which it performs for other organs. First among these is the storage in the form of glycogen of cabohydrate absorbed in the intestine after meals. The glycogen reserve in the liver of a well-nourished man amounts to about 90 g. The glycogen can be broken down at need and liberated into the blood as glucose which can be used by all the tissues, particularly the brain. If this store of glycogen were not available the blood glucose level would probably fall in the intervals between meals with serious impairment of brain function.

Another important role of the liver is in gluconeogenesis. We have seen that the cells of the blood convert approximately 36 g glucose a day to lactate and in vigorous exertion the muscles can produce up to 100 g lactate in a few minutes. Some of the lactate is taken up by other tissues such as the heart, and perhaps by resting skeletal muscles, and oxidized to carbon dioxide and water; about half, or perhaps more, is converted to glucose or glycogen in the liver (Fig. 6.2). An athlete exerting himself maximally can in 2½ minutes perform mechanical work equivalent to 300 kJ with the liberation of about 100 g lactate, most of which is removed from the blood in about an hour. The liver is also capable of forming glucose or glycogen

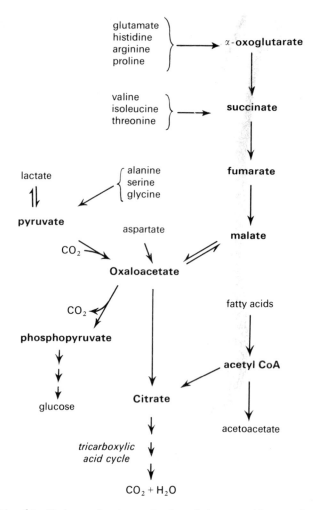

Fig. 6.2 Pathways for the production of glucose and ketones from lactate, glycogen, triglycerides and some amino acids. Oxaloacetate is a key intermediate.

from amino acids (Fig. 6.2) and this source of glucose is important for the brain in brief periods of fasting.

The liver itself does not appear to make extensive use of carbohydrate as an energy source. In a normal well-fed individual the liver seems to subsist mainly by the oxidation of amino acids; in starvation, when the amino acids are required for glucose formation, it can maintain itself by the oxidation of fatty acids.

Kidneys. The kidneys, like the liver, are able to form glucose from amino acids. This capacity is particularly important in prolonged starvation.

Energy Metabolism in the Whole Organism

It is convenient to consider first a fasting subject at rest. The brain and other nervous tissue requires about 144 g glucose per day, virtually all of which is completely oxidized to carbon dioxide and water. A further 36 g glucose is required by the blood cells, which convert it to lactate. The lactate is to a large extent converted back to glucose in the liver. The energy requirements of all other tissues (heart, muscle, kidney and the liver itself) are met almost exclusively by the metabolism of fatty acids liberated from adipose tissue. It is therefore only brain and nervous tissue which deplete the body of glucose. Their requirements are met, when the liver's reserve of glycogen is exhausted, by glucose produced in the liver from fatty acids and amino acids and in the kidney from amino acids. The amino acids are derived almost entirely from muscle.

If starvation is prolonged, and initially obese individuals have been known to fast for several months without ill-effect, the brain and nervous tissue adapt their metabolic pathways to use increasing amounts of fatty acids.

In a fasting subject at rest the muscle protein and adipose tissue are being depleted to maintain his metabolism and these processes may continue at a steady rate for a long time. On the other hand eating a meal produces a transient sequence of biochemical events. If we consider a well nourished 75 kg man in the 6 h period after a substantial dinner made up of, say, 200g carbohydrate, 75 g protein and 75 g fat we could expect to find that the carbohydrate had been disposed of as follows.

1. The fructose and galactose would all have been converted to glucose or glycogen.

2. The nervous system and blood cells would have metabolized a proportion of their daily requirements of carbohydrate (about 40 g).

3. As carbohydrate began to be absorbed from the gut, the liver would stop releasing glucose and would instead start taking up carbohydrate from the portal blood and converting it to glycogen. About 20 g glucose would be added to the liver's reserve of glycogen, though more would be laid down in this form if the liver glycogen reserve had been depleted as a result of either fasting or exertion. The amount of glucose laid down as glycogen in muscle would similarly depend on the pre-existing muscle glycogen reserve.

4. The remaining glucose would largely be taken up by the adipose tissue and converted to triglycerides.

CONTROL MECHANISMS

Several levels of control of carbohydrate metabolism can be distinguished. At the level of the individual cell, metabolic pathways are largely controlled by allosteric mechanisms. Thus the rate of the overall glycolytic process is determined principally by the activity of the enzyme fructokinase (Fig. 6.3). This activity is enhanced by ADP and AMP and inhibited

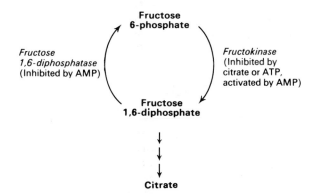

Fig. 6.3 The factors controlling the interconversion of fructose 6-phosphate and fructose 1,6-diphosphate, a key reaction in the breakdown and formation of carbohydrate.

by ATP. Similarly the generation of ATP in mitochondria is largely determined by the availability of ADP. Thus when there is a sudden increase in energy output by muscle, and therefore increased ATP breakdown, the consequent increase in ADP itself stimulates ATP generating reactions. Under resting conditions the ATP content of tissues rises while that of AMP falls to a minimum. In the liver the inhibition of fructose 1,6-diphosphatase by AMP is relieved so that there is an increase in the reconversion of glucose to lactate.

Storage of glucose as glycogen and the subsequent breakdown of glycogen are under more elaborate control.

Glycogen is broken down by *phosphorylase* and other enzymes to glucose 1-phosphate, which is converted by *phosphoglucomutase* to glucose 6-phosphate which can then be metabolized by either the glycolytic or pentose phosphate pathway (Fig. 6.4). In liver, but not in muscle, glucose 6-

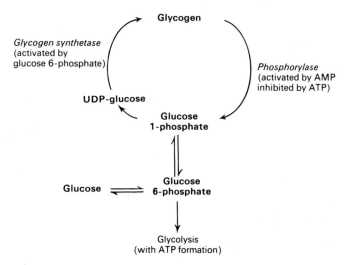

Fig. 6.4 The factors controlling the activity of enzymes involved in the synthesis and breakdown of glycogen.

phosphate can be converted to free glucose by the enzyme glucose 6-phosphatase. Muscle phosphorylase exists in two forms *a* and *b* which appear to be respectively a tetramer and a dimer of the same subunit. The *b* form requires AMP as an activator and is inhibited by ATP and glucose 6-phosphate. Its activity is therefore increased when the demand for ATP or glucose 6-phosphate is increased. Phosphorylase *a*, on the other hand, is *not* dependent on AMP for activity and its function is therefore independent of the demand for either glucose 6-phosphate or energy. It can be formed from phosphorylase *b* by the action of the calcium-requiring enzyme *phosphorylase kinase* which catalyses the transfer of a phosphoryl group from ATP to a serine residue on each of the phosphorylase subunits. This conversion can be reversed by the enzyme phosphorylase phosphatase.

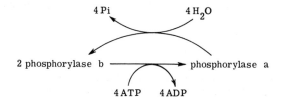

Conversion of *b* to *a* is accelerated, apparently indirectly, by the presence of the cyclic nucleotide, cAMP. The direct effect of cAMP is to activate an enzyme called cyclic AMP dependent protein kinase (Fig. 6.5). A minute quantity of cAMP can by this 'cascade system' rapidly transform a large quantity of muscle phosphorylase from the *b* to the *a* form and therefore quickly free the rate of glycogen breakdown from its normal dependence on AMP. Cyclic AMP is formed from ATP by the enzyme adenyl cyclase which is activated by adrenaline.

The phosphorylase in liver also exists in two forms, *a* and *b*, which have properties analogous to the muscle enzymes and are interconvertible by similar mechanisms. In this case however the *a* form is a dimer not a tetramer as in muscle.

The synthesis of glycogen is active when glycogen breakdown is inhibited and less active when glycogen breakdown is stimulated. Glycogen synthetase exists in a phosphorylated 'D' form which is *dependent* on the presence of glucose 6-phosphate for activation and in a non-phosphorylated 'I' form which is *independent* of glucose 6-phosphate. Conversion of the independent 'I' to the dependent 'D' form is brought about by the same cyclic AMP dependent protein kinase which favours glycogen breakdown.

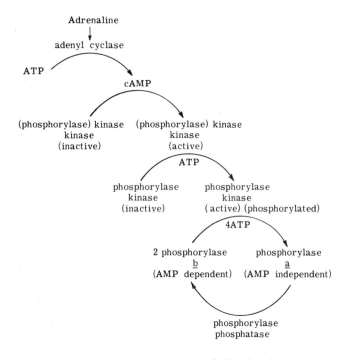

Fig. 6.5 Mechanism of the activation of phosphorylase.

At this level metabolic pathways are largely self-regulating. They are activated by high concentrations of their starting materials or low concentrations of their products and inactivated under the reverse conditions. A second level of control which regulates the activity of whole tissues can be illustrated by the *glucose tolerance test* (p. 93) in which 50 g glucose is given orally to a fasting subject. This amount of glucose is normally absorbed within half an hour. If it were evenly distributed throughout half the body mass, as lactate appears to be, the blood glucose concentration would increase by about 8 mmol/l and return to the fasting level only after 4

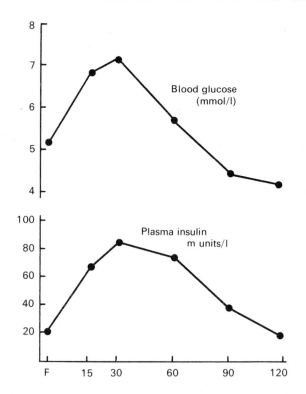

Fig. 6.6 Blood glucose and plasma insulin responses to the administration of 50 g glucose by mouth in 34 normal subjects. F = fasting level. (K. D. Buchanan & M. T. McKiddie (1967) *Diabetologia*, 3, 461.)

hours or so. In fact the increase in blood glucose level is normally much less (about 3 mmol/l over the fasting level of 3 to 5 mmol/l) and the return to the fasting level is normally complete in about 90 minutes (Fig. 6.6). The explanation of these differences is that although glucose is continually taken up by the brain and can readily diffuse into the liver, it cannot by itself enter muscle cells. In a healthy subject, a small increase in blood glucose level causes the β-cells of the islets of Langerhans in the pancreas to liberate the hormone, *insulin*, which facilitates the entry of glucose into muscle cells and adipose tissue. In diabetes mellitus (see below) the deficiency or defective action of insulin means that glucose is only slowly removed from the circulation.

The secretion of insulin by the β-cells is therefore a mechanism by which an influx of carbohydrate activates the mechanisms for its storage as glycogen in liver or muscle, or its conversion to fat in the adipose tissue. Consequently the blood glucose level does not normally rise above, say 9 mmol/l. If the blood glucose level falls below 5 mmol/l a second mechanism comes into play.

Glucagon, formed in the α-cells of the islets of Langerhans in the pancreas, is secreted when the blood glucose falls. Glucagon appears to act on carbohydrate metabolism chiefly by increasing formation of cAMP in the liver. This, as we have seen, increases the breakdown of glycogen to glucose and inhibits the reverse process.

Insulin and glucagon together regulate the storage of incoming glucose and the release of glucose from liver glycogen to meet the demands of brain and other tissues. In an emergency, particularly one requiring violent muscular exertion, some means of overriding this normal homeostatic control is required. This is provided by *adrenaline*, released in such situations from the adrenal medulla.

Insulin

The structure of the pancreas has been described on p. 66. It contains about two million interalveolar cell islets (islets of Langerhans) which together weigh about 1 g. Each of these small vascular bodies contains many β-cells which secrete insulin and a smaller number of α-cells which secrete glucagon.

Source. A normal human pancreas contains about 8 mg insulin and secretes about 2 mg or 50 units per day. Insulin is a small protein (mol. wt. 6000 daltons) containing an *A* chain of 21 amino acid residues, and a *B* chain of 30 residues. The chains are linked by disulphide bonds. Insulin is a derivative of a much larger single polypeptide chain of 84 amino acids known as pro-insulin first found in the study of islet cell tumour tissue. The connecting chain (*C-peptide*) of 33 amino acids is split off by the action of two enzymes (Fig. 6.7). Pro-insulin has a low biological activity but it reacts like insulin in many radioimmunoassays. The amino acid sequences in the insulins of different species differ but pig and ox insulins are very similar to the human hormone and patients can be treated with these insulins. Although they develop measurable amounts of antibodies, adverse antigenic reactions are rare.

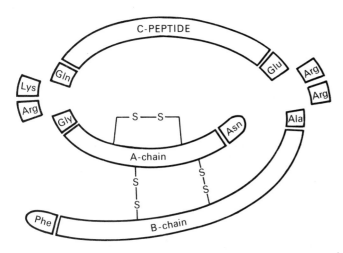

Fig. 6.7 Conversion of pro-insulin to insulin by the action of protease enzymes.

Metabolism. Insulin is stored in a relatively insoluble granular form, possibly as a complex with zinc and proteins, in the islet cells. The granules are thought to migrate to the cell surface and fuse with the plasma membrane at the time of insulin release. Insulin is rapidly metabolized in the liver and has a half-life of about 5 minutes.

Plasma levels. Plasma insulin concentrations have been measured by bio-assays based on the fact that insulin increases the uptake of glucose by isolated rat tissues, for example diaphragm or epididymal fat pad. Values of 30 to 100 micro-units per ml (25 units = 1 mg) have been reported for normal fasting individuals. Shortly after a carbohydrate meal these values may be increased tenfold. Bio-assays measure the total 'insulin-like activity' rather than insulin alone and thus give falsely high values.

Radioimmunoassay provides greater specificity and is readily adapted to the analysis of large numbers of samples. The technique is based upon the competition between radioactive (^{125}I)-insulin and non-radioactive insulin for binding sites on a specific antibody. The non-radioactive insulin may be in a standard solution or that present in a plasma sample. The insulin levels in the samples are determined by comparing the radioactivity in the insulin-antibody complex from the test samples with that in the complex from standard solutions. Under the best conditions, less than 0·1 micro-units of insulin may be measured by radioimmunoassay. This method, however, measures immunological activity and consequently immunologically active pro-insulin and insulin fragments with little or no biological activity may be measured as insulin.

The radioimmunoassay method shows that normal fasting subjects have a fasting plasma insulin level of about 10 micro-units per ml. After oral administration of glucose, insulin levels increase sharply (Fig. 6.6), the shape of the plasma insulin response resembling the blood glucose curve. The intravenous administration of glucose, though producing higher circulating blood glucose levels, has a smaller effect on insulin secretion. The greater effect of oral glucose is thought to be due to gastrointestinal hormones which are released when glucose enters the gut and stimulate insulin secretion.

Secretion. The secretion of insulin in response to a rising blood glucose concentration takes place in two phases: an initial rapid phase as some stored insulin is released, followed by a slower phase as newly synthesized insulin is secreted. Glucose is not the only substrate that can stimulate insulin release. Insulin secretion can be provoked by amino acids, notably arginine,

Insulin secretion is stimulated by a number of hormones including the gastrointestinal hormones gastrin, secretin, pancreozymin and enteroglucagon, and pancreatic glucagon.

Adrenaline inhibits the first stage of the secretion of insulin stimulated by rising blood glucose levels. Since the effect of orally administered glucose is unaffected, it appears that the action of gastrointestinal hormones overrides the inhibitory effect of adrenaline. Another hormone which inhibits insulin release is *somatostatin* (growth-hormone release inhibiting factor, Chap. 28) which is produced not only in the hypothalamus but also by the δ-cells of the pancreatic islets.

The pancreatic islets are supplied with both sympathetic and parasympathetic nerves. It is possible that the impairment of glucose tolerance seen in stress results from inhibition of insulin release mediated by the sympathetic nervous system. Parasympathetic activity (or the administration of acetyl choline) stimulates insulin release but the physiological importance of this is still unknown.

Effects of insulin administration. When insulin is given by injection to a healthy man the blood glucose falls rapidly (Fig. 6.8). If it should fall below about 2·2 mmol/l symptoms and signs of *hypoglycaemia* (low blood glucose) develop. The subject becomes apprehensive and irritable; he finds it difficult to concentrate and often has a headache; he feels hungry and sweats. Since the metabolism of the brain is ordinarily dependent on a supply of glucose, hypoglycaemia may produce confusion, convulsions, loss of consciousness and death. Many

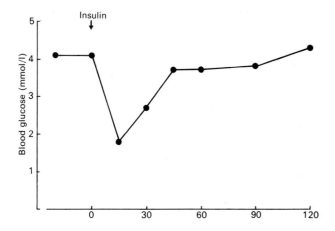

Fig. 6.8 Changes in blood glucose concentration after the intravenous injection of insulin in a dose of 0:15 units/kg. (*Courtesy of T. E. Isles and Hazel Barker.*)

of the symptoms of hypoglycaemia are due to adrenaline liberated from the adrenal medulla in response to the low blood glucose level. Hypoglycaemia can be quickly remedied by giving glucose or sucrose by mouth or by injecting glucose intravenously.

Actions. The lowering of blood glucose by insulin was for long regarded as its fundamental action. Insulin facilitates the passage of glucose through cell membranes but this is by no means the only action of insulin. Insulin has widespread effects on many metabolic processes (Table 6.9). Some of these are immediate but others take several hours or days to achieve. In all of these roles insulin acts with a complicated system of hormonal checks and balances which modify both the release and the peripheral effects of insulin.

Insulin is the principal anabolic and anticatabolic hormone controlling carbohydrate, lipid and protein metabolism with the overall effect of promoting synthetic pathways and putting energy into store. On a maintenance diet insulin has simply a homeostatic role; when food is in excess it also has an anabolic role.

Insulin acts by binding to receptors on the cell surface. There is evidence of two distinct types of receptors with different

Table 6.9 Principal actions of insulin on cells

Membrane effects
    Uptake of glucose increased
    Uptake of amino acids increased
    Uptake of fatty acids increased
    Uptake of Mg^{2+} and K^+ increased

Metabolic effects
    Increased synthesis of DNA and RNA
    Increased protein synthesis
    Increased synthesis of glycogen (in liver and muscle)
    Increased synthesis of triglycerides (in adipose tissue)
    Increased fatty acid synthesis (in liver)
    Decreased protein breakdown (in muscle)
    Decreased glycogenolysis (in liver)
    Decreased gluconeogenesis (in liver and kidney)
    Decreased ketone production (in liver)
    Decreased triglyceride breakdown (in adipose tissue)

affinities for insulin. It is likely that in adipose tissue the low affinity receptor is involved in the promotion of triglyceride formation while binding of insulin to the high affinity receptor inhibits triglyceride breakdown. Thus the inhibition of lipolysis is an action that is seen at low plasma insulin levels while higher insulin levels are needed to stimulate glucose uptake and triglyceride synthesis.

Insulin operates by controlling the functions of key enzymes, possibly by altering the intracellular content of cAMP. For example in carbohydrate metabolism glucose utilization is stimulated by the activation of glucokinase, phosphofructokinase and pyruvate kinase while glycogen synthesis is promoted by an action on glycogen synthetase (p. 87). Gluconeogenesis is inhibited by actions on the enzymes responsible for reverse glycolysis.

The action of glucagon in stimulating insulin release has already been mentioned. This stimulatory effect is limited by an inhibitory effect of insulin on the production of glucagon by the pancreatic α-cells.

Insulin antagonists. Changes in the concentration of plasma insulin are closely related to changes in concentrations of certain other hormones (Fig. 6.10), and the action of insulin is opposed by several hormones including cortisol, adrenaline

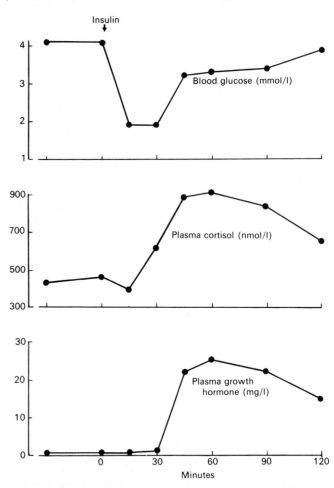

Fig. 6.10 Responses in blood glucose, plasma cortisol and plasma growth hormone levels to the intravenous injection of insulin in a dose of 0·15 units/kg in a normal subject (*Courtesy of Hazel Barker, Margaret Browning and T. E. Isles.*)

and, when present in excess, thyroxine. In general these insulin antagonists favour catabolic processes while insulin increases anabolism.

Growth hormone, the most important hormonal antagonist of insulin, is diabetogenic in adults, causing impaired glucose tolerance (p. 92) and lack of response to insulin. Placental lactogen, a placental hormone (Chap. 29) found in plasma during pregnancy, is also an insulin antagonist. A decreased response to insulin is a feature of pregnancy.

Administration of cortisol to human subjects decreases glucose tolerance. Cortisol influences carbohydrate metabolism in many ways not directly related to insulin principally by stimulating gluconeogenesis (Chap. 28). In this way cortisol appears to oppose the action of insulin.

Adrenaline blocks insulin release and at the same time promotes the breakdown of glycogen in the liver.

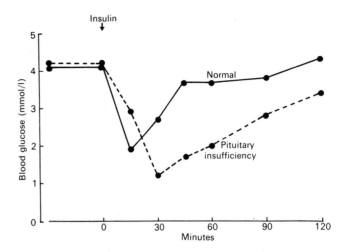

Fig. 6.11 Changes in blood glucose in a patient with pituitary insufficiency, compared with those in a normal subject, after the intravenous injection of insulin in a dose of 0·15 units/kg. (*Courtesy of Hazel Barker and T. E. Isles.*)

Glucagon

Glucagon is a polypeptide of 29 amino acid residues and like insulin has a precursor, *proglucagon*. In response to hypoglycaemia, the α-cells of the pancreatic islets secrete glucagon which stimulates glycogen breakdown by the liver and so raises the blood glucose level. An intravenous injection of glucagon causes the blood glucose concentration to double in a few minutes. It returns to normal values in about 90 minutes. As might be expected, both the rise and duration of effect are less pronounced in circumstances such as starvation in which liver glycogen stores are low.

The main physiological role of glucagon is the prevention of hypoglycaemia during fasting or when insulin release is provoked by factors other than hyperglycaemia. For example a rise in the plasma levels of amino acids after a protein meal leads to rises in the production of both insulin and glucagon and hypoglycaemia does not occur. Glucagon acts by enhancing the production of cAMP. This in turn stimulates liver phosphorylase which catalyses the first step in glycogenolysis. Another effect of glucagon is its stimulation of insulin production.

Adrenaline

Adrenaline, like glucagon, operates by stimulating the formation of cAMP and so the release of glucose from stored glycogen. Adrenaline also stimulates gluconeogenesis and inhibits insulin secretion. Hypoglycaemia is a powerful stimulus to adrenaline secretion.

Growth Hormone (Somatotrophin)

Patients with excessive production of growth hormone (Chap. 28) frequently have high plasma glucose levels with high plasma insulin levels. Conversely extreme insulin sensitivity occurs after removal of the pituitary gland in animals and a similar sensitivity to insulin is also found in patients with pituitary insufficiency (Fig. 6.11).

Hypoglycaemia promotes growth hormone secretion (Fig. 6.10). At least one role of growth hormone seems to be to spare glucose when it is in short supply. During exercise muscles readily use glucose, even when there is a lack of insulin. Growth hormone tends to prevent this by increasing fatty acid uptake by muscle and promoting triglyceride breakdown in adipose tissue. Ultimately, this action spares amino acids which would otherwise become precursors of glucose in glucoeogenesis. Such amino acids are essential for processes of growth and repair. Thus, growth hormone favours protein anabolism.

Cortisol

Cortisol, secreted by the adrenal cortex (Chap. 28) has a potent effect on carbohydrate metabolism, as do its various synthetic analogues such as prednisolone and dexamethasone. When cortisol concentrations rise protein synthesis is reduced and an increased amount of amino acids becomes available to the liver for gluconeogenesis. In addition glycogen synthetase seems to be activated, probably because of the increasing amounts of insulin secreted in response to the rising blood glucose level.

In general the effect of cortisol on carbohydrate metabolism is to maintain gluconeogenesis by provision of amino acids and by induction of enzymes as required. It may thus be regarded as a slow, or second line, defence against hypoglycaemia. Cortisol also facilitates the actions of glucagon, adrenaline and growth hormone by inhibiting peripheral glucose utilization, and by its synergistic effect on lipolysis in adipose tissue.

The Thyroid Hormones

The thyroid hormones (Chap. 28) increase gluconeogenesis, glycogenolysis and amino acid production from protein and so tend to raise the blood glucose level. However, they also stimulate insulin secretion so that, overall, they have little effect on blood glucose concentration. Disturbances of carbohydrate metabolism are, however, observed in thyroidectomized animals and in patients with excess thyroid hormone. Hyperthyroidism exacerbates diabetes mellitus.

DISORDERS OF CARBOHYDRATE METABOLISM

Glycosuria. When urine gives positive tests for reducing substances the cause is likely to be glucose and the condition *glycosuria*; if a method involving glucose oxidase, such as 'Clinistix' or the appropriate square of 'Labstix', gives a positive result, the sugar is certainly glucose. However, in certain circumstances reducing sugars other than glucose may be present. Lactose, for example, is frequently found in the urine of pregnant or lactating women and galactosuria has been reported in breast-fed infants. Galactose and fructose may be found in the urine of persons with rare inborn errors of carbohydrate metabolism. Pentoses may appear in the urine after ingestion of large amounts of certain fruits.

Although the concentration of glucose in the blood of healthy people varies in the course of the day between 3 and 9 mmol/l only small amounts are found in the urine and the usual tests for glycosuria are negative. Although glucose is filtered in the glomeruli (Chap. 15) it is subsequently almost completely reabsorbed by the proximal tubules. The capacity of the tubules to reabsorb glucose is limited and, when the concentration of glucose in the blood rises above about 9 mmol/l, the maximum reabsorptive capacity is exceeded and glycosuria occurs.

The reabsorptive capacity of the renal tubules for glucose varies from one person to another. In some otherwise healthy individuals the reabsorptive capacity is less than normal so that glycosuria is present even when the blood glucose level is within normal limits (renal glycosuria). Glycosuria may occur in pregnancy because the glomerular filtration rate is increased. In the presence of a constant maximum tubular reabsorptive capacity a rise in the glomerular filtration rate means that the 'renal threshold' is readily exceeded.

We have already seen that the concentration of glucose in the blood is greatly influenced by the rate at which it enters the blood from the alimentary tract and the rate at which it is removed from the blood by the liver. Sometimes, after surgical removal of a large part of the stomach, glucose may be absorbed from the small intestine into the blood at a rate greater than that at which, initially, the liver and muscles can convert it into glycogen; a transient hyperglycaemia with glycosuria ('alimentary glycosuria') therefore occurs.

Glycosuria can be produced in animals by the administration of alloxan or phlorizin and the investigation of their actions has thrown much light on carbohydrate metabolism. *Alloxan* given by injection to animals damages the pancreatic islets so that a condition resembling diabetes mellitus ensues. *Phlorizin* causes glycosuria when taken by mouth or injected into animals or man. It inhibits phosphorylase and reduces the ability of the renal tubule cells to reabsorb glucose from the glomerular filtrate. After the administration of phlorizin the blood glucose level falls as the result of the continuous excretion of glucose and the carbohydrate stores eventually become exhausted. A fasting phlorizinised animal maintains its blood glucose level by converting the amino acids of its own tissue proteins into glucose with consequent loss of tissue.

Diabetes Mellitus

This disorder is characterized by hyperglycaemia and glycosuria, accompanied by alterations in fat and protein metabolism. It is the result of lack of effective insulin action. In most patients the disease develops spontaneously, probably as a result of a hereditary predisposition. However insulin deficiency can also occur if the pancreas is destroyed by disease or removed surgically.

There are two main clinical groups though the distinction between them is not absolute.

Type 1 (juvenile-onset type) occurs characteristically with an abrupt onset in patients under 25 years of age. These patients are deficient in insulin; there is little or no insulin in their plasma and no insulin response to a glucose load. They are liable to ketosis (see below) and require insulin for the control of their diabetes.

Type 2 (maturity-onset type) develops insidiously in middle-aged, usually obese, patients; symptoms, if present, have often lasted several months before medical advice is sought. Population surveys have shown that many apparently healthy people have mild diabetes of this type. The total amount of islet tissue in the pancreas may be greater than normal and the plasma insulin levels may be normal or raised. In these patients the fasting blood glucose level may be normal but after a glucose load the blood glucose level rises higher than in normal people and remains high longer (Fig. 6.12). Plasma insulin levels may also start within the normal range but the maximum insulin response may not be seen until 90 or 120 minutes after the administration of glucose. This slow response is quite unlike the brisk response seen in normal subjects (Fig. 6.6). The cause of these abnormalities is still unknown.

Clinical features. The initial symptoms of diabetes develop because large amounts of glucose are excreted in the urine. The loss of so much solute causes an osmotic diuresis (Chap. 15) and a large volume of urine (*polyuria*). In spite of drinking

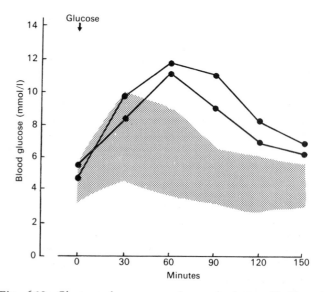

Fig. 6.12 Glucose tolerance tests in two patients with Type 2 diabetes. Although the fasting blood glucose is normal the response to 50 g glucose is abnormal. The normal range is indicated by the dotted area.

large amounts of fluid (*polydipsia*) the patient is thirsty. These two symptoms alone may persist for many months in maturity-onset diabetes.

In type 1, further features develop if treatment is not begun quickly. Although the tissues, in particular the muscles, receive glucose from the blood, they are unable to utilize it efficiently in the absence of insulin so that the diabetic patient feels weak and tired. In adipose tissue triglycerides are broken down and the level of free fatty acids in the blood rises. The disproportionate metabolism of fat in diabetes results in the overproduction of ketone bodies (acetone, acetoacetic acid and β-hydroxybutyric acid) which can be detected in the blood and urine. When this *ketosis* is severe the patient's breath has a characteristic smell. As acetoacetic and β-hydroxybutyric acids are produced faster than they can be metabolized, the patient develops *acidaemia* which causes hyperventilation (*air hunger*) (Chap. 16). Along with the abnormal metabolism of carbohydrate and fat there is an excessive breakdown of protein, the amino acids being converted to glucose in the liver.

At this stage, as a result of the ketosis, the patient develops *anorexia* (lack of appetite), nausea and vomiting; the continued loss of water and electrolytes in the urine leads to increasing saline depletion. The 'keto-acidosis' is associated with increasing drowsiness and, if untreated, the patient may become unconscious (diabetic coma) and die from a combination of hyperglycaemia, ketosis and acidaemia. This outcome can be prevented by treatment with insulin and intravenous fluids.

Treatment. While type 1 diabetics generally require insulin, which must be given by injection, type 2 diabetics do not usually need insulin. Those who are overweight generally respond to dietary restriction and weight reduction. Most of the remainder can be controlled by oral hypoglycaemic drugs, either *sulphonylureas* such as tolbutamide and chlorpropamide, which act partly by increasing the release of insulin from the pancreas, or *diguanides*, such as phenformin or metformin, which are thought to act mainly by increasing the peripheral utilization of glucose.

Diagnosis: the glucose tolerance test. The diagnosis of juvenile-onset diabetes is based on finding some of the clinical features described above and confirmed by finding a very high blood glucose level. In the milder case of maturity onset diabetes, fasting or random blood glucose levels may be normal and a glucose tolerance test may be needed to establish the diagnosis (Fig. 6.12). The procedure is as follows.

After a fast of at least 8 hours, a blood sample is taken for determination of the fasting blood or plasma glucose concentration. A sample of urine is obtained and a solution of 50 g glucose in 200 ml water is drunk. Samples of blood and urine are collected at 30-minute intervals over a period of 2½ hours and their glucose concentration determined. The results obtained in normal subjects are shown by the dotted area in Figure 6.12. In normal subjects the fasting blood glucose is about 4 to 5 mmol/l; the maximum values are reached in about 30 minutes and fasting values are regained within two hours. In the later part of the test, the blood glucose frequently falls below the initial level.

In fasting subjects the concentration of glucose is only 0·1 mmol/l higher in the arterial than in the venous blood, because during fasting the tissues take very little from the blood. The concentration of glucose in free-flowing capillary blood, obtained by stabbing a warmed finger-tip, is virtually the same as found in arterial blood. The arteriovenous difference is increased to 1·5 mmol/l or more after a carbohydrate meal, on account of the rapid uptake of glucose by the tissues from the blood (Fig. 6.13). Plasma glucose is now often measured instead of blood glucose; the results obtained are about 20 per cent higher than those obtained with whole blood.

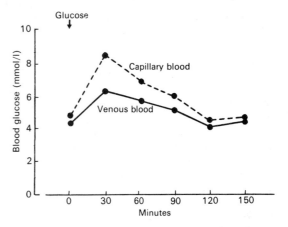

Fig. 6.13 Changes in blood glucose after the ingestion of 50 g glucose in a healthy man (A) on a high fat low carbohydrate diet and (B) on a high carbohydrate low fat diet.

The shape of the glucose tolerance test curve is influenced by the type of food taken in the days before the test. If it contained little carbohydrate the curve rises more sharply and to a higher level, indicating a relatively poor glucose tolerance. On the other hand, if the meals taken before the test have been largely carbohydrate, the rise in blood glucose is smaller indicating a better glucose tolerance (Fig. 6.14). Standardization of the diet before the test is therefore important: not less than 150 g carbohydrate should be taken in each of the three days before the test.

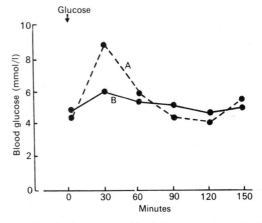

Fig. 6.14 Capillary and venous blood glucose levels in a healthy man after the ingestion of 0·75 g glucose per kg body weight.

Insulin Excess

An insulin-producing tumour is one cause of spontaneous hypoglycaemia. Patients may first be noted to be behaving oddly particularly when some time has elapsed after a meal or after a missed meal. The patient may be confused and be thought to be drunk. In severe cases the hypoglycaemia may cause convulsions and coma. Some patients learn that they can avoid symptoms by taking carbohydrate-rich snacks; they tend to gain weight.

Among the investigations that are helpful in the diagnosis of this disorder are the extended glucose tolerance test, the prolonged fast and insulin assay. In the extended glucose tolerance test the procedure is continued for four hours since hypoglycaemia may not be seen sooner. In a prolonged fast, say 48 hours, symptoms of hypoglycaemia usually develop and can be relieved by glucose administration. Both tests must be carried out under supervision since dangerous hypoglycaemia can occur. In both tests regular measurements of blood glucose and plasma insulin are made; in patients with insulinomas the plasma insulin may be inappropriately high for the blood glucose value.

The disorder is treated surgically but it is often very difficult because tumours may be small or multiple. Where surgery has been unsuccessful the drug diazoxide may be given; this inhibits insulin secretion from the β-cells.

Obesity

The physiology of obesity was outlined on page 18. The excessive deposition of energy in the form of triglyceride in adipose tissue is the result of an excess of energy intake over energy expenditure; in many cases a low energy expenditure is as important as a high food intake.

Many metabolic abnormalities have been found in obese patients. These include a high production of cortisol from the adrenal cortex and high plasma levels of insulin which rise still further after a glucose load (Fig. 6.15). Many of these patients also have impaired glucose tolerance. While the cause of these abnormalities is not known it is clear that they are the result rather than the cause of the obesity; the abnormalities disappear as weight is lost.

Very occasionally obesity may be the result of endocrine disorders such as glucocorticoid excess or thyroid insufficiency (Chap. 28).

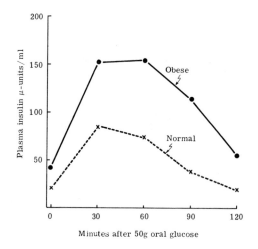

Minutes after 50g oral glucose

Fig. 6.15   Plasma insulin response to glucose ingestion in obese subjects compared with the response in normal subjects. The fasting level is raised and the response to glucose excessive. (*By courtesy of Margaret McKiddie.*)

REFERENCES

Bajaj J S (ed) 1977 Insulin and metabolism. Elsevier, Amsterdam
Gerisch J E, Charles M A, Grodsky G M 1976 Regulation of pancreatic insulin and glucagon secretion. Annual Review of Physiology 38: 353–388
Goldsmith S J 1975 Radioimmunoassay: review of basic principles. Seminars in Nuclear Medicine 5: 125–152
Hers H G 1976 Control of glycogen metabolism in the liver. Annual Review of Biochemistry 45: 167–189
Marks V, Turner D S 1978 The gastrointestinal hormones with particular reference to their role in the regulation of insulin secretion. In: Marks V, Hales C N (eds) Essays in medical biochemistry 3. Biochemical Society, Colchester
Newsholme E A 1976 Carbohydrate metabolism in vivo. Clinics in Endocrinology and Metabolism 5: 568–578
Newsholme E A, Start C 1973 Regulation in metabolism. Wiley, London
Oakley W G, Pyke D A, Taylor K W 1978 Diabetes and its management, 3rd edn. Blackwell, Oxford
Sherwin R, Felig P 1978 Pathophysiology of diabetes mellitus. Medical Clinics of North America 62: 695–711
Siperstein M D 1975 The glucose tolerance test: a pitfall in the diagnosis of diabetes mellitus. Advances in Internal Medicine 20: 297–324
Unger R H, Orci L 1976 Physiology and pathophysiology of glucagon. Physiological Reviews 56: 778–825

7 Hepatic and Biliary Function

The liver is the largest internal organ, weighing 1500 g in the adult, or approximately 2 per cent of the total body weight. Its many functions include the synthesis of plasma proteins, the metabolism of amino acids, carbohydrates, lipids, ethanol, hormones and drugs, the formation and excretion of bile, the storage of glycogen, vitamins and iron, and the removal of antigens absorbed from the gastrointestinal tract.

Structure

The liver cells are arranged in units or lobules. Each lobule has a central vein which drains into sub-lobular veins which join the hepatic venous system, and peripheral portal tracts, each containing a branch of the hepatic artery, a branch of a portal vein, bile ducts and lymphatics (Fig. 7.1). Alternatively the liver may be thought of as consisting of acini, each of which has a portal tract at the centre and hepatic venules at the periphery. The liver parenchymal cells or hepatocytes are arranged in plates one or two cells thick extending between the portal tracts and the central vein. These plates are separated by spaces, the sinusoids, which convey mixed hepatic arterial and portal venous blood from the portal tracts to the central vein. The sinusoids are lined by endothelial cells, some of which, the Kupffer cells, are capable of phagocytosis. Between the liver cells is a network of bile canaliculi which convey bile to the bile ducts of the portal tract.

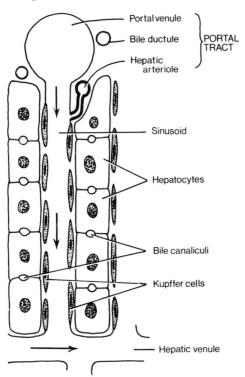

Fig. 7.1 A hepatic sinusoid. The blood it contains is derived both from the portal vein and the hepatic artery.

The hepatocytes nearest the portal tract, the periportal hepatocytes, are supplied with more highly oxygenated blood than that reaching the centrilobular hepatocytes adjoining the central vein. The centrilobular hepatocytes are more vulnerable than the periportal hepatocytes to damage by anoxia or by liver toxins such as carbon tetrachloride. There are other functional differences between periportal and centrilobular hepatocytes; for example, the periportal hepatocytes contain higher concentrations of enzymes such as glucose-6-phosphatase and succinate dehydrogenase.

Electron microscopy shows that the hepatocytes contain all the organelles such as mitochondria, endoplasmic reticulum and Golgi apparatus found in other metabolically active cells.

Circulation Through the Liver

The liver has a dual blood supply from the hepatic artery and the hepatic portal vein. The hepatic artery, a branch of the coeliac axis, delivers fully oxygenated blood with a Po_2 of 95 mm Hg (13 kPa) at a mean pressure of approximately 100 mm Hg (13 kPa). The hepatic portal vein, formed by the junction of the splenic and superior mesenteric veins, receives blood from the stomach, small intestine, part of the large intestine, spleen and pancreas, and delivers this partially deoxygenated blood with a Po_2 of 60 to 75 mm Hg (8 to 10 kPa) at a pressure of approximately 8 mm Hg (1 kPa). Absorbed foodstuffs and drugs, pancreatic hormones such as insulin and glucagon, and other gastrointestinal hormones such as secretin are thus carried to the liver in the portal venous sytem before reaching the systemic circulation.

Hepatic blood flow has been estimated by the Fick principle and by the use of flow meters attached directly to the major abdominal blood vessels during abdominal surgery. Under basal conditions, the blood flow in the hepatic artery is 500 ml/min and in the portal vein, 1 l/min. This total blood flow of 1·5 l/min is 30 per cent of the cardiac output at rest. The hepatic artery provides 40 per cent of the oxygen delivered to the liver. After a meal, the intestinal, and therefore portal, blood flow increases, oxygen saturation in the portal vein falls, and the blood flow through the hepatic artery increases. Exercise reduces hepatic blood flow.

In some animals, blood from the superior mesenteric vein perfuses mainly the right lobe of the liver, whilst blood from the splenic vein is preferentially distributed to the left lobe. In man, mixing of the blood stream in the portal vein seems to be more complete and this differential perfusion does not occur.

Within the liver, branches of the hepatic artery supply the bile ducts before being distributed to the sinusoids. Blood flow in the sinusoids is controlled by sphincter mechanisms at the points of entry of the hepatic artery and portal vein radicles. The sinusoids form an anastomotic vascular channel so that a reduction in inflow may temporarily reverse the direction of sinusoidal blood flow. As there are anastomotic channels between the hepatic artery and portal vein and between the portal vein and hepatic veins, some of the blood entering the liver does not pass through the sinusoids. The central lobular veins empty via the hepatic veins into the inferior vena cava. Hepatic venous blood has a Po_2 of 40 mm Hg (5 kPa).

The liver produces 1 ml of lymph per minute, ten times that produced by an equivalent mass of skeletal muscle.

FUNCTIONS OF THE LIVER

The liver has an essential role in the metabolism of carbohydrates, lipids and proteins, and in the secretion of bile.

Synthetic functions. All the plasma proteins except the immunoglobulins are synthesized in the liver. These plasma proteins include albumin, the clotting factors, transport proteins and enzymes. Approximately 150 to 200 mg of albumin are synthesized per kg body weight per day (10 to 14 g/day for a 70 kg man); 6 to 10 per cent of the plasma albumin pool is degraded daily. The synthesis of albumin may be impaired in liver disease.

The liver is responsible for the synthesis of the majority of blood *clotting factors* (p. 116), including factors I, II, V, VII, IX and X. Synthesis of factors II, VII, IX and X requires vitamin K. Fibrinolytic factors (p. 118) are also produced by the liver. Abnormalities of blood coagulation are common in acute and chronic liver disease.

Proteins responsible for the transport of lipids, hormones, and some minerals are synthesized in the liver. These include the protein moiety of plasma lipoproteins, thyroid-binding globulin, sex-hormone binding globulin, and transcortin (Chap. 28), transferrin (p. 110) and caeruloplasmin responsible for the carriage of copper.

Plasma enzymes, such as lecithin-cholesterol acyl transferase, and enzyme inhibitors, such as α_1-antitrypsin, are produced in the liver.

Detoxication. Many drugs are metabolized by the liver, and the stages in drug metabolism have been classified as phase I and phase II reactions (Fig. 7.2). In a phase I reaction the drug undergoes oxidation, reduction, or hydrolysis, and in a phase II reaction either the drug or the product of a phase I reaction is conjugated with glucuronic acid, glycine, or sulphate. Such transformations produce metabolites which are more polar (and therefore more water-soluble) than the parent drug. Most of the conjugates are excreted into bile; some re-enter the circulation to be excreted by the kidney.

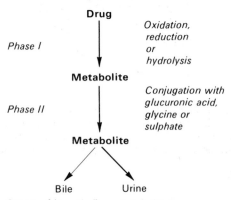

Fig. 7.2 Stages of hepatic drug metabolism.

The hepatic oxidative drug-metabolizing enzymes are associated with the smooth endoplasmic reticulum, forming the non-specific 'mixed function oxidase system'. One feature of this system is the increase in enzyme activity which follows the long-term administration of a substrate drug, a process known as *enzyme induction*. Drugs which act as enzyme inducers include barbiturates and ethanol. Enzyme induction is non-specific, so that the metabolism of drugs other than that of the inducing drug is increased. For example, long-term administration of a barbiturate enhances the rate of metabolism of the anticoagulant drug warfarin (Fig. 7.3).

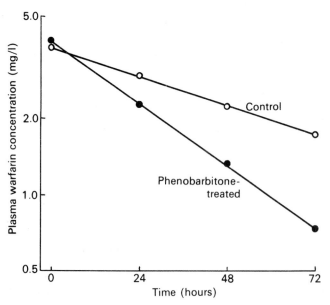

Fig. 7.3 Mean plasma warfarin levels in 10 subjects who were given a single dose of warfarin on two occasions. On one (−○−○−) no active drug was given at the same time. On the other occasion (−●−●−) the subjects had been pretreated with phenobarbitone. It is seen that after phenobarbitone treatment warfarin levels fall much more rapidly because of the induction of the enzymes of warfarin metabolism. The zero time values represent an extrapolation from the values obtained at 24, 48 and 72 hours. (Data of M. G. McDonald, D. S. Robinson, D. Sylvester & J. J. Jaffe (1969) *Clinical Pharmacology and Therapeutics*, 10, 80–84.)

A drug taken by mouth and absorbed from the gastro-intestinal tract must pass through the liver before entering the systemic circulation. Metabolism of the drug in the intestinal mucosa or liver during this initial transit is referred to as 'first pass metabolism' and may lead to lower peripheral blood levels of the drug than those obtained from the same dose given parenterally.

Not all hepatic drug transformations produce metabolites with reduced pharmacological activity; in some cases the result is activation of the drug. For example, the corticosteroid drug prednisone is reduced to the active metabolite prednisolone, and metabolism of the immunosuppressive agent azathioprine produces the pharmacologically active product 6-mercapto-purine. Some vitamins undergo conversion in the liver to metabolically active forms, for example pyridoxine is converted to the active coenzyme, pyridoxal-5′-phosphate.

Metabolism of ethanol. Only 2 to 10 per cent of ingested ethanol is excreted unchanged in urine and breath, the remainder being metabolized to acetaldehyde in the liver. Three pathways of ethanol oxidation have been identified (Fig. 7.3).

(i) involving alcohol dehydrogenase, a cell sap (cytosol) enzyme which utilizes NAD. This is the principal mechanism of ethanol oxidation.

$$CH_3CH_2OH + NAD^+ \xrightarrow[\text{dehydrogenase}]{\text{Alcohol}} CH_3CHO + NADH + H^+$$

(ii) acting via the mixed function oxidase system localized on the microsomes of the smooth endoplasmic reticulum.

$$CH_3CH_2OH + NADPH \atop +H^+ + O_2 \xrightarrow[\text{oxidase system}]{\text{Mixed function}} CH_3CHO + NADP \atop + 2H_2O$$

(iii) using hydrogen peroxide (generated from NADPH, H^+ and O_2) and the enzyme catalase. This pathway accounts for only about one per cent of the ethanol oxidizing capacity of the liver.

$$NADPH + H^+ + O_2 \longrightarrow NADP + H_2O_2$$

$$H_2O_2 + CH_3CH_2OH \longrightarrow CH_3CHO + 2H_2O$$

The acetaldehyde formed from these reactions is itself oxidized further in the mitochondria of the liver cell.

Storage. The liver stores energy, chiefly in the form of glycogen but also as triglyceride. Hepatic stores of vitamin B_{12} are sufficient to last up to four years. Copper and iron (as ferritin in the Kupffer cells), the fat-soluble vitamins A, D, and K, and the water-soluble vitamins riboflavin, nicotinamide, pyridoxine and folic acid are stored in the liver.

Inactivation of hormones. The liver is a principal site of inactivation of many hormones including insulin, glucagon, cortisol, aldosterone, testosterone, and thyroid hormones. It is the site of de-iodination of thyroxine (T_4) to tri-iodothyronine (T_3) (Chap. 28).

Antigen clearance. The Kupffer cells are macrophages and are responsible for the removal of antigens (including bacteria) entering the portal vein from the gastrointestinal tract.

BILIARY SYSTEM

Bile is secreted by the hepatocytes into the *bile canaliculi*, a series of narrow spaces between adjacent liver cells. The surface area of the canaliculi is increased by microvilli which protrude into the canalicular lumen (Fig. 7.4). The canaliculi drain via bile ductules into the bile ducts which run in the portal tracts; the bile ducts themselves discharge into the right and left hepatic ducts which unite to form the common hepatic duct at the hilum of the liver.

The gall-bladder is a sac-like structure with a capacity of 30 to 50 ml. Its smooth muscle coat is covered by serosa and lined by a mucous membrane covered with columnar epithelium. It fills and empties via the cystic duct which joins the common hepatic duct to form the bile duct; this in turn empties into the duodenum via the ampulla of Vater (Fig. 7.5). At this point of entry into the duodenum the bile duct and the adjacent pancreatic duct are surrounded by a circular band of smooth muscle, the choledocho-duodenal sphincter (sphincter of Oddi).

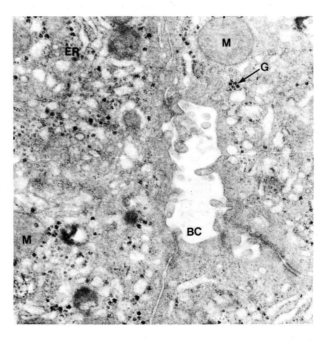

Fig. 7.4 Electron micrograph of parts of three liver cells, showing a bile canaliculus lined by microvilli (BC), endoplasmic reticulum (ER), glycogen deposits (G) and mitochondria (M). (By courtesy of D. Hopwood.)

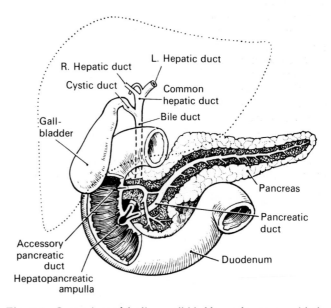

Fig. 7.5 Connexions of the liver, gall-bladder, and pancreas with the duodenum. The anatomical arrangement of the entry of the pancreatic duct and the bile ducts is not always as shown here; they enter the duodenum separately in 29 per cent of persons.

Composition of bile. Bile is an aqueous solution of organic compounds and electrolytes. The composition of hepatic bile is shown in Table 7.6. In the gall-bladder, electrolytes and water are resorbed producing bile more concentrated than that in the hepatic duct. The osmolality of bile is similar to that of plasma, approximately 300 mmol/kg. This osmolality is due mainly

Table 7.6   Composition of hepatic bile

Organic compounds

	Concentration (mg per 100g)	Percentage of total solids
Bile acids	140 – 2230	8 – 53
Phospholipid	140 – 810	9 – 21
Cholesterol	100 – 320	3 – 11
Bile pigments	10 – 70	0·4 – 2
Protein	30 – 300	1·3 – 10

Inorganic ions

	Concentration (mmol/l)
Na^+	146 – 165
K^+	2·7 – 4·9
Ca^{2+}	5·0 – 9·6
Mg^{2+}	2·8 – 6·0
Cl^-	88 – 115
HCO_3^-	27 – 55

to the presence of inorganic ions which account for only a small percentage of the total solids. The cations Na^+, K^+, Ca^{2+}, and Mg^{2+} are present in approximately the same concentration as in plasma, but the concentration of chloride is lower in bile than in plasma. This electrochemical difference is made up by organic ions, chiefly bile acids, which exist in ionized form at the biliary pH of 5·7 to 8·6.

Bile may also contain non-physiological substances such as drugs (for example penicillin), radiographic contrast media such as iopanoic acid, and organic dyes such as bromsulphthalein (BSP).

Bile acids are steroid acids derived from cholesterol. The rate-limiting step in bile acid synthesis is 7 α-hydroxylation of cholesterol and the rate of bile acid formation is regulated by negative feed-back inhibition of the enzyme cholesterol 7 α hydroxylase. The principal bile acids are shown in Figure 7.7. The primary bile acids, cholic acid and chenodeoxycholic acid are synthesized in the liver, conjugated with either glycine or taurine (Fig. 7.8) in the hepatocyte, and secreted into the canaliculus. In the gut, some of the primary bile acids are metabolized by intestinal bacteria. They are deconjugated and then either reabsorbed, returning to the liver via the portal vein (see 'enterohepatic circulation', p. 101), or undergo dehydroxylation in the 7α position to form the secondary bile acids deoxycholic acid and lithocholic acid. The secondary bile acids are themselves partially resorbed and re-conjugated in the liver.

The predominant *phospholipid* in bile is lecithin.

Bile pigments are conjugates of bilirubin, the breakdown product of haem. Bilirubin leaves the blood and enters the hepatocyte in the unconjugated form; it is bound to the intracellular protein *ligandin* and is conjugated with glucuronic acid. Conjugated bilirubin is then secreted into the bile canaliculus. The secretion of conjugated bilirubin proceeds independently of the secretion of bile acids.

Cholesterol is insoluble in water. In bile it is held in solution by the formation of *micelles* which also contain bile acids and phospholipid. Each bile acid molecule consists of the non-polar, hydrophobic steroid nucleus and the polar, hydrophilic side arm and hydroxyl groups. Bile acids thus have detergent properties. When incorporated into a micelle, the bile acid molecules (usually 10 to 12 per micelle) become oriented with the polar groups on the outside. The phospholipid and

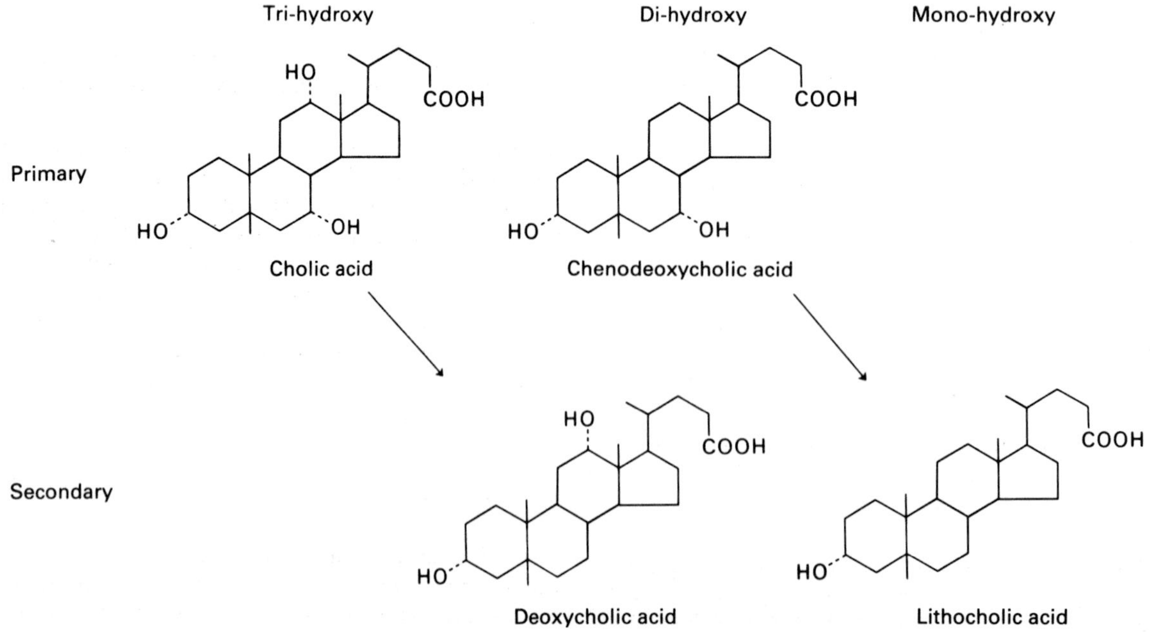

Fig. 7.7   The principal bile acids.

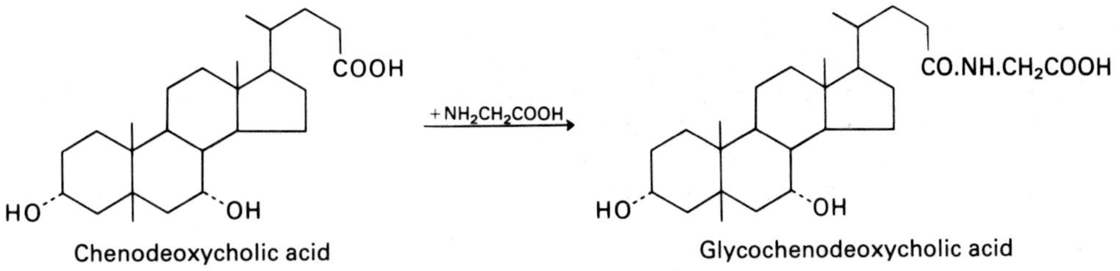

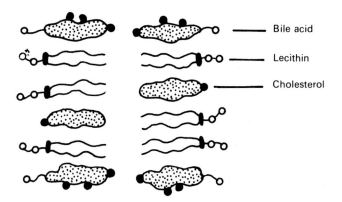

Fig. 7.8 Conjugation of chenodeoxycholic acid with glycine.

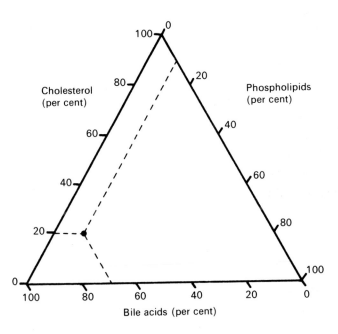

Fig. 7.9 Diagrammatic representation of a bile acid micelle. The polar (hydrophilic) parts of each molecule are on the outside of the micelle while the hydrophobic components are on the inside. (After K. W. Heaton (1972): *Bile Salts in Health and Disease.* Edinburgh: Churchill Livingstone.)

cholesterol molecules interdigitate with the bile acids (Fig. 7.9). Such a micellar solution can remain stable only if the relative proportions of the constituents remain within certain limits. Outside these limits either the phospholipid, the cholesterol, or both, come out of solution. The relative concentrations of bile salts, phospholipid and cholesterol can be shown graphically on a system of triangular co-ordinates (Fig. 7.10). The molar concentration of each constituent is

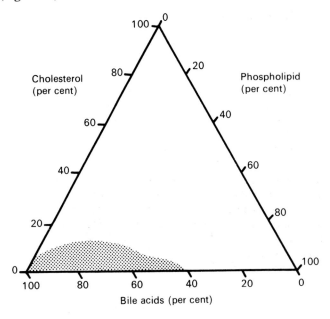

Fig. 7.11 Solubility of cholesterol in bile. Only bile samples which lie within the shaded area are unsaturated with cholesterol.

expressed as a percentage of the total molar concentration of the solution and plotted along the appropriate axis. The composition of the mixture is represented by a point which lies at the intersection of three lines (Fig. 7.10). It has been shown experimentally that only mixtures whose composition lies in the lower left-hand corner of the triangle (Fig. 7.11) can exist in micellar solution. In subjects who regularly produce bile which is supersaturated with cholesterol, the cholesterol may be deposited in the gall-bladder with the formation of gall-stones.

Bile Secretion

The formation of bile involves the uptake or synthesis of a variety of substances by the hepatocytes, their discharge into the bile canaliculi and the modification of the composition of bile during its passage through the bile ducts and gall-bladder.

Fig. 7.10 Molar composition of bile plotted on triangular co-ordinates. The point A represents a bile sample with a molar composition of 10 per cent phospholipid, 20 per cent cholesterol and 70 per cent bile acids.

Bile is secreted into the canaliculi at a pressure of 14 to 20 mm Hg (2 to 2·6 kPa). Since bile flow is independent of the perfusion pressure in the sinusoid hydrostatic pressure cannot be the principal mechanism for the production of bile. Bile flow is derived from the active secretion of solutes into the canaliculi, accompanied by the passive transfer of water along the osmotic gradient so created. The total bile flow is the sum of two components, termed the 'bile-acid-dependent', and the 'bile-acid-independent' fractions.

Bile-acid-dependent bile flow. Infusion of bile acids into the liver of animals produces an increase in bile flow (choloresis) and the rate of bile flow shows a linear relationship to the rate of excretion of bile acids. This has also been demonstrated in man. In the experiment illustrated in Figure 7.12, a cannula was inserted into the bile duct during a surgical operation, so that bile could be collected and its volume measured. Postoperatively, a tube was passed into the duodenum and bile acids were infused into the small intestine. The exogenous bile acids were incorporated into the entero-hepatic circulation and produced an increase in biliary secretion of bile acids. The rate of bile flow increased in proportion to the change in bile acid secretion (Fig. 7.12). Biliary secretion of phospholipid is also proportional to bile acid secretion but the rate of secretion of bilirubin and cholesterol is largely independent of that of bile acids.

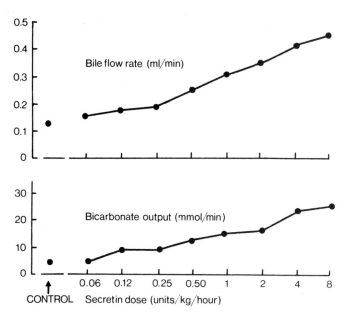

Fig. 7.13 Increase in flow rate of bile and in biliary bicarbonate output in response to secretin. (R. S. Jones & M. I. Grossman (1969) *American Journal of Physiology*, 217, 533.)

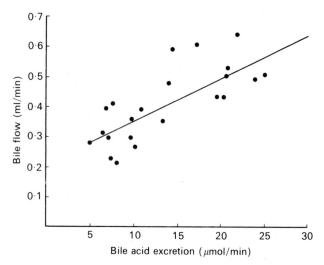

Fig. 7.12 The relationship between bile flow and bile acid excretion in man. (*After* T. Schersten, C. S. Nilsson, E. Cahlin, M. Filipson and G. Brodin-Persson (1971) *European Journal of Clinical Investigation*, 1, 242–247.)

Bile-acid-independent bile flow. Extrapolation of the regression line in Figure 7.12 intercepts the vertical axis at 0·2 ml/min. This is the bile flow which would theoretically occur when bile acid secretion is zero, and is referred to as the 'bile-acid-independent' fraction of bile flow. It depends on the Na^+-K^+-ATPase dependent active secretion of sodium, and can be blocked by inhibitors of active sodium transport.

The production of bile by the hepatocytes is estimated to be 5 l/day in man. The composition of bile is modified during its passage through the biliary tree. In the bile ducts, active secretion of bicarbonate and passive transfer of water increase bile volume and bicarbonate concentration and reduce the

concentration of bile acids. Such ductular secretion of bicarbonate is under the control of several hormones, particularly secretin (compare its effect on pancreatic secretion), CCK-PZ, gastrin, and glucagon (Fig. 7.13).

In the gall-bladder, sodium, chloride, and bicarbonate are actively resorbed; this is followed by the inevitable passive transfer of water, resulting in a ten-fold increase in the concentration of non-absorbable organic solutes. The daily output of bile into the duodenum is approximately 500 to 600 ml.

Control of gall-bladder contraction. Filling of the gall-bladder depends on the positive pressure gradient brought about by the active secretion of bile together with the contraction of the sphincter at the choledocho-duodenal junction and on the adaptive relaxation of the gall-bladder wall. The resting intraluminal pressure of the human gall-bladder ranges from 0 to 11 mm Hg (1·6 kPa).

Food in the upper small intestine induces contraction of the gall-bladder and relaxation of the choledochal sphincter by causing the release of CCK-PZ and secretin from the mucosa of the small intestine. The CCK-PZ exerts a direct stimulant action on the muscle of the gall-bladder so that the pressure in the gall-bladder increases up to 30 cm H_2O (3·0 kPa). The cholecystokinetic effect of CCK-PZ is greatly augmented by small amounts of secretin and by vagal stimulation (Fig. 7.14). After total vagotomy (or section of the anterior hepatic branch) the resting volume of the gall-bladder is doubled.

Control of the choledocho-duodenal sphincter. The pressure gradient between the lumen of the bile duct and the duodenal lumen is determined by contraction of the sphincteric muscle at the choledocho-duodenal junction. The sphincteric contraction is mediated by cholinergic mechanisms, so that the flow of bile into the duodenum decreases when the antrum contracts or when hydrochloric acid reaches the duodenum in high concentration. On the other hand,

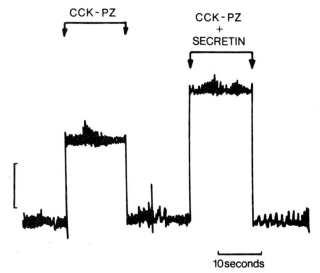

Fig. 7.14 Pressure response of gall-bladder of dog to CCK-PZ alone and to CCK-PZ plus secretin. Secretin alone did not cause contraction of the gall-bladder but it augmented contraction when given with CCK-PZ. The vertical bar represents a pressure change of 10 cm water (1·0 kPa). (*From* M. I. Grossman (1970) *Origin, Chemistry, Physiology and Pathophysiology of the Gastrointestinal Hormones,* ed. W. Creutzfeld. Stuttgart: Schattauer.)

sphincteric resistance is reduced by vagotomy and atropine, and by CCK-PZ. Other reflex effects have been described but the results of all experiments are so variable that the effects of vagal and sympathetic innervation of the biliary tract are still open to question.

Functions of Bile Acids

Bile acids inhibit the enzyme cholesterol 7α-hydroxylase in the liver and thus control their own rate of synthesis by negative feedback. They may inhibit the synthesis of cholesterol in the liver and small intestinal mucosa. Bile acid secretion increases bile flow by the bile-acid-dependent mechanism and increases the biliary secretion of phospholipid. Bile acids are essential for maintaining the solubility of cholesterol in bile by the formation of micelles.

Bile acids are important in the absorption of lipids from the small intestine. They aid the emulsification of fat, and with phospholipids, fatty acids and monoglycerides form mixed micelles (p. 73). Cholesterol and fat-soluble vitamins must be incorporated into mixed micelles before they can be absorbed.

Bile acids stimulate pancreatic secretion, probably by the release of CCK-PZ, and activate pancreatic lipase in the gut lumen. They inhibit resorption of water and electrolytes in the colon and increase colonic motility.

The Enterohepatic Circulation

Some of the bile acids secreted into the duodenum are deconjugated and dehydroxylated in the 7α position by enzymes from anaerobic bacteria. This produces a mixture of conjugated and unconjugated primary and secondary bile acids. Most of these are reabsorbed from the terminal ileum, where over 90 per cent of the bile acids are removed by an active transport mechanism (Fig. 7.15). Cholic acid is absorbed more efficiently than chenodeoxycholic acid, and conjugated bile acids are absorbed better than unconjugated bile acids. Some dihydroxy bile acids, such as chenodeoxycholic acid, are absorbed in the jejunum, and some unconjugated bile acids are absorbed passively from the colon.

The reabsorbed bile acids return via the portal vein to the liver where they are reconjugated and re-secreted into the bile, which thus contains a mixture of conjugated primary and secondary bile acids. Hepatic 7α-hydroxylation of secondary bile acids to reform primary bile acids does not occur. The uptake of bile acids by the liver is 70 to 90 per cent efficient so that the concentration of bile acids in peripheral venous blood (3·5 μmol/l when fasting) is much lower than that in the portal vein (20 μmol/l).

Faecal losses of bile acids of 500 to 700 mg/day are replaced by hepatic synthesis from cholesterol, so that the total bile acid pool remains constant at 2 to 4 g. Since 20 to 30 g of bile acids enter the duodenum each day, the total bile acid pool must traverse the enterohepatic circulation six to ten times during each 24-hour period.

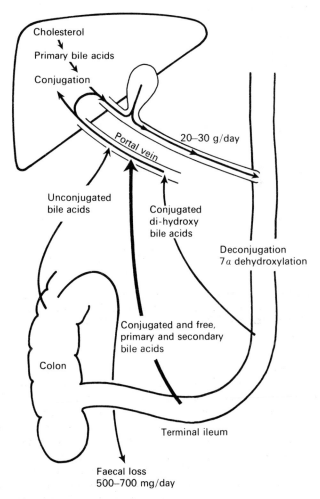

Cholesterol
Primary bile acids
Conjugation
Portal vein
20–30 g/day
Unconjugated bile acids
Conjugated di-hydroxy bile acids
Deconjugation 7α dehydroxylation
Conjugated and free, primary and secondary bile acids
Colon
Terminal ileum
Faecal loss 500–700 mg/day

Fig. 7.15 Diagrammatic representation of the enterohepatic circulation of bile acids.

A number of substances in addition to the bile acids have an enterohepatic circulation. Vitamins B_{12} and D, hormones such as thyroxine, and certain drugs are secreted in bile and reabsorbed from the intestine.

DISORDERS OF HEPATIC FUNCTION

The normal plasma concentration of bilirubin is 0·1 to 1·0 mg/dl (2 to 17 μmol/l). Excretion of bilirubin may be impaired in patients with liver disease and in those with obstruction to the extrahepatic biliary tract (as occurs, for example, when a gall-stone becomes impacted in the bile duct). Failure of bile to reach the duodenum is termed 'cholestasis'. Bilirubin then accumulates in the blood, and when the plasma bilirubin level exceeds 40 μmol/l the sclera and skin show a yellow discolouration recognized clinically as jaundice.

The reduced secretion of bile acids into the duodenum impairs absorption of lipids and fat-soluble vitamins. The malabsorption of vitamin K aggravates the defects of blood coagulation seen in liver disease. Reduced synthesis of plasma proteins, particularly albumin, leads to hypoproteinaemia and the development of oedema according to the Starling equilibrium (Chap. 16).

In some liver diseases such as cirrhosis the normal arrangement of portal tracts, sinusoids and central veins becomes distorted and the resistance to blood flow through the liver is increased. The pressure in the portal vein rises and may reach 35 mm Hg (4·7 kPa). When portal hypertension is established, blood is diverted from the portal venous system to the systemic circulation through the gastric and oesophageal veins which become dilated and form oesophago-gastric varices which are a potential source of gastrointestinal bleeding. Portal hypertension and hypoproteinaemia combine through the Starling equilibrium to produce ascites, an abnormal collection of transudated fluid in the peritoneal cavity.

Some patients with severe liver disease develop *hepatic encephalopathy*, with a flapping tremor of the hands, mental confusion or coma, and abnormalities of the electroencephalogram. It is thought to be the result of accumulation of toxic metabolites such as ammonia, short-chain fatty acids, and certain amino acids in the blood and brain. Abnormal metabolism of the amino acid tyrosine produces octopamine (Fig. 7.16) which resembles noradrenaline chemically but which acts as a 'false neurotransmitter' by having lower neurotransmitter activity than noradrenaline at noradrenergic receptor sites.

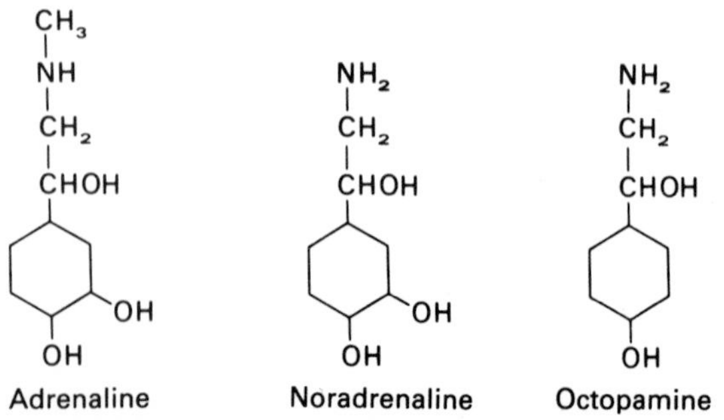

Investigation of Hepatic and Biliary Function

The secretory capacity of the liver can be assessed by the estimation of serum bilirubin and bile acids, and the synthetic capacity by the measurement of the clotting factors (for example by estimation of the prothrombin time) and the concentration of serum albumin. If hepatocyte necrosis occurs, intracellular enzymes such as aspartate aminotransferase are released into the blood and can be estimated in the serum.

Excretion of the dye bromsulphalein (BSP) can be used to assess liver function. BSP is taken up by hepatocytes, conjugated with glutathione, and excreted into bile. A dose of BSP is given intravenously and the plasma level estimated 45 minutes later. At this time more than 95 per cent of the injected dose should have been removed by the liver. Abnormal retention of BSP is a sensitive index of liver disease.

Hepatic scanning. Particulate matter is removed from the blood by the macrophages. A colloidal substance such as microaggregated albumin or sulphur-colloid injected intravenously is taken up by the Kupffer cells. If the colloid has been labelled with a radioactive isotope (as in [99]technetium microaggregated albumin), scanning of the abdomen with a scintillation counter gives a visual representation of the liver (Fig. 7.17). Such hepatic scans can reveal metastatic malignant deposits in the liver.

Breath tests. A substance labelled with radioactive ^{14}C is ingested, absorbed and metabolized by the liver with the release of [14]CO_2 which can be measured in a sample of expired air. One breath test uses ^{14}C-aminopyrine and the rate of

Fig. 7.16 Adrenaline, noradrenaline, and octopamine.

Adrenaline   Noradrenaline   Octopamine

Fig. 7.17 Hepatic scan obtained after the intravenous injection of [99]technetium labelled microaggregated albumin. (*Courtesy of F. Hutchinson.*)

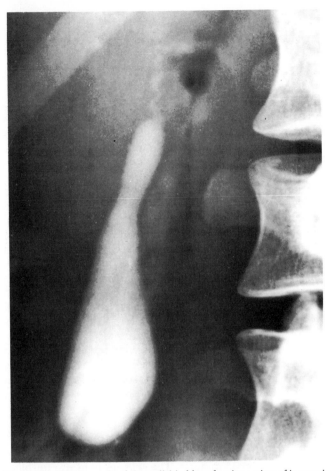

Fig. 7.18 Radiograph of the gall-bladder after ingestion of iopanoic acid. The cystic duct is also outline by contrast material. (*Courtesy of J. W. McNab.*)

excretion of $^{14}CO_2$ gives an indication of the metabolic activity of the liver. Low rates of $^{14}CO_2$ excretion occur in patients with liver disease, and high rates of excretion are seen in patients on long-term treatment with enzyme-inducing drugs (see p. 96).

Radiology. Radiographic contrast media such as iopanoic acid are excreted into the bile canaliculi by the same pathway as is used for excretion of bilirubin. They can be given orally or intravenously to outline the gall-bladder (Fig. 7.18) or bile ducts. Alternatively, contrast material can be injected directly into the biliary system, either through a needle passed into the liver or through a cannula passed into the bile duct via the ampulla of Vater. Such techniques are used to demonstrate the presence of gall-stones, obstruction to the biliary tree, and impaired gall-bladder function.

Jaundice

In normal plasma bilirubin is all in an unconjugated form. Within the hepatocyte it is rendered water-soluble by conjugation to glucuronic acid. In jaundiced patients it is often helpful to identify which form of bilirubin predominates; unconjugated bilirubin is present in excess in jaundice due to excessive haemolysis or to disorders affecting the uptake or conjugation of bilirubin, such as inborn errors or competition by drugs. Conjugated bilirubin is present in excess in patients with defects of bilirubin secretion, due to viral diseases or drugs or inherited defects or caused by mechanical obstruction of the biliary tree by gall-stones or by a tumour (*obstructive jaundice*). Unconjugated bilirubin is insoluble and circulates bound to plasma albumin. Conjugated bilirubin is water-soluble; the urine of a patient with obstructive jaundice is dark because of its bilirubin content.

REFERENCES

Bissell D M 1975 Formation and elimination of bilirubin. Gastroenterology 69: 519–538
Branch R A, Nies A S, Read A E 1975 The liver and drugs. Modern Trends in Gastroenterology 5: 289–317
Connor H 1978 Assessing the metabolic function of the liver. Topics in Gastroenterology 6: 281–298
Heaton K W 1972 Bile salts in health and disease. Churchill Livingstone, Edinburgh
Javitt N B 1976 Hepatic bile formation. New England Journal of Medicine 295: 1464–1469 and 1511–1516
Jones R S, Meyers W C 1979 Regulation of hepatic biliary secretion. Annual Review of Physiology 41: 67–82
Paumgartner G (ed) 1977 Bile acids. Clinics in Gastroenterology 6: no 1
Sherlock S 1975 Diseases of the liver and biliary system, 5th edn. Blackwell, Oxford
Schiff L 1975 Diseases of the liver, 4th edn. Lippincott, Philadelphia
Tavill A S, Swain C P 1979 The protein secretory activities of the liver. In: Duthie H L, Wormsley K G (eds) Scientific basis of gastroenterology. Churchill Livingstone, Edinburgh, p 249–287

8 The Blood

Blood consists of a pale, straw-coloured fluid, the *plasma*, in which the *formed elements*, red cells, white cells and platelets are suspended. The chief functions of the blood are the transport of oxygen and food materials to all the cells of the body and the removal of carbon dioxide and waste materials to the organs of excretion. The red cells are the main agents of oxygen transport; leucocytes are involved in reaction to infection and in other scavenging functions; platelets are involved in the prevention of loss of blood (haemostasis).

Total Volume of Plasma and Blood

The volume of plasma can be measured by the principle of dye dilution or isotope dilution. A known volume of the non-toxic dye Evans Blue is injected intravenously. After a slight delay for mixing a sample of blood is taken and the concentration of dye in the plasma is measured. From this the plasma volume is calculated. Dyes usually begin to leave the circulation in a few minutes, thus the use of human albumin labelled with radioactive iron may be more accurate, but only relatively so as even that combination may leak.

The total blood volume can be estimated from the plasma volume and the proportion of plasma and cells (haematocrit) obtained by centrifugation. However, these dilution methods make the assumption that the ratio of plasma to cells is the same throughout the body, but the haematocrit value of the blood as a whole is about 10 per cent lower than the haematocrit in a large vessel. This may be because of the preferential accumulation of red cells in the more rapidly moving axial stream of smaller vessels or because some capillaries contain plasma but no red cells. The volume of the red cells can, however, be obtained independently by incubating a sample of the subject's blood with tracers such as ^{32}P, ^{51}Cr, ^{42}K or CO which combine with the red cells. A known amount of the sample is injected intravenously and the extent of dilution is measured.

In a normal adult the haematocrit rises about 3·5 per cent on changing from the lying to the standing position, presumably because fluid leaves the capillaries in which the hydrostatic pressure is increased. At the same time the plasma protein level rises about 7 g/l.

Table 8.1 Blood volume values in children. (*After* Osgood, E. (1955) Pediatrics 15, 733.)

Age	Blood volume (ml/kg)
24 hours	83
3 months	87
6 months	86
1 year	80
6 years	80
10 years	75
15 years	71

The blood volume in an adult male is about 5 litres. In a female 3·5 to 4·5 litres are usual; higher values are found in pregnancy. The blood volume of children is best expressed in relationship to the child's weight (Table 8·1); typical values for total blood volume are 0·3 l in the newborn, 0·6 l at the age of 1 year and 1·6 l at the age of 6.

The 5 litres of blood are contained in the heart, arteries, capillaries and veins. Of the 1300 ml in the pulmonary circulation about 400 ml are in the arteries, 60 ml in the capillaries and 840 ml in the venules and veins. Of the 3000 ml in the systemic circulation about 550 ml are in the arteries, about 300 ml in the capillaries and 2150 ml in the venules and veins. The veins are regarded as blood reservoirs, partly because they contain a large proportion of the blood and partly because they can accommodate an increased amount with little rise in pressure (Chap. 11).

The effects of haemorrhage. The effects of loss of blood depend on the amount lost and the rapidity of bleeding. The loss of small amounts of blood, for example from bleeding haemorrhoids, intermittently or continuously over many months does not disturb the circulation but it may produce anaemia.

In healthy normal subjects a large amount of blood can be lost before the arterial pressure falls. In one experiment 11 normal human subjects were bled about 17 per cent of their blood volume in 35 minutes. The changes in heart rate, blood pressure and cardiac output were insignificant. However, the splanchnic blood volume was reduced by 30 per cent so that the splanchnic vascular bed contributed about half the volume of blood removed. These findings show the importance of the splanchnic circulation as a blood reservoir in man; they can best be explained by supposing that there is active venous vasoconstriction without arterial vasoconstriction.

For a short time after a haemorrhage the concentrations of haemoglobin and of plasma protein may remain normal but within two or three hours both fall because of the entry into the circulation of protein-free fluid as a result of the fall in capillary filtration pressure produced by arteriolar constriction. In this way the circulating blood volume is restored within about 24 hours and during this period the concentrations of plasma protein and haemoglobin fall progressively. Between 2 and 4 days after the loss of blood the plasma protein concentration is restored; the concentration of haemoglobin returns to normal more slowly by increased production of red cells by the bone marrow. The period needed for complete restoration of the haemoglobin level depends on the amount of blood lost and upon the availability of iron in the body stores; about 20 days are required after the loss of 200 ml of blood.

Plasma Proteins

Proteins constitute the major part of the dissolved solids of the blood plasma; their total concentration is about 65 to

75 g/l. They comprise a mixture of simple and conjugated proteins and include lipoproteins and glycoproteins.

At one time plasma proteins were divided into only two fractions, albumin and globulin, but the use of electrophoresis showed that the globulin fraction could be divided into five components: α_1-, α_2-, β- and γ-globulin and fibrinogen (Fig. 8.2). It is now known that each of these fractions contains several individual proteins. These can be identified by the technique of immunoelectrophoresis.

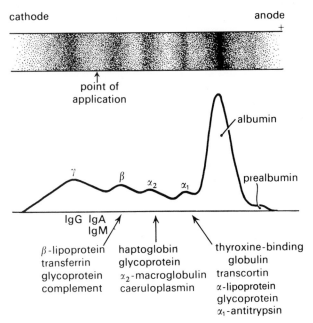

Fig. 8.2 Electrophoretic separation of the plasma proteins. With the exception of albumin it is seen that each band represents several distinct proteins.

Albumin. Albumin, the most abundant of the plasma proteins, is a globular protein of molecular weight about 67 000. It is synthesized in the liver and its main function is to maintain the colloid osmotic pressure of the plasma and so promote the return of fluid from tissues into the venous ends of the capillaries (Chap. 16). It also carries many substances (such as bilirubin and some drugs) which would otherwise be insoluble in plasma.

No disorder characterized by increased plasma albumin levels has been described. Low levels are found whenever synthesis is impaired (in liver disease or when amino acids are scarce as in malnutrition or malabsorption syndromes) or when excessive albumin is lost from the plasma (in some kidney diseases, some intestinal disorders and after burns).

Thyroxine binding globulin. This globulin, with a molecular weight of 40 000 to 50 000, is responsible for the transport of thyroxine, a hormone produced by the thyroid gland. Inherited disorders with deficiency of this protein are recognized but cause little clinical abnormality. Some thyroxine is also carried in the plasma on *pre-albumin*.

Haptoglobin. This is an α_2-globulin with several distinct heritable variants. It binds haemoglobin which has been released into the plasma after red blood cells have been damaged and prevents the loss of haemoglobin in the urine. The breakdown of haemoglobin begins as soon as it is bound to haptoglobin. It is likely that little haptoglobin is used when red cells are destroyed by the macrophages at the end of their normal life span but that haptoglobin is used up when breakdown of red cells (*haemolysis*) occurs elsewhere. In patients with haemolytic diseases plasma levels of haptoglobin fall and haptoglobin may even disappear entirely from the plasma.

Caeruloplasmin. This is a copper-containing protein of molecular weight about 160 000. It is an enzyme with oxidase activity and may be important in the transport of copper in the plasma. In *Wilson's disease*, or *hepatolenticular degeneration*, an inherited disorder with low plasma levels of caeruloplasmin, copper is deposited in several tissues.

α_1-antitrypsin. This protein (molecular weight about 45 000) inhibits the action of many proteolytic enzymes, notably trypsin, chymotrypsin and plasmin (pp. 66, 119). High plasma levels are found in acute illnesses; low levels are found in a rare inherited form of the pulmonary disease, emphysema, in which there is a progressive loss of lung tissue in adult life.

α_2-macroglobulin. This large protein (molecular weight about 820 000) is another inhibitor of proteolytic enzymes. Normal children have higher plasma levels of this protein than adults. High values are also found in diseases characterized by deficiency of albumin but the reason for this is not known.

Transferrin. This β-globulin, of molecular weight about 90 000, is responsible for the transport of iron in the plasma. The plasma level of transferrin is increased in patients with iron deficiency and decreased in some inherited disorders.

Other plasma proteins. Other important plasma proteins are the *lipoproteins*, responsible for the carriage of lipids in plasma, the *immunoglobulins* (antibodies) (p. 125) and the components of *complement* (p. 127). *Fibrinogen* is the precursor of the fibrin formed when blood clots (p. 116).

THE ERYTHROCYTES

Normal human erythrocytes (red cells) are circular biconcave discs without nuclei (Fig. 8.3). Their main constituent is haemoglobin and their principal function is the transport of oxygen from the lungs to the tissues where it is used. The haemoglobin in the erythrocyte is in a higher concentration (approximately 340 g/l of red cell mass) than could be achieved in simple solution.

When a specimen of blood, in which coagulation has been prevented, is centrifuged it separates into two main layers: a clear, normally straw-coloured upper layer of plasma (approximately 55 per cent of the volume), and a lower layer of packed erythrocytes with a small amount of trapped plasma between them. Between these two layers is a narrow band (*buffy coat*) comprising about 1 per cent of the volume and consisting of an upper creamy-white layer of platelets and a lower grey-white layer of white cells or leucocytes. The percentage of blood volume occupied by the packed red corpuscles, the packed cell volume (P.C.V.) or haematocrit, is normally about 45 per cent and is used in medicine as an index of anaemia, since the more anaemic a patient is the lower is the haematocrit; or, in a subject who is not anaemic, the P.C.V. is an index of the

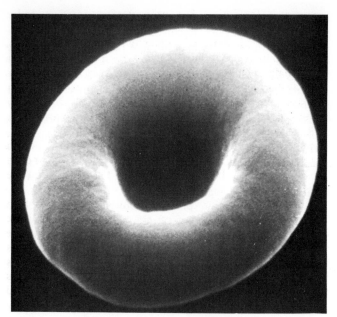

Fig. 8.3 Photograph of a normal erythrocyte taken with the scanning electron microscope. $\times$ 11 000. (*By courtesy of P. G. Toner.*)

relative amount of fluid in the plasma (dehydration, Chap. 16).

There are normally about 5×10^{12} red cells per litre of circulating blood. Since the blood volume is about 5 litres, there are approximately 25×10^{12} red cells (or 2·5 kg) in the circulation. In the healthy adult the red cell count varies from 4·2 to $6·4 \times 10^{12}$ per litre, the average count in the male being $5·5 \times 10^{12}$, and in the female $4·8 \times 10^{12}$. In healthy subjects there are circadian variations equivalent to 4 per cent of the mean value for the day.

In health the erythrocytes have an average diameter of 7·2 μm (measured on a fixed and stained film of blood) and a thickness of 1·9 μm. In disease these proportions may be altered so that in pernicious anaemia (p. 28) for example the mean corpuscular diameter is greater than normal (macrocytes) and there is a larger than normal variation in size between the cells.

From the haematocrit and the red cell count it is possible to calculate the mean corpuscular volume (M.C.V.) which is normally from 78 to 94 μm³.

Erythrocyte sedimentation rate (E.S.R.). When blood to which an anticoagulant has been added stands in a narrow tube the red cells form aggregates (*rouleaux*) which gradually sediment leaving a clear zone of plasma above. The sedimentation rate is measured as the length of the column of clear plasma after one hour. The E.S.R. depends mainly on the relative concentrations in the plasma of fibrinogen and the α_2- and γ-globulins. The asymmetry of these macromolecules promotes the aggregation of red cells into rouleaux and clumps. Almost all infections, whether acute or chronic, are accompanied by a rise in α_2- and γ-globulins and most wasting and destructive diseases by an increase in fibrinogen. The E.S.R. is useful in detecting the presence and activity of disease but it is quite unspecific. The sedimentation rate also varies according to the red cell count, the lower the red cell count the greater the sedimentation rate.

The Structure and Metabolism of Erythrocytes

Since the red cell can be bisected without its contents escaping it seems likely that it consists of a close network or of a jelly which is none the less flexible enough to allow the cells to assume the paraboloid form in which they pass through capillaries as a succession of tiny plugs separated by plasma (Fig. 11.23) The usual biconcave disc shape is regained immediately when the cells pass into a larger vessel. The elongated form of the erythrocyte when passing through a capillary presents a larger surface area to the capillary wall for the transference of oxygen.

Although erythrocytes have no nuclei and normally contain no glycogen they are metabolically quite active, utilizing some 1·5 to 2·2 mmoles of glucose per litre per hour equivalent to the liberation of 100 J. This energy is required to pump out sodium and pump in potassium against electrochemical gradients and to reduce methaemoglobin to haemoglobin.

The metabolism of glucose in the red blood cell, which is essential for its survival, involves both glycolysis and the pentose phosphate pathway, 80 per cent of the glucose being broken down by the former and 20 per cent by the latter. The red cell has no mitochondria and therefore no tricarboxylic acid cycle.

In the pentose phosphate pathway, the first enzyme involved is the *glucose-6-phosphate dehydrogenase (G-6-PD)* in the operation of which large amounts of reduced NADP are formed. This reduced NADP is utilized by the red blood cell to maintain glutathione (GSH) in the reduced state

$$\text{glucose 6-phosphate} + \text{NADP}^+ + \text{H}_2\text{O}$$
$$\downarrow G\text{-}6\text{-}PD$$
$$\text{6-phosphogluconic acid} + \text{NADPH} + \text{H}^+$$
$$\text{GSSG} + \text{NADPH} + \text{H}^+$$
$$\downarrow glutathione\ reductase$$
$$\text{2 GSH} + \text{NADP}^+$$

The function of the reduced glutathione within the erythrocyte is not clearly understood, but it probably prevents the oxidation of haemoglobin to methaemoglobin and its sulphydryl groups play a part in maintaining the structure of the red cell and also of the globin part of the haemoglobin molecule.

In the population of many parts of the world, there is a deficiency of the G-6-PD in the red blood cells. This is an inherited condition which affects more than 100 million people in the world. This deficiency is a common cause of jaundice in babies; it also causes haemolysis after the administration of antimalarial and antibacterial drugs, the consumption of the bean *Vicia faba* and the occurrence of infections. Many enzyme deficiencies in red cells have been discovered but only a few have serious effects.

Hydrogen peroxide is formed in small amounts in normal red cells and in increased amounts after the administration of certain drugs, including those which cause haemolysis in G-6-PD deficiency. If not destroyed as rapidly as it is produced, hydrogen peroxide oxidizes haemoglobin to methaemoglobin and then, irreversibly, to oxidized degradation products. Excess of hydrogen peroxide also affects the integrity of the cell membrane; vitamin E seems to have a role in the protection against this effect because the red cells of patients with vitamin E deficiency are readily lysed by peroxide.

There are two protective mechanisms against hydrogen peroxide within the red cell. Glutathione peroxidase uses hydrogen peroxide to oxidize reduced glutathione. Normal activity of glutathione peroxidase depends on the presence of adequate amounts of reduced glutathione which requires normal functioning of the pentose phosphate pathway, including G-6-PD. The other protective agent is the enzyme catalase which decomposes hydrogen peroxide to water and oxygen. Chemically, catalase resembles haemoglobin in being an iron-containing haemoprotein. Of the two mechanisms glutathione peroxidase is probably the more important.

At least 100 enzyme systems have been identified in the mature red cell but because it has no nucleoprotein it cannot synthesize proteins, including enzymes.

Erythrocytes of various abnormal shapes, for example spherocytes, elliptocytes, sickle cells and target cells occur in disease. Many of these abnormal erythrocytes have a shorter life-span than normal so that the patients tend to be anaemic. Spherocytes by reason of their shape can swell only a little when put into a hypotonic solution of sodium chloride; they therefore rupture more readily and their osmotic fragility is said to be increased.

Origin of the Erythrocytes

The formation of erythrocytes is one of the most active anabolic processes in the body for in the adult approximately 2×10^{11} of these cells are replaced by the red bone marrow 24 hours. Specimens of marrow can be obtained by puncturing the sternum or the ilium with a stout needle. For many years studies on erythropoiesis were mainly morphological, but more recently much information has been gained from isotopic labelling, especially with radioactive iron. In the classical methods of studying blood cell formation the cells are stained with various mixtures of methylene blue (a basic dye) and eosin (an acid dye). Nuclei, because of their DNA content, stain blue (basophilic) and early red cell precursors have blue (basophilic) cytoplasm from RNA. The concentration of haemoglobin is shown by the degree of eosinophilic staining. The term *polychromatic* is used when the cytoplasm stains with both basic and acid dyes owing to the presence of both RNA and haemoglobin.

The earliest precursor of the erythrocyte which can be recognized by morphological methods is the *proerythroblast* but these cells are not able to maintain their own numbers while providing the cells which mature into erythrocytes. It is clear, therefore, that proerythroblasts are continually being formed from precursors. Such cells are known as *stem cells* and the size of the stem cell population is maintained by the continuous production of new cells which replace those that are lost. Recently evidence has been obtained that the stem cell is a small round cell with little cytoplasm.

It is likely that the stem cells which provide the precursors of the erythrocyte also provide the precursors of other blood cells, notably the granulocytes and platelets. Whether the precursors of lymphocytes are derived from the same stem cell population is uncertain. The factors that decide in which way a particular stem cell differentiates are not known.

Cells maturing into erythrocytes have a variety of names, pro-erythroblast (E_1), large basophilic (early) normoblast (E_2), small basophilic normoblast (E_3), polychromatophilic (intermediate) normoblast (E_4), late non-dividing normoblast (E_5), reticulocyte (E_6) and erythrocyte (E_7). Cells in the early stages of their development contain a relatively large amount of RNA (more than 5 per cent) and are basophilic; at the E_4 stage they have reached a degree of differentiation at which further divisions cease as the RNA content falls to 0·5 per cent. Subsequently the cells lose their nuclear material so that the mature erythrocyte contains neither RNA nor DNA.

The term reticulocyte is used to denote an erythrocyte which shows a blue staining network when exposed to certain basic dyes, for example 'brilliant cresyl blue' or 'new methylene blue'. The reticulum, an aggregation of traces of RNA, appears in either nucleated or non-nucleated red cells and indicates immaturity. When for any reason the bone marrow produces red cells at a greater rate than normal, immature red cells tend to appear in the blood and the percentage of reticulocytes may rise (see Fig. 8.6).

It seems likely that cells do not proceed along their maturation pathway as a cohort but that the number of divisions as well as the maturation times may vary. Further, a small number of cells normally die during the process (ineffective erythropoiesis), but the death rate is much greater in a number of diseases, for example pernicious anaemia. The average number of divisions occurring during maturation is estimated to be 3 or 4 and the time for the whole process 120 hours.

The Life-Span of the Erythrocyte

The life-span of red cells in the circulating blood is about 120 days. Transfusion experiments using compatible, but antigenically different erythrocytes have been confirmed by radioactive techniques. Thus when the haem of the haemoglobin molecule is labelled by the incorporation of glycine containing ^{15}N the life-span can be shown to be 127 days. The most frequently used isotope in clinical work is ^{51}Cr. A sample of blood is incubated with radioactive sodium chromate, $Na_2{}^{51}CrO_4$. The red cells take up ^{51}Cr rapidly and, after they have been washed with saline to remove the radioactive plasma, the labelled red cells are returned to the subject by intravenous injection. The rate at which radioactivity leaves the blood is a measure of the survival time of the erythrocytes in circulation. The apparent half life, 28 to 38 days in normal persons, is less than the true value (about 60 days) because the decline in radioactivity is due partly to loss of old cells and partly to loss of ^{51}Cr from the cells. Nevertheless the test is useful in the diagnosis of haemolytic disease and also, from the radioactivity of the stools, in the detection of bleeding into the alimentary tract. The haem is degraded in macrophages to bilirubin which is transported attached to albumin to the liver and there conjugated with glucuronic acid and excreted into the bile. Excessive breakdown of erythrocytes and disorders of the liver or the biliary tree (p. 103) may cause *jaundice*.

Since the mean life span of erythrocytes is normally 120

days, one hundred-and-twentieth of the circulating red cells (about 25 g) must be removed each day from the circulation by the macrophages. The spleen is the most important site of erythrocyte breakdown.

When the life-span of the erythrocytes is reduced a state of *haemolytic disease* exists. This is not necessarily followed by anaemia since the bone marrow may produce enough new cells to compensate even if the survival time of circulating erythrocytes is only 20 or even 15 days.

The destruction of erythrocytes is to some extent random but older cells are more likely to be destroyed. Normally the ageing of these cells is not accompanied by any morphological change but, in subjects from whom the spleen has been removed surgically or in whom it is congenitally absent or destroyed by disease, the red cells show a variety of shapes, for example 'target', 'burr' and fragmented forms. Ageing is accompanied by a progressive loss of lipid and diminution in glycolytic enzyme activity. By differential centrifugation it can be shown that red cells increase in density with age.

The sites of erythropoiesis change with development (Fig. 8.4): in blood vessels in the yolk sac membrane in the embryo, in the liver and spleen in the fetus, throughout the skeleton in the infant and in membrane bones (thoracic cage, vertebrae and pelvis) in the adult. Even red marrow contains some adipose cells. These cells disappear when erythropoiesis is very active, as in haemolytic anaemia, and become more abundant in the elderly and after poisoning with, for example, benzene.

The Control of Erythropoiesis

In health the concentration of red cells (and of haemoglobin) remains remarkably constant because the destruction of old red cells is balanced by the production of new. There must therefore be a control mechanism but its details are far from clear.

Erythropoietin. The fundamental stimulus to erythropoiesis is hypoxia; it has been known for many years that arterial hypoxia, whether it is the result of chronic lung disease (Chap 14) or of the reduced oxygen tension in the air at high altitude (Fig. 8.5) increases erythropoiesis. An explanation was provided by the discovery in 1953 of the hormone *erythropoietin*. Erythropoietin is a glycoprotein (containing sialic acid) with a molecular weight of about 28 000 which moves electrophoretically as an α_2-globulin. It has not yet been

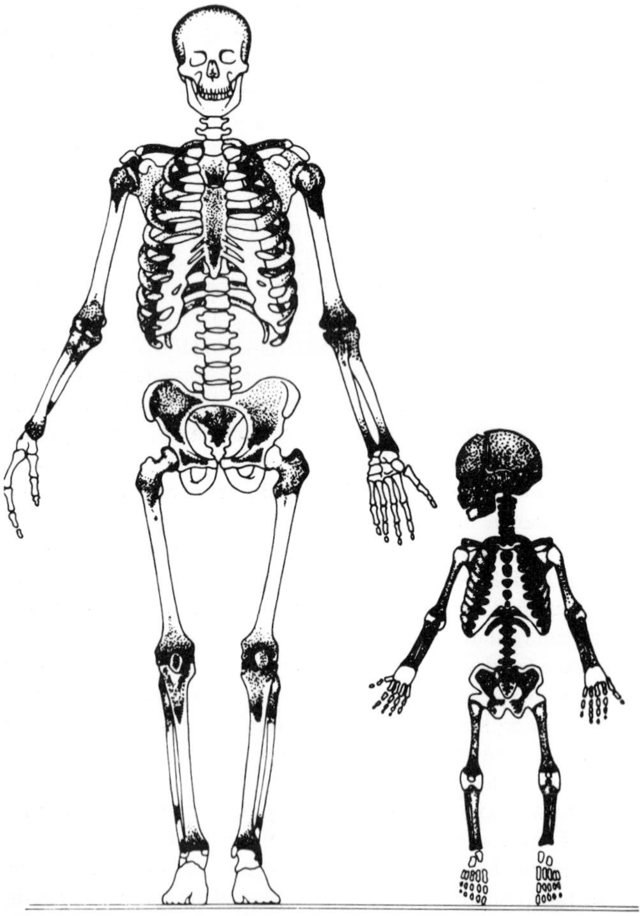

Fig. 8.4 Sites of active haematopoietic marrow (red marrow) in children and adults. There is a similar amount of red marrow (1000 to 1500 g) in each despite the differences in body weight. (*From* Bierman, H. R. (1961) In *Functions of the Blood*, ed. MacFarlane, R. G. & Robb-Smith, A. H. T., p. 357. Oxford: Blackwell.)

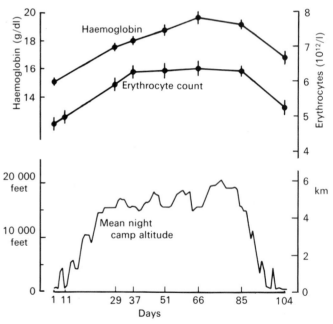

Fig. 8.5 Mean red blood cell count and blood haemoglobin level and mean night camp altitude of the ten expedition members (aged 24 to 38) during the attempt in 1954 to reach the summit of Makalu on the Nepal–Tibet border. They spent 62 days continuously above 4·6 km (15 000 ft). The increase in red cells and haemoglobin did not reach its maximum until 6 or 7 weeks had been spent at high altitude. On the other hand the descent to sea level brought the red cell and haemoglobin values in 17 days very nearly to the original sea-level values. Even if it is assumed that on descent erythropoiesis ceased entirely the rate of disappearance of the red cells is greater than can be accounted for on the basis of normal red cell destruction. The vertical bars represent the mean ± standard error of mean. (N. Pace, L. B. Meyer & B. E. Vaughan (1956) *Journal of Applied Physiology*, 9, 141–144.) It is of interest to note that in the Andes and Himalayas people live and work in permanently occupied settlements at 4 to 4·6 km (13 000 to 15 000 ft) above sea level.

crystallized but highly potent concentrates have been prepared and its plasma level can be measured by bioassay.

Erythropoietin is produced mainly in the kidney possibly by the juxtaglomerular cells (Chap. 15). It cannot normally be detected in blood but it is present within a few hours of the onset of hypoxia in experimental animals and it disappears again when the hypoxia is relieved. Erythropoietin is also present in the blood of animals made anaemic by repeated bleedings. It is presumably responsible for the reticulocytosis and blood regeneration in such animals because serum taken from them can induce a reticulocyte response in a normal animal.

High levels of erythropoietin have been demonstrated in the plasma or urine in most types of anaemia in man, the only notable, but not unexpected, exception being the anaemia of renal failure. Erythropoietin levels may be increased in patients with renal tumours. In the bone-marrow the chief action of erythropoietin is to increase the rate of formation of proerythroblasts from stem-cells after which proliferation and maturation proceed in the normal way.

It may well be that there are other humoral factors governing erythropoiesis.

Cobalamin and folic acid. These vitamins, discussed on B₁₂ pp. 28 and 29, have an important role in the synthesis of DNA. In the absence of either, the pro-erythroblasts of the bone-marrow, instead of maturing into normoblasts, give rise to immature cells called megaloblasts which later lose their nuclei and appear as large red cells, called macrocytes. These cells enter the peripheral circulation which therefore contains red cells on the average bigger than normal. This type of anaemia is thus called *macrocytic* or more specifically, *megaloblastic*. When it is due to deficiency of vitamin B_{12} and is associated with atrophy of the gastric mucosa it is called pernicious or Addisonian anaemia. Although most patients with vitamin B_{12} deficiency have this disorder, others become deficient because of other gastric or ileal lesions or from radical surgical removal of these parts of the alimentary canal.

Megaloblastic anaemia can also be caused by deficiency of folic acid which can arise from lack of folic acid in the diet or of its impaired absorption in the upper part of the small intestine in patients with malabsorption (p. 79); the body's stores of folic and folinic acids are small.

In cobalamin deficiency and folic acid deficiency the nuclei of the megaloblasts are large and finely stippled compared with those of normoblasts. Chromosomes derived from them are longer, more slender and less tightly coiled than normal. The time required for DNA synthesis is prolonged but, since other synthetic processes are not slowed down, more haemoglobin than usual accumulates in each cell and leads to macrocytosis.

As early as 6 hours after the injection of vitamin B_{12} into a patient with pernicious anaemia cytological changes are observed in the bone-marrow, the numerous primitive megaloblasts being replaced by more mature cells. Three to 4 days later the bone-marrow contains only a few megaloblasts, the predominant erythroblastic cell being the normoblast. In the circulating blood the number of reticulocytes usually begins to rise on the fourth or fifth day and reaches a maximum at 7 days or a little later, thereafter falling and eventually reaching the normal level (less than 2 per cent) (Fig. 8.6).

Other erythropoietic factors. The value of copper in the regeneration of blood has been demonstrated in animals and

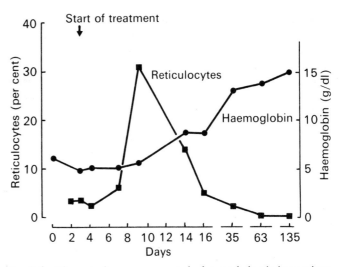

Fig. 8.6 The reticulocyte response to hydroxocobalamin in a patient with pernicious anemia. The arrow indicates the time at which the treatment was started. (*By courtesy of H. B. Goodall and the late D. G. Adamson.*)

also in children. Pyridoxine plays an essential role in the synthesis of haem, but it is only rarely that deficiency of this vitamin is the cause of anaemia in man. Anaemia is a feature of scurvy (p. 29) and is cured by giving ascorbic acid. Apart from its effects in promoting the absorption of iron it is doubtful if ascorbic acid is useful in the treatment of other types of anaemia.

Iron metabolism. The total amount of iron in the body of a 70 kg man is about 3 to 4 g. About 70 per cent of this is in the haemoglobin and myoglobin; the remainder consists of storage iron, transport iron and enzyme iron.

Iron released from the breakdown of red cells is not excreted but returns to the iron pool and is re-utilized. In the absence of external haemorrhage less than 1 mg of iron is lost from the body each day. The inevitable iron loss occurs from desquamated cells from the mucosae and skin and from traces in the bile and urine. In the adult male and the postmenopausal female this is the total amount of iron which has to be replaced from the diet, but the physiological requirements for growth, menstruation and pregnancy make additional demands. (Table 8.7). The median loss of blood during menstruation is 30 ml but many women lose far more than this. The upper limit of normality is 80 ml; above this signs of iron deficiency are likely to appear. In a normal pregnancy about 300 mg of iron are needed for the fetus and placenta, and the considerable increase in maternal red cell mass requires a further 400 to 500 mg. Most of this is needed during the second half of pregnancy and is achieved by an increase in the absorption of iron by the gut and mobilization of storage iron. Some of the iron from the increased red cell mass may go back into storage after delivery but some is lost in the bleeding after parturition. Breast feeding accounts for an iron loss of about 0·5 mg per day.

The physiological iron requirements may therefore be as much as 2 to 3 mg a day in non-pregnant women or up to 6 mg per day towards the end of a pregnancy (Table 8.7). Pathological losses from haemorrhage, notably from excessive menstrual loss or ulcerative lesions in the gastrointestinal tract may make the requirement even higher.

In Britain the average daily iron intake is about 14 mg and

Table 8.7 Estimated physiological iron requirements

	mg/day
Minimal obligatory loss	0·5–1·0
Growth: 0–1 year	0·7–0·8
1–11 years	0·3
Adolescence	0·5
Normal menstruation	0·5–1·6
Lactation	0·5

	Average total *iron requirement
Pregnancy	
Obligatory loss	180 mg
Fetus	250 mg
Placenta	70 mg
Increase in maternal red cells	400 mg
	900 mg

* This is accumulated mainly in the second half of pregnancy when the average daily iron requirement could be as high as 6 mg per day.

this might be thought to provide a generous margin, even for pathological iron losses. However, normally only about 10 per cent or less of the iron ingested is absorbed (Table 8.8) This amount is usually sufficient for adult men and postmenopausal females but children and younger women may be in precarious balance.

The iron in food is either in the form of *ferric iron complexes* or as *haem iron*. The latter is absorbed as haem and the iron is split off within the intestinal mucosal cell. Non-haem iron needs to be brought to the absorbing surface of the duodenum or upper part of the jejunum as a soluble chelate of small molecular weight. Reducing agents and substances such as ascorbic acid which produce soluble chelates enhance the absorption of non-haem iron while phytates and phosphates reduce absorption. For these reasons the composition of the diet is often more important than the total iron content in relation to the actual amount of iron absorbed. Thus vegetarian diets, especially those based almost exclusively on cereals, may provide a total iron intake several times that of the average Western type of diet, and yet be inadequate to prevent iron deficiency because of the excessively high phytate content.

Haem iron absorption is independent of such factors. Iron from meat is well absorbed and the meat protein itself aids absorption of non-haem iron. The *gastric secretion* may also be important in relation to the absorption of non-haem iron; acid aids solubility and chelating substances in normal gastric juice help to keep the iron in solution as the pH is raised. *Duodenal secretions* are important in the absorption of haem iron because they prevent the formation of large polymers which are not well absorbed. Conversely the *pancreatic secretion* by virtue of its bicarbonate content may reduce iron absorption by encouraging the formation of precipitates of non-haem iron and large polymers of haem iron.

The absorption of iron is adjusted in response to increased demand for iron. Thus absorption of a simple ferrous iron salt may be increased four-fold in iron deficiency. Absorption of iron from food is usually not more than doubled (Table 8.8). The change in absorption is probably determined by the

Table 8.8 Iron absorption in normal and iron deficient subjects measured with radioactive iron

	Mean percentage absorption iron ingested	
	Normal	Iron deficiency
Ferrous ascorbate	9·2	40·1
White bread	2·2	7·3
Oat cakes and porridge	4·0	10·0
Eggs	2·2	5·6
Chicken muscle	6·9	17·0
Haemoglobin	10·0	22·0

The data for white bread were obtained by adding radioactive iron to the flour. The remaining foods were labelled biologically with radioactive iron. Iron absorption was measured with a total body counter. (*Courtesy of Sheila Callendar.*)

amount of iron incorporated into ferritin of the mucosal cells as they are formed in the intestinal glands. Normally some of the iron entering the intestinal mucosal cell is taken by an unidentified carrier through the transport pool to be absorbed into the plasma; the rest is trapped in the ferritin apparatus and is ultimately lost when the cell is sloughed into the lumen of the bowel (Fig. 8.9).

The amount of iron incorporated into the mucosal cells as they are formed is in turn determined by the rate of erythropoiesis and the state of the body iron stores. Increased erythropoiesis or diminished iron stores both increase iron absorption probably by diverting iron from the mucosal cell. Conversely reduced erythropoiesis or increased iron stores result in diminished iron absorption.

When the iron enters the plasma most is attached to the specific iron binding protein *transferrin* which transports iron to and from the various compartments, for example from gut to bone marrow and from destroyed red cells back to the bone marrow. Transferrin is normally about one-third saturated with iron and the iron binding capacity is about 60 μmol/l.

A small proportion of the iron in the plasma is in the form of *ferritin*. Ferritin is a water soluble protein consisting of *apoferritin* and a variable amount of iron. When fully saturated the ferritin molecule contains 26 per cent of iron. Apoferritin is synthesized in response to the presence of iron in cells, and the plasma level of ferritin provides a useful measure of the iron stores in the body. Plasma ferritin levels are normally about 140 μg/l in normal men and 40 μg/l in normal women. In iron-deficiency anaemia plasma ferritin levels are usually less than 10 μg/l, but there is conflicting evidence about the relationship between plasma ferritin concentrations and iron stores.

Iron which is used for erythropoiesis is stored, mainly in the liver and the macrophages. The amount of storage iron depends upon the state of iron balance. It constitutes a reserve which may be called upon where iron requirements are increased, for example after blood loss. Storage iron consists of ferritin and *haemosiderin*. Ferritin can be visualized with the electron microscope and has a characteristic appearance. Haemosiderin is found in the liver and consists of iron-rich water insoluble granules which when appropriately stained are visible with the light microscope.

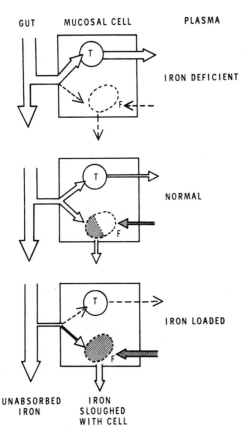

GUT   MUCOSAL CELL   PLASMA

IRON DEFICIENT

NORMAL

IRON LOADED

UNABSORBED   IRON
IRON   SLOUGHED
              WITH CELL

Fig. 8.9 Diagrammatic representation of the control of iron absorption by the mucosal cell. Absorption is determined primarily by the amount of iron incorporated into the ferritin apparatus (F) of the mucosal cell. In iron deficiency mucosal cells are deficient in ferritin and virtually all the iron entering the mucosal cell enters the transport pool (T) and passes on into the plasma. Little iron is shed into the lumen of the gut. In normal mucosa some ferritin is present hence less iron enters the cells. Of this smaller amount some enters the transport pool (T), the remainder enters the ferritin pool (F) and is shed as the cells slough off. In iron loaded states the increased quantity of ferritin in the cell allows little iron to enter from the gut. Of that which does most goes to the ferritin and is lost with the death of the cell. Little, if any, enters the transport pool. (Modified from M. E. Conrad (1970) In *Iron Deficiency*, ed. L. Hallberg, H. G. Harwerth & A. Vannotti. London and New York: Academic Press.)

Iron is also intimately concerned with the *respiratory enzymes*, for example the catalases and cytochromes. Reduction in the amount of these enzymes may be responsible for the degenerative tissue changes seen in association with iron deficiency.

Anaemia due to iron deficiency is particularly likely to occur in children and adolescents and in women during reproductive life. Normal infants are born with appreciable stores of iron but iron stores may be inadequate in premature infants who may also develop folate deficiency. Surveys made in Western Europe show a prevalence of iron deficiency in women of between 15 and 25 per cent. In the tropics iron deficiency is very common; it is often caused by infestation with worms, particularly hookworms in the duodenum. In general iron in vegetables and cereals is less well absorbed than that from animal sources (Fig. 8.10), thus vegetarian diets are likely to contribute towards iron deficiency by making the balance more

precarious. Another important cause of iron deficiency is chronic blood loss, especially from the gastrointestinal tract, as in patients with peptic ulcers, gastric or intestinal neoplasms or piles.

Before iron deficiency results in anaemia the tissue stores are depleted and the serum iron falls below 60 μg/100 ml. This is accompanied by an increase in the total iron binding capacity of the serum. With further iron depletion the haemoglobin concentration in the red cell (MCHC) falls and the cells appear hypochromic (*hypochromic anaemia*). Treatment with iron corrects the abnormalities but in order to replenish the iron stores, treatment has to be continued for some time after the haemoglobin has reached normal levels.

While a hypochromic anaemia is most commonly due to lack of iron, other causes include abnormalities of the synthesis of haem or globin. A disorder of haem synthesis causes a rare type of anaemia, *sideroblastic anaemia*. In this condition there is a massive accumulation of ferritin round the nucleus of the erythroblast which is known as a ring sideroblast. The causes

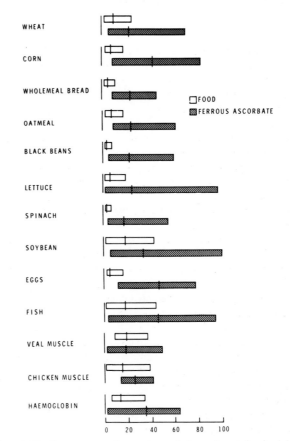

WHEAT

CORN

WHOLEMEAL BREAD

OATMEAL

BLACK BEANS

LETTUCE

SPINACH

SOYBEAN

EGGS

FISH

VEAL MUSCLE

CHICKEN MUSCLE

HAEMOGLOBIN

☐ FOOD
▨ FERROUS ASCORBATE

0   20   40   60   80   100

Fig. 8.10 Percentage absorption of iron from foods labelled biologically with radioactive iron compared with that from a similar dose of iron as a ferrous iron salt (ferrous ascorbate) in the same subjects. The vertical lines indicate the mean values and the horizontal bars indicate the limits. The vegetable sources were labelled with radioactive iron by growing them in tanks with radioactive iron added to the nutrient solution. In the case of the animal sources, the radioactive iron was given by injection and thus incorporated into the tissues. (Data derived from M. Layrisse, J. D. Cook, C. Martinez, M. Roche, I. N. Kuhn, R. B. Walker & C. A. Finch (1969) *Blood*, 33, 430–443; and S. T. Callender (1971) *Gerontologia Clinica*, 13, 44–51; and also unpublished data by S. T. Callender.)

of sideroblastic anaemias are complex but some cases respond to pyridoxine (p. 27).

Haemoglobin

Haemoglobin is a conjugated protein consisting of the protein globin and an iron-containing porphyrin ring *haem*. Each haemoglobin molecule contains four polypeptide chains, four haem units and therefore four iron atoms. At least three haemoglobins are normally found in man. Haemoglobin A comprises 98 per cent and haemoglobin A_2 the remaining 2 per cent of adult haemoglobin. Haemoglobin F forms more than half of the haemoglobin in the fetus and newborn child but is almost entirely replaced by haemoglobin A during infancy.

The various forms of haemoglobin all contain two identical α-polypeptide chains, but differ in the other chains: haemoglobin A contains two β-chains, haemoglobin A_2 two δ-chains and haemoglobin F two γ-chains. The amino acid sequence of a human β-chain is shown in Figure 8.11. In each chain the haem molecule is suspended between two residues of histidine with its iron linked directly to one of them. The other histidine residue is also associated with the iron but there is a gap into which oxygen molecules are introduced when haemoglobin is oxygenated.

Disorders of globin synthesis. These disorders, known as *haemoglobinopathies*, are common and usually inherited. Some are caused by abnormal amino acid sequences while others are caused by a failure of synthesis of one of the normal chains.

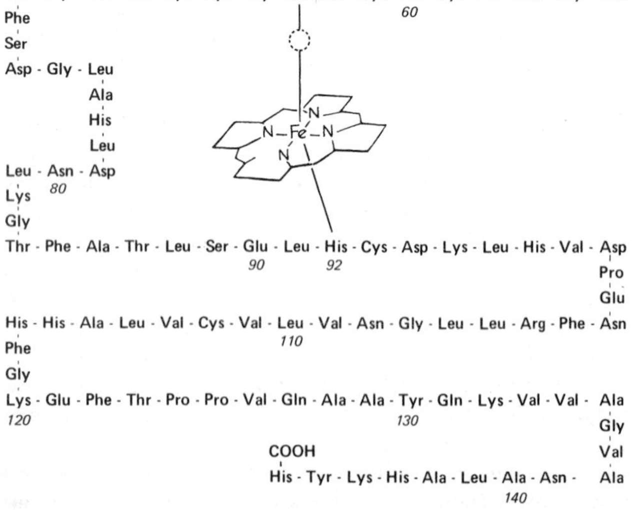

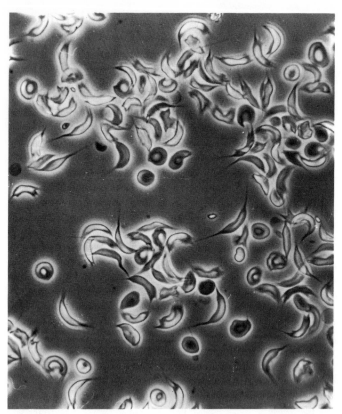

Fig. 8.12 Positive sickle test. This preparation was made by incubating a drop of blood in 2 per cent sodium metabisulphite for a few hours. The sample was from a Nigerian man with the sickle-cell trait. Phase contrast. × 280. (*By courtesy of A. S. Todd.*)

In sickle-cell anaemia sickling of the erythrocytes is due to the presence of an abnormal haemoglobin, HbS, with a single substituted amino acid in the β-chain (valine at position 6). The sickling phenomenon is precipitated by exposure to low oxygen tension (Fig. 8.12). Only slight hypoxia is required if the condition is inherited from both parents (homozygous) but more severe hypoxia is required to cause sickling in heterozygotes. In the homozygote severe haemolytic anaemia occurs from childhood, though not in the neonate who is protected by persistence of fetal haemoglobin; crises with thrombosis from sickling occur frequently, especially in relation to infection, particularly malaria. Yet curiously the heterozygote appears to succumb to malignant (falciparum) malaria less readily than normal individuals; this may help to explain the high prevalence of sickling in tropical Africa and Greece.

Single amino acid substitutions are also the basis of the other common haemoglobinopathies, C, D and E. HbC has apparently originated in a small area of West Africa (Ghana and Volta) whereas there are large pockets of HbD in various parts of the world (such as the Punjab) and HbE has a wide distribution throughout South-East Asia. These haemoglobinopathies cause no trouble in heterozygotes and only slight anaemia in homozygotes, but the combination of HbC with HbS (sickle-cell disease) can lead to more severe anaemia and vascular disease, especially in pregnancy.

Rare amino acid substitutions at key points in the globin chains may lead to unstable haemoglobin formation or to

Fig. 8.11 The β chain of human haemoglobin showing the haem moiety suspended between histidine residues numbers 63 and 92. The dotted circle represents the site for the attachment of oxygen.

abnormal handling of oxygen and consequent polycythaemia or cyanosis.

Thalassaemia (Mediterranean anaemia) is due to quantitative failure of synthesis of either the α- or β-globin chains of the haemoglobin molecule. The classical type is β-thalassaemia which is mild in the heterozygote but severe in the homozygote. In α-thalassaemia the condition is insignificant in the heterozygote yet lethal in the homozygote because of severe haemolysis in the fetus.

LEUCOCYTES

The circulating blood contains colourless cells called *white cells* or *leucocytes* which possess nuclei. There are three varieties of white cells—the *granulocytes* (so called because of their numerous cytoplasmic granules), the *lymphocytes* and the *monocytes*. From the time of birth onwards all the granular cells are formed in the bone-marrow and they are, therefore, often termed the myeloid series. Although a few lymphocytes are formed in the marrow, most are produced in the lymphatic tissues. The precise site of production of the monocytes is not known.

The Granulocytes

The granular leucocytes are formed in the bone-marrow, outside the blood vessels, from non-granular myeloblasts, themselves derived from the stem cells (p. 107). The myeloblasts give rise to three varieties of myelocyte, neutrophil, eosinophil and basophil, so-called from the behaviour of the granules toward Romanowsky stains which contain both (acid) eosin and (basic) methylene blue. When the myelocytes mature they become the neutrophil, eosinophil and basophil polymorphonuclear leucocytes of the blood (Fig. 8.13).

Polymorphonuclear leucocytes. These cells have lobed nuclei which vary greatly in shape, the number of lobes increasing with the age of the cell up to four or more. The neutrophil polymorphs, about 10 to 12 μm in diameter, are amoeboid and phagocytic when examined fresh on a warm stage. The movements are brought about by filaments of actin and myosin. The diameter of these, and all other leucocytes, as seen in a blood film depends on the thickness of the film. The small cytoplasmic granules stain faintly pink with Romanowsky stains and are, therefore, not strictly neutrophil. The electron microscope shows that the granules are 0·02 to 0·5 μm in diameter and that some contain much lipid. The metabolism of polymorphonuclear leucocytes is much more active than that of erythrocytes; glucose is metabolized mainly aerobically. They contain glycogen, glutathione, histamine and a number of enzymes including amylase, lipase, protease, catalase, nucleotidases, β-glucuronidase and phosphatases. In all, some thirty enzymes have been isolated from human neutrophil granules and almost all chemical bonds known in nature can be broken by them.

One intracellular enzyme of neutrophils, alkaline phosphatase, is of genetic interest. Its amount is increased in mongolism (trisomy 21) and it is usually absent in chronic myeloid leukaemia which is characterized by the *Philadelphia chromosome*, a small chromosome 21 (Chap. 32). Inter-

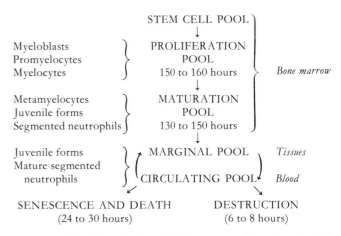

Fig. 8.13 The life-cycle of myeloid leucocytes. (*After* E. P. Cronkite & T. M. Fliedner (1964) *New England Journal of Medicine*, 270, 1347–1352.)

pretation of assays of neutrophil alkaline phosphatase is difficult because high values are found in infections and also when plasma levels of corticosteroids are high.

The mature granulocytes are distributed between the bone-marrow, the circulating blood and the tissues. Some idea of this distribution can be obtained in man by studying the effects of an injection of foreign proteins. This, after no more than an hour, can produce a great influx of mature polymorphs into the 'circulating pool' from a 'marginal pool' in the bone-marrow and other tissues.

The life-cycle of the granular leucocyte in man has been studied by autoradiography after the DNA has been labelled with tritiated thymidine. The life span of the mature polymorph in the blood and tissues is no more than about 30 hours.

One of the main functions of the polymorphonuclear leucocytes is the protection of the body from infection, because where the circulating and marginal pools are small (*leucopenia*) infection, general or local, readily occurs. Phagocytosis is the main way by which these leucocytes exert this function (p. 123). When a neutrophil polymorph engulfs a micro-organism its oxygen consumption increases immediately with production of hydrogen peroxide and superoxide which kill the micro-organism.

The eosinophil leucocyte. This cell has usually a bilobed nucleus. Large red-staining granules, 0·7 to 1·3 μm across, are scattered through the cell. The eosinophils show amoeboid movements but they are not actively phagocytic. They contain plasminogen and a variable amount of histamine.

Eosinophil leucocytes are formed in the bone-marrow and released into the circulating blood where they remain for a few hours only. They are attracted towards local tissue concentrations of histamine which they render physiologically inactive by some chemical means not yet understood. They also antagonize 5-hydroxytryptamine (Chap. 28). They probably leave the tissues through the lymphatics.

Basophil leucocyte. This cell has large cytoplasmic granules about 1 μm in diameter which stain a deep blue and contain heparin, 5-hydroxytryptamine and relatively large amounts of histamine. These cells, and similar cells found in the tissues, are often called 'mast' cells.

The Lymphocytes

Several different cell types have been given the name 'lymphocyte', the most characteristic being a small round cell with a densely staining nucleus and little cytoplasm—the so called small lymphocyte. Two main types of large lymphocyte are recognized microscopically: one form with basophilic cytoplasm ('irritation lymphocyte', 'activated lymphocyte' or Türk cell) and another form with a pale cytoplasm containing azurophil granules ('stress lymphocyte').

So far as their life-cycle is concerned the lymphocytes can be divided into two categories, those with a short life-span of the order of two to three days and a relatively rapid rate of production and a second group with a long life-span (perhaps 200 days or even more) and a much slower rate of production. Both types are found in the blood. The function of lymphocytes is described on pages 123 to 125.

Monocytes

The monocyte, 16 to 22 μm in diameter, the largest leucocyte in the blood, is recognized by its oval or horseshoe-shaped nucleus. The cytoplasm of the monocyte is pale-staining and frequently contains vacuoles and a few small reddish granules. Monocytes are actively phagocytic.

Leucocytosis and Leucopenia

The number of leucocytes in the circulating blood is very variable but ranges from 4×10^9 to 11×10^9 per litre, 60 to 70 per cent of which are neutrophil polymorphs (Table 8.14). Somewhat higher polymorph counts are found in pregnancy and in the newborn. An increase in blood leucocytes above 11×10^9 per litre is called a *leucocytosis* and a fall below 4×10^9 is known as *leucopenia*. As a rule abnormal fluctuations in the total leucocyte count are produced largely by changes in the number of neutrophil polymorphs but the factors responsible for such changes are not known in any detail. Violent exercise, fever and haemorrhage are followed by a leucocytosis and some increase occurs a few hours after a protein meal. Damage to, or destruction of, tissue as in accidents, fractures, surgical operations as well as infections lead within a few hours to a considerable and often prolonged increase in circulating polymorphonuclear cells.

Table 8.14 Numbers of white cells in normal adult blood. Lower numbers of neutrophil leucocytes are normally found in Africans.

	Numbers expressed as 10^9/litre	Percentage of total cells
Neutrophil polymorphonuclears	3 to 6	60 to 70
Lymphocytes	1·5 to 2·7	20 to 30
Monocytes	0·1 to 0·7	2 to 8
Eosinophil polymorphonuclears	0·1 to 0·4	2 to 4
Basophil polymorphonuclears	0 to 0·2	0 to 2
All leucocytes	5 to 9	100

It seems likely that leucocytosis is brought about by humoral factors which affect both release of leucocytes from the marginal pool as well as granulocytopoiesis—the production of more leucocytes by the bone-marrow. It is difficult at present to separate these two effects. A number of extracts prepared from various tissues, some of them containing a high proportion of nucleic acids, have been claimed to contain LPF (leucocyte-promoting factor) and a water-soluble, heat-stable, dialysable substance, leucopoietin G has been found in plasma. Adrenocortical steroids (Chap. 28) produce an increase in the polymorph count and a decrease in the number of lymphocytes and eosinophils.

Little is known about the ultimate fate of granular leucocytes and it is not known whether there is a feed-back mechanism governing granulocytopoiesis. Considerable numbers pass into the alimentary canal and are destroyed.

The concentration of circulating eosinophils varies by as much as 50 per cent during the day, the lowest counts with the least variation being found during the early afternoon. An increase in the eosinophil count (*eosinophilia*) is characteristic of certain skin diseases, infestation with parasites and allergic disorders such as asthma and hay-fever.

Leucopenia occurs in malnutrition or starvation and occasionally after administration of certain drugs, for example sulphonamides. Deficiency of vitamin B_{12} or folic acid commonly causes leucopenia; pyridoxine deficiency does so occasionally. Infection in a patient with megaloblastic anaemia may cause a further dangerous lowering of the leucocyte count. The leucocytes, particularly the neutrophils, may be reduced in some patients with enlargement of the spleen (hypersplenism). A severe leucopenia is dangerous because of the increased risk of infection.

THE PLATELETS

The platelets (thrombocytes) are the smallest of the formed elements of the blood, measuring 2 to 3 μm in diameter. They are formed by division of the cytoplasm of *megakaryocytes*, large cells 40–150 μm in diameter found in bone marrow, lungs and to a less extent in other tissues.

The megakaryocytes are polyploid cells containing, on average, four times the diploid number of chromosomes in a large, usually lobulated nucleus. Individual platelets are demarcated before release by a system of membranes derived from and continuous with the plasma membrane of the megakaryocyte. The rate of platelet production is partly controlled by the number of circulating platelets (normally 100 $\times 10^9$ to 500 $\times 10^9$ per litre) and it now seems likely that a humoral substance *thrombopoietin* mediates this influence in much the same way as does erythropoietin in haemopoiesis. Since a megakaryocyte has a volume 3000 to 4000 times that of a single thrombocyte it seems likely that each may produce more than a thousand platelets.

The mature platelet is a biconvex disc with a complex structure, a living cell which, like the erythrocyte, consumes oxygen in spite of the absence of a nucleus. It contains a system of microfilaments and microtubules (pp. 6, 7), granules containing lysosome-like enzymes, glycogen particles, electron dense granules (probably serotonin storing bodies), a few mitochondria, a Golgi apparatus and a smooth endoplasmic reticulum.

In man platelets have a life-span of 7 to 14 days. Some 10 to 15 per cent are lost by consumption in haemostasis and the maintenance of vascular integrity. The remainder are destroyed by the macrophage system, especially in the spleen; thus the platelet count rises if the spleen is removed. The main functions of platelets seem to be in haemostasis (see below) but it has now been shown that labelled platelets can contribute part of their cytoplasm to endothelial cells and may therefore have a role in supporting the metabolism of injured intima. Platelets also contain, and can release, a protein (β-thromboglobulin) able to increase vascular permeability and thus contribute to the humoral control of inflammatory reactions.

HAEMOSTASIS

Haemostasis describes the homeostatic mechanisms which operate to maintain the blood within the vessels and in a fluid state. Four main systems are concerned in haemostasis (Fig. 8.15): the plasma coagulation factors, platelet adhesion and aggregation, the reactions and surface properties of the blood vessels and, modifying all these, the fibrinolytic system. These systems are also modified by the reactions of the complement (p. 127) and kinin systems (Chap. 28).

Blood Coagulation

When blood is withdrawn from a vein in the arm, and emptied into a test-tube, clotting takes place in about 5 minutes at room temperature. The time of coagulation depends on the conditions under which the estimation is made. The reactions leading to the clotting of blood are modified by factors from injured tissue, by changes in the electrical charge on the surface of the container and by changes in temperature. When blood clots in a test-tube it becomes a solid mass but if the tube is left for some time, the clot contracts (*retracts*) to leave a supernatant yellow fluid called *serum*. Microscopic examination of the clot shows it to be composed of irregularly arranged fibrils of a protein material called *fibrin*, in the interstices of which the cells are trapped. The cells are not necessary for coagulation since plasma free from erythrocytes, leucocytes and platelets can still be made to clot within 3 to 5

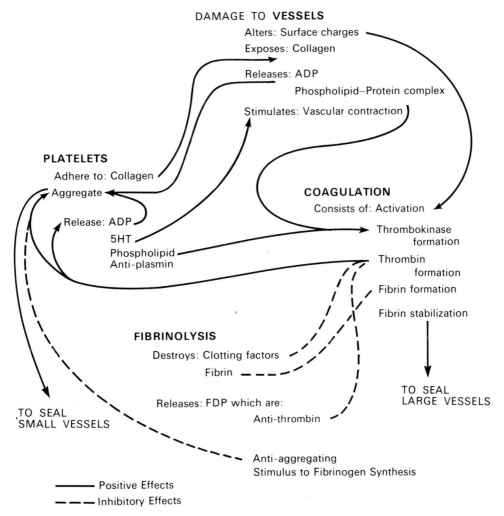

Fig. 8.15 Mechanisms involved in haemostasis and their interactions. FDP = Fibrin degradation products. (*By courtesy of A. S. Todd.*)

mins. The platelets, however, release factors which accelerate coagulation. For example in siliconed tubes the clotting time is shortened by the addition of platelets.

Fibrin is produced by polymerization of a soluble precursor *fibrinogen* normally present in the blood plasma. Fairly pure fibrinogen with a molecular weight of 340 000 can now be prepared. Work with rat tissues maintained by perfusion has shown that fibrinogen is formed in the liver; the formation rate is increased when the blood level of fibrinogen is low. The fibrinogen molecule (Fig. 8.16) is a dimer, each subunit being composed of three peptide chains, united by a complex of disulphide linkages known as the 'disulphide knot'. The amino-terminal segments play an important part in the formation of fibrin. The conversion of fibrinogen to fibrin is brought about by the enzyme *thrombin* which splits arginyl-glycine bonds to liberate the small peptides A and B (Fig. 8.16). This 'unmasks' sites which allow hydrogen bonds to form between adjacent fibrin monomers. Polymers of fibrin formed in this way are relatively unstable and may be dissolved for example in strong urea solution; they repolymerize if the concentration of urea is reduced. On the other hand, fibrin formed in whole blood or from plasma containing calcium ions is insoluble in urea; the fibrin polymer has been 'stabilized' by the formation of peptide linkages between adjacent monomers. The cross-links are formed by another enzyme, usually called *fibrin stabilizing factor*. This enzyme, an aminotransferase, forms glutamyl-lysine linkages at three or four specific sites on the fibrin monomer. The resulting 'stable fibrin' is mechanically stronger, more compact structurally and more resistant to attack by proteolytic enzymes. The diminution or absence of stable fibrin may explain the impairment of wound

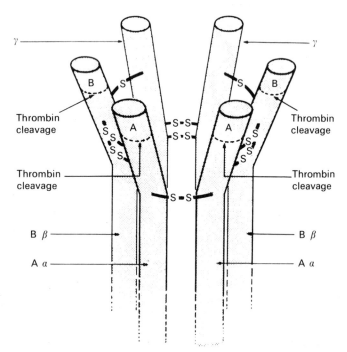

.Fig. 8.16 The amino-terminal part of the fibrinogen molecule to show the six peptide chains. The whole molecule has a molecular weight of 680 000. The action of thrombin is to release peptides A and B from the α and β chains. (*After* B. Blombäck (1969) *British Journal of Haematology*, **17**, 145.)

Table 8.17 International nomenclature of blood coagulation factors with synonyms

Factor	Synonyms
I	Fibrinogen
II*	Prothrombin
III	Thromboplastin
IV	Calcium
V	Labile factor, proaccelerin, Ac-globulin
VII*	Stable factor, proconvertin, serum prothrombin conversion accelerator (SPCA)
VIII	Antihaemophilic globulin (AHG), antihaemophilic factor A
IX*	Christmas factor, plasma thromboplastin component (PTC), antihaemophilic factor B
X*	Stuart-Prower factor
XI	Plasma thromboplastin antecedent (PTA), anti-haemophilic factor C
XII	Hageman factor
XIII	Fibrin stabilizing factor, fibrinase, fibrinoligase

The first four factors are well known by their names which are likely to remain in use, but the international nomenclature (Roman figures) for the other factors is now becoming general.

* These factors are affected by the anticoagulant drugs (coumarins and indanediones) much used in the treatment of thrombotic diseases.

healing seen in persons with an inborn deficiency of fibrin stabilizing factor. The precursor of the aminotransferase is activated by thrombin in the presence of calcium ions. These linkages may account for the characteristic periodicity of fibrin seen in electron micrographs. Thrombin also has a powerful accelerating effect on blood coagulation because of its ability to increase the rate of formation of other enzymes of the coagulation system.

The conversion of fibrinogen to stable fibrin by thrombin, fibrin stabilizing factor and calcium ions is the end of a complex chain of enzyme reactions involving at least 10 other factors. Knowledge of these was in the past gained by studying patients with an inborn, or acquired, deficiency of single factors but modern biochemical methods now allow us to describe the process of coagulation in the form of a chain of reactions. Traces of the history of blood coagulation research remain in the numerical nomenclature of the clotting factors which relates to the order of their discovery rather than to their position in the chain of reactions (Table 8.17). It should be noted: (1) that the substrate for each enzyme is a proenzyme which becomes the active enzyme for the next reaction; (2) that this arrangement can function as an 'enzymic amplifier', so that a small change at the beginning of the system may result in the formation of large amounts of thrombin and fibrin at the end; (3) that the 'amplifier' can be modified by negative or positive 'feed-back'. Positive feed-back is exemplified by the ability of thrombin to accelerate the rate of activation of factor X. Negative feed-back is exemplified by the neutralization of thrombin by fibrin; (4) that the system has two 'inputs' (the intrinsic and extrinsic systems of thromboplastin generation, see below); (5) that calcium ions are required at several stages of the reaction.

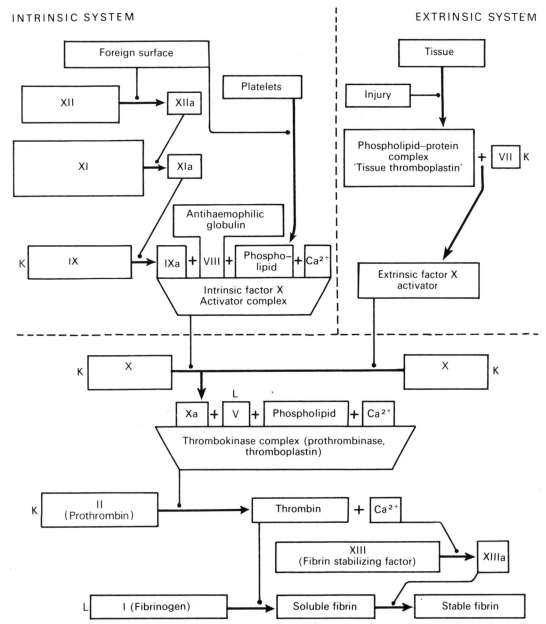

Fig. 8.18 Scheme of the coagulation system: a, after the number of a factor indicates the activated form of that factor, for example IXa is activated factor IX; K, factors requiring vitamin K for their synthesis in the liver; L, factors synthesized in the liver, not needing vitamin K. A heavy arrow indicates a chemical transformation; a line ending in a dot indicates a factor promoting a reaction. For synonyms see Table 8.17. (*By courtesy of A. S. Todd.*)

The train of coagulation reactions may be initiated in two different ways (Fig. 8.18). The first is by exposure of the plasma to an altered surface, the important feature of which is a change in the electrical charge. In some way this causes activation of factors XI and XII. The product of this reaction is activated factor XI—usually designated as XIa which then acts on factor IX to give IXa. Factor IXa then combines with factor VIII and with phospholipid from platelets to activate factor X. Factor X similarly complexes with factor V, calcium and phospholipid to form thrombokinase (sometimes called thromboplastin). Thrombokinase activates factor II (prothrombin) to form thrombin. It will be noted that apart from the 'altered surface' all the components of this reaction chain are contained within the blood, hence the name *intrinsic coagulation system*.

In the second reaction sequence, the *extrinsic system*, the surface-activated reactions of the intrinsic system are by-passed; phospholipid and protein from injured tissue (also sometimes called thromboplastin) combine with factor VII and calcium to activate factor X; from this point onwards the reactions are as in the intrinsic system. In both systems the function of the phospholipid seems to be 'physical' rather than 'chemical', the lipid-protein micelles ensuring that the components have the correct conformation and interrelationship for the reactions to proceed.

Clinical tests of the coagulation system. To study these reactions it is first necessary to obtain blood in the unclotted state, usually by removing calcium ions from the system. Oxalates precipitate the calcium as insoluble oxalate; citrate and salts of ethylene-diamine-tetraacetic acid (EDTA, seques-trene) chelate calcium ions. In some cases *heparin* (see below) may be used to prevent clotting both *in vitro* and *in vivo* but it is generally unsatisfactory in coagulation studies. Substances which prevent blood clotting are collectively known as anti-coagulants. It should be noted that this term is also applied to drugs which act on the liver to inhibit the synthesis of clotting factors and impair coagulation *in vivo*.

The simplest test used is the *whole blood clotting time*, the time taken for blood to clot in a glass tube under standard conditions. This tests factors in the intrinsic system.

The *one stage prothrombin time* tests factors from the extrinsic system and factors common to both systems, notably fibrinogen and factors V, VII and X. The test is carried out by adding tissue extract and calcium to a plasma sample and measuring the time taken for the mixture to coagulate. It is used to assess the effect of anticoagulant drugs, such as dicoumarin.

The *thromboplastin (thrombokinase) generation test* illus-trates the use of two stage systems, and also the technique of partial fractionation of the blood to identify coagulation deficiencies. Three fractions are used: (1) fresh plasma containing factor V and factor VIII, other factors having been removed from the plasma by adsorption on to aluminium hydroxide; (2) serum containing factors VII, IX and X, other factors having been destroyed by incubating the serum at 37°C; (3) platelet extract providing phospholipid. Phospholipid extracted from tissue may be used instead of that from platelets. When these three fractions are incubated at 37°C together with calcium ions thrombokinase is formed. The amount of thrombokinase formed after any given time may be measured by adding a sample of the incubated mixture to normal plasma and measuring the rate of coagulation. By substituting each normal fraction in turn by the corresponding fraction from the patient's plasma, the probable position of the defect in the reaction scheme can be detected. This type of test is frequently used in the diagnosis of haemophilia (factor VIII deficiency) and Christmas disease (factor IX deficiency), but the identification of other defects in the clotting system and assay of individual clotting factors are also possible by using variations of this technique.

Another method often used to identify a clotting disorder is to add the plasma under investigation to plasma from a patient with a known single deficiency, to see whether the plasmas are mutually corrective. Correction of the clotting functions implies a disorder different from that in the 'known' sample, failure to correct implies identity of deficiency.

Disorders of coagulation. The best known of the genetic-ally determined disorders is haemophilia (a functional defect of the clotting factor VIII molecule). It is inherited as an X-linked recessive (Chap. 32). The haemophiliac patient suffers from crippling haemorrhage into tissues and joints after minor injury and bleeds excessively if wounded. Factor IX deficiency (Christmas disease) is almost indistinguishable clinically from haemophilia and is inherited in the same way.

The treatment for episodes of bleeding in haemophilia is the administration of factor VIII. Whole blood is inefficient for this purpose because the volume needed to supply sufficient factor VIII to correct the deficiency is very large. For this reason concentrated forms of factor VIII are nearly always used for treatment and prophylaxis of haemophilia. Major diffi-

culties in the treatment of haemophilia by replacement are the liability of factor VIII *in vitro*, its short half-life *in vivo* (12 to 14 hours) and the tendency for a few patients to become immunized to the protein. Of the acquired coagulation disorders, those associated with liver disease have provided useful information about the clotting system. Fibrinogen, prothrombin, factors V, VII, IX and X are all synthesized in the liver and their production may be severely depressed in liver disease. Of these factors all but factor V and fibrinogen seem to require vitamin K for their synthesis. Thus clotting abnormalities closely resembling those due to liver disease may be seen in patients with vitamin K deficiency due to impairment of fat absorption in the gut especially when that is caused by biliary obstruction.

Anticoagulant drugs. Some chemical analogues of vitamin K are effective as anticoagulant drugs because they inhibit the synthesis of factors VII, IX and X by the liver; they can be given by mouth and are widely used in medicine. Their effects can be reversed by administration of vitamin K_1 (the water-soluble form of this vitamin).

Heparin is another widely used anticoagulant. It is a proteoglycan and is active *in vitro* and *in vivo* but it must be given by injection. Its anticoagulant activity is attributed to its sulphate groups which react with free basic groups on protein clotting factors; it interferes especially with the actions of factor Xa and of thrombin. The action of heparin in the circulation may be neutralized by administration of *protamine*, a basic nuclear protein obtained from fish sperm. Although heparin is widely distributed in the mast cells, there is little evidence that, in man, it functions physiologically as an anticoagulant.

An extract from the venom of the Malayan pit viper has been used to produce a different kind of anticoagulant effect, *defibrination*. This extract (arvin) splits fibrin peptide A (Fig. 8.16) from the fibrinogen molecule to produce a weakly aggregated unstable fibrin which is rapidly removed from the circulation by the macrophages. In this way all the circulating fibrinogen is consumed.

In normal circumstances clotting does not occur in the blood vessels partly because the tendency to clot is prevented by inhibiting reactions and partly because any fibrin formed is removed by fibrinolysis. Inhibitory control of the coagulation reaction occurs mainly at the stage of fibrinogen conversion, in the form of *antithrombin* effects. Six antithrombin effects have been described—not all of them well characterized or generally recognized. The best established are the *antithrombin I* effect, that is the neutralization of thrombin by adsorption on to fibrin and *antithrombin III*, which is greatly enhanced in its activity by the addition of heparin.

Fibrinolysis

In the living animal fibrin formation is an intermediate step in a variety of physiological and pathological processes: as in haemostasis during menstruation and at parturition, in the inflammatory response and in reactions to cancer cells in the circulation and tissues. In many cases fibrin formed within blood vessels is rapidly dissolved to restore the fluidity of the blood, in others the fibrin becomes hyalinized or is removed by phagocytes and replaced by connective tissue. The process of liquefaction of fibrin is known as fibrinolysis; it may occur as rapidly as blood coagulation itself. Fibrinolysis also resembles blood clotting in being the end result of a chain of enzyme reactions involving components from both plasma and tissues.

The main plasma component of the fibrinolytic system is *plasminogen*, inactive precursor of the proteolytic enzyme *plasmin*. Plasmin is a serine protease capable of splitting peptide linkages involving arginine or lysine. Plasmin also splits other proteins including factors V, VIII and IX, the immunoglobulins, some components of the complement system (p. 127) and the kininogens (to produce vasoactive kinins such as bradykinin and kallikrein). Plasmin activity is abolished by *antiplasmins*, from the α_1- and α_2-globulin fractions of plasma. Plasmin and antiplasmin form complexes which are dissociated by fibrin. For this reason plasmin is not detectable in blood unless fibrin is added to dissociate the α_2-globulin-plasmin complex. These unique inhibitory arrangements render the action of this non-specific protease highly selective for fibrin. Many drugs have been used as inhibitors of fibrinolysis, the most effective are tranexamic acid and aprotinin, a polypeptide which also inhibits trypsin and kallikrein.

The transformation of the enzyme precursor, plasminogen, to the active form, plasmin, requires the presence of an activator simply referred to as *plasminogen activator*. Substances having an activating effect on plasminogen are found in small amounts in the blood and in high concentration in the tissues, especially in the endothelium of blood vessels (Fig. 8.19). Urine contains a plasminogen activator, urokinase. Proteolytic enzymes such as trypsin and leucocyte protease can activate plasminogen, as can the lysosomal enzymes of many types of cell.

In addition to endogenous agents, activators of plasminogen have been obtained from various bacteria, moulds and plants. Of these the most important is *streptokinase*, a protein from cultures of haemolytic streptococci. In purified form this material is widely used to promote fibrinolytic activity in the circulating blood of patients with thrombosis. Streptokinase acts by converting some of the plasminogen into a plasminogen activator.

Fibrinolytic activity in whole blood is commonly measured by the *dilute whole blood clot lysis time technique*. Blood is diluted to diminish the effect of inhibitors, clotted by thrombin and then incubated. The time taken for the clots to dissolve is a measure of spontaneous fibrinolytic activity. The other widely used method is the *euglobulin lysis time technique*. The plasma under test is diluted and acidified to precipitate a protein fraction containing fibrinogen, plasminogen and plasminogen activator; much of the inhibitory activity remains in the supernatant. The precipitate is redissolved, clotted by the addition of thrombin, and the time taken for the clot to dissolve at 37°C is measured.

Fibrinolytic activity is detectable in the blood of normal subjects; it is increased after exercise, after injection adrenaline and in emotional stress; it follows a circadian rhythm being increased by day and diminished at night. Arterial blood contains less activator than venous and in man the activator content of the endothelium in arteries is generally less than that in the venous intima. The endothelium of arteries supplying the retina, myocardium and kidneys is an exception

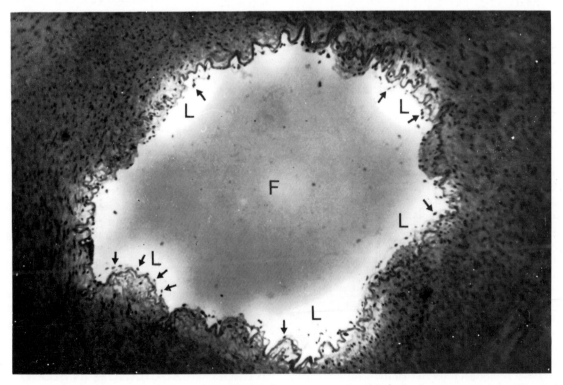

Fig. 8.19 Histological demonstration of plasminogen activator. The tissue is a small branch of a coronary artery. The section has been mounted on a thin layer of plasminogen-rich fibrin, incubated then fixed and stained. The fibrin shows as a uniform dark background (F). The light areas (L) show where the fibrin has been digested and are related to endothelial cells (indicated by arrows). The activator in the endothelium has converted plasminogen to plasmin and fibrinolysis has followed. × 170. (*By courtesy of A. S. Todd.*)

to this rule and has a high content of activator. One method for demonstrating the plasminogen activator content of tissues is shown in Figure 8.19.

Fibrinolysis seems to go on continuously in the circulating blood since fibrin degradation products (FDP) can be detected in the blood of healthy subjects. In cases of thrombosis and of excessive fibrinolysis the plasma level of FDP may be increased from the normal value of 2 to 10 mg/l to as much as 760 mg/l. When first formed FDP have a heparin-like action on the thrombin-fibrinogen reaction.

Platelets

Platelets (p. 114) are essential for haemostasis but have so far been mentioned only in connexion with their ability to release phospholipid for the formation of the activator of factor X in the intrinsic system. Platelets have other important actions in haemostasis: (1) *Adhesion reactions.* Platelets have the ability to adhere to foreign surfaces. The most important of these are collagen (*in vivo*) and glass (in laboratory experiments). (2) *Reversible aggregation.* Platelets adhere to each other in a reversible fashion under the influence of certain substances especially adenosine diphosphate, noradrenaline and 5-hydroxytryptamine. This reaction is not at first accompanied by changes in fine structure. (3) *Irreversible aggregation.* This reaction is triggered by thrombin, by ADP in high concentrations and by exposure to collagen. All these agents seem to stimulate release of endogenous ADP from the platelets which have easily recognized morphological changes such as rupture of the cytoplasmic membrane and degranulation. *In vivo* masses of irreversibly aggregated platelets form haemostatic plugs in damaged small blood vessels. (4) *The release phenomenon.* During the aggregation reactions, especially irreversible aggregation, substances important in coagulation and in the control of vascular tone are released from the platelets. The substances released include ATP and ADP, 5HT, K^+, platelet factor 3 (phospholipid), platelet factor 4 (a basic protein with an antiheparin action), thromboxane A_2 (a prostaglandin) and lysosomal enzymes. (5) *Contractile function.* Platelets contain an actomyosin-like protein, thrombasthenin, which contracts in the presence of magnesium ions, using ATP as its energy source. This protein is responsible for the phenomenon of *clot retraction.* The contractile protein may have important functions in altering the configuration of the platelet membrane and in discharging cytoplasmic contents during the release reaction. Clot retraction is a weak effect and may be little more than a vestigial function, of interest only as a laboratory indicator of platelet activity.

Prostaglandins play an important part in platelet metabolism and function. Platelets synthesize from arachidonic acid prostaglandins including thromboxane A_2, one of the most powerful platelet aggregating agents known. This synthesis may be arrested by commonly used anti-inflammatory drugs such as aspirin and indomethacin which inhibit the enzyme cyclo-oxygenase. It is of great interest that the endothelial cells of human blood vessels synthesize a prostaglandin, *prostacyclin.* This substance is a most potent *inhibitor* of platelet aggregation and also a strong vasodilator. It is released from the lungs and circulates in the blood. These observations are the basis of a new approach to the prevention of arterial thrombosis by the use of drugs modifying prostaglandin metabolism.

Methods of studying platelets and their functions. In the *clot retraction* test the proportion of serum expressed from whole blood by clot retraction under standard conditions is measured. Clot retraction is impaired if either the number, or the contractile function, of the platelets is diminished. The *proportion of adhesive platelets* is assessed by measuring the loss of platelets when blood is exposed to a foreign surface. This test can be modified by addition of aggregating agents such as ADP which increase adhesion. *Platelet aggregation* can be measured by the changes in the light extinction of platelet suspensions resulting from the addition of aggregation reagents such as ADP, collagen, noradrenaline and thrombin.

Platelet disorders. The most important platelet disorder is a reduction in number—*thrombocytopenia.* This may be due to excessive utilization in abnormal coagulation processes; excessive destruction by the spleen; impaired production from megakaryocytes damaged by poisons, immune reactions or the presence of neoplasms. Major disorders of platelet function are rare and are usually hereditary; they are referred to as *thrombasthenia.* Minor impairment of function can be produced by a variety of drugs. Aspirin inhibits endogenous ADP release and thromboxane A_2 production, impairing aggregation in response to collagen, while prostaglandin E_1 increases the amount of cyclic AMP. Platelet disturbances lead to haemorrhage from small vessels, a prolonged bleeding time and spontaneous capillary haemorrhages into the skin, known as purpura. Bleeding due to thrombocytopenia may be relieved temporarily by the transfusion of platelet concentrates.

The Blood Vessels

The action of platelets and the coagulation of the blood modified by fibrinolysis are directed towards the achievement of haemostasis (Fig. 8.15). A fourth element is also concerned, namely the vasomotor response not only to injury but also to pharmacologically active peptides released during clotting and fibrinolysis.

Thrombosis. Thrombosis is the formation of solid masses of fibrin and platelets in blood vessels. It may occur in the course of haemostasis especially when larger vessels have been injured. It may also occur in response to changes in the intimal lining of vessels or when the balance of the coagulation and fibrinolytic systems is disturbed. One result may be the obstruction of blood flow in an important vessel such as a coronary artery or a leg vein.

An increase in blood coagulability is often seen 8 to 12 days after a surgical operation and also after childbirth. It is caused by an elevated platelet count, an increased platelet adhesiveness, altered concentration of clotting factors and inhibitors. At the same time thrombotic disease is more likely to occur.

PHYSIOLOGICAL CHANGES IN BLOOD IN INFANCY AND CHILDHOOD

The haemoglobin content of the blood (Fig. 8.20) at birth is about 21 g/dl, but it declines from this high value during the first two or three months of infancy to about 12 g/dl, rising again to about 13 g/dl in the succeeding three months. The iron released by breakdown of the haemoglobin of the destroyed red cells remains within the body and is used again for the synthesis of haemoglobin, but the initial fall in the red cell count is not prevented by the administration of iron even in large amounts.

Fetal haemoglobin (HbF) was mentioned earlier. It forms about 50 per cent of the haemoglobin at term but after birth the proportion declines rapidly. Little is known of the factors which control the switch from HbF to HbA. Fetal haemoglobin takes up oxygen more readily and gives up carbon dioxide more easily than does adult haemoglobin. This property is no doubt of value to the fetus which is exposed to relatively low oxygen tensions.

The red cell count is high at birth (Fig. 8.20) but declines in parallel with the haemoglobin level. This rapid destruction of red cells together with the relatively low activity of UDP glucuronyl transferase in the infants' 'immature' liver is responsible for the 'physiological jaundice' that is seen in some 30 per cent of all new-born babies, maximal on the third day. A few nucleated red cells are found in the peripheral circulation for a short time after birth. About 5 to 10 per cent of reticulocytes occur in the blood of the newborn but adult numbers (1 per cent or less) are reached in a few days. The red cells at birth contain only one quarter of the adult amount of carbonic anhydrase; premature infants have even less. The infant starts off with 300 to 500 mg of iron provided by the mother; after birth the iron requirements must be provided in the food.

At birth there is a polymorphonuclear leucocytosis lasting only several days; this is followed by a lymphocytosis which persists for a year or so. The platelets, unlike the other cellular elements, are present at birth in reduced numbers, normal adult values being attained within the first 10 days of life.

The haematological changes in premature infants are of particular importance. At birth many such infants have a very high haemoglobin level, often of the order of 20 or 21 g/dl. This appears to be due to fetal anoxia, particularly in the so-called dysmature infant suffering from placental failure. The premature infant is born with poor iron stores and, if his mother has not received folic acid, may develop megaloblastic anaemia. Tocopherol (p. 31) may be important in protecting the erythrocyte of the premature infant from haemolysis.

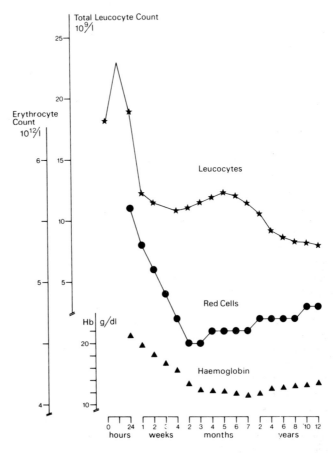

Fig. 8.20 A graphic representation of mean values for erythrocyte count (★), total leucocyte count (●) and haemoglobin (Hb) content of whole blood (▲) from birth to 12 years. (Data obtained from *Documenta Geigy: Scientific Tables.* 7th edition. Basle: Geigy.)

REFERENCES

Aledort L M (ed) 1975 Recent advances in hemophilia. Annals of the New York Academy of Sciences 240: 1–426
Barbior B. M 1975 Cobalamin: biochemistry and pathophysiology. Wiley, New York
Beeson P B, Bass D A 1977 The eosinophil. Saunders, London
Biggs R (ed) 1976 Human blood coagulation, haemostasis and thrombosis, 2nd edn. Blackwell, Oxford
Brewer D B 1972 Activities of the neutrophil polymorph. British Medical Journal 2: 396–400
Cawley J C, Hayhoe F G J 1973 Ultrastructure of haemic cells. Saunders, London
Chanarin E, Brozovic M, Tidmarsh E, Waters D A W 1976 Blood and its diseases. Churchill Livingstone, Edinburgh
Cline M J 1975 The white cell. University Press, Harvard
Dacie J V, Lewis S M 1975 Practical haematology, 5th edn. Churchill Livingstone, Edinburgh
Dawson A A, Walker W 1974 Blood formation and the pathogenesis of anaemia. British Medical Journal 2: 260–262
Giblett E R 1969 Genetic markers in human blood. Blackwell, Oxford
Gordon J L (ed) 1976 Platelets in biology and pathology. North Holland, Amsterdam
Hardisty R M, Weatherall D J (ed) 1974 Blood and its disorders. Blackwell, Oxford
Hirsh J, Brain E A 1979 Haemostasis and thrombosis. Churchill Livingstone, Edinburgh
Humbert J R (ed) 1975 Neutrophil physiology and pathology. Seminars in Haematology 12: 1–160
Katz D H 1977 Lymphocyte differentiation, recognition and regulation. Academic Press, London
Lehman H, Huntsman R G 1974 Man's haemoglobins. North Holland, Amsterdam
MacFarlane R G, Robb-Smith A H 1961 Functions of the blood. Blackwell, Oxford

Moncada S, Vane J R 1979 Arachidonic acid metabolites and the interactions between blood-vessel walls. New England Journal of Medicine 300: 1142–1147

Murphy P 1976 The neutrophil. Plenum, New York

Ogston D, Bennett R 1977 Haemostasis. Wiley, New York

Poller L (ed) 1977 Recent advances in blood coagulation: 2. Churchill Livingstone, Edinburgh

Porter R, Fitzsimmons D W (eds) 1977 Ciba foundation symposium: iron metabolism. Elsevier, Amsterdam

Surgenor D M (ed) 1974 The red blood cell, 2nd edn. Academic Press, New York

Suttie J W, Jackson C M 1977 Prothrombin structure, activation and biosynthesis. Physiological reviews 57: 1–70

Thomas D (ed) 1978 Thrombosis. British Medical Bulletin 34: No. 2

Thomas D (ed) 1977 Haemostasis. British Medical Bulletin 33: 183–288

Thomson, Jean M (ed) 1979 Blood coagulation and haemostasis. Churchill Livingstone, Edinburgh

Watts G 1979 What are mast cells for? New Scientist 28 June 1104–1106

Weatherall D J (ed) 1976 Haemoglobin. British Medical Bulletin 32: No. 3

9 Immunity and the Defence Mechanisms against Foreign Substances

This chapter is concerned with the body's defence mechanisms against foreign materials such as bacteria, viruses and also proteins from other animals. Some of these mechanisms are non-specific and do not depend on previous exposure of a person to the foreign substance. Other defence mechanisms, particularly the immune response, operate only when a person has been previously exposed to a particular substance.

Examples of non-specific defence mechanisms include those of the skin (Chap. 17), whose outer horny layer is a physical barrier to the entry of bacteria, and the mucous membranes of the respiratory tract, whose cilia dispose of particulate matter by sweeping it into the pharynx where it is swallowed. The acid of gastric juice destroys many organisms. The sweat and sebaceous secretions of the skin contain bactericidal and fungicidal substances while tears contain *lysozyme*, a bactericidal protein. Nasal secretions not only trap organisms but also contain proteoglycans capable of inactivating some viruses.

Within the tissues and blood stream there are phagocytic cells which ingest and destroy foreign particles. These include the polymorphonuclear leucocytes of the blood and the larger cells of the *macrophage system*, namely the monocytes in the blood and the histiocytes in the tissues. The process of phagocytosis is shown in Figure 9.1.

The polymorphonuclear leucocytes (p. 113) provide an important early defence against bacterial invasion by migrating from the blood to sites where bacteria are multiplying. These cells are capable of engulfing and digesting many of the bacteria that cause acute infections; some bacteria are engulfed but not digested. The ingestion of foreign particles or of some endogenous material such as damaged erythrocytes is enchanced when they are coated by specific antibodies. Bacteria are destroyed not only by lysosomal enzymes but also by hydrogen peroxide produced within the cell in glucose metabolism. This mechanism is initiated by phagocytosis.

Many bacterial infections are controlled at an early stage by the local action of the polymorphonuclear leucocytes; pus contains the remains of these cells. If an infection is too severe to be controlled in this way, bacteria escape into the blood vessels and lymphatics and are carried to the lymph nodes and spleen. There they are trapped by the macrophages (p. 127) which play a part in stimulating the immune response.

The remainder of this chapter is concerned with the specific defence mechanisms of immunity. Substances capable of stimulating immune responses are known as *antigens* and generally have a molecular weight greater than 5000. Examples include proteins, polysaccharides (such as those of bacterial cell walls) and complex lipids. There are two kinds of immune mechanism: *humoral immunity* which involves the production of antibodies, and *cell-mediated immunity* in which lymphocytes react directly with foreign material. Both mechanisms involve lymphocytes.

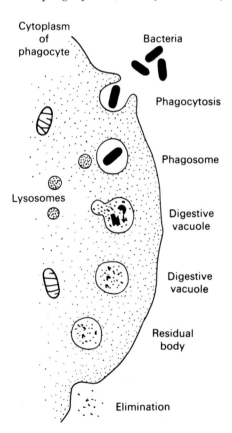

Fig. 9.1 The mode of action of a phagocytic cell such as a polymorphonuclear leucocyte or a macrophage. A bacterium is ingested by pinocytosis, and lysosomal enzymes are poured into the resulting vacuole.

The Lymphocytes

Lymphocytes are formed in the bone marrow in adults; in the fetus, the yolk sac, the liver and possibly the thymus are additional sources. Lymphocytes are found in all tissues except the central nervous system. The lymphatic tissue contains 100 g of lymphocytes, the bone marrow 70 g and the blood 3 g; the total amount in the body is about 1300 g. Stress or the administration of adrenal corticoids inhibits the production of lymphocytes.

Lymphocytes are continually circulating from the blood into the tissues and then into lymphatic vessels and back to the blood (Fig. 9.2). This circulation of lymphocytes is of great importance in ensuring that all parts of the body are surveyed for foreign material. Furthermore, when lymphocytes pass through the lymph nodes and spleen they are brought into close proximity to macrophages containing foreign antigens.

There are two classes of lymphocytes, T-lymphocytes and B-lymphocytes. Their different functions are described below. T- and B-lymphocytes cannot be distinguished by light microscopy but can be identified by complicated *in vitro* tests. About 75 per cent of circulating lymphocytes are T-cells.

person (allografts). T-lymphocytes also regard as 'foreign' some antigens found in malignant neoplasms.

The T-lymphocyte is derived from a stem cell in the bone marrow which migrates to the thymus and is there processed to become effective or *immunologically competent* (Fig. 9.3). This process is marked by the acquisition of new surface antigens of which the best known (in the mouse) is designated theta (θ). This maturation in the thymus is under the influence of a local polypeptide hormone known as *thymosin*.

The immunologically competent T-lymphocyte then circulates until it meets a foreign antigen, generally in a lymph node or another lymphoid tissue such as the spleen or the aggregated lymph follicles (Peyer's patches) in the intestine. There the T-lymphocyte undergoes *blast-transformation* giving rise to numerous progeny which have specific receptors for that antigen on their surface. When an activated T-lymphocyte encounters its antigen it releases a number of humoral factors of low molecular weight (*lymphokines*) which include factors responsible for the attraction (chemotaxis) of macrophage cells and also *lymphotoxin* (which kills foreign cells) and *interferon* which inactivates viruses. Recent evidence suggests that there are two subgroups of T-lymphocytes: *suppressor cells* whose role is to modify the immunological response by other lymphocytes, and *helper*

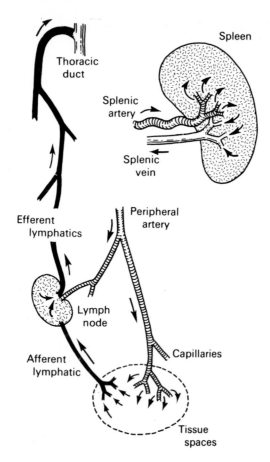

Fig. 9.2 The main pathways of lymphocyte circulation.

The thymus. The thymus consists of a peripheral cortex densely packed with lymphocytes and a central medulla in which the lymphocytes are less numerous. The medulla also contains epithelial cells and 'Hassall's corpuscles', spherical structures composed of keratin and concentric layers of spindle-shaped cells which may possibly be macrophages.

The thymus in mammals arises from the endoderm of the third and fourth branchial clefts and usually consists of two or more lobes on each side of the midline. In the evolutionary development of the immune response, the thymus appears at the same time as immunological activity. In the fetus, the thymus is the first tissue in which lymphocytes can be recognized. In the young child the thymus is large and very active. It contains many dividing lymphocytes and the thymus appears to be the organ responsible for the production of 'competent' T-lymphocytes (see below).

After adolescence the thymus becomes much smaller. As a result the lymphoid tissues dependent on it, the spleen and lymph nodes, are less active and the effectiveness of cell-mediated immunity declines.

T-lymphocytes and Cellular Immunity

The T-lymphocytes (thymus-dependent lymphocytes) are concerned with cellular immunity and once stimulated migrate to sites of foreign antigens like tuberculous lesions or grafts such as transplanted kidneys or skin grafts taken from another

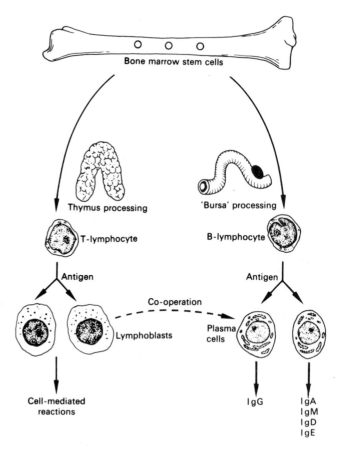

Fig. 9.3 Processing of bone marrow cells by the thymus and by the lymphoid tissue of the alimentary tract to become immunocompetent T- and B-lymphocytes, respectively. On antigenic stimulation, lymphocytes proliferate and transform themselves into lymphoblasts and plasma cells. (*From* I. M. Roitt (1971) *Essential Immunology.* Oxford: Blackwell.)

cells which co-operate with B-lymphocytes in the production of antibodies.

Most of our knowledge of the function of T-lymphocytes is based on studies on mice. Much of this is probably also true of man because, in a child whose thymus is congenitally absent, there is a severe deficiency of T-lymphocytes, defective reaction to grafts and an increased susceptibility to certain infective organisms.

Cellular immunity is the cause of *delayed hypersensitivity reactions* such as the tuberculin reaction. When products of *Mycobacterium tuberculosis* are injected into the skin of a person who has had a previous infection with the same organism, a red indurated area appears at the site of the injection in three or four days. Cellular immunity plays an important role in the body's defence against viral, bacterial and fungal infections, in transplant rejection, and in the defence against neoplastic growths. Inappropriate action by the cell-mediated immunity may cause some auto-immune diseases (p. 130). T-lymphocyte function may be suppressed by steroid hormones or by the drug azathioprine. These substances are used to treat patients with auto-immune disease and to prevent rejection of a tissue or organ graft.

B-lymphocytes and Humoral Immunity

B-lymphocytes are concerned with humoral immunity. When exposed to foreign antigens they synthesize RNA and differentiate into the histologically distinctive *plasma cells* (Fig. 9.4) which produce immunoglobulins (antibodies). A group of plasma cells which produce an antibody against a single antigen is known as a *clone*. B-lymphocytes are so

called because in the chicken they disappear, and antibody production ceases, after excision of the bursa of Fabricius, a mass of lymphoid tissue near the cloaca. Mammals do not possess a bursa of Fabricius but the corresponding tissue may be the lymphoid tissue of the tonsils, intestine and appendix.

Antibody activity in the plasma is found in the proteins called immunoglobulins which form the gamma-globulin band on electrophoresis. When an antigen is introduced into the body, antibodies which react specifically with it are produced after a few days. The specificity of this reaction is a fundamental characteristic of the immune response.

Antigen-antibody reactions. A number of tests can be carried out *in vitro* to demonstrate the reaction between an antigen and its antibody. They are widely used in medicine.

1. *Precipitation.* A precipitate forms when a soluble antigen and antibody react to form an antigen-antibody complex.

2. *Agglutination.* Bacterial or other cells clump in the presence of their antibodies.

3. *Opsonization.* Bacteria are engulfed by phagocytes in the presence of the antibacterial antibody.

4. *Complement fixation.* The complement system (p. 127) is activated when an antigen and antibody react in the presence of complement. This activation can be demonstrated by tests using reagents which react with non-activated complement.

5. *Neutralization tests.* These include neutralization of a toxin (such as tetanus toxin) by its antitoxin *in vivo* in animals, and neutralization of a virus by its antiserum *in vitro* in cell culture.

The immunoglobulins. Five classes of immunoglobulins are known, namely IgM, IgG, IgA, IgD and IgE (Table 9.5). Immunoglobulin G (IgG), the most abundant immunoglobulin in man, is a protein with a molecular weight of about 150 000, consisting of four polypeptide chains, two identical heavy chains each having a molecular weight of about 50 000 and two identical light chains each with a molecular weight of about 25 000. The chains are held together by disulphide bonds (Fig. 9.6).

There are two binding sites for antigen at the amino-terminal ends of the chains and each binding site is made up of the amino-terminal segment of one heavy and one light chain. Two types of light chain are recognized, κ (kappa) and λ (lambda): both occur in all classes of immunoglobulin. The heavy chains, on the other hand, are specific for each class of immunoglobulin: γ (gamma) for IgG, μ (mu) for IgM, α (alpha) for IgA, δ (delta) for IgD and ε (epsilon) for IgE.

The structure of IgM is unique in that it consists of five units linked together by a small polypeptide known as a J-chain (Fig.

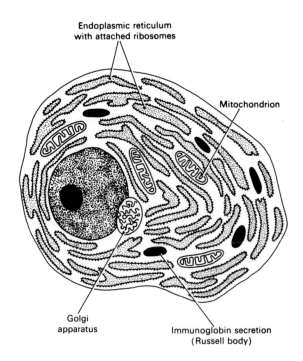

Fig. 9.4 A diagram of a plasma cell (immunocyte) to show the abundant endoplasmic reticulum with attached ribosomal (RNA) granules. (*After* D. M. Weir (1973) *Immunology for Undergraduates.* Edinburgh: Churchill Livingstone.)

Endoplasmic reticulum with attached ribosomes

Mitochondrion

Golgi apparatus

Immunoglobin secretion (Russell body)

Table 9.5 Human immunoglobulins

	IgG	IgA	IgM	IgD	IgE
Heavy chains	γ	α	μ	δ	ε
Light chains	κ & λ	κ & λ	κ & λ	κ & λ	κ & λ
Molecular weight	150 000	170 000	960 000	184 000	188 100
Normal serum concentration	8·0–16·0 g/l	1·4–4·0 g/l	0·5–2·0 g/l	0–0·4 g/l	0·1–1·3 mg/l
Complement activation	Yes	No	Yes	No	No
Ability to cross placenta	Yes	No	No	No	No

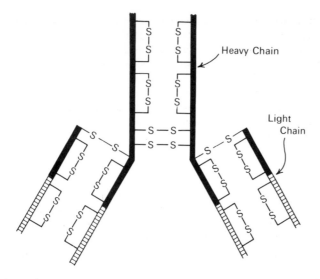

Fig. 9.6 Structure of immunoglobulin G (IgG), to show the two heavy chains and the two light chains linked by disulphide bonds. The amino acid composition of the black parts of each chain is constant whereas that at the amino-terminal end, which is the antigen binding site, is variable (striped). A number of IgG classes with differences in the numbers and position of the disulphide bonds are recognized.

9.7). IgA circulates in the plasma as a monomer, like IgG: it is secreted on to a mucosal surface as a dimer held together by a small protein known as the *secretory piece* (Fig. 9.13, p. 130).

The immunoglobulins are secreted by B-lymphocytes which have been stimulated by antigen either directly or after having been processed by macrophages. The active B-lymphocyte appears as a plasma cell on microscopy. IgM, IgA and IgE are produced by B-lymphocytes which have the corresponding immunoglobulin determinants on their surfaces. Most IgG is produced by co-operation between B-lymphocytes and T-lymphocytes in the presence of macrophages.

IgM antibodies are found in the circulation and, because they have at least five sites for attachment to antigens, are very efficient in reacting with bacteria and foreign cells. The isoagglutinins of blood groups A and B belong to this class (p. 131), as do antibodies against the bacterial body, or somatic, antigens of typhoid and paratyphoid bacilli.

IgG antibodies are found throughout the tissue spaces and are directed against a large variety of antigens. Most virus antibodies and antitoxins belong to this class of immunoglobulin which is the only one that crosses the human placenta. IgG antibodies probably prevent or 'block' hypersensitivity reactions due to IgE. An example of the clinical use of this 'blocking' reaction is the injection of pollen extracts to reduce the likelihood of hay fever in susceptible patients.

IgD has little or no antibody activity but may be important in early life as an antigen-trapping determinant on the surface of some B-lymphocytes. IgE is involved in hypersensitivity reactions such as asthma and hay fever. Its physiological function is not certain but it may have a role in the defence against intestinal parasites such as roundworms and tapeworms. The function of IgA in the plasma is unknown; the principal role of IgA appears to be the protection of mucous membranes.

Primary and secondary immune response. When an antigen such as bovine serum albumin is injected into a rabbit, antibodies appear in the rabbit's serum after a few days (the latent period). The amount of antibody increases rapidly to a peak and then declines. The first antibodies to be produced are IgM; later IgG antibodies appear and the IgM antibodies disappear. These features constitute the *primary response* to the bovine serum albumin.

If the same rabbit is again injected with bovine serum albumin the response occurs sooner and the amount of antibody is greater. Most of the antibody produced on this occasion is IgG. This is the *secondary response* to the bovine serum albumin. The more rapid appearance of antibody and the greater production are due to the activity of long-lived B-lymphocytes, sometimes called *memory cells*, stimulated during the primary response. In the secondary response not only is the antibody concentration higher, but it also remains high for much longer than in the primary response (Fig. 9.8).

Passive immunity. Passive immunity may be given to a patient by injection of gamma globulin (containing the immunoglobulins) from the plasma of another human being or of an animal which has already been actively immunized against a particular disease. Human gamma globulin is used in the treatment of tetanus and in the prevention of infectious hepatitis.

Some newborn animals acquire passive immunity by

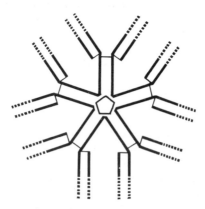

Fig. 9.7 Structure of immunoglobulin M. The J-chain is represented by the pentagon at the centre of the molecule. The dotted areas indicate the parts of the molecule whose amino acid content varies according to the antigen which it recognizes as in Figure 9.6.

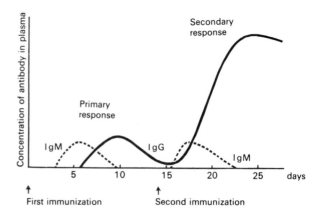

Fig. 9.8 The primary and secondary responses to immunization with an antigen.

absorbing antibodies from the mother's colostrum, but the human baby obtains antibodies almost entirely via the placenta. These antibodies are all IgG since none of the other immunoglobulins can cross the placenta.

The complement system. It has been known since the late nineteenth century that a heat-labile substance in serum can cause the lysis of red blood cells and the destruction of certain bacteria when the appropriate antibody is also present. This substance is called 'complement'. Since that time nine components of complement called C'1 to C'9 have been characterized; all are proteins. These components react in an orderly sequence (C'1, C'4, C'2, C'3, C'5, C'6, C'7, C'8, C'9) when an antigen-antibody complex has formed which causes the activation of the first component. A cascade reaction involving all nine components leads to the enzymic lysis of cells or destruction of bacteria.

In addition to causing lysis, complement has a number of important functions which occur as the various components are activated. One of these is *leucocyte chemotaxis*, that is the attraction of leucocytes to areas where there are complexes of antigen, antibody and complement, as occur, for example, at sites of bacterial invasion. Another is *immune adherence:* antigen–antibody–complement complexes adhere to surfaces where they are readily ingested by phagocytic cells. Activation of the third component of complement (C'3) is probably the most important function of the system. While this occurs ordinarily in a classical antigen-antibody reaction with activation of C'1, C'4 and C'2, C'3 may also be activated directly in some circumstances (the 'complement by-pass') by, for example, trypsin, cobra venom, plasmin, thrombin and tissue proteins.

The Macrophage System

Certain cells found in all parts of the body are able to engulf particulate material including micro-organisms, effete erythrocytes, disintegrating fibrin, tissue debris and any finely divided or colloidal substance that may be introduced parenterally into the body whether accidentally, therapeutically or experimentally. Thus, if an animal is killed some days after the intravenous or intraperitoneal injection of Indian ink or the dye trypan blue, it is found that the particles of carbon or dyestuff are not distributed generally throughout the body but are concentrated in cells in certain organs in amounts depending on their content of phagocytic cells. These cells comprise the macrophage system (Table 9.9), formerly called

Table 9.9 The Macrophages

In blood
  Monocytes
In tissues
  Histiocytes
  Microglia (in CNS)
Lining sinuses and sinusoids
  Lymph nodes
  Spleen
  Liver
  Bone marrow

the reticulo-endothelial system. Together with the lymphocytes they are known as the *lymphoreticular system*.

There are differences between species in the distribution of macrophages and also, within a species, variations in the behaviour of the macrophages in different sites. Caution is therefore needed both in applying to man information derived from experimental animals and in assuming that one foreign substance is treated in the same way in all sites.

Tissue histiocytes. Cells of the macrophage type occur in most connective tissues. Many of them appear to be long-term residents and are sometimes referred to as 'fixed' tissue histiocytes or macrophages. In most sites they are scanty, but they are relatively abundant in the omentum of the fetus and the newborn where these cells appear beneath the peritoneum as pale milky aggregates. When the need arises for histiocytes in greater number, as in some forms of inflammation, the 'fixed' histiocytes are rapidly supplemented by others, the 'wandering' histiocytes, that appear to be constantly 'on patrol' in most tissues. These in turn are supplemented by yet others, formerly circulating blood monocytes but now, in response to the stimulus, extravascular. It may be that most 'wandering' histiocytes are of intravascular origin.

Monocytes. Monocytes arise mostly in bone marrow and spleen. Many of these in the circulating blood are destined to become wandering tissue histiocytes.

Lymph nodes. At the lymph nodes, lymphocytes are brought into close contact with particulate matter which has been collected by the lymph and fixed by macrophages.

Figure 9.10 shows the ways in which lymphocytes pass through a lymph node. The lymph (p. 128) enters the node in afferent lymphatics which penetrate the capsule; it leaves through the efferent lymphatic at the hilum. From there the lymph is collected into larger and larger lymphatics. The lymph from most parts of the body passes into the thoracic duct and so into the great veins of the neck. During the passage of lymph through a lymph node small molecules are transferred to the blood stream but proteins, including antibodies, are added to it. In the fasting state the lymph from the thoracic duct is pale yellow and transparent. After a fatty meal it becomes milky because the lymph from the intestine then contains chylomicrons (p. 78). Lymph also contains large numbers of lymphocytes, mainly T-lymphocytes.

Within a lymph node a meshwork of reticular cells gives it its fibrous structure. Embedded in the cortical area are large numbers of lymphocytes. The endothelial lining of the sinuses consists of macrophages with many dendritic processes.

The spleen. The spleen has an unusual circulation (Fig. 9.11). The splenic artery enters at the hilum and breaks up into numerous branches with few anastomoses. Near their terminations the arterioles are surrounded by sleeves of lymphoid tissue (Malpighian bodies). It is difficult to trace the pathway of the blood through the spleen from this point, but probably the arterioles, after a terminal dilatation, link up in a loose way with sinuses; the flow by this direct route is fairly rapid. The incomplete walls of these sinuses are made up of rod-like cells with narrow gaps between them lying parallel with the long axis of the sinus. Blood seems to pass from the sinus through the gaps in the wall into the pulp and back again into the sinus, but circulation by this indirect route must be slow. Most of the plasma and some of the red cells go by the direct path to the sinuses where they are joined by red cells

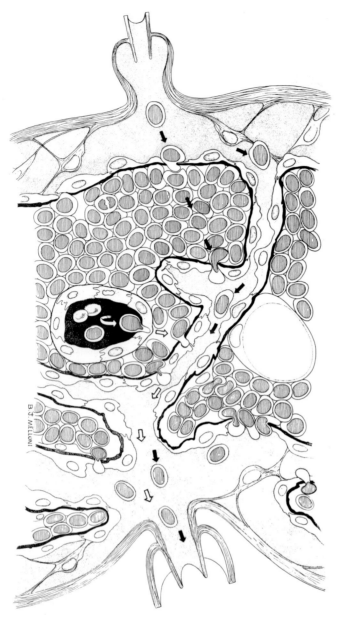

Fig. 9.10 The circulation of lymphocytes within a lymph node. The sinuses are lined by macrophages. Note that lymphocytes come both from afferent lymphatics (black arrows) and from post-capillary venules (white arrows). (*From* J. A. Bellanti (1971) *Immunology*. Philadelphia: Saunders.)

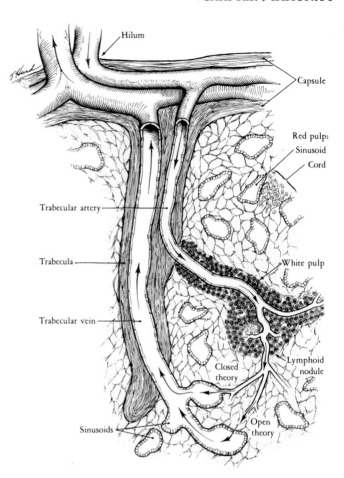

Fig. 9.11 Structure of the spleen to show the lymphoid tissue adjacent to the terminal arterioles and the possible routes from arteriole to sinuses. (*From* J. A. Bellanti (1971) *Immunology*. Philadelphia: Saunders.)

which have taken the indirect path. The sinuses either link up with one another or join a venule. The veins unite in the hilum to form the splenic vein. The slow element of the circulation through the spleen leads, in effect, to a sequestration of red cells and affords an opportunity for the phagocytosis of aged red cells or of foreign substances such as bacteria.

The Malpighian bodies make up the white pulp of the spleen and consist principally of lymphocytes and macrophages surrounding the arterioles. Thus the spleen, like the lymph nodes, has an architecture which allows the lymphocytes to come into contact with foreign particles. The significance of the spleen is underlined by the fact that after splenectomy patients have an increased liability to serious infections. The defensive activity of the spleen may be partly due to its production of a tetrapeptide hormone *tuftsin* which stimulates phagocytosis.

Liver. If an animal is injected intraperitoneally or intravenously with colloidal carbon, sections of liver obtained only minutes later show numerous carbon-laden cells, the *Kupffer cells*, which form part of the endothelial lining of the sinusoids. It seems likely that all the endothelial cells have phagocytic ability, and are therefore potentially 'Kupffer' cells, but some react more promptly or more avidly than others, perhaps due to their age or metabolic status at the time. Some of these cells, when laden with particles, become detached and pass in the hepatic veins or the lymphatics to the lungs and regional lymph nodes; replacement is achieved by division of adjacent sinusoidal endothelial cells.

Bone marrow. The experimental intravenous injection of appropriate suspensions has shown that the disposition of phagocytes in the bone marrow is similar to that in the spleen. The endothelium of the marrow is discontinuous, and thus particulate material and ageing erythrocytes have ready access to the extravascular compartment.

Microglia. Histological methods involving metallic impregnation reveal cells within the central nervous system, especially around small arteries and arterioles, that are neither astrocytes nor oligodendrocytes. Such cells change their appearance in areas of brain damage and become clearly recognizable as macrophages. They are known as the microglia. Their origin is not yet clear, but the use of labelled blood monocytes has shown that in areas of injury cells of apparently microglial type rapidly become supplemented by macrophages that were formerly blood monocytes. In health microglial cells do not engulf material from dyestuffs or colloidal suspensions injected intravenously presumably because such material does not cross the blood brain barrier (Chap. 19).

Macrophages in other situations. A few endothelial cells in the sinusoids of the adrenals and pituitary show phagocytic activity but their significance is not known. In the lung, phagocytes are abundant. They do not comprise a formal 'system' as do the Kupffer cells in the liver but are present as relatively large numbers of wandering histiocytes. Macrophages cannot be seen unless particulate matter enters the lung but as a result of atmospheric pollution macrophages with engulfed carbon or other material are virtually always present in the alveoli and airways and can be easily seen in bronchial secretion or expectoration. The origin of these cells is still uncertain; they may be derived from circulating blood monocytes (which become wandering tissue histiocytes), alveolar epithelial cells or the fibroblastic mesenchymal cells that support the alveolar epithelium. Larger particles are trapped directly in the mucus of the respiratory tract and then coughed up or swallowed. Smaller particles are engulfed by macrophages which are then likewise removed in the mucus (Fig. 9.12); some are carried by the macrophages into the lymphatics from which they eventually become deposited in the small foci of lymphoid tissue in the lung or in the regional lymph nodes. In persons exposed to dust, the material may travel even further; in coalminers carbon is commonly found in the lymphatics and lymph nodes of the diaphragm, posterior abdominal wall and neck.

Function of macrophages. Macrophages differ from polymorphonuclear leucocytes in their much greater avidity for, or ability to engulf, inorganic particulate material such as carbon and dust particles in general. Macrophages have also the unusual capacity, when confronted by particularly insoluble or foreign material, to fuse together with the formation of multinucleated giant cells. Most forms of organic foreign material such as a thorn, a spicule of fish bone or surgical catgut can be destroyed by enzyme action and lysis. Most forms of inorganic material cannot be destroyed by lysis; some of this is transported to lymph nodes by the macrophages but the rest remains undisturbed throughout life. Bile pigment, haemosiderin, melanin, lipid substances and carbon may be seen in different circumstances within macrophages. In damaged tissues macrophages may also contain dead and dying microorganisms and polymorphonuclear leucocytes, tissue debris, sterol crystals and fibrin. Cells of the macrophage system are also responsible for the phagocytosis and breakdown of erythrocytes and for the catabolism of haemoglobin.

Relationship to immune mechanisms. Macrophages can ingest and store antigens but cannot manufacture antibodies; the recognition of antigen and the manufacture of antibody are functions of lymphocytes. The macrophage either presents antigen, or antigen modified in some way, to the T- and B-lymphocytes so that the lymphocyte can develop cellular immunity or a humoral response. The macrophage by

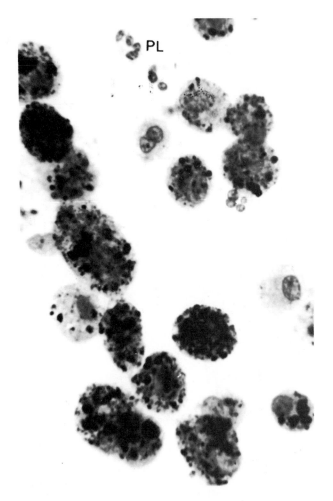

Fig. 9.12 Macrophages of bronchial origin in sputum. The cells are relatively large and contain different amounts of particulate material (mostly soot and dust). The amount is so great in some cells as to obscure the nucleus completely. At the top may be seen the multilobed nuclei of two polymorphonuclear leucocytes (PL); their cytoplasm is devoid of particles. Papanicolaou. ×900. (*By courtesy of W. W. Park.*)

retaining antigens prevents the exposure of lymphocytes to excess antigenic material with a resulting loss of their activity.

Immune Mechanisms on Mucosal Surfaces

Immunity and the gastrointestinal tract. The presence of bacteria or other foreign substances in the diet stimulates the immune system. The major humoral defence is IgA formed by plasma cells found around the intestinal glands. IgA is transported through the epithelial cells attached to a glycoprotein known as a *secretory piece* (Fig. 9.13). The complex of secretory piece with two molecules of IgA passes into the lumen where it carries out its antibody activity. This IgA is specific and people can be immunized against certain diseases, such as poliomyelitis, by an oral vaccine which stimulates IgA production in the gut.

Cellular immunity is also important in the gut which has a large population of lymphocytes. The lymphocytes often occur in follicles, and large collections in the small intestine are called *aggregated lymph follicles* or *Peyer's patches*. Proteins

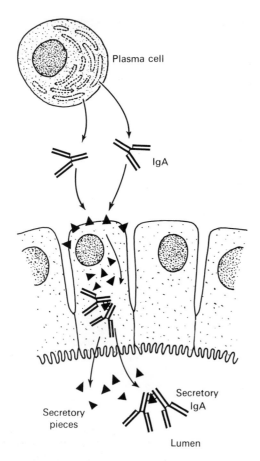

Fig. 9.13 The formation of secretory IgA in the gut. IgA is synthesized by plasma cells in the submucosa. The secretory pieces are synthesized within the mucosal cell and migrate to the cell membrane where each is linked by J-chains to two IgA molecules. This complex is then transported across the cell and released into the lumen of the gut together with some free secretory pieces. (*After* P. Brandtzaeg (1974) *Immunology*, **26**, 1101–1114.)

reach the lymphocytes in the mucosa in two different ways. In the *Peyer's patches* the lymphoid tissue is covered by a layer of membranous epithelial cells, the M cells, which have a markedly folded surface. These pick up antigens from the gut lumen and present them to the lymphocytes beneath. In other parts of the intestine antigens are picked up by enterocytes and passed to adjacent lymphocytes.

Immunity and the respiratory tract. As in the gastro-intestinal tract the major humoral defence is IgA which is especially important in viral infections of the respiratory tract such as influenza. IgA is produced in plasma cells in the submucosa of the trachea, becomes a secretory molecule as it passes through the epithelial cells and emerges on to the surface.

Cell-mediated immunity is also important in the respiratory tract especially in tuberculosis. The role of macrophages in the bronchial tree was discussed earlier (p. 129).

Disorders of the Immune Mechanisms

Although the immune mechanisms are essential for survival, their action may at times be damaging as in allergic

reactions and autoimmune disease. Other defects are caused by an excessive production of immunoglobulins (as with *myeloma*) or by failure of immune responses.

Myeloma. After a malignant change in a clone of plasma cells there is an increase in immunoglobulin production. Such a clone produces a single class of immunoglobulin. In some patients with this disorder light chains appear in the urine and are known as Bence–Jones protein.

Immunodeficiency. A number of diseases, some of which are inherited, are due to impaired immune responses. There may be a failure of antibody response or a failure of cellular immunity or a combination of both. The diseases reveal themselves by recurring bacterial or fungal infections.

Autoimmune diseases. The early immunologists did not believe it was possible for antibodies to be produced against a person's own tissues but it is now known that in several diseases antibodies are produced in the body against its own tissues. Examples are autoimmune diseases of the thyroid gland, of the stomach (pernicious anaemia, p. 29 and p. 109), of the adrenal glands and a large group of diseases called 'collagen diseases'. It is not known whether the antibodies actually cause the autoimmune disease or are produced as part of the disease process, but the detection of antibodies in plasma is useful in diagnosis.

BLOOD GROUPS AND TISSUE ANTIGENS

The *blood-group antigens* are found on the surface of erythrocytes. Over 100 of these antigens have now been demonstrated, and no doubt others remain to be discovered. They are inherited characteristics and most have been shown to belong to genetically independent blood-group systems, of which there are at least 14. The best known are ABO, Rh, MNS, P and Lewis. With the exception of Xg, which is controlled by a gene on the X-chromosome, all the blood-group antigens are controlled by autosomal genes (Chap. 33).

A, B, H and Lewis blood-group substances can also occur in soluble form in certain secretions such as saliva and gastric mucin. These soluble blood-group substances are glyco-proteins but the blood-group antigens on the red cell surface are thought to be glycolipids. In both types of molecule the antigenic specificity is associated with differences in the carbohydrate moiety, for example Group A with *N*-acetyl-galactosamine and Group B with D-galactose. In general a blood-group antigen (for example the Rh-antigen designated D) possessed by an individual is detected only when a suspension of his red blood cells is mixed with serum containing the equivalent antibody (in this case, anti-D). Agglutination of the red cells then occurs and the individual concerned is classified as 'D-positive'. The red cells of another person lacking the D antigen are not agglutinated by this antibody and this individual is called 'D-negative'.

When red cells containing a blood-group antigen are mixed with plasma containing the equivalent antibody agglutination is followed in some cases by lysis of the cells (*haemolysis*) if complement is present. Lysis of incompatible red cells may also occur *in vivo* within the circulation. More commonly, however, the interaction between blood-group antibody and antigen, after the transfusion of incompatible red cells, results in these cells being removed intact from the circulation by the macrophages, particularly those of the liver and spleen.

Blood-group Antibodies

These immunoglobulins may be divided into two broad classes, immune and naturally occuring antibodies. However the distinction between them is not always clear cut.

Immune antibodies. If red cells containing a blood-group antigen, for example D, are introduced into the circulation of a person who lacks that antigen (in this case a D-negative person) that person may be immunized and the equivalent antibody, anti-D, will appear in his plasma.

This type of immunization can be caused by blood transfusion, and particularly by repeated transfusions, but even the intramuscular injection of a small quantity of blood may stimulate the formation of antibodies. Moreover, red cells from a fetus carrying an antigen, inherited from its father but absent in the mother, may enter the maternal circulation and immunize the mother. Immune blood-group antibodies are usually IgG. They have a molecular weight of about 150000 and can cross the placenta easily.

Naturally occurring antibodies. A blood-group antibody may be present in the plasma of an individual who, as far as can be determined, has never been immunized by the equivalent antigen. It was the regular occurrence of the antibodies anti-A and anti-B which led to the discovery by Landsteiner in 1900 of the A and B substances—the first antigens to be recognized in human red cells. Naturally occurring antibodies are usually IgM with a molecular weight of about 900000. They do not cross the placenta.

ABO System

The ABO group of a person depends on whether his red cells contain one, both, or neither of the two blood-group antigens A and B. There are, therefore, four main ABO groups, AB, A, B and O.

If the A antigen is *not* present in the person's cells (that is, he is group B or group O) his plasma contains naturally occurring anti-A (α). Similarly, if the cells lack the B antigen (that is, he is group A or group O) the plasma contains anti-B (β). The plasma of a group AB person contains neither of these antibodies (Table 9.14).

Table 9.14

Group	Antigens present in red cells	Antibodies present in serum
AB	A and B	—
A	A	anti-B (β)
B	B	anti-A (α)
O	—	anti-A+anti-B ($\alpha+\beta$)

Subgroups of A. As early as 1911 it was discovered that group A individuals could be divided into two categories, A_1 and A_2. More recently other, weaker, subgroups of A (A_3, A_4, etc.) have been recognized, but they are rare. Similarly, minor variations within group B have also been found.

Group O. The red cells of a group O person lack both the A and B antigens. No clear evidence has yet been obtained of a true 'O antigen' or an anti-O antibody. With rare exceptions all human red cells contain a blood-group substance called H substance, and the corresponding antibody, anti-H, has been found in the plasma of certain human beings and animals. There is good evidence that H may be a precursor from which the A and B substances are made under the influence of the A and B genes.

Rhesus System

In 1940 Landsteiner and Wiener discovered that an antibody, produced in rabbits by injecting them with the blood of a rhesus monkey, agglutinated not only the red cells of the monkey but also the cells of 85 per cent of a large series of human blood samples. The antibody was called anti-rhesus (anti-Rh) and the cells agglutinated by it were called rhesus-positive (Rh-positive).

Soon after this discovery, immune anti-Rh was demonstrated in the plasma of certain Rh-negative human beings. These were Rh-negative persons who had been transfused with Rh-positive blood, or Rh-negative women who had borne Rh-positive children.

More recently it was shown that anti-rhesus antibody produced in animals such as rabbits or guinea-pigs by injection of rhesus monkey red cells is not of the same specificity as the anti-Rh found in Rh-negative humans who have been immunized by human Rh-positive red cells.

Fisher postulated in 1943 that the inheritance of Rh antigens was controlled by three pairs of closely linked allelic genes, *Cc, Dd, Ee*, each gene determining an antigen denoted by the same letter. The antigen D was thought to be the original Rh antigen and an Rh-positive individual was one whose red cells contained D. A person inherited three Rh genes (one of each pair) from each of his parents, for example *CDe* from one parent and *cde* from the other, giving a genotype which could be expressed *CDe/cde*.

Fisher's original theory no longer explains the observations made since 1943. For example, it postulates the existence of an antigen 'd' controlled by the gene 'd' allelic to 'D', but no antibody with the specificity anti-d has ever been discovered and so there is no direct evidence for the existence of the 'd' gene. While Fisher's theory of separable Rh genes is now accepted with reserve, his notation still remains the most convenient in use.

Haemolytic disease of the newborn. Blood-group antibodies of the immune type present in the blood of a pregnant woman can cross the placenta and gain access to the fetal circulation. Then, if the fetal red cells contain the equivalent antigen, haemolysis may ensue. It should be noted, however, that whereas most children possess blood-group antigens inherited from the father but absent from the mother, it is comparatively uncommon for a woman to develop immune antibodies, even after repeated 'incompatible' pregnancies. Moreover, when immunization of the mother does occur and the fetus is affected, the severity of the condition varies very greatly. In the most severe cases destruction of the fetal red cells may be so rapid and widespread that the fetus dies. Most cases are more mildly affected and some have no evidence of red cell destruction at all.

Many blood-group antigens and their equivalent antibodies may cause haemolytic disease of the newborn but the most frequently implicated is the Rh antigen, D. Until recently the incidence of haemolytic disease due to Rh incompatibility in Britain was approximately 1 in 150 in all pregnancies. Cases of haemolytic disease of the newborn due to ABO incompatibility (in particular where the mother is group O and the child group A) are probably as common as those due to Rh. Only rarely, however, are such cases severe.

Prevention of Rh immunization by administration of Rh antibody. Rh(D) positive fetal red cells, in numbers sufficient to cause immunization of an Rh(D) negative mother, may cross the placenta at any time during pregnancy but most commonly when the placenta is separating from the uterus during delivery or abortion. In the absence of any treatment, between 10 and 20 per cent of Rh(D) negative women delivered of Rh(D) positive babies were actively immunized and anti-D could be detected in the mothers' plasma.

D-positive fetal red cells can be cleared rapidly from the circulation of a D-negative mother by injecting her with a concentrated immunoglobulin (IgG) fraction prepared from plasma containing powerful anti-D antibody. In many countries it is now routine practice to give all D-negative women an injection of an anti-D immunoglobulin preparation as soon as possible after delivery of a D-positive infant or after an abortion. This has dramatically reduced the number of women who, in a subsequent pregnancy, show evidence of active Rh(D) immunization and, therefore, the number of babies with haemolytic disease of the newborn.

Blood Transfusion

Before a transfusion is given precautions must be taken to ensure that the bloods of donor and recipient are compatible. The greatest danger is that the patient's plasma may contain an antibody, or antibodies, active against the equivalent antigen or antigens present in the donor's red cells. The effect on the patient of such an incompatible transfusion varies, but a severe and even fatal reaction may be caused.

ABO incompatibility is particularly dangerous since anti-A and anti-B in the plasma can cause rapid destruction of transfused red cells containing the equivalent A and B antigens. Next in importance is the Rh antigen, D. Although a D-negative person rarely possesses naturally occurring anti-D, anti-D may be present as a result of a previous transfusion of D-positive blood or a pregnancy with a D-positive infant. Any subsequent transfusions of D-positive blood would then be liable to cause a severe and perhaps fatal reaction. Serious reactions due to blood-group antigens other than A, B or D are uncommon but not unknown.

Antibodies in the *donor's* plasma against antigens in the recipient's red cells seldom cause reactions, mainly because they are rapidly diluted in the patient's circulation.

For these reasons it is advisable for transfusion to select blood of the same ABO and D groups as those of the patient and in addition to *crossmatch* a sample of the patient's plasma against a suspension of the donor's red cells. The cross-matching tests should reveal the presence in the patient's plasma of any antibody that is active against an antigen in the donor's cells.

Tissue Typing

Just as erythrocytes have isoantigens on their surface so do nucleated cells. These *tissue antigens* or *histocompatibility antigens* may stimulate an immune response whenever a person receives, for example in a graft from another person, nucleated cells with antigens different from those of his own cells. This immune response consists of both antibody production and lymphocyte sensitization and leads to the rejection of the grafted tissue in 7 to 10 days. Only between identical twins is it possible to graft tissues successfully without the need for drugs which suppress the immune responses; the likelihood of rejection is greatly reduced by the best possible matching of donor and recipient cells by tissue typing.

Histocompatibility antigens are found on nucleated tissue cells and also on leucocytes and platelets. In practice lymphocytes and platelets in the peripheral blood are used in tests for these antigens. The ABO antigens of eythrocytes are also important tissue antigens, but few of the other red cell groups appear to be important in the rejection of grafts. The most important system of tissue antigens is known as the *HL-A system* (human leucocyte-A system) which is determined by a number of genes situated on chromosome 6. The determination of HL-A compatibility as well as ABO compatibility is usually made before renal transplants, skin grafts and bone marrow transfers are undertaken.

One further histocompatibility antigen, the H-Y antigen, is specific to the Y-chromosome and may play a part in the normal differentiation of gonadal tissues according to their sex-chromosome composition.

REFERENCES

Bodmer W F (ed) 1978 The HLA system. British Medical Bulletin 34: No 3
Cohen A B, Gold W M 1975 Defense mechanisms of the lungs. Annual Review of Physiology 37: 325–350
Festenstein H, Demart P 1978 HLA and H2— Basic immunogenetics and clinical relevance. Arnold, London
Freedman S O, Gold P (eds) 1976 Clinical immunology. Harper & Row, Hagerstown Md
Gell P G H, Coombs R R A, Lachmann P J 1974 Clinical aspects of immunology, 3rd edn. Blackwell, Oxford
Holborow E J 1974 An ABC of modern immunology, 2nd edn. Lancet, London
Holborow E J, Reeves W G (eds) 1977 Immunology in medicine. Academic Press, London
Mollison P L 1978 Blood transfusion in clinical medicine, 6th edn. Blackwell, Oxford
Race R R, Sanger R 1975 Blood groups in man, 6th edn. Blackwell, Oxford
Roitt I M 1977 Essential immunology, 3rd edn. Blackwell, Oxford
Rosen F 1974 Primary immunodeficiency. Pediatric Clinics of North America 21: 533–550
Scientific American 1976 Immunology. Freeman, San Francisco

Taylor G (ed) 1975 Immunology in medical practice. Saunders, London
Thompson R A 1978 The practice of clinical immunology, 2nd edn. Arnold, London
Trainin N 1974 Thymic hormones and the immune response. Physiological Reviews 54: 272–315

10 The Heart

STRUCTURE AND FUNCTION

The mammalian heart possesses two *atria* separated by the *interatrial septum*, and two *ventricles* separated by the thicker *interventricular septum*. In the human thorax all four chambers lie at approximately the same level. Blood flows from each atrium into the immediately adjacent part of the ventricle, the *inflow tract*, and passes out via the *outflow tract* into the aorta or pulmonary artery. The whole muscular structure, together with a certain amount of epicardial fat, is enclosed within a serous membrane, the *serous pericardium* (p. 135).

The walls of the atria are thin, appropriate to the small amount of work required to force their contents into the ventricles. The thick-walled ventricles do most of the work of the heart, expelling the blood into the system of branching arteries which offer considerable impedance to the onflow of the blood. The wall of the left ventricle is about three or four times thicker than the wall of the right ventricle at the corresponding position for the left ventricle functions as a pressure pump, while the right ventricle acts as a volume pump.

The cavities may contain roughly 400 ml of blood (*end-diastolic volume*), an amount that is much greater than the quantity expelled by both ventricles each time they contract (about 140 ml). In other words the cavities are not completely empty even at the end of systole; the ratio end-systolic volume/end-diastolic volume is about 0·55. The left ventricular residual volume at the end of systole in untrained persons is estimated to be about 50 ml and in endurance athletes about 120 ml. These values have been obtained by angiocardiography (p. 158) and also by calculation from the dye dilution method of measuring cardiac output (p. 162).

Each ventricle has the same capacity and each expels the same amount of blood during systole (*stroke volume*). If this were not so the circulation would eventually cease. Let us consider what would happen if the right ventricle were to deliver, say, 0·1 ml more blood per contraction than the left. If the left expels 60 ml per beat and the right 60·1 ml per beat then in one hour, if the heart beats 80 times a minute, the left expels 288 000 ml and the right 288 480 ml. The difference, 480 ml, would have to be accommodated in the pulmonary vessels and the lungs, with grave effects upon the pulmonary circulation and respiration. This does not mean, however, that for *short* periods the amounts of blood expelled by the two ventricles must be exactly the same; at certain phases of the respiratory cycle, for example, there are small, temporary differences between the stroke volumes of the right and left ventricles. In health, though, the average outputs must be equal. In heart failure a discrepancy between the two outputs has serious consequences. In some types of congenital heart deformities in which blood is shunted from one side of the circulation to the other there may be quite large differences between the ventricular outputs.

The atria and the ventricles are completely separated by the fibrotendinous ring which gives attachment to most of the muscular fibres and to the atrio-ventricular valves. The only muscular connexion between atria and ventricles is the atrio-ventricular (junctional) bundle of His. Closely connected with the main fibrous ring are other fibrous rings that surround the arterial orifices and serve for the attachment of the great vessels and semilunar valves and some of the ventricular muscle fibres. The arrangement of the cardiac muscle (the *myocardium*) in both atria and ventricles is complicated and includes the *papillary muscles* that project into the cavities of the ventricles, and to which the chordae tendineae are attached.

Heart valves. The heart valves (Fig. 10.1) are formed by

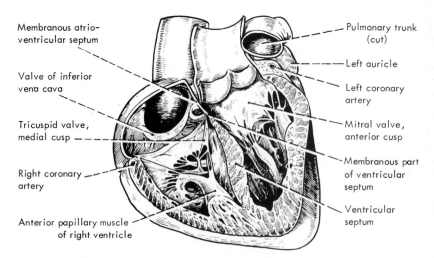

Membranous atrio-ventricular septum

Valve of inferior vena cava

Tricuspid valve, medial cusp

Right coronary artery

Anterior papillary muscle of right ventricle

Pulmonary trunk (cut)

Left auricle

Left coronary artery

Mitral valve, anterior cusp

Membranous part of ventricular septum

Ventricular septum

Fig. 10.1 Section through the human heart to show the valves. On the right side the atrioventricular orifice has been cut across. On the left side the section passes through the aortic valve and in front of the mitral valve. The AV valve system includes cusps, chordae and papillary muscles. The cusps make the open valves funnel-shaped (After *Gray's Anatomy*, 31st edition (1954), p. 694.).

cusps of fibrous tissue attached to the fibrous rings and covered on both sides by endocardium. All the valves are formed so that they permit the blood to flow only from the atria to the ventricles and onward into the arteries. The points of entry of the veins into the atria have no functional valves.

The cusps of the *atrioventricular valves* are large, sail-like structures that arise from the atrioventricular rings and pass down into the cavity of the ventricles (Fig. 10.1). Their margins are connected by thin cords (*chordae tendineae*) to the papillary muscles that form part of the muscular mass of the ventricles. As the ventricles contract the papillary muscles pull on the chordae tendineae so that the cusps cannot prolapse into the atria. On the left side, between the left atrium and left ventricle, two cusps form the mitral valve. Closure of the tricuspid valve is brought about mainly by the more mobile anterior cusp. Functionally the cusps, chordae and papillary muscles normally act as a single atrioventricular valve mechanism, and damage to any one component may make the valve incompetent.

The aortic and pulmonary valves each have three semilunar cusps of very thin fibrous tissue covered by endocardium. In the intact heart the three pockets meet along three lines and prevent blood from flowing back into the ventricle.

Coronary vessels. Three bulges of the aortic wall just above the aortic valve are termed the aortic sinuses. It is thought that eddies in the blood in these sinuses prevent the cusps of the aortic valve from obstructing the orifices of the coronary arteries, and may play a part in closure of the valve. The right coronary artery most frequently supplies the right atrium, right ventricle, diaphragmatic surface of the left ventricle and sinu-atrial and AV nodes, while the left coronary artery supplies the greater part of the left heart (Fig. 10.2). The coronary arteries and their larger branches lie in the sub-epicardium but from them smaller vessels pass into the substance of the myocardium where their branches form rich plexuses of arterioles, capillaries and venules. From these vessels arise luminal vessels which may open into any of the four chambers of the heart. From 30 up to 60 per cent of the coronary artery blood flow may be returned to the heart by these luminal vessels rather than by the veins leading to the coronary sinus. The luminal vessels may either drain or nourish the myocardium, according to the difference between the pressure in them and the pressure in the chambers of the heart. Numerous arterial anastomoses of the order of 100 to 300 μm in diameter occur in all areas of the heart, especially in the deeper layers of the left ventricle and interventricular septum. The capillary supply of heart muscle is about six times as rich as that of skeletal muscle, and greater in the inner than in the superficial parts of the myocardium.

The pericardium. The heart is enclosed in a conical sac, the *pericardium*, the neck of which merges with the fibrous covering of the walls of the great vessels at the base of the heart; inferiorly the sac is attached to the central tendon of the diaphragm. Its inner surface and the outer surface of the heart are lined by the *serous pericardium*. The two serous surfaces are separated by a thin film of fluid which allows free movement of the layers over one another.

The Size of the Heart

A knowledge of cardiac size can be derived only by X-rays. Radiographs taken with a tube-to-film distance of two metres,

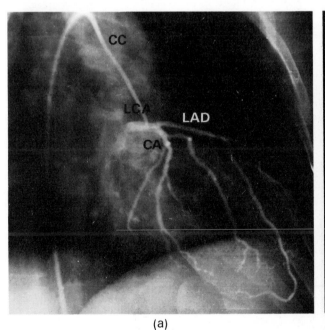
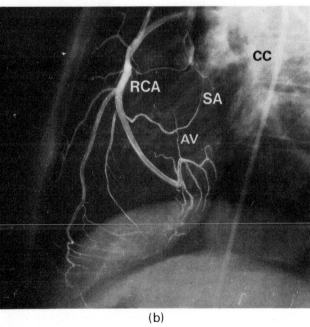

(a)   (b)

Fig. 10.2 Radiographs of the human coronary arterial system. In (a) and (b) contrast medium has been injected into the left (a) and right (b) coronary arteries of a beating heart through a cardiac catheter (CC) sited accurately in the ostium (*selective coronary arteriography*). In (a) the 'trunk' of the tree is the left coronary artery (LCA), the uppermost main branch is the left anterior descending artery (LAD) and its smaller branches, the lower main branch is the circumflex artery (CA) and its branches. In (b) the right coronary artery (RCA) is shown with its branches including those to the sinu-atrial node (SA) and AV node (AV). (By courtesy of the Cardiac Department, Victoria Infirmary, Glasgow).

at the end of a quiet expiration with the patient as close as possible to the film, give little distortion with a magnification of the cardiac area of 2 to 10 per cent.

The silhouette of the normal heart and blood vessels is remarkably variable (Fig. 10.3), depending on the position of the subject and on the phase of respiration, weight, build and muscular activity. Long-distance runners tend to have large hearts. Information about enlargements and movements of the individual chambers of the heart can be obtained by watching the cardiac silhouette on a fluorescent X-ray screen.

The Myocardial Cells

Heart muscle is not a syncytium but consists of discrete cells of different types. The two main varieties may be regarded as 'working' myocardial cells and specialized 'conducting' cells. Within each of these two groups there are differences: for example, working cells in the atrium are anatomically and physiologically different from working cells in the ventricle, and there are similar differences between the cells of different parts of the specialized conducting tissue (p. 140).

Working myocardial cells. The main bulk of the atria and ventricles consists of working myocardial cells arranged in columns. Each cell contains one central nucleus, many myofibrils aligned along the cell's axis and an exceptionally large number of mitochondria. Each cell is enclosed by its membrane, or sarcolemma, the structure through which the cardiac electrical activity exerts its important function (Fig. 10.4).

The myofibrils, as in skeletal muscle (Chap. 21), are both structurally and functionally the fundamental contractile units of the myocardium. The microstructure of the cardiac sarcomere resembles that of skeletal muscle (Fig. 21.5, p. 330), with sets of actin and myosin myofilaments hexagonally arranged. The modulating proteins tropomyosin and troponin are also present in the thin filaments of cardiac muscle though there is some evidence that all four proteins may not be chemically identical with those in skeletal muscle. It is probable, however, that they act in essentially the same way as described for skeletal muscle (Chap. 21).

The large and numerous mitochondria constitute at least 35 per cent of the total volume of cardiac muscle and lie close to the myofibrils.

The sarcolemma. The myocardial cell membrane resembles other cell membranes (Fig. 10.5). Adjacent cells are held together by a complicated system of interdigitating projections, which appear on light microscopy as the 'intercalated discs' (Fig. 10.5) and which consist of the two surface membranes of adjacent cells within the same column and the intercellular space between them. They are similar in structure to the rest of the cell membranes and continuous with them. The thin actin myofilaments seem to be attached to the inner surfaces of these areas, and here and there desmosomes are present.

As in skeletal muscle invaginations of the sarcolemma extend into the substance of the cell to form the *transverse tubules* of the sarcoplasmic reticulum lying in relation to the Z-lines of the sarcomeres as shown in Figure 10.4. The *longitudinal sarcoplasmic reticulum*, a true intracellular

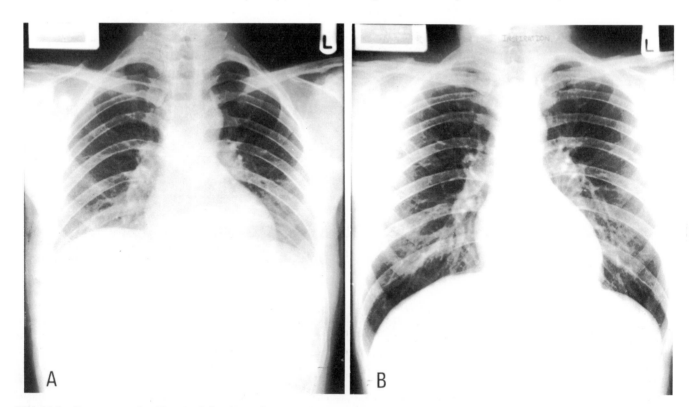

Fig. 10.3 Postero-anterior X-rays of the chest of a normal young man. A, during expiration; B, during inspiration. Note that during inspiration the diaphragm descends and that the cardiac silhouette and the 'shadows' of the pulmonary vessels and the bronchial tree appear altered.

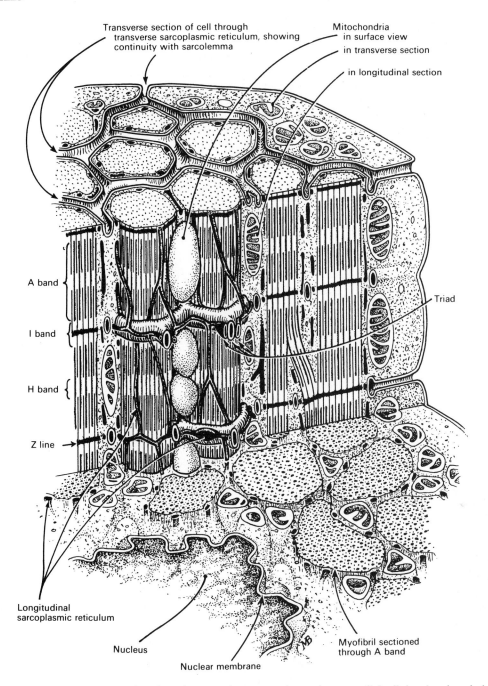

Transverse section of cell through
transverse sarcoplasmic reticulum, showing
continuity with sarcolemma

Mitochondria
in surface view
in transverse section
in longitudinal section

A band

I band

H band

Z line

Triad

Longitudinal
sarcoplasmic reticulum

Nucleus

Nuclear membrane

Myofibril sectioned
through A band

Fig. 10.4   Three-dimensional reconstruction, based on electron microscopy, of part of a myocardial cell showing the relationship between the transverse tubular system of the sarcoplasmic reticulum, the terminal cisternae of the longitudinal sarcoplasmic reticulum (triads) and the Z lines of sarcomeres. The transverse system has some horizontal branches (not shown) and cisternae are also in apposition to them and to the sarcolemma.

organelle, is finer and scantier in cardiac muscle than in skeletal muscle but in the neighbourhood of the Z-lines it forms flattened *terminal cisternae* which are separate from, but closely apposed to, the transverse tubules. The terminal cisternae and transverse tubules appear in electron microscope sections as '*triads*' or '*diads*' (Fig. 10.4).

Another important modification of the sarcolemma is found especially in areas along the longitudinal surfaces of the cells where the contact between two adjacent cells is closer than elsewhere and the surface membranes seem to be fused with obliteration of the intercellular space. These regions are called '*nexuses*' or '*tight junctions*' and seem to contain a system of intercellular pores (Fig. 10.5). The intercalated discs and the nexuses probably account for the relatively low electrical resistance between adjacent cardiac muscle cells.

The physiological differences between cardiac and skeletal muscle are probably related to three ways in which the membranes of the two kinds of striated muscle cells differ. First, unlike skeletal muscle, which contracts in response to a stimulus conveyed by a motoneurone (Chap. 21), cardiac

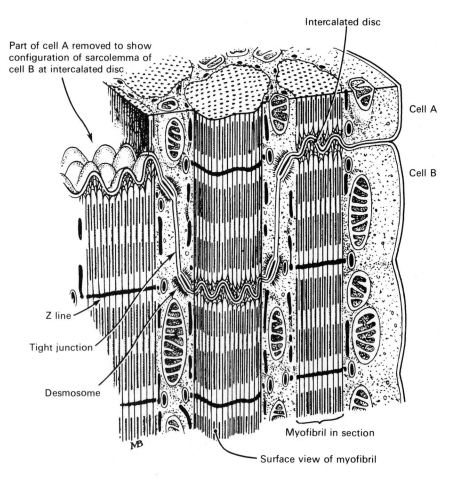

Part of cell A removed to show configuration of sarcolemma of cell B at intercalated disc

Intercalated disc

Cell A

Cell B

Z line

Tight junction

Desmosome

Myofibril in section

Surface view of myofibril

Fig. 10.5   Three dimensional reconstruction of adjacent parts of two myocardial cells (A and B) separated by part of the intercalated disc, showing the tight junctions (nexuses) where the surface membranes of the two cells seem, on electron microscopy, to be fused.

muscle of all kinds has, at least in certain circumstances, the fundamental property of contracting with *innate rhythmicity*. This property is particularly well developed in the modified myocardial cells forming the *specialized conducting tissue*, and especially in cells in certain regions, called *pace-makers*, that generate electrical current, spontaneously and fairly regularly, at inherent rates characteristic of different sites in the system. Secondly, the myocardium is very sensitive to the *direct action of neurohumoral transmitters* such as adrenaline and acetylcholine. Thirdly, the *duration of the action potential* of myocardial cells is very much greater than that of skeletal muscle: the upstroke is no slower, but the return to the resting potential takes much longer, especially in ventricular muscle (Fig. 10.6).

These three features have an important bearing on the functioning of the heart. The innate rhythmicity of a hierarchy of potential pace-makers ensures the continued beating of the heart; the direct action of neurohumoral transmitters powerfully affects the contractility of the muscle (p. 148); the plateau of the action potential prolongs the *refractory period* of the cell (Fig. 10.8), making it incapable in ordinary physiological conditions of producing summated contractions. Tetanic contraction of the myocardium would prevent the coordinated rhythmic contraction and relaxation that constitute the normal beating of the heart (p. 154).

THE ELECTRICAL EXCITATION OF THE HEART

Transmembrane resting and action potentials can be obtained from myocardial cells by the same techniques that are applied to nerve and are the result of differences of ionic concentrations and ionic fluxes across cell membranes. There are however important differences between the transmembrane potentials and ion fluxes of myocardium and those of nerve: in myocardium there is a slow inward calcium current not found in nerve and the potassium gating mechanisms are more complicated (Fig. 10.7).

The transmembrane *resting potential* recorded from inside cardiac cells is about −90 mV, evidence that the inside is negatively charged with respect to the outside ('polarized'). After excitation the polarity of charge on the membrane is reversed, and the transmembrane potential changes very rapidly to perhaps +30 mV. The subsequent voltage-time curve of the membrane *action potential* is much longer than that of nerve (Fig. 10.6). The prolonged depolarization, which lasts 400 to 500 msec in Purkinje cells and ventricular working cells is mainly the result of the slow inward calcium current. For the greater part of this time the cardiac cell is refractory to further stimuli (Fig. 10.8). In working muscle cells and non-pace-making special conducting tissue phase 4 is the resting potential of the cell and remains constant until the cell

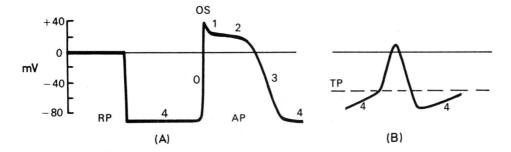

Fig. 10.6 The thick line shows the potential recorded by a microelectrode at first just outside the resting myocardial cell (0 mV), then inserted into the cell to give the transmembrane resting potential. The diagram on the left (A) shows the transmembrane potential in a working ventricular muscle cell; the diagram on the right (B) that of a nodal pace-maker cell. RP, resting potential. AP, action potential. TP, threshold potential. OS, overshoot. Phase 0 of the action potential represents the depolarization of the cell. Phases 1, 2 and 3 represent stages of repolarization. Phase 4 = RP in A, the pace-maker potential in B.

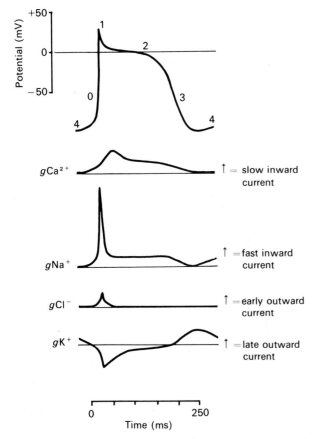

Fig. 10.7 Idealized model of a membrane action potential (MAP) and pacemaker activity of a Purkinje cell. The conductances (g) of the sarcolemma for various ions are shown non-quantitatively. In pace-making cells of the SA, and possibly AV, node the important inward channel may be that related to Ca^{2+} influx. In ventricular working muscle Cl flux is not important. (Adapted from Katz, A. M. (1977) *Physiology of the Heart*, New York: Raven Press, p. 237, and Noble, D. (1979) *The Initiation of the Heartbeat*, Oxford: Clarendon Press, p. 165).

membrane is excited again. The cell is then rapidly depolarized with a sudden and explosive increase in the membrane permeability to sodium; sodium ion moves rapidly into the cell down its electro-chemical gradient and a new action potential begins.

The special conducting system. The innate rhythmicity of cardiac muscle contraction is normally controlled by the electrical activity of the heart initiated by *pace-making cells* in the specialized myocardial cells of the *conducting system*. Although experimentally, in unphysiological conditions, working myocardial cells are capable of spontaneous depolarization they are normally excited by an electrical current passing along the surface of the cell membrane and from cell to cell through the intercalated discs and tight junctions.

Cells of the special conducting tissue vary greatly in size and character, some being smaller and some larger than working myocardial cells but they have a higher glycogen content and appear paler on staining than working cells; the electron microscope shows that they contain fewer myofibrils and mitochondria and poorly developed sarcoplasmic reticulum. With the exception of a group of cells at the centre of the atrioventricular node, which seem to exert only a delaying effect on conduction, it is likely that all the cells in the special conducting tissue are potential pace-maker cells, and together they act like a series of electrical oscillators whose rates are locked to that with the fastest inherent frequency.

The specialized conducting system (Fig. 10.9) consists of the *sinu-atrial node* near the junction of the superior vena cava and the right atrium; a diffuse area of cells, known as the *atrio-ventricular (AV) node*, lying above the right annulus fibrosus and near the mouth of the coronary sinus and the opening of the inferior vena cava; the *bundle of His* with its main left and right branches and the terminal ramifications of the *Purkinje network* in the subendocardial muscle.

The duration of the action potential in cells of the special conducting tissue increases progressively from the atrio-ventricular node to the Purkinje fibres (Fig. 10.10). Thus, as the electrical impulse is conducted down the system, the distal fibres with their longer effective refractory period may fail to respond to the higher rate of stimulation of proximal fibres. The abnormal condition called 'heart block' (p. 171) may result.

Another important feature of the special conducting tissue is that the inherent rate of discharge of the pace-maker cells declines progressively from the sinu-atrial node to the cells of the Purkinje network. Thus under ordinary conditions the sinu-atrial node, which has the fastest intrinsic rate, controls the rate of excitation of the whole heart because of the extremely rapid conduction of the excitatory current along the

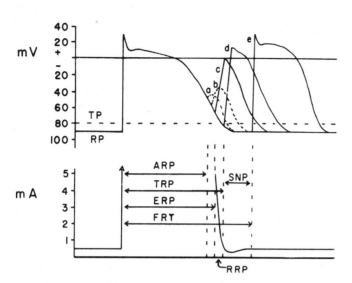

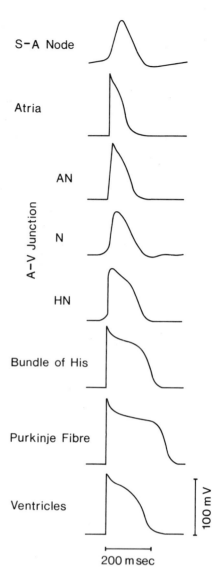

Fig. 10.8 Diagram to show the effect of the refractory states of a myocardial cell on attempts to elicit an action potential. Above is a normal membrane action potential (MAP). a-e, MAPs evoked by stimuli applied at times as indicated. The diagram below shows the excitability of the cell to cathodal stimulation. ARP, absolute refractory period. ERP, effective refractory period. TRP, total refractory period. RRP, relative refractory period. FRT, full recovery time. TRP−ERP = RRP. FRT−TRP = supranormal phase (SNP). The first potential to be *propagated* at all (c) arises at the end of ERP. The response, d, is not propagated normally. The first normal response (e) occurs at the end of FRT. (B. F. Hoffmann & D. Singer (1964) *Progress in Cardiovascular Disease*, 7, 226–260.)

Fig. 10.10 Characteristic shapes of the action potential from various types of myocardial cell. The duration is prolonged progressively from the atria to the peripheral Purkinje fibre. N denotes cells in the central part of the AV node; AN, cells nearer the atrium; HN, cells nearer the bundle of His. (Y. Watanabe & L. S. Dreifus (1968) *American Heart Journal*, 76, 114–135.)

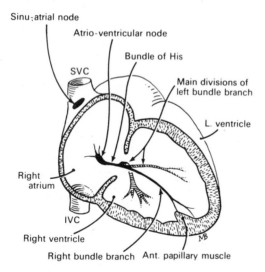

Fig. 10.9 Diagram to show the main parts of the cardiac specialized conducting system. The heart is viewed from the front and right, into the right atrium and ventricle, and has been cut in a plane parallel with the septa, which, in this display, are assumed to be transparent. The AV nodal tissue lies in the right atrium, the bundle of His runs below the membranous part of the interventricular septum, the two main divisions of the left bundle-branch lie beyond the septum. The Purkinje network, which ramifies in the subendocardium of both ventricles, is not shown.

Table 10.11 Speeds of conduction in the mammalian heart

Tissue	Approx. diameter cell (μm)	Velocity (m per sec)
Atrial fibres	10	0·3 to 0·5
AV node	5	0·05
Purkinje fibres	30	2·0 to 5
Ventricular cells	9 to 16	0·4 to 1

special conducting tissue. Table 10.11 shows conduction velocities through various parts of the conduction system and the working myocardium.

The action potential of pace-making cells differs from that of working myocardium: for example the rate of rise of the upstroke is less, the peak is more rounded and there is no great overshoot. There is considerable evidence to suggest that these features are the result of the action of the slow calcium current, with little or no contribution from a sodium flux. The most important physiological difference, however, lies in phase 4 (Fig. 10.6). In active pace-making cells the resting potential steadily lessens ('pace-maker potential'), probably because of increasing permeability to K^+ and Na^+.

Transmembrane potentials from the sinu-atrial node (Fig. 10.12) have all the characteristics of pace-making cells and the rate of automatic discharge can be varied in three ways. The threshold can be altered, as with changes in external Ca^{2+} concentration; the slope of the diastolic depolarization (Phase

4) can change, as under the influence of catecholamines; the level of the initial membrane resting potential can change, as with an altered K^+ concentration or under the influence of acetylcholine or drugs such as the digitalis glycosides.

Normally electrical current spreads from the pace-maker cells in the sinu-atrial node to excite the neighbouring atrial cells and then spreads from cell to cell along the working myocardial fibres of the atrium, 'depolarizing' them. The excitation leads to contraction of the sarcomeres.

The excitatory local membrane currents run from cell to cell through the atrial muscle towards the atrio-ventricular (AV) ring. This structure would act as a complete barrier to the spread of electrical activity from the atria to the ventricles were it not for the gap through which the specialized *atrio-ventricular junctional system* runs in the form of the bundle of His (p. 140).

The AV node lies subendocardially on the atrial side of the right annulus fibrosus and consists of successive layers of cells. Those near the atrial working muscle (AN in Fig. 10.10) propagate the impulse increasingly slowly, a property that seems to be associated with the slow upstroke and blunter peak of the action potential. Propagation through the middle zone of the node (N in Fig. 10.10) is remarkably slow and accounts for about 30 msec of the total delay in atrio-ventricular conduction. After the impulse crosses this central zone of the AV node its conduction velocity increases progressively to the main branches of the bundle of His. The first fibres to leave the bundle of His are those that form the posteroinferior division of the left bundle-branch. The next to leave are those that form the anterosuperior division of the left bundle-branch. Finally the remaining fibres become the right bundle-branch. The two main divisions of the left bundle-branch fan out under the endocardium of the left side of the interventricular septum and adjacent ventricle and end in the Purkinje network in the septum and near the two left-ventricular papillary muscles. The right bundle-branch runs to the Purkinje network near the anterior papillary muscle of the right ventricle.

Ventricular excitation. The first parts of the ventricles to

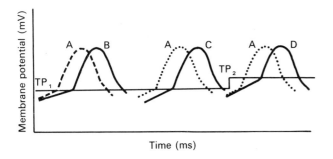

Fig. 10.12 Diagram to show how the rate of firing of transmembrane action potentials recorded from a cell in the SA node may be slowed by three different mechanisms. When the pace-maker potential (Phase 4, Fig. 10.6) reaches the normal threshold potential (TP_1) the cell fires (A). If the rate of depolarization is slower (slope of Phase 4 less) it fires as B. If the resting potential is increased it fires as C. If the threshold potential is raised to TP_2 the cell fires as D. The shape and height of the action potentials are purely diagrammatic.

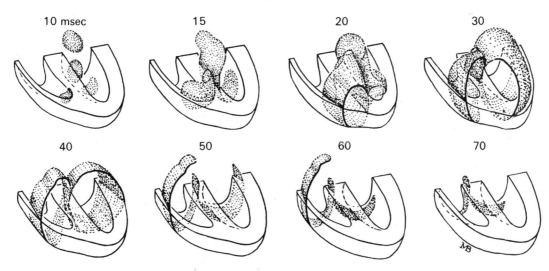

Fig. 10.13 Diagram to show the wavefronts of electrical excitation spreading through the human ventricles at successive instants after the start of ventricular depolarization. When a wavefront reaches the epicardium it is no longer moving and is therefore not represented in this diagram. The first part of the epicardium to be excited is the apical part of the right ventricle at about 20 msec. The septum is excited from both sides, and excitation in both ventricles moves from endocardium to epicardium, in the left fairly concentrically, in the right more tangentially.

be excited are small subendocardial areas on the left side of the interventricular septum. A few milliseconds later the subendocardial muscle of the right ventricle is excited near the anterior papillary muscle. During the next 60 msec or so the electrical activity spreads through the ventricular muscle from endocardium to epicardium as shown in Figure 10.13. The epicardium is first depolarized near the apex of the right ventricle about 20 msec after ventricular excitation begins. Excitation of both ventricles in complete in about 70 to 80 msec. This intrinsic cardiac electrical activity is to the heart what the impulse in the motoneurone is to skeletal muscle, an essential prerequisite for normal contraction.

By appropriate electrical techniques the electrical activity can be recorded from the surface of the body in terms of potential difference (voltage). Such a record is the basis of the *electrocardiogram* (ECG), so useful in clinical medicine (see p. 150).

Excitation-contraction coupling. The electrical excitation of a myocardial cell membrane is the result of the generation of a local circuit current by the membrane action potential, similar to that in unmyelinated nerve. This current, by positive feedback, is responsible for the propagation of the explosively self-perpetuating action potential. In addition, the tight junctions and intercalated discs provide a low electrical resistance between cells probably because of their high permeability to current-carrying K^+. The membrane current is transmitted toward the interior of the cell along the surfaces of the transverse tubular system. In the region of the 'triads' the electrical impulse in some way allows Ca^{2+}, sequestered in the nearby cisternae of the longitudinal system, to move out into the myofibrils. Ca^{2+} is bound to troponin C; the tropomyosin molecules then shift, removing their inhibiting action on contraction. ATP is split by the myosin ATPase in the presence

of Mg^{2+} and the filaments are propelled past each other to successive new sites for reaction with making or breaking of actin-myosin bonds. The sarcomere shortens and the myofibril contracts (Fig. 10.14).

The relaxation of the sarcomere is probably associated with the active transfer of Ca^{2+} from the vicinity of the myofibrils back into the cisternae, and the resumption of the inhibiting actions of troponin and tropomysin.

If the function of the heart and lungs is taken over by a pump and oxygenator it is possible to open the ventricles of the dog and study the mechanical movements of the myocardium by high-speed cinephotography. The order of contraction agrees with the order of electrical excitation already described. In the left ventricle contractions are seen first in the papillary muscles and in the adjacent septum and reach their maximum in 40 msec. The contraction waves spread from this area in such a way that the maximal contraction of the inflow tract occurs in 60 msec, of the outflow tract in 100 msec and of the aortic infundibulum in 120 msec. Relaxation occurs in the same order. The sequence of events in the right side is the same but the time course is shorter because of the shorter conduction time through the thinner walls. The early contraction of the papillary muscles tightens the chordae and so prevents the cusps of the AV valves from bulging much into the atrium during systole. This sequential contraction of the muscular wall of the ventricles is reminiscent of the peristaltic wave in the coiled tube of the embryonic heart and it is likely to aid the pumping mechanism.

MYOCARDIAL METABOLISM

The muscular tissue of the heart resembles skeletal muscle cells in containing glycogen, ATP and phosphocreatine but its metabolic behaviour is somewhat different from that of skeletal muscle.

The metabolism of the heart is normally almost entirely aerobic and accounts for about 7 per cent of the body's oxygen consumption. At rest, the heart consumes 6·5 to 10 ml/100 g tissue per minute and extracts 65 to 75 per cent of the oxygen in the coronary arterial blood. Apart from oxygen the main metabolic substrate of the heart is free fatty acids which supply about two-thirds of its energy when the body is in the fasting state. Important amounts of glucose and lactate are also consumed, 11 g of glucose and 10 g of lactic acid per day accounting together for about 35 per cent of the total oxygen extracted. Glucose is used especially after meals, and the lactate normally comes from the metabolism of skeletal muscle; when free fatty acids are available glucose utilization is suppressed. Lesser amounts of pyruvate and ketone bodies are also used by the myocardium, but only very small amounts of amino acids although the myocardium contains a higher concentration than any other tissue in the body of the enzyme aspartate aminotransferase (AST). When part of the muscle dies as the result of interruption of its blood supply, for example, after coronary artery occlusion, this enzyme is liberated into the blood and the serum AST activity rises for 2 to 3 days. The increase in the serum of this and other cardiac intracellular enzymes is often useful in the diagnosis of myocardial infarction.

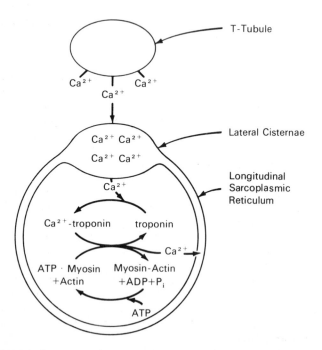

Fig. 10.14 Suggested mechanism of excitation-contraction coupling (B. Morkin & P. J. LaRaia (1974) *New England Journal of Medicine*, **290**, 445.)

Cardiac metabolism is often considered in three stages. In the stage of *energy liberation* the major substrates are metabolized in the mitochondria to acetyl co-enzyme A which enters the citric acid cycle. The hydrogen released is then moved along the electron transport chain with a stepwise release of energy from carbon hydrogen bonds. In the stage of *energy conservation* most of the energy thus liberated as hydrogen or its electron is converted by oxidative phosphorylation to the terminal-bond energy of creatine phosphate (CP) and adenosine triphosphate (ATP). The utilization of the high energy bonds of ATP (*energy utilization*) involves its hydrolysis by a Mg^{2+}-activated myofibrillar enzyme, myosin-ATPase, which is inactive in the absence of calcium. The breakdown of ATP at the myofibrillar bridges releases energy for the contraction of the myofibrils. A transphorylation equilibrium between ATP and CP ensures that ATP is rapidly replaced through the hydrolysis of CP which acts as a reserve of high-energy bonds.

If the heart becomes hypoxic, metabolism becomes partly anaerobic with increased glucose transport into the cell, increased glycogenolysis and a marked increase in anaerobic glycolysis. The glycolysis produces increased pyruvate which is reduced to lactate. This excess lactate is released by the heart into the blood in the coronary sinus.

When ventricular contraction is increased to overcome a raised arterial impedance (pressure load, afterload) the oxygen consumption is greater than that involved in a corresponding contraction to expel an increased end-diastolic volume of blood (volume load, preload).

MYOCARDIAL CONTRACTION

The length–tension relation. Spiral and transverse muscle bundles have been described in the myocardium but since they were only seen after very crude methods of preparation they are likely to be artifacts. In a papillary muscle all the fibres are aligned in much the same direction, so these thin cardiac muscles provide simpler samples than the more complex ventricular wall. The behaviour of isolated papillary muscles subjected to a *preload* and *afterload* has been much studied with a myograph (Fig. 10.15). With such a preparation, the unstimulated muscle is progressively stretched and the 'resting (passive) tension' rises. When the muscle is then held at a fixed length and electrically stimulated, an isometric force can be measured at one end. If, at various lengths, the muscle is stimulated, active contraction is superimposed on the resting *length-tension relationship* for each length, giving a curve of 'total tension' (Fig. 10.16). The 'actively developed' tension can be derived from the total tension by subtracting the resting tension. Figure 10.17 shows a '*length-tension curve*' for papillary muscle. The range of muscle lengths at which the active tension is almost maximum (L_{max}) is relatively wide, and corresponds to the rounded peak of the active tension curve. As the muscle is shortened the actively developed tension and the resting tension both fall.

The length–tension curves of cardiac and skeletal muscle are similar in shape. Figure 10.17 also shows the curve for the sartorius muscle of the frog, corrected for the different cross-sectional areas and for the proportions of the contractile

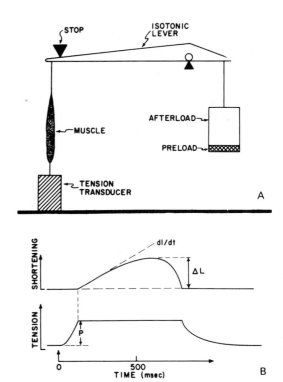

Fig. 10.15 Diagram showing (A) the experimental arrangement for studying the loaded contraction of a papillary muscle with a myograph. The initial length is set by a 'preload' and held constant by the stop. When the muscle shortens it lifts the 'afterload'. B illustrates tension and shortening of a typical after-loaded contraction. Starting at 0 the isometric tension increases until, when it reaches P, the muscle begins to shorten and the afterload is lifted. The initial velocity of shortening of the subsequent isotonic contraction is given by d*l*/d*t*. ΔL indicates the maximum shortening during the contraction. (E. H. Sonnenblick (1966) The mechanics of myocardial contraction. In *The Myocardial Cell*, ed. Briller, S. A. & Conn, J. J. p. 173. Philadelphia: University of Pennsylvania Press.)

material in the two types of striated muscle cell. The peak active tension at L_{max} is generally the same for cardiac and skeletal muscle. By contrast the resting tension at L_{max} is considerable in cardiac muscle and exists during the major part of the ascending limb of the length-active-tension curve, while in skeletal muscle resting tension is minimal at L_{max}, rising only appreciably during the descending limb of the length–active-tension curve. Cardiac muscle therefore operates along the ascending limb of the length-active-tension curve while skeletal muscle operates mainly near the apex. It is not certain why cardiac muscle has this relatively high resting tension.

The length–tension curves in Figure 10.17 are related to sarcomere lengths that correlate closely with the theoretical limits to the shortening of sarcomeres in the ventricles. These relationships, and the fact that the length of the sarcomere is directly proportional to muscle length along the ascending limb of the length–active-tension curve, form the ultrastructural basis of Starling's 'Law of the Heart' which is considered later.

Length–tension curves of this general form have been derived experimentally from mammalian and human papillary muscle, and from the human heart *in situ* (Fig. 10.16). The

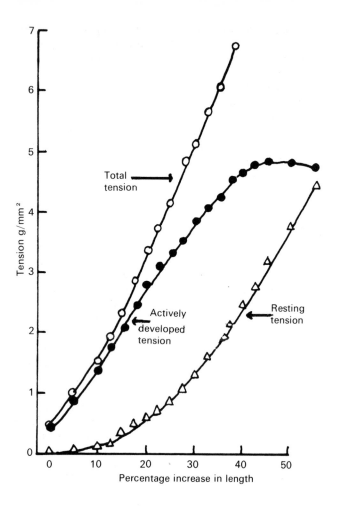

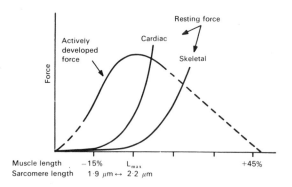

Fig. 10.17 The relationship between tension (force) and initial muscle length for cat papillary muscle and for the sartorius muscle of the frog. Muscle length has been normalized relative to that length where the actively developed tension is maximum (L_{max}). Active tension is normalized relative to the tension developed at L_{max}. Resting tension is the tension produced by the passively stretched muscle. Active tension is the tension the striated muscle generates when stimulated. (R. A. Leyton & E. H. Sonnenblick (1971) The sarcomere as the basis of Starling's law of the heart in the left and right ventricles. In *Functional Morphology of the Heart: Methods and Achievements in Experimental Pathology*, ed. Bajusz, E. & Jasmin, G. Vol. 5, p. 22. Basel: Karger.)

Fig. 10.16 Length-tension curves for human papillary muscle removed at a cardiac operation (E. H. Sonnenblick, E. Braunwald & A. G. Morrow (1965). *Journal of Clinical Investigation*, 44, 966). Similar curves are obtained from human ventricular myocardium *in situ* at operation.

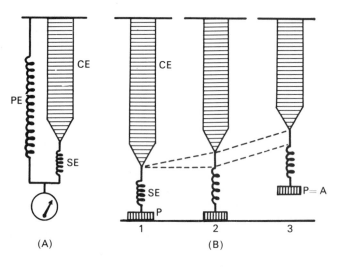

Fig. 10.18 A. V. Hill's model of muscle contraction. (A) CE, contractile element (actin–myosin mechanism); SE, series elastic component; PE, parallel elastic component. (B) during contraction— 1, initial resting state; 2, the CE shortens, the SE is stretched but the preload, P, is not moved (isometric contraction); 3, further shortening of CE lifts the preload, which now becomes an afterload, A (isotonic contraction).

concepts of preload and afterload (Fig. 10.18) of the whole heart are used in clinical medicine.

The force-velocity relation. A. V. Hill's model to explain the mechanical activity of skeletal muscle (Fig. 10.18 and Chap. 21) has proved useful in considering cardiac muscle as well, although the series elastic (SE) component of myocardium seems to be more compliant than that of skeletal muscle, and the parallel elastic component (PE), to be stiffer. Hill studied the relation between the load on a muscle and the velocity of its shortening, the *'force–velocity relation'*, which is a fundamental property of the contractile element (CE), that is the actinmyosin mechanism (Fig. 10.19). When the force, or load, (*P*) approaches zero the velocity of initial shortening (*V*) is maximal and is termed V_{max}. As the load is increased the amount and the velocity of contraction both decrease progressively until no shortening can occur and the maximum isometric force (P_0) is reached.

The 'active state' of myocardium is a measure of the processes that generate force and shortening at contractile sites. It is characterized by instantaneous relations between muscle length, force and velocity of contraction, during the

whole course of a contraction. The activation of heart muscle is relatively slow, so early in the contraction the slow increase in the active state gives low values for the shortening velocity of the lightly loaded muscle. Late in the contraction the load is heavy and this fact and the sensitivity of the CE to displacement give low velocities of shortening. During most of the contraction, however, when the muscle acts most intensely, it operates on this *force–velocity curve*. The intensity of the active state' is thus an expression of the capacity of the

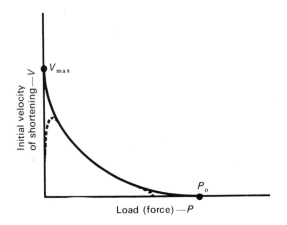

Fig. 10.19 A force-velocity curve for muscle. Theoretically a hyperbolic relationship exists between the initial contraction velocity (V) and the muscle tension (P). V_{max}, maximum velocity of initial shortening at zero load:P_0, maximum tension at zero shortening (isometric). Experimentally, the force-velocity relations of a muscle are not expressed by this curve either early, or late, in contraction, but are as indicated by the dashed lines.

contractile mechanism of muscle at any moment after stimulation to produce tension, force and motion.

If the ends of the muscle are fixed and the isometric tension developed is maximal, all the active sites that generate tension to bring about shortening would tend to be in a 'combined', rather than a 'free', state: thus the maximum tension (P_0) should be determined by the total number of actin–myosin sites that are combined, which in turn may be related to the amount of Ca^{2+} present, to the action of troponin and to the sarcomere length. With progressively lighter loads fewer and fewer actin-myosin sites would be combined, and more would be free, until eventually both the rate of release of energy and the speed of shortening of the muscle are maximal, and the muscle shortens freely with no load. Because almost all active sites are now free, V_{max} would be determined by the maximal intrinsic rate at which energy can be released to allow an actin–myosin interaction to produce the cyclic changes in position that lead to shortening. This is related to myosin ATPase, and the rate of activity of this enzyme has been found to provide an excellent index to the V_{max} of muscle. Force-velocity curves for cardiac muscle have been obtained experimentally from animal and human papillary muscle, canine left ventricle and intact human ventricle (Fig. 10.20). The value for V_{max} must be obtained by extrapolation.

Changes in force-velocity relations characterize the two most important general properties of cardiac muscle: the change in *initial muscle length*, the basis of the 'Starling mechanism' to be considered later, and changes in the *contractile state* of the myocardium. An increase in the initial length of the muscle produces a rise in P_0 without a change in V_{max}. A change in the contractile state of the myocardium alters V_{max} with or without a change in P_0

This behaviour of the myocardium contrasts with that of skeletal muscle. Under physiological conditions the force-velocity curve of a skeletal muscle does not alter; its force is altered mainly by its innervation, which controls the number of contracting fibres, each of which contracts almost maxi-

mally, though at varying rates. The nerve supply of the heart, however, cannot change the total number of contracting fibres; the contractile force of myocardium depends on the point on the ascending part of the length–tension curve at which the cardiac muscle cells are operating.

Length, force and velocity. Let us consider a papillary muscle preparation at a given contractile state. Both the force-velocity and the length–tension relations apply to it: that is to say, the greater the load, the slower is the contraction, and, within limits, the longer the fibre the greater is the force developed. It has been shown that during myocardial contraction the velocity of shortening at any instant is a function of the length of the muscle and also of its afterload at that moment. Three variables are concerned: the force or 'load', the velocity of contraction and the fibre length. A three-dimensional plot is therefore needed to demonstrate adequately the course of events during a single contraction. The framework for such a three-dimensional representation can be constructed by displaying *a family of force–velocity curves* for different lengths of the muscle (Fig. 10.21).

Bearing in mind A. V. Hill's model (Fig. 10.18), let us now consider the moment-to-moment state of the papillary muscle during a single contraction. In Figure 10.21B the muscle is activated at 0. When the active state has developed maximally the force–velocity relationship is as shown at 1. Here the contractile element starts to shorten, stretching the SE and building up isometric force. As the force increases the velocity of shortening of the CE drops towards 2. Here the force developed by the CE equals the load, which is therefore lifted,

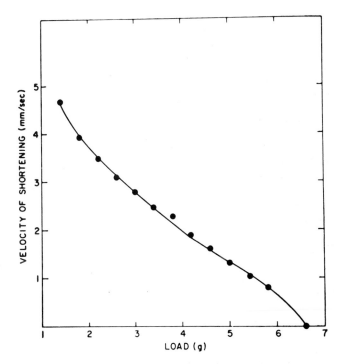

Fig. 10.20 Force–velocity curve for human papillary muscle removed at a cardiac operation. Initial velocity of isotonic shortening on ordinate, afterload on abscissa. (E. H. Sonnenblick, E. Braunwald & A. G. Morrow (1965) *Journal of Clinical Investigation*, 44, 966.) Similar curves have been obtained during isovolumetric contraction of intact ventricle.

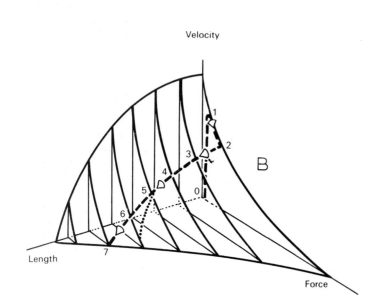

the contraction now becoming isotonic. The rate at which the muscle then shortens falls in accordance with the length of the CE, and the pathway of the three-dimensional relationship moves from one force–velocity curve to another, as shown by the numbers 3 to 7 in Figure 10.21B. The plane on which this pathway runs, encompassing force, velocity and length, may be regarded as defining the mechanical correlates of the contractile state of the muscle.

The contraction of an intact left ventricle is, of course, more complicated. Loading conditions are different: the preload, or circumferential fibre length at the onset of contraction, is a function of the end-diastolic ventricular volume, and the afterload, or aortic impedance, also varies. Despite these limitations the three-dimensional framework can be modified to form a basis for understanding several important general principles.

In Figure 10.22 a left ventricular contraction starts at 0, where the circumferential fibre is at its end-diastolic length. Ventricular contraction is isovolumetric (p. 155) at the start, so that the velocity of contraction rapidly increases and then follows the force–velocity relation for isometric contraction until the aortic valve opens (2). The subsequent ejection phase (see p. 155) is characterized by 'auxotonic' contraction against an increasing resistance, that is the afterload or aortic impedance; at each instant during ejection the length of the muscle fibres and the velocity of contraction are correspondingly related. At the end of ejection, when muscular shortening is maximal, the pathway that has characterized the ventricular contraction has reached point 3. Isovolumetric relaxation then

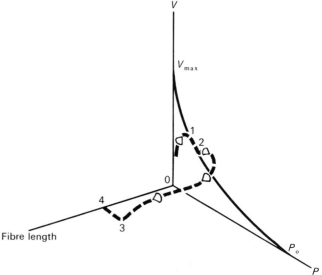

Fig. 10.21   (A) Length–tension and force–velocity curves combined in a three-dimensional construction to illustrate the contraction of a papillary muscle. Note that the usual convention regarding magnitude has been reversed in the axis representing length. (B) A family of force–velocity curves appropriate to different muscle lengths occupies the framework shown in A. During contraction, which starts at 0, the changing relationship between initial velocity, length and force is indicated by the dashed line and solid arrows. Early and late in the contraction the force–velocity relationships determined experimentally (dotted line) are not exactly in accordance with theory.

Fig. 10.22   Diagram to illustrate theoretical relations between force (load), velocity of contraction and circumferential fibre length during the contraction of an intact left ventricle. Symbols are as in Fig. 10.19. 0 denotes the end-diastolic length of the fibre. 1–2 represents isovolumetric contraction (p. 155). At 2 the aortic valve opens and, since the aortic impedance increases during the early ejection phase (p. 155),, contraction is not isotonic, but auxotonic, that is against an increasing load. 3–4, isovolumetric relaxation. 4–0, diastolic increase in fibre length. (*After* E. Braunwald, J. Ross & E. H. Sonnenblick (1967) *Mechanisms of Contraction of the Normal and Failing Heart*. London: Churchill.)

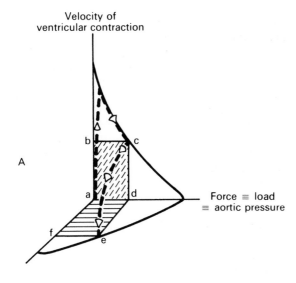

Velocity of
ventricular contraction

A

Force ≡ load
≡ aortic pressure

Circumferential fibre length
≡ ventricular volume

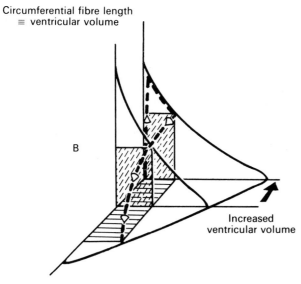

B

Increased
ventricular volume

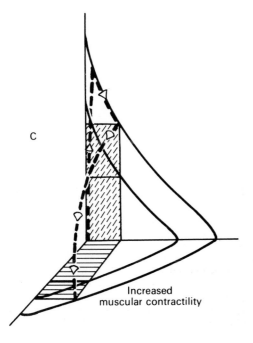

C

Increased
muscular contractility

occurs (3 to 4) and during diastole (4 to 0) the ventricle fills and the fibre length increases.

In this three-dimensional framework the axis representing the muscular tension or load (*P*) can also represent the aortic impedance (afterload) and the axis representing the circumferential length can also represent the ventricular volume. In Fig. 10.23A af can therefore represent the *stroke volume*, or the volume of blood ejected during one complete ventricular contraction (p. 162). There is an almost linear relationship between ventricular systolic pressure and the length of end-diastolic muscle segments, or the ventricular volume, in the physiological range. Because of this, and because power = aortic pressure × velocity, and work = stroke volume × pressure, the 'power' and 'work' of the ventricle during the contraction can be indicated in the three dimensional diagram as shown in Figure 10.23. However, the 'power', 'work' and 'mechanical efficiency' of the heart are not nearly such useful concepts as the Starling mechanism and the contractile state of the myocardium.

To illustrate these two important mechanisms Figure 10.23 also provides three-dimensional diagrams showing (B) the effects of an increased ventricular end-diastolic volume (Starling mechanism) and (C) the effect of increased muscle contractility. Similar analyses can be made of contraction against an increased aortic impedance (afterload) and during an increased heart rate (tachycardia).

Starling's law of the heart. In E. H. Starling's famous experiments with the isolated and denervated *heart-lung preparation* the venous return to the heart or the arterial resistance could each be increased independently. As a result of either change the heart responded by an increase in both the end-diastolic volume and the contractile activity. As a result of his experiments Starling enunciated his 'Law of the Heart': *"that the energy of contraction, however measured, is a function of the length of the muscle fibre"*.

Starling suggested that the increased force of contraction was associated with a change in energy along active surfaces disposed longitudinally, so seeming to anticipate modern theories based on the ultrastructure of the sarcomere, of which he was ignorant. At first he believed that his law described the way in which the cardiac output of the healthy heart was automatically adjusted to the varying needs of the body, but in fact that adjustment is mainly achieved by the nervous and hormonal control of myocardial contractility, as Starling himself later seems to have realized. The function of the Starling mechanism is to ensure that over any period of time the outputs of the left and the right ventricle are approximately equal, so that the total blood volume is distributed in proper proportions between the systemic and pulmonary circulations.

McMichael and Sharpey-Schafer first produced experimental evidence to suggest that in the intact human heart the

Fig. 10.23 Simplified diagrams to illustrate some important aspects of ventricular contraction. (A) af represents stroke volume. Power = afterload (aortic pressure) × velocity (abcd). Work = stroke volume × pressure (adef). (B) The effect of increased ventricular volume, the Starling mechanism. (C) The effect of increased muscular contractility. (*After* E. H. Sonnenblick (1966) The mechanics of myocardial contraction. In *The Myocardial Cell*, ed. Briller, S. A. & Conn, H. J. P. 1973. Philadelphia: University of Pennsylvania Press.)

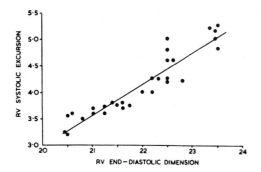

Fig. 10.24 Beat-to-beat relations between right ventricular (RV) end-diastolic dimensions and systolic shortening during the subsequent cycle in a patient with sinus rhythm during and after release of a Valsalva manoeuvre. Both variables were measured from cineradiographs of patients whose ventricular epicardium had been previously marked by radio-opaque clips at the time of cardiac operation. (E. Braunwald (1965). *British Heart Journal*, 27, 1–16.)

end-diastolic length of ventricular muscle is a major determinant of the strength of contraction. In general this concept is now accepted (Fig. 10.24).

Non-contractile components in heart muscle. Consideration of the force of contraction of cardiac muscle is complicated by the fact that some of the resting tension is maintained by non-contracting elastic structures, Hill's SE and PE (Fig. 10.18). Anatomically they cannot yet be identified and, indeed, need not even be structurally separate. Further, during a cardiac contraction more and more of the force exerted in the resting state may be transferred from the elastic elements to the myofilaments, and during ventricular systole a significant amount of the tension may be borne by the PE, though the SE probably plays no part in alterations to the contractile state of the myocardium. The PE, moreover, determines the resting (diastolic) pressure-volume relationship of the ventricle.

VENTRICULAR PERFORMANCE

Starling showed that the stroke volume of a heart that was not failing is a function of the diastolic fibre length, or ventricular diastolic volume, which in turn is related to the diastolic filling pressure. This last relationship is, however, complicated by the law developed by Laplace for arteries, modified to apply to a ventricle: it implies that the tangential force in the myocardial wall needed to produce a given intraventricular pressure is a direct function of the ventricular radius ($T = (P \times R)\, 2h$, where T = tangential intramyocardial tension, P = intraventricular pressure, R = internal radius of ventricular cavity, h = thickness of ventricular wall). If the diastolic volume of the ventricle is increased a greater intramyocardial tension is needed to keep the intraventricular pressure constant.

Ventricular function curves. Sarnoff and his colleagues correlated the ventricular stroke volume with mean atrial, or ventricular end-diastolic, pressures, using these as a measure of the diastolic volume. Ventricular performance, measured in this way, can be expressed in the form of *ventricular function curves* (Fig. 10.25). Alterations in the ventricular performance

are represented in this graph as a family of ventricular function curves, the position of each curve corresponding to a different state of ventricular contractility. Rushmer's work on conscious, fully active animals, to whose hearts various measuring instruments had previously been attached at a surgical operation, has suggested that the situation is even more complicated. In such animals Starling's length–tension relationships appeared to hold during some simple activities: for example, when a dog lies down from the sitting position the diameter of the left ventricle increases for a few beats and during this time the rate of flow through the aortic valve and the ventricular stroke volume also increase; minor alterations in heart rate such as sinus arrhythmia are accompanied by similar changes. On the other hand the cardiac response to exercise in these animals, and probably in man, does not seem to conform to any simple intrinsic mechanism. It seems clear that changes in the contractility of the muscle and the heart rate, brought about by reflex and humoral mechanisms, and modified by posture, often over-rule the effects of the simple Starling mechanism.

Despite these complexities it is still useful to think of cardiac performance in terms of ventricular function curves, if we remember that many factors play a part in both main variables—the ventricular end-diastolic volume and the myocardial contractility. Factors that affect the ventricular end-diastolic volume are shown in Figure 10.26, those that affect the contractile state of the myocardium in Figure 10.27.

When the blood volume is drastically reduced by a sudden severe haemorrhage ventricular performance is impaired. On standing, the blood tends to pool in the lower parts of the body so the intrathoracic volume and ventricular end-diastolic blood volume are reduced; lying with the legs raised, however, tends to raise the cardiac output unless the heart is failing. The normal negative intrathoracic pressure is an important factor in maintaining the diastolic filling of the heart. Artificial positive-pressure ventilation can interfere with this mechanism and, by impairing the venous return to the heart, may

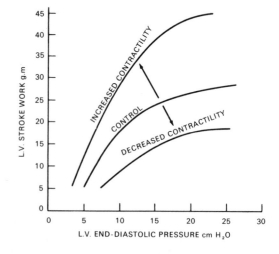

Fig. 10.25 Diagrammatic representation of ventricular function curves obtained under control conditions, during the administration of a positive inotropic agent (increased contractility) and during a negative inotropic state (decreased contractility). LV, left ventricle. (E. Braunwald, J. Ross & E. H. Sonnenblick (1967) *Mechanisms of Contractions of the Normal and Failing Heart*. London: Churchill.)

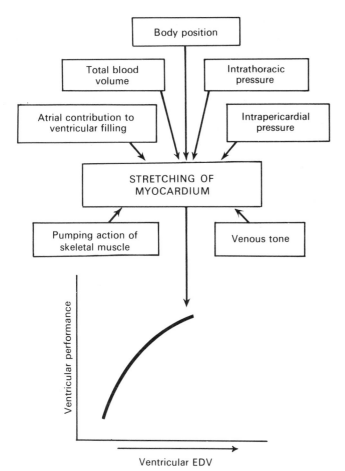

Fig. 10.26 Diagram of a Starling curve, relating ventricular end-diastolic volume (EDV) to ventricular performance and the major influences that determine the degree of stretching of the myocardium, that is, the magnitude of the EDV. (After E. Braunwald, J. Ross & E. H. Sonnenblick (1967). *Mechanisms of Contraction of the Normal and Failing Heart*. London: Churchill.)

reduce the cardiac output. During exercise the smooth muscle in the walls of the veins is constricted, probably by sympathetic stimulation, and tends to increase the filling of the heart, as does the pumping action of skeletal muscles on the veins (p. 164). The *atrial transport function* can increase the ventricular end-diastolic volume (p. 154) by acting like a 'booster-pump'.

The contractile state, or 'inotropy', of the myocardium, can be increased ('positive inotropy') or decreased ('negative inotropy'), by physiological, pharmacological or pathological causes. In physiological conditions the main positive inotropic factor is the noradrenaline released by the sympathetic nerve endings in the heart and acting upon the β-adrenergic receptors in the myocardium. The amount of this noradrenaline depends on the frequency of sympathetic nervous impulses arriving at the heart, but circulating catecholamines also have a direct effect on the myocardium and increase its contractility. Many drugs have a positive or negative inotropic action: for example, the glycosides of digitalis are frequently used to increase the power of ventricular contraction in heart failure, and drugs that block the β-adrenergic receptors in the

myocardium may impair ventricular contractility. In pathological conditions hypoxia, hypercapnia and acidosis of the myocardium and damage to the muscle itself all reduce the contractile power of the ventricle.

The inotropic state of the heart, independent of changes in afterload and preload, has so far proved difficult to quantify, and it is likely that V_{max} in isolated myocardium can be altered by several inotropic stimuli though there is some doubt about its validity as an index of contractility independent of fibre length. If the ventricular end-diastolic pressure (preload) and the aortic pressure (afterload) are held constant in the intact heart, positive and negative inotropic stimuli increase and diminish the stroke volume, and the ejection velocity and maximum rate of rise of pressure (dP/dt) of the left ventricle (Fig. 10.38). However, these measurements can also be altered by changes in loading.

The left ventricular stroke volume expressed as a percentage of the end-diastolic volume is known as the 'ejection fraction' and may be estimated by various methods, including biplane cine-angiocardiography. The left ventricular ejection fraction

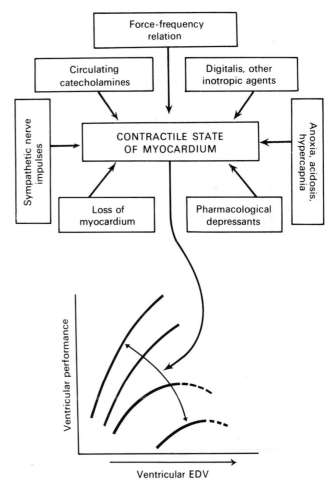

Fig. 10.27 Diagram showing the major influences that elevate or depress the contractile state of the myocardium, and the manner in which alterations in the contractile state of the myocardium affect the level of ventricular performance at any given level of ventricular end-diastolic volume. (After E. Braunwald, J. Ross & E. H. Sonnenblick (1967) *Mechanisms of Contraction of the Normal and Failing Heart*. London: Churchill.)

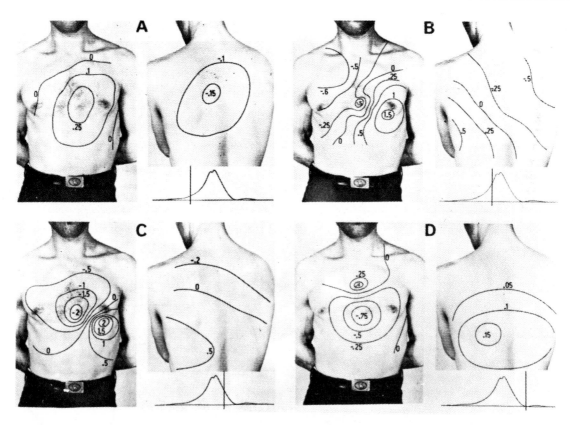

Fig. 10.28 Distribution on the chest surface of a normal subject of electrical potentials arising from cardiac excitation at four instants of time during ventricular activation ('isopotential field map'). The vertical lines intersecting the QRS complex of the electrocardiograms (p. 153) at the bottom of the figures indicate the instants of time to which the maps are related. (B. Taccardi (1963) *Circulation Research*, **12**, 341.)

for a wide range of animals at rest is about 50 per cent, ranging in man between about 50 and 65 per cent. Positive inotropic agents increase the ejection fraction from any given end-diastolic volume.

THE ELECTROCARDIOGRAM

We have already briefly considered the generation of the electrical currents and potential differences in cardiac pacemaker cells and their conduction from cell to cell during the electrical excitation leading to mechanical contraction (p. 138). This electrical activity can be recorded as a potential difference on the surface of the body by electrodes applied to the skin and linked to a system of amplifiers and galvanometers called an *electrocardiograph*. The distribution of these potentials on the skin of the thorax can be mapped by computerized techniques. The *isopotential map* thus recorded varies at different moments during ventricular excitation (Fig. 10.28). Accordingly an electrode at any one site on the body records potential differences that vary as a function of time. The electrocardiograph usually records these voltage–time curves on moving paper throughout each cardiac cycle and from beat to beat: such a record is called an *electrocardiogram* (ECG) (Fig. 10.29 and 35).

The electrocardiogram is useful to the physiologist because its various 'deflections' or 'waves' allow the timing of various events in the cardiac cycle. In clinical medicine it is even more valuable, for it provides the most accurate available infor-

mation about the rhythm of the heart and about abnormalities of the spread of excitation through the myocardium, for example, when it is damaged by disease.

Wavefronts of depolarization. The electrical excitation of a cardiac muscle cell spreads from the point of stimulation, accompanied by the regenerating membrane action potential set up by the ion fluxes through the sarcolemma and membrane currents (Fig. 10.30A) which are transmitted from cell to cell through the low resistance pathways of the intercalated discs and the tight junctions. As the excitation advances along a cell the distribution of charges at the junction between the resting and active regions is as shown in Fig. 10.30B. The excitation is conducted so rapidly from cell to cell that this distribution of charges may be regarded as an advancing 'wavefront' of excitation through the myocardium. Such a wavefront carries opposite electrical charges on its two surfaces and therefore produces appropriate fields of potential and current.

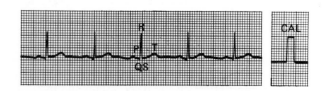

Fig. 10.29 Normal electrocardiogram (ECG) recorded by 'standard lead II' (p. 153). Time intervals (horizontal), 40 and 200 msec. Voltage scale (vertical), 0·1 and 0·5 mV. CAL, calibration signal (1 mV).

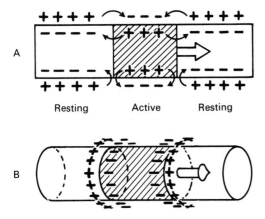

Fig. 10.30 Diagram of a myocardial fibre during the passage of excitation (depolarization) and recovery (repolarization). In the resting state the outside of the cell membrane is positively charged with respect to the inside; in the active state the polarity is reversed. Local membrane currents flow as indicated by the small arrows in (A) at the junctions of active and resting parts of the cell. These junctions form charged wavefronts of excitation and recovery (depolarization and repolarization). These wavefronts have direction, polarity and magnitude and so each can be represented as a vector: the solid arrow in (B) represents the advancing wavefront of excitation.

Electrical current seems to flow in the heart much as it does between two terminals immersed in a *volume conductor*, such as a large volume of electrolyte solution, through which the current can flow in three dimensions. The lines of current-flow in a volume conductor are accompanied in the usual manner by appropriate isopotential lines, also distributed in three dimensions (Fig. 10.31). Although the thorax contains organs with electrical resistances different from that of the heart, for example the lungs, it is probable that the intrathoracic contents act as a volume conductor, extending that of the heart and providing a more or less homogeneous conducting

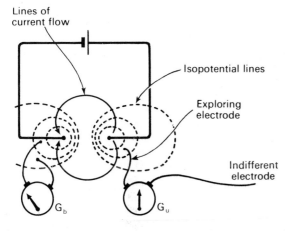

Fig. 10.31 Diagram to show the lines of current flow and the lines of equal potential (isopotential field) between two terminals immersed in a large volume of electrolyte solution ('volume conductor'). G_b represents the galvanometer of a 'bipolar' lead system recording the potential difference between two points of relatively high potential that are close together. G_u represents the galvanometer of a 'unipolar' lead system where the electrodes are at points far apart, and one ('indifferent electrode') is at a point of relatively very low potential.

medium for the three-dimensional fields of current and potential. The potentials are greatest near the positive and negative terminals of the 'cardiac electrical generator' and diminish as the square of the distance from them. When the isopotential lines meet a limiting surface such as the skin they are slightly distorted, but the small increases in magnitude thus produced seem to be approximately balanced by the internal shunting effect of the blood inside the heart.

During the excitation of the heart charged wavefronts move through the muscle of the atria and the ventricles (Fig. 10.13). At any instant the apparent cardiac generator is the vectorial resultant of several complex and differently directed wavefronts. Figure 10.32 shows the *resultant vectors* at 10, 40, and 70 msec after the onset of ventricular excitation. Figure 10.33 shows how these early, middle and late vectorial forces contribute to the formation of characteristic deflections in the electrocardiogram recorded from conventional electrode sites

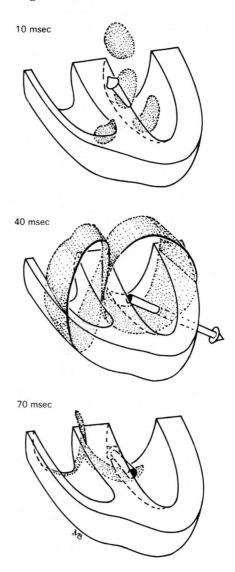

Fig. 10.32 Diagrammatic representation of the wavefronts of excitation of the ventricles at 10, 40 and 70 msec after the onset of ventricular depolarization (see Fig. 10.13). The solid arrows indicate vectors representing the total unbalanced electrical activity at each instant.

on the surface of the body during ventricular depolarization. Similar principles can be applied to the consideration of atrial depolarization.

Repolarization. The same general principles also apply to the repolarization of both the atria and the ventricles. Since the polarity of the charged wavefront that accompanies the restoration of the resting state is opposite to that of the depolarizing wavefront (Fig. 10.30), one might expect that the deflections in the ECG representing repolarization would

always be opposite in direction to those that represent depolarization. However, repolarization does not proceed through the intact heart in the same order as depolarization: excitation lasts longer at the base of the heart than at the apex.

During the first rapid phase (0) of the membrane action potential (Fig. 10.6) the depolarization of the 'working' cell is associated with the sudden increase in the permeability of the sarcolemma that allows the passive inward Na^+ flux. Repolarization, on the other hand, involves the active

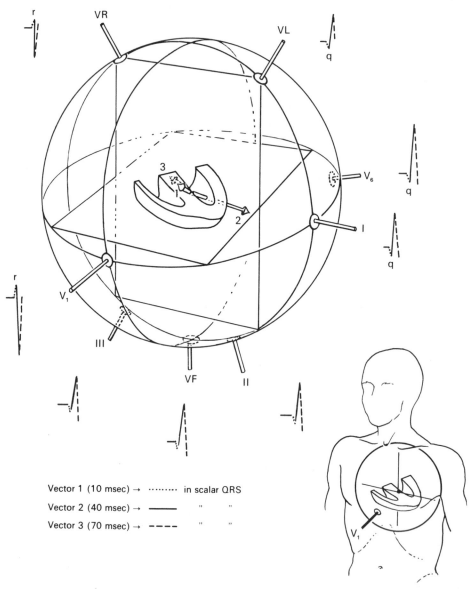

Vector 1 (10 msec) → ········ in scalar QRS

Vector 2 (40 msec) → ——   "   "

Vector 3 (70 msec) → – – – –   "   "

Fig. 10.33 Simplified diagram to show how the three vectors shown in Figure 10.32 can be considered as arising at the centre of a spherical volume conductor in the thorax, and indicating the positions on the surface of this sphere of some conventional electrode positions used in electrocardiography. Beside each electrode is an indication of the contribution made by each of the three vectors to the surface (scalar) QRS complex recorded at each site. The magnitude and sign of each scalar deflection in the QRS complex is determined by the relationship between the size and position in space of the vectors and a plane passing through the origin of the vectors and at right angles to the 'lead axis'. In this diagram the lead axes are not shown but each runs from the site of a surface electrode to the origin of the vectors. Thus, the 10 msec vector, being short and directed upward and to the right toward the electrode sites for scalar leads VR and V_1, gives a small positive (upward) deflection (r) in these leads; it is, however, directed away from the electrode sites of other leads and so gives negative (downward) deflections (q) in them. The unipolar exploring electrodes VR, VL and VF are actually applied to the right and left arms and the left leg respectively; V_1 is sited on the precordium as shown in the smaller diagram, V_6 is sited in the left axillary region. The standard bipolar leads (Roman numerals) record complexes similar to those recorded by unipolar exploring electrodes sited as shown, though the actual lead arrangements are more complex (p. 153).

extrusion of Na$^+$ by the much slower mechanism of the Na$^+$-K$^+$ pump, which involves metabolic work and the action of ATPase, and is much more readily disturbed by changes such as altered electrolyte concentrations and oxygen tension in the myocardium. It has been suggested that repolarization may be delayed in the subendocardial myocardium because the high blood pressure in the ventricles affects the inner part of the myocardium more than the outer. There is, however no direct experimental evidence about the course of repolarization through the heart under normal conditions, but it is certainly true that the segment of the ECG that reflects repolarization (ST–T, Fig. 10.35) is much more readily altered by comparatively small changes in the state of the myocardium than that which reflects depolarization (QRS) (Fig. 10.34).

Atrial repolarization is not usually recognized in the normal ECG because it occurs during the inscription of the QRS deflections that accompany ventricular depolarization. When AV conduction is delayed atrial repolarization can sometimes be recognized as a low-voltage negative deflection following that of atrial depolarization (P wave).

'Lead systems' and terminology. To record the ECG two electrodes and a galvanometer in the electrocardiograph apparatus are used to detect potential differences between the sites of the electrodes. In a volume conductor the potential far away from the source of current is negligible, so an electrode sited far from the source can be regarded as providing a reference point of virtually zero potential and is then called the 'indifferent' electrode. The other, 'exploring', electrode can then be used to measure potentials in any part of the volume conductor or on its surface (Fig. 10.31) This is the basis of the *unipolar lead* system devised by Wilson for experimental work and for clinical electrocardiography: they are called 'V' leads because they record values that approach meaningful voltages.

Where both electrodes are comparatively near the source of current the galvonometer records the difference between two potentials of considerable size, each of which is constantly changing throughout the cardiac cycle. In this case the potentials recorded by the electrocardiograph represent the differences between two variables, and are therefore less meaningful. This is, however, the basis of the original *bipolar lead* systems, such as were used by Waller and Einthoven in their early work on the ECG. Bipolar leads are still used, in addition to unipolar recording, in clinical practice, for example

the three 'standard limb leads', for which the electrodes are connected to the arms and legs as follows: Lead I, right arm and left arm; Lead II, right arm and left leg; Lead III, left arm and left leg. Because the dry skin surface has a considerable electrical resistance it is usual to reduce the resistance between the body and the metal electrode by briskly rubbing the skin with a jelly containing an electrolyte.

A normal electrocardiogram (lead I) is represented diagrammatically in Figure 10.35, which is enlarged for ease in labelling. The standard record is made with the apparatus adjusted so that a vertical movement of 1 cm is produced by a potential change of 1 millivolt (mV).

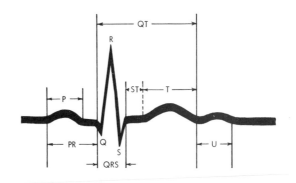

Fig. 10.35 A diagram showing the beginning and end of the various parts of the electrocardiogram, namely the P wave, QRS complex, T and U waves, the PR and QT intervals, and the PQ and ST segments. The TP segment from the end of T to the beginning of P is not labelled. By an agreed convention an upward deflection in the finished record indicates electrical negativity of right arm in leads I and II and of left arm in lead III.

The P wave begins as the excitatory process passes from the SA node to the atria, its duration indicating the time taken for excitation to spread throughout the atrial muscle. The QRS complex indicates the depolarization of the ventricles. The T wave signals the last part of repolarization in the ventricles; the U wave, not always seen, is probably related to after-potentials (See p. 303). The PR interval gives the time taken by the excitatory process to travel over the atria and through the AV junctional tissue to the ventricular muscle. During the ST segment all parts of the ventricles have been depolarized; the record is, however, not quite isoelectric (horizontal) but inclined slightly in the same direction as the T wave, because repolarization begins very slowly during this period. Ventricular repolarization is completed during the T wave. In the TP or UP interval, that is between two cycles of cardiac activity, the whole heart is in the resting polarized state and the record is isoelectric.

The P wave lasts from 60 to 110 msec. The PR interval usually lasts from 120 to 200 msec and, like QT, varies inversely with the heart rate. The QRS complex varies considerably in form, lasting from 60 to 110 msec. Values greater than this indicate either that the electrical events are prolonged in one ventricle or that the ventricles are not being excited simultaneously. The amplitude of the QRS complex is usually from 0·5 to 1·5 mV in leads I, II and II, but is considerably higher in unipolar leads from electrodes sited on the precordium ('chest leads').

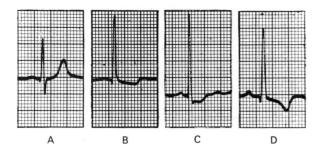

A   B   C   D

Fig. 10.34 A, single PQRST complex from a normal electrocardiogram (see Fig. 10.35). B, C and D are abnormal complexes, with characteristic changes in the ST segment and T wave (ventricular repolarization) while QRS (ventricular depolarization) is hardly altered. B, patient receiving a digitalis glycoside; C, low serum K$^+$ level (1·3 mmol/l); D, left ventricular hypertrophy.

THE CARDIAC CYCLE

In considering the *cardiac cycle* we are concerned with the working of the pump, not simply in terms of the contraction of one ventricle, but with the cyclical contraction (*systole*) and relaxation (*diastole*) of the two atria and the two ventricles (Fig. 10.36). During diastole each chamber fills with blood, during systole the blood is expelled. Although the blood moves through the two cardiac pumps in series (p. 2), the right and left hearts are arranged anatomically in parallel and both atria and both ventricles contract almost simultaneously (Fig. 10.41).

Atrial function. Although the thin walled atria act as central venous reservoirs their contraction produces comparatively small, but important, increases in atrial blood pressure. Atrial systole begins at about the peak of the P wave of the ECG, contraction of the right atrium usually very slightly preceding that of the left. The muscular contraction forces blood from the atria through the funnels of the AV valves into the ventricles during the last phase of passive ventricular filling; it causes small increases in the pressures in both the atria (*atrial 'a wave'*, Fig. 10.44) and ventricles, because at this stage the AV valves are still open. Since there are no valves between the right atrium and the venae cavae, some blood is expelled backwards during atrial systole into the superior vena cava where it causes a rise in the pressure and in the volume.

These changes are transmitted upward to the internal jugular vein and cause a wave in the jugular phlebogram (p. 155, Fig. 10.37 and Fig. 11.26 p. 187).

In normal hearts, beating with a normal rhythm, the volume of blood transported by the atria into the ventricles by atrial systole varies with the heart rate. When the heart is beating slowly diastole is long and passive ventricular filling is almost complete; atrial transport is small. When the heart rate is faster ventricular filling may never be complete and the atria may contract soon after the end of the rapid filling phase of the ventricles (Fig. 10.41) when there is a relatively high pressure gradient between the atria and the ventricles; the atrial transport function is then considerable. At even faster rates, when the atria contract during the phase of rapid ventricular filling, it may be the transport function of the atria that maintains the adequate filling of the ventricle and so prevents a fall in cardiac output. In the common cardiac dysrhythmia called *atrial fibrillation* (p. 171) atrial contraction is not coordinated and there is therefore no transport function. The patient is rarely handicapped while the ventricular rate remains low, but when it is fast the patient's cardiac output may be reduced and can only be restored to normal when the ventricular rate is reduced by a drug, such as digitalis, that slows the discharge rate of the AV nodal pace-makers. Clinical studies of patients with atrial fibrillation and complete heart block (p. 171) indicate that the atrial transport function can be

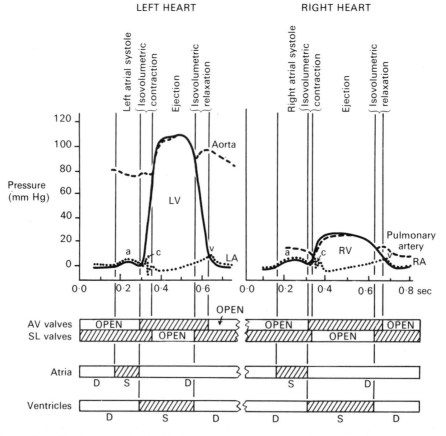

Fig. 10.36   The main haemodynamic events associated with the cardiac cycle on the left and right sides of the heart in man. LV, left ventricle; RV, right ventricle. LA, left atrium; RA, right atrium. AV, atrioventricular; SL, semilunar. D, diastole; S, systole. See also Figures 10.37, 10.38, 10.41, 10.43, 10.44 (pressure pulses), 10.39 (angiocardiogram), 10.46 and 10.47 (phonocardiogram), 11.26 (jugular phlebogram) and Table 10.42.

responsible for increases in the cardiac output varying from about 10 to about 40 per cent.

Atrial function may also normally play a part in closing the AV valves. At the end of atrial systole the blood continues to move through the valve because of its inertia, causing a momentary reduction in atrial pressure which tends to 'suck' the valve cusps towards each other.

When the electrical excitation of the atria is complete the excitation of the ventricles begins after a delay caused mainly by the slow conduction velocity through the central part of the AV node. This delay is responsible for most of the PR interval in the ECG and normally allows the atria to contract completely before ventricular contraction starts.

Ventricular function. Ventricular contraction (Figs 10.36 to 10.42) begins soon after the start of ventricular excitation denoted by the beginning of the QRS complex of the ECG. The pressure of blood in the ventricles begins to rise while that in the relaxing atria is falling. About 50 ms after the atrial and ventricular pressure curves cross the cusps of the atrio-ventricular valves close and then bulge momentarily backward into the atria. In ordinary circumstances the valves do not leak, the surfaces of their cusps being held in apposition by the pull of the papillary muscles on the chordae tendineae attached to the cusp edges. This momentary backward bulging of the AV valve cusps produces slight transient increases of pressure in the atria (*c wave*), (Figs 10.37 and 10.44). These intra-atrial c waves are not the same as the c waves in the jugular phlebogram, which are caused by the transmitted pulsation of the underlying carotid artery (Figs 10.37 and 11.26).

After the closure of the AV valves the blood pressure rises in both ventricles but because both the AV and the semilunar valves are closed the volume of intraventricular blood remains constant. During this *isovolumetric* (isometric) phase of ventricular contraction the ventricles alter their shape, becoming plumper, and the apex and AV ring move nearer to

one another. This 'descent of the base' stretches the right atrium and the consequent reduction in intra-atrial pressure contributes to the descending limb of the atrial a wave. When the rising ventricular pressures exceed the pressures in the aorta and pulmonary artery the semilunar valves open, the isometric phase ends and the *ejection* (isotonic) phase of contraction begins.

The ejection phase of ventricular contraction is strongly influenced by changing impedances in the great arteries. The early, short, rapid ejection phase is one of auxotonic contraction and the maximum velocity of blood flow is in fact attained earlier than the peak of the ventricular pressure curve (Fig. 10.38). The volume of blood ejected (*stroke volume*) from each ventricle is partly accommodated in the root of the great vessels by a transient expansion which is the origin of the arterial pulse wave. It also displaces the blood expelled by the

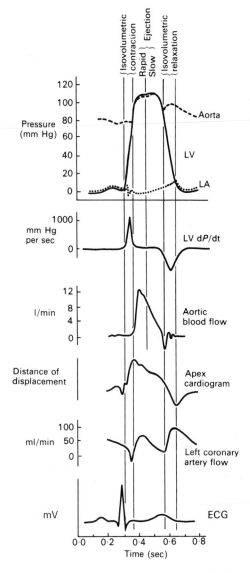

Fig. 10.38 The main haemodynamic events associated with the left atrium (LA) and left ventricle (LV) and the aorta throughout one cardiac cycle. Above downwards: pressure pulses (see Table 10.42); maximum rate of rise of LV pressure, dP/dt; aortic blood flow; apex cardiogram (p. 161); left coronary artery blood flow (p. 168); ECG.

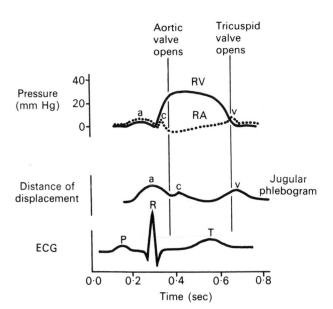

Fig. 10.37 Above downwards: pressure pulses (see Table 10.41) in right atrium (RA) and right ventricle (RV) during one cardiac cycle; jugular phlebogram (Fig. 11.26 and p. 188); electrocardiogram.

POSTERO-ANTERIOR   LEFT LATERAL

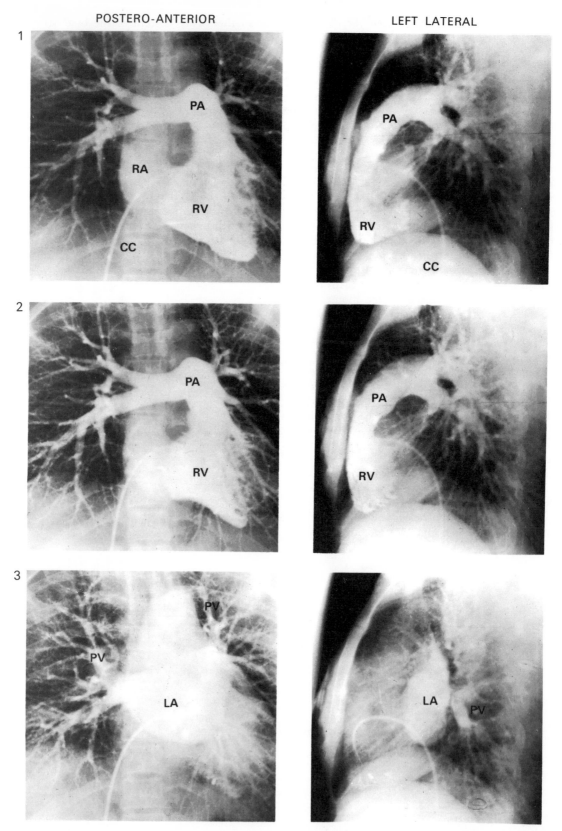

Fig. 10.39 Frames from simultaneous postero-anterior and left lateral rapid still radiographs during angiocardiography of a normal human heart. The contrast medium was injected through a cardiac catheter (CC) sited in the right ventricle (RV) during a previous cardiac cycle, and fills various cardiac chambers and vessels at subsequent stages of the cardiac cycle: (1) right ventricular diastole, with slight filling of the right atrium (RA) because of tricuspid incompetence caused by the catheter; (2) RV systole expels contrast into the pulmonary arteries (PA); (3) the contrast has passed through the pulmonary capillaries and is returning through the pulmonary veins (PV) to fill the left atrium (LA); (4) systole expels blood from the left ventricle (LV) into the aorta (AO) and in the lateral view an aortic sinus (S) is evident; (5) by the time the LV has relaxed in diastole the contrast has moved farther down the descending aorta. (*By courtesy of the Royal Postgraduate Medical School, London.*)

POSTERO-ANTERIOR   LEFT LATERAL

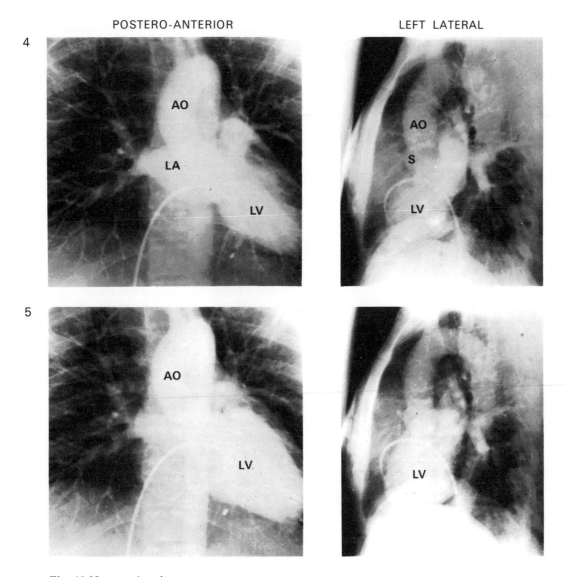

Fig. 10.39   (continued)

previous systole (p. 176). The later, longer phase ('reduced ejection') characterized by a fall in both the ventricular and the aortic and pulmonary arterial pressures takes place during the T wave of the ECG. During this time the flow of blood from the aorta to the periphery exceeds that from the ventricle to the aorta, the shortened muscle fibres generating progressively less tension. At the end of this phase the ventricular muscle relaxes, and when the ventricular pressures fall below those in the aorta and pulmonary artery the semilunar valves shut. The closure of the aortic valve may be assisted by the effects of vortices in the blood in the aortic sinuses.

Throughout ventricular systole the ventricular volume, as measured by a bell cardiometer, falls steeply (Figs 10.40 and 10.41). At the same time blood has been returning to the atria, assisted by the negative intrathoracic pressure; because the AV valves are closed the intra-atrial pressure gradually rises to form the ascending limb of the intra-atrial *v wave* (Fig. 10.44).

After the closure of the semilunar valves isovolumetric ventricular relaxation continues rapidly, the pressures in the ventricles soon falling below those in the atria. At this point,

the summit of the v wave in the atrial pressure curve, the atrioventricular valves open and the blood flows passively from the atria to the ventricles, at first very fast, later more slowly. Immediately after the end of systole an elastic recoil of muscle rapidly lowers the ventricular pressure causing an increased

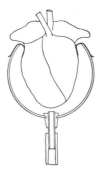

Fig. 10.40   The bell cardiometer for measuring changes in biventricular volume of the exposed heart of an animal.

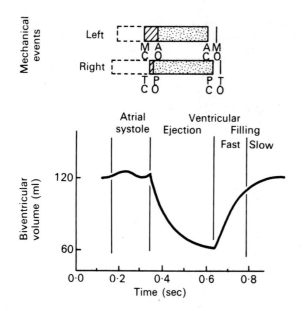

Fig. 10.41 The relationship between the main mechanical events in the right and left sides of the heart and the biventricular volume. Above, systolic events in the right and left atrium and ventricle are asynchronous: open areas enclosed by dashed lines indicate atrial systole; hatched areas indicate ventricular isovolumetric contraction; dotted areas indicate ventricular systole. MC, mitral valve closure; TC, tricuspid valve closure. AO, aortic valve opening; PO, pulmonary valve opening. AC, aortic valve closure; PC, pulmonary valve closure. MO, mitral valve opening; TO, tricuspid valve opening.

flow of blood from the atria. Negative pressures up to 11 cm H_2O have been recorded in the left ventricle of dogs with the mitral valve temporarily clamped.

In diastole, during the first rapid phase of ventricular filling, the pressures in both atria and ventricles continue to fall but the ventricular volume increases sharply. At normal heart rates the first rapid phase of ventricular filling is succeeded by a slower phase in which the slope of the curve of the ventricular volume is flatter. If the ventricular rate is slow enough the volume curve may eventually become almost level because the ventricles are full (*ventricular diastasis*).

Cardiac Catheterization

In 1929 Forssmann passed a thin, flexible ureteric catheter from an arm vein into his own heart, watching its progress by the help of an X-ray screen and a mirror held by a nurse. This brave experiment opened a new era in human cardiovascular physiology based on the technique of cardiac catheterization, which is now used routinely by clinical cardiologists.

Cardiac catheters intended to explore the great veins, the right side of the heart, the coronary sinus and the pulmonary artery are usually introduced through the antecubital or femoral vein. The left atrium and left ventricle can be catheterized from the right atrium by the use of a special catheter with a tip sharp enough to penetrate the interatrial septum. The aorta and left ventricle are usually catheterized from the femoral artery.

Special catheters can be used to obtain samples of blood from the great veins, any of the four chambers of the heart, the

coronary sinus, the aorta or the pulmonary artery. Analysis of the oxygen content of mixed venous blood from the pulmonary artery can be used to calculate the cardiac output by the Fick principle (p. 161). The catheters can be attached to manometers to record intravascular pressures and to demonstrate pressure gradients by withdrawal of the catheter tip across valves. Table 10.42 shows normal intracardiac pressures in

Table 10.42 Normal average values of intracardiac pressures in man (from various authors). LV peak systolic pressure is approximately the level of the systolic blood pressure recorded in the brachial artery, that is about 110 mm Hg. (See also Figs 10.43 and 10.44.)

Site	Mean	Range
RA	3 mm Hg	1–5 mm Hg
RV (peak systolic)	26 mm Hg	19–31 mm Hg
(end-diastolic)	4 mm Hg	2–6 mm Hg
PA (mean)	14 mm Hg	10–18 mm Hg
(peak-systolic)	23 mm Hg	16–29 mm Hg
(end-diastolic)	9 mm Hg	5–13 mm Hg
LA (mean)	8 mm Hg	2–12 mm Hg
LV (end-diastolic)	9 mm Hg	5–12 mm Hg

man and Figures 10.43 and 10.44 show records of intracardiac pressure curves obtained by cardiac catheterization. Special catheters with electrodes at the tip are used to record the intracardiac electrocardiogram and direct recordings can be made of the electrical impulse travelling through the AV nodal tissue, the bundle of His and the right and left bundle–branches of the special conducting system (Fig. 10.45). Tiny microphones at the tips of cardiac catheters have been used to identify the sources of normal and abnormal cardiac sounds (p. 159) (Fig. 10.44). Some cardiac catheters have at the tip a special platinum electrode capable of producing an electric potential in the presence of hydrogen: with such a 'hydrogen electrode' sited in a cardiac chamber a lung-to-electrode circulation time can easily be determined by making the subject inhale a breath of pure hydrogen gas. Other catheters end in an electrode capable of delivering a stimulating electrical impulse ('pacing').

A radio-opaque fluid ('contrast medium') can be injected into any chamber of the heart or into the great vessels (*selective angiocardiography*). The passage of this opaque

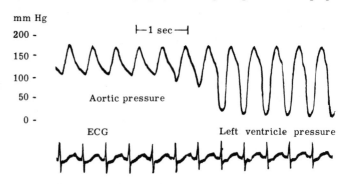

Fig. 10.43 Pressure records from the aorta and left ventricle in a female patient aged 39 with a normal aortic valve. As the catheter is gradually withdrawn from the aorta into the ventricle there is a fairly sudden change (diastolic pressure gradient) in the record which is normal in this patient. (H. A. Fleming, E. W. Hancock, B. B. Milstein & D. N. Ross (1958). *Thorax*, 13, 97–102.)

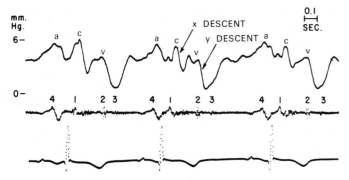

Fig. 10.44 Normal pressures and heart sounds simultaneously recorded from inside the right atrium. Above down: right atrial pressure pulse, intra-atrial phonocardiogram, surface ECG for reference. (H. L. Moscovitz, E. Donoso, I. J. Gelb & R. J. Wilder (1963) *An Atlas of Haemodynamics of the Cardiovascular System.* p. 31. New York: Grune & Stratton.)

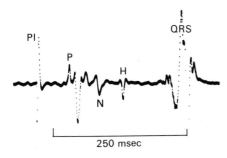

Fig. 10.45 Direct recording made by an electrode catheter of the electrical impulse in the special conducting system in the human heart. PI, artificial pacing impulse in the right atrium. Between the excitation of the atrium (P) and that of the ventricles (QRS) the electrode records the activity of the AV node (N) and the bundle of His (H) as smaller polyphasic deflections. (A. N. Damato, S. H. Lau, W. D. Berkowitz, K. M. Rosen & K. R. Lisi (1969). *Circulation,* 39, 435.)

medium through the heart can be recorded by rapid still, or cine, X-ray photography, and gives useful information about the anatomy of the chambers and the flow of blood between them (Fig. 10.39, pp. 156, 157). The right and left coronary arteries can be selectively catheterized, and the *coronary arteriograms* thus obtained demonstrate the coronary arterial circulation (Fig. 10.2 p. 135).

Not only has cardiac catheterization yielded a great deal of knowledge about the physiology of the normal heart but it is an invaluable part of the investigation of many patients with heart disease, providing information obtainable by no other means. Cardiac pacing is used to treat cases of heart block (p. 171).

Heart Sounds

The heart and great vessels may be considered as an elastic fluid-filled system that responds to a change in equilibrium of any part by oscillating as a whole. Rushmer has used the analogy of a fluid-filled balloon, tapped sharply: although the tap is only applied at a single point, the elastic walls of the balloon and the fluid it contains vibrate as a whole.

Because of the haemodynamic events of the cardiac cycle the blood flows through the heart with sharply varying velocities and both accelerations and decelerations of flow produce vibrations of the cardiac muscle and valves, the walls of the great vessels and the blood they contain. The vibrations have a relatively low frequency and are rapidly damped, but some of their components lie above the threshold of human hearing (see Chap. 27) and can therefore be appreciated as *heart sounds.*

The two main groups of normal heart sounds can usually be heard if the listener presses his ear firmly against the skin of the precordium. They are more easily heard by the use of various types of stethoscope which amplify the sounds and help to cut out other distracting noises. A graphical recording of heart sounds, a *phonocardiogram* (PCG), can be made by using microphones, amplifiers and filters to overcome some of the limitations imposed by the human ear. The PCG usually shows four main groups of vibrations in every cardiac cycle (Figs 10.44, 10.46 and 10.47, pp. 159 and 160).

Studies by intracardiac phonocardiography strongly suggest that changes of velocity and turbulence in the blood produce vibrations that are most intense 'downstream' from their site of production. This technique, combined with that of echocardiography (p. 161), has thrown some fresh light on the origin of these four normal heart sounds.

The two sounds heard by the unaided ear are called the 'first'

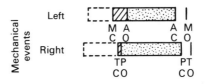

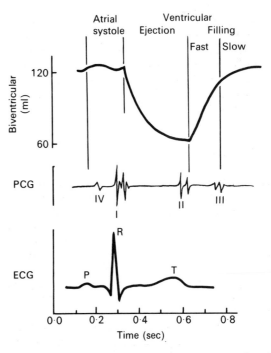

Fig. 10.46 The relationships between the heart sounds (phonocardiogram) and mechanical events in the heart. Above downwards: mechanical events and biventricular volume (labelled as in Fig. 10.41); phonocardiogram (PCG); electrocardiogram (ECG).

and 'second' heart sounds. The *first heart sound* is the longest and loudest of the normal heart sounds. The PCG shows a group of vibrations of mixed frequency occurring at the end of the QRS complex. It is associated with the beginning of ventricular systole and is mainly caused by vibrations set up by the closure of the AV valves. Often there are two main groups of vibrations and on auscultation with the stethoscope the first sound is heard to be 'split'. This splitting is the result of the closure of, first, the mitral, and then the tricuspid, valve. Because the vibrations are most intense 'downstream' from the AV valves the first heart sound is best heard at an area of the chest wall near the apex beat (p. 161). Because of its length and the comparatively low frequency of its components it is traditionally represented by the syllable, *lub*.

The *second heart sound* shows on the PCG as two shorter groups of vibrations of higher frequency occurring about the end of the T wave in the ECG. These sounds are caused by the sudden closing of, first, the aortic, and then the pulmonary, valve. They are best heard 'downstream' from these valves in an area on the chest wall about the second intercostal space just to the right and left of the sternum. The untrained ear may not appreciate the split between the aortic and pulmonary components. The second heart sound, being shorter and of higher pitch than the first heart sound, is traditionally represented by the syllable *'dupp'*. Careful auscultation, however, during slow continued respiration, or phonocardiography, confirms that the second heart sound is usually only single during the phase of full expiration. During the inspiratory phase the increase in the negative intrathoracic pressure increases the volume of blood in the right ventricle

which significantly delays the closure of the pulmonary valve, and hence the pulmonary component of the second heart sound. The second heart sound then sounds more like *'trupp'*. At the height of inspiration the delay in the closure of the pulmonary valve is maximal, the split between the aortic and pulmonary components is widest and the sound may be represented as *'tu-rupp'*. During expiration the split narrows again. This 'movement' of the splitting of the second heart sound is most easily heard in young people in the erect position (Fig. 10.47).

The *third heart sound* is heard in children and young adults. In the PCG it is shown as a short group of vibrations of very low frequency in early diastole, occurring towards the end of the phase of rapid ventricular filling. These vibrations are probably set up in the blood at a time when the left ventricular wall is changing from a state of active relaxation to one of passive distension and when the whole mitral valve system reaches a certain tension (Fig. 10.46, p. 159).

The fourth heart sound, or *atrial sound* is inaudible in normal people and can usually only be demonstrated by phonocardiography. It consists of a few low frequency vibrations during the PR interval of the ECG and is caused by the contraction of the atria and the flow of blood through the AV valves. In abnormal conditions, such as delayed AV conduction when the PR interval is long, the atrial sound may be heard on auscultation as a faint low thud.

In abnormal hearts altered cardiac haemodynamics may give rise to abnormal vibrations or turbulence. These may be heard on auscultation as extra sounds, such as the 'opening snap' of a pliant cusp in a narrowed mitral valve (mitral stenosis), or as

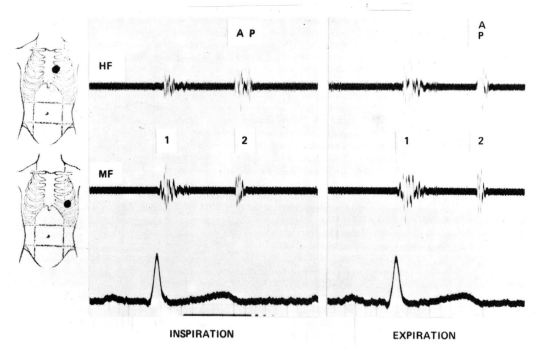

Fig. 10.47 Phonocardiogram of a normal young adult. One microphone at the left sternal edge provides a high-frequncy (HF) record, the other, at the region of the cardiac apex provides a medium frequency (MF) record. 1 and 2, first and second heart sounds. A and P, vibrations associated with closure of the aortic and pulmonary valves. The lowest trace is ECG, Lead II. On inspiration the increased negative intrathoracic pressure increases the filling of the right ventricle in diastole. The increased right ventricular volume delays closure of the pulmonary valve: the pulmonary valve closure sound (P) is delayed, causing audible splitting of the second heart sound (0·04 sec. in this record). On expiration, pulmonary valve closure occurs so soon after aortic valve closure that the second heart sound seems single on auscultation.

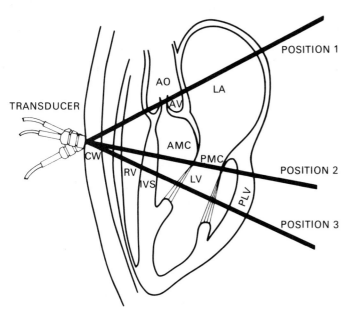

Fig. 10.48 Sagittal section of the heart showing normal anatomical relationships of the cardiac chambers and aortic and mitral valves. The ultrasound beam of the echocardiograph is directed along positions 1, 2 and 3 to explore areas of interest. CW, chest wall; AO, aorta; AV, aortic valve; LA, left atrium; LV, left ventricle; RV, right ventricle; IVS, interventricular septum; AMC, anterior mitral valve cusp; PMC, posterior mitral valve cusp; PLV, posterior left ventricular wall. (D. Vérel and R. G. Grainger (1978) *Cardiac Catheterization and Angiocardiography* Edinburgh: Churchill Livingstone.)

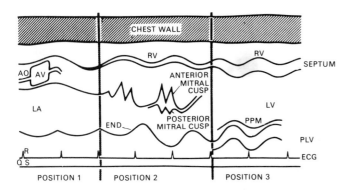

Fig. 10.49 Diagram of echocardiogram obtained as the direction of the ultrasonic beam is gradually changed from position 1 to position 3 in Fig. 10.48. Position 1 demonstrates opening and closing of the aortic valve. Position 2 shows movements of anterior and posterior cusps of the mitral valve and the size of the ventricles in systole and diastole. Position 3 shows the movements of the interventricular septum and the posterior papillary muscle of the left ventricle. END, endocardium posterior wall LV; PPM, posterior papillary muscle; other abbreviations as in Fig. 10.48 (D. Vérel & R. G. Grainger (1978) *Cardiac Catheterization and Angiocardiography* Edinburgh: Churchill Livingstone.)

cardiac 'murmurs', such as the sound that occupies the whole of systole caused by the turbulence of the blood regurgitated into the left atrium through an incompetent mitral valve.

Movements of the Heart

The heart is quite soft in diastole, its shape being determined mainly by the amount of blood within it and by the position of the body. When the ventricles contract the heart becomes hard and there is an increase in the antero-posterior, and a decrease in the transverse, diameter. The movement of the heart within the chest, as a diffuse *cardiac impulse*, can often be felt by a hand laid on the precordium. A localized pulsation (*apex beat*) is often felt in the fifth left intercostal space about the midclavicular line. X-rays show that the actual apex is about 2 cm lower down.

The pulsations of the apex beat can be more critically analysed if they are recorded by appropriate techniques in the form of the *apex cardiogram*. The main outward pulsation is caused by ventricular systole, but this is preceded by the smaller pulsation associated with atrial contraction and followed by an inward pulsation marking the opening of the AV valves (Fig. 10.38, p. 155).

In patients with abnormal hearts some of these features may be pronounced enough to be seen, or felt by the hand: hypertrophy of one or other ventricle produces a prolonged and more powerful pulsation of appropriate parts of the precordium, while hypertrophy of the atria may be associated with a palpable atrial component of the apex beat, associated with an audible atrial sound.

Echocardiography. Appropriately directed beams of ultrasound can be reflected as echoes from moving structures in the heart. The echoes are detected and displayed by the *echocardiograph*. Fig. 10.48 shows the general principles involved, and Fig. 10.49 indicates how the movement of various cardiac structures can be shown. Echocardiography gives information about the opening and closing of aortic and mitral valves and the movement and thickness of ventricular walls and the interventricular septum.

CARDIAC OUTPUT

The Fick Principle. For the determination of the cardiac output in man only indirect methods are applicable. Fick pointed out in 1870 that in a given time the total amount of any gas gained or lost in the lungs must be equal to the difference between the amounts of the gas brought to the lungs in the arterial blood and the amount leaving the lungs in the venous blood. Thus if we can measure (a) the amount of oxygen passing from the lungs into the blood per unit of time (b) the oxygen content of the arterial blood and (c) the oxygen content of mixed venous blood, then the output of the heart is easily calculated. An average value for (a) is 250 ml per minute, for (b) is 19 ml per 100 ml blood, and for (c) is 14 ml per 100 ml blood. Each 100 ml of blood in passing through the lungs gains 5 ml of oxygen, that is the arteriovenous difference. Since 250 ml of oxygen actually passes into the blood per minute (see Fig. 10.50)

$$\frac{250}{5} \times 100\,\text{ml} = 5000\,\text{ml or 5 litres}$$

of blood are needed to carry that amount of oxygen, and this is the cardiac output per minute. If the heart contracts 71 times per minute then the stroke volume of each ventricle is $5000 \div 71 = 70\,\text{ml}$.

The oxygen consumption can be determined by a spirometer or by the Douglas bag technique (p. 14). The oxygen content of arterial blood can be measured directly in a specimen obtained by arterial puncture. A specimen of mixed venous blood can be obtained only by catheterizing the pulmonary artery since there are large regional differences in the oxygen content of blood from superficial veins, and even between streams within the right ventricle.

The results obtained in this way represent the effective output of each ventricle but do not allow for any run-back of blood into the ventricles such as may occur with valvular disease. If all the oxygen taken up from the inspired air is carried in the blood and none is utilized in the lungs the results should be correct for normal persons. The average arterio-venous oxygen difference at rest is $4 \cdot 5$ ml O_2 per 100 ml blood. Since the average oxygen consumption is 240 ml per minute the average cardiac output is $240/4 \cdot 5 \times 100 = 5 \cdot 3$ litres per minute. The range in normal adults under basal conditions is from 4 to 7 litres per minute, with an average of $5 \cdot 3$ litres. This corresponds to a stroke volume from each ventricle of 70 to 80 ml.

The cardiac output in exercise may be increased to as much as 40 litres per minute, partly by an augmented stroke volume and partly by an increase in heart rate. The rise in cardiac output with exercise is, however, not accompanied by a parallel rise in venous pressure (see also Chap. 21). Apprehension and anxiety may be accompanied by an increase of some 10 to 20 per cent over the basal value. The output is some 10 per cent lower during sleep. In healthy persons there is an increase in cardiac output up to about 25 per cent on lying down, presumably the result of an increased venous return. It seems reasonable to expect that the cardiac output would be closely correlated with body size and for many years it has been customary to express the *cardiac index* as the minute volume per m² of body surface (about $3 \cdot 1\,\text{l}$).

Indicator dilution. The cardiac output in man may also be measured by the indicator dilution method. A known amount (X mg), of a non-diffusible dye is injected into the pulmonary artery or a central vein and the rapid rise and fall of its concentration in arterial blood is followed by sampling from, say, the brachial artery. The falling concentration, before recirculation of the dye begins, can be plotted as a graph which, if extrapolated to zero concentration or $0 \cdot 1$ mg/l in Figure 10.51, gives the time after injection at which all the dye must have been ejected from the heart if there had been no recirculation (Y seconds). Since the concentration falls off exponentially it can be plotted as a straight line on semilog paper (Fig. 10.51). If the average concentration of the dye in the blood is calculated for this period (Z mg/litre) then X/Z litres is the amount of blood required for the ejection of X mg of dye. Since this took place in Y seconds the cardiac output in litres per min must have been $X/Z \times 60/Y$. The indicator does not enter the red cells but is carried in the plasma so this formula gives the plasma flow from which the blood flow can be calculated (see Chap. 8). Brachial artery puncture can be avoided by measuring the rise and fall of the concentration of the dye by shining a light through the vasodilated lobe of the ear on to a photocell (*oximetry*).

If the dye is injected rapidly into the left ventricle the end-diastolic volume EDV (as well as the cardiac output) can be calculated from the exponential curve provided that the heart beat is recorded simultaneously. If the concentration of the dye in the blood ejected at one ventricular contraction is C_N and the concentration at the previous beat is C_{N-1} then

$$\text{EDV} = \frac{\text{SV}}{1 - \left(\dfrac{C_N}{C_{N-1}}\right)}$$

where SV is stroke volume

For example if the concentration is halved at each beat the ventricle must eject half its contents into the aorta and admit the same volume from the left atrium; EDV must be twice SV. The residual volume at the end of systole is of course EDV − SV. Serum albumin, labelled with a radio-isotope, may be used instead of a dye, and estimated in the blood by an

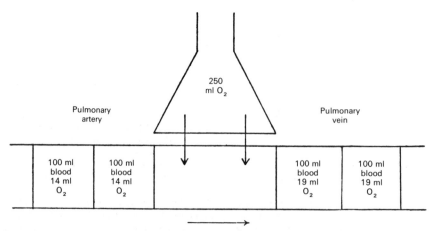

Fig. 10.50 Scheme to illustrate the determination of cardiac output by the Fick principle. Each rectangle represents 100 ml of blood which gains 5 ml of oxygen in passing through the lungs. 250 ml of oxygen disappears from the lungs per minute. This volume would be accounted for by 250/5 or 50 rectangles. The flow is therefore $250/5 \times 100\,\text{ml}$, or 5 litres per minute.

appropriate isotope-counting technique. With the thermo-dilution technique cold fluid is injected into the right atrium and 'detected' in the pulmonary artery by a special catheter which carries thermistors. An analogue computer calculates the cardiac output. The indicator–dilution method of estimating the cardiac output is unreliable for giving a single 'absolute' value, but useful to compare short-term changes in one subject as shown in Figure 10.51.

Examples of cardiac outputs and regional blood flows during rest and exercise in subjects with normal and abnormally functioning hearts are given in Table 10.52.

RETURN OF BLOOD TO THE HEART

The most important cause of the venous return is the action of the heart in pumping blood round the circulation. The pressure within the chest, but outside the lung, that is the *intrathoracic pressure*, is normally negative, that is a little below atmospheric pressure. Accordingly blood flows from the abdomen and other parts where the pressure is above atmospheric into the thoracic veins where the pressure is lower. The effective filling pressure of the right side of the heart is therefore the difference between the extrathoracic venous pressure and the diastolic pressure in the right atrium, the pressure in the relaxed atrium being the same as the intrathoracic pressure. The intrathoracic pressure becomes more negative during inspiration and the filling pressure therefore higher. During inspiration the descent of the diaphragm causes an increase of intra-abdominal pressure which aids the return of blood to the thorax.

The importance of this *respiratory pump* is shown in the performance of static effort, such as pulling on a tug-of-war rope or blowing a trumpet (Fig. 10.53). Both require considerably expiratory effort so the pressure in the thorax becomes positive (*Valsalva manoeuvre*, Fig. 10.53). The return of blood to the heart is much reduced or ceases entirely, the superficial veins of the head and neck become engorged and the mean arterial blood pressure falls. The blood flow through the brain

may be so much reduced that the subject feels giddy and may lose consciousness (*syncope*, p. 200).

The return of the blood to the heart is also assisted by the contraction of muscles all over the body, especially in the legs. When the muscles contract blood is squeezed out of the capillaries and smaller veins within the muscles into the larger veins between the muscles. The alternate contractions and relaxations of the leg muscles that occur in walking serve to drive the blood back through the venous valves to the heart. The intramuscular pressure in the calf muscles in man can be measured by passing a fine catheter into them; at rest it is about 10 mm Hg, on standing 30 mm Hg, while a maximal contraction may raise the pressure to 200 mm Hg. Thus the *muscle pump*, as Figure 10.54 shows, is quite powerful. A person standing rigidly at attention for a prolonged period may eventually faint because the reduced venous return to the heart caused by inactivity of the muscle pump results in a diminished cardiac output and a decreased blood supply to the brain.

The distensibility of the pericardial sac sets a limit to the filling of the heart in diastole. If the sac contains fluid neither

Table 10.52 Distribution of the cardiac output at rest and during the steady state of supine leg exercise in a normal subject and a patient with mitral valve stenosis and cardiac failure (oxygen uptake during exercise 500 ml/min/m²)

Blood flow (ml/min)	Normal subject		Patient with mitral stenosis	
	Rest	Exercise	Rest	Exercise
Splanchnic	1400	1300	800	400
Renal	1100	900	650	300
Cerebral	750	750	600	600
Coronary*	250	450	300	500
Resting skeletal muscle	700	700	700	350
Leg—muscle	500 ⎫	5000	500 ⎫	3400
skin	250 ⎭		50 ⎭	
Skin (other than leg)	250	1000	100	50
Other organs	600	400	300	200
Cardiac output	5800	10500	4000	5800

*It is likely that when the rise in cardiac output due to exercise reaches high levels the proportion passing through the coronary circulation falls below 4 per cent.

O. L. Wade & J. M. Bishop (1962) *Cardiac Output and Regional Blood Flow.* Oxford: Blackwell.

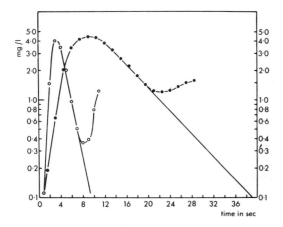

Fig. 10.51 Dye concentration curves (Evan's Blue) plotted on semi-logarithmic paper. ●——●. Rest experiment. Cardiac output 4:73 litres per minute. ○——○ Work experiment. 1260 kg m per minute. Cardiac output 21·9 litres per minute. The second upward trend of the curves is due to recirculation of dye. (E. Asmussen and M. Neilsen (1952–53) *Acta physiologica scandinavica,* 27, 217.)

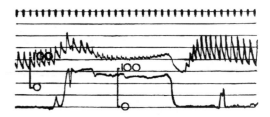

Fig. 10.53 Professional trumpet player blowing Concert A against a pressure of about 80 mm Hg for 17 seconds, effectively performing Valsalva's manoeuvre (forced expiration against a closed glottis). Upper curve, arterial pressure. Lower curve, mouth pressure. Calibration in mm Hg and time marker in seconds. (M. Faulkner & E. P. Sharpey-Schafer (1959) *British Medical Journal,* i, 685–686.)

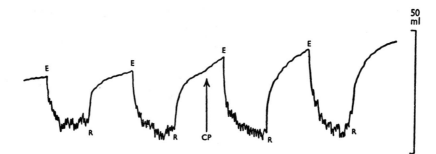

Fig. 10.54   A record in the changes in volume of the calf of the leg measured with a plethysmograph (p. 181) to show the effects of the 'muscle pump'. A fall in volume is indicated by a downward movement of the trace. At E a pedal was pressed down once per second for 10 secs; R indicates the beginning of a rest period of 10 sec. At CP a cuff just above the knee was inflated to 90 mm Hg until the end of the trace. During each period of exercise blood was forced out of the calf and its volume diminished. Even when the venous pressure was raised to 90 mm Hg blood was forced out of the calf by the exercise. (H. Barcroft & A. C. Dornhorst (1949) *Journal of Physiology*, 109, 402.)

atria nor ventricles can dilate fully, and so the cardiac filling falls. The output per beat is therefore diminished (cardiac tamponade). If the pericardial pressure rises above the venous pressure, as may happen after perforation of a ventricle, blood cannot enter the heart and the circulation ceases.

Cardiac Output and Venous Return

The transport function of the atria has been described earlier: we must now consider the central role played by the *right atrial pressure* in controlling both the venous return and the cardiac output. At first its action may seem paradoxical, for in a rise in right atrial pressure both increases the cardiac output and reduces the venous return. The cardiac output is increased, by the Starling mechanism, in response to the increased filling of the ventricle caused by the raised right atrial pressure. The venous return tends to be reduced because the raised right atrial pressure slows down the inflow of blood from the periphery. Except for periods of time lasting not more than a few seconds, the cardiac output is equal to the venous return, equilibrium being maintained by the overall velocity of blood flow through the heart–lung system.

Guyton has proposed an elegant graphical model to display the relationships between the venous return, the cardiac output and the right atrial pressure. Figure 10.55a shows the relationship between the right atrial pressure and the venous return, a 'venous pressure curve'. The venous return decreases when the right atrial pressure increases. Figure 10.55b shows a 'cardiac output curve', where the right atrial pressure is plotted against the cardiac output, the cardiac output increasing with right atrial pressure. Because the right atrial pressure or *central venous pressure* is plotted along the abscissa in each graph and the units are the same (mm Hg for pressure and litres per minute for blood flow) the venous pressure curve may be superposed on the cardiac output curve as in Figure 10.55c. The point at which the curves intersect represents the 'equilibrium point' of the system where the cardiac output equals the venous return. The regulation of the circulatory system, when considered in this way, involves the recovery of the equilibrium point after transient disturbances of the system, or the establishment of new equilibrium points when homeostatic mechanisms are ineffective: for example, in Fig.

10.56 if the venous pressure rises from the equilibrium point to point A, the total blood volume remaining constant, the cardiac output of the next ventricular contraction would be increased to B because of the Starling mechanism. This increased stroke volume would reduce the venous pressure to point C, and so the adjustment would go on during the next few beats until the original equilibrium point is reached again. If we consider again the family of ventricular function curves shown in Figure 10.25 we can see that a change in the contractile state of the muscle will alter the cardiac output in Figures 10.55 and 10.56 and the equilibrium point will be a different one.

NERVOUS REGULATION OF THE HEART

The heart–lung preparation shows that even the denervated heart has considerable powers of regulating its activity according to need. In the intact animal, however, the activity of the heart is regulated to a large extent by the activity of the vagus and the sympathetic nerves and by circulating catecholamines.

The Vagus Nerve

Fibres of the vagus nerve pass through the cardiac plexuses to supply predominantly the SA and AV nodes and the atrial muscle; some fibres do reach the ventricles though the vagal effect on the ventricles is not great. Vagal stimulation in general decreases the contractility of atria and ventricles, reduces the heart rate and slows the spread of excitation through the AV node.

The Sympathetic Nerves

The heart receives branches of the sympathetic nerve from the upper thoracic region of the spinal cord which synapse in the cervical sympathetic ganglia. Terminal fibres supply the whole of the atria and ventricles and both the SA and AV nodes. Sympathetic stimulation in general has opposite effects to vagal stimulation, increasing the contractility of atria and ventricles, the heart rate and the speed of excitation of the AV node.

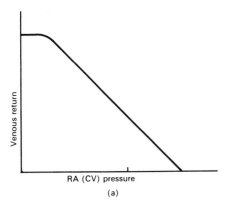

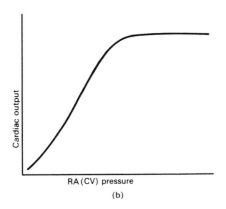

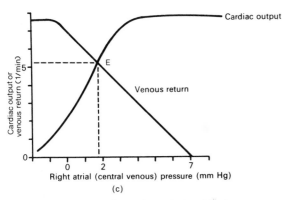

inhibits the effect of vagal impulses on the heart, his heart rate rises. The slow heart rate of athletes is mainly the result of vagal slowing of intrinsic pace-maker activity. It is well known that fear and anger can produce sudden striking increases in cardiac output and heart rate.

If a man is given atropine which inhibits the vagus and propranolol which blocks the sympathetic β-receptors (Chap. 25) his heart can be regarded as pharmacologically de-nervated. At rest the heart rate remains steady and the cardiac output varies according to Starling's law. When propranolol is given alone the cardiac output and heart rate are both reduced.

The effect of the autonomic innervation of a cardiac pace-maker can be appreciated by observing the membrane action potentials recorded by intracellular microelectrodes from spontaneously beating cells in the sinus venosus of the frog's heart. When the vagus nerve is stimulated weakly, or a small dose of acetylcholine is given, the pace-maker potential (Fig. 10.6B) rises more slowly so the critical value for the sudden rise in depolarization is reached more slowly and the heart beats more slowly. Stronger vagal stimulation (Fig. 10.57) suppresses the pace-maker potentials and stabilizes the

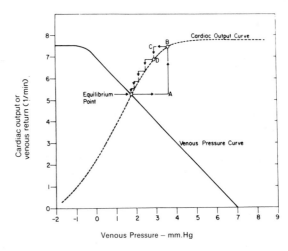

Fig. 10.56 Diagram to show how the equilibrium point is regained after a sudden shift to A (increased venous pressure) by subsequent beat-to-beat changes in cardiac output and central venous pressure. (R. M. Berne & M. N. Levy (1967) *Cardiovascular Physiology*. St. Louis: Mosby.)

Fig. 10.55 Diagrams to show the relationship between cardiac output and venous return to the heart. (a) Shows the relation between venous return and right atrial (central venous) pressure. Contrary to the usual convention the central venous pressure is plotted on the abscissa. (b) Shows the relation between cardiac output and right atrial pressure. (c) Shows the curves in (a) and (b) superposed. The axes remain the same. E, equilibrium point, where cardiac output equals venous return. (*After* A. C. Guyton (1963) *Circulatory Physiology: Cardiac Output and its Regulation*. London: Saunders.)

Cardiac Autonomic Balance

Cardiac autonomic balance is maintained by the generally opposing effects of the vagus and the sympathetic nerves on the heart. Inhibitory impulses are continually passing down the vagus nerves to decrease the heart rate and it is mainly by variations in this *vagal tone* that alterations in heart rate are produced: if a man is given an injection of atropine which

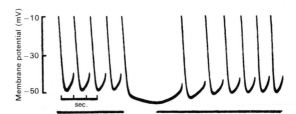

Fig. 10.57 Inhibitory polarization of frog's sinus venosus during vagal stimulation. The record is taken at an amplification that shows only the lower part of the action potential. During the fifth cycle, vagus stimulation at 20/sec starts and continues for about 3 sec as indicated by the break in the reference line. This causes a suppression of pace-maker potentials and a gradual increase in the membrane potential (downward deflection) to a value 9 mV higher than that usually reached during diastole. (O. F. Hutter & W. T. Trautwein (1956) *Journal of General Physiology*, 39, 715–733.)

membrane potential at an even greater value and so arrests the heart. The effect of acetylcholine is the result of an increased permeability to potassium ions.

When the sympathetic nerve is stimulated (Fig. 10.58) the results are in obvious contrast to those obtained on vagal stimulation; the pace-maker potential rises more quickly, the threshold for impulse propagation is reached more quickly and the heart beats follow one another more closely. Adrenaline causes an increase in Ca^{2+} and K^+ currents and in the activity of the $Na^+–K^+$ pump.

Afferent Nerves and Cardiac Reflexes

The efferent vagal fibres arise in the dorsal nucleus of the vagus, and the afferent fibres of the vagus end in the same region, so it is convenient to speak of this area of the medulla oblongata as the *cardio-inhibitory centre* (Fig. 10.59). The vasomotor centre controlling the calibre of the blood vessels is also situated in this part of the brain and the two centres have numerous interconnecting fibres.

It has not been possible to define exactly the position of the *cardio-accelerator centre* which may lie near the cardio-inhibitory centre in the medulla or perhaps in the hypothalamus. Nerve fibres pass down from the centre to the cells in the intermediolateral tract of the grey matter of the spinal cord from which arise the sympathetic cardiac nerves.

The two chief afferent nerves concerned in the regulation of cardiac activity are those which arise in the heart and aorta and pass up the vagus, and those which arise in the carotid sinus and pass by the glossopharyngeal nerve to the medulla oblongata (Fig. 10.59). The cardio-aortic and the carotid sinus nerves should be regarded as two afferents of one regulating mechanism for preventing any undue rise of blood pressure and for avoiding an excessive load being put on the heart. For this reason these are sometimes called 'buffer' nerves.

Cardio-aortic nerve. The main afferent nerve, the cardio-aortic nerve, arises from endings in the left ventricle and aortic arch. The cardio-aortic nerve endings are stimulated when the pressure in the left ventricle and aorta is high, that is, they are baroceptors (Fig. 12.6). If a record of the nerve impulses is made at the same time as a record of the blood pressure it is found that a burst of impulses passes up the cardio-aortic nerve at each systole and a similar burst passes down the vagus nerve to the heart to produce slowing and sometimes a fall in blood pressure. The higher the aortic pressure the greater is the

frequency of discharge which at any *mean* pressure is related to the pulse pressure. The changes in frequency of discharge per unit rise of pressure are greatest when the blood pressure of the animal is within the usual ('normal') range.

The carotid sinus. The dilatation at the beginning of the internal carotid artery, the carotid sinus (Fig. 10.60), has a very rich sensory innervation; the receptors, which lie in the adventitia, are sensitive to stretching like those of the cardio-aortic nerve. The fibres pass to the medulla in a branch of the glossopharyngeal nerve. It has been shown that the number of action potentials in a single afferent fibre in the carotid sinus nerve is proportional to the carotid sinus pressure and that

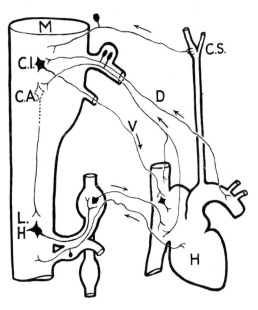

Fig. 10.59 Simplified diagram of the nerve supply of the heart. C.I. = cardio-inhibitory centre. C.A. = cardio-accelerator centre. M = medulla oblongata. L.H. = lateral horn of spinal cord. D = depressor fibre (afferent vagal). V = efferent vagal fibre. C.S. = carotid sinus. H = heart.

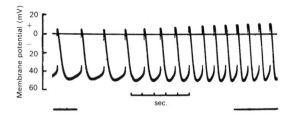

Fig. 10.58 Action potentials during sympathetic stimulation. Frog sinus venosus treated with atropine 1 in 10^6. Stimulation of vagosympathetic trunk as indicated by break in reference line. Note the increase in the slope of the pace-maker potentials and in the amplitude of the action potentials. (O. F. Hutter & W. T. Trautwein (1956) *Journal of General Physiology*, 39, 715–733.)

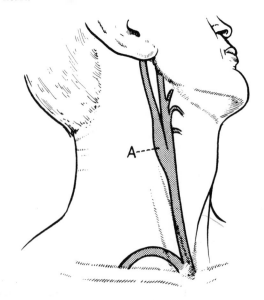

Fig. 10.60 Diagram showing the position of the carotid sinus (A) in the neck.

during diastole, when the pressure is falling, the frequency of the impulses is less (Fig. 10.61). Electrical stimulation of the carotid sinus or its nerve, or distension of the sinus by increase of the pressure within it, produces a reflex slowing of the heart and a fall of blood pressure exactly as described in the case of the cardio-aortic nerve. If the carotid sinus is encased in a rigid cement that does not allow it to expand no reflex effects are obtained. The effect of stimulation of the endings in man can be shown by digital pressure over the bifurcation of the carotid artery lying behind the medial edge of the sternomastoid muscle at the level of the hyoid bone (Fig. 10.60). Such pressure will often produce some slowing of the heart beat even in normal individuals but the effect is more striking if the beat is rapid (Fig. 10.62). After denervation of the carotid sinus in man baroceptor activity disappears at once and recovers very little; the systemic blood pressure is usually raised about 25 mm Hg.

The carotid body. The carotid body situated at the bifurcation of the common carotid artery contains numerous sinusoidal capillaries which bring the blood into close contact with glomus cells richly supplied with afferent nerve fibres that join the carotid sinus nerve. The nerve endings are sensitive to alterations in the composition of the blood in the sinusoids and are, therefore, called *chemoceptors*. Similar chemoceptor tissue is found at various positions on or near the arch of the aorta.

The chemoreflexes can be studied by isolating the carotid bifurcation, care being taken to keep the nerve supply and the

venous drainage of the carotid body intact. In animals, perfusion of the bifurcation with blood of low oxygen tension (Po_2) causes a rise of blood pressure by increasing the sympathetic outflow. In man hypoxia produces tachycardia before and after removal of the carotid bodies; the increased heart rate could be due to stimulation of aortic bodies or due to liberation of adrenaline or a direct effect on the SA node. It is possible that in man, as in the dog, the carotid bodies are mainly concerned with respiratory reflexes while the aortic bodies take part mainly in circulatory reflexes. Reduction of Po_2 causes a great increase in the numbers of impulses in the nerves from the chemoceptors (Fig. 12.7). A fall of blood pressure, as after severe haemorrhage, reduces the carotid blood flow so severely that the glomus cells are stimulated by hypoxia. Chemoceptor impulses produced by hypoxia usually cause the heart to slow if ventilation is controlled but if the ventilation is allowed to increase secondary reflexes from the lungs may cause an acceleration of the heart.

Atrial reflexes. The stimulation of atrial receptors, situated on the right side of the heart at the junctions of the superior and inferior venae cavae with the right atrium and on the left side of the heart at the junction of the pulmonary veins with the left atrium, causes an increase in heart rate; the afferent limb of this reflex is in the vagal nerves and the efferent limb in the sympathetic nerves to the heart. Surprisingly the efferent limb of this reflex involves only the sympathetic nerves to the sinu-atrial node so that there is no accompanying sympathetic effect on the cardiac muscle, only an effect on heart rate.

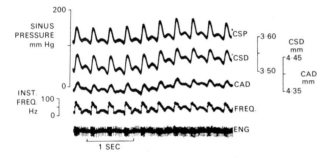

Fig. 10.61 Simultaneous recordings from a normal anaesthetized dog of carotid sinus pressure (CSP); carotid sinus diameter (CSD); carotid artery diameter (CAD); electroneurogram (ENG), showing action potentials from a single fibre dissected from the carotid sinus, and the instantaneous frequency of the action potentials (FREQ). The records of dimension changes were obtained from ultrasound crystals placed in the tissue on either side of the carotid sinus and carotid artery. The shape of the record of FREQ closely resembles that of CAD (*By courtesy of P. Sleight*).

The Rate of the Heart

The heart rate in young healthy adult males under basal conditions lies between 60 and 65 beats per minute, the figures for women being somewhat higher. However, under ordinary conditions the heart rates of men average about 78, and of women 84 beats per min and the American Heart Association accepts between 50 and 100 heart beats per minute as the normal range. The heart rate tends to fall as childhood advances (Fig. 10.63). The heart rate increases progressively with increasing exercise up to some 200 beats per minute but the rate of increase is less in trained subjects. The rate at which the cardiac frequency returns after exercise to the pre-exercise level is used an index of physical fitness, the initial rate ideally being restored within 2 minutes of the end of exercise.

The heart rate is increased by all kinds of emotional disturbances (Fig. 10.64), but it falls progressively during sleep. The heart rate is also affected by body temperature, increasing on the average by 20 beats per min per °C rise in temperature.

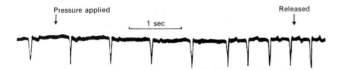

Fig. 10.62 Effect of left carotid pressure on heart rate as shown on the ECG of a human subject. The rate at the beginning of the trace is about 150 and at the end 75/min. The nerve endings in the adventitia of the carotid sinus normally discharge when the pressure in the sinus rises but these baroceptor endings also discharge if the sinus is distorted by traction on the carotid artery or, as in this case, by direct pressure.

THE CARDIAC RESPONSE TO EXERCISE

Muscular exercise is the main challenge to the transport function of the circulation. During exertion a man's oxygen consumption can increase twenty-fold and the cardiac output during exercise is directly related to the oxygen consumption. Studies on athletes have shown that they can attain cardiac outputs of over 40 litres per minute with stroke volumes of over 200 ml. The increased oxygen needs of actively contract-

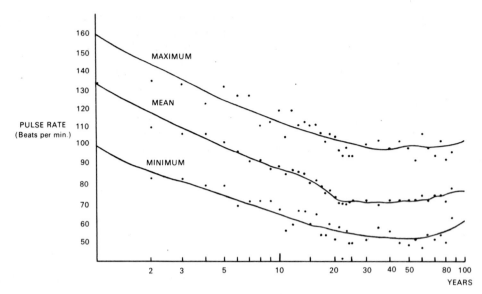

Fig. 10.63 Diagram to show variation of resting pulse rate with age constructed from data of Tigerstedt, *Lehrbuch der Physiologie des Kreislaufes*.

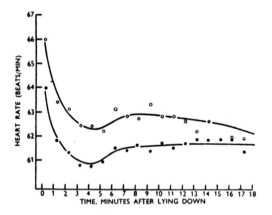

Fig. 10.64 Mean heart rate of forty-six healthy young men for 18 min after lying down. O——O, on first visit to laboratory; ●——●, on second visit, approximately 8 days later. (J. M. Tanner (1951) *Journal of Physiology*, 115, 391–409.)

ing skeletal muscle are met by several mechanisms which include an increase in cardiac output, redistributions of the flow of available blood from inactive to active tissues, an increase in the amount of oxygen extracted by the tissues from the blood, increased use of lactate as a metabolic substrate and a small amount of anaerobic metabolism. We are concerned in this chapter with the increase in the cardiac output although, even while limiting our attention to the way in which the heart achieves this, we must refer to important peripheral factors that are discussed elsewhere.

The two main mechanisms for increasing the cardiac output are an increase in the heart rate (tachycardia) and increase in the stroke volume; both mechanisms may operate together. The tachycardia of exercise is the result of adrenergic influences on the cardiac pace-maker. The heart rate of a resting subject can be increased, without the action of the autonomic nervous system, by the use of electrical artificial pace-makers. When the heart rate is increased in this way from about 80 to 120 beats per minute the cardiac index does not

change, and even falls slightly at the faster heart rates, with an inverse linear relationship between the stroke volume and the heart rate. However, in these circumstances the tachycardia is accompanied by reduced dimensions of both the right and the left ventricles, the reduction in end-diastolic volume being about half a normal stroke volume. These findings accord with the fact that tachycardia is achieved mainly at the expense of diastole when the ventricles are filling. Moreover, during this experimental tachycardia the force–velocity curve is displaced upward, V_{max} being increased with no change in P_0. This indicates an increased contractility of the ventricular muscle attributable purely to the heart rate and independent of any direct effect of neurohumoral stimuli on the myocardium.

During exercise, however, only part of the displacement of the force–velocity curve is produced by an increase in rate alone, and during severe exertion the tissue requirements can only be met by a cardiac output that is further augmented by an increased stroke volume. In addition, the increased sympathetic stimulation of the myocardium and the increase in the circulating adrenergic amines both lead to an increased contractile state of the muscle. Peripherally, vasodilatation in the active skeletal muscles reduces the aortic impedance (afterload) and thus encourages the increased cardiac output.

Hyperventilation, the pumping action of the exercising muscles and constriction of the veins all contribute to the increase of venous return and ventricular filling (preload) but, as part of the general 'hyperkinetic circulatory state', the increased velocity of blood flow through the heart and lesser circulation is great enough to prevent the central venous pressure from rising much. The Starling mechanism therefore does not account for the greater stroke volume expelled during exercise.

THE CORONARY CIRCULATION

About 4 per cent of the output of the left ventricle passes into the coronary vessels so the blood flow in the aorta is not the total cardiac output; that can only be found by measuring the flow in the pulmonary artery.

The peculiarities of the venous drainage (p. 135) make it difficult to estimate human coronary blood flow accurately. Samples of blood can be obtained from the coronary sinus through a cardiac catheter (p. 158) introduced into the mouth of the sinus through the right atrium. If a sample of arterial blood is obtained while the patient is breathing nitrous oxide or radioactive krypton, the arterio–venous gas difference can be obtained. This method measures only the blood flow through the left ventricle but it is unlikely that the flow through the right ventricle is substantially different. The coronary blood flow at rest is about 200 ml per min (65 ml per 100 g per min). About 70 per cent of the total coronary blood flow occurs during diastole.

During systole the coronary vessels lying within the heart muscle are compressed. This compression increases the total resistance of the coronary vascular bed and actually momentarily reverses the flow in early systole (Fig. 10.38). Since the blood pressure in the left ventricle during systole is slightly higher than it is in the aorta the intramyocardial tissue pressure in the inner half of the ventricular wall is greater than the arterial blood pressure, and the total blood flow, systolic and diastolic, in subendocardial muscle is about half that in the superficial part of the myocardium. This flow gradient is partly offset by the greater density of capillaries in the deeper myocardium. Nevertheless cells in the subendocardial myocardium tend to be most severely damaged by hypoxia (ischaemic necrosis).

The pressure in the right ventricle is, of course, at all times much lower than the pressure in the aorta so perfusion of the coronary vessels in the right ventricle is much more efficient. It is probably for these reasons that ischaemic necrosis (myocardial infarction) affects mainly parts of the left ventricle rather than the right.

When the heart beats faster and more strongly its oxygen consumption is increased: during exercise, therefore, the myocardial blood flow is increased, like the blood flow to the skeletal muscle and the skin. The coronary blood flow during severe exercise with a cardiac output of 25 litres per minute could amount to 1 litre per minute (but see Table 10.52). The coronary vessels are dilated or constricted by an autoregulatory system in which the myocardial oxygen tension (Po_2) determines the blood flow by altering the coronary vascular resistance.

Hypoxia can cause vasodilatation and an increase of flow of as much as 500 per cent. Since neither carbon dioxide nor lactic acid can increase the flow by more than 50 per cent it is assumed that the hypoxic muscle fibres liberate a vasodilator substance. A vasodilator metabolite has not been identified but adenosine is a likely candidate. If the coronary circulation is occluded the Po_2 of the myocardium falls and when the occlusion is released the blood flow increases (reactive hyperaemia, p. 190) and the Po_2 rises above normal. This suggests that the capillaries, not arterio–venous shunts, carry the increased flow. Large changes of pressure in the aorta can also influence coronary perfusion. When the arterial pressure falls the consequent release of adrenergic substances from the adrenal medulla produces coronary vasodilatation and increased coronary blood flow while the flow through the skin, kidneys and splanchnic vessels is severely restricted. The

circulation through the heart, like that through the brain, is therefore maintained.

The coronary blood vessels are supplied with both sympathetic and parasympathetic nerves. In animals sympathetic stimulation and noradrenaline and adrenaline produce an increase in blood flow but whether this is due to vasodilatation, to alteration in heart rate and aortic pressures, or to metabolic effects is not yet clear. Drugs that block either the α or β-adrenergic receptors have been used to study the effect of sympathetic stimulation on the coronary vascular bed of the dog. Sympathetic vasoconstriction in cardiac muscle is only slight, in contrast to that in skeletal muscle, and is largely overcome by local chemical vasodilatation. Unlike skeletal muscle vessels, the coronary vascular bed is not supplied by sympathetic vasodilator fibres. During exercise, although diastole is shortened because of tachycardia a normal heart does not suffer from a reduced blood supply. If the coronary arteries are diseased, however, the myocardium can become hypoxic during exercise: this is the cause of ischaemic cardiac pain on exertion (angina pectoris).

DISORDERED CARDIAC RHYTHMS

The clinical aspects of cardiac arrhythmias lie outside the scope of this book but their mechanisms are of interest to students of physiology because they illustrate some important principles.

The mechanism of many of the commonest arrhythmias was first suggested by Mackenzie after careful observation of the jugular venous pulse and later by recording the venous pulse at the same time as the arterial pulse with his famous 'polygraph'. It was, however, Lewis's use of the electrocardiograph that confirmed their nature. The precise mechanisms of many of the more complicated arrhythmias have been elucidated by the technique of intracardiac electrocardiography, excitation being directly recorded from various parts of the special conducting system (Fig. 10.45).

Ectopic pace-makers. The premature discharge of a pacemaker cell lower than the sinus node (ectopic focus) produces premature excitation and contraction of the chamber where it is sited (extrasystole). When the ectopic focus lies above the AV node there is a premature excitation of the whole heart (*supraventricular ectopic beat*) (Fig. 10.65). Because the spread of atrial excitation is abnormal it may cause an abnormal P wave, but ventricular excitation occurs normally through the AV node and bundles; the QRST complex is therefore normal.

When the ectopic focus lies below the division of the bundle of His into its main right and left bundles, or in the potential pace-making cells of the Purkinje network in the ventricles, there is a premature and abnormal spread of excitation in the ventricles (*ventricular ectopic beat*). An abnormal QRST occurs with no preceding P wave (Fig. 10.66). If the excitation spreads backward up the AV conducting system there will be retrograde excitation of the atria, and a P wave may follow the QRS complex. During ventricular ectopic beats the abnormal ventricular contraction is inefficient, and the intraventricular pressure and stroke volume are low. The distension of the aortic root is therefore small and a pulse wave may not be propagated to the wrist.

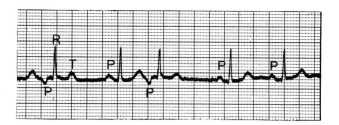

Fig. 10.65 Electrocardiogram, lead II, showing two *supraventricular extrasystoles*. The ectopic focus is low in the atrium or in the AV junctional tissue. Atrial excitation occurs in a direction the reverse of normal. The first and third P waves are therefore inverted. Ventricular conduction is normal so the abnormal premature P waves are followed by normal premature QRST complexes.

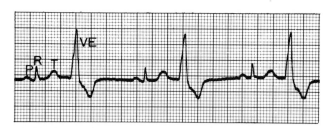

Fig. 10.66 ECG, lead II, showing *ventricular extrasystoles* (VE) following each normal complex. The abnormal spread of excitation from the ectopic pace-maker below the divisions of the conducting tissue (p. 140) causes wide and abnormally shaped QRST complexes.

The premature excitation of the myocardium after the discharge of an ectopic focus may leave the muscle refractory to the next pace-making stimulus arising in the sinu-atrial node. Sometimes retrograde atrial excitation prematurely discharges the SA node. Ectopic beats are then followed by a longer diastole than usual ('compensatory pause'). The patient may feel that his heart has 'missed a beat'. A series of ectopic beats arising from a focus in the atria or ventricles can produce a paroxysm of tachycardia (atrial or ventricular) that may impede filling of the heart and so lower the cardiac output (Figs. 10.67A and B).

Atrial fibrillation and flutter. During atrial systole in a normally functioning heart all the atrial muscle fibres contract practically simultaneously and, in the ventricular systole that follows, all the ventricular muscle fibres contract in an orderly sequence. In certain diseases of the heart, or after electrical or chemical stimulation, this orderly contraction may be replaced by very irregular activity, in which the individual muscle fibres contract in a disorderly sequence all out of step with one another so a fine rapid tremulous movement (*fibrillation*) is seen over the surface of either the atria or the ventricles. The affected chambers of the heart do not contract as a whole and their pumping action is lost. If the ventricles fibrillate (Fig. 10.68) the blood is not pumped out into the systemic or pulmonary circulations and death rapidly results from anoxia of the brain. If, however, fibrillation is confined to the atria the ventricles still force the blood round the circulation and a patient with atrial fibrillation may have a reasonably efficient circulation (p. 171).

If an atrium of the exposed heart of the dog is subjected to a brief period of rapid electrical stimulation (300 to 600 per minute) the atria may change their rhythm and beat about 300

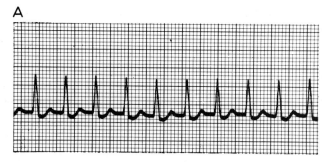

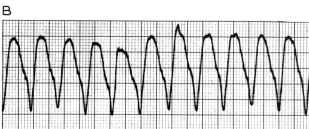

Fig. 10.67 Paroxysms of tachycardia. A. *Supraventricular (atrial) tachycardia*; because the ectopic pace-maker discharges above the division of the AV conducting system (p. 140) the QRST complexes have a normal shape. B. *Ventricular tachycardia*; the ectopic pace-maker lies below the division of the AV conducting tissue, so the complexes are bizarre, like ventricular extrasystoles.

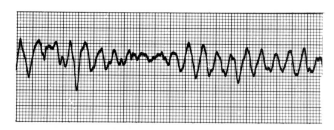

Fig. 10.68 *Ventricular fibrillation*. There are no recognizable P waves or QRS complexes. The chaotic cardiac electrical activity gives rise to random oscillations only.

times per minute (*atrial flutter*). This abnormal rhythm also occurs in diseased or even normal human hearts (Fig. 10.69).

The mechanism of atrial flutter and fibrillation was studied by Prinzmetal and his colleagues with high-speed cinephotography (2000 frames per second) and a cathode-ray oscillograph. In atrial fibrillation minute irregular contractions occur continuously throughout the atrial muscle each one involving an area from 0·03 to 3 mm in diameter. Superimposed on these are larger contractions which sweep across the atrium fairly regularly at rates of 400 to 600 per minute giving an appearance of fibrillation to the unaided eye. Prinzmetal claimed that all the atrial arrhythmias arose from the discharge of a single ectopic focus. At rates of impulse formation in the ectopic focus below the normal sinus rate premature atrial systoles are produced; when the rate of impulse formation is in the range 100 to 250 per minute atrial tachycardia is the result. Flutter and fibrillation are found at rates of impulse formation of approximately 300 to 400 per minute respectively. Not all workers agree with Prinzmetal. For example Rytand has marshalled much evidence in support of the earlier idea that atrial flutter, when it occurs in patients and is not induced experimentally, is caused by 'circus movement'; that is to say the wave of excitation is trapped in a circular pathway in the atria because of the refractory period and so becomes perpetuated.

In both atrial flutter and fibrillation the rate of stimulation is so rapid that the AV node is incapable of responding to every impulse reaching it from the atria. When flutter is present the ventricles usually respond in a regular manner to every third or fourth atrial contraction (Fig. 10.69) while in atrial fibrillation the response of the ventricles is irregular (Fig. 10.70) and often rapid, giving an irregular rapid pulse, and a systolic blood pressure that varies from beat to beat because of the varying length of diastole.

Any disorder of cardiac rhythm that causes very rapid ventricular contractions tends to reduce the cardiac output and may lead to heart failure (see below). Many fast abnormal rhythms, however, can be converted to normal sinus rhythm by a single direct-current electric shock applied across the patient's thorax. The high voltage shock, which lasts only a few milliseconds, is usually triggered by the R wave of the ECG and has an energy value of between 50 and 400 joules.

Heart block. Since the conduction of excitation in the AV junctional tissue does not normally occupy more than 210 msec a PR interval above this value denotes impaired AV conduction (*incomplete heart block*) (Figs. 10.71 A and B). *In complete heart block* (Fig. 10.72) the contractions of the atria and ventricles are completely dissociated from one another, the atria being activated from the SA node and the ventricles from a pace-maker with a slower rate of impulse formation in the bundles. In such a case the ECG shows regularly recurring P waves of normal form and, superimposed upon this, a regular succession of ventricular complexes at a slower rate (*idio-ventricular rhythm*).

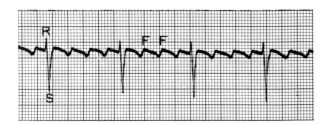

Fig. 10.69 ECG, lead II, showing *atrial flutter*. A regular succession of characteristically abnormal P waves (F or flutter waves) indicates the abnormal excitation of the atria but the ventricles respond only to every fourth beat. There is therefore '4:1 AV block'.

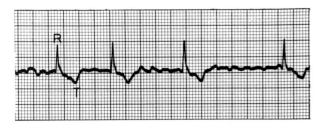

Fig. 10.70 ECG, lead II, showing *atrial fibrillation*. Low voltage irregular oscillations of the base line represent the atrial arrhythmia. The QRS complexes occur irregularly because the AV node can only transmit some of the impulses it receives. In this record the T wave is inverted because of an abnormality of repolarization (see Fig. 10.34).

Circulatory arrest. When the ventricles either do not contract at all, or do not do so efficiently enough to maintain an adequate cerebral circulation, consciousness is lost and death occurs unless artificial ventilation and cardiac massage are used.

By rhythmic pressure on the lower third of the sternum the heart can be compressed between the sternum and the vertebral bodies, lateral movements being restricted by the pericardium. Relaxation of the pressure allows the heart to fill again. By repetition of this *external cardiac massage* 60 to 70 times per minute it is usually possible to produce a radial pulse and a systolic blood pressure of 60 to 100 mm Hg (mean pressure 10 to 20 mm Hg). If the heart stops when the patient is on the operating table the surgeon can pass a hand through an incision and compress the patient's heart rhythmically (*internal cardiac massage*).

The appearance of the ECG gives no information at all about

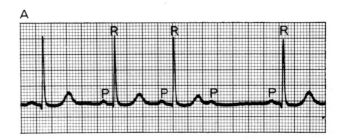

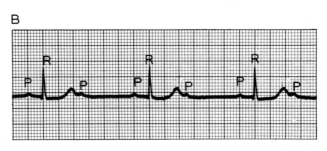

Fig. 10.71 Two forms of *incomplete heart block*. A. The PR interval increases from complex to complex because the impulse takes an increasingly long time to traverse the AV node; eventually the impulse is not conducted to the ventricles and no QRS complex follows the P wave. The cycle then begins again ('Wenckebach periods'). B. There is no QRS complex after every second P wave because of failure of AV conduction ('fixed' 2:1 AV block, 'dropped beats').

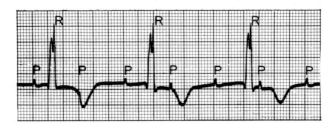

Fig. 10.72 *Complete heart block*. The P waves occur regularly at a rate of 100 per minute and represent atrial systole at this rate. The wide and abnormal QRS complexes also occur regularly, but at a much slower rate (45 per minute) and represent the discharge of an independent ventricular pace-maker. Atrial and ventricular activities are entirely dissociated.

the force of cardiac contraction: indeed, evidence of electrical activity can be present in the ECG when the heart has stopped contracting.

CARDIAC FAILURE

In his experiments with the isolated dog's heart Starling related the cardiac output to the venous pressure. He also emphasized the difference between a good, that is to say healthy, heart and a fatigued or failing heart. For a given output the healthy heart was working at a low venous pressure and a low diastolic size while the failing heart worked at a high venous pressure and a large diastolic size. Although the heart in an intact man differs considerably from an animal's heart in a heart–lung preparation these observations are still relevant to cardiac failure, which has been defined by Wood as 'a state in which the heart fails to maintain an adequate circulation for the needs of the body despite a satisfactory venous filling pressure'. Starling also pointed out that the right and left sides of the heart might fail separately according to the load imposed

upon them and this also to some extent has analogies in clinical practice.

Cardiac failure is a complicated and somewhat controversial subject. Briefly, however, whatever the actual cardiac output at the time, failure involves a reduction of output from previous levels and an increase in the venous pressure, apparent at first only during exercise, but later also at rest. The fall in output is accompanied by a redistribution of blood throughout the body (Table 10.52) and an alteration in the function of many organs and tissues. Retention of sodium and water occurs early in cardiac failure and leads to an increased blood volume that further overloads the heart. In some patients the secretion of aldosterone (Chap. 28) is increased and in many there is an increased release of antidiuretic hormone (Chap. 28). Both may contribute to the fluid retention, the mechanism of which is not yet fully understood. The increase of systemic venous pressure must also be a factor in producing oedema and may interfere with hepatic function. Increased pulmonary venous pressure and volume is associated with pulmonary oedema which reduces the compliance of the lungs and may cause the breathlessness that is such a prominent feature of heart failure.

REFERENCES

Bergel D H (ed) 1972 Cardiovascular fluid dynamics. Academic Press, London

Berne R M, Levy M N 1977 Cardiovascular physiology. St Louis, Mosby

Bloomfield D A (ed) 1974 Dye curves. University Park Press, Baltimore

Braunwald E, Ross J, Sonnenblick E H 1976 Mechanisms of contraction of the normal and failing heart. Little Brown, Boston

Braunwald E 1974 Regulation of the circulation. New England Journal of Medicine 290: 1124–1129

Burch G E, De Pasquale N P 1964 A history of electrocardiography. Year Book Publishers, Chicago

Chapman C B, Mitchell J H 1965 Starling on the heart: Facsimile reprints including the Linacre lecture on the law of the heart, analysis and critical comment. Dawsons, London

Deuchar D C 1964 Clinical phonocardiography. English Universities Press, London

Dickinson C J, Marks J (ed) 1978 Developments in Cardiovascular Medicine. MTP Press, London

Durrer D, Van Dam R T, Freud G E, Janse M J, Meijler F L, Arzbaecher R C 1970 Total excitation of the isolated human heart. Circulation 41: 899–912

Fabiato A, Fabiato F 1979 Calcium and cardiac excitation-contraction coupling. Annual Review of Physiology 41: 473–484

Folkow B, Neil E 1971 Circulation. Oxford University Press, London

Guyton A C, Jones C E, Coleman T G 1973 Circulatory physiology: cardiac output and its regulation. 2nd edn. Saunders, London

Hainsworth R, Kidd C, Linden R J 1979 Cardiac receptors. University Press, Cambridge

Harris P, Opie L H (eds) 1971 Calcium and the heart. Academic Press, New York and London

Harvey W 1628 Exercitatio anatomica de motu cordis et sanguinis. Fitzer, Frankfurt. Translated into English by Gweneth Whitteridge 1976 Blackwell, Oxford

Henry J P, Meehan J P 1971 The circulation. Year Book Publishers, Chicago

Hurst J W (ed) 1978 The heart, arteries and veins. McGraw-Hill, New York

Hutter O F 1957 Mode of action of autonomic transmitters on the heart. British Medical Bulletin 13: 176–180

Jackson J R 1972 Mechanism of ventricular ejection. British Medical Journal iv: 166–169

James T N, Sheriff L 1968 Ultrastructure of myocardial cells. Americal Journal of Cardiology 22: 389–416

Katz A M, Brady A J 1971 Mechanical and biochemical correlates of cardiac contraction. Modern concepts of cardiovascular disease 40: 39–45

Katz A M 1977 Physiology of the heart. Raven Press, New York

Kelman G R 1977 Applied cardiovascular physiology. Butterworth, London

Langer G A 1973 Heart: excitation-contraction coupling. Annual Review of Physiology 35: 55–86

Leatham A 1975 Auscultation of the heart and phonocardiography. Churchill Livingstone, Edinburgh

Leyton R A, Sonnenblick E H 1971 The sarcomere as the basis of Starling's law of the heart in the left and right ventricles. In: Bajusz E, Jasmin G (eds) Methods and achievements in experimental pathology. Vol. 5: Functional morphology of the heart. Karger, Basel, p. 22

Linden R J, Snow H M 1974 The inotropic state of the heart. Recent Advances in Physiology 9: 148–190

Mills P G, Chamusco R F, Craige E 1976 Echophonocardiographic studies of the contribution of the atrioventricular valves to the first heart sound. Circulation 54: 944–951

Mitchell J H, Wildenthal K 1974 Static (isometric) exercise and the heart: physiological and clinical considerations. Annual Review of Medicine 25: 369–381

Morkin E, La Raia P J 1974 Biochemical studies on the regulation of myocardial contractility. New England Journal of Medicine 290: 445–451

Noble D 1974 Cardiac action potentials and pacemaker activity. Recent Advances in Physiology 9: 1–50

Noble D 1979 The initiation of the heartbeat. Clarendon Press, Oxford

Opie L H 1968–69 Metabolism of the heart in health and disease. American Heart Journal 76: 685–698

Porter Ruth, Fitzsimons D W (eds) 1974 The physiological basis of Starling's law of the heart. Ciba Foundation Symposium 24 (new series). Associated Scientific Publishers, Amsterdam

Randall W C (ed) 1977 Neural regulation of the heart. University Press, Oxford

Reuter H 1979 Properties of two inward membrane currents in the heart. Annual Review of Physiology 41: 413–424

Ross J, Sobel B E 1972 Regulation of cardiac contraction. Annual Review of Physiology 34: 47–90

Rushmer R F 1976 Structure and function of the cardiovascular system. Saunders, London

Sarnoff S J, Mitchell J H 1961 The regulation of the performance of the heart. American Journal of Medicine 30: 747–771

Shepherd J T, Vanhoutte P M 1979 The human cardiovascular system. Raven Press, New York

Smith O A 1974 Reflex and control mechanisms involved in the control of the heart and circulation. Annual Review of Physiology 36: 93–123

Sonnenblick E H 1966 The mechanics of myocardial contraction. In: Briller S A, Conn H J (eds) The myocardial cell. University of Pennsylvania Press, Philadelphia, p 173

Sperelakis N 1979 Propagation mechanisms in heart. Annual Review of Physiology 41: 441–457

Stenger R J, Spiro D 1961 Structure of the cardiac muscle cell. American Journal of Medicine 30: 653–665

Trautwein W 1973 Membrane currents in cardiac muscle fibres. Physiological Reviews 53: 793–835

Vasalle M 1979 Electrogenesis of the plateau and pacemaker potential. Annual Review of Physiology 41: 425–440

Vérel D, Grainger R G 1978 Cardiac catheterization and angiocardiography. Churchill Livingstone, Edinburgh

Wade O L, Bishop J M 1962 Cardiac output and regional blood flow. Blackwell, Oxford

Weidman S 1974 Heart: electrophysiology. Annual Review of Physiology 36: 155–170

Wellens H J J, Lie K I, Janse M J (ed) 1978 The conduction system of the heart. Nijhoff, The Hague

11   The Circulation

The circulatory system brings blood close enough to individual cells to hold their local environment relatively constant by diffusion between blood plasma and extracellular fluid. Diffusion takes place across the thin-walled capillary vessels and the rest of the circulatory apparatus is arranged to keep these vessels adequately supplied with blood.

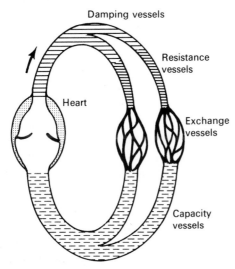

Fig. 11.1 Functional components of the circulation. Of the total blood volume the arteries contain about 20 per cent, the capillaries 5 per cent, and the veins about 75 per cent.

It is often helpful to think of the circulation in functional rather than in anatomical terms (Fig. 11.1). We can think of the blood vessels as arranged in a large number of circuits in parallel. Thus there will be one circuit for the renal circulation, one for the skin circulation, one for the muscle circulation and so on. Each of these individual circuits consists of a number of sections arranged in series. The chief function of the first section of each circuit is to damp the huge pressure fluctuations generated by the heart to give a fairly steady driving pressure. Anatomically, these *damping* vessels correspond fairly closely with the arteries. The second section is composed of vessels which offer a high and variable resistance to the flow of blood around the circuit. They act as taps which regulate the flow in any particular circuit. They may be referred to as *resistance vessels* and correspond anatomically to the arterioles. The third section in each circuit is composed of the vessels which permit exchange of material by diffusion across their walls. These may be referred to as the *exchange vessels* and correspond anatomically to the capillaries and some of the thin-walled venules. The final section in each circuit consists of the vessels that contain the bulk of the blood volume. These are referred to as *capacity vessels* and correspond anatomically to the veins and venules. By altering their dimensions, they adjust the capacity of the circulation to meet variations in the volume and distribution of blood in the circulatory system.

Although it is useful to think about each section of the

circulation in terms of the chief feature it presents, that is damping, resistance, exchange or capacity, it should be stressed that all vessels present all these features to some extent. For example, all vessels offer some resistance to flow but the greater part of the resistance lies in the arterioles. Similarly, all vessels have the capacity to hold blood but a very large fraction of the blood volume is contained in the venules and veins. Each functional variety of blood vessel and its features will now be considered in turn.

THE ARTERIAL OR DAMPING VESSELS

These vessels have three main features. They convert the intermittent pressure generated by the heart into a fairly steady pressure head. They distribute blood to the tissues at low energy cost and the pressure head within them is maintained at a fairly constant value by a number of complex control systems.

Structure of Arteries

All the blood vessels of whatever size have a smooth inner lining of flattened *endothelial cells* joined edge to edge. This inner lining is continuous from the arteries through the capillaries to the veins and to the internal lining of the heart (the *endocardium*).

The arteries have three main coats and the following description refers mainly to a medium-sized artery (Fig. 11.2). The endothelial layer is surrounded by an elastic layer, the two together forming the *tunica intima*, or inner coat. After death, when the internal pressure falls, the elastic tissue contracts and forms the wavy inner border of an artery seen in histological preparations. The tunica intima is surrounded by smooth muscle fibres which pass circularly round the vessel, forming the *tunica media*, or middle coat. Finally there is an external coat, or *tunica adventitia*, of collagen-rich connective tissue which blends with the general tissue of the body (Chap. 17). In the larger arteries the elastic layer takes the form of a fenestrated membrane and there is also a certain amount of subendothelial fibrous tissue. The muscle fibres of the middle coat are reinforced by a network of elastic fibres and the outer coat contains elastic fibres in addition to collagen fibres. The large arteries, and particularly the aorta, thus contain a greater proportion of elastic tissue in their walls than do the smaller arteries. The walls of the arterioles are almost entirely muscular. At the point where an artery gives off a branch, or divides into two, the combined cross-sectional area of the two divisions is somewhat greater than that of the original artery. The total cross-sectional area of the vascular system, therefore, gradually increases as the vessels themselves become smaller (Fig. 11.13) so that at the capillaries it may be one thousand times that at the aorta.

The walls of the veins are very much thinner than those of

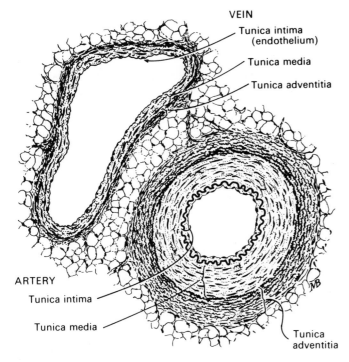

VEIN
Tunica intima
(endothelium)
Tunica media
Tunica adventitia

ARTERY
Tunica intima
Tunica media
Tunica adventitia

Fig. 11.2 Cross-section of a medium sized artery and its accompanying vein (×80). The cross-sectional area of a major vein is more than twice that of the corresponding artery; small veins draining a tissue may have six or seven times the cross-section of the little arteries supplying it. Recent measurements suggest that the post-capillary venules may have a larger total cross-sectional area than the capillaries. (M. P. Wiedman (1963) *Circulation Research*, **12**, 375–378.)

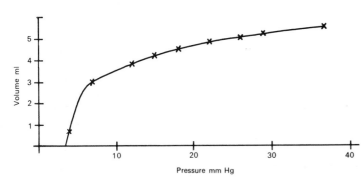

Fig. 11.3a The volume-pressure curve of the vena cava of a dog. Note that the vein is easily distended by a relatively small pressure compared with that required to distend an artery, but once distended it becomes resistant to further stretch. A distended vein can be shown to be stiffer than an artery. (*After* H. Blömer (1954–55) *Zeitchrift für Biologie*, **107**, 468–480.)

the corresponding arteries and their internal diameter is generally greater (Fig. 11.2). The elastic tissue is usually quite inconspicuous and some veins, for example those of the bones and placenta, are said to have little or no muscular tissue.

The veins are easily distended by a small rise of pressure (Fig. 11.3a); the arteries, on the other hand, withstand a considerable increase of internal pressure with a relatively small increase in volume as indicated in Fig. 11.3b. The elasticity of the aorta gradually diminishes as age increases. The veins, unlike the arteries, can accommodate relatively large volumes of added (transfused) fluid with only small changes in pressure.

Role of the elastic tissue. When the left ventricle contracts, all the energy imparted to the blood does not appear immediately as kinetic energy. Some is used to stretch the elastic fibres in the arterial walls and is stored there as potential energy. During systole this 'give' in the arterial wall limits the rise in the systolic arterial pressure. If the walls were rigid, the systolic pressure would be much higher. With increasing age the elastic tissue degenerates and the arterial walls become stiffer. As this happens the systolic pressure tends to rise. During diastole the recoil of the elastic tissue returns the energy stored in the wall to the blood and this limits the fall in arterial pressure. If the walls were rigid, diastolic pressure would be much lower. Thus the elastic tissue tends to damp pressure fluctuations in the arterial system to provide a fairly constant pressure head.

Role of the arterial smooth muscle. The media in the major arteries is predominantly elastic in character, but it also contains a considerable amount of smooth muscle. It is not clear what function this muscle serves. The resistance offered

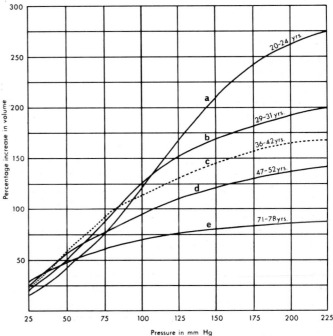

Fig. 11.3b Mean volume-elasticity curves of thoracic aortas in various age groups showing the relation of the percentage increase in volume to the increase in pressure. (P. Hallock & I. C. Benson (1937) Elastic properties of human aorta. *Journal of Clinical Investigation*, **16**, 597.)

by the larger arterial vessels is so low that changes in their calibre would not greatly affect the total resistance offered by the circuit. In the smaller muscular arteries the smooth muscle may be important in determining local vascular resistance.

The smooth muscle can be excited by mechanical damage. It may be that the muscle has a protective function so that in a severe injury when an artery is severed the irritation of the vessel wall may induce spasm which reduces blood loss.

Smooth muscle in blood vessels, like smooth muscle elsewhere, responds to stretch by contracting. When a person stands up the arterial pressure in his feet rises by about 100 mm Hg, the hydrostatic equivalent of the column of blood from the heart to the feet. This would tend to distend the arteries. However, the smooth muscle contraction induced by stretch tends to prevent excessive distension.

The Arterial Pulse

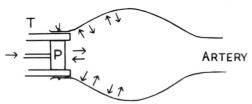

Fig. 11.4 Diagram to illustrate the initiation of a pulse wave in the aorta.

The rapid rise of pressure following the ejection of some 60 ml of blood from the left ventricle at each systole expands the aorta and a pressure wave or pulse passes along its wall. The pulse is *not* due to the passage of blood along the arteries—the blood travels at only 0·5 m per s—but to a pressure wave travelling about 7 m per s. If the piston P in Fig. 11.4 is driven towards the right in the tube T tied into an artery the vessel is distended locally, because the blood is incompressible. This produces a local increase of pressure that has little effect on the advancing piston, which is in fact a mass of incompressible blood; instead the next section of the artery is stretched so that a wave of pressure travels along the vessel wall without involving actual transmission of blood. Indeed the pulse wave can travel down such an elastic tube even if the distant end is closed; there it may be reflected back in an attenuated form. Reflexion of pressure waves occurs at every branching point in the arterial tree and may make records of the arterial pulse very complex.

Pulse wave velocity. If the pulse is recorded simultaneously from the carotid and the radial arteries, the velocity of the pulse wave is found to be about 5 m per sec at 5 years and 8 m per sec at 60 years; the difference in the velocities is due to the fact that arteries become stiffer with increasing age.

It is useful to know that the pulse wave normally arrives at almost the same moment at the beginning of the femoral artery and at the radial artery at the wrist. If the femoral pulse is later than the radial it is probable that the wave is reaching the femoral artery along collateral channels developed as the result of a congenital narrowing of the aorta (coarctation).

The shape of the pulse wave. The record (Fig. 11.5) of the pulse wave in the brachial artery shows a steeply ascending limb, due to ventricular systole, followed by a more gradual fall in diastole. However, the curve in diastole is not smooth as

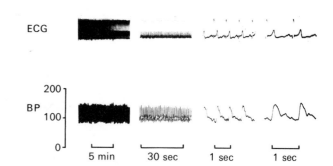

Fig. 11.5 Records of arterial blood pressure recorded directly by an indwelling catheter from the brachial artery of a normal ambulant subject who wore the miniature tape-recording apparatus, perfusing pump and transducer in a harness. The records were made at different speeds; the first two provide information such as is shown in Figure 11.9, the last shows the shape of the brachial arterial pressure pulse. (*Courtesy of P. Sleight.*)

would be expected if it were merely the result of a slow decline of pressure, but contains several minor oscillations. The most constant of these is the dicrotic wave, the largest wave on the descending line of the trace. It has been ascribed to rebound from the closed aortic valves but it is more probable that this wave, together with other smaller subsidiary waves often observed, represents oscillations of the aorta at its own natural frequency. The difference between the systolic and diastolic pressures is about 40 mm Hg in normal people and is called the *pulse pressure.*

The form of the pulse wave is changed as it passes to the periphery by the frictional resistance of the arterial walls and by reflected waves, so that interpretation of the wave form is difficult. For clinical purposes, however, useful information about the shape of the pulse wave can be obtained by feeling the carotid artery. A wave that rises slowly and dies away slowly (plateau pulse) is a good indication that the aortic valve is narrowed (stenosed); on the other hand, a pulse wave that rises and falls quickly (collapsing pulse) may mean that the aortic valve is incompetent, allowing a proportion of the systolic discharge to run back (regurgitate) into the left ventricle.

The pulse rate. The pulse rate varies considerably from individual to individual and in the same subject at different times, depending on a large number of factors which are considered in Chapter 10. The resting pulse rate tends to fall as a child grows up, as shown in Figure 10.63.

The pulse, judged by the fingers, is not quite regular. Accurate records show that there is a slight acceleration during inspiration and a slight deceleration during expiration (Fig. 11.6) provided that the respiratory rate is low. This is termed *sinus arrhythmia.* In children this fluctuation in rhythm is much more marked than in adults. During inspiration the thoracic pressure falls while the abdominal pressure rises and, therefore, blood flows more readily into the thoracic veins, producing a rise of atrial and central venous pressure and an acceleration of the heart. This is only a partial explanation of sinus arrhythmia, since alterations of heart rate related to respiratory activity also occur independently of any alteration in venous pressure.

In heart disease when the cardiac rhythm is irregular (atrial fibrillation, premature beats, p. 169) the rate of the heart may

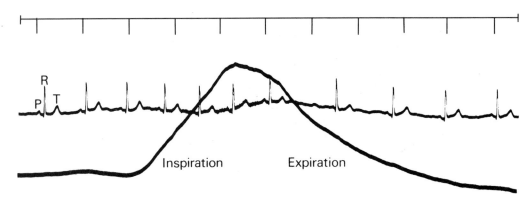

Fig. 11.6 Sinus arrhythmia. ECG (Lead II) from a healthy male aged 24 showing cardiac acceleration during inspiration and slowing during expiration. Timing marks, 1·0 second apart.

exceed the pulse rate because the volume of some of the systolic discharges is insufficient to promote a pulse wave in the arterial walls great enough to reach the wrist. This is called a *pulse deficit*.

Arterial Pressure

Measurement. It is well known that blood escapes from a cut artery under considerable pressure, and the first attempt to measure the pressure was made by Stephen Hales in 1732. After occluding the artery with a temporary ligature he tied a brass pipe into the femoral artery of a mare and connected to it a glass tube 9 ft (2·7 m) long. When he loosened the ligature on the artery the blood rose 8 ft 3 in (about 250 cm) above the level of the heart. He noted that alterations in pressure occurred with each beat of the heart and with the movements of respiration. These results are of great historical interest but the method is not very useful because the blood clots in the manometer in a few minutes.

Nowadays accurate and continuous records of arterial blood pressure in man can be obtained with strain-gauge or condenser manometers communicating directly with an artery through a needle or catheter (Fig. 11.5).- Such records show oscillations between the maximum or systolic pressure and the minimum or diastolic pressure. A point half-way between the maximum and minimum pressures does not represent the *mean arterial pressure* which is, in fact, closer to the diastolic than to the systolic pressure. For convenience it may be taken as the diastolic pressure plus one-third of the pulse-pressure but more strictly it is the level of the line halving the area between the pulse wave contour and the diastolic pressure level. This value can be calculated and recorded electronically.

The direct method just referred to is obviously unsuitable for routine clinical use but the blood pressure can be estimated in man indirectly, although less accurately, by a *sphygmomanometer*, a mercury manometer with one wide and one narrow limb (Fig. 11.7). A rubber bag of standard size (18 cm × 12 cm for adults) covered with cloth is wrapped round the upper arm, leaving the cubital fossa exposed, and connected to the manometer and pump with which it is rapidly inflated to a point above the systolic blood pressure. The pressure in the bag is allowed to fall gradually while the operator auscultates through a stethoscope whose diaphragm or bell is placed lightly over the brachial artery at the bend of the elbow. The

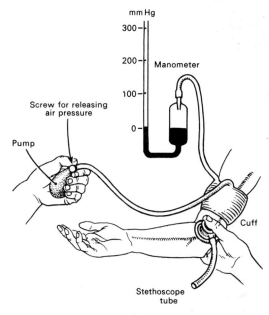

Fig. 11.7 Auscultatory method of measuring blood pressure in man. The cuff should be at heart level.

pressure in the cuff is raised rapidly until the radial pulse disappears. When the pressure is allowed to fall slowly a series of sounds is heard (Fig. 11.8). If the pressure in the bag is above the systolic pressure, SBP, the artery is occluded throughout the pulse cycle. When the pressure falls a little below SBP (line A) the artery opens momentarily when the internal pressure is greater than the external (cuff) pressure and a soft thudding sound is heard at each pulse. As the pressure is further reduced these sounds are gradually succeeded by a distinct tapping which becomes louder as the pressure is reduced. As the pressure in the cuff is allowed to fall, the character of the sound suddenly changes from a sharp, loud tapping to a softer thudding or muffled noise ('fourth phase') (Fig. 11.8, line C). This is taken as the diastolic blood pressure, DBP. Finally the sounds disappear, usually quite suddenly ('fifth phase'), when the pressure in the bag falls below a certain pressure (line D) because below this pressure the internal pressure in the brachial artery is always greater than the pressure applied externally by the bag; the flow of blood along the artery is not interrupted and usually no sound is heard.

Several investigators have compared the pressure readings obtained from a cannula inserted into the brachial artery in one arm with the readings obtained in the other by the auscultatory method. Considerable discrepancies have been observed. The indirect method usually gives readings of SBP about 25 mm Hg lower than the 'true' SBP given by the direct method. The DBP reading by the indirect method is on average 8 mm Hg higher at line C but about 2 mm Hg higher at line D. Although indirect sphygmomanometry does not give an accurate (absolute) measurement of either SBP or DBP yet, since the direct and indirect readings are highly correlated, the indirect method is of great practical value in medicine.

Normal values. When the subject is supine the mean arterial pressures in the brachial and femoral arteries are approximately the same that is, about 100 mm Hg. When the subject is standing however, the femoral pressure is higher than that in the brachial artery, the difference being the pressure of a column of blood equal in height to the vertical distance between one artery and the other.

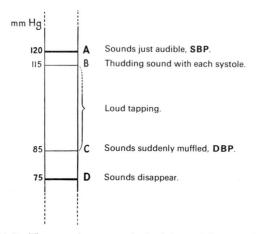

Fig. 11.8 The auscultatory method of determining arterial blood pressure.

In any individual arterial pressure is not constant but subject to appreciable variations over short intervals of time (Fig. 11.9). It also varies with each respiratory cycle (Fig. 11.10). During sleep the SBP may fall below 80 mm Hg (Fig. 11.9). The pressure recorded at some moment in ordinary conditions of life is referred to as the *casual* blood pressure. The figure is higher, sometimes much higher, than the *basal* blood pressure, that is the pressure recorded when the subject is in a state of complete physical and mental rest.

Many attempts have been made to define normal values for blood pressure but all such efforts have been unsatisfactory. The pressure obtained by the sphygmomanometer is affected by the thickness of the arm, the thicker the arm the higher the value obtained. Arterial pressure increases with age (Fig. 11.11), more in some subjects than in others, and no dividing line can properly be set at any age below which the pressure is normal and above which it is abnormal. Indeed, it is considered by some that arterial pressure is inherited as a graded characteristic (like height) and that the range of variation includes values hitherto regarded as abnormal. It seems likely that at least three factors are concerned in the production of high blood pressure, namely age, heredity and environment.

Factors determining arterial pressure. Blood enters the arterial system from the left ventricle and leaves through the arterioles. The amount entering is determined by the cardiac output and the amount leaving is determined by the resistance offered by the arterioles (peripheral resistance). If more blood enters, that is if the cardiac output increases or if less blood leaves, that is if the peripheral resistance rises, the pressure in the arterial system rises. Conversely if cardiac output or peripheral resistance falls, the arterial pressure decreases. Blood pressure is therefore directly proportional to cardiac output and peripheral resistance. Changes in the elasticity of the arteries affect pulse pressure more than mean pressure in the arterial system.

Factors regulating arterial pressure. Control systems within the body tend to maintain mean arterial pressure within fairly strict limits. In this way the head of pressure in the arteries perfusing a tissue is maintained relatively constant despite the changes that frequently occur in both cardiac output and peripheral resistance. Stretch receptors are found

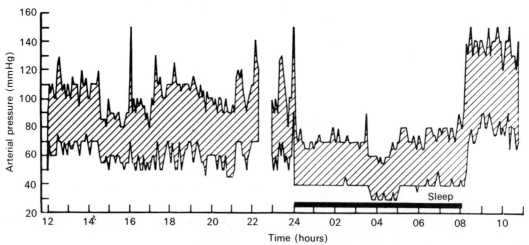

Fig. 11.9 Continuous record of arterial blood pressure of a healthy man during 24 hours made by means of an indwelling arterial cannula. (Fig. 11.5) Note the fall of SBP and DBP during sleep. The high pressure shown at 16.00 is due to a painful stimulus, that at 24.00 to coitus. (A. T. Bevan, A. J. Honour & F. H. Stott (1969) *Clinical Science*, **36**, 329–344.)

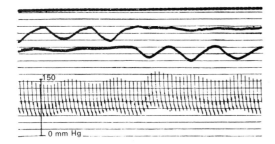

Fig. 11.10 Tracings in a normal man of, from above downwards, time in seconds, thoracic and abdominal breathing and arterial blood pressure. The respiratory records were made with spirometers; a downward movement indicates inspiration. The blood pressure was measured with an electrical (capacitance) manometer communicating with the inside of an artery. The arterial pressure shows variations corresponding to respiration which do not alter in phase when the breathing changes from thoracic to abdominal. (A. C. Dornhorst, P. Howard & G. L. Leathart (1952) *Circulation*, 6, 554.)

in the wall of the proximal arterial tree, especially in the region of the aortic arch and carotid sinuses. When the arterial pressure rises there is increased stimulation of these nerve endings. The increased traffic of impulses up the vagus and glosso-pharyngeal nerves leads to reflex vagal slowing of the heart and reflex release of vasoconstrictor tone in the peripheral blood vessels. The resulting fall in cardiac output and the reduction of peripheral resistance tend to restore the blood pressure to the normal value. Similarly a fall in arterial pressure decreases the stimulation of the arterial stretch receptors. The reflex tachycardia and vasoconstriction that ensue tend to raise the blood pressure towards its normal value.

Even when the arterial baroreceptors are denervated a rise of blood pressure can still be regulated to some extent. The exact mechanism of the control system responsible is not understood. However, it is known that a fall in renal blood flow, such as would occur if arterial pressure fell, results in the release of the hormone renin from the kidney. Renin converts the plasma protein angiotensinogen to the angiotensin polypeptides which constrict blood vessels and cause the release of aldosterone from the adrenal cortex. The salt and water retention brought about by aldosterone together with the vasoconstriction produced by angiotensin tend to raise arterial pressure to the set value.

Arteries as Transport Vessels

Arteries transport blood at high velocity and low energy cost from the heart to the periphery. The high velocity of flow (about 0·5 m per sec) is due to the relatively small cross-sectional area of the arterial system (Fig. 11.13). The total cross-sectional area of the arteries is smaller than that of any other part of the vascular system. The mean pressure in the radial artery is only 5 mm Hg or so lower than that in the aorta (Table 11.12). Because of the extremely low resistance to flow offered by the arteries, blood is transported from the heart to the wrist with the loss of only 5 mm Hg pressure.

Table 11.12 Table of mean blood pressure at various points in the vascular system in man (supine) (referred to the pressure in the right atrium)

	mm Hg
Large artery (for example carotid)	90
Medium artery (for example radial)	85
Capillary	10 to 30
Small veins of arm	9
Intestinal capillaries	over 10
Portal vein	10
Inferior vena cava	3
Large veins of neck	0 to −2
Pulmonary artery	15

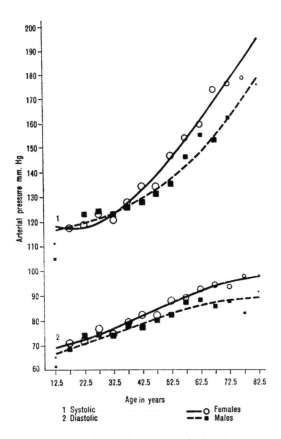

Fig. 11.11 Systolic and diastolic pressures for females (open circles) and males (black squares) for each five-year age group of the population sample, together with the fitted curves. The area of each circle or square is proportional to the number of subjects in that age group. (M. Hamilton, G. W. Pickering, J. A. F. Roberts & G. S. C. Sowry (1954). *Clinical Science*, 13, 11–35.)

THE ARTERIOLES OR RESISTANCE VESSELS

The changes in intravascular pressure, intravascular cross-sectional area and velocity of blood flow at various points of the vascular system are indicated diagrammatically in Figure

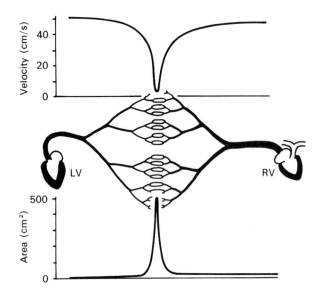

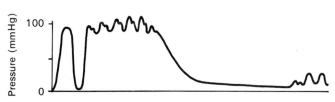

Fig. 11.13 Diagram showing the relations between blood pressure, blood velocity and the total cross-sectional area in arteries, capillaries and veins (Adapted from R. F. Rushmer (1976) *Structure and Function of the Cardiovascular System*, 2nd edn. Philadelphia: Saunders).

11.13. The biggest fall in arterial pressure occurs in the arterioles which offer the largest resistance to flow. Regional blood flow is regulated by variations in the resistance they offer.

Arterioles have a mean diameter of about 100 μm. Like the rest of the vascular system they are lined with endothelium but have a relatively thick coat of smooth muscle. Thus the ratio of wall thickness to lumen in arterioles is about 1:1, much higher than in any other type of blood vessel.

Peripheral Resistance

Peripheral resistance is the functional resistance offered by the circulatory system to the flow of blood around it. From the wall to the centre of a blood vessel the blood flows along the vessel in a series of concentric laminae with increasing velocity. The laminae are moving at different velocities relative to one another and it is the lack of slipperiness or the cohesive forces between adjacent layers that is responsible for the friction. All the energy imparted to the blood by the heart is used up in overcoming this functional resistance in one transit round the circulatory system.

Peripheral resistance (R) can be measured using the hydraulic equivalent of Ohm's law, that is $R = \dfrac{\Delta P}{F}$ where ΔP is the pressure drop across and F the flow around the circulation. For the calculation it is necessary to measure mean arterial pressure, mean venous pressure and the cardiac output.

From Poiseuille's law which describes the factors governing the laminar flow of fluid through capillary tubes with rigid walls it can be derived that peripheral resistance (R) is directly proportional to the length of the tube (l), the viscosity of the fluid (η), and inversely proportional to the fourth power of the radius (r) that is $R \propto \dfrac{l\eta}{r^4}$.

Since the length of the vessels and the viscosity of the blood are relatively constant, changes in peripheral resistance are usually induced by changes in the radius of the vessels. Because of the fourth power relationship small changes in radius can cause large changes in resistance; for example, a doubling of the radius of a vessel would cause a sixteenfold decrease in the resistance if offered.

Blood flow in the circulation is normally *laminar* as shown in Figure 11.14. If it becomes *turbulent* peripheral resistance is increased. As the rate of flow of a fluid in a tube is gradually increased there comes a point at which laminar flow is replaced by turbulence and the conditions mentioned above no longer apply. By injecting a stream of dye into a stream of water flowing in a long straight tube Reynolds (1883) found that turbulence developed if the expression rVd/η, in which r is the radius of the tube, V the mean velocity of flow, d the density and η the viscosity, exceeded a certain value. Reynolds' number is about 1000 for water and slightly less for blood. It is obvious that *turbulent flow* occurs more readily when the fluid is of low viscosity and the velocity relatively great and that it tends to develop first in large vessels. These conditions are found in the

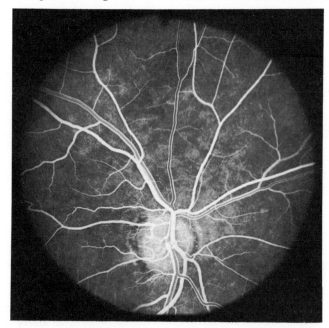

Fig. 11.14 A retinal fluorescein photograph of the fundus of the right eye taken after a single intracarotid injection of 4 ml 5 per cent fluorescein in a healthy male aged 30 years. Fluorescein appears white in the photograph taken 12 seconds after the injection of fluorescein. The arteriolar system is filled with fluorescent blood. The main veins are seen filling from the smaller branches and the fluorescein maintains its position at the edge of the vein, demonstrating laminar flow. Just inferior to the optic disc, two veins showing laminar flow unite. A thin central stream has formed in the main vein from the merging of the streams at the walls of the tributary veins. (*By courtesy of D. F. J. Archer.*)

heart and aorta of severely anaemic patients and turbulence possibly accounts for the cardiac murmurs readily audible with the stethoscope over the heart and large arteries in such people. The relatively high velocity of the flow of blood through narrowed valves in the heart, for example, may be sufficient in itself to cause turbulence and the development of audible murmurs.

The experiments of Poiseuille and Reynolds were carried out with homogeneous fluids, steady flow and rigid tubes. Blood with its cellular content is certainly not homogeneous, its flow is pulsatile and the arteries are elastic. However, although the various laws suggested by these workers may not be exactly applicable to the circulation they are probably a good approximation.

Regulation of peripheral resistance. Since most of the resistance offered by the circulation lies in the arterioles, changes in the calibre of these vessels cause much greater changes in peripheral resistance than comparable changes in other vessels. If perfusion pressure is held constant, flow is inversely proportional to peripheral resistance. This is the situation which obtains in man because control systems hold the arterial pressure steady. Thus changes in the calibre of arterioles, more than changes in the calibre of any other vessels, determine the amount of blood flowing around the circulation. Through regulation of the calibre of arterioles local peripheral resistance and hence local blood flow is controlled. It should be noted that arterioles control blood flow not blood velocity. Flow depends on resistance whereas velocity depends on the total cross-sectional area of the vascular bed.

The arterioles are particularly well designed for the precise regulation of their internal diameters. Their walls are very muscular. In the transverse section of an arteriole, the ratio of the area occupied by muscle to the area occupied by the lumen is about one to one. This ratio, known as the *wall to lumen ratio*, is higher in arterioles than in other types of blood vessel. The muscle is very reactive and its tone is influenced by nervous and other factors. Although changes in arteriolar calibre are usually brought about to alter the rate of blood flow, they are sometimes made to control blood pressure. Peripheral resistance influences blood pressure and a reflex increase in resistance may be induced when the baroreceptors detect a fall in arterial pressure.

Measurement of Blood Flow

The simplest method of determining the blood flow through an organ is to collect and measure over a given period of time all the blood emerging from its veins. Various methods of measuring blood flow without loss of blood have been invented. In Rein's flow meter heat is applied to an artery in the living animal by a coil situated midway between two thermocouples placed upstream and downstream on the artery. If the flow is fast the temperature difference between the two couples is small, if slow the difference is large. The apparatus is calibrated by noting the galvanometer deflexions at various known rates of flow through an excised artery of the same size. The electromagnetic flow meter depends on the fact that an electromotive force is induced in a conductor (in this case the blood) moving through a magnetic field. The e.m.f. is picked up by two electrodes placed on opposite sides of the

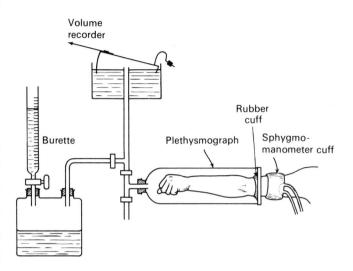

Fig. 11.15 Diagram of a plethysmograph for measuring the rate of blood flow through the arm. A thin rubber cuff makes an air-tight junction just above the elbow. The sphygmomanometer cuff is connected to a pump and manometer as in Figure 11.7; it is inflated to obstruct the venous return but not the arterial inflow. The forearm swells and expels air into the volume recorder. The excursion of the volume recorder is calibrated by running water from the burette into the Wolff's bottle.

unopened artery at right angles to the direction of flow and to the magnetic field.

The changes of volume of a limb or part of a limb can be recorded by means of a *plethysmograph* (Fig. 11.15). This is a rigid box which can be slipped over the part so as to make a closed system in which small changes of volume can be recorded. If the veins are obstructed for a *short* time (without obstructing the arterial inflow) the record shows an increase in volume which indicates the flow of blood into the part during the period of obstruction. The rigid plethysmograph has now largely been replaced by the strain gauge plethysmograph. It consists of a thin plastic tube, with a narrow lumen filled with mercury, which is fastened around the arm to measure its circumference, and hence the volume of the part of the limb. If the venous return is prevented the swelling of the limb increases the length of the column of mercury and increases its resistance. This is easily recorded electronically; the records are similar to those in Figure 11.16.

Since the heat loss from a part is directly related to its blood flow it is possible to assess the flow in a hand or a finger in which the heat loss is high by measuring the heat gained by a water-calorimeter in which the part is immersed. Since the temperature of the skin is determined by the rate of blood flow through it, measurements of surface temperature may be used as an index of blood flow in superficial tissues. The Fick principle (p. 161) can be applied to the determination of the blood flow through an organ, for example the heart (cardiac output), the kidney (pp. 163, 182) or the brain.

The blood flow through various organs is given in Table 11.17. These values are approximate only, since they depend upon the state of activity of the part.

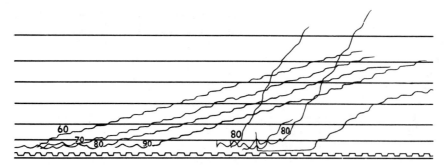

Fig. 11.16 Plethysmograph records. The first four records were made during rest; the following ones at short intervals after exercising the hand within the plethysmograph. The figures on the graph give the pressure in mm Hg in the cuff occluding the venous return. Each space between horizontal lines represents 5 ml increase in arm volume. Time mark in seconds. (A. W. Hewlett & J. G. van Zwaluwenburg (1909–10) *Heart*, 10, 92.)

Table 11.17 Approximate values for resting blood flow through different organs in man in ml per 100 g per minute obtained by various methods

	Blood flow
Carotid bodies	2000
Thyroid	560
Kidney	150
Liver	150
Heart (coronary circulation)	100
Intestine	70
Brain	65
Spleen	40
Stomach	25
Hand	7 to 12
Finger	15 to 40
Forearm (mainly muscle)	1 to 3
Leg (mainly muscle)	1 to 2

THE CAPILLARIES OR EXCHANGE VESSELS

Structure and organization. The circulatory system conveys substances in solution to and from the capillaries where the exchanges between blood and tissue cells take place. The capillaries are minute vessels of the order of 10 μm in diameter connecting arterioles with venules but differing from them in having no muscular coat. Single capillaries differ in diameter, length, and in the nature of their connexions with the smallest arteries and veins. Each capillary consists of a tube of endothelium composed of a single layer of flat cells, about 30 μm by 10 μm. The edge of one cell is fitted closely into the edge of its neighbour by slight overlapping or by interdigitations which leave only a very narrow slit between adjacent cells. Each endothelial cell possesses mitochondria and other organelles like those in other cells; its thickness varies from 0·2 μm at the periphery to 3 μm at the bulge containing the nucleus.

With the aid of the electronmicroscope three types of capillary structure have been described. A *continuous (non-fenestrated) capillary* is one whose endothelium is an apparently continuous sheet. Though no channels can be seen by ordinary electronmicroscopy, intercellular slit-like pores can be identified by the use of a tracer which when injected into the blood passes out through the pores and enables them to be visualized. These capillaries are found in many tissues, including muscle and the central nervous system, and it is known that their walls behave as porous membranes. A *fenestrated capillary* is one whose walls show *intra*cellular fenestrations. The holes are usually less than 0·1 μm in diameter. Such capillaries are seen in renal glomeruli, choroid plexus and ciliary body and are thought to permit large and rapid transfer of fluid across their walls. Since there is little protein in glomerular filtrate, these capillaries cannot be freely permeable to protein. A *discontinuous (sinusoid) capillary* is one in which there are large gaps between adjoining endothelial cells. Such capillaries are found in the liver, spleen and bone marrow. They permit the passage of macromolecules, and probably blood cells, across their walls.

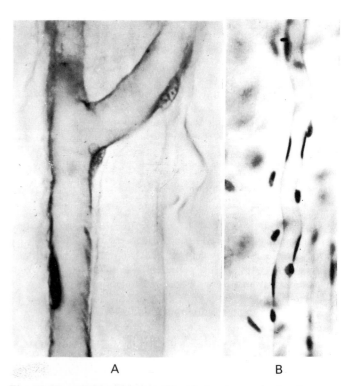

A   B

Fig. 11.18 (A) Branching capillary in frog's muscle showing two Rouget nuclei and one endothelial nucleus. (B) Mesenteric capillary of the rat showing Rouget nuclei sessile on the wall. Endothelial nuclei are also shown. × 1000. (*By courtesy of H. P. Gilding.*)

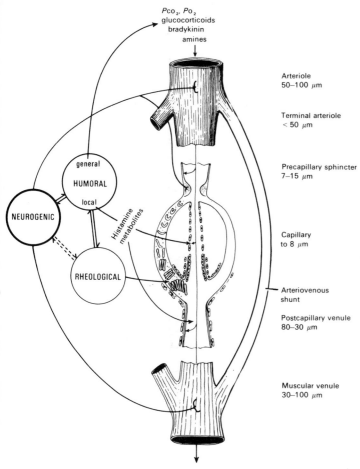

Fig. 11.19 Diagrammatic representation of the normal micro-circulation and its control (*Adapted from* A. L. Stalker (1970) *Journal of Clinical Pathology*, **23**, (Suppl. 4), 11.)

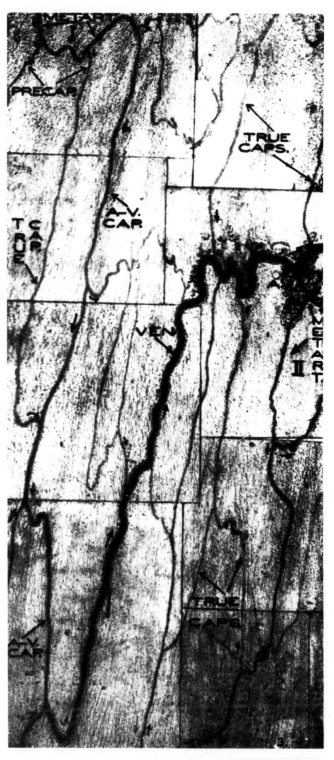

A basement membrane about 25 nm thick completely surrounds the endothelial tube and outside it is a pericapillary sheath supporting the vessels and continuous with the surrounding connective tissue matrix. Embedded in the pericapillary sheath, or possibly attached to the surface of the endothelium, are at intervals large branched cells called *pericytes* or *Rouget cells* (Fig. 11.18).

Zweifach, by microscopic observation of the circulation in the capillary beds of the dog's omentum and the meso-appendix of the rat, has shown that the capillaries are arranged in functional units (Figs. 11.19 and 11.20). A metarteriole, which contains muscular elements, leads into a *thoroughfare channel*, or *AV-bridge*, larger than a true capillary but resembling it in having no muscle tissue in its walls. The thoroughfare channels which may be as long as 1·5 mm lead

Fig. 11.20 Topographical view (approx. × 100) of a portion of capillary bed in the meso-appendix of a rat photographed during moderate hyperaemia to render visible most of the blood vessels in the field. Prominently displayed is the venule which drains this region. Two metarterioles, I and II, are shown, I starting at upper left and II at middle of right margin. Metarteriole I, along its course, gives off three precapillaries with sphincters, then passes down as the a-v capillary which gives off one precapillary at its right, and further

down receives, in succession, two post-capillaries. At lower left corner it joins with another a-v capillary to form the non-muscular venule. The venule courses up as a prominent vessel and passes out of the figure at the right after receiving several post-capillaries. The true capillaries carry the flow between pre- and post-capillaries. Metar-teriole II, shortly after appearing at the right of the figure, is connected with a neighbouring venule by a short anastomosing vessel vessel (A.V.A.) which may serve to short-circuit the blood of this region. (R. Chambers & B. W. Zweifach (1944) *American Journal of Anatomy*, **75**, 173–200.)

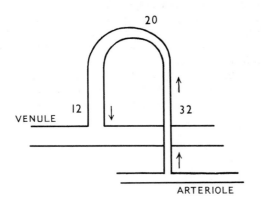

Fig. 11.21 Average pressures in mm Hg in a skin capillary in man. (*After* E. M. Landis (1930) *Heart*, 15 213.)

directly from arterioles to venules while the true capillaries, shorter in length, open from them and from the metarterioles and arterioles themselves. The true capillaries may be open or closed according to the needs of the tissue for at the origin of each capillary there is a *precapillary sphincter* by means of which blood flow through the capillary may be slowed or arrested. The precapillary sphincter is a functional one; anatomically it may only be represented by the last smooth muscle cells. The capillaries themselves are probably not contractile. In tissues such as muscle, which require a very variable blood flow, the proportion of true capillaries to thoroughfare channels is high (of the order of four to one) while in others, in which the flow is relatively much more constant, there is a higher proportion of thoroughfare channels. Certain organs, for example the nail bed and the renal glomerulus, have their own special capillary pattern. Whereas the arterioles are mainly under nervous control the more peripheral metarterioles are mainly, but not entirely, under hormonal control; the precapillary sphincters are almost entirely under hormonal control. It is thought that at rest the

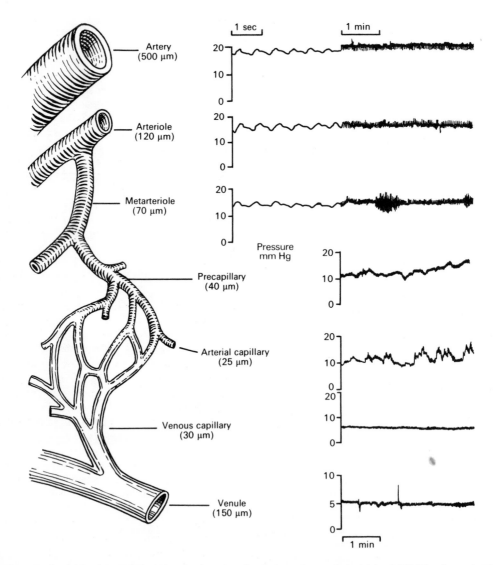

Fig. 11.22 Pressure records obtained at various points in the microcirculation. (C. A. Wiederhielm, J. W. Woodbury, S. Kirk & R. F. Rushmer (1964) *American Journal of Physiology*, **207**, 173.)

metabolic needs of a tissue can be met by exchange through thoroughfare channels and that when the tissue becomes active the precapillary sphincters open according to the metabolic needs.

Capillary pressure. Since the circulation of the blood depends on a pressure gradient the pressure in the capillaries must be lower than that in the smallest arteries and greater than that in the smaller veins (Fig. 11.13). The first satisfactory method of measuring intracapillary pressure was that devised by Landis in 1930. He inserted a micropipette with an aperture of about $10 \mu m$ into various parts of the capillary loops of the skin of the nail bed. The pipette, moved by a micromanipulator and observed through a binocular microscope, was connected by a system of tubes containing citrate solution to a mercury manometer. When the pipette was inserted into a capillary the pressure was adjusted until blood neither entered nor left the micropipette. This pressure was taken as the internal capillary pressure. The average pressure (Fig. 11.21, in the arterial limb was 32 mm Hg with a range of 21 to 44 mm Hg: the summit of the loop gave a mean pressure of 20 (range 15 to 32) and the venous end a mean of 12 mm Hg (range 6 to 18). There is thus a considerable gradient of pressure along the capillaries near the root of the nail. The pulse pressure at the arteriolar end of the loop was at least 5 to 10 mm Hg and at the venous end usually zero.

Because of the inertia of the mercury column, Landis's method can measure only mean pressure. Rapid fluctuations in capillary pressure can now be detected by inserting a microelectrode into a capillary and recording changes in its resistance. The microelectrode with a tip diameter of $0·5 \mu m$ is filled with NaCl solution (2 mol/l) which is a good electrical conductor. If the capillary pressure rises, plasma is forced up

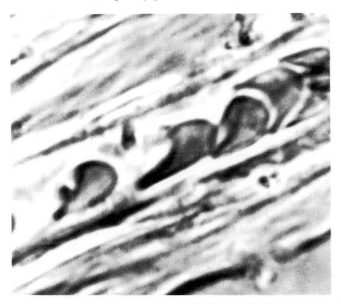

Fig. 11.23 Red cells in a mesenteric capillary of the dog: direction of flow left to right: rate of flow 1 mm per sec: magnification $\times 3000$: exposure time $5 \mu sec$. The red cells which are biconcave discs in the large vessels become paraboloid with a bell-shaped hollow in the capillaries. The leading part becomes convex and the trailing part becomes concave so that the shape resembles a thimble or parachute. Further details are to be found in M. M. Guest, T. P. Bond, R. G. Cooper & J. R. Derrick (1963) *Science, New York*, 142, 1319–1321. (*By courtesy of M. Mason Guest.*)

the tip of the microelectrode and increases its resistance. This system has a good frequency response and rapid fluctuations in capillary pressure can be recorded. The pressure fluctuations observed in the minute vessels of the frog's mesentery are shown in Figure 11.22.

Blood flow in capillaries. When the frog's tongue, lung, or web of the foot is observed under a microscope a network of vessels is seen. In the arterioles the red cells move forward in jerks corresponding to the beats of the heart but the pulsatile nature of the flow is lost in the capillaries unless there is peripheral vasodilatation. If the capillaries are narrow the red cells follow one another in single file and may become deformed (Fig. 11.23), but they recover their shape on reaching a wide vessel. The capillaries show great variations in calibre, with corresponding alterations in flow. In the venules the red blood cells pass along in a steady axial stream, leaving a clear peripheral stream of colourless plasma.

The capillaries in the nail bed of the human finger are easily observed under the microscope if the skin is illuminated by an oblique beam of light. A drop of oil makes the skin more translucent by replacing the air in the surface layers of the epidermis. The capillaries are of the order of $10 \mu m$ in diameter but the capillary loops vary greatly in size, in shape and in lumen, the venous side being usually much wider than the arterial side. Spontaneous alterations in the capillary diameter and the rate of flow of corpuscles occur often at the bases of the nail, and frequently in the back of the hand, capillaries opening and closing in the absence of any apparent stimulus. Thus although the pulsatile flow characteristic of the arterial system is absent in the capillaries the flow through these vessels is anything but continuous.

The velocity of blood flow in capillaries, about $0·5$ mm/sec, is about 1000 times lower than that in the aorta. This is because the total cross-sectional area of the capillary bed is so enormous. It is not because the capillaries offer very much resistance to flow. The slow flow in the capillaries provides a relatively long time for exchange to take place between the plasma and tissue fluid.

Capillary permeability. The rate at which fluid passes through the capillary membrane is determined not only by its permeability under different conditions but also by the pressure and flow within it. In defining capillary permeability it is necessary to know (a) the volume or mass of substances passing through (b) unit area in (c) unit time, under the influence of (d) unit hydrostatic or osmotic pressure (e) per unit thickness of membrane. Finally, the rate of fluid transfer is affected by the hydrostatic and osmotic pressures of the fluid outside the capillary. There are therefore considerable difficulties in the way of understanding the factors that govern the passage of materials across capillary walls, and it is seldom that all these factors are known.

Various possible routes across the capillary endothelium have been identified by electron microscopy including pinocytic vesicles, various types of fenestration and larger intercellular gaps. Fluids, ions, metabolites, proteins and even blood cells are known to cross the endothelium but there is no agreement about the exact route taken by each.

After injection of plasma dyed with sulfoflavin which has a high affinity for plasma proteins, fluorescence indicating the passage of protein is seen only at the venous end of long capillaries (11.24). This is not a contradiction of the Starling

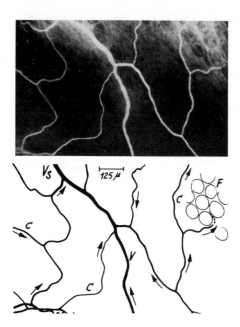

Fig. 11.24 Part of the capillary bed of the duodenal mesentery of a cat 10 minutes after the injection of albumin-conjugated fluorescein isothiocyanate. The dye escaped mainly from the venule V–V$_s$. F = fat globules. C = capillary. V$_s$ = collecting vein. (G. Hauck & H. Schröer (1969) Pflügers Archiv European Journal of Physiology, 312, 32–44).

hypothesis described in Chapter 16, which is concerned with the passage of small molecules. It is likely that there is an increase in the size of the pores, that is a 'gradient of permeability', from small arteries to small veins.

Normally there is a dynamic balance between loss of fluid from the capillaries and reabsorption into the capillaries and removal of excess by the lymphatics so that the fluid does not accumulate. If, however, the venous pressure is increased the balance is upset and fluid accumulates.

Tracer studies indicate that the quantities of fluid and dissolved substances that exchange across the capillary walls each day are enormous. It has been estimated that, in man, about 100 000 litres of fluid can pass out of and back into the vascular system every 24 hours. The bulk of this exchange is due to simple diffusion forces. The fluid exchange dependent on the hydrostatic and colloid osmotic pressure gradients and the lymphatic system accounts for only a tiny fraction (about one five-thousandth) of the total.

Capillary fragility. Capillary permeability and capillary fragility (or resistance) refer to different, and probably distinct, properties of the capillary wall. In clinical usage 'capillary fragility' refers to the production of minute haemorrhages (*petechiae*) in the skin when the capillary pressure has been raised in the forearm by the application of a venous occluding pressure to the upper arm by a sphygmomanometer cuff, or to the production of petechiae by the application of suction to the skin.

Landis has pointed out that frequently there is a striking lack of association between increased capillary permeability and

increased fragility. Thus, the oedema fluid of inflammation contains few red cells but a great deal of protein representing, therefore, a relatively pure increase in permeability. On the other hand, the petechiae that occur in certain blood diseases consist chiefly of red cells with little or no oedema fluid or protein.

Despite the fact that the walls of capillaries are so thin, they can withstand very large distending pressures. For example, when a person is standing without making rhythmical contractions of his leg muscles, the pressure in the capillaries in his feet rises to about 100 mm Hg. This is because of the hydrostatic effect of the column of blood above the feet. The law of Laplace explains why this pressure does not burst the capillaries. The tension in the wall of a cylindrical tube (T) depends on the pressure difference across the wall of the tube (P) and the radius of the tube (*r*), that is T = P*r*. In a capillary high internal pressures do not increase the wall tension very much because the radius is so small.

THE VEINS OR CAPACITY VESSELS

Veins have thinner walls, less elastic tissue and a larger internal diameter than the corresponding arteries and they are more easily distended than arteries (Fig. 11.3a). The valves made of folds of internal endothelium have already been described (p. 3). The veins have two main functions. They transport blood at high velocity and low energy cost from the tissues back to the heart. Secondly, by alterations of tone in the smooth muscle in their walls they adjust the capacity of the circulation to meet the blood volume and so regulate the filling pressure of the heart.

Venous Pressure

The venous pressure in man is best measured directly by connecting a long thin, flexible cannula, introduced into a vein, to a manometer filled with a solution of isotonic saline. Measurement of the hydrostatic pressure within a vein, say at the level of the elbow is of little value since the figure obtained depends on the position of the vein relative to the heart. If the arm is raised the pressure falls and if the arm is lowered it rises. The upper level of fluid in the manometer tube does, however, occupy a constant relation to the level of the heart, or to the sternal angle which is a convenient reference point whose relation to the heart is reasonably constant. Thus if there is no obstruction or constriction between the manometer tube and the right atrium the difference in level between the height of the meniscus and the sternal angle represents the pressure in the right atrium. As a rule this lies between zero and –2 cm of water but there is a great deal of individual variation in *central venous pressure*, values as high as 9 and 12 cm being found not infrequently in apparently healthy young men; values over 20 cm H$_2$O may be found in congestive heart failure. The pressure in the atria and in the great veins is not constant but varies with the cardiac cycle and with respiration. It also varies with the position of the patient, being somewhat higher if the patient is recumbent.

The internal jugular vein may be made to act as its own manometer since it usually has no functioning valves. The

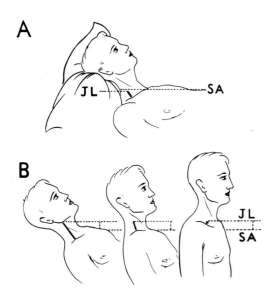

Fig. 11.25 The upper diagram, A, represents the level of blood in the internal jugular vein when the subject is lying with the head supported on pillows. The upper level of the column of blood in the jugular vein (JL) lies a little below the level of the sternal angle (SA). In the lower diagram, B, the upper level of the column of blood in the internal jugular vein is above the sternal angle, indicating an increase of venous pressure. Note that as the position of the patient alters the upper level of the column of blood occupies different positions in the neck although its relation to the sternal angle remains the same. (T. Lewis (1949) *Diseases of the Heart*, London: Macmillan.)

vessel collapses at the point at which the external pressure (that is the atmospheric pressure) is greater than the internal pressure (the venous blood pressure). The upper level of the column of blood in the internal jugular vein is identified by the upper level of outward venous pulsation and is conventionally measured from a horizontal plane passing through the sternal angle (Fig. 11.25) which is arbitrarily taken as the reference point. With the patient propped up, his head supported on a pillow, the level is from 0 to 3 cm above this line and the venous pressure is said to be, therefore 0 to -3 cm (of blood). Higher values are found when the heart is failing or when the blood volume is much increased. The use in this way of the external jugular vein as a manometer is unreliable.

The venous pressure in the superficial veins of the dorsum of the foot with the subject erect and motionless is from 70 to 100 mm Hg, which is the same as the calculated hydrostatic pressure from the right atrium. On exercise, owing to the action of the muscle pump (p. 164), the reading falls to less than 30 mm Hg. If, however, the leg veins are varicose, with incompetent valves, there may be little difference between the readings during exercise and at rest.

Venous Pulse

At rest the flow of blood in the larger veins is continuous except near the heart. The variations of atrial pressure usually pass back a short way into the great veins near the heart since they are not equipped with valves. A volume pulsation at the

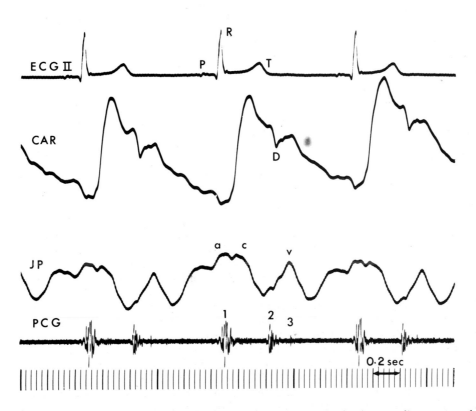

Fig. 11.26 Simultaneous records from a normal male aged 22 years. From above downwards: electrocardiogram (standard lead II) (ECG II), external carotid arteriogram (CAR), jugular phlebogram (JP) and apical phonocardiogram (PCG). D marks the dicrotic notch, *a, c, v* the three main peaks of the phlebogram. 1, 2, 3 First, second and third heart sounds.

root of the neck in the internal jugular vein is therefore often seen in normal people. The pulsations of the internal jugular vein, which lies deep to the sternomastoid muscle, are seen as lateral, not as vertical movements. The venous pulse can be recorded by placing a metal cup on the right side of the neck above the sternal end of the clavicle. A rubber tube leads from the cup to a membrane manometer and a suitable recorder. Such a record is shown in Figure 11.26; it cannot be fully analysed unless either an electrocardiogram or a record of the arterial pulse is made simultaneously.

In the venous pulse there are three positive waves during each cardiac cycle. The *a* wave is produced by atrial systole. It is replaced by a rapid fluttering movement when the atria flutter and disappears when they fibrillate (p. 170). The *a* wave becomes more prominent when the pressure in the right side of the heart is raised because of valvular disease or chronic lung disease, and is very prominent should the right atrium contract against a closed tricuspid valve as sometimes happens with complete heart block. The *a* wave is followed shortly by the *c* wave. In the jugular pulse this is a disturbance imparted to the recording apparatus by the pulse in the underlying carotid artery. Some time later the *v* wave appears. This is due to the gradual increase of venous pressure during ventricular systole and the summit of the *v* wave is coincident with the opening of the mitral and tricuspid valves. The first negative wave, between *a* and *c*, is the result of atrial diastole. The trough between *c* and *v* is produced by descent of the heart during ventricular systole and the third negative wave (after *v*) is due to the sudden release of pressure in the veins as the tricuspid valve opens.

The tracing of the jugular pulse in Figure 11.26 should be compared with the record of the changes in intra-atrial pressure obtained from a manometer communicating directly with the interior of the right atrium (Fig. 10.37).

Veins as Transport Vessels

After passing slowly through the capillaries the blood speeds up as it passes through the venules and veins because the total cross-sectional area of the venous bed is so much smaller than that of the capillaries. The blood is transported from the periphery to the heart with very little expenditure of energy. The pressure gradient of about 10 mm Hg is enough to return blood from a small vein in the arm to the right atrium because the veins offer very little resistance to blood flow.

Gravity can affect the transport function of the veins. Above heart level, gravity aids the return of blood to the heart. Below heart level the hydrostatic pressure of the dependent blood tends to distend the venous system. The tendency to impair the venous return to the heart is counteracted by the muscle pump. When muscles in the leg contract they compress the veins lying in the fascial planes between them. Because of the system of valves the blood is normally driven towards the heart.

Veins as Capacity Vessels

The volume of blood accommodated in veins depends very much on the pressure gradient across their walls (*transmural pressure*). Small changes in transmural pressure can produce large changes in the internal dimensions of veins. When the transmural pressure is low, for example below 5 mm Hg, the venous lumen appears on cross-section as a flattened ellipse and holds little or no blood. With modest increases in transmural pressure, the venous cross-section becomes more and more circular and its capacity rises rapidly (Fig. 11.3a). Further increases in transmural pressure when the cross-section has become circular cause little further increase in capacity; at this stage the venous walls are quite stiff.

Although the veins are easily distensible and have little muscle in their walls they should not be thought of as simple inert tubes. They have a resting tone and are capable of constriction and dilatation, in part governed by baroceptor reflexes from the aorta and right atrium and in part, as during exercise, by chemical substances in the blood. Venoconstriction is produced by a rise in venous pressure in the right side of the heart seen in cardiac failure or induced by the Valsalva manoeuvre (p. 163) or by a fall in arterial blood pressure. Both adrenaline and noradrenaline constrict veins. When the effective blood volume is reduced by approximately 500 ml, either by removing this quantity of blood or by inflating cuffs round the thighs, the hand volume decreases and the distensibility of the hand vessels, mainly veins, decreases. If the changes occur generally in the body they would be useful since they tend to reduce the amount of blood in the vascular dead space of the veins and so maintain the central venous pressure in spite of the reduction in blood volume.

Barcroft H (ed) 1963 Peripheral circulation in man. British Medical Bulletin 19: 97–162

Bevan J A, Godfraind T, Maxwell R A, Vanhoutte P M (eds) 1979 Vascular neuroeffector mechanisms. Raven Press, New York

Cliff W J 1976 Blood vessels. University Press, Cambridge

Florey, Lord 1968 The missing link. The structure of some types of capillary. Quarterly Journal of Experimental Physiology 53: 1–5

Folkow B, Neil E 1971 Circulation. Oxford University Press, London

Gauer O H, Thron H L 1962 Properties of veins *in vivo*: integrated effects of their smooth muscle. Physiological Reviews 42: Suppl 5, 283–327

Grayson J, Zingg W 1976 Microcirculation Vols 1 and 2. Plenum Press, New York

McCally M 1967 The effect of weightlessness. Science Journal 3: 39–43

McDonald D A 1974 Blood flow in arteries, 2nd edn. Arnold, London

Marks J, Birkett D A, Shuster S 1972 'Capillary permeability' in patients with collagen vascular diseases. British Medical Journal, i, 782–784

Mellander S, Johannson B 1968 Control of resistance exchange in capacitance functions in the peripheral circulation. Pharmacological Reviews 20: 117–196

Merrill E W 1969 Rheology of blood. Physiological Reviews 49: 862–888

Roberts C (ed) 1972 Blood flow measurement. Sector Publishing, London

Russell W J 1974 Central venous pressure: its clinical use and role in cardiovascular dynamics. Butterworth, London

Shepherd J T, Vanhoutte P M 1975 Veins and their control. Saunders, London
Spector W G (ed) 1964 The acute inflammatory response. Annals of the New York Academy of Sciences 116: 747–1084
Wells R 1973 The microcirculation in clinical medicine. Academic Press, London and New York
Wood J E 1965 The veins. Churchill, London
Zweifach B W 1973 Microcirculation. Annual Review of Physiology 35: 117–150

12   Vasomotor Control

Just as the activity of the heart is modified by local, humoral and nervous factors, so is that of the blood vessels. The behaviour of blood vessels is usually modified by contraction or relaxation of the smooth muscle in their walls. Sometimes other mechanical factors may influence behaviour but active control of the smooth muscle is thought to be the most important mechanism. However, just as vessels differ in structure and function, the regulatory mechanisms controlling all types of blood vessel are not identical. It is therefore best to think in terms of the regulatory systems for each variety of blood vessel, the damping, resistance, exchange and capacity vessels.

CONTROL OF THE RESISTANCE VESSELS

Although all blood vessels offer some resistance to the flow of blood, the main resistance lies in the small arteries and arterioles (p. 179). These vessels are controlled by the local action of chemical or physical factors, hormones circulating in the blood or by the autonomic nerves which supply them. Although changes in the calibre of resistance vessels tend to change the pressure levels and gradients in the circulation, the main effect is on blood flow. Blood flow to any tissue is normally regulated by local factors to serve the needs of that tissue but it may be subordinated to supply the needs of the entire body by hormonal or nervous factors.

Local Control

Effect of metabolites. Figure 12.1 shows schematically the effect of temporary occlusion of blood flow in a limb on resistance blood vessels. On release of the occlusion the blood flow is raised well above the resting level and then gradually returns towards the resting level. The increase in blood flow after occlusion is known as *reactive hyperaemia*. The excess blood flow after release is sometimes referred to as the *blood flow repayment* for the *blood flow debt* incurred during occlusion. Though there is not a precise relationship, the bigger the debt incurred, the bigger the repayment made. Increasing the period of occlusion tends to increase both the intensity and duration of the reactive hyperaemia. This phenomenon is confined to those tissues whose circulation has been reduced. It is not mediated by vasomotor nerves since it is unaffected by severance of the autonomic nerves to the limb.

A similar increase in blood flow is seen after a period of exercise in a limb. When the exercise stops the blood flow is increased greatly above the resting level and then falls in an exponential fashion towards the resting level. This phenomenon is called *exercise hyperaemia*. Like reactive hyperaemia it is confined to the exercising tissues and still occurs after section of the autonomic nerves to the tissue. The intensity of the exercise hyperaemia is related to the severity and duration of the exercise.

In both exercise and reactive hyperaemia, the increase in blood flow is thought to be due to an increased concentration of metabolites in the tissues which can cause blood vessels to dilate. In the case of circulatory arrest, metabolism continues to produce metabolites even when the blood flow is stopped. So the concentration of metabolites, and hence the vasodilatation in the tissue, increases with an increase in the period of circulatory arrest. When the circulation is re-established, the increased blood flow through the dilated vessels washes away the metabolites in an exponential fashion until their concentration in the tissues, and hence the blood flow, has returned to normal. The increase in blood flow that occurs in muscles during exercise is not adequate to supply the needs of the increased metabolism. Metabolites therefore accumulate in the tissues and the resulting vasodilatation is responsible for the hyperaemia which follows exercise. When the raised blood flow has cleared the excess of metabolites the blood flow returns to normal.

It is the local control of resistance blood vessels by metabolites which ensures that the blood supply to tissues is precisely regulated to meet their metabolic needs. If heart muscle has to do more work, the increased local metabolism that this entails increases the local production of metabolites and hence local coronary blood flow. The parts of the heart muscle which experience the greatest increases in work get the greatest increases in blood flow. The occurrence of metabolic

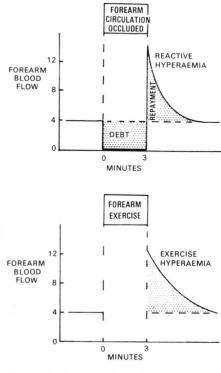

Fig. 12.1   Change in forearm blood flow (ml/100 ml/min) after occlusion of the circulation (above) and exercise of the forearm muscles (below) (*By courtesy of I. C. Roddie.*)

hyperaemia is most evident in tissues such as muscle and liver where blood flow is mianly determined by metabolic needs. In tissues, such as skin and kidney, where blood flow is related to functions other than metabolism, metabolic hyperaemia is less evident.

There is still no agreement about the metabolic factors responsible for dilating the blood vessels. Among those suggested are carbon dioxide and hydrogen ion excess, oxygen lack, potassium excess, an increase in the osmolality of the local tissue fluids, adenosine triphosphate, adenosine, phosphate and bradykinin. All can dilate blood vessels; some, such as adenosine triphosphate and bradykinin, do so strongly and others, such as potassium and phosphate, weakly. It is likely that most of the above substances contribute to metabolic hyperaemia, the contribution of any particular substance varying in different tissues and under different conditions. Oxygen lack seems to be particularly important in regulating myocardial blood flow whereas carbon dioxide tension seems to have an important influence in the regulation of cerebral blood flow (Chap. 19).

Effect of local temperature. If the hand or foot is put into warm water at 45°C the blood flow through the part increases several fold. The increase is local, being restricted to the part that is immersed. It is independent of the autonomic nerve supply since it can occur even if the part is denervated. This vasodilatation serves to protect the extremity from the damaging effect of heat. If the extremity is immersed in water at 45°C with the circulation occluded, it becomes painful as the tissue temperature rises. The vasodilatation that normally occurs tends to keep the tissues relatively cool by increasing their perfusion with blood at central body temperature. Since heat causes vasodilatation in denervated tissues it is likely that its effect is a direct local one on the smooth muscle in the wall of the resistance vessel. In intact tissues the stimulating effect of heat on local tissue metabolism may contribute to the dilatation.

The immersion of an extremity in moderately cold water normally causes vasoconstriction which reduces the loss of heat from the blood to the environment. In people whose limbs are exposed to cold water for prolonged periods, say after shipwreck, the prolonged decrease in blood flow may lead to local tissue death (necrosis) in the toes and feet (immersion foot syndrome).

An extremity exposed to near freezing temperatures, for example 0 to 4°C, shows a characteristic pattern of events (Fig. 12.2). The local blood flow falls to about zero initially and the part becomes painful. Blood flow then starts to rise rapidly to a value well above the resting level. At this time pain disappears.

After another short interval flow falls again and pain reappears. This cyclic pattern of blood flow persists while the immersion in ice continues. It is referred to as *cold vasodilatation*, and is a 'hunting reaction'.

This vasodilatation may be elicited locally in the fingers, toes, ears and the tip of the nose, parts which are particularly rich in A-V anastomoses. It does not depend on an intact nerve supply but the exact mechanism underlying it is not fully understood. Its effect is clearly protective since it tends to prevent tissue damage due to freezing of the extremities.

Effect of transmural pressure. The pressure difference across the wall of a blood vessel is measured by subtracting the external tissue pressure from the intravascular pressure. It is referred to as the *transmural pressure*. Changes in transmural pressure cause local changes in the resistance vessels.

As the transmural pressure in the vessels rises, one would expect the resistance vessels to dilate due to distension and the blood flow to increase. However, as Figure 12.3 shows schematically, this expectation is not fulfilled. If the arterial pressure is raised above the normal value of about 100 mm Hg, blood flow rises only very slowly until, at a high critical pressure, it rises sharply. The fact that flow does not change very much when the pressure is raised suggests that the increase in transmural pressure elicits an increase in vascular resistance. The large increase in flow at very high pressures is thought to be due to the distending forces overcoming the vasoconstrictor response.

If the pressure is lowered below normal, the blood flow at first does not fall proportionately; this indicates that a fall in transmural pressure decreases the vascular resistance. How-

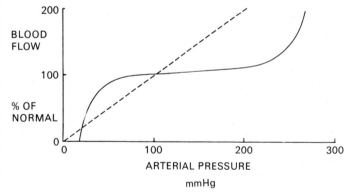

Fig. 12.3 The effect of arterial pressure on blood flow. The broken line shows the relationship which would be expected if the blood vessels behaved as rigid tubes. (*By courtesy of I. C. Roddie.*)

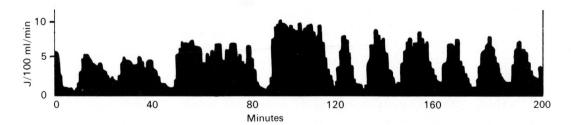

Fig. 12.2   The heat loss in J/100 ml tissue/min from the right index finger to water at 0 to 6°C. The black area represents the heat loss from the circulating blood. Pain was felt when heat loss was at a minimum (*After* A. D. M. Greenfield, J. T. Shepherd & R. F. Whelan (1951) *Irish Journal of Medical Science,* **309**, 415.)

ever, at very low perfusion pressures the flow stops even while there is still a positive perfusion pressure head. This closure of the vessels below a certain critical transmural pressure has been referred to as *critical closure* by Burton who predicted such instability at low pressure values from the law of Laplace.

The diagram also shows that over a very wide range of perfusion pressures the blood flow is relatively independent of the pressure head. This phenomenon, referred to as *auto-regulation,* is seen to some extent in most vascular beds but is a marked feature in kidney, brain and muscle. It is a useful phenomenon since it tends to keep blood flow to an organ fairly constant despite fluctuations in blood pressure provided its metabolic requirements do not change.

A number of mechanisms have been suggested to account for autoregulation. According to the *myogenic theory* a rise in transmural pressure tends to stretch the walls of the resistance vessels. Smooth muscle is excited by stretching and responds by contracting. The resulting vasoconstriction increases vascular resistance and limits the tendency for flow to increase. The converse reaction would explain the decrease in resistance when transmural pressure is lowered. A second possible mechanism is contained in the *tissue pressure theory.* In an encapsulated organ such as the kidney a rise in transmural pressure would result in a rise in tissue fluid formation. The accumulation of tissue fluid would increase tissue pressure and result in a mechanical compression of the resistance vessels. This would also tend to limit the increase in blood flow when transmural pressure rises. A third possibility is contained in the *tissue metabolite theory.* The increase in blood flow resulting from a rise in transmural pressure would tend to wash away local metabolites and reduce the metabolite concentration in the tissues. This in turn would cause vasoconstriction and so limit the increase in blood flow.

It is likely that all these mechanisms contribute to different degrees to the autoregulation seen in different tissues.

Effect of oxygen partial pressure in pulmonary alveoli. As mentioned earlier oxygen lack may cause vasodilatation. In the myocardium oxygen lack seems to be the most important factor in the coronary vasodilator response to an increase in myocardial work. When the pressure of oxygen in the alveoli of one part of the lungs falls, vasoconstriction occurs in the blood vessels perfusing that part. In this situation hypoxia acts as a vasoconstrictor agent. This response ensures that blood is not sent to poorly ventilated alveoli and so helps to maintain the normal ventilation to perfusion ratio in the lungs. It may also contribute to pulmonary arterial hypertension in people with chronic lung disease. (See also p. 218).

Nervous Control

Vasoconstrictor nerves. These are nerves, which, when stimulated, cause blood vessels to constrict. Impulses reaching their nerve terminals release noradrenaline which excites the smooth muscle in the walls of the blood vessel.

The existence of a nervous control of the blood vessels was first shown in 1852 by the French physiologist Claude Bernard who cut the cervical sympathetic nerve in the neck of a rabbit and found that the blood vessels in the ear of the same side became dilated and the ear became warmer. Since electrical stimulation of the end of this nerve going to the ear caused a constriction of the vessels and a lowering of the temperature of the ear the blood vessels must normally have been kept constricted by impulses continually passing along the nerve.

The central origin of the vasoconstrictor nerve impulses can be traced in animals by making sections through the brain stem at various levels, starting at the cranial end and gradually passing caudad. A large number of cells and fibres in the medulla are concerned with the transmission of impulses to blood vessels and this area is, therefore, called for convenience the *vasomotor centre.* Afferent impulses are constantly reaching the vasomotor centre from all parts of the body, especially from the pressor receptors in the carotid sinus and aortic arch and from the cardiac and respiratory centres in the medulla itself; efferent impulses are thus initiated or modified and appropriate adjustments made in the circulatory system via the sympathetic nervous system. In disease of the afferent nervous system, as for example in the neuropathy of diabetes mellitus, reflex alterations of vascular tone may be disturbed.

The vasoconstrictor impulses pass down from the medulla into the cord and leave by the thoracic and upper lumbar nerves since electrical stimulation of the anterior spinal roots of the thoracic and upper lumbar part of the cord, or of the corresponding white rami communicantes, or of any of the sympathetic nerves arising from them, causes a vasoconstriction in the area supplied.

The fibres leave the lateral horn of the grey matter in the anterior (ventral) root, passing by way of the white ramus communicans to the sympathetic ganglion (*preganglionic fibres*) (Fig. 25.2). Here new fibres (*postganglionic fibres*) arise, some going straight to the main blood vessels, others returning to the mixed spinal nerves, to be carried in them to the blood vessels in the periphery.

If the sympathetic nerves to the extremities of man are cut, the blood flow through the extremities increases. This increase is most marked in the skin of the hands and feet, but is also transiently seen in the skeletal muscles of the forearm and calf. It can be concluded that the blood vessels of these parts are normally subjected to considerable vasoconstrictor tone. It also follows that blood flow to these parts may be increased by release of vasoconstrictor tone.

The frequency of impulses in vasoconstrictor nerves is usually quite low compared with that in somatic motor fibres. It has been shown that almost complete vasoconstriction is produced when vasoconstrictor nerves are stimulated at rates of about 8 impulses per second. The resting level of vasoconstrictor tone could be mimicked by about 1 impulse per second. In somatic fibres, maximum contractions of skeletal muscle are achieved with impulse frequencies of about 50 per second.

Vasodilator nerves. These are nerves which, when stimulated, cause dilatation of the blood vessels they innervate. They are thought to do this by releasing acetylcholine at their nerve endings. Vasodilator nerve fibres occur in both sympathetic and parasympathetic systems.

Stimulation of the following parasympathetic nerves produces vasodilatation in the part supplied: chorda tympani to the submandibular gland, small petrosal nerve to the parotid gland, lingual nerve to the tongue and the pelvic splanchnic nerves to the external genitalia. The nerves to the salivary glands might not be regarded as true vasodilators since vasodilatation may be brought about by bradykinin.

After a muscle has been treated with atropine to make its blood vessels insensitive to acetylcholine, stimulation of the vasodilator nerves to that muscle is without effect. However, atropinization of the muscles in a limb of an intact animal does not reduce the limb blood flow. This shows that vasodilator fibres, unlike vasoconstrictor fibres, are not tonically active under normal circumstances. They appear to be brought into action whenever the need for them arises.

Vasomotor Reflexes

These permit the general circulatory requirements of the body to override the local requirements of the tissues. Though in some reflexes the effects may be fairly well localized, in most cases their effects are seen throughout the body. Vasomotor reflexes are most evident in those tissues such as skin, muscle and gut where the blood supply can be restricted without an immediate severe threat to the tissue. The flow through some tissues, such as the heart and the brain, that cannot tolerate prolonged restriction of flow is only partly controlled by vasomotor nerves (see p. 169 and Chap. 19). Hundreds of vasomotor reflexes have been described but only some of the more important ones that can be elicited in man are described below.

Thermoregulatory reflexes. When a subject is heated by immersing his legs in warm water, the blood flow to his hands increases. This is reflexly mediated by release of sympathetic vasoconstrictor tone since it does not occur if the sympathetic nerves to the hand are cut or if the vasoconstrictor fibres are selectively blocked (Fig. 12.4). A similar release of vasoconstrictor tone occurs in the other extremities, such as the ears, nose and lips. Vasodilatation also occurs in the skin of other parts of the body but this is the result of activity in the

sympathetic cholinergic nerves which supply the sweat glands in these parts. The dilatation may be secondary to the release of bradykinin-forming enzyme by these active glands. Reflex visodilatation in response to body heating is not seen in vascular beds such as muscle which lie deep to the skin. Skin vasodilatation, by raising skin temperature, normally leads to increased heat loss from the body.

The co-ordinating centres for these reflexes are thought to lie in the hypothalamus (Chap. 26). The centres are controlled not only by changes in the temperature of the blood impinging upon them but also by afferent impulses travelling from thermoreceptors in the heated parts. The introduction of warm saline into the internal carotid artery causes reflex vasodilatation in the skin. However, if, in the experiment described in the previous paragraph, blood warmed in the legs is prevented from passing to the brain by inflating cuffs on the thighs the reflex vasodilatation in the hand is reduced but not abolished. This suggests that the residual vasodilatation in the hand results from impulses arising from temperature receptors in the heated skin.

If the body is cooled a reflex increase in vasoconstrictor tone occurs in most of the skin areas of the body. The vasconstriction, by decreasing skin temperature and therefore the temperature gradient between the body and the environment, helps the body conserve heat (see also Chap. 26).

Blood shift reflexes. Many stimuli, which have in common the effect of shifting blood towards or away from the chest, can produce reflex alterations in vasoconstrictor tone. These reflex changes are most evident in the blood vessels of the muscles. Tilting a person into the foot-down position, the application of negative pressure to the lower part of the body, breathing at positive pressure (Fig. 12.5) and the Valsalva manoeuvre all tends to shift blood away from the chest towards the feet. These stimuli are associated with a reflex increase in vasoconstrictor tone in muscle blood vessels. Tilting a person into the foot-up position, the application of positive pressure to the lower limbs and squatting, all tend to move blood

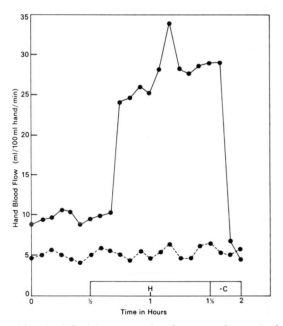

Fig. 12.4 Blood flow in a normal and a sympathectomized hand during body heating. H represents time during which feet were in hot water (45°C); C represents time during which feet were in cold water (12 to 16°C). (G. T. C. Hamilton (1947) *Ulster Medical Journal*, 16, 18–26.)

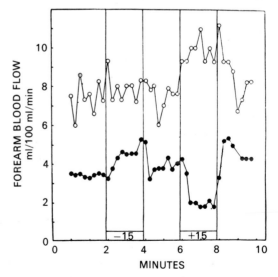

Fig. 12.5 Blood flow in normal (●) and nerve-blocked (○) forearms during pressure breathing. During the two periods indicated, the subject breathed air at pressures 15 mm Hg below and 15 mm Hg above atmospheric pressure, respectively. (D. A. Blair, W. E. Grover & B. S. L. Kidd (1959) *Clinical Science*, 18, 9.)

towards the chest and result in reflex vasodilatation. The efferent limb of these reflexes is composed of sympathetic vasoconstrictor fibres. The reflex changes are not seen in sympathectomized tissues. Neither the location nor the nature of the receptors concerned in the afferent limb of the reflexes is known. The receptors may be one of the large number of stretch receptors that have been identified in the walls of the low pressure vessels in the thorax. They are not thought to be the baroreceptors in the arterial system, since alteration of the activity in these does not have much effect on vasoconstrictor tone in man. When the blood pressure at the carotid sinus is altered in man the changes in blood flow in the limbs are small and can be explained by the changes that occur in arterial pressure (Fig. 12.6). However, in animals such as the dog arterial baroreceptor stimulation does lead to reflex alterations in vasoconstrictor tone. This species difference may be an expression of the very different gravitational stresses experienced by the circulations of man and dogs.

Chemoreceptor reflexes. As mentioned earlier the direct effect of carbon dioxide on the blood vessels is to dilate them. However, when carbon dioxide is breathed by man in high concentration a reflex increase in peripheral vascular resistance occurs in the muscles. This is mediated by way of sympathetic vasoconstrictor fibres. If these fibres are blocked, peripheral vasodilatation occurs when high concentrations of carbon dioxide are breathed. Carbon dioxide is thought to act directly on the vasomotor centre in the medulla but it probably acts on the peripheral chemoreceptors also. Severe oxygen lack also produces some reflex increase in peripheral resistance (Fig. 12.7) but its effect is small relative to that of carbon dioxide.

Exercise reflexes. When a subject exercises his muscles, strong local vasodilatation is brought about by metabolities in the active muscles. However, in other tissues, such as the muscles which are not taking part in the exercise, there is a

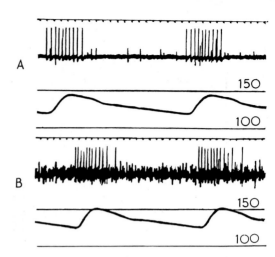

Fig. 12.7 Cat. Thiopentone anaesthesia. Right carotid sinus nerve cut centrally and a thin slip laid on saline wick electrodes. Action potentials recorded on oscillograph via resistance-capacity coupled amplifier. Blood pressure recorded from femoral artery by condenser manometer. Records from above downwards: time trace 20 msec, electroneurogram of this slip of sinus nerve, blood pressure. Calibration lines for pressures of 150 and 100 mm Hg are shown. A = Cat breathing air spontaneously. B = Cat breathing 10 per cent. O_2 in N_2 spontaneously. The large spikes, about 7 mm in the diagram, are baroreceptor discharges; the smaller (2 mm) spikes are chemoreceptor discharges. Note the increase in chemoreceptor activity during hypoxia. (C. Heymans & E. Neil (1958) *Reflexogenic Areas of the Cardiovascular System*. London: Churchill.)

reflex vasoconstriction. Figure 12.8 shows the changes which occurred when a subject exercised his legs on a bicycle ergometer. Blood pressure and heart rate rose. Blood flow rose in the forearm, whose sympathetic nerves had been blocked, probably because the increase in the arterial blood pressure drove more blood through the tissue. However, in the normally innervated forearm, the blood flow fell slightly in spite of the rise in mean arterial pressure. This showed that the peripheral vascular resistance in the forearm rose reflexly during leg exercise. This reflex helps to redistribute blood from the non-active to the active muscles during exercise. The efferent limb of the reflex consists of sympathetic vasoconstrictor fibres but the nature and location of the receptors on the afferent limb and the reflex centre are not known.

If all the sympathetic vasoconstrictor fibres are blocked pharmacologically, exercise cannot be sustained for very long. The peripheral vasodilatation produced by the exercise results in such a fall in total peripheral resistance that the arterial pressure falls dramatically and unconsciousness ensues.

Emotional stress reflexes. When a subject is frightened or given difficult mental arithmetic to do, vasodilatation occurs in muscle tissue (Fig. 12.9). This response is reduced or abolished by blocking the sympathetic nerves supplying the tissue and by atropine. These results indicate that sympathetic cholinergic vasodilator nerves are involved in the response. It is likely also that adrenaline released from the adrenal medulla contributes to the response. Cholinergic vasodilator fibres to skeletal muscle blood vessels have been described in animals but the adequate stimulus for their reflex excitation has not been identified. They are not involved in the reflex responses to baroreceptor stimulation. However, stimulation through

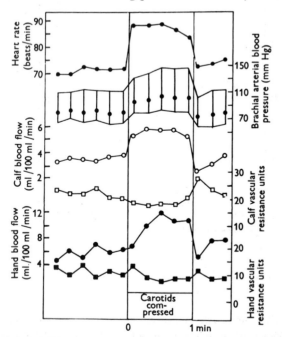

Fig. 12.6 The effect of bilateral carotid artery compression on heart rate, brachial arterial pressure, and blood flow, and resistance to flow in the calf and the hand. (I. C. Roddie & J. T. Shepherd (1957) *Journal of Physiology*, 139, 381.)

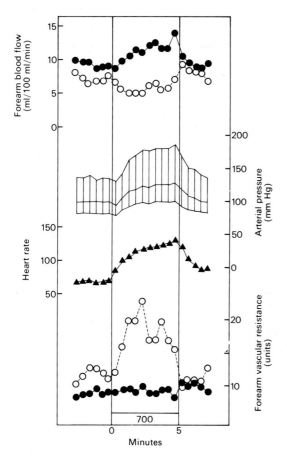

Fig. 12.8 The effect of deep nerve block on forearm blood flow and forearm vascular resistance during 5 min leg exercise. Nerve-blocked forearm (●); normal forearm (○); heart rate (▲). The rectangle represents the period of leg exercise. The increase in oxygen consumption above the resting level during exercise was 700 ml. (D. A. Blair, W. E. Glover & I. C. Roddie (1961) *Circulation Research*, 9, 264–274.)

electrodes implanted in the hypothalamus in cats in areas which excite 'flight or fight' responses also excite the sympathetic cholinergic vasodilator pathway. This suggests that, as in man, these fibres are involved in the muscle vasodilatation accompanying stressful situations. It is interesting in this respect that vasodilator fibres to muscle seem to be involved in the vasodilatation in muscle seen during fainting (Fig. 12.19).

Lung inflation reflexes. Taking a deep breath causes a reflex vasoconstriction in the skin of the peripheral parts in man. It does not occur if the sympathetic fibres have been severed (Fig. 12.10). In fact, a large number of relatively trivial stimuli, such as a sudden noise, a pinch or the inflation of a cuff on an arm, can cause well marked reflex vasoconstrictions in the hand. The muscle blood vessels are not involved in these responses. Some of these responses form part of the alerting reaction in man but their physiological significance is obscure.

Hormonal Control

Compared with the local and nervous control of resistance vessels, hormonal control is relatively unimportant. Some of the more important humoral agents which affect resistance vessels are mentioned below.

Adrenaline and noradrenaline. When the splanchnic nerves are stimulated the initial rise of blood pressure is probably due to vasoconstriction in the abdominal organs. This is followed about half a minute later by a second rise due to the liberation of adrenaline and noradrenaline from the adrenal medulla. A similar effect to this will be described in asphyxia (p. 231). Again, when the pressure in the carotid sinus is reduced the rise of arterial blood pressure which follows is due partly to the reflex activity of the vasoconstrictor nerves and partly to liberation of adrenaline and noradrenaline. Liberation of these hormones also occurs in flight or fight reactions or when the subject is exposed to emotional stress.

When it is injected intravenously into an animal adrenaline produces an immediate and transient fall of arterial pressure at once succeeded by a sudden rise. The increase in blood pressure lasts but a few minutes. Adrenaline causes constriction in the cutaneous and other vessels; however, at the same time the blood vessels of the skeletal muscles dilate so that the total peripheral resistance is slightly lowered (Figs 12.11 and 12.12). The increased cardiac output must therefore be responsible for the rise in systolic pressure; the mean blood pressure may not be altered.

Injection of noradrenaline is not followed by an initial fall in arterial pressure and the rise in systolic pressure is greater than

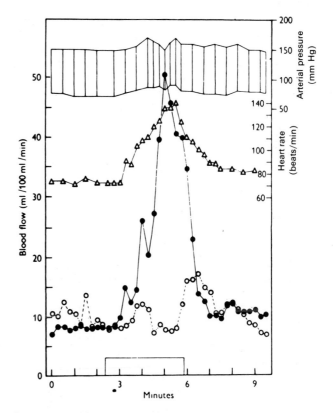

Fig. 12.9 Results showing that active cholinergic vasodilator nerves to human muscle contribute to the vasodilatation in the forearm muscles during stress. ○, hand blood flow; ●, forearm blood flow; △, heart rate. During the time represented by the rectangle it was suggested to the subject that he was suffering from severe blood loss. (D. A. Blair, W. E. Glover, A. D. M. Greenfield & I. C. Roddie (1959) *Journal of Physiology*, 148, 633.)

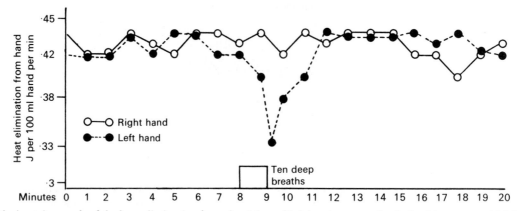

Fig. 12.10 Calorimetric records of the heat elimination from the right and left hands separately of a healthy man aged 38. Before the record began the median and ulnar nerves on the right side had been infiltrated with procaine. Beginning at the eighth minute as indicated by the open rectangle the subject took ten deep breaths, following which the heat elimination from the left hand fell, indicating vasoconstriction. The absence of vasoconstriction in the right (blocked) hand shows that this is mediated through efferent nerves.

that after adrenaline. In spite of the reduction in cardiac output brought about through the aortic and carotid sinus reflexes the mean blood pressure rises. Noradrenaline is therefore a general vasoconstrictor (Fig. 12.11), and may be used as such in clinical medicine. The α and β receptors, on which adrenaline and noradrenaline act, are described in Chapter 25.

Noradrenaline is normally present in the walls of the arteries and veins, and in the heart; the aorta of the rabbit, for example, contains an average amount of $0\cdot5$ μg per gram. The noradrenaline in the walls of vessels is thought to lie in stores associated with vasoconstrictor nerve endings. These stores are mobilized when the constrictor nerves are stimulated, and can be depleted by certain drugs, such as reserpine, that can be used in the treatment of high blood pressure in man. Certain substances such as nicotine, and (in the presence of atropine) acetylcholine, cause vasoconstriction in the vessels of the rabbit ear. This vasoconstriction is due to the release of noradrenaline from the artery wall, since it does not occur in the ears of rabbits treated with reserpine.

Angiotensin. The octapeptide angiotensin II (Chap. 15) produces generalized vasoconstriction and thus increases arterial pressure. It also stimulates the production of aldosterone (Chap. 28) and therefore tends to increase the volume of the extracellular fluid and the blood volume.

Kinins. A number of peptides are powerful vasodilators. Bradykinin (Chap. 28) formed during the active secretion of sweat and salivary glands enormously increases the blood flow in these secreting tissues. The intra-arterial injection of as little as $0\cdot01$ μg may, and $0\cdot1$ μg always does, increase the blood flow in the forearm (muscle blood flow) or in the hand (blood flow through the skin); intravenous infusion of bradykinin produces large increases in blood flow in both forearm and hand and a visible flushing of the face. On a molar basis, bradykinin (mol. wt. 1934) is the most active substance known to produce vasodilatation in man. The kinins may take part in the vasodilatation associated with the activity of all tissues, not only glandular tissues.

Histamine has very pronounced effects on the circulation. When injected intra-arterially or intravenously it causes vasodilatation of the resistance vessels, flushing of the skin and a fall in arterial pressure. It also increases the permeability of the capillaries which then permit loss of protein and fluid from the circulation (see also Chap. 28).

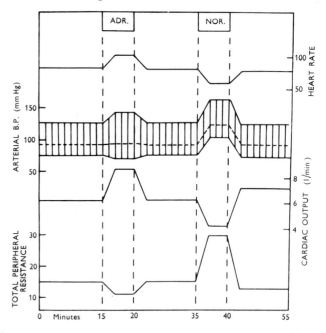

Fig. 12.11 The effects of intravenous infusions of adrenaline and noradrenaline on heart rate, arterial blood pressure, cardiac output and total peripheral resistance. (The initial transient drop in blood pressure that occurs during infusions of adrenaline is not shown.) (H. Barcroft & H. J. C. Swan (1953) *Sympathetic Control of Human Blood Vessels.* London: Arnold.)

CONTROL OF THE DAMPING VESSELS

The large elastic arteries convert the large pressure fluctuations generated by the heart into a fairly steady perfusion pressure. They also contain sensory nerve endings which detect stretching of the arterial wall for the control system that stabilizes arterial pressure.

The arterial wall contains smooth muscle and there is good evidence that it is innervated. However, the precise role of this muscle in arterial function is not clear. The large elastic arteries offer so little resistance to blood flow that changes in their calibre make practically no difference in the total resistance offered by the circulation. Changes in muscle tone in the large arteries have, therefore, no appreciable effect on

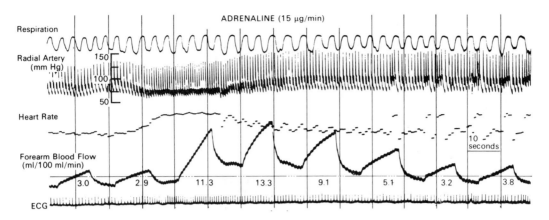

Fig. 12.12 Intravenous infusion of adrenaline bitartrate at 15 μg/min. Respiration was recorded by a nasal thermocouple. The pressure in the radial artery was measured by a strain-gauge manometer. Note the calibration 50, 100, 150 mm Hg. The heart rate was obtained electronically from the electrocardiogram (ECG). The forearm blood flow was obtained by venous occlusion plethysmography; the values in ml/100 ml/min are given below, 3·0, 2·9, etc. The vertical lines are 10 sec apart. The infusion began 30 sec before the first vertical line and continued throughout. (M. J. Allwood, E. W. Keck, R. J. Marshall & J. T. Shepherd (1962) *Journal of Applied Physiology*, 17, 71.)

blood flow. Arterial muscle responds to circulating hormones such as adrenaline by constricting and to local metabolites such as carbon dioxide by relaxation. The muscle is attached to the elastic fibres in the artery wall and by contracting it increases the elastic tension in the wall and reduces the distensibility of the arteries. This reduces the amount of blood contained in the arteries at any arterial pressure and also changes the characteristics of the arterial pulse wave. The smooth muscle might also regulate the sensitivity of the stretch receptors in the aortic arch and carotid sinus by altering the distensibility of their walls. Arteries respond vigorously to local mechanical irritation by contraction. This may limit blood loss when the arterial wall is cut or damaged.

CONTROL OF THE EXCHANGE VESSELS

The true capillaries do not seem to have either nerve fibres or muscle cells but the precapillary sphincters and arteriovenous anastomoses are supplied by non-myelinated nerve filaments. Stimulation of a sympathetic vasoconstrictor nerve probably constricts the metarterioles and the precapillary sphincters and prevents blood flowing into and through the capillaries (Fig. 11.19). The blood cells and plasma gradually drain away into the veins and the capillaries close but they open immediately if the precapillary sphincters relax. It seems likely that nervous control provides a background tone but it is much less important than the control by hormones such as adrenaline and by tissue metabolites such as histamine, 5-hydroxytryptamine, acetylcholine and carbon dioxide and the various kinins. The small vessels without nerves are much more sensitive to hormones than are the innervated arterioles. The reflex responses arising from the baroceptors depend on changes in the calibre of the arterioles; the microvessels do not show any active change in calibre.

Chemical Control of the Capillaries

Vasomotion is the term applied to the spontaneously occurring periodic relaxation and constriction of the thorough-

fare channel and of its precapillaries (p. 184). In uninjured resting tissue the blood-flow through the thoroughfare channel is fairly constant and its hydrostatic pressure relatively high. Vasomotion of the precapillary offshoots, manifested by an opening and closing of their sphincters, governs flow through the true capillaries and produces areas of varying hydrostatic pressure which are maintained for periods of time that differ greatly under different conditions. The fluid exchange in the capillary bed is thus greatly influenced by vasomotion. This delicately balanced activity depends on vasoconstrictor nervous influences and on humoral factors, both vasodilator and vasoconstrictor. The origin in the tissue itself of some of the humoral factors provides a local mechanism for the distribution of blood and, therefore, the extent and duration of fluid exchange.

The number of capillaries per unit area of tissue can be approximately determined by examining microscopically sections of the tissues of animals injected before death with India ink. In active muscles the capillaries are not only much more numerous than in resting muscles but also much wider. Thus in the resting muscle of a guinea-pig Krogh found 200 capillaries per mm² with an average diameter of 3·5 μm, against 2500 per mm² in an active muscle with an average diameter of 5·0 μm. A transverse section of an active skeletal muscle may show three or four times as many capillaries as muscle fibres. Activity is thus accompanied by capillary dilatation and in addition the size of the capillary bed is enormously increased by the opening up of vessels which were closed during the resting state. This opening up of new capillaries is believed to be initiated by the local release of chemical substances.

Nervous Control of Capillary Function

Though the capillaries are not innervated, the vessels upstream and downstream from them are. Nervous influences, by controlling the inflow and outflow from the capillary beds, can control the hydrostatic pressure in the capillaries and thus the net movement of fluid across the capillary wall. Stimulation of the vasoconstrictor fibres to a muscle vascular

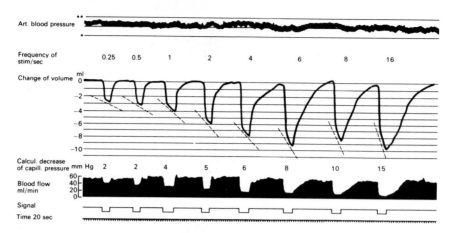

Fig. 12.13 Effects on resistance and capacitance vessels and net transcapillary fluid shift produced in the hindquarters of a cat by maximal lumbar vasoconstrictor fibre stimulation at different frequencies. Changes in blood flow reflect effects on resistance vessels (inflow and outflow pressures kept constant). The initial and rapid decreases in volume reflect effects on capacitance vessels and the subsequent slower and continuous decreases in volume (slopes indicated by dashed lines), transcapillary influx of extravascular fluid. Reductions in mean hydrostatic capillary pressure calculated in approximate figures. (S. Mellander (1960) *Acta physiologica scandinavica*, **50**, Suppl. 176, 35.)

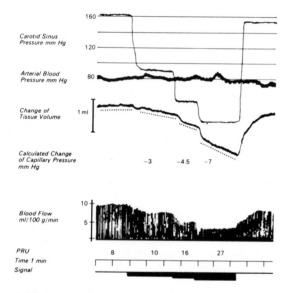

Fig. 12.14 Effects of stepwise reductions of pressure in the isolated, bilaterally perfused carotid sinus regions upon tissue volume and blood flow in the cat's hindquarters, while arterial inflow pressure and venous outflow pressure are kept constant in this region. Note how there occurs a reflex decrease of hindquarters blood flow at every stepwise decrease of carotid sinus pressure. Also, tissue volume decreases in a stepwise fashion, where each step is characterized by a first rapid phase and a second slow, but continuous, phase. The slope of this second phase is well graded to the reflex decrease in blood flow. PRU, blood flow resistance. (B. Öberg (1964) *Acta physiologica scandinavica*, **62**, Suppl. 229, 33.)

bed (Fig. 12.13) causes three main effects, (1) a decrease in blood flow due to constriction of the resistance vessels, (2) a decrease in the volume of blood contained in the muscle due to constriction of the capacity vessels and (3) mobilization of fluid from the tissue spaces into the blood. The third effect is thought to be due to the fall in capillary pressure which follows constriction of the precapillary resistance vessels.

In certain animals it has been found that stimulation of the carotid sinus nerve causes not only a reflex vasodilatation but

also an increase in the rate of tissue fluid formation (Fig. 12.14). Such a change may also result from a shift of blood to the chest. However, all situations in which blood flow is increased by vasodilatation are not associated with increased tissue fluid formation. Unless the precapillary sphincters are relaxed blood will not flow through the true capillary bed.

CONTROL OF THE CAPACITY VESSELS

Contraction of the smooth muscle in the walls of the veins has a number of effects. It reduces the capacity of the venous system to hold blood at any particular venous pressure. By raising the mean pressure in the venous system it tends to raise the filling pressure of the heart. The resulting increase in filling leads to stronger contractions and an increase in cardiac output. The rise in mean venous pressure also tends to cause capillary pressure to rise with a consequential increase in the formation of tissue fluid.

The term *venous tone* is often used to describe the degree of contraction of venous smooth muscle. When the smooth muscle is contracted, venous tone is said to be high. In these conditions venous distensibility is reduced; higher venous pressures are required to fill the veins to particular volumes so that their pressure-volume curves become flatter (Fig. 12.15).

Measurement of venous tone. There is no completely satisfactory way of doing this but a number of methods may be employed. One is to compress both ends of a superficial segment of a vein under the skin which does not show any side branches opening from, or draining into it. If the pressure in the segment is measured through an indwelling needle or catheter, venoconstriction is signalled by a rise, and venodilatation by a fall of pressure in the segment. Another method is to expose the venous system to gradually increasing or decreasing steps of pressure and construct pressure-volume curves. Flattening of the pressure-volume curves indicates venoconstriction (Fig. 12.15). A third method is to fill the veins to a constant high pressure by venous congestion. A decrease in the volume of the tissue at constant venous pressure indicates venoconstriction. It is important to realize

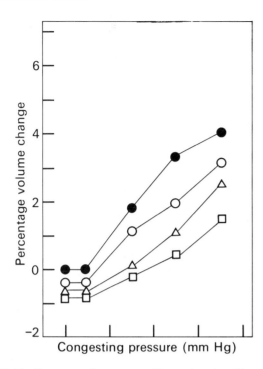

Fig. 12.15 Pressure-volume curves illustrating the effect of intra-arterial infusions of adrenaline on the high- and low-pressure capacity vessels of the forearm. Infusion of saline, ●; adrenaline infusions 0·1 μg/min, ○; 0·4 μg/min, △; 1·0 μg/min, □. Increasing doses of adrenaline progressively decrease the resting volume of the forearm and the distension of the forearm caused by raised venous pressure. This suggests that adrenaline constricts capacity blood vessels. (W. E. Glover, A. D. M. Greenfield, B. S. L. Kidd & R. F. Whelan (1958) *Journal of Physiology*, **140**, 113.)

that distension by itself is not evidence that the smooth muscle in the venous wall has relaxed. The dilatation of veins in parts of the body below heart level is a passive consequence of the increase in transmural pressure and not, of course, due to relaxation of the venous muscle. Further, when resistance vessels dilate, the inflow of blood into the capacity vessels raises the pressure in these vessels and distends them.

Venomotor Responses

Since the venous system is mainly concerned in integrated responses of the entire circulatory system, the responses of the venous system are usually integrated through vasomotor nerves or hormones.

Local factors. The local application of cold causes venoconstriction which may be intense and prolonged. This constriction may be proportionately greater than the constriction of the resistance vessels and account for the oedema seen in hands being rewarmed after exposure to cold. Local hypoxia and carbon dioxide excess relax venous smooth muscle, but these responses may be outweighed by the reflex effects of these stimuli acting centrally.

The pharmacological properties of the circular and longitudinal smooth muscle of the veins are different and species variation is considerable. Adrenaline and noradrenaline both cause venoconstriction (Fig. 12.15) due to the stimulation of α-

receptors which are predominant in this muscle. Isoprenaline which stimulates β-receptors causes relaxation of venous muscle. Both histamine and 5-hydroxytryptamine cause venoconstriction. The female sex hormones oestradiol and progesterone tend to reduce spontaneous activity in veins and make their contractions weaker. Nitrites and adenylic acid have also been found to cause venodilatation.

Nervous factors. Most of the stimuli that cause constriction of the resistance vessels seem also to cause constriction of the capacity vessels. As mentioned in the section on exchange vessels, stimulation of the sympathetic nerves to a tissue causes a fall in blood flow and blood capacity in that tissue. Stimuli which are thought to cause reflex venoconstriction include systemic hypoxia and hypercapnia, carotid sinus hypotension, body cooling, emotional stress, the shifting of blood away from the chest, exercise and the taking of deep breaths. Reflex venodilatation has been described in carotid sinus hypertension, fainting and sleep.

When a subject exercises his legs on a bicycle ergometer the capacity of the forearm veins is reduced (Fig. 12.16). The response is graded to the severity of the work. This does not occur if the sympathetic nerves to the arm have been cut. It can be demonstrated that the venoconstriction is generalized and occurs also in the muscles taking part in the exercise. Such an increase in venous tone is likely to play an important part in the circulatory adaptation to exercise. When the resistance vessels in the exercising muscles dilate the capillary and post-capillary pressures rise. If this were not accompanied by an adjustment of tone in the capacity vessels, blood would tend to pool in them. This tendency is antagonized by the pumping effect of the contracting muscles. The increase in venous tone acts in the same direction.

Stimuli which shift blood away from the chest cause reflex reductions in venous capacity. Thus venoconstriction has been reported after the Valsalva manoeuvre and on exposing the entire lower part of the body to a pressure below atmospheric. Figure 12.17 shows this response which is abolished by drugs which block the sympathetic nerves to the arm. This type of response would help to maintain the filling pressure of the heart when blood tended to pool in the lower extremities.

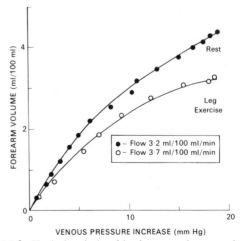

Fig. 12.16 Typical relationship between increase in forearm volume and pressure in a large forearm vein at rest (●) and during supine leg exercise (○). Note that forearm blood flow was similar in both circumstances. (B. S. Bevegard & J. T. Shepherd (1968) *Journal of Applied Physiology*, **20**, 1.)

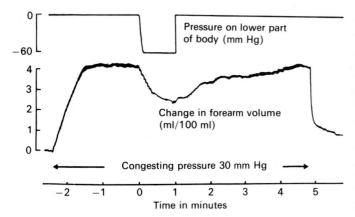

Fig. 12.17 The increase in volume of a forearm after congestion by a cuff at a pressure of 30 mm Hg. When the volume becomes constant, the lower body is exposed to a negative pressure of 60 mm Hg and the arm volume falls. When the suction is removed from the body the forearm volume does not return to its previous level for 4 minutes. (*After* B. V. Ardill, B. M. Bhatnagar & P. H. Fentem (1968) *Journal of Physiology*, 194, 627.)

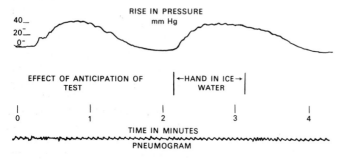

Fig. 12.18 Pressure changes recorded from a segment of a superficial vein of the forearm that had been isolated between wedges and kept at constant volume. (J. J. Duggan, V. Logan Love & R. H. Lyons (1953) *Circulation*, 7, 869.)

Figure 12.18 shows the result of an experiment in which pressure was measured in a segment of superficial forearm vein. With the subject at rest, the pressure in the segment was about zero mm Hg. When he became anxious about the nature of the forthcoming test, the pressure rose to about 40 mm Hg and then fell again. Immersing one hand in ice water had a similar effect. The increase in vasomotor tone during emotional stress would help to prevent pooling of blood in the extremities which might result from the concomitant dilatation of the resistance vessels.

SYNCOPE

Syncope, usually called fainting, means a transient loss of consciousness due to reduction in cerebral blood flow. At the same time skeletal muscular tone is diminished and the patient slumps or falls to the ground if unsupported; the faint is thus usually self-limiting.

Cerebral blood flow is remarkably constant over a wide range of blood pressure (p. 291), and fainting only occurs when the fall of blood pressure is severe. The reduction in blood pressure is usually the result of either a reflex vasomotor

depression which produces marked vasodilatation or the loss of the baroceptor reflexes that normally maintain cerebral perfusion in the upright posture. Fainting therefore occurs most frequently when the person is upright and consciousness usually returns quickly when he lies flat, unless the syncope is caused by a failure of cardiac output caused for example by ventricular fibrillation or arrest or by extreme bradycardia as in heart block (p. 171).

The commonest cause of fainting is probably strong emotions, particularly conflicting ones, as those aroused by sudden confrontation with an unpleasant sight such as a road traffic accident or surgical operation. Such emotions cause vasodilatation of skeletal muscle, perhaps because of an increase in circulating adrenaline and the activation of cholinergic vasodilator fibres. The heart rate is often low, and this bradycardia is abolished by atropine, so the syndrome of bradycardia, muscle vasodilatation and systemic hypotension with fainting was named *vaso-vagal syncope* by Lewis. Pallor, 'cold' sweating, nausea and yawning may be associated with fainting, and other precipitating factors may include fatigue, hunger or standing in a crowded room. Syncope can also be induced by depletion of the circulating blood volume. A sudden loss of blood may lead to syncope: in blood donors it is uncommon when less than 400 ml of blood are withdrawn, but occurs in about half the subjects if 1 litre is removed (Fig. 12.19).

When a subject stands up, blood is normally prevented from pooling in the legs under the influence of gravity by reflex

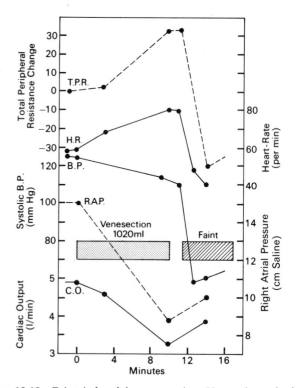

Fig. 12.19 Faint induced by venesection. Up to the end of the venesection, arterial pressure was maintained by peripheral vasoconstriction (increased total peripheral resistance) in spite of a decreasing cardiac output. During the faint, the cardiac output increased slightly, and the fall in blood pressure was, therefore, due to decrease in peripheral resistance. (H. Barcroft, O. T. Edholm, J. McMichael & E. P. Sharpey-Schafer (1944) *Lancet*, i, 189.)

adrenergic vasoconstriction. If for some reason the vaso-constriction fails to oppose the tendency of the blood to pool, *orthostatic hypotension* with syncope may result. This is a common complication induced by the adrenergic-blocking drugs used to treat high blood pressure (hypertension), and sometimes after the reduction of blood volume and sodium produced by powerful diuretic drugs.

Rarely syncope is caused by cardiac inhibition due to reflex vagal effects triggered by pressure on the carotid sinus, by micturition and sometimes by prolonged coughing that virtually amounts to a Valsalva manoeuvre.

PERIPHERAL CIRCULATORY FAILURE

There are two main ways in which the circulatory system may fail to provide the tissues with a blood flow that is adequate for their needs. The primary fault may lie in the heart so that it is unable to deliver an adequate cardiac output despite an adequate filling pressure; this is called *central circulatory failure* or *cardiogenic 'shock'* (see p. 172) and occurs, for example, after myocardial infarction and pulmonary embolism. On the other hand, the basic fault may lie peripherally so that the circulation cannot provide an adequate filling pressure for the otherwise normal heart; this is called *peripheral circulatory failure*. Both types of failure can result in underperfusion of the tissues with consequent inadequate function of organs such as the kidney, brain and liver. However, the conventional distinction between central and peripheral circulatory failure is a crude over-simplification. The whole circulatory system, heart, arteries, arterioles, capillaries, venules and veins, functions as an integrated whole; a break-down in any one part can hardly fail to influence events in other parts of the system.

Shock is also the term given to the clinical condition in which the patient is pale, cold and sweaty. The pulse is rapid and the arterial pressure is low, with a systolic level often less than 80 mm Hg and a small pulse pressure. The cardiac output is reduced. The patient has little pain or interest in his surroundings. Physical and mental activities are depressed, the metabolic rate reduced and the temperature low. No satisfactory explanation of these phenomena has yet been discovered.

The most important factor in peripheral circulatory failure is a relative disproportion between the blood volume and the volume of the vascular bed; the blood volume and the central venous pressure are usually both reduced. This reduction may be caused by sudden external loss of blood; by pooling of blood in capillary beds; as a result of plasma loss from extensive burns; or because of loss of extracellular fluid (as in diabetic keto-acidosis or severe gastroenteritis). These are all examples of *hypovolaemic shock*. Peripheral circulatory failure also occurs in some cases of self-poisoning with hypnotic drugs that cause paralysis of the vasomotor centres and relaxation of the venous system, leading to a reduction of the central venous pressure. The so-called 'traumatic shock' that occurs after road accidents or under battle conditions is probably the result of a combination of several of these factors. Peripheral circulatory failure may also occur in some bacterial infections, particularly those involving gram-negative organisms ('bacteraemic' shock), but its underlying mechanism is not yet clear.

An unusual type of circulatory failure occurs as a result of adrenocortical insufficiency, either in Addison's disease (Chap. 28) or when adrenal function has been suppressed by previous corticosteroid therapy: severe hypotension develops when the patient is subjected to stress such as severe infection or an operation and is associated with an inadequate rise in the level of corticosteroids in the plasma. In some patients central and peripheral circulatory failure coexist especially when hypovolaemic shock has persisted for some time and secondary myocardial failure results from continued poor coronary artery perfusion.

REFERENCES

Berne R M, Levy M N 1977 Cardiovascular physiology. St Louis, Mosby
Bannister R 1979 Chronic autonomic failure with postural hypotension. Lancet ii: 404–406
Braunwald E 1974 Regulation of the circulation. New England Journal of Medicine 290: 1124–1129, 1420–1425
Daly M de Burgh 1972 Interaction of cardiovascular reflexes. The Scientific Basis of Medicine Annual Reviews, 307–332
Folkow B, Neil E 1971 Circulation. Oxford University Press
Greenfield A D M 1963 The circulation through the skin. In: Handbook of Physiology. Section 2, Vol. 2, 1325–1351. American Physiological Society, Washington DC
Heymans C, Neil E 1958 Reflexogenic areas in the cardiovascular system. Churchill, London
Hilton S M 1962 Local mechanisms regulating peripheral blood flow. Physiological Reviews 42: Suppl. 5, 265–282
Johnson R H, Spalding J M K 1974 Disorders of the autonomic nervous system. Blackwell, Oxford
Lundgren O, Jodal M 1975 Regional blood flow. Annual Review of Physiology 37: 395–414
Maggis E 1965 Microhemocirculation. Observable variables and their biological control. Charles C Thomas. Springfield, Illinois
Roddie I C 1966 Nervous control of limb blood flow. Scientific Basis of Medicine Annual Reviews, 260–278
Whelan R F 1967 Control of the peripheral circulation in man. Charles C Thomas. Springfield, Illinois
Zweifach B W 1961 Functional behaviour of the microcirculation. Blackwell, Oxford

13 Respiration

In unicellular organisms oxygen can diffuse from the watery environment to all parts of the cell. With increasing size and complexity of the animal, however, the distance between the surface and the tissues becomes so great that special means are required to carry oxygen to the individual cells. In mammals the oxygen is taken up in the capillaries of the lungs and is conveyed by the blood to the tissues. At the same time the carbon dioxide produced in the tissues is carried to the lungs and there leaves the body. A scheme of the processes involved in respiration is given in Figure 13.1.

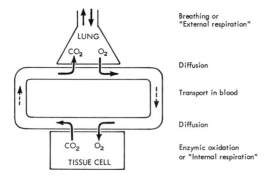

Fig. 13.1   Respiratory processes.

Air is moved in and out of the lungs by their 'bellows action' (*ventilation*). It is then distributed within each lung so that alveoli which are also perfused by blood are adequately ventilated (*distribution*). Oxygen and carbon dioxide are then exchanged between the gas mixture in the alveoli and the blood in the pulmonary capillaries (*gas transfer*). The gases are then *transported* in the blood to the tissues.

RESPIRATORY TRACT

The nose. The nasal passages are lined by a very vascular mucous membrane characterized, except at the entrance, by ciliated columnar epithelium which warms and moistens the entering air and removes larger particles (more than $10 \mu m$ effective diameter) of dust. The warming is very effective; air inspired at 6°C, for example, has been heated to 30°C by the time it reaches the back of the nose. As it passes down the trachea its temperature rises to body temperature and it is completely humidified by the time it arrives at the bifurcation. The temperature of the expired air is always below 37°C because the air loses heat as it passes out through the nose.

Electrical, chemical or mechanical irritation of the nasal mucous membrane causes apnoea, closure of the larynx and constriction of the bronchi, and also slowing of the heart and variable changes in blood pressure. This reflex which is related to the diving reflex (p. 231) helps to prevent the inhalation of liquids and noxious gases. When the mucous membrane is congested or inflamed resistance to inflow increases and

breathing through the nose is correspondingly difficult. Mouth breathing is uncomfortable because an important part of the warming and humidifying surface is by-passed.

The air passages. The *trachea* is a nearly circular tube about 16 mm in diameter and 12 cm long. It is kept patent by incomplete rings of cartilage, the deficiency on the posterior aspect being filled in with fibrous and muscular tissue. This structure allows free movement of the head and neck without the danger of kinking and obstructing the airway. During a deep inspiration the trachea increases in diameter by about one-tenth and in length by about one-fifth. The trachea divides into two main *bronchi* and these in turn subdivide, giving about ten further generations of small bronchi. All these air passages have a fibrous outer layer, and are supported by irregular pieces of cartilage. Internal to this is a layer of smooth muscle, the *bronchial musculature*, arranged in helical bands. Between the muscle fibres there is a considerable amount of elastic tissue. The bronchi are easily distended; an increase of 10 cm H_2O in the internal pressure can increase their volume by 50 per cent. Conversely they collapse if the intrathoracic pressure exceeds the intraluminar pressure by 50 cm H_2O, as it may in a violent expiration. The bronchi are lined by a ciliated columnar epithelium. In the trachea and larger bronchi numerous muco-serous glands innervated by the vagus lie below the epithelium. The mucus of the bronchi is produced by large numbers of goblet cells: the bronchioles have neither glands nor goblet cells but club-like apocrine cells have been found between the ciliated cells.

The total cross-sectional area of the airways increases at each branching. There are four generations of *terminal bronchioles*, the muscle of which is particularly well developed, and these open into *respiratory bronchioles* of equal diameter which have a well-marked muscle layer (Fig. 13.2). There are three generations of respiratory bronchioles and, since they have scattered alveoli in their walls, they are a transition zone between the conducting and exchanging parts of the airways. The respiratory bronchioles open into alveolar ducts whose walls are composed entirely of alveoli. Alveolar ducts are continued into alveolar sacs, each possessing about 17 alveoli. In man about 14×10^6 alveolar ducts open into about 250×10^6 alveoli. The alveoli are from 70 to 300 μm in diameter, being somewhat smaller in the more dependent parts of the lungs. Adjacent alveoli are connected by small pores which pass between the branches of the pulmonary capillaries.

The respiratory tract from the nose to the bronchioles is lined by ciliated columnar epithelium. The free border of each cell has several hundred hair-like processes or cilia 1 to 5 μm long and 0·3 μm in diameter. The ciliated cells occur in little groups which beat synchronously. The cilia impel the fluid on the surface in one direction by a rapid forward movement (the effective beat) followed by a slower return movement. This movement can be seen on the surface of a nasal polypus recently removed from the human nose. The cilia beat about 20 times per minute and particles of powder are carried along the trachea about 0·4 mm per sec; the rate depends on the depth of the layer of mucus lying over the cilia. The ciliary movement propels mucus and foreign bodies to the main bronchi and trachea from which they are finally cleared by coughing; in this way the healthy lung is kept free of inhaled bacteria. The cilia of excised mucous membrane are readily depressed by noxious agents and hypoxia but *in vivo* they are hardier and are unaffected by cigarette smoking. Ciliary activity continues independently of all nervous connexions and indeed continues for some hours after death. Small particles that reach the lower respiratory tract (effective diameter less than $10 \ \mu m$) are trapped by the mucus and removed by the phagocytic activity of free macrophages in the alveoli. About 100 ml of tracheo-bronchial mucus, containing albumin and secretory IgA, is produced per day.

Bronchial muscle. The activity of the bronchial muscle is controlled by the autonomic nervous system. Stimulation of the vagus or experimental perfusion with acetylcholine produces bronchial constriction while sympathetic stimulation produces bronchodilatation; perfusion of adrenaline also produces bronchodilatation by stimulation of β_2-receptors in the bronchial muscle. The central origin of these fibres is not known.

In asthma the patient has difficulty in breathing and has a sense of suffocation, both of which are produced by a spasm of the bronchial musculature, especially during expiration—an exaggeration of the normal constriction on expiration. The spasm can often be relieved by the subcutaneous injection of adrenaline or the inhalation of fine particles or droplets of related chemical substances that act as bronchial dilators, for

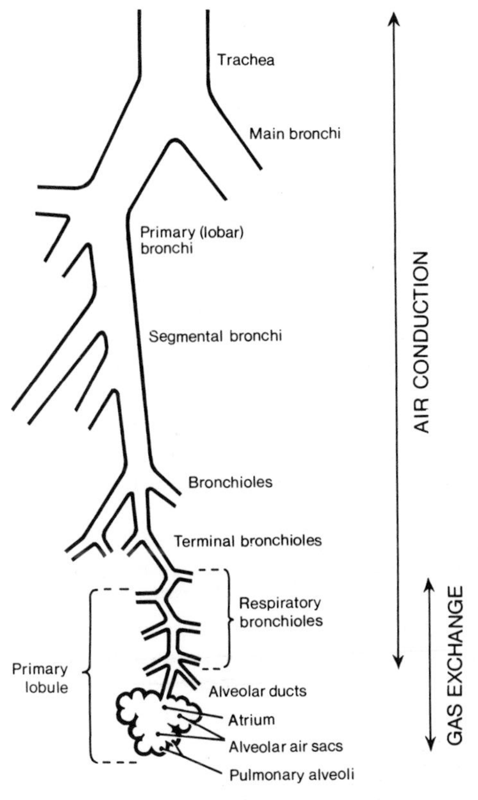

example isoprenaline or salbutamol. These mimic the effects of β_2-stimulation by endogenous neurotransmitters.

Inhalation of the prostaglandin $PGF_{2\alpha}$ produces broncho-constriction, especially in asthmatic patients. This effect is probably mediated through cholinergic receptors. The inhalation of PGE_2, on the other hand, causes bronchodilatation by stimulation of β receptors. Both prostaglandins are present in human lung tissue.

The injection of histamine in the guinea-pig causes a powerful bronchoconstriction which is probably the cause of death in anaphylactic shock in this animal. Histamine has usually very little effect on the bronchi in man but in asthmatics histamine inhaled as an aerosol can produce bronchoconstriction and an asthmatic attack.

If a conscious man is given atropine the dead space (p. 212) increases and the airway resistance decreases; vagotomy in man increases the bronchial calibre. These facts show that the muscle of the trachea and bronchi is normally in tonic contraction produced by cholinergic vagal nerves. Inflation of the lungs or a deep inspiration relaxes the bronchial muscle whereas deflation contracts it. These reflex effects may account for the changes in calibre of the bronchi in breathing but the changes in calibre in ordinary quiet respiration are probably merely passive, that is they are part of the change in the size of the lungs. So many interacting reflexes affect bronchial tone that no simple description is possible. Vagal afferents from airway receptors are important in these and other reflexes (p. 230).

The respiratory parts of the lungs. The structures distal to each first order respiratory bronchiole are spoken of as a *primary lobule* or *acinus* (Fig. 13.2), which is the physiological unit of the lung, but the capillary networks extend across several acini. The respiratory bronchioles are lined by a cubical, non-ciliated epithelium which becomes progressively flatter as it is traced towards the pulmonary alveoli. Minute vents connect adjacent alveoli within each primary lobule, and epithelium-lined tubules connect terminal or respiratory bronchioles with adjacent alveoli; a communication is thus provided between the ultimate alveoli and their parent bronchioles.

The exchange of gases between the air and blood takes place in the alveoli where, as the electron microscope shows (Fig. 13.13), the air and the blood are separated by two very thin cellular membranes, the endothelium of the pulmonary capillary and the flattened epithelium of the alveolus. The thickness of the tissue between the alveolar air and the blood is about $0 \cdot 5 \ \mu m$ overall. The total area of the aveolar membrane of both lungs is estimated to be 70 to 80 m^2 in adult man; the area depends on the state of expansion of the lungs.

The passage of fluid across a tissue capillary is discussed on p. 185 but in a pulmonary capillary the situation is much more complicated. The force tending to keep the alveoli dry is the osmotic pressure of the plasma proteins (say 25 mm Hg) less the capillary blood pressure (say 10 mm Hg), that is a total of about 15 mm Hg. This readily explains the occurrence of pulmonary oedema when the blood pressure in the left atrium rises above 20 mm Hg but it takes no account of the surface tension.

The surface tension of a fluid in a Langmuir trough tends to reduce its surface area but when a liquid surface is curved as in an alveolus there is a resultant force towards its centre. The

Fig. 13.2 The air passages. (*After* Macklin.) There are approximately 23 orders of branching between the bifurcation of the trachea and the alveolar sacs. In man there are about 130 000 primary lobules, each containing 2000 alveoli.

pressure P is given by Laplace's equation $P = 2\gamma/r$ where γ is the surface tension and r is the radius of the sphere. A small alveolus with a radius of $50\,\mu m$, or 50×10^{-4} cm, if lined with plasma with a surface tension of $55\,dyn/cm$ (or in S.I. units, $55 \times 10^{-3}\,N/m$) would have a pressure of $110\,dyn/cm \div 50 \times 10^{-4}$ cm $= 2\cdot2 \times 10^4 dyn/cm^2 = 16\cdot5\,mm\,Hg$. This pressure, acting in the same direction as the pulmonary capillary pressure, would overcome the osmotic pressure of the plasma proteins and would not only draw fluid out of the capillaries but would cause the alveolus to collapse. However, the fluid lining the alveoli contains a 'surfactant' (Fig. 13.13), a lipoprotein containing much fully saturated di-palmitoyl lecithin which reduces γ considerably (5 to 10 dyn/cm). The pressure towards the centre of the alveolus would, in the example given, be only $1\cdot5$ to $3\,mm\,Hg$. When the oedema foam (that is lining fluid) from the lungs is spread on a Langmuir trough the surface tension rises somewhat as the area is increased; this effect is probably present in the lungs as the alveoli expand on inspiration but the increase of surface tension may be partly balanced by the increase in radius so that P is not much altered. Conversely the surface tension (γ) falls as the alveoli become smaller on expiration; in this way collapse during expiration is prevented. The surfactant is thought to be produced by the giant alveolar cells which lie in the septa between the alveoli. It appears first at the twenty-eighth week of intrauterine life just at the time the fetus becomes viable. If excised gas-free lungs are filled with saline to abolish the air/fluid interface in the alveoli only half the pressure is required to expand them to a given volume. Since this treatment cannot affect the elastic tissue it shows clearly that the suface tension at the air/fluid interface is as important as the elastic tissue in recoil of the lungs. The *respiratory distress syndrome* in premature neonates is probably due to lack of surfactant.

Like every other tissue the lungs consume oxygen and the adult lung can account for as much as 4 per cent of the total oxygen uptake of the body.

The pleura. The outer surface of the lung is covered by a delicate serous membrane, the *visceral pleura*, which is reflected from the roots of the main bronchi on to the inside of the thoracic walls and upper surface of the diaphragm, the *parietal pleura*. The surface of the visceral and parietal pleurae consists of a single layer of flattened cells, and normally the two pleurae are separated by a thin film of serous fluid, sufficient only to lubricate the surfaces so that they move over one another easily during breathing. So long as this film is intact the two pleurae cannot be separated except by considerable force. The potential space between the two plurae is known as the *pleural cavity*. When the pleurae are separated by an accumulation of fluid, or the entry of air, the pleural cavity becomes apparent and a hydrothorax or a pneumothorax (bilateral or unilateral) is said to exist (see p. 206).

MECHANICS OF BREATHING

Ventilatory Movements

The movement of air into and out of the lungs (*ventilation*) is brought about by alterations in the size of the thoracic cavity, the lungs following these variations passively. When the thoracic cavity enlarges during inspiration the lungs must

also expand because the visceral pleura cannot part from the parietal pleura on the thoracic wall. Air flows through the airways into the lungs because at that instant the air in the atmosphere is at a higher pressure than the air in the lungs. Bulk flow of air brings the respiratory gases as far as the terminal bronchioles. In the respiratory parts of the lungs diffusion is the main driving force. On expiration the changes are in the opposite direction.

The most important muscle of inspiration is the dome-shaped *diaphragm*, separating the thoracic and abdominal cavities; it is made up of a central tendon with muscle fibres radiating from it to the circumference of the lower parts of the thoracic wall. When it contracts the central tendon is pulled down and the intra-abdominal pressure is raised; at the same time the costal margins move up and out because of the vertical position of the fibres attached to them which expand the base of the thorax. In quiet inspiration the diaphragm may be the only respiratory muscle in action but some activity has been recorded in the internal intercostals. However, the diaphragm can be paralysed in man by cutting both phrenic nerves without producing serious respiratory difficulty at rest.

The liver is so much denser than the lungs that its upper edge can be clearly seen on the fluorescent X-ray screen. Since the liver lies immediately below the diaphragm the upper edge of its shadow can be used to mark the level of the diaphragm. On quiet inspiration the downward movement is approximately 12 mm but on violent inspiration it may be 70 to 100 mm. The height of the diaphragm, and thus the capacity of the chest, varies with the position of the body—the diaphragm is highest in the supine position, a little lower in the erect position, and still lower when the subject is sitting because the abdominal muscles are relaxed in this position. Since the cross-sectional area of the thorax increases from above downwards, any given air intake can be accomplished by a smaller diaphragmatic movement the lower the resting position of the diaphragm. This is one of the reasons why a patient with respiratory disease is often most comfortable when sitting up. The diaphragm is the last muscle to cease functioning during progressively deepening anaesthesia, and the fact that it is innervated by nerves arising in the cervical region of the cord means that it is not affected by spinal injuries below the neck (see p. 371).

The movements of the ribs on inspiration are of two kinds: (1) 'pump-handle' in which the sternal end of the downward sloping rib is raised and (2) the 'bucket-handle' in which the middle of the rib is moved upwards and outwards about an anteroposterior axis. If the intercostal nerves supplying the intercostal muscles are cut the amplitude of these rib movements is reduced and the tissues of the intercostal spaces bulge or recede according to the variations in intrathoracic pressure.

Action potentials have been recorded in the intercostal muscles by inserting into them very fine bipolar needles which picked up impulses from a small volume of muscle. The intercostal muscles seem to contribute very little to the effort of quiet respiration. No activity could be detected in the external intercostals in these circumstances. The internal intercostals showed some activity in two restricted areas—in the parasternal region (upper four interchondral spaces) on inspiration and in the lower lateral part of the chest on expiration. In vigorous respiration, however, the two layers of muscle showed reciprocal activity all over the chest wall, the external intercostals contracting on inspiration and the internal intercostals on expiration.

When the subject is lying completely relaxed no electrical activity can be recorded during inspiration from the muscles of the anterior abdominal wall. The elastic properties of the abdominal wall keep up the viscera and the diaphragm. The abdominal muscles are true muscles of expiration but they are little used in quiet breathing and the variations in intragastric, that is intra-abdominal, pressure are correspondingly small. They seem to go into vigorous action only when the ventilation is high or when the subject is coughing or straining; even then they are much less active than they are during postural movements. In maximum voluntary breathing efforts, such as occur in the vital capacity test, the lower ribs are drawn downwards and medially by the abdominal muscles with a large rise of intragastric pressure. A limit may be put to the depth of inspiration by the abdominal muscles which contract at the end of a maximal inspiration.

The only accessory muscles of any importance in inspiration are the scaleni and the sternomastoids. The former may be in action in some persons in quiet inspiration; they elevate and fix the first two ribs. The sternomastoids are used only in deep breathing and in dyspnoea; they raise the sternum and increase the anteroposterior diameter of the thorax. In deep breathing the extensors of the vertebral column may help inspiration. In the deepest inspiration that can be made the circumference of the chest is increased by 5 to 11 cm; in quiet inspiration the increase is only 1 cm.

In expiration the inspiratory muscles relax and the movements of the thorax and the lungs just described are reversed. During this largely passive phase the ribs fall and untwist partly by their own elasticity and partly by the contractions of the muscles attached to them. The elastic recoil of the lungs also contributes. Even when there is obstruction to respiration this is true because the usual effect of obstruction is to increase inflation: the obstruction is thus overcome by increased passive recoil rather than by contraction of the abdominal muscles, or indeed of the other accessory muscles of respiration.

Radiographic and other indirect methods of measuring the relative contributions of the descent of the diaphragm and of the movements of the rib cage have led to the conclusion that the diaphragm is responsible for three-quarters of the tidal volume, but the movement of the rib cage is responsible for two thirds of the vital capacity.

Expansion of the lungs. During inspiration the vocal folds move apart, the bronchi dilate and, as the lungs expand, the bronchial tree is elongated, and the alveoli become wider. At the same time the intrathoracic pressure falls, the venous return increases and the right ventricular output increases and the amount of blood in the pulmonary circuit increases.

Since the lungs expand quite passively, the parts next to the most mobile portions of the thoracic cage expand most and the mediastinal portions least. As the lungs expand they occupy the potential space lined by pleura between the diaphragm and the lower ribs (*costo-diaphragmatic recess*) which is obliterated at expiration by the coming together of the two layers of the parietal pleura.

Quantitative records of changes in lung volume can be obtained by using a recording *spirometer* (Fig. 13.3) or a

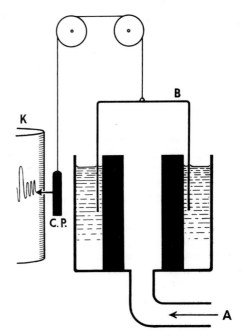

Fig 13.3 Spirometer designed for high respiratory rates. The subject breathes into A and raises the bell B and the index attached to the counterpoise C.P. moves down the kymograph K. (L. Bernstein, J. L. D'Silva & D. Mendel (1952) *Thorax*, 7, 255.)

pneumotachograph both of which require the use of a mouthpiece or face-mask which are liable to disturb the normal pattern of breathing. Methods depending on recording the thoracic dimensions are a little less reliable but provide valuable information about natural breathing patterns. These methods include the strain-gauge or stethograph (measuring chest circumference), the inductance test, the impedance monitor and magnetometer (chest diameter), and an oeso-phageal catheter (measuring intrathoracic pressure).

Intrapleural pressure. The pleural space contains only a very thin film of fluid which because of surface tension makes it very difficult to separate the two pleural layers. The situation is comparable to that in which a wet rubber 'sucker' is stuck to a piece of glass. When the sucker is applied firmly to the glass and released the atmospheric pressure holds it in position. If the film of water between the rubber and glass evaporates, the sucker is easily dislodged. Similarly, in the case of the lungs, the parietal and visceral layers of the pleura are kept pressed together by the atmospheric pressure and remain in firm contact. Alterations in the volume of the lungs during breathing occur because of the movements of the thoracic cage. In the process of expansion the elastic tissue of the lung is stretched and provides a force tending to collapse the lungs—this gives rise to the *negative intrapleural pressure*. It is greater, the greater the expansion of the lungs and the stretch of the elastic tissue. The intrapleural pressure can be measured by injecting a very small quantity of air between the two layers of pleura and connecting this air pocket to a water manometer. Such a record is shown in the upper portion of Figure 13.4. In quiet respiration the intrapleural pressure varies between about plus 1 and minus 4 cm water; in forced inspiration it may decrease to minus 20 cm or even minus 40 cm water and in forced expiration it may increase to plus 30 cm. It is more convenient to measure the intrapleural pressure with a fine polythene tube attached to a thin-walled balloon lying in the lower third of the oesophagus. In the upright position this has been shown to give pressure readings that agree closely with those recorded in the intrapleural space.

The abdominal pressure, measured through a tube passed into the stomach, varies in the opposite direction to that in the thorax; on inspiration, when the diaphragm descends, the intrapleural pressure becomes more negative and the intra-abdominal pressure more positive.

The elasticity of the lungs can be demonstrated by passing a hollow needle through the chest wall to allow air to enter and break the 'seal' between the two layers of the pleura. Air continues to pass in until the intrapleural pressure rises to atmospheric pressure and the lung on that side collapses by the retraction of its elastic tissue (see also p. 204). This condition is called a *pneumothorax*.

Work of breathing. The volume of air contained in the chest at the resting respiratory level is called the functional residual capacity (FRC, see Fig. 13.6). If this volume is to be

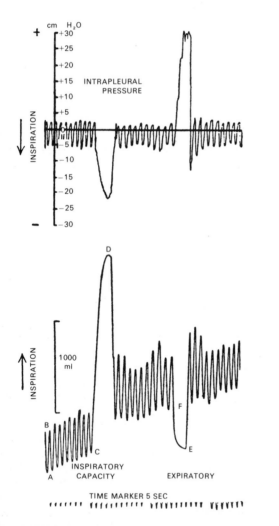

Fig. 13.4 Simultaneous traces of intrapleural pressure recorded by a water manometer (upper trace) and respiratory record made with a recording spirometer (lower trace). Note on the respiratory trace that AB = tidal volume; CD = inspiratory capacity; EF = expiratory reserve volume; CD + EF = vital capacity (p. 208). (R. V. Christie & C. A. McIntosh (1934) *Journal of Clinical Investigation*, 13, 292.)

increased or decreased, work must be done (1) against the tendency of the lungs and chest wall to recoil to their resting position, (2) to overcome the resistance to air flow through the airways, and (3) to overcome the resistance to movement of the tissues themselves. These three forces, all tending to oppose the change of volume of the thorax, are called elastic resistance, airway resistance and tissue ('viscous' or 'non-elastic') resistance. The first depends only on the change of volume itself, while the latter two are proportional to the rate of change of volume, that is, on air flow. During normal quiet breathing, the active contraction of muscles provides the energy to overcome these resistances during inspiration during which potential energy is stored in the stretched elastic tissues. This energy is then available to overcome the airway and tissue resistance during expiration. This combination of elastic and viscous resistance makes the relationship between intrapleural pressure and tidal volume somewhat complex. If the lungs were perfectly elastic and the resistance to air flow through the bronchi negligible, the two curves would be in phase so that the maximum negative pressure coincided with the maximum volume at the end of inspiration and the least negative pressure with the minimum volume at the end of expiration. But, as Figure 13.5 shows, the peaks of the pressure curve occur a little before the peaks of the volume curve; the curves are not in phase. In other words, because of the viscous resistance of the lungs and the airway resistance, the volume curve lags behind the pressure curve. When simultaneous values of pressure and volume for a single cycle are read off from these curves and plotted in a graph with pressure as ordinate and volume as the abscissa an 'ellipse' OIAE is obtained. The area OIAN is the total work of inspiration, the area OAN representing the work done against elastic forces and the area OIA the work done against viscous resistance during inspiration. The energy OAN stored in the lungs at the end of inspiration is available to do the work OAE necessary to overcome the viscous resistance to expiration.

The large airways, trachea and bronchi of more than 2 mm diameter account for 80 to 90 per cent of the resistance to flow, the distal airways account for only 10 to 15 per cent. It is difficult therefore to detect changes in flow due to small or early changes in the calibre of the distal airways.

A relatively small amount of work is expended in respiration at rest; it is of the order of 4J (0·4 kg.m) per min, of which 60 per cent is elastic work and 40 per cent is used in overcoming airway and viscous resistance. Even in severe exercise the work of breathing is only about 3 per cent of the total energy output.

In *bronchial asthma* the airway resistance is much increased by reason of narrowing of the bronchi and therefore the work of breathing is much increased. The shape of the pressure/volume curve is markedly altered in emphysema (see insert in Fig. 13.5).

Conscious subjects can easily recognize quite small increases, of the order of 25 per cent, in elastic resistance produced experimentally by breathing into and out of rigid drums or of viscous resistance produced by breathing through a narrow airway. In both cases increased respiratory effort is needed. Vagal block does not relieve the feeling of distress associated with breathing against resistance. The sensation may arise in the muscles of the thoracic cage or more probably in the joint receptors.

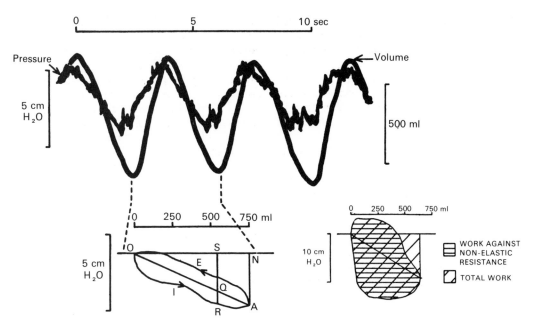

Fig. 13.5   A simultaneous tracing of intraoesophageal pressure and tidal volume in a normal subject at rest. The pressure trace is reserved so that a fall in intraoesophageal pressure is shown as an upward deflexion. The pressure-volume diagram derived from one breath is shown below. The pressure exerted against non-elastic resistance is obtained by subtracting the elastic pressure from the total pressure exerted at any point of the inspiratory cycle. At the point S this is SR — SQ = QR. Inserted on the lower right is a pressure-volume diagram obtained from a patient with emphysema. (M. B. McIlroy, R. Marshall & R. V. Christie (1954) *Clinical Science*, 13, 128 and 148.)

Compliance. Compliance is the change in volume produced by unit change in pressure. A high compliance means that a given change of pressure moves a large volume of air; the compliance is lowered if the lungs become stiff or if the surface tension of the fluid lining the alveoli is raised. The pressure required is the transpleural pressure, usually obtained by measuring the pressure difference between the intrathoracic oesophagus and the mouth. Measurements of compliance must be made under static conditions if the elastic properties only of the lungs are to be measured since in breathing part of the air pressure is used to overcome the viscous resistance of the tissues and the resistance to flow of air and part to expand the lungs against elastic resistance. If the measurements are made at the end of inspiration (A in Fig. 13.5) there is no air flow and the non-elastic tissue and airway resistances are zero. In Figure 13.5, about 750 ml of air move into the lungs for a change of pressure of about 3·5 cm of water. This gives a compliance of 0·22 litre/cm water. The range of compliance in the adult healthy male is from 0·09 to 0·26. The value in the new-born child is only 0·005; as in other small mammals the lungs are less easily inflated. At age 10 years the value is about 0·06 litre/cm water. In old age the compliance decreases.

Breath sounds. When a stethoscope is applied over the chest, various sounds of different character, and of different temporal and spatial distribution can be heard. The precise cause of these sounds is conjectural but it is likely that the loud blowing *bronchial* sounds heard over the trachea and large bronchi are caused by turbulence of the air in the larynx, and it is possible that the soft hissing *vesicular* sound is due to the opening of air sacs.

The velocity of sound in hydrogen is nearly four times that in air, and consequently if a subject breathes hydrogen all sounds which depend on the resonance of gas columns in the lungs become higher in pitch. The tracheal and bronchial sounds rise

in pitch but the vesicular sound is not altered, so its causation must be quite different from that of the other sounds. In specific lung disorders there are sometimes characteristic local variations in these sounds that may be helpful in diagnosis.

Lung Volumes and Capacities

The volume of air breathed in and out in a single quiet respiration is about 500 ml. This *resting tidal volume* (V_T) is measured by causing the subject to breathe from a recording spirometer (Fig. 13.3). A violent inspiratory effort can take into the lungs about 2500 ml measured from the resting respiratory level which by convention is taken as the end of a normal expiration (Fig. 13.6, and A, C, or F in Fig. 13.4). This is called the *inspiratory capacity*; it includes the resting tidal volume and the *inspiratory reserve volume* as shown in Figure 13.6. After a quiet expiration (500 ml) it is possible by a violent expiratory effort to blow out approximately 1300 ml of air; this is the *expiratory reserve volume*. Even after the deepest possible expiration the lungs and respiratory passages still contain about 1600 ml of air; this is the *residual volume*. At the end of a quiet expiration the lungs contain the expiratory reserve volume and the residual volume which together are called the *functional residual capacity* (2900 ml) (see Fig. 13.6). This large volume prevents rapid changes in the composition of the alveolar air and collapse of the alveoli. Normally (see p. 211) only 360 ml of fresh air (tidal volume minus dead space) is added to the functional residual capacity on inspiration.

Functional residual capacity (FRC). This can be measured by a dilution technique. The subject breathes at the end of expiration into a spirometer filled with oxygen. After a few minutes of quiet breathing the nitrogen originally in his lungs

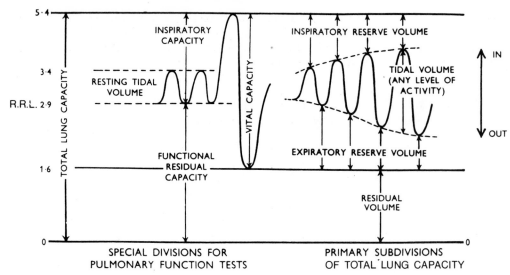

Fig. 13.6 A representation of a recording obtained by a spirometer (Fig. 13.3) to illustrate the subdivisions of the lung capacity. The figures on the left are the average values in litres for an adult man. (*Federation Proceedings* (1950) 9, 602.) R. R. L. = resting respiratory level. Note that the word 'volume' is used for the simple subdivisions; where two or more of these subdivisions are involved the word 'capacity' is used.

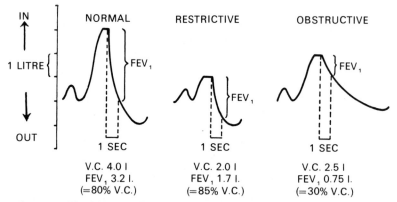

Fig. 13.7 *Forced expiratory spirograms*. The three records are taken from spirometer tracings. Inspiration is up and expiration down, and the records read from left to right. After a deep inspiration the subjects breathed out as rapidly and forcibly as they could. The total volume expired is the *forced vital capacity* and the volume expired in the first second is the *forced expired volume* in 1 second (FEV₁). The 'restrictive' record was obtained from a patient with kypho-scoliosis; the 'obstructive' record from a patient with airway obstruction. Kypho-scoliosis is a deformity of the bony structure of the chest that interferes with movement; although the vital capacity is more severely reduced in the patient with kypho-scoliosis than in the patient with airway obstruction the proportion of the vital capacity expired in the first second is normal. (E. J. M. Campbell, C. J. Dickinson & J. H. D. Slater (1968) *Clinical Physiology*. 3rd edition. P. 124. Oxford: Blackwell.)

is distributed evenly between his lungs and the spirometer. The functional residual capacity is calculated from the reduction in nitrogen content of the spirometer. In another method the subject breathes a mixture of helium (or hydrogen) and oxygen from a spirometer, into which oxygen is run to keep the trace level.

The size of the FRC reflects the balance between the tendency of the lungs to deflate because of their own elasticity and the opposite tendency of the thorax to expand.

Vital capacity. If, after the deepest possible inspiration, a subject makes as forcible an expiration as possible into a spirometer we obtain a reading of the *vital capacity* (Figs. 13.6 and 13.7). Using the figures already quoted we find that this is composed of

Inspiratory capacity	2500
Expiratory reserve volume	1300
	3800 ml

The vital capacity depends on the size, age, sex and ethnic origin of the subject and useful predictions of the vital capacity from height, weight or surface area can be made. The vital capacity in any one individual is sufficiently reproducible to be a useful guide to the progress of the lung disease and it is used in certain clinical tests of ventilatory performance (Fig. 13.7). Chest expansion as given by a tape-measure during a deep inspiration is not a reliable indication of the vital capacity.

The estimates of the subdivisions of the lung volume depend somewhat on the position of the subject. The slight reduction in vital capacity in the supine position as compared with the sitting position may be due to the increase in the amount of blood in the pulmonary vascular bed. The small increase in the inspiratory capacity and the considerable reduction in the expiratory reserve volume which occur on lying supine are explained by the changes in position of the diaphragm which lies higher in the thorax when the subject is supine.

The vital capacity is reduced by conditions that interfere

with thoracic movements, and in diseases in which the air in the spongy lung is replaced by fluid or solid material, and when expansion of the lung is impaired by the presence of fluid or air between the layers of the pleura. In patients with heart failure the vital capacity may be reduced 10 to 30 per cent, partly by an accumulation of blood in the engorged vessels of the pulmonary system, and partly by fluid extravasated into the alveolar spaces. When the vital capacity of a patient is reduced to about 40 per cent of normal, he can no longer perform even the simplest movements without becoming breathless. Such patients are much more breathless lying down than sitting up (*orthopnoea*), partly because of the decline in vital capacity in the recumbent position (see also p. 208) and partly because of the decrease in compliance which increases the work of respiration in the horizontal position.

The vital capacity (3800 ml) and the residual volume (1600 ml) added together give the *total lung capacity* (5400 ml).

Dynamic Tests of Bellows Function

Tests of ventilation, designed to measure the 'bellows action' of the lung, are commonly used in clinical medicine. Many factors are involved and, although airway resistance is probably the most important, lung size and compliance, muscular co-ordination and power are also included. Because airway resistance is so often raised in the common lung diseases, such as asthma and chronic bronchitis, tests of ventilatory efficiency are the most widely used of all the tests of lung function.

Much information can be obtained by an easy test procedure. The patient is asked to make a maximal inspiration followed by a single forced expiration. The volume expelled in the first second of expiration (FEV_1) has been found to correlate well with the subject's disability. Normal values for FEV_1 vary with age, sex and to a smaller extent with body size but healthy persons can expel 75 per cent or more of the vital capacity within the first second. When the resistance of the airways is greatly increased the proportion may fall to 30 per cent or less (Fig. 13.7).

The spirometers usually employed to measure FEV_1 and VC cannot respond quickly enough to provide a measure of the high flow rates achieved at the start of a forced expiration. A *peak flow meter* is commonly used to provide further information about dynamic ventilatory function. Airway resistance can also be measured directly by means of a *body plethysmograph* where pressure changes in a box completely enclosing the subject reflect the alveolar pressure changes during the breathing cycle where flow is also measured.

Artificial Ventilation

Artificial or assisted ventilation may be required whenever breathing is depressed or absent, for example, during the administration of an anaesthetic or after a head injury. When a muscle relaxant is administered all skeletal muscles including the diaphragm are paralysed, so artificial ventilation is essential.

Assisted ventilation is usually given by mechanical venti-lators which provide intermittent positive pressure ventilation (IPPV) through a cuffed endotracheal tube. Positive end-expiratory pressure (PEEP) promotes more efficient gas exchange by preventing the closure of small airways in apnoeic patients. Continuous positive airway pressure (CPAP) is useful in patients who are breathing spontaneously, but whose respiration is inefficient, such as infants with the 'respiratory distress syndrome'.

Artificial ventilation is also required in emergencies, such as drowning, cardiac arrest, electric shock and carbon-monoxide poisoning. It is obviously difficult in such emergencies to say whether the heart or the respiration fails first but if the activity of the medulla oblongata is depressed respiration becomes sluggish and may cease. The heart, on the other hand, can continue to beat independently of the central nervous system, provided that it receives an adequate supply of oxygen. Thus, if oxygen can reach the patient's blood promptly enough, the circulation can be maintained until the cause of the respiratory depression is removed or alleviated so that the respiratory centre is given time to recover its rhythmic activity and restore natural respiration.

An equally important reason for prompt action is that asphyxia of only a few minutes' duration does irreparable damage to the cortical cells of the brain. The oxygen content of the blood falls from 20 to 15 ml per 100 ml blood during the first few minutes, to 2 to 3 ml after 6 min, and to zero in 8 min. Although it may be possible to restore breathing after periods of apnoea of 8 to 10 min there is rarely complete recovery of cerebral function after 2 or 3 min. *Not a single second* should therefore be lost in applying artificial ventilation. No time should be wasted in loosening clothing or in prolonged attempts to drain water out of the lungs or in moving the victim to a more convenient situation. A few victims of immersion have survived up to 40 minutes below the surface and have regained cerebral function. Resuscitation procedures should not be abandoned early.

In fresh water drowning death is usually due primarily to cardiac arrest. In electric shock death is due primarily to ventricular fibrillation (occasionally asystole). In these two emergencies and, of course, in cardiac arrest from any cause, both external cardiac massage (p. 171) and artificial venti-lation are required.

The essentials of a good first-aid method of artificial ventilation are: (1) it should produce adequate ventilation of the lungs: (2) if any apparatus is needed it must be of the simplest kind which should be readily available anywhere; (3) no damage should be done to the patient by violent handling; (4) the strain on the operator should be minimal so that he can apply the method for long periods; (5) the position of the patient should be such that the airway is kept open.

Expired air resuscitation. This ancient method used by Elisha (2 Kings, 4, 34), was 'rediscovered' about 1957; it is easy to learn and is in every way superior to manual methods. The patient is placed on his back on a firm surface, if possible with his head at a slightly lower level than his stomach. The operator should quickly clear out mucus, food or other materials from the mouth and throat. It is most important to extend the patient's head as far as possible (Fig. 13.8) so that the airway is opened up. The operator pinches the patient's nostrils to prevent leakage, takes a deep breath and blows into the patient's mouth until the chest is seen to rise; the operator

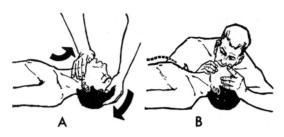

Fig. 13.8 Intermittent positive-pressure breathing. (a) Head hyperextended and chin raised. (b) Mouth-to-mouth resuscitation. Look for chest rise with each inflation. (M. H. Brook, J. Brook & G. M. Wyant (1962) *British Medical Journal*, ii, 1564–1566.)

then takes his mouth quickly away to allow passive exhalation. The process is repeated about 10 times a minute in adults. Mouth-to-nose ventilation is superior to mouth-to-mouth because full extension of the neck can be combined with complete closure of the mouth and lifting forward of the lower jaw; also inflation of the stomach is less likely. In resuscitating an infant the operator can place his mouth over the subject's nose and mouth and the lungs can be inflated with little puffs at say 30 per min.

There is no doubt that this is an effective method; investigation has shown that a tidal volume of 1 litre can readily be maintained. The expired air of the operator, though containing 16 per cent of oxygen (instead of 21 per cent as in air) is capable of maintaining adequate oxygenation of the subject's blood with adequate carbon dioxide elimination.

External cardiac massage (p. 171) should also be applied if the absence of carotid or femoral pulsations indicates that cardiac arrest has occurred; but artificial ventilation must be continued since external cardiac massage alone does *not* ventilate the lungs. Artificial ventilation and external cardiac massage must be continued until either the patient recovers, or a doctor pronounces him dead.

Ventilators. Prolonged artificial ventilation is sometimes required when spontaneous respiration is depressed. It is necessary when the chest is unable to expand the lungs, for example during and after thoracic surgery, or when the muscles of the thorax are paralysed, for example after high injuries to the cervical spine, in poliomyelitis, and after administration of muscle relaxants during general anaesthesia for surgical operations. Mechanical ventilators are then employed. Almost all such machines now operate on the principle of 'intermittent positive pressure', the lungs being inflated at a predetermined pressure and rate through a tube inserted into the trachea either through the mouth or nose or directly through a small incision below the cricoid cartilage (tracheostomy). This endotracheal tube has an inflatable cuff that blocks the rest of the tracheal lumen. Old methods by which the chest was expanded by negative pressure applied to the outside of the thorax are now seldom used.

In carbon monoxide poisoning, as in all other forms of hypoxia and asphyxia, pure oxygen is always to be preferred to oxygen-carbon dioxide mixtures. Normal man at rest breathing air eliminates half the carbon monoxide in his blood in 250 min; if he breathes pure oxygen, half of his carbon monoxide is eliminated in 40 min. Even more efficient is the oxygen pressure chamber in which pure oxygen is supplied at a pressure of two atmospheres (hyperbaric oxygen); not only

does the oxygen drive off the carbon monoxide but the plasma itself is able to carry twice as much oxygen at two atmospheres.

Although carboxy-haemoglobin is cherry coloured the skin of a patient poisoned with carbon monoxide is cyanosed and pale. It is only at necropsy that the cherry colour is seen. Unless the patient is moribund hyperventilation is usual; it reduces the Pa_{CO_2} but because of hypoxia the arterial pH is low. Administration of CO_2 with oxygen is therefore contra-indicated since it would lower the pH still further.

VENTILATION

The amount of air breathed in or out per minute is called the respiratory minute volume or pulmonary ventilation. It is usually measured as expired ventilation ($\dot{V}_E$) and expressed as litres (BTPS) per minute. Even in the steady-state there is some spontaneous variation from minute to minute, and care has to be taken to minimize the influence of conscious control and extraneous stimuli, including the discomfort of the apparatus used for collecting the expired air. Resting ventilation depends on body size and metabolism and is

Table 13.9   Respiratory data at different ages

Age	Respiratory frequency (breaths per min)	Tidal volume (V_T) (ml)	Basal oxygen requirement (V_{O_2}) (ml per min)
At birth	14–60	10–20	23
First year	25–35	—	78
2–4 years	20–30	—	87–100
5–14 years	20–25	200–350	100–175
Adult man	10–18	350–900 av. 500	240
Adult woman	10–18	200–650 av. 340	200

The figures in the last column have been calculated from the data in Fig. 2.15 The range of respiratory data is very wide indeed (see for example *The Handbook of Respiration* (1958) London: Saunders). The figures given in this table can only be regarded as representative.

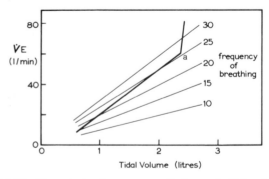

Fig. 13.10 The relation between ventilation and tidal volume in human subjects when breathing is stimulated by any factor except hyperthermia. Note that the observed relation appears to be linear over a wide range of tidal volumes and crosses the iso-frequency lines, and that there is usually an inflexion a, beyond which the tidal volume rises little above half the vital capacity. (*After* E. N. Hey, B. B. Lloyd, D. J. C. Cunningham, M. G. M. Jukes & D. P. G. Bolton (1966) *Respiration Physiology*, 1, 193–205.)

between 5 and 7 litres/min. Considerable reserve capacity is available for ventilation in normal subjects, and minute ventilation can exceed 100 litres in heavy exercise.

Respiratory frequency. The respiratory frequency at rest varies considerably from subject to subject but in the adult it is 10 to 18 per minute. Higher frequencies are normally found in young children (Table 13.9). The respiratory frequency is increased along with tidal volume by almost any respiratory stimulus such as exercise. It is under voluntary control and for this reason a true resting frequency is not likely to be obtained if the subject is aware that his breathing is being observed. The relationship between ventilation, tidal volume and respiratory frequency is shown in Figure 13.10.

Composition of the Respired Air

The effect of respiration, so far as oxygen is concerned, is that an adult man at rest acquires about 250 ml of oxygen per min. At the same time about the same quantity of carbon dioxide is breathed out.

Expired air can be collected by making the subject breathe through valves into a Douglas bag (p. 15). A sample of *alveolar air* can be obtained by the method devised by Haldane and Priestley. A tube 120 cm long and 2·5 cm in diameter is fastened to a mouthpiece provided with an evacuated gas sampling tube or an air-tight syringe. At the end of a normal expiration the subject closes his nose and breathes out as deeply and as quickly as possible through the tube, finally closing the mouthpiece by putting his tongue against it. Immediately, a sample of the air last expelled from the lungs is taken. In this method the dead space air coming first into the long tube is washed out by the alveolar air coming later, so that alveolar air only is taken into the sampling tube. This technique is open to the objection that, by interrupting the rhythm of respiration, it may alter the composition of the alveolar air. Alternative methods that sample a small quantity of the gas at the end of each normal expiration over a period of time ('end-tidal sampling') have the advantage of providing continuous and sensitive monitoring of the alveolar composition in the undisturbed subject. Neither method gives accurate results when there is abnormal distribution of gases in the lungs such as occurs in many patients with chronic disease of the lungs or even in normal patients being ventilated by artificial means.

Air samples can be analysed by a variety of methods, but the most precise is Lloyd's modification of Haldane's volumetric apparatus. The volume of the sample is first accurately measured and it is then passed over potassium hydroxide solution to absorb carbon dioxide and the volume is measured once more. Finally the oxygen is absorbed by alkaline pyrogallol solution and the oxygen content is shown by the further reduction in the volume of the sample. More rapid but less precise methods depend on the paramagnetic properties of oxygen, the infra-red absorption of carbon dioxide or on the thermal properties of gases (catharometry). Mass spectrometry is now widely used.

The following table of experimental results shows how the percentage composition of typical expired and alveolar air samples from a resting subject differs from that of inspired atmospheric air which is remarkably constant the world over.

The values for nitrogen in the table include small quantities of argon and other inert gases that behave physiologically like nitrogen. Nitrogen is not given out from the body as the increase in nitrogen content of the expired air might at first sight suggest. Since the respiratory quotient (RQ),

Percentage composition of dry gas	Inspired air	Expired air	Alveolar air
Oxygen	20·93	16·89	14·50
Nitrogen	79·04	79·61	79·95
Carbon dioxide	0·03	3·50	5·55

$$\frac{\text{Volume of } CO_2 \text{ produced}}{\text{Volume of } O_2 \text{ used}},$$

is usually less than 1 (see p. 13), the volume of carbon dioxide escaping from the blood is less than the volume of oxygen taken into the blood. The RQ calculated from the expired air composition in the example given above is 0·83. Thus the volume of air expired is less than the volume of air inspired although both contain the same absolute amount of nitrogen, given by $\dot{V}_I \times F_{I,N_2}$ or $\dot{V}_E \times F_{E,N_2}$ where F stands for fraction of dry gas volume. The equivalence of these expressions means that the ratio of the expired to inspired ventilations is the ratio between the inspired and expired nitrogen fractions. This formula is used in the calculation of the RQ from the equation above which first becomes

$$\frac{\dot{V}_E \times F_{E,CO_2}}{\left(\dot{V}_E \times \dfrac{F_{E,N_2}}{F_{I,N_2}} \times F_{I,O_2} \right) - (\dot{V}_E \times F_{E,O_2})}$$

and therefore simplifies to

$$\frac{F_{E,CO_2}}{(0·265 \times F_{E,N_2}) - F_{E,O_2}}$$

Alveolar values can be substituted throughout for expired values, and partial pressures can be used instead of fractions. The inspired CO_2 fraction in atmospheric air is small enough to be ignored in this equation.

The alveolar air is not so variable in composition as the tidal air. During quiet breathing the small quantity of air drawn into the alveoli with each breath, about 360 ml, is not sufficient to disturb very greatly the composition of the large volume, about 2900 ml, of air in the functional residual capacity but in deep breathing the composition of the expired air approaches more closely that of the alveolar air. It might be thought that such a system of ventilation of the alveoli is inefficient since the alveoli are not swept through with fresh air at each breath. However, the known rates of diffusion of oxygen and carbon dioxide are more than sufficient to allow the rapid transfer of carbon dioxide and oxygen through the space occupied by the functional residual air.

Alveolar Dead-space

Of the 500 ml of air taken in at a quiet inspiration only a part reaches the respiratory parts of the lungs; the remainder occupies the mouth, pharynx, trachea (25 to 30 ml) and air passages up to the terminal bronchioles (that is the ('anatomical' dead-space) and is unchanged in composition because no respiratory exchange takes place. On expiration the unchanged air in the dead-space is breathed out first, to be followed by air from the alveoli; the mixed expired air contains both dead-space air and alveolar air. If 500 ml of expired air contains 4 per cent carbon dioxide, the total amount of carbon dioxide breathed out is $4/100 \times 500 = 20$ ml. But this 20 ml carbon dioxide came from only X ml of alveolar air which contained 5·5 per cent carbon dioxide (for method see p. 211); therefore $X \times 5·5 \div 100 = 20$ and $X = 364$ ml. The dead-space in this simplified example is 136 ml which is approximately the value in young men. The value varies with the position of the subject and it increases if the lungs are distended (see also p. 202).

The dead-space ventilation equals the dead-space volume times the respiratory frequency, and thus increases as breathing gets faster. For any given volume of total (expired) ventilation, the proportion that is wasted in ventilating the dead-space rises with the respiratory frequency.

From the functional point of view, it is more important to measure the volume or ventilation of the *physiological dead-space*, which includes, in addition to the anatomical dead space, a further volume known as the *alveolar dead-space*. This comprises those alveoli that are not perfused and a proportion of those that are partially perfused; that is, it allows for the relatively inefficient ventilation of all those alveoli with a $\dot{V}/\dot{Q}$ ratio (see p. 219) higher than normal. Physiological dead-space is defined, therefore, as that part of the tidal volume which does not participate in gaseous exchange; in practice its measurement requires the sampling of arterial blood. Then Bohr's mixing equation gives:

Physiological dead-space

$$= \text{Tidal volume} \left\{ \frac{\text{arterial } P_{CO_2} - \text{mixed expired } P_{CO_2}}{\text{arterial } P_{CO_2} - \text{inspired } P_{CO_2}} \right\}$$

This equation is parallel to the one that is the basis for the calculation of anatomical dead-space above:

Anatomical dead-space

$$= \text{Tidal volume} \left\{ \frac{\text{alveolar } F_{CO_2} - \text{mixed expired } F_{CO_2}}{\text{alveolar } F_{CO_2} - \text{inspired } F_{CO_2}} \right\}$$

(P = partial pressure and F = fraction. In both equations inspired CO_2 is usually taken as zero.)

The expired ventilation can be thought of as comprising two portions: dead-space (wasted) ventilation and alveolar (effective) ventilation.

By convention all values for the subdivisions of the lung volume and all results of pulmonary function tests should be given at body temperature and atmospheric pressure and saturated with water vapour, BTPS, and not at 0°C as are metabolic data. The values quoted on pages 210 to 211 are the mean values for adult males in a population varying widely in age and size. The values in women are about 25 per cent lower.

Uneven Distribution

All parts of the lungs are not ventilated uniformly even in normal persons; the distribution of ventilation in disease may be extremely uneven. The nitrogen content of an alveolar air sample taken after breathing pure oxygen for 7 min should be less than 2·5 per cent; in emphysema, in which the ventilation is very uneven, it may be 10 per cent because the oxygen has not succeeded in washing the nitrogen out of the less well ventilated parts of the lungs. Uneven ventilation may also be detected by recording continuously the nitrogen content of the air expired immediately after a single maximal inspiration of oxygen. After the oxygen in the dead-space is blown out the nitrogen level in normal persons climbs rapidly to a nearly flat plateau: a slow increase of nitrogen content up to a high level indicates defective distribution or mixing of the large breath of oxygen because the poorly ventilated alveoli that received little oxygen during inspiration empty slowly during expiration. This is called the 'nitrogen washout' test.

Closing Capacity

It has recently been discovered that during expiration significant closure, or at least restriction of airflow, may occur in the gravitationally dependent airways at the lung bases. The lung volume at which this occurs is called the *closing capacity*. It is the sum of the residual volume and the *closing volume*. Such closure can be demonstrated by a simple test involving the continuous rapid monitoring of a tracer gas (for example argon or helium) in the respired air. If the tracer is administered as a bolus early in a deep inspiration starting from residual volume (see p. 208), it is preferentially distributed to the uppermost parts of the lung because of the normal trans-pulmonary pressure gradients. During a slow expiration, a sudden rise in the concentration of the tracer shows that the expired air is now coming predominantly from those upper parts, and it is presumed that the lower parts have been closed off by airway collapse.

Closing volume is increased in older subjects, in pulmonary oedema and in smokers, and it may eventually exceed the functional residual capacity, particularly when this is reduced as it is when the subject is in the supine position. Closure then occurs during the normal tidal volume. In these circumstances the impairment of ventilation may lead to significant hypoxaemia. The increase in closing volume in old age may be, at least partly, responsible for the lower resting arterial P_{O_2} in the elderly.

Fetal and Neonatal Respiration

From the age of 12 weeks the fetus makes occasional respiratory movements. If radio-opaque material is injected into the amniotic fluid before Caesarean section, X-ray photographs of the fetus immediately after birth show shadows in its lungs and intestinal tract. Since the radio-opaque material is concentrated in the lungs, the water of the amniotic fluid must be absorbed through the lungs into the fetal circulation. During intra-uterine life respiratory movements are intermittent and irregular. At birth, air is breathed instead of fluid and the respirations become deeper and more regular. The extent of the expansion of the lungs is indicated by the change in specific gravity; lungs removed from the body before respiration has begun sink in water (sp. gr. 1·06) whereas aerated lungs float (sp. gr. 0·34).

When air enters the lungs at the first breath an air–liquid interphase is formed, the surface tension of which resists ingress of air. Since the resistance is inversely proportional to the radius of the tube it is not surprising to find that an air pressure of the order of 30 cm H₂O is needed to inflate fully an excised lung of a full-term baby. This resistance does not seem to present undue difficulty to the baby since intraoesophageal swings of 90 cm H₂O have been recorded during the first breath. The first inspiratory effort must therefore be violent, but as the residual air builds up subsequent breaths need not be so vigorous. The low surface tension fluid lining of the alveoli (p. 204) must form at the first breath; if it does not the infant experiences respiratory distress due to its efforts to expand the lungs. The amniotic fluid in the lungs is carried off by the lymphatics in the first three or four hours after birth.

The respiratory frequency at birth is usually about 30 per minute (range 14 to 60); since the average respiratory minute volume is 500 ml the average tidal volume is about 17 ml. Breathing may be quite irregular in the first few days of extra-uterine life but later becomes regular. The Hering-Breuer reflex (p. 230) is active during the first week of life only. The respiration of the new-born infant is stimulated by administration of carbon dioxide just as is the respiration of the adult. In the new-born the dead-space is 4·4 ml, the functional residual capacity is 75 ml, and the crying vital capacity is 56 to 110 ml.

PULMONARY CIRCULATION

The primary function of the lungs is gas exchange which is carried out by a network of capillaries surrounding the alveoli. The blood vessels of the lungs consist of two sets originating from different sources and performing functions of a different character. One set is derived from the pulmonary artery and gives rise to the alveolar capillaries; the other set takes origin directly or indirectly from the aorta, and furnishes the nutrient vessels of the lungs by way of the bronchial arteries.

The Lung Blood Vessels

The main pulmonary artery divides into two, one to each lung. Within each lung the pulmonary artery follows the bronchi in all their sub-divisions and breaks up into arterioles and a network of capillaries situated in the walls of the air spaces (Fig. 13.11). Structurally the pulmonary artery is a predominantly elastic vessel with a thin medial coat. After entering the lungs the pulmonary arteries become less elastic and more muscular. Maximum muscularity appears in vessels of 100 to 200 μm diameter; then between 100 and 30 μm diameter the vessels rapidly lose their muscle coat.

The capillaries are each about 8 μm diameter and 8 μm long and form a dense network or mesh with an estimated area of 30 to 50 m² (Fig. 13.12). An alternative way of depicting the alveolar capillaries is to consider the vascular bed as consisting of two endothelial sheets of tissue held apart by 'stays' or 'posts' of septal tissue. This 'sheet-flow' concept appears to a red cell as an underground parking garage with floor, ceiling and intervening support posts. The capillary vessels are so short and communicate so frequently with one another that the concept of a 'sheet' is more helpful than the notion of a series of tubes.

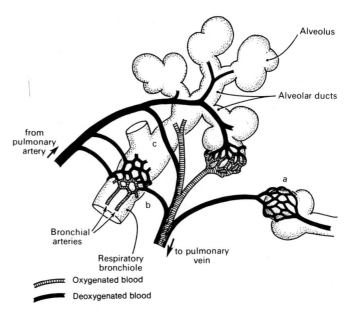

Fig. 13.11 General scheme of a primary lobule showing vascular communications between the pulmonary and bronchial vascular systems in the region of the respiratory bronchiole and some intra-pulmonary causes of venous admixture with arterial blood. The latter include (1) uneven alveolar ventilation of different parts of the lungs. Under-ventilation of alveoli with a normal pulmonary capillary blood flow (indicated by adjacent lobule (a)) leads to hypoxaemia. (2) Venous blood from the bronchial circulation draining into the pulmonary veins (b). (3) Pulmonary artery-pulmonary vein shunts (c). The bronchial artery blood flow is exceedingly difficult to measure but is probably about 1 per cent of the pulmonary flow. The bronchial circulation has few veins of its own, the drainage is mainly as at (b) into the pulmonary veins which go to the left atrium. The bronchial arteries also supply a small amount of blood to mediastinal structures which drain into the azygos vein and left atriu. *(By courtesy of M. de Burgh Daly.)*

Fig. 13.12 The network of capillaries in the walls of the alveoli (W. S. Miller (1947). *The Lung*, 2nd edition, p. 76. Illinois: C. C. Thomas).

The air in the alveoli is separated from the blood in the capillaries by 0·3 to 0·7 µm (Fig. 13.13). In disease however the potential space between them may be occupied by oedema fluid or an inflammatory exudate so the distance through which oxygen and carbon dioxide have to diffuse is greatly increased. All the pulmonary capillary blood returns by the pulmonary veins containing oxygenated blood to the left atrium. The pulmonary circulation is in series with the systemic circulation and therefore the outputs of the left and right ventricles must be equal except for very short periods when circulatory adjustments are taking place. Otherwise the lungs would either become overfilled with blood or depleted of blood depending on the relative outputs of the two ventricles (p. 134).

The *bronchial arteries* enter each lung, and break up into two or three branches which accompany each of the larger bronchi and bronchioles. Their capillary networks supply arterial blood to the smooth muscle wall of the whole length of the bronchial tree as far as the respiratory bronchioles, and to intrapulmonary nerves and nerve ganglia, pleura, interstitial lung substance and lymphoid tissue, and are the vasa vasorum of the pulmonary arteries. Blood is carried away from the bronchial circulation by two routes: first, by true bronchial veins draining blood from the first two dividing points of the bronchial tree into the right atrium, and secondly, by broncho-

pulmonary veins which drain blood from the venous plexus surrounding the bronchi and bronchioles as far as the respiratory bronchioles into the pulmonary veins (Fig. 13.11). Blood from the systemic circulation can therefore reach the pulmonary circulation by way of the bronchial vascular system.

Not only do the systemic and pulmonary vascular system anastomose on the venous side of the pulmonary circulation, but also at a capillary level (Fig. 13.11), and possibly at a pre-capillary level as well. The clinical significance of these anastomotic channels is that in forms of congenital heart disease associated with stenosis (narrowing) of the main pulmonary artery, patent interventricular septum and arterial hypoxaemia, these channels open up enormously thereby increasing the bronchial artery blood flow from a normal value of 1 to 2 per cent of the left ventricular output to as much as 20 per cent. This blood now goes through the pulmonary capillaries so that the systemic arterial (hypoxic) blood is given a 'second chance' of being oxygenated.

The lungs receive a nerve supply from both the para-sympathetic and sympathetic divisions of the autonomic nervous system. The pulmonary circulation (pre- and post-pulmonary capillary blood vessels), the bronchial circulation and the bronchial smooth muscle receive a nerve supply from the vagus and sympathetic nerves. In addition there are now

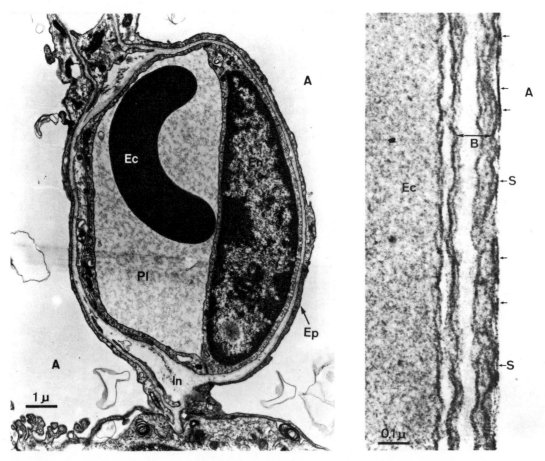

Fig. 13.13 Electron micrographs of monkey lung. The picture on the left shows two alveoli (A) with the capillary between them in cross section. Ep, epithelium; In, interstitial space; En, endothelial cell; Pl, plasma; Ec, erythrocyte. (E. R. Weibel (1969) In *The Pulmonary Circulation and Interstitial Space*, eds. A. P. Fishman & H. H. Heckt, p. 11. Chicago: University of Chicago Press.) The picture on the right shows the alveolar endothelium of rat lung at higher magnification. B, tissue barrier (endothelium, interstitial space and epithelium). S, surfactant (arrows point to osmophilic surface layer). *(By courtesy of Joan Gil.)*

believed to be three functionally different types of receptors in the lungs: (1) pulmonary stretch-receptors in the walls of the airways (responsible for the Hering–Breuer respiratory reflex) (p. 230), (2) lung irritant receptors (for example, those in the wall of the trachea responsible for the cough reflex (p. 231), and (3) juxta-pulmonary capillary receptors ('J'-receptors) situated in the interstitial space next to the pulmonary capillaries. The afferent fibres conveying the information to the central nervous system run largely in the vagus nerves.

The ensemble of the respiratory bronchiole and its subdivisions (Fig. 13.2 and Fig. 13.11), together with its accompanying pulmonary and bronchial blood vessels, lymph vessels and nerves, forms a *primary lobule*.

Pressures in the pulmonary blood vessels. The pressure in the pulmonary artery in man can be measured directly by catheterization through the right side of the heart. The values for pulmonary arterial pressure are: systolic, 20 to 23 mm Hg, which is the same as the right ventricular systolic pressure; diastolic 5 to 9 mm Hg, and mean pressure, 11 to 15 mm Hg. Typical pressure waves are shown in Fig. 13.14.

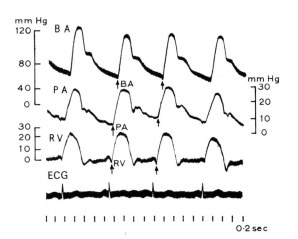

Fig. 13.14 Simultaneous records of pressure in brachial artery (BA), pulmonary artery (PA) and right ventricle (RV) obtained by optical manometers attached to cardiac catheters. An ECG, lead II, is also shown. *(By courtesy of A. Cournand.)*

When studying pulmonary haemodynamics, it is often important to know the value of the left atrial pressure which may be measured by passing a catheter into the pulmonary artery and then advancing it until it can pass no further and oxygenated blood can be withdrawn from it. Its tip must block a small branch of the pulmonary artery and the pressure may be recorded. This is known as pulmonary arterial *wedge pressure* and usually corresponds fairly closely with the pressure in the left atrium. Although the method is relatively simple it can give values for pulmonary wedge pressure which do not agree with those in the left atrium, and a more reliable method is to measure the left atrial pressure directly by transatrial septal catheterization through the right atrium (p. 158). The mean left atrial pressure varies from 0 to 5 mm Hg, so the pressure gradient across the lungs, pulmonary arterial pressure minus left atrial pressure, is 12 mm Hg. The blood flow through the

lungs is about 5 l per minute at rest, and therefore the resistance to blood flow offered by the pulmonary circulation (see formula (p. 180) is only about one-eighth that of the systemic circulation.

The pressure in the lung capillaries must lie between the pulmonary arterial pressure and the left atrial pressure, and is about 8 mm Hg. This pressure is much lower than that in the capillaries of the systemic circulation. The osmotic pressure exerted by the plasma proteins is, however, the same in the two vascular territories so the tendency for fluid to remain within the pulmonary capillaries or for fluid to enter them from the alveolar spaces is greater than in the systemic capillary bed. In failure of the left ventricle, the left atrial pressure rises and this rise is transmitted backward to the pulmonary capillaries. When the capillary pressure reaches 20 to 30 mm Hg, fluid passes into the alveoli resulting in pulmonary oedema.

Flow in the pulmonary blood vessels. Mean blood flow through the pulmonary circulation of man may be measured by the Fick, dye dilution or thermal dilution methods, and the normal value at rest, expressed as cardiac index, is 3·2 l per min per m² body surface area. The output of the right ventricle is not distributed equally between the two lungs because of their different size; about 45 per cent passes through the left lung and 55 per cent through the right. The pulmonary circulation time, that is the time taken for the blood to pass from the pulmonary artery to the left atrium is about 5 sec, of which about 0·75 sec represents the time the blood takes to traverse the pulmonary capillaries at rest. During strenuous exercise the latter figure is reduced to about 0·3 sec which is still long enough for adequate gas change to occur. The pressure is pulsatile not only in the pulmonary arteries (Fig. 13.14) but also in the pulmonary capillaries and veins.

Distribution of pulmonary blood flow. The mean pressure in the pulmonary artery of 11 to 15 mm Hg is

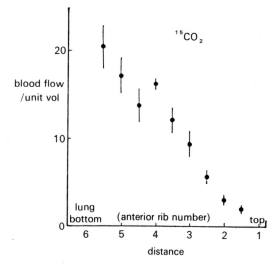

Fig. 13.15 Distribution of blood flow in the normal upright lung as measured with radioactive carbon dioxide. Data from 16 normal subjects; means and standard errors of clearance rates. Note that blood flow decreases steadily from the bottom to the top of the lung, there being virtually no flow at the apex. (J. B. West (1970) *Ventilation Blood Flow and Gas Exchange.* 2nd edition, p. 19. Oxford: Blackwell.)

equivalent to 15 to 20 cm of blood and is barely sufficient to perfuse the vessels in the apices of the lungs which are about 15 cm above the level of the pulmonary artery when the body is erect. On the other hand the pressure in the arteries in the bases of the lungs is equal to the pressure in the pulmonary artery plus the hydrostatic pressure of about 15 cm of blood, the vertical distance of the vessels below the pulmonary artery. The lower parts of the lungs (Fig. 13.15) are therefore relatively better perfused. The blood flow in different parts of the lungs varies therefore with their vertical position in relation to the level of the pulmonary artery. Thus in a person lying supine the apices and bases of the lungs are equally perfused, but the vessels in the posterior parts of the lungs are better perfused than those in the anterior parts.

The blood flow through the various parts of the lungs can be investigated quantitatively. The subject is seated between a pair of scintillation counters sensitive to the radiation from a particular anteroposterior volume of lung. If he takes a single breath of carbon dioxide containing $^{11}CO_2$, the counting rate rises quickly indicating the amount of gas coming into the part of the lung being investigated. If he holds his breath the $^{11}CO_2$ is carried off in the pulmonary circulation and so the count falls, the rate of fall indicating the rate of blood flow. Such experiments (Fig. 13.15) show that the blood flow is maximal at the bases of the lungs and is minimal (nearly zero) at the apices of the lungs when the subject is in the upright position. In exercise the flow increases in all parts of the lungs due to an increase in cardiac output and pulmonary arterial pressure, but especially in the apical regions so that the flows now become more even. In diseases of the heart in which pulmonary blood flow is augmented or in which the left atrial and pulmonary venous pressures are increased, the pulmonary flow is also more evenly distributed within the lungs.

It must be realized that if the pulmonary vessels behaved as a series of rigid tubes, the siphon effect would ensure that blood flow in all parts of the lungs was uniform. *In vivo*, the vessels are very distensible and collapsible and this is responsible for the blood being delivered in the lungs unevenly largely because of gravitational effects. This can be accounted for by consideration of the mechanical effects of the pressure inside and outside the vessels, that is the transmural pressure.

The lungs may be arbitrarily divided into three zones by the relative sizes of the pulmonary arterial, pulmonary venous and alveolar pressures (Fig. 13.16). In *zone 1* there is little blood flow because the pulmonary arterial pressure is less than the alveolar pressure to which the collapsible vessels are exposed. In *zone 2* the pulmonary arterial pressure exceeds the alveolar pressure, but the alveolar pressure is higher than the pulmonary venous pressure. In this situation the vessels are partly compressed (Fig. 13.16) and the blood flow is proportional to the difference between the pulmonary arterial and alveolar pressures, rather than between the pulmonary arterial and pulmonary venous pressures. This situation has been compared with a sluice or waterfall and has given rise to the term 'sluice' or 'waterfall' effect. In *zone 3* the pulmonary venous pressure exceeds the alveolar pressure so the blood flow is determined by the difference between the pulmonary arterial and pulmonary venous pressures. Thus the blood flow increases down this zone because the transmural pressure increases, thereby distending the vessels.

Figure 13.17 shows that, in addition to the variation in blood flow from the apex to the base of the lung, ventilation also varies, but not to such a great extent. So far as oxygenation of the blood is concerned an important factor is the ratio of ventilation to blood flow in different parts of the lungs, known as the alveolar ventilation ($\dot{V}A$)–pulmonary capillary blood

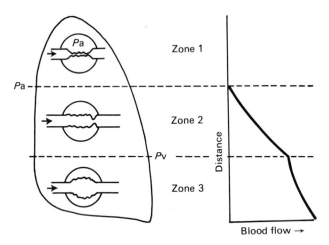

Fig. 13.16 Scheme which accounts for the distribution of blood flow in the lung. In zone 1, alveolar pressure (Pa) exceeds pulmonary arterial pressure (Pa) and no flow occurs, presumably because collapsible vessels are directly exposed to alveolar pressure. In zone 2, pulmonary arterial pressure exceeds alveolar pressure, but alveolar exceeds venous pressure (Pv). Here the vessels are partly compressed and flow is determined by the arterial-alveolar pressure difference which steadily increases down the zone. In zone 3 venous pressure now exceeds alveolar pressure and flow is determined by the arterial-venous pressure difference which is constant down the line. However the pressure across the walls of the vessels increases down the zone so that their calibre increases and so does the flow. (*After* J. B. West (1977) *Ventilation/Blood Flow and Gas Exchange*, 3rd edition, p. 22. Oxford: Blackwell.)

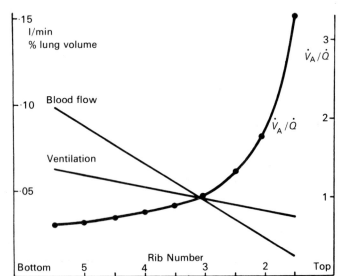

Fig. 13.17 Distribution of ventilation, blood flow and ventilation-perfusion ratio up the normal upright lung. Because blood flow falls more rapidly than ventilation with distance up the lung, the ventilation-perfusion ratio rises, slowly at first, then rapidly. (J. B. West (1977). *Ventilation/Blood Flow and Gas Exchange* 3rd edition, p. 30. Oxford: Blackwell.)

flow ($\dot{Q}$c) ratio or the ventilation–perfusion ratio. This varies from 3·3 at the apex to 0·63 at the base of the lungs (Fig. 13.17). The physiological significance of this ratio is discussed in the next section.

Pulmonary Blood Volume

The total blood volume in the body is about 5 litres of which 1·8 l, or 1·14 l per m² body surface area, are within the thorax, the intrathoracic blood volume. The pulmonary blood volume is 1·18 l, or 0·77 l per m² or 29 per cent of the total blood volume. The estimate of pulmonary blood volume includes about 100 ml in the pulmonary capillaries.

The pulmonary blood volume is not constant but varies widely under a variety of conditions, the changes being brought about by the transference of blood from the lungs to the systemic circulation and vice versa. While these changes are occurring the outputs of the two ventricles must momentarily be unequal. Because the volume of blood in the lungs can vary so much and is apparently in excess of that required for respiratory function the concept has arisen that the lungs act as a blood reservoir. The reserve blood in the lungs is important in determining the diastolic filling of the left side of the heart and thus the stroke volume and output of the left ventricle.

Complex changes in the pulmonary circulation occur during normal breathing. With the fall of intrathoracic pressure during inspiration there is an increased filling of the right ventricle and therefore an increased right ventricular output.

The mean pulmonary arterial pressure rises, causing distension of the pulmonary blood vessels and an increase in pulmonary blood volume. At the same time the capacity of the pulmonary vascular bed increases but, in spite of the increased pulmonary artery inflow volume, the pulmonary venous outflow decreases, resulting in a reduction in left ventricular outflow and a small fall in systemic blood pressure. In expiration the increased volume of blood in the lungs is expelled through the pulmonary veins with the result that the left ventricular output increases causing a rise in systemic blood pressure. Simultaneously the higher intrathoracic pressure reduces the return of blood to the right ventricle and the mean pulmonary arterial pressure falls.

Other factors modify pulmonary blood volume. It is greater in the supine than in the erect position. The application of intermittent positive pressure artificial respiration reduces pulmonary blood volume, as does venesection. Procedures such as warming the body, general and spinal anaesthesia, and injection of systemic vasodilator drugs, for example, amyl nitrate and nitroglycerine, cause displacement of appreciable quantities of blood from the thorax. Thus changes in vascular tone in the systemic circulation causing changes in systemic blood volume lead to inverse changes in pulmonary blood volume.

The volume of blood in the lungs increases if a back-pressure is imposed on the pulmonary circulation by a rise in left atrial pressure, such as results from mitral stenosis. In left ventricular failure, the left atrial pressure and the pulmonary blood volume increase.

Regulation of Pulmonary Blood Vessels

It is evident, then, that an important determinant of the pulmonary arterial pressure is the cardiac output. Thus in exercise when cardiac output increases several-fold, there is usually an accompanying rise in pulmonary arterial pressure (Fig. 13.18).

Active changes in calibre of the pulmonary blood vessels can also occur, thereby altering pulmonary vascular resistance and pulmonary arterial pressure. Vasoconstriction is caused by the stimulation of sympathetic fibres going to the lungs, and by injections of adrenaline, noradrenaline and 5-hydroxytryptamine. Certain reflexes also modify the pulmonary vascular resistance; thus stimulation of the carotid sinus baroreceptors causes a decrease in pulmonary vascular resistance, whereas stimulation of the carotid body chemoreceptors increases

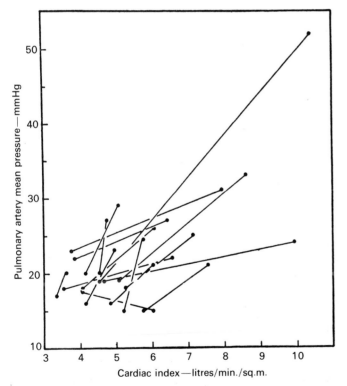

Fig. 13.18 Mean pulmonary arterial pressure and cardiac output at rest and during the fifth minute of exercise in 16 normal subjects. Individual resting and exercise values are joined. (Donald, K. W., Bishop, J. M., Cumming, G. and Wade, O. L. (1955), *Clinical Science*, 14, 37–73.)

Table 13.19 Pressure in pulmonary artery in relation to altitude and arterial hypoxia

Altitude		Mean pulmonary arterial pressure (mmHg)	Arterial oxygen saturation (per cent)
(ft)	(m)		
0	0	13	97
5 280	1 610	16	95
10 150	3 094	25	92
14 900	4 542	28	78

After J. H. K. Vogel, W. F. Weaver, R. L. Rose, S. G. Blount & R. F. Grover. Quoted from *Lancet* (1962) ii, 233–234.

pulmonary vascular resistance. There is still doubt, however, about the functional significance of the sympathetic innervation to the lungs in man.

A particularly potent constrictor agent is hypoxia. Acute hypoxia causes a rise in pulmonary arterial pressure from constriction of the small pulmonary vessels involving both arterioles and venules. This is the result of a direct effect of hypoxic alveolar air or of unsaturated blood in the vessels. An increase in cardiac output is also partly responsible for the rise in pulmonary arterial pressure. Chronic hypoxia at high altitudes causes a rise in pulmonary arterial pressure (Table 13.19); the pressure returns to normal if the subject is brought down to sea level. At high altitudes breathing is much deeper than at sea level (p. 235) and a reduction of intrathoracic pressure (p. 235) combined with increased capillary pressure may account for pulmonary oedema in mountain climbers and in mountain cattle (Brisket disease). Chronic disease of the lungs with hypoxia leads to generalized pulmonary vasoconstriction, persistent increase in mean pulmonary arterial pressure and, ultimately, to failure of the right ventricle. Localized hypoxia in poorly ventilated areas of the lungs causes local vasoconstriction so that blood is diverted to better aerated parts of the lung. An increase in alveolar P_{CO_2} also causes pulmonary vasoconstriction.

Dilatation of the pulmonary blood vessels occurs in response to injections of acetylcholine.

Non-respiratory Function of the Lungs

Although the lungs act primarily to oxygenate the blood and to excrete CO_2, it is now apparent that they have other important functions. They are in a unique position to act as filters. Particles of fibrin, fat and pieces of placental tissue are trapped in the lungs and removed by enzymes. The lungs take up leucocytes and platelets and contribute factors involved in blood coagulation and fibrinolysis; prostaglandins are removed. The lungs possess many enzymes; for example the conversion of angiotensin I to angiotensin II probably occurs in the lungs; noradrenaline is removed in the lungs but adrenaline passes through unchanged. Other activities, including the initiation of reflexes, are described elsewhere.

VENTILATION-PERFUSION AND GAS EXCHANGE

Ventilation-Perfusion Relations

Since about 4 litres of air enter the alveoli per minute and about 5 litres of blood pass through the lungs per minute the overall ventilation-perfusion ration ($\dot{V}_A/\dot{Q}$) is about 0:8 but this average or ideal value does not apply to all alveoli even in a healthy man. Since in the steady-state the quantity of oxygen taken up by the blood is the same as the quantity lost by the alveolar air, and the quantity of carbon dioxide added to the alveolar air is the same as that lost by the body, the overall respiratory exchange ratio (R) of the blood and ideal alveolar air are the same, and this would be true for every alveolus if they all had the same ventilation-perfusion ratio. However, even in normal lungs there is a wide range of ratios from one

extreme where no blood perfuses a well-ventilated alveolus ($\dot{V}/\dot{Q} = \infty$) to the other where no air ventilates a well-perfused alveolus ($\dot{V}/\dot{Q} = 0$). Because of the different shapes of the dissociation curves of carbon dioxide and oxygen, these extremes do not in general balance each other out, and even in normal lungs there is a difference between the P_{O_2}, the P_{N_2} and to a smaller extent the P_{CO_2} of mixed alveolar gas and mixed pulmonary venous blood. This also results in a difference between the respiratory exchange ratios of individual alveoli (Fig. 13.20).

Measurement of the physiological dead space (p. 212) gives a clue to the ventilation-perfusion ratio since the space may be considered to include the anatomical dead space (where no gas exchange takes place) together with a contribution from alveoli with a high ventilation-perfusion ratio (where less than average exchange occurs). If the dead space is more than 30 per cent of the tidal volume a significant proportion of the alveoli is better ventilated than perfused if the anatomical dead space can be assumed to remain normal.

By taking samples of alveolar air through catheters introduced into different parts of the lung it is possible to obtain direct information about regional ventilation-perfusion relationships. By using oxygen or carbon dioxide labelled with $^{15}O_2$ (half-life 2 min) ventilation and perfusion can be assessed without the disturbance and discomfort of catheterization. The gamma radiation produced by decay of the isotope is detected by scintillation counters, one on the front and one on the back of the chest. The subject takes a single breath of air containing a trace of the labelled gas and holds his breath for 12 sec. The counting-rate rises in about 5 sec to a peak value, falls slowly during breath-holding and more rapidly when breathing of room air is resumed. The peak value indicates the amount of air entering the volume of lung between the counters, that is the ventilation. The slow fall during breath-holding measures the uptake of gas by the blood, that is the perfusion.

Such experiments show, when the subject is standing erect, a progressive fall in ventilation-perfusion ratio from 3·3 to 0·63 from apex to base of the lung. West has calculated that the alveolar P_{O_2} falls by 40 mm Hg from apex to base but because of the shape of the oxygen dissociation curve of haemoglobin the change in oxygen saturation of blood leaving the alveolar capillaries in the lower parts of the lungs is reduced by only 4 per cent. The P_{CO_2} and P_{N_2} increase on passing from the apex to the base of the lungs. The ventilation-perfusion inequality produced on changing from the horizontal to the vertical position has however little effect on the overall gas exchange.

In disease ventilation of an area of lung is reduced if the airways are narrowed or if the lung tissue becomes stiffer, that is its compliance is reduced. Neither condition allows the alveoli to fill up within the time of a single inspiration. Impaired alveolar ventilation with normal capillary perfusion produces a *physiological right-to-left shunt* of underoxygenated blood (*venous admixture*) causing arterial hypoxia which may be severe enough to produce 'central' cyanosis (p. 238). Many disease processes affect the pulmonary blood vessels and reduce capillary perfusion locally. The disturbed $\dot{V}/\dot{Q}$ ratio is usually accompanied by increased ventilation of other alveoli, but this cannot compensate entirely, and disturbed $\dot{V}/\dot{Q}$ ratios constitute a major cause of hypoxia (p. 237).

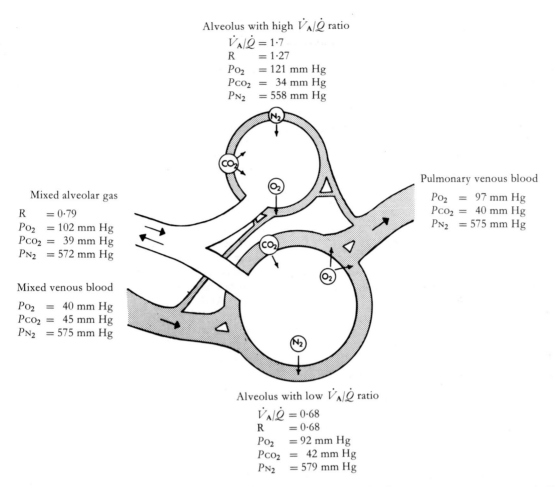

Alveolus with high $\dot{V}_A/\dot{Q}$ ratio

$\dot{V}_A/\dot{Q} = 1\cdot7$
$R \quad = 1\cdot27$
$P_{O_2} \quad = 121$ mm Hg
$P_{CO_2} = 34$ mm Hg
$P_{N_2} = 558$ mm Hg

Mixed alveolar gas

$R \quad = 0\cdot79$
$P_{O_2} \quad = 102$ mm Hg
$P_{CO_2} = 39$ mm Hg
$P_{N_2} = 572$ mm Hg

Mixed venous blood

$P_{O_2} \quad = 40$ mm Hg
$P_{CO_2} = 45$ mm Hg
$P_{N_2} = 575$ mm Hg

Pulmonary venous blood

$P_{O_2} \quad = 97$ mm Hg
$P_{CO_2} = 40$ mm Hg
$P_{N_2} = 575$ mm Hg

Alveolus with low $\dot{V}_A/\dot{Q}$ ratio

$\dot{V}_A/\dot{Q} = 0\cdot68$
$R \quad = 0\cdot68$
$P_{O_2} \quad = 92$ mm Hg
$P_{CO_2} = 42$ mm Hg
$P_{N_2} = 579$ mm Hg

Fig. 13.20 Diagram to illustrate possible variations in the ventilation-perfusion ratio, $\dot{V}_A/\dot{Q}$. R = respiratory exchange ratio. The stippled pathways represent the pulmonary capillaries; the two open circles represent two alveoli, one with a high $\dot{V}_A/\dot{Q}$ and the other with a low $\dot{V}_A/\dot{Q}$. The respiratory exchange ratios of the two alveoli vary considerably from each other and from that of an alveolus which is normally ventilated and perfused (R = 0.79). In the alveolus with high $\dot{V}_A/\dot{Q}$ ratio the P_{ACO_2} is relatively low while the P_{AO_2} is high. The volume of CO_2 exchanged is greater than that of O_2 (that is R is high) because of the different shapes of their dissociation curves (see Figs. 14.5 and 14.8). The N_2 in this alveolus is diluted by evolution of CO_2 to a greater extent than it is concentrated by absorption of O_2; the final P_{AN_2} is therefore relatively low. In the alveolus with low $\dot{V}_A/\dot{Q}$ ratio P_{ACO_2} is relatively high while P_{AO_2} is relatively low, and the volume of CO_2 exchanged is low relative to that of O_2, that is R is low. The N_2 in the alveolus is concentrated to a greater extent than it is diluted by the evolution of CO_2; the final P_{AN_2} is therefore high. For calculation of R see p. 211. (J. E. Cotes (1975) *Lung Function—Assessment and Application to Medicine*, Oxford: Blackwell.)

Alveolo-capillary Gas Transfer

Although respiratory gas exchange is commonly referred to as occurring across the 'alveolar' or 'alveolo-capillary' membrane the gases actually pass through five separate media (Fig. 13.13): the alveolar epithelium, the interstitial space, the capillary endothelium, the blood plasma and the membrane of the red cell. Surfactant (p. 204) is also present on the epithelial surface of the alveoli (Fig. 13.13). It is the first three of these media that are regarded as the 'alveolo-capillary membrane'. The alveolar membrane acts in a purely passive manner and the transference of oxygen or carbon dioxide takes place by diffusion. To calculate if diffusion can account for the passage of the gases it is necessary to know (1) the partial pressures of the gases in the alveolar air and in the blood of the pulmonary artery and pulmonary veins, and (2) the rate of diffusion of gases through the alveolar membrane and (3) the distances involved.

The methods for obtaining samples of alveolar air and for calculating the partial pressure of the gases are given on page 222. The partial pressures of gases in blood or plasma are measured by electrode methods (Figs 14.1 and 14.4).

Krogh showed that the carbon dioxide tension of the arterial blood (P_{aCO_2}) of the rabbit was nearly the same as the partial pressure of carbon dioxide in the alveolar air (P_{ACO_2}); usually the former was slightly greater. Although the free diffusion coefficient of carbon dioxide in water is a little less than that of oxygen, the solubility coefficient of carbon dioxide in water is twenty-four times greater than that of oxygen. This explains how it is that carbon dioxide is transferred about thirty times more rapidly than oxygen across the alveolar membrane and that a pressure difference of only 0·03 mm Hg is needed to transfer across the membrane all the carbon dioxide lost from the lungs.

When mixed venous blood with an oxygen tension of about 40 mm Hg enters the alveolar capillary it is exposed to alveolar air with an oxygen tension of 105 mm Hg, that is an alveolar-capillary difference of 65 mm Hg. As the blood flows through the capillary its oxygen tension rises and within 0·3 sec at rest approaches that in the alveolar air up to a final value of almost 105 mm Hg. The alveolo-capillary gradient at the venous end of the capillary is less than 1 mm Hg but the mean gradient over the whole length of the capillary is about 15 mm Hg. The membrane gradient at the venous end of the capillary is little altered in exercise but is greatly increased at low barometric pressures at which the oxygen content of the blood is reduced. The value of this gradient at an altitude of 5000 metres (16 400 feet) at rest is about 8 mm Hg although the average gradient along the whole of the capillary is still 15 mm Hg. This pressure is needed to transfer the required volume of oxygen across the alveolar membrane.

However, at sea-level the P_{O_2} of the arterial blood in young adults breathing atmospheric air is about 5 mm Hg lower than that of alveolar air. In old age the difference may be about 15 mm Hg. A small part of the difference in P_{O_2} between alveolar air and arterial blood is due to right to left shunts in the lungs; a larger part is due to bronchial veins and to minute veins from the heart muscle which drain into the left atrium. About half of the total difference is due to unevenness in the ventilation–perfusion ratio in the different parts of the lungs (venous admixture, p. 218).

In exercise the oxygen requirements are greatly increased and large quantities of oxygen must pass across the alveolar membrane. The pulmonary capillary bed enlarges considerably but, although the overall rate of blood flow through the pulmonary circuit is increased many times, the time spent by each red corpuscle in passing through a pulmonary capillary is reduced by only a half (p. 225). The oxygen saturation of arterial blood in exercise is as high as it is in the resting state unless the work is severe. The increased oxygen demand of the skeletal muscles is met partly by the opening up of capillaries closed in the resting state and by the greatly augmented blood flow through the muscle resulting from arteriolar dilatation. The increased uptake of oxygen by the muscles reduces the oxygen content of the blood returning to the lung. For example in mild exercise requiring 800 ml oxygen per min the arteriovenous oxygen difference may be 10 ml per 100 ml of blood instead of the resting value of about 4 ml. The increased oxygen consumption is more or less balanced by the concurrent hyperventilation, so that P_{AO_2} and P_{aO_2} remain nearly constant.

Transfer factor. The characteristics of the alveolar membrane of whole lung can be stated in terms of its transfer factor (T_L) which is the number of ml of a gas which can traverse it per minute per mm Hg gradient of pressure across the membrane. To measure T_L it is necessary to use a gas which is much more soluble in blood than in tissue fluids and plasma, otherwise the rate of uptake of the gas in the lungs would depend more on the amount of blood flowing past the alveoli than on the diffusion characteristics of the membrane. Two such gases exist, namely oxygen and carbon monoxide, and their increased solubility in blood is due to their chemical combination with haemoglobin. Of these two gases carbon monoxide uptake is easier to measure since the capacity of haemoglobin for it is such that even if the pulmonary blood flow were stopped during the period of measurement (less than one minute) at the concentrations used, the haemoglobin would still remain unsaturated at the end of the period. Further, in calculating the pressure difference between the gas in the alveolus and the plasma, it can be assumed (in non-smokers) that the plasma value is nearly zero. (In smokers it is often necessary to measure the 'back-tension' of CO.) When oxygen is the measuring gas this of course is not the case and the main difficulty is in calculating the mean alveolar to capillary gradient. Both gases measure the same function and the resting adult value of T_{CO} is 25 ml per min per mm Hg. According to the laws of diffusion and solubility T_{O_2} must be $1·23 \times 25 = 31$ ml/min/mm Hg. Individual values vary with the size of the subject. The T_{CO_2} on the other hand is of the order of 500 ml/min/mm Hg.

The speed with which these gases can pass from alveolar air to the haemoglobin of the red cells is obviously affected by the permeability of the structures crossed, the area over which the haemoglobin is spread and the rate of uptake by haemoglobin. It is now possible to measure separately two of the factors limiting the diffusion of gases: that due to the alveolocapillary membrane itself, and that due to the red blood cell and the haemoglobin. It can be calculated that the membrane T_{O_2} is of the order of 70 ml/min/mm Hg. The transfer factor is increased up to three times in healthy persons in exercise probably because many capillaries open up as a result of an increase in cardiac output and this increases the surface area available for diffusion. The resting value is reduced if the lung parenchyma is reduced in diseases which particularly affect the interstitial tissue of the lungs alveolar-capillary block). Where there is a reduction in the normal pulmonary capillary reserve, as in emphysema, low values for T_L in exercise have been reported.

REFERENCES

Angell James Jennifer E, Daly M de B 1972 Some mechanisms involved in the cardiovascular adaptations to diving. Symposia of the Society for Experimental Biology 26: 313–341
Asmussen E, Neils-Gunnar K 1968 The 'diving bradycardia' in exercising man. Acta Physiologica Scandinavica 73: 527–535
Avery M E, Normand C 1965 Respiratory physiology in the new-born infant. Anaesthesiology 26: 510–521
Bates D V, Christie R V 1964 Respiratory lung function in disease: An introduction to the integrated study of the lung. Saunders, London
Bennett P B, Elliott D H 1975 The physiology and medicine of diving and compressed air work, 2nd edn. Bailliére Tindall, London
Bonhuys A 1977 The physiology of breathing. Grune & Stratton, London
Buist A Sonia, Ross B B 1973 Predicted values for closing volumes using a modified single breath nitrogen test. American Review of Respiratory Diseases 107: 744–752
Campbell E J M, Agostini E, Davis J N 1971 The respiratory muscles: Mechanics and neural control, 2nd edn. Lloyd-Luke, London
Caro C G (ed) 1966 Advances in respiratory physiology. Edward Arnold, London
Comroe J H 1974 Physiology of respiration: An introductory text. 2nd edn. Lloyd-Luke, London
Cotes J E 1979 Lung function: Assessment and application in medicine, 4th edn. Blackwell, Oxford

Cumming G, Semple S J G 1973 Disorders of the respiratory system. Blackwell Scientific Publications, Oxford

Cunningham D J C 1973 The control system regulating breathing in man. Quarterly Reviews of Biophysics 6: 433–484

Daly I de B 1966 Pulmonary and bronchial vascular systems. Arnold, London

Fisher A B, Steinberg H, Bassett D 1974 Energy utilization by the lung. American Journal of Medicine 57: 437–446

Fishman A P, Renkin E M (eds) 1979 Pulmonary oedema. American Physiological Society (Clinical Physiology Series) Quest, London

Forgacs P 1978 Lung sounds. Baillière, London

Forster R E, Crandall E D 1976 Pulmonary gas exchange. Annual Review of Physiology 38: 69–93

Guz A 1975 Regulation of respiration in man. Annual Review of Physiology 37: 303–323

Haldane J S, Priestley J G 1935 Respiration, 2nd edn. Clarendon Press, Oxford

Harris L 1975 Clinical respiratory physiology. John Wright, Bristol

Heinemann H O, Fishman A P 1969 Non-respiratory functions of mammalian lung. Physiological Reviews 49: 1–47

Howell J B L, Campbell E J M (eds) 1966 Breathlessness. Blackwell, Oxford

Hughes D T D, Empey D W 1975 Clinical pulmonary physiology. Academic Press, London

Hunter A R 1972 Essentials of artificial ventilation of the lungs, 3rd edn. Churchill Livingstone, Edinburgh

Jones J D 1972 Comparative physiology of respiration. Arnold, London

Kinosita H, Murakami A 1967 Control of ciliary motion. Physiological Reviews 47: 53–82

Macklem P T 1978 Respiratory mechanics. Annual review of physiology 40: 157–184

Nunn J F 1977 Applied respiratory physiology, 2nd edn. Butterworth, London

Pattle R E 1965 Surface lining of lung alveoli. Physiological Reviews 45: 48–79

Porter, Ruth (ed) 1970 Breathing: Hering–Breuer centenary symposium. Churchill, London

Randell H W 1971 Aerospace Medicine. Churchill Livingstone, Edinburgh

Reid Lynne 1973 Properties of mucus. The scientific basis of medicine annual reviews 130–150

Saunders K B 1977 Clinical physiology of the lung. Blackwell, Oxford

Strang L B 1978 Neonatal respiration: physiology and clinical studies. Blackwell, Oxford

Sykes M K, McNicol M W, Campbell E J M 1976 Respiratory failure, 2nd edn. Blackwell, Oxford

Tierney D F 1974 Lung metabolism and biochemistry. Annual Review of Physiology 36: 209–232

Wagner P D 1977 Diffusion and chemical reaction in pulmonary gas exchange. Physiological Reviews 57: 257–312

Weibel E R 1973 Morphological basis of alveolar capillary gas exchange. Physiological Reviews 53: 419–495

West J B 1974 Respiratory physiology: the essentials. Blackwell, Oxford

West J B 1977 Pulmonary pathophysiology: the essentials. Blackwell, Oxford

West J B (ed) 1977 Regional differences in the lung. Academic Press, London

Weyer E M (ed) 1966 Interdisciplinary investigation of mucus production and transport. Annals of the New York Academy of Science 130: 869–973

Widdicombe J G (ed) 1974 Respiratory physiology, vol 2 of MTP. International Review of Science. Butterworth, London

Widdicombe J G 1974 Reflexes from the lungs in the control of breathing. Recent Advances in Physiology 9: 239–278

Widdicombe J G (ed) 1977 Respiratory physiology II. International Reviews of Physiology, vol 14. University Park Press, London

Yousef M K, Horvath S M, Bullard R W (eds) 1972 Physiological adaptations: desert and mountain. Academic Press, New York

See also references at the end of Chapter 14.

14 Respiratory Gases and the Control of Breathing

TRANSPORT OF GASES IN THE BLOOD

Gas tensions. The partial pressure of a gas, P, in a mixture of gases is obtained by multiplying the pressure of the mixture by the percentage of the gas in it. For example, the partial pressure of oxygen, Po_2, in dry atmospheric air (about 21 per cent oxygen) at 760 mm Hg is $21/100 \times 760 = 160$ mm Hg. The amount of a gas dissolved in water at 37°C exposed to a gas is given by the partial pressure multiplied by the solubility coefficient; for oxygen 0·00003, for carbon dioxide 0·0007, for nitrogen 0·000016 ml per ml water per mm Hg. When equilibrium is established between the gas and the water as many molecules of the gas enter the water as leave it; the *tension* of the gas in the water is then the same as the pressure (or partial pressure) of the gas. Since arterial blood is nearly in equilibrium with alveolar air the tensions of the gases in arterial blood (Pa) are approximately the same as their partial pressures in the alveolar air (PA). The table below shows the amounts of gases held in solution by 100 ml of water at 38°C exposed to alveolar air.

	Oxygen	Carbon dioxide	Nitrogen
	ml	ml	ml
100 ml water in equilibrium with alveolar air	0·3	2·6	0·9

When blood is exposed to a vacuum the whole of its contained gas is removed and the average volumes obtained from 100 ml of blood are as follows:

	Oxygen	Carbon dioxide	Nitrogen
	ml	ml	ml
Arterial blood	19	54	0·9
Venous blood	14	58	0·9

Thus the amount of oxygen in the blood is greater than can be accounted for by simple solution; most must be in some combination. Similarly, the greater part of the carbon dioxide must be present in combination. Nitrogen, on the other hand, is in simple solution.

Estimation of oxygen and carbon dioxide in blood. Whatever method is used for these measurements it is important that the blood sample should be collected in such a way as to avoid exposure to atmospheric air which would cause loss of carbon dioxide or gain of oxygen. In addition the assays must be done as quickly as possible because of the continuing metabolism of the blood cells.

In Haldane's classical method for blood gas analysis oxygen is driven off from a sample of blood by the addition of potassium ferricyanide solution. The reaction takes place in a closed apparatus so that the total volume of oxygen can be measured. Similarly carbon dioxide can be driven off, and its volume measured, by the addition of tartaric acid.

If the amount of oxygen carried in the plasma (0·3 ml per 100 ml per mm Hg) is subtracted from the total oxygen, we have the amount of oxygen carried by the haemoglobin, that is the *oxygen content*. If the estimation is repeated on another sample of the same blood which has first been shaken with air to saturate it with oxygen, the figure obtained is higher than the oxygen content of the first sample and represents the *oxygen capacity*. The *percentage saturation* of the first sample is given by (Oxygen content/Oxygen capacity) $\times$ 100.

In the Van Slyke apparatus the blood is put into an acidified air-free ferricyanide solution and subjected to a vacuum. The ferricyanide drives off the oxygen, the acid drives off the carbon dioxide and the vacuum the nitrogen. The gas evolved is analysed by absorbing first the carbon dioxide and then the oxygen.

In current clinical practice Po_2 is almost always measured by the use of electrodes such as that illustrated in Figure 14.1. Pco_2 can also be measured with a Pco_2 electrode (Fig. 14.4).

Since the light transmissions of haemoglobin and oxy-haemoglobin are different, the oxygen saturation of blood can be approximately determined by shining a light through the lobe of the ear on to two photo-cells one of which is covered with a red filter and the other with a blue filter (the *oximeter*). The ratio of the photocell currents is related to the saturation of the blood with oxygen. This method, which is very rapid and convenient, has been successfully used in the investigation of hypoxia during flying at high altitudes and has found applications in clinical medicine.

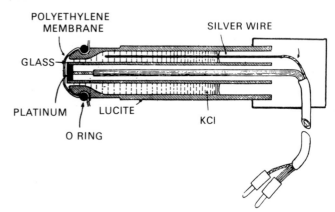

Fig. 14.1 The polarographic oxygen electrode. Blood is made to flow past a platinum electrode (charged to –0·5 V) covered with a polyethylene membrane permeable to oxygen molecules. At the platinum surface the dissolved molecules receive electrons, becoming either OH⁻ or H_2O_2. The current passing from the platinum electrode to the silver-silver chloride electrode in saturated KCl is linearly related to the number of dissolved oxygen molecules at its surface, which depends on the Po_2. If there is no oxygen there is practically no current. (J. W. Severinghaus (1959) *Symposium on pH and Blood Gas Measurement*, ed. Woolmer, R. F. Chap. 10. London: Churchill.)

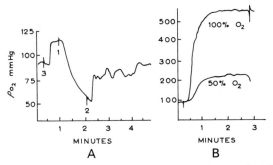

Fig. 14.2 A and B A. Polarographic electrode records. Effect of breath holding and hyperventilation on arterial oxygen tension while subject breathes room air. (1) Voluntary breath holding for 72 seconds during which the arterial P_{O_2} dropped to 51 mm Hg. (2) Recovery followed by normal respiration. (3) Preparatory hyperventilation lasting 36 seconds during which the P_{O_2} increased 20 mm Hg. The time lag after (1), (2) and (3) to the change of P_{O_2} is due to the dead space of the electrode and the circulation time. B. Continuous measurement of arterial oxygen tension of two individuals during administration of 50 and 100 per cent oxygen. The downward deflexion at the beginning indicates the time of application of the face mask. The interval between this deflexion and the upswing of the arterial oxygen tension (10 seconds) represents the dead space of the electrode plus the circulation time of the left brachial artery. (S. T. Koeff, M. U. Tsao, A. Vadney, T. O. Wilson & J. L. Wilson (1962) *Journal of Clinical Investigation*, 41, 1125.)

The partial pressures of oxygen and carbon dioxide in the tissues may be measured directly by suitably modified electrodes similar to those shown in Figures 14.1 and 14.4. Transcutaneous methods are also being developed.

By means of an oxygen electrode similar to that shown in Figure 14.1 through which blood from the brachial artery is passed continuous records of arterial P_{O_2} can be obtained (Fig. 14.2).

Table 14.3 The approximate differences between arterial and mixed venous blood in a healthy subject at rest

	Arterial blood	Mixed venous blood
Oxygen		
content (ml per 100 ml whole blood)	19	14
partial pressure (P_{O_2}) (mm Hg)	95	40
saturation of haemoglobin (percentage)	95	70
ml dissolved (in plasma of 100 ml blood)	0·3	0·12
Carbon dioxide partial pressure (P_{CO_2}) (mm Hg)	40	46
Carbon dioxide as ml total in 100 ml blood	48	52
content in plasma of 100 ml blood		
(60 ml plasma)	36	38
as bicarbonate in plasma of 100 ml blood	34	36
dissolved in plasma of 100 ml blood	1·6	1·8
total in ml carried by red cells in 100 ml blood	12·5	13·8
carbamino content of red cells of 100 ml blood	2·2	3·2
as bicarbonate in red cells of 100 ml blood	9·1	9·9
dissolved in red cells of 100 ml blood	0·8	0·9
pH	7·4	7·38
Chloride ions (mmol/l of plasma)	103	101

For some purposes it is convenient to use moles. The conversion is easily made since 1 mmol CO_2=22·3 ml CO_2 or 1 ml CO_2=0·045 mmol CO_2.

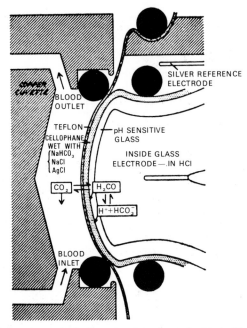

Fig. 14.4 Schematic design of a CO_2 electrode. The pH sensitive glass membrane is covered with cellophane soaked in bicarbonate solution saturated with silver chloride. This in turn is covered with teflon which is permeable to CO_2 gas but not to hydrogen ions. The blood sample passes through the apparatus as shown and CO_2 passes through the teflon from the blood into the bicarbonate solution and equilibrium is reached in a few minutes. The voltage measured between the two electrodes is linearly related to P_{CO_2}.

Transport of Oxygen

The amount of oxygen which a given amount of haemoglobin takes up depends on the partial pressure of the oxygen, P_{O_2}, in the atmosphere in contact with it. The graph (Fig. 14.5) showing the relation between the percentage saturation of haemoglobin and the partial pressure of oxygen, the *dissociation curve*, is obtained in the following way. A small quantity of blood, say 5 ml, is placed in a 250 ml bottle (tonometer) filled with gas of known oxygen concentration. The bottle is rotated for 20 minutes in a water-bath at 37·5°C, so that a large area of blood is exposed to the gas. Then the percentage saturation is measured as described above. The results of a series of determinations at different pressures of oxygen when plotted give a sigmoid curve as shown in Figure 14.5.

Since each haem group is a binding site for oxygen, a haemoglobin molecule can combine with up to four molecules of oxygen. When some of the binding sites combine with oxygen a change occurs in the arrangement of the protein subunits and the affinity of the haem groups for oxygen is increased. Because the sites of oxygen binding are at some distance from one another, this co-operation of the four sites in binding oxygen is an example of an allosteric effect.

The oxygen dissociation curve of myoglobin (Fig. 14.6) which has only one haem group is a simple hyperbola. The sigmoid relationship shown by haemoglobin makes oxygen transport by the blood a much more efficient process than it would be if blood contained a simple oxygen carrier like myoglobin. To dissociate half of the bound oxygen from

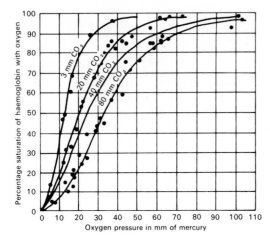

Fig. 14.5 Oxygen dissociation curves of human blood exposed to partial pressures of 3, 20, 40 and 80 mm Hg of carbon dioxide. The percentage saturation was measured by Van Slyke's apparatus. (A. V. Bock, H. F. Field & G. S. Adair (1924) *Journal of Biological Chemistry*, 59, 366.)

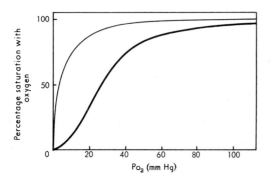

Fig. 14.6 Oxygen dissociation curves of myoglobin (thin line) and haemoglobin (thick line) at P_{CO_2} = 40 mm Hg.

arterial blood, the oxygen partial pressure need only be reduced to about 24 mm Hg at 38°C and pH 7.4. Under these conditions myoglobin is more than 80 per cent saturated (Fig. 14.6) and to dissociate half of its bound oxygen the partial pressure must be reduced to about 6 mm Hg. The oxygen dissociation curve of haemoglobin thus allows the tissues to function at a relatively high oxygen tension without at the same time limiting too severely the amount of oxygen which is delivered.

When fully saturated one molecule of haemoglobin with molecular weight 64460 combines with four molecules of oxygen which at s.t.p. occupy 4×22.4 1. Each gram of haemoglobin can therefore carry 1.39 ml oxygen.

Bohr found in 1910 that the position of the dissociation curve depended on the P_{CO_2} in the gas mixture in the tonometer—the greater the P_{CO_2} the further to the right was the dissociation curve (Fig. 14.5). Barcroft shortly afterwards found that this displacement could be produced by any acid; a fall in pH moves the curve to the right. A rise in temperature also shifts the dissociation curve to the right (Fig. 14.7); blood parts with its oxygen more readily at higher temperatures. Conversely a fall of temperature shifts the dissociation curve to the left.

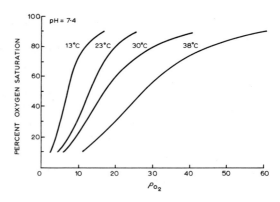

Fig. 14.7 The effect of temperature on the oxygen dissociation curve of oxyhaemoglobin of human blood at pH 7.4. (*From* data in P. Astrup, K. Engel, J. N. Severinghaus & E. Munson (1965) *Scandinavian Journal of Clinical and Laboratory Investigation*, 17, 520.)

The modification of the dissociation curve produced by the carbon dioxide tension of the blood (the Bohr effect) has biological advantages. Since the P_{CO_2} is lower in the lungs than in the tissues, haemoglobin has a higher affinity for oxygen where oxygen is being taken up than it has where oxygen is being set free. The reduction of P_{CO_2} of the blood as it passes through the pulmonary capillaries enables the haemoglobin to take up only a small additional amount of oxygen. (The dissociation curves (Fig. 14.5) are very close to one another at P_{O_2} of 95 mm Hg.) However, in the tissues where the P_{O_2} is between 10 and 40 mm Hg the effect of P_{CO_2} on the oxygen carrying capacity of the blood is quite large as shown by the wider separation of the oxygen dissociation curves (Fig. 14.5). An active tissue has a relatively high P_{CO_2}, low pH and raised temperature and all these changes set free more oxygen for its respiratory processes.

Another factor with an important influence on the oxygen dissociation curve is the high concentration of 2,3-diphosphoglycerate (DPG) in the red cell. The reduced haemoglobin molecule can bind one molecule of DPG very tightly in a site between its two β-chains. Oxyhaemoglobin with its altered arrangement of subunits binds DPG much less tightly if at all. Hence in the presence of DPG the reduced form of haemoglobin is stabilized and the affinity of haemoglobin for oxygen is greatly diminished. In other words the oxygen dissociation curve is shifted to the right and oxygen release in the tissues is facilitated.

The DPG content of the red cell is not constant. If blood is stored *in vitro* at 37° for 24 hours most of the red cell DPG is lost. DPG is synthesized in the red cell from a metabolite of the normal glycolytic pathway, 1,3-diphosphoglycerate, by the enzyme diphosphoglyceromutase. The synthesis is somehow stimulated by hypoxia such as is found in anaemia or at high altitudes. The increased DPG levels achieved in such conditions are important in facilitating the unloading of oxygen in the tissue capillaries.

In man the oxygen tension in the systemic arteries (Pa_{O_2}) is about 95 mm Hg and the carbon dioxide tension 40 mm Hg. Figure 14.5 shows that haemoglobin is 95 per cent saturated in these circumstances. In mixed venous blood the oxygen and carbon dioxide tensions are about 40 and 46 mm Hg respectively. The haemoglobin in mixed venous blood is, therefore, about 70 per cent saturated.

Because the dissociation curve is obtained from steady-state measurements it cannot tell us anything about the kinetics of the reaction between haemoglobin and oxygen.

The speed of the reaction $Hb + O_2 \rightarrow HbO_2$ has been measured by driving a dilute haemoglobin solution through one jet into a mixing chamber and water containing oxygen in solution through another jet into the same mixing chamber from which the mixed fluids travel steadily down a glass observation tube. While the mixed fluids pass down the tube the haemoglobin becomes oxyhaemoglobin. The point at which 50 per cent saturation occurs can be detected spectroscopically. The rate of flow can be calculated from the diameter of the tube and the volume flowing out of it. Half-saturation is reached in about 0·003 seconds but if a suspension of red cells is used the half-time is about 0·07 sec because the oxygen has to penetrate the membrane and diffuse through the substance of the cell. Nevertheless this time is so much less than the half-second or so spent by a corpuscle in the alveolar capillary that the speed of this reaction cannot normally be a factor limiting the uptake of oxygen. In severe anaemia, however, when the oxygen-carrying capacity of the blood is reduced and when the rate of blood flow through the pulmonary capillary increases, the Po_2 of the plasma in the capillaries increases, and the Po_2 gradient across the alveolo-capillary membrane is diminished with a consequent reduction in oxygen diffusion. In health the rate of diffusion across the alveolar membrane is not a limiting factor but when the characteristics of this membrane are altered by disease the prolonged diffusion rate results in arterial unsaturation (p. 237). The time for the reverse reaction, $HbO_2 \rightarrow Hb + O_2$, to reach half completion is 0·004 sec in solution and 0·038 sec in the red cell, so that release of oxygen to the tissues from the blood can be very rapid.

The Carriage of Carbon Dioxide

As indicated already, the carbon dioxide content of the blood is much more than can be explained by simple physical solution. At 38°C and 40 mm Hg 100 ml of water can dissolve about 2·6 ml of carbon dioxide, whereas blood may contain 50 or 60 ml carbon dioxide per 100 ml. Since all the carbon dioxide can be obtained from blood by addition of an acid the carbon dioxide must be carried partly as dissolved gas but mainly as bicarbonate. Further, since the total anions (chloride, phosphate, and others) are insufficient to combine with the sodium ions found in plasma, the combined carbon dioxide must be present as sodium bicarbonate. Both corpuscles and plasma transport carbon dioxide; the former carries about one-quarter of the total and the latter about three-quarters (Table 14.3).

By exposing blood to various partial pressures of CO_2 we can obtain data to draw a dissociation curve showing the relationship between the pressure of carbon dioxide and the total amount of carbon dioxide contained in the blood sample. Figure 14.8 shows dissociation curves for both oxygenated and reduced blood.

The metabolism of the tissues produces carbon dioxide and when the Pco_2 in the tissues is greater than the Pco_2 in the arterial end of the capillaries carbon dioxide diffuses into the

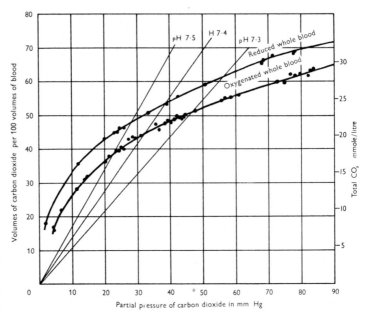

Fig. 14.8 Carbon dioxide dissociation curves for reduced and oxygenated blood. (*After* A. V. Bock, H. F. Field & G. S. Adair (1924) *Journal of Biological Chemistry*, 59, 371.) The pH values are calculated from the Henderson-Hasselbach equation,

$$pH = pK_a + \log \frac{[\text{base}]}{[\text{acid}]}.$$

capillaries. The greater part of the carbon dioxide goes directly into the red cell as shown in Figure 14.11 but a small additional quantity, due to the increase in Pco_2, is dissolved in the plasma where it is *slowly* hydrated to form bicarbonate and hydrogen ions.

$$CO_2 + H_2O \rightleftharpoons HCO_3^- + H^+$$

Some carbon dioxide is taken up by the plasma proteins to form carbamino compounds.

$$CO_2 + PrNH_2 \rightleftharpoons PrNHCOOH = PrNHCOO^- + H^+$$

The H^+ ions produced in these reactions are buffered by the proteins and phosphate of the plasma. At pH 7·4, which is on the alkaline side of their iso-electric point the proteins are weak acids.

$$H^+ + Na \text{ proteinate} \rightarrow Na^+ + H \text{ proteinate}$$

When carbon dioxide enters the red cell bicarbonate and hydrogen ions are formed *very rapidly* by the enzyme *carbonic anhydrase* discovered by Roughton. The speed of the reaction $CO_2 + H_2O = H^+ + HCO_3^-$ is about 13000 times greater in the red cells than in the plasma. In this way, and because of the high solubility of CO_2 in aqueous media, we can account for the rapid removal of carbon dioxide from the blood in the short transit time in the pulmonary capillaries and also for the rapid uptake when the blood is traversing the capillaries in the tissues. The H^+ ions formed in the red cells by the reaction

$$CO_2 + H_2O \rightleftharpoons H^+ + HCO_3^-$$

are buffered by the protein part of the haemoglobin molecule

$$H^+ + KHb \rightarrow K^+ + HHb.$$

Because haemoglobin is present in higher concentration in the red cells and because it is a more powerful buffer than the proteins of the plasma and because bicarbonate is formed more quickly in the red cells, the concentration of HCO_3^- ions is greater in the red cells than in the plasma; accordingly HCO_3^- ions pass into the plasma and, since cations such as Na^+ and K^+ cannot pass easily through the red-cell membrane, anions (mainly Cl^-) pass into the cell to maintain electrical neutrality. At the same time a small amount of water moves into the red cells to maintain osmotic equilibrium. The plasma of venous blood contains about 2 per cent less chloride than the plasma of arterial blood (Table 14.3). This *chloride shift* was discovered by Hamburger in 1918. The result of this shift of HCO_3^- ions from the red cells back into the plasma is that the plasma of the capillary blood carries the greater part, about two-thirds, of the additional carbon dioxide and the red cells only one-third although the major part of the buffering occurs in the red cells. When the venous blood is oxygenated in the lungs the chloride shift is reversed. (See also Figs. 14.10 and 14.11.)

Some of the carbon dioxide entering the red cells from the tissues is taken up by the haemoglobin to form carbamino-haemoglobin.

$$CO_2 + HbNH_2 \rightleftharpoons HbNHCOOH \rightleftharpoons HbNHCOO^- + H^+$$

This rapid reaction does not require a catalyst. Although the carbaminohaemoglobin accounts for only 5 to 10 per cent of the total carbon dioxide of blood (Table 14.3 and Fig. 14.9) it is mobile and easily exchanged and hence of considerable physiological importance. About one-quarter of the change in carbon dioxide content of the whole blood (the arterio-venous difference) in ordinary respiration can be accounted for by the change in carbon dioxide bound as carbaminohaemoglobin.

The H^+ ions produced by the hydration of CO_2 and by the ionization of carbaminohaemoglobin are buffered by haemoglobin and by the phosphate esters which the red cells contain. Haemoglobin is an effective buffer in the pH range 7.0 to 7.6 because it contains many histidine residues whose imidazole groups buffer in this range. However, the greater part of the buffering needed during respiratory exchange is carried out by a few of the ionizing groups on haemoglobin which are influenced by the oxygenation and deoxygenation of the haem groups. These oxygen-linked groups have now been identified; the α-amino group of valines 1α and the imidazole side chains of histidines at 122α and 146β all contribute to the effect (for positions see Fig. 8.11). On oxygenation of the haemoglobin these groups become less basic and release hydrogen ions. When the oxygen dissociates they become more basic again and hydrogen ions are taken up. To keep the pH constant when 1 gram molecule of oxygen dissociates, 0.7 gram molecule of hydrogen ions must be added. These hydrogen ions could be produced by the hydration of 0.7 gram molecule of CO_2. Thus when the R.Q. is 0.7 the red cell can bring about respiratory exchange without changing its internal pH. At higher RQs the remainder of the buffering is carried out by the other buffers in the red cell. When haemoglobin takes up oxygen in the lungs, H^+ ions are given to the solution since oxyhaemoglobin is a stronger acid, the reaction catalysed by carbonic anhydrase, $H^+ + HCO_3^- \rightarrow CO_2 + H_2O$, occurs and the CO_2 so formed is got rid of through the lungs.

The amount of carbon dioxide which can be carried by haemoglobin is affected by the oxygen tension (Haldane effect). Just as reduced whole blood (Fig. 14.8) can contain more carbon dioxide than oxygenated blood so reduced haemoglobin (Fig. 14.9) can carry more carbamino-bound carbon dioxide than oxyhaemoglobin. If in dogs the carbonic anhydrase is inhibited by giving them acetazolamide intravenously carbon dioxide transport and excretion are severely disturbed. Since the blood is moving slowly through the tissue capillaries there may be time for the hydration of carbon dioxide but since the blood passes through the lung capillaries in only 0.75 sec (p. 215) the reaction $H^+ + HCO_3^- \rightarrow H_2O + CO_2$ is too slow to allow transfer of the normal amount of carbon dioxide to the alveolar air. Therefore carbon dioxide is dammed back and the P_{CO_2} of the blood and the tissues rises until a new steady state is reached.

The factors involved in transport of carbon dioxide have been summarized by Roughton in diagrams (Figs 14.10 and 14.11) which illustrate both its uptake in the tissues and its release in the lungs.

The importance of haemoglobin in the carriage of carbon dioxide can be illustrated by considering the effect of breathing oxygen under pressure. At three atmospheres ($3 \times P_B$) of pure oxygen the P_{O_2} of the alveolar air is

$$(3 \times P_B) - P_{CO_2} - P_{H_2O} \text{ or } (3 \times 760) - 40 - 47.$$

The amount of oxygen carried in 100 ml plasma is therefore $2193 \times 0.003 = 6.6$ ml. Since this is sufficient (p. 14) to supply the metabolic needs of the body at rest if the cardiac output is in the usual range of about 5 l/min there is little or no need for oxyhaemoglobin to part with its oxygen. Since the carbon dioxide carrying capacity of oxyhaemoglobin is less than that

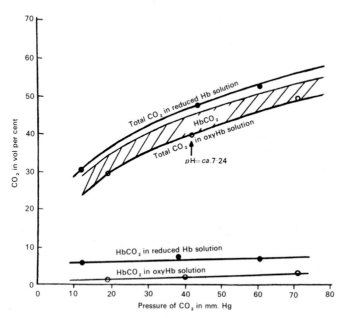

Fig. 14.9 The upper two curves are carbon dioxide dissociation curves of reduced and oxygenated human haemoglobin solution respectively. In the change from the oxygenated to the reduced state the carbon dioxide represented by the shaded area is taken up in the carbamino form—this is quite a considerable part of the change in the carbon dioxide content. The absolute amounts of carbamino compounds are shown in the lower pair of curves. (J. K. W. Ferguson (1937) *Journal of Physiology*, **88**, 49.)

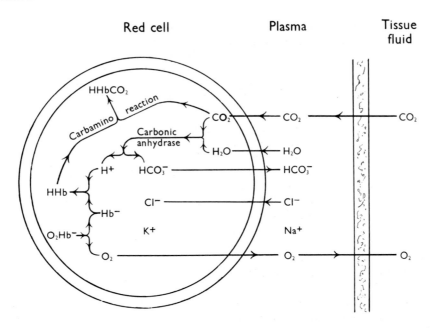

Fig. 14.10 A schematic summary of the chemical processes which occur when haemoglobin takes up oxygen in the lungs. See also legend to Figure 14.11. (F. J. W. Roughton (1935) *Physiological Reviews*, **15**, 293.)

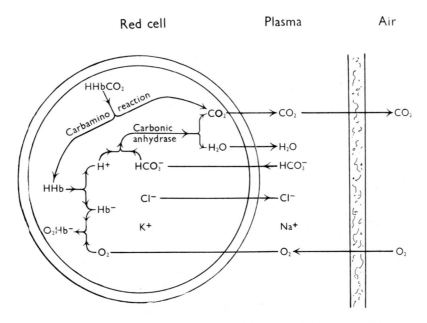

Fig. 14.11 A schematic summary of the chemical processes which occur when haemoglobin parts with its oxygen in the tissues. The chloride shift is represented as a movement of ions. The shaded part represents the capillary wall. Most of the CO_2 goes into the red blood cell as shown; a small quantity is dissolved in the plasma and some links up with H_2O slowly since there is no carbonic anhydrase in the plasma. Some is taken up by the plasma proteins to form carbamino compounds. These two reactions produce H^+ ions (see pp. 226 and 268) which are taken up by the plasma buffers. Inside the red cell HCO_3^- is formed very quickly in the presence of carbonic anhydrase. The H^+ ions resulting from the hydration of CO_2 and the formation of carbaminohaemoglobin are buffered by haemoglobin.

of haemoglobin the tissue P_{CO_2} rises and stimulates the respiratory centre. This paradoxical stimulation of ventilation, with its consequent lowering of alveolar and arterial P_{CO_2} is also seen to a smaller extent when pure oxygen is breathed at normal atmospheric pressure, though an initial fall in ventilation due to a withdrawal of the normal peripheral chemoreceptor drive (see p. 233) is usually seen.

THE CONTROL OF BREATHING

The complexity of the control of breathing is indicated by Dornhorst's description of the respiratory centre as a computer which receives information from the brain, muscles and tissues via nerves and from the blood by chemical stimuli, from which it calculates the demand for ventilation (Fig.

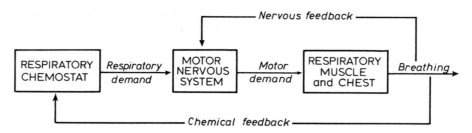

Fig. 14.12   Organization of breathing. In this simple model the organization of breathing is represented as two control systems, one within the other. The outer one maintains the long-term stability of the blood gases and in fact depends for its operation on information about them, notably the partial pressure of carbon dioxide in arterial blood ('chemical feedback'). The inner system attends to the performance of each breath and depends upon proprioceptive information ('nervous feedback'). (E. J. M. Campbell (1965) *British Medical Journal*, i, 1452.)

14.12). The important chemical control of respiration is described on p. 231, but a rather crude idea of the organization of this computer, gained from surgical experiments on the central nervous system of animals, is outlined here, and the nervous control of respiration is described below.

The Respiratory Centre

If the upper parts of the brain down to the mid-brain are cut away respiration continues but section through the posterior part of the medulla brings respiration to a stop. When the spinal cord is cut across in the thoracic region the intercostal muscles innervated from levels below the section are paralysed but the diaphragm, supplied by the phrenic nerves continues to move. Division above the roots of the phrenic nerves (3rd, 4th and 5th cervical) arrests diaphragmatic movements and the animal dies of asphyxia, although for a time movements of the alae nasi may be seen. The respiratory centre must therefore lie somewhere in the hind-brain and must send impulses out along the phrenic and intercostal nerves.

Lumsden found that, after cutting the vagus nerves in the cat (Fig. 14.13B, a–b), respiration became slower and deeper. A subsequent cut through 1 (Fig. 14.13A) produced no change in respiration. Section between 2 and 3 produced *prolonged inspiration* as at (c). Section at 4 produced *gasping respiration* (d). Section at 6 abolished all respiratory movements. These results suggest that there is a controlling or *pneumotaxic centre* in the upper (cranial) part of the pons which controls the activities of lower (caudal) groups of neurones, that is, those causing prolonged inspiration and gasping. If the vagal fibres which pass mainly to the expiratory centre are left intact after cutting between 2 and 3 (Fig. 14.13A) breathing is still regular. Thus to maintain rhythmic breathing the respiratory centres in the lower part of the medulla must be influenced either by the pneumotaxic centre or by afferent impulses through the vagus nerves (Fig. 14.14). Experiments on the dog have amplified Lumsden's findings. The apneustic state after section at level 2 (Fig. 14.13A) is greatly reduced by denervation of the carotid bodies. (Apneusis is a prolonged inspiration.) Dogs transected at level 4 with the vagus nerves cut can breathe regularly for many hours.

Micro-electrodes have been used to stimulate or record from localized areas of the brain stem. The results of these studies have been interpreted in a variety of ways and several alternative models have been constructed in an attempt to

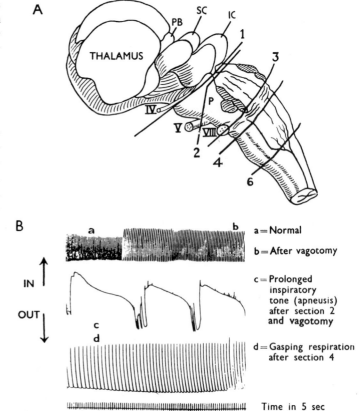

a = Normal

b = After vagotomy

c = Prolonged inspiratory tone (apneusis) after section 2 and vagotomy

d = Gasping respiration after section 4

Time in 5 sec

Fig. 14.13   Diagram (not to scale) of the brain stem of a cat to show the position of sections which produced the alterations in respiratory rhythm shown in the lower part of the figure. PB, pineal body; SC and IC superior and inferior colliculi; P, pons; IV, V, VIII, cranial nerves. (T. Lumsden (1923) *Journal of Physiology*, 57, 153, 354; 58, 81, 111.)

explain the findings. Burns has suggested that there are two independent networks of neurones, inspiratory and expiratory, with reciprocal innervation between them, both showing self-excitation and self-limitation. Von Euler's model (Fig. 14.14) of the control of the normal rhythm of breathing has an inspiratory ramp generator (A) whose output drives a second neurone pool (B) which also receives afferent information from the lungs through the vagus nerves. The output from B therefore increases with time during an inspiration, and when a threshold level is reached, the group of neurones C is

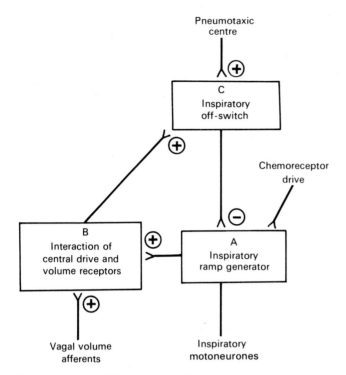

Fig. 14.14 Simplified model of the brain-stem mechanisms responsible for the generation of rhythmic breathing movements. The neurones in the ramp generator (A) slowly increase their inspiratory activity and are influenced mainly by the chemoreceptor drive. This activity interacts with information about the volume of the lungs arriving through the vagus (B), and this eventually reaches the threshold of the off-switch (C). When that discharges, the inspiratory ramp generator is reset. (After J. G. Widdicombe).

triggered to inhibit A. C is called the inspiratory off-switch, and appears to receive input from the pontine pneumotaxic centre.

While both the frequency and the depth of respiration can to some extent be controlled voluntarily, and even arrested altogether for a short time, the respiratory centre seems to possess a rhythmic activity of its own. This was first clearly demonstrated in the goldfish since after removal of the brain from the body the medulla shows rhythmic electrical variations with the same frequency as the gill movements. An analogous intrinsic rhythm in mammals after complete denervation is abolished by artificial respiration with oxygen and increased if carbon dioxide is added to the inspired air.

Stimulation of certain parts of the premotor cortex increases respiratory movements, whereas stimulation of other cortical areas inhibits them. Since lesions in the lateral hypothalamus diminish respiration it is likely that this region exerts a facilitatory action on the respiratory centre. Cooling the medulla slows respiration. If the body temperature of an animal is raised, or if the blood going to the medulla is warmed, respiration becomes faster but not deeper (*tachypnoea*). During sleep the respiratory centre is less active so the alveolar carbon dioxide may rise above the waking value.

Motor fibres from the respiratory centre nuclei cross over in the medulla and pass down through the anterior and anterolateral columns of the cord to the nuclei of the phrenic and intercostal nerves in the anterior horns of the grey matter. Commissural fibres must join the nuclei across the spinal cord, and thus hemisection of the cervical cord does not always cause paralysis of the diaphragm on the same side.

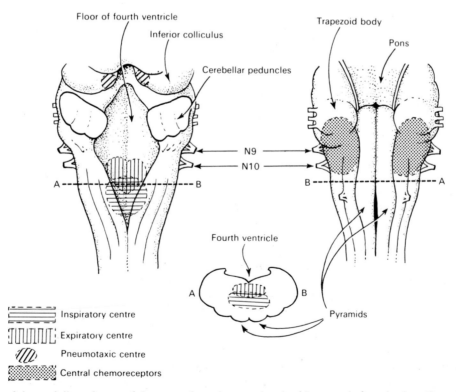

Fig 14. 15 Diagrams of the medulla and pons of the cat to show the areas involved in control of respiration. (Compiled from diagrams by various authors.)

Reflex Regulation of Respiration

The most important factor in the regulation of respiration is undoubtedly the carbon dioxide tension of the blood supplying the central chemoreceptors (p. 231). The activity of the respiratory centre, however, is modified by afferent impulses which are continuously arriving at the medulla in the vagus nerves and in the nerves from the carotid body and carotid sinus and from the cerebral cortex; the centre is also influenced, especially in man, by impulses arising in receptors in the chest-wall.

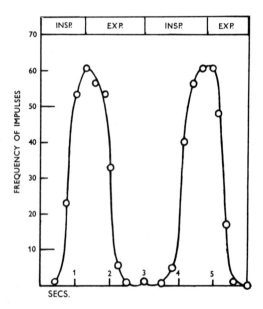

Fig. 14.16 Frequency of afferent impulses in a single fibre of the vagus of a decerebrate cat during normal breathing. The frequency of nerve impulses at the end of expiration need not necessarily be zero. For example, another fibre discharged at the rate of 50 impulses per sec at the end of expiration and at 80 impulses per sec at the height of a normal expiration. The response of these stretch receptors is also affected by the physical state of the lung, for example by changes in pressure in lung vessels, size of bronchi and speed of inflation. (*After* E. D. Adrian (1933) *Journal of Physiology*, 79, 337.)

On inspiration the lungs are stretched and impulses travel up the vagus to the medulla. The frequency of the impulses increases with increasing stretch of the lungs (Fig. 14.16) until the peak of inspiration is reached when the frequency declines as expiration occurs. The receptors giving rise to these impulses seem to lie in the bronchioles close to the bronchial muscles since drugs which increase bronchial tone increase the discharge and drugs which cause bronchodilatation decrease the discharge. However, some of the nerve impulses in the afferent vagus during expansion of the lungs have been traced to *stretch receptors* lying in the lower end of the trachea and in the main bronchi. The following experiments show that these impulses inhibit the respiratory centre. Inflation of the lungs or stimulation of the central end of a cut vagus nerve in an anaesthetized animal arrests inspiration. This inhibition of inspiration by lung inflation was first described in 1868 by Hering and Breuer. This reflex is an important mechanism for the control of breathing in many laboratory animals and also for a few days in the newborn baby but in the conscious man it

is seen only if the inflation is large provided that the vagi are intact. After section of both vagus nerves in animals (see Fig. 14.13A and B) inspiration is prolonged and the frequency of breathing is reduced. In man stretch receptors discharge as in the cat (Fig. 14.16), but bilateral vagus block does not alter the pattern of quiet breathing at rest. It does, however, substantially affect the degree and the pattern of the response to respiratory stimuli like CO_2, virtually abolishing the usual increase in frequency of breathing and thus reducing the total ventilation achieved. Under these conditions, the relation between ventilation and tidal volume lies along one of the frequency isopleths of Figure 13.10 (p. 210). Vagal block also diminishes the unpleasant sensation associated with rebreathing and breath-holding.

Breathing can be made more difficult by making a subject breathe in and out of a closed tank to simulate increase of elastic forces or by making him breathe through narrow orifices to simulate increase of viscous forces. An increase in the expiratory load causes an immediate increase in the volume of the lungs without any change in the rate of breathing (Fig. 14.17). The adjustment to inspiratory loading also occurs immediately—too quickly to be a response to alteration in blood $P\mathrm{CO}_2$. Since vagal block in man does not affect the ability to detect additional loads it seems likely that adjustments to loading (Fig. 14.17) are dependent on receptors in the muscles and joints of the chest wall.

Many other reflex alterations of breathing have been described; they may arise from receptors in the lungs or heart or large vessels. If the lungs of an anaesthetized animal are

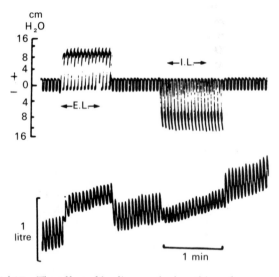

Fig. 14.17 The effect of loading on the breathing of an anaesthetized man. The upper record shows the pressure at the mouth relative to atmospheric pressure. The lower records shows the movements of a spirometer bell (inspiration upwards); the general upwards slope is due to the gradual absorption of oxygen. Expiration was loaded (10 cm water) at E. L. and inspiration was loaded at I. L. The expiratory load immediately increased both end-expiratory and end-inspiratory lung volumes (lower record); when the load was removed they both decreased to the previous value; the respiratory rate was unaffected. Inspiratory loading reduced end-inspiratory lung volume without affecting the respiratory frequency. The effect on conscious subjects is similar. (E. J. M. Campbell, C. J. Dickinson, O. P. Dinnick & J. B. L. Howell (1961) *Clinical Science*, 21, 311.)

deflated the rate and force of inspiration are increased if the vagus nerves are intact. In man deflation or collapse of the lungs as in the formation of a pneumothorax is followed by increase of ventilation. In animals increased pressure in the pulmonary capillaries, brought about by temporary occlusion of the mitral valve orifice, is associated with rapid shallow breathing which is abolished by section of the vagus nerves. Small pieces of blood clot (thrombo-emboli) lodged in the small blood vessels of the lungs, have variable reflex effects, usually apnoea and then rapid shallow breathing and pulmonary vasoconstriction and oedema. Part of this complicated response may be due to stimulation of *juxta-capillary (or J-) receptors* in the lungs p. 215 which send impulses up the vagus nerves.

A rise of venous pressure in the great veins near the heart, produced for example by rapid injection of fluid, or occurring in cardiac failure, stimulates respiration. Swallowing, which usually occurs during expiration, is attended by a reflex inhibition of respiration (p. 39) via the glosso-pharyngeal nerve.

Application of cold water to the skin causes gasping followed by hyperventilation. This reflex may sometimes be responsible for drowning. Breath-holding by itself has little effect on heart rate but if the face is immersed in cold water (2°C) the heart slows. This effect is much more obvious in diving animals. Their stay under water is longer than would be expected from their store of oxygen because the cardiac output is reduced and only the blood supply to heart and brain is maintained; the supply to organs not damaged by temporary asphyxia is reduced.

A *cough* is a sudden inspiratory effort with a wide open glottis followed by an expiratory effort against a closed glottis which suddenly opens to let the air rush out under pressure. During the expiratory effort the intrathoracic pressure rises to 100 or even 300 mm Hg and narrows the trachea and bronchi as in any forced expiration. Coughing is useful in bringing foreign bodies up the bronchi and trachea. The velocity of airflow in the trachea of a normal subject during a vigorous cough may reach 600 miles/hour (Mach 1). *Sneezing* is a somewhat similar reflex arising from irritation of the nasal mucosa through the nasal branch of the fifth nerve; the expiratory blast passing through the nose may propel droplets up to 6 m. Stimulation of the nasal mucosa in dogs by water or tobacco smoke depresses or abolishes breathing; it also causes bradycardia, reduction of cardiac output, vasoconstriction in most areas of the body but not in the head. *Hiccup* is a repetitive spasmodic contraction of the diaphragm and external (inspiratory) intercostal muscles in the course of which the glottis closes suddenly and further entrance of air into the chest is prevented. The sudden arrest of the column of entering air produces the characteristic sound and sensation. The peculiar involuntary, 'infectious' respiratory act, the *yawn*, is accompanied by facial and limb-stretching gestures and is remarkable for a marked dilatation of the pharynx. Apart from the temporary vasoconstriction associated with a large inspiration (p. 196), there is no accompanying circulatory alteration in the brain or elsewhere. The cause and function of yawning are quite obscure.

The cough reflexes in man are difficult to analyse. The results of experiments with cats are only assumed to apply to man; these reflexes vary greatly between species. In the cat coughing can be brought about by mechanical irritation of the larynx or trachea but not of the main bronchi. Such irritation also produces broncho-constriction, bradycardia and hypertension. The reflex is not obtained if the mucosa is first sprayed with a local anaesthetic. The receptors, which adapt rapidly, are probably knob-like subepithelial endings derived from large afferent fibres. Inhalation of sulphur dioxide or other noxious gases also causes coughing but in this case the *irritant receptors* must be situated more deeply in the lungs since the reflex is not abolished by anaesthetizing the trachea. The afferent pathways for both reflexes are mainly in the vagus but the sympathetic pathway may also be involved to a small extent.

Chemical Regulation of Respiration

The chemical regulation of respiration is maintained by central and peripheral chemoreceptors. Its importance is illustrated by *asphyxia*, in which there is a simultaneous lack of oxygen and an excess of carbon dioxide in the alveolar gas mixture. Asphyxia has long been studied in experimental animals and in human subjects who are allowed to rebreathe their own expired air from a spirometer without the removal of the accumulating carbon dioxide by soda lime.

Three stages are described in asphyxia. (1) The respiratory movements are first increased in depth and rate. The breathing becomes violent and the expiratory efforts more and more powerful. Consciousness is lost at the end of this stage which is followed by (2) the stage of convulsions involving practically all the muscles of the body, with stimulation of many central neurones, resulting in vasoconstriction, salivation, contraction of pupils and contraction of muscles of alimentary canal and bladder. This is followed quite suddenly by (3) a stage of slow deep inspirations in which most bodily activities are in abeyance and reflexes are absent. Finally the respirations become infrequent and ineffective and the animal dies in a few minutes.

Effect of carbon dioxide. The effects of asphyxia on respiration and on the circulation are produced partly by excess of carbon dioxide and partly by lack of oxygen in the blood and in the tissues. The effect of carbon dioxide was first demonstrated in the experiments of Haldane and Smith in which the subject re-breathed air containing rising concentrations of carbon dioxide up to 6 per cent. The depth and rate of respiration both increase. The subject may not notice the effect of low concentrations of carbon dioxide in the inspired air, but at concentrations above 3 per cent the subject is well aware of the increased respiratory effort. If air containing between 3 and 5 per cent carbon dioxide is breathed respiration becomes very deep and very rapid; at concentrations over 10 per cent cardiac and respiratory functions are depressed and confusion and headache occur.

The total ventilation of the lungs per minute (strictly, the alveolar ventilation, $\dot{V}A$) and the alveolar P_{CO_2} (P_{ACO_2}) are interdependent. When air containing added CO_2 is inspired the P_{ACO_2} rises, and so does the P_{CO_2} in the pulmonary venous blood and therefore in the arterial blood. This rise stimulates the central chemoreceptors and the ventilation is increased. The remarkably linear relation between $\dot{V}A$ and the P_{ACO_2} under these conditions is called the CO_2 response line (Fig.

14.18). However, at a given inspired P_{CO_2} (P_{I,CO_2}), the greater the ventilation the lower the P_{ACO_2}, because the extra volume of air breathed effectively dilutes the metabolically produced CO_2 which is diffusing into the alveoli at a constant rate.

Algebraically this can be expressed as

$$\dot{V}_A \cdot (P_{ACO_2} - P_{ICO_2}) = \dot{V}_{CO_2} \cdot P_B$$

or

$$P_{ACO_2} = \frac{\dot{V}_{CO_2} \cdot P_B}{\dot{V}_A} + P_{ICO_2}$$

(where P_B = barometric pressure and $\dot{V}_{CO_2}$ = volume of metabolic CO_2 per minute). Graphically, this relation between $\dot{V}_A$ and P_{ACO_2} is a hyperbola that is shifted to the right by progressive increments of inspired CO_2 (Fig. 14.18A). In Figure 14.18B the straight CO_2-response line has been superimposed on these hyperbolae, and the air-breathing point is marked X. The points of intersection between the hyperbolae and the response line are the $\dot{V}_A$, P_{ACO_2} co-ordinates in the steady-state at each different P_{ICO_2}, and the double-ended arrows (marked 40, 21 and 6) indicate that although the P_{ACO_2} rises with the

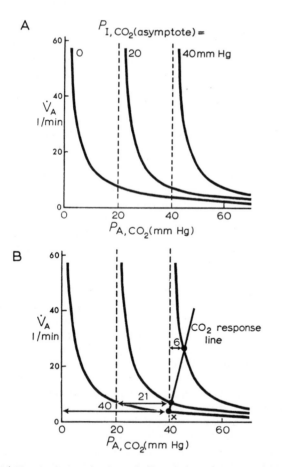

Fig. 14.18 A shows the hyperbolic relations between alveolar ventilation ($\dot{V}_A$) and alveolar CO_2 (P_{ACO_2}) at three different partial pressures (0, 20 and 40 mm Hg) of inspired CO_2. B also shows the straight CO_2 response line; the horizontal bars represent the difference between inspired and alveolar P_{CO_2}. X shows the position when the subject is breathing atmospheric air. The dotted vertical lines are the asymptotes representing P_{ICO_2}.

P_{ICO_2} when CO_2 is added to the inspired air, the difference between them becomes smaller. The overall effect of this increased ventilation is to minimize the change in the alveolar and the arterial P_{CO_2} and is a good example of an important homeostatic regulatory mechanism. The concentration of H^+ ions in the blood is also regulated in part through this reflex (see below). The relation between ventilation and inspired P_{CO_2} is distinctly non-linear: in this example, the first increment of 20 mm Hg produces only a slight change in ventilation while a further identical increment in inspired P_{CO_2} gives rise to a substantial increase.

The carbon dioxide tension in the alveoli (P_{ACO_2}) is calculated as follows. In alveolar air at sea level the carbon dioxide content is about 5·5 per cent and the pressure of water-vapour 47 mm Hg. Since the atmospheric pressure is 760 mm Hg the P_{CO_2} is equal to 5·5 per cent of (760 minus 47) mm Hg, that is 39 mm Hg. At high altitudes or in a pressure chamber where the barometric pressure is much less or much greater than normal, the carbon dioxide content of alveolar air is correspondingly different but the alveolar P_{CO_2} remains the same at a given alveolar ventilation. For most purposes the really important quantity is the arterial P_{CO_2} and this is measured in hospital practice by electrochemical methods (p. 223). Where these methods are not available, indirect methods may be used. Carbon dioxide diffuses so rapidly through the lung tissues that the arterial and alveolar partial pressures are equal, and therefore measurement of P_{ACO_2} gives a theoretically good indirect estimate of P_{aCO_2}. However, the difficulties in obtaining the true alveolar air have already been mentioned (p. 211). An alternative indirect approach to the arterial P_{CO_2} has been via the mixed venous P_{CO_2} ($P_{\bar{v}CO_2}$). Direct studies with cardiac catheters and arterial needles have shown that $P_{\bar{v}CO_2}$ is about 6 mm Hg greater than P_{aCO_2}. Many bloodless methods of measuring $P_{\bar{v}CO_2}$ indirectly have been described but none is able to give a continuous estimate. One way is to use the lungs as an equilibrating device. The subject is asked to rebreathe from a bag containing 1 or $1\frac{1}{2}$ l oxygen for a minute and a half or until an increase in depth or rate of respiration is noticed. The bag then contains a mixture of gases with a P_{CO_2} slightly higher than that in mixed venous blood. After a rest (at least 2 minutes) the subject rebreathes the mixture for 20 seconds only to make a fine adjustment between the bag P_{CO_2} and mixed venous P_{CO_2} before recirculation of the blood can take place. For greater accuracy this 20-second rebreathing may be repeated. The P_{CO_2} of the gas in the bag and of the mixed venous blood are now very nearly the same and thus the arterial P_{CO_2} is taken to be 6 mm Hg less than the P_{CO_2} of the contents of the bag. Campbell has recently shown that this relation is more accurately expressed as $P_{aCO_2} = 0.8\ P_{\bar{v}CO_2}$.

Stimulation of central chemoreceptors. When excess carbon dioxide is breathed the P_{CO_2} of all the tissues rises and may alter, for example, the state of the blood vessels in them. However, only at two sites, the carotid bodies and the medulla, is there an influence on breathing. The carotid body chemoreceptors, if the rise of P_{CO_2} is high enough, cause reflexly an increase in breathing, but the changes represented by the straight line in Figure 14.18 can almost certainly be accounted for by the chemoreceptors of the medulla (see Fig. 14.15). The peripheral chemoreceptors in man may normally have only an emergency function or a supporting role to the more important medullary centre. With long residence at high altitude the medullary carbon dioxide chemoreceptors become more sensitive because of a fall in the bicarbonate concentration of the cerebrospinal fluid (CSF) while the carotid and aortic body chemoreceptors retain their sensitivity to hypoxia except in chronic mountain sickness. Since a rise of Pco_2 in the blood and an increase in hydrogen ion concentration in the CSF both stimulate the medullary chemoreceptors, it is pertinent to ask whether the effect of carbon dioxide is a specific property or whether it is due simply to the alteration of pH. Pappenheimer has shown by perfusing the cerebral ventricles of goats with mock-CSF at different Pco_2 and bicarbonate concentrations that the ventilation is best related to the hydrogen ion concentration close to the surface of the medulla. In intact man, however, the commonest cause of alterations in the pH of the CSF is a change in the arterial Pco_2. The apparent specificity of carbon dioxide as a respiratory stimulant is due to the fact that carbon dioxide passes through cell membranes very rapidly whereas H^+ ions penetrate very slowly. This slow penetration could account for the slow effect of lactic and other acids. But since H^+ ions are formed when the carbon dioxide reaches the interior of a cell the final stimulus may in fact be an increase in $[H^+]$.

There is good evidence that the chemoreceptor cells sensitive to carbon dioxide are quite distinct from the cells of the respiratory centre responsible for the reflex adjustment of breathing. For example, chloralose and other anaesthetics reduce the stimulating effect of carbon dioxide without reducing the stimulating effect of afferent impulses. Perfusion of the fourth ventricle with cerebrospinal fluid of high Pco_2 stimulates breathing and local application of such solutions or of acetylcholine or nicotine to the anterior lateral medullary area (see Fig. 14.15) increases respiratory movements within a few seconds. Similar experiments show that such chemoreceptors are situated at various positions in the brain stem, that is at varying distances from the cells of the respiratory centre itself. Nevertheless, such chemoreceptors have not been localized histologically. When air rich in carbon dioxide is breathed the Pco_2 and the $[H^+]$ of the cerebrospinal fluid rise a little more slowly than the Pco_2 of the arterial blood; but since it has little protein to act as a buffer, the cerebrospinal fluid shows eventually a much greater rise in $[H^+]$ than does the well-buffered blood. The slow rise of $[H^+]$ in the cerebrospinal fluid fits in very well with the slow rise in depth and rate of respiration on breathing air rich in carbon dioxide; the slow return to the normal level of respiration when the subject breathes room air once more is explained by the relatively slow fall in Pco_2 and in $[H^+]$ in the cerebrospinal fluid.

Not all variations in ventilation are due to variations in the CO_2 stimulus. For example breathing is deeper in exercise although the Pco_2 of the alveolar air is at its usual level (Chap. 21). The excessive breathing of fever may be accompanied by a low arterial Pco_2. If the respiratory centre is severely depressed by drugs the addition of CO_2 to the inspired air may not stimulate respiration. The effect of a given rise of alveolar Pco_2 is greater if the Po_2 of the arterial blood is low, that is, the CO_2-response line (Fig. 14.18B) is made steeper by hypoxia. Lack of oxygen has a depressant action on the cells of the respiratory centre but in the intact animal inhalation of a gas with a low oxygen content results in increased ventilation. The stimulant effect of hypoxia on respiration is a reflex effect

through the chemoreceptors of the carotid body (Fig. 14.19).

Carbon dioxide retention. A higher than normal partial pressure of CO_2 in the arterial blood ($Paco_2$) is referred to as *hypercapnia*. This is frequently the result of ventilatory impairment as in chronic bronchitis. When the $Paco_2$ rises to a certain level, which varies in individual patients, the clinical features of 'CO_2 narcosis' may be evident: change of personality, drowsiness and coarse tremor. The skin, though cyanosed, may be warm, and the pulse bounding, because of a high pulse pressure. The drowsiness may proceed to stupor, convulsions, coma and death.

Carotid body. Chemoreceptors sensitive to changes in the Pco_2 and Po_2 of the blood are found in the carotid bodies, ellipsoidal structures usually about 6 mm long at the bifurcation of the common carotid artery. Their weight is very variable but is on average about 12 mg. They are heavier in people living at high altitudes. Similar aortic bodies lie between the ascending aorta and the pulmonary artery. Histological preparations of the carotid body show large glomus cells, presumably chemoreceptors, containing catecholamines. One pole of these cells lies close to the sinusoidal capillaries, at the opposite pole are the afferent endings of the glossopharyngeal nerve. Efferent synpathetic fibres come from the superior cervical ganglion to these glomus cells. The glossopharyngeal nerve also contains efferent fibres. Vagal fibres also end in the carotid body. Presumably impulses in these efferent fibres are able to modify the afferent discharge in the glossopharyngeal nerve passing to the brain stem.

Oxygen lack induced in man by breathing, for example, 10 per cent oxygen in nitrogen produces hyperventilation but after removal of the carotid bodies the same degree of hypoxia produces very little if any change in breathing. It can be inferred that the human aortic bodies, like those in the dog, have very little effect on respiration; they are more concerned in cardiovascular reflexes (p. 167). The respiratory centre is itself depressed by lack of oxygen but the impulses sent to the respiratory centre by the chemoreceptors of the carotid bodies are able to overcome the central depression. Inhalation of 3 per cent carbon dioxide in air increases ventilation in man before and after removal of the carotid bodies, presumably by stimulation of the central medullary chemoreceptors but, in the presence of hypoxia, carbon dioxide is a further stimulus to the carotid bodies (see Fig. 14.19). If a person is given pure oxygen to breathe at sea level breathing is depressed slightly for a few minutes. This suggests that even at normal arterial Po_2 there is some discharge from the carotid and aortic bodies.

The carotid body contains acetylcholine and dopamine and catecholamines which could act as transmitters to stimulate the nerve endings but the nature of the transmitter is still uncertain. Hypoxia in rats decreases the dopamine content of the glomus cells. Eyzaguirre believes that in hypoxia or hypercapnia an acetylcholine-like substance is responsible for initiating the nerve impulses but in more intense chemoreceptor activity, induced by exposure to nitrogen or sodium cyanide, acetylcholine and other substances are released. The blood flow through a 2 mg carotid body of the cat is about 40 $\mu l/min$; this is much greater than the supply to any other tissue in the body (Table 11.17). It is at first sight difficult to explain how a tissue with such a large blood supply could be affected by mild hypoxia but it is likely that only a small fraction of the total blood flow traverses the capillaries supplying the glomus

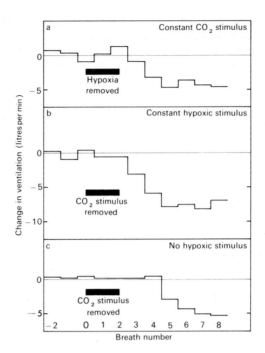

Fig. 14.19 The time course of the fall in ventilation in man when respiratory stimuli are removed for three breaths during the period marked by the black bars. The subjects were previously in a steady-state of hyperventilation caused by hypercapnia (inspiring 6 per cent CO_2) with or without hypoxia (10 per cent or 94 per cent O_2). (a) Hypoxia is removed, leaving a constant background CO_2 stimulus. Ventilation is falling by the third breath. (b) CO_2 stimulation removed, leaving a constant background hypoxic stimulus. Time-course of fall in ventilation is the same as in (a), and is therefore probably under the control of the peripheral chemoreceptors. (c) As (b) but in hyperoxia. The fact that the ventilatory depression is delayed for about 6 seconds longer suggests that the peripheral chemoreceptors are not responding to CO_2 in the absence of hypoxia but the central chemoreceptors are responding when the blood with a reduced P_{CO_2} reaches the brain a few seconds later. (*After* D. J. C. Cunningham, B. B. Lloyd, J. P. Miller & J. M. Young (1965) *Journal of Physiology*, 179, 68P.)

cells and even this may be reduced by opening up of arteriovenous anastomoses when the sympathetic nerve is stimulated. Hypoxia and hypercapnia cause a rise in blood flow but a fall in oxygen consumption provided that the sympathetic nerves are intact. After section of the sympathetic nerves the total blood flow may increase by one-third. Stimulation of the sympathetic nerve to the carotid body reduces the blood flow and increases the chemoreceptor discharge and also increases the tidal volume. Limb movements cause an increase in activity in the cervical sympathetic nerve and an increase in chemoreceptor activity; this may account for the increase in respiration occurring a few seconds after the beginning of exercise. The rate of discharge from the carotid body chemoreceptors is related inversely to its oxygen usage and not to its total blood flow. Oxygen consumption is related mainly to sympathetic activity. It is likely that in hypoxia anaerobic metabolites accumulate and stimulate the nerve endings. This would account for the chemoreceptor discharge which continues for 30 min or so after death.

Carotid sinus. A rise in blood pressure tends to depress, and

a fall to stimulate, respiration. These effects are initiated by the pressure receptors (baroreceptors) in the aorta and carotid sinuses. When a large dose of adrenaline is injected into an intact animal, the blood pressure rises and breathing stops (adrenaline apnoea). This is a carotid sinus and an aortic reflex and not a direct effect of adrenaline on the respiratory centre, because it is abolished after the vagus nerves and sinus nerves are cut or if the rise in blood pressure is prevented by a compensator included in the circulation. If the two common carotid arteries are clamped, the pressure within the carotid sinuses falls temporarily to zero; respiration is stimulated and the blood pressure rises (Fig. 14.20A). After denervation of both carotid sinuses this effect is absent (Fig. 14.20B). Clamping the carotid arteries reduces the number of impulses from the baroreceptors and, since it makes the carotid bodies anoxic, it increases the discharge from the chemoreceptors.

Both adrenaline and noradrenaline given intravenously to man at the rate of 10 to 20 μg per min stimulate respiration. Also in the hypertensive crises produced by a sudden discharge of these substances from a tumour of the adrenal medulla the breathing may be deep and rapid. These amines increase the sensitivity to hypoxia of the respiratory apparatus by stimulating the carotid bodies; they do not appear to act directly on the respiratory centre since injection into the vertebral or carotid arteries of a man at a rate of 1 to 2 μg per min has no such effect.

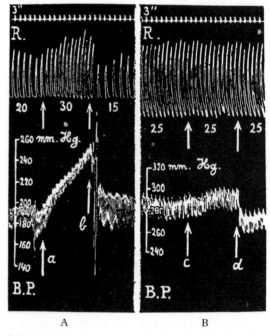

Fig. 14.20 Dog 10·5 kg anaesthetized with chloralose. Depressor nerves cut. R, respiratory movements. BP femoral blood pressure recorded with a mercury manometer. ↑ a, common carotid arteries clamped. This was followed by increased rate and depth of respiration with acceleration of the heart and rise of BP. ↑ b, common carotid arteries opened. This was followed by a return to original conditions. The two carotid sinus nerves were cut between A and B. This was followed by a rise of BP with acceleration of the heart and increase in rate and depth of respiration. ↑ c, common carotid arteries closed. ↑ d, common carotid arteries opened. Only very slight mechanical effects on the BP. (C. Heymans & J. J. Bouckaert (1930) *Journal of Physiology*, 69, 261.)

Effects of lack of oxygen. The alveolar oxygen tension is not regulated so precisely as the P_{CO_2}. It depends on the percentage of oxygen in the atmosphere, upon the atmospheric pressure (Fig. 14.21) and on the depth of ventilation. At sea-level the percentage of oxygen can be reduced from 21 to 13 without producing any marked alteration of breathing. This is because the arterial chemoreceptors (carotid bodies) are less active over this range than when the hypoxia is more intense, and because any reflex hyperventilation is immediately offset by the simultaneous reduction in P_{CO_2} as the carbon dioxide is blown off. The effects of lowering the oxygen tension still further can be seen by making a subject breathe in and out of a spirometer through a soda-lime container to absorb carbon dioxide. His skin and mucous membranes become bluish in colour (cyanosis, p. 238) as the oxygen is used up but he may not show any respiratory distress. When the oxygen percentage falls below 12 breathing is stimulated by the intense hypoxia and more oxygen is taken into the alveoli. If CO_2 is allowed to build up in the spirometer by removing the soda-lime, the ventilation is substantially stimulated by the interaction of hypoxia and hypercapnia.

Effect of high altitude. Although the percentage of oxygen in the air remains the same at all levels, the atmospheric pressure and therefore the partial pressure of oxygen, P_{O_2}, vary according to the height above sea-level.

The newcomer who has ascended rapidly to, say 4 km (13 000 ft) is dyspnoeic on exertion and may become unconscious if he attempts to go up a stair quickly. He may also suffer from mountain sickness, the symptoms of which, namely weakness, nausea, loss of appetite, headache and sleeplessness, are due to cerebral hypoxia. At first respiration is stimulated by the chemoreceptors so that the alveolar P_{O_2} is raised and the alveolar P_{CO_2} is reduced; in consequence the pH of the blood and CSF rises. In a few hours active transport of HCO_3^- out of the CSF brings the pH of the CSF back to its normal value, respiration is then once more under the control of both central and peripheral chemoreceptors.

The kidneys, in a slower compensatory adaptation, excrete more HCO_3^- and bring back the arterial pH to its normal value. Alkalosis by itself cannot explain the symptoms of mountain sickness; there may be an accompanying potassium deficiency and sodium retention. It has been recommended that men exposed to high altitudes should have a high intake of K but a limited intake of Na. Continued residence at a high altitude produces acclimatization and when this is complete the blood volume may have increased as much as 25 per cent, mainly

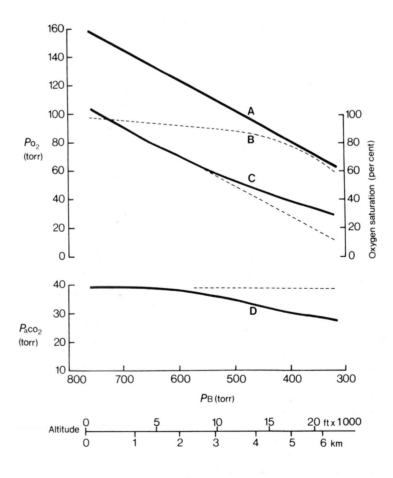

Fig. 14.21 The effect of acute exposure to simulated altitudes while breathing air. Curves show (A) partial pressure of oxygen in the inspired air, (B) percentage oxygen saturation of haemoglobin in arterial blood, (C) alveolar partial pressure of oxygen and (D) alveolar partial pressure of carbon dioxide. The broken lines on curves C and D depict the alveolar gas pressure which would occur in the absence of any ventilatory response to hypoxia. Note that the barometer scale is linear but the altitude scales are not. (*By courtesy of the Royal Air Force, Institute of Aviation Medicine.*)

because of the increase of red cells (Fig. 8.5). The resulting increase in viscosity of the blood is offset by a general vasodilatation so that the resting blood pressure may fall a little. The right ventricle hypertrophies probably because of pulmonary arterial hypertension. These adaptive changes have enabled fit men to carry out for a short period moderately hard physical work on mountains at 6 km (20 000 ft). Even acclimatized persons at high altitudes (above 5·5 km) complain of insomnia. Administration of oxygen encourages sound sleep at night. The changes in Po_2 and Pco_2 of the alveolar air and in the oxygen saturation of the blood at various heights are shown graphically in Figure 14.21.

When the change from sea-level to high altitude is very rapid, as in modern jet fighter aircraft, there is no time for acclimatization and the pilot must breathe oxygen from sea-level. Even in the 'slow' fighter aircraft used at the beginning of the Second World War, pilots, if they did not breathe oxygen, were apt to behave abnormally above 3 km (10 000 ft) without their being aware of it. Above this altitude increasing cerebral hypoxia produces defects in judgment and reasoning with a spurious feeling of confidence, reduction in visual acuity and visual field, weakness of arms and legs with muscular incoordination and twitching, hilarity or pugnacity, and eventual unconsciousness. In unpressurized aircraft when the barometric pressure is less than 150 mm Hg even pure oxygen must be administered under pressure.

Jet passenger aircraft fly at 6 to 14 km (20 000 to 46 000 ft) and supersonic aircraft fly at 18 to 21 km (59 000 to 69 000 ft) where the atmospheric pressure is only 33 mm Hg. Since sudden exposure to the ambient pressure at these altitudes would cause loss of consciousness in approximately one minute the cabin must be pressurized, the simulated 'altitude' being in the range 1·5 to 2·5 km (5000 to 8000 ft). The usual operating 'altitude' is about 1·5 km, only very rarely is it necessary to 'go up' to 2·5 km. Inspection of curve B of Figure 14.21 shows that the arterial oxygen saturation at 1·5 and 2·5 km is 92 and 90 per cent respectively. The small reduction in saturation from the sea level value of 97 per cent is accounted for by the 'flatness' of the oxygen dissociation curve of haemoglobin (Fig. 14.5) from 100 to 60 mm Hg, in other words from sea level to 3 km (10 000 ft). The small amount of hypoxia at these 'altitudes' is of no importance to a healthy person but even before these 'heights' are reached expansion of gas in the middle ear may give rise to pain unless it is relieved by repeated swallowing movements. If a defect occurs which allows the cabin 'altitude' to rise above 4·3 km (14 000 ft) masks delivering oxygen are supplied automatically to each passenger.

Cheyne-Stokes respiration. The commonest type of *periodic breathing* is the occurrence of a series of respirations which gradually increase in depth from a barely perceptible movement to a maximum and then progressively decline to terminate in a period of apnoea lasting from a few seconds to as long as a minute (Fig. 14.22). This 'hunting' behaviour is possible because the chemoreceptors, especially those in the medulla, are separated from the lungs, and there is a time lag between the changes imposed on the blood gases in the lungs by changes in ventilation, and information about these changes reaching the respiratory controller (see the feedback diagram, Fig. 14.12). Usually this lag is small and the hunting is smoothed. A prolonged lung-to-brain circulation time exaggerates the oscillations. If there is damage to supramedullary

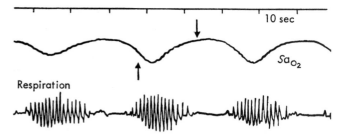

Fig. 14.22 Periodic 'Cheyne-Stokes' respiration. When the oxygen saturation of the blood (Sao_2) and therefore the Po_2 of the peripheral chemoreceptors falls to a certain level (↑) the breathing is stimulated, the Sao_2 rises and breathing diminishes or ceases (↓). The oxygen saturation was determined in the ear, see oximeter, page 222. (R. Hegglin (1961) *Triangle*, 5, 130–137.)

nervous pathways that normally inhibit the respiratory centres there is an excess ventilatory response to CO_2 that overcomes the normal smoothing effect. During the apnoeic phase the patient may become confused or even unconscious but breathing gradually begins again and the whole cycle is repeated. Cheyne-Stokes breathing occurs in healthy people at high altitudes, after hyperventilation and occasionally in deep sleep; it is quite common in healthy infants. When it occurs in an adult during waking hours it usually indicates serious disease of the heart or brain.

Breath holding. At the end of an inspiration the breath can be held for 30 to 50 sec. This is called the *period of voluntary apnoea* or *breath-holding time*. The subject is forced to breathe again when the alveolar Pco_2 is 47 to 50 mm Hg. When breathing is resumed there is an almost immediate relief of respiratory distress as the alveolar air composition returns to normal. If instead of breathing air at the end of a period of voluntary apnoea the subject is allowed a few breaths of a gas mixture containing say, 8·2 per cent oxygen and 7·5 per cent carbon dioxide ($Pco_2 = 53$ mm Hg) relief of respiratory distress is obtained which is sufficient to allow another short period of apnoea in spite of the continuing decrease in oxygen saturation of the blood and increased alveolar Pco_2. The period of voluntary apnoea is prolonged if the vagus nerves are blocked. If a subject is completely paralysed with tubocurarine except for one hand used for signalling it is found that the time during which he has no desire to breathe is prolonged. Afferent impulses from the stretch receptors in the lungs and from the respiratory muscles must therefore contribute to the desire to breathe. Thus although the breaking point of apnoea depends mainly upon raised $Paco_2$ (hypercapnia) other factors are involved.

After a short period of forced breathing (*voluntary hyperpnoea*) the period of voluntary apnoea is much longer. This cannot be due to an increased oxygen content of the blood since it is normally very nearly (95 per cent) saturated with oxygen. The hyperpnoea reduces the initial blood Pco_2 and therefore lengthens the time taken for the metabolic CO_2 (not excreted because the breath is held) to raise the central chemoreceptor Pco_2 to the breaking-point threshold. Paradoxically, however, this threshold is lower for prolonged breath-holds. There seems to be some time-dependent mechanism, probably linked to the afferent information about thoracic muscle tension and lung volume, that supplements the drive to breathe caused by CO_2.

Conversely the breath-holding time immediately after exercise is relatively short because the pH of the blood is lowered by its increased content of carbon dioxide and by the appearance in it of organic acids produced by muscle metabolism. Breathing oxygen during the preparatory hyperpnoea does not greatly increase the period of apnoea. There is thus no doubt that the carbon dioxide tension of the blood is the main factor determining the length of the breath-holding time, although when there is hypoxia the breaking-point is reached somewhat sooner.

If hypernoea is prolonged so much carbon dioxide is blown off that the pH of the blood rises and tetany may occur (p. 286). Unanaesthetized persons, whether hyperventilation is carried out voluntarily or by a pump, rarely become apnoeic even when the arterial P_{CO_2} is as low as 16 mm Hg; apnoea significantly longer than the spontaneous interval between breaths is an indication of brain damage. Hyperventilated anaesthetized subjects may become apnoeic when the pump is stopped.

Drowning accidents have been reported in which the victim hyperventilated before diving in an attempt to prolong the duration of underwater swimming. Such exercise after hyperventilation may reduce the blood P_{O_2} to less than 34 mm Hg, a degree of hypoxia which may result in unconsciousness before the P_{CO_2} rises to the level that would force the swimmer to come to the surface.

Dyspnoea. No satisfactory explanation has yet been offered for the sensation of breathlessness and distress, usually called dyspnoea, which occurs if the lungs are stiff or if the airways are obstructed. Impulses going up from the lungs in the vagus nerves or from the joint receptors in the thoracic cage to the central nervous system have been implicated, as has stimulation of chemoreceptors by altered blood-gas tensions. It has been suggested that dyspnoea arises when the actual expansion of the chest achieved is not appropriate to the ventilation which the central nervous system demands.

HYPOXIA AND CYANOSIS

Hypoxia

When the oxygen supply to the tissues becomes inadequate, hypoxia is said to be present. Some aspects of this problem have already been discussed on page 235. Although the effects upon the human subject depend to some extent on the way in which the hypoxia is produced, and on the rapidity with which it develops, the commonest effects are cerebral, namely, confusion, excitement, hallucinations, restlessness and unconsciousness. There are four types of hypoxia.

Hypoxic hypoxia. This type differs from others mentioned below in that the oxygen content of the arterial blood is reduced below its normal level because the arterial P_{O_2} is reduced. Its causes include obstruction of the air passages and paralysis of the respiratory muscles. Breathing air at high altitudes where the oxygen tension is low or a mixture of anaesthetic gases with too low a content of oxygen also leads to this type of hypoxia. It may occur also when parts of a lung are thrown out of action by collapse or compression or pneumonia or when the mixing of gases in the lungs is imperfect, as in emphysema. This type of hypoxia may also result from impaired diffusion of oxygen across the boundary zone between blood and alveolar air when the pulmonary tissues are infiltrated by disease; the hypoxia is then not accompanied by retention of carbon dioxide because this gas is transferred about 30 times faster than oxygen across the alveolar membrane. The commonest cause of hypoxic hypoxia in lung disease is simply the inequality of ventilation-perfusion ratios throughout the lung. As explained in Figure 13.20 such inequality gives rise to a difference in P_{O_2} between mixed alveolar air and pulmonary venous blood. In diseased lungs this mechanism may reduce the pulmonary venous (and hence the arterial) P_{O_2} to half its normal value. Hypoxic hypoxia can also occur in certain congenital anomalies of the heart or great vessels in which the oxygenated blood in the aorta becomes mixed with poorly oxygenated blood that has not traversed the lungs (anatomical right-to-left-shunt).

In all these circumstances oxygen is supplied to the tissues of the body at a tension lower than normal and may be inadequate for their needs, especially during activity. Acute hypoxic hypoxia is accompanied by an increase in cardiac output of 10 to 20 per cent and the hypoxia stimulates respiration through the carotid bodies; hyperventilation is produced and the elimination of carbon dioxide is increased. The hyperventilation reduces the inspired-alveolar partial pressure for both oxygen and carbon dioxide (Fig. 13.20) and this compensatory mechanism reduces the fall in alveolar and arterial P_{O_2} that would have occurred without it. The rise in cardiac output is also a compensatory response because it reduces the arteriovenous difference for oxygen and prevents too great a fall in venous, and therefore tissue, P_{O_2}. Chronic hypoxia of this type stimulates the production of erythropoietin (p. 108), with a consequent increase in the numbers of red cells in the circulating blood ('secondary polycythaemia'). It may also cause constriction of the pulmonary arterioles and pulmonary arterial hypertension which can in turn cause right ventricular failure. Hypoxic pulmonary heart disease often afflicts patients with chronic airways obstruction, such as chronic bronchitis.

Anaemic hypoxia. This results from interference with oxygen transport either because the amount of circulating haemoglobin is reduced (anaemia), or because the haemoglobin is rendered unavailable by being combined with a substance with which it forms a stable compound. In this type of hypoxia the oxygen load, that is the oxygen carried per 100 ml of blood, is reduced but, since the oxygen tension in the alveolar air and in the arterial blood is normal, the tissues receive their oxygen at a normal tension. The carotid bodies are little affected by this type of hypoxia, so there is no compensating hyperventilation.

As the blood flows through the capillaries in the tissues the oxygen tension falls very rapidly so that, if no compensation occurred, the greater part of the oxygen would be supplied to the tissues at a much reduced tension. In anaemia this disadvantage is compensated for by an increase in the cardiac output; the circulation rate is more rapid, and each 100 ml of blood is required to part with less of its oxygen load to the tissues than would otherwise be the case. Oxygen is thus supplied to the tissues at tensions higher than could occur with the normal circulation rate. In patients with slowly developing anaemia the oxyhaemoglobin dissociation curve (see Fig. 14.5) may be displaced to the right probably by an increased concentration of 2,3 DPG (p. 224) so that a greater proportion of the oxygen is released in the tissue capillaries. As a result of such compensatory mechanisms anaemic patients are rarely breathless at rest but they may rapidly become so with exercise.

Haemoglobin may be rendered unavailable for oxygen transport by drugs such as chlorates and nitrates which convert it to methaemoglobin, or by carbon monoxide which has an affinity for haemoglobin about 250 times greater than that of oxygen. For this reason concentrations of carbon monoxide as low as 0·1 per cent in the atmosphere produce dangerous hypoxia; where there is prolonged exposure, 0·01 per cent is the maximum concentration which can be tolerated. According to J. B. S. Haldane 10 per cent of COHb in the blood causes breathlessness on exertion; 30 per cent COHb causes headache, irritability and impaired judgement; 60 per cent unconsciousness and convulsion; 80 per cent death by asphyxia. The blood of a healthy non-smoker may contain 0·4 per cent COHb derived from destruction of red cells. The binding of CO to myoglobin is greater than it is to haemoglobin. CO therefore interferes with oxygen transport in the myocardium and consequently damages heart muscle and is also likely to cause permanent damage to the central nervous system. The blood of cigarette smokers may have 5 per cent or more of their haemoglobin combined with CO. The treatment of carbon monoxide poisoning is discussed on page 210.

In anaemic hypoxia, although the venous Po_2 is much reduced, the concentration of reduced haemoglobin may yet be insufficient to produce cyanosis.

Stagnant hypoxia. In this type of hypoxia slowing of the circulation may occur locally as the result of vasoconstriction by cold or obstruction to the venous outflow from a part, or because of cardiac failure or peripheral circulatory failure. In this condition arterial oxygen saturation, the partial pressure of oxygen and the oxygen load are all normal but the circulation rate is slowed and the blood dwells longer in the capillaries. Thus the arteriovenous oxygen difference is increased and much of the oxygen is delivered to the tissues at a reduced tension. A small degree of compensation can, however, occur since the retarded flow leads to increase in the capillary blood carbon dioxide tension which encourages the dissociation of oxyhaemoglobin and thus increases the supply of oxygen to the tissues. The cyanosis sometimes seen in persons with polycythaemia in whom the concentration of red cells is over eight million per mm³ and of haemoglobin over 23 g per 100 ml is mainly the result of stagnant hypoxia produced by the increased viscosity imparted to the blood by its much greater content of cells.

Histotoxic hypoxia. Cyanide poisoning is the only important example of histotoxic hypoxia. Cyanide interferes with tissue oxidation by paralysing the cytochrome system and other iron-containing enzyme systems. The cells are, therefore, unable to utilize the oxygen conveyed to them and the arteriovenous oxygen difference is much reduced. Narcotics may have a similar effect by interfering with dehydrogenase systems.

Cyanosis

The colour of the skin is determined by the amount and condition of the blood in the minute vessels and, especially, in the veins of the subpapillary plexus. *Cyanosis* is a violet, bluish or sometimes greyish colour of the skin produced by abnormally large amounts of reduced haemoglobin, or, less frequently, by abnormal pigments such as methaemoglobin and sulphaemoglobin.

Central cyanosis. As explained on page 237 hypoxic hypoxia may arise in lung disease associated with abnormal $\dot{V}/\dot{Q}$ ratios; a less common cause is reduction of the transfer factor to the extent that blood reaches the pulmonary veins insufficiently oxygenated. When cyanosis occurs in this way the patient's extremities are warm and pulsatile, the peripheral blood flow is usually relatively rapid, the heart rate rapid and the pulse pressure increased. There is, in short, vasodilatation and the cyanosis is said to be *central*. The oxygen saturation may fall to 80 per cent before cyanosis is readily apparent; the Pao_2 is then about 45 mm Hg.

Peripheral cyanosis. In contradistinction some cyanosed patients may be cold and blue, with peripheral pulses difficult to feel. Blood flow through the tissues is reduced as the result of vasoconstriction and cyanosis occurs because of the longer time available in the tissues for gaseous exchange. This is *peripheral* cyanosis which is an index of the stagnant hypoxia that may occur in cardiac and peripheral circulatory failure. The oxygen saturation of the arterial blood is normal.

Oxygen Therapy

The administration of oxygen often benefits strikingly hypoxic hypoxia and relieves cyanosis. When the arterial oxygen saturation is normal, as in the stagnant, anaemic and histotoxic forms, less is to be expected of oxygen therapy than in the hypoxic type. Although efficient administration of oxygen can raise the partial pressure of this gas in the alveolar air from 100 to 650 mm Hg it does not necessarily follow that the arterial oxygen tension is correspondingly increased. However, in the hypoxia due to paralysis of the muscles of respiration, to rapid shallow breathing and to many diseases of the lung in which a considerable proportion of the pulmonary blood flow perfuses areas that are not well aerated, the administration of oxygen relieves cyanosis rapidly and the effects of hypoxia more slowly. Such a dramatic relief is not to be expected when there is a large shunt of venous blood from the right to the left side of the heart, or when the diseased pulmonary tissue has been largely deprived of its blood, because in these conditions the blood leaving the functioning alveoli is already 95 per cent saturated.

Efficient oxygen administration at atmospheric pressure is capable of increasing the concentration of oxygen in solution in the plasma from the normal level of about 0·3 ml per 100 ml to values of the order of 1·8 ml per 100 ml. Administration of oxygen may, therefore, make a worthwhile contribution to the oxygen supply of the tissues, equivalent perhaps to an increase of 30 per cent in cardiac output. For this reason the administration of oxygen is useful in all kinds of hypoxia, however produced; its value can be judged in practice by observing its effect in dispelling cyanosis.

When it is intended that the concentration of oxygen in the inspired air should be as high as possible it should be administered through a mask that covers both nose and mouth and has a non-return valve. The mask is used either with a reservoir bag, or a demand-valve on the supply of oxygen.

A lower concentration, about 60 per cent, of oxygen in the inspired air is often adequate and can be provided by cheap, disposable plastic masks which fit the patient's face fairly well and into which oxygen is delivered at not less than 6 litres/min.

Children and very restless patients may sometimes need to be nursed in an 'oxygen tent' of flexible transparent plastic within which they can move fairly freely. The temperature of the enclosed atmosphere must be kept at about 18·5°C. The flow rate of O_2 is usually about 8 litres/min. The oxygen must be humidified when any of these methods is used. It is important to remember that there is a considerable fire risk involved in all methods of oxygen administration.

In certain chronic respiratory diseases such as chronic bronchitis the inadequate ventilation causes a raised Pa_{CO_2} as well as a reduced Pa_{O_2}. This chronic hypercapnia leads to a reduced central chemo-sensitivity to carbon dioxide, and ventilation is largely driven by the hypoxic stimulus acting through the carotid body reflexes. If the hypoxia is suddenly corrected by administration of oxygen, respiration may become dangerously depressed, causing a higher Pa_{CO_2}, carbon dioxide narcosis and even death. In these circumstances the percentage of oxygen in the inspired air should be carefully controlled to provide the highest concentration of oxygen that will not cause a rise of Pa_{CO_2}: that concentration may vary between about 23 and 30 per cent. However, accurate control is difficult in clinical practice. Nasal cannulae can deliver 25 to 30 per cent O_2 into the nostrils with a flow-rate of 1 litre O_2/min; control is not very accurate but the method avoids masks and may be convenient. More accurate methods involve the use of loosely-fitting masks designed on the Venturi principle to deliver a more finely-controlled oxygen concentration. To avoid hypoxia and hypercapnia the Pa_{CO_2} and Pa_{O_2} should ideally be measured at regular intervals.

Oxygen in a chamber at a pressure of two atmospheres (*hyperbaric oxygen*) is sometimes used in the treatment of circulatory disorders. It increases the concentration of oxygen dissolved in the plasma and may sometimes allow the survival of tissues which have had their blood supply seriously impaired. Hyperbaric oxygen is probably the best treatment for carbon monoxide poisoning.

Respiratory Gases in Divers

As a diver descends through water the gas mixture he breathes comes under increasing pressure. For example, the partial pressure of O_2 in air at atmospheric pressure is 160 mm Hg but at a depth of 37·6 m it is 760 mm Hg (101·3 kPa) (atmospheric pressure); the effect of O_2 on a diver breathing air at this depth would be the same as if he were breathing pure O_2 above the surface of the water. Thus, during descent, increasing amounts of respiratory gases diffuse through body fluids and tissues and are dissolved in them. Nitrogen is five times more soluble in lipids than in water, so fatty tissues, including nervous tissue, take up relatively more N_2 during compression. These facts are responsible for several important dangers to divers and caisson workers. Carbon dioxide narcosis has been discussed on p. 233.

Oxygen poisoning. A brief exposure to a Po_2 of over twice atmospheric pressure induces *acute oxygen poisoning* that affects the nervous system, causing lip-twitching, dizziness, nausea and convulsions. Less often, a much lower Po_2 (a half to a little over atmospheric pressure), exerted over several days, irritates the bronchi and lungs, even causing pulmonary oedema (*chronic oxygen poisoning*).

Premature and sick new-born infants given high concentrations of O_2 to breathe develop fibrosis and proliferation of the retinal vessels (*retrolental fibroplasia*) which causes blindness. Oxygen concentrations of 40 to 60 per cent are, however, safe and properly controlled oxygen therapy is an essential part of the care of such babies.

Nitrogen narcosis. At a depth of 30 m the pressure on a diver is four times the atmospheric pressure. Between 30 and 75 m down the increased Pa_{N_2} causes, at first, light-headedness, euphoria and lessened concentration (Cousteau's 'rapture of the deeps'), and later delayed reaction times, inco-ordination and mental depression.

Decompression sickness. When a diver ascends, the partial pressures of gases in his body are reduced. If decompression is too fast, however, gases come out of solution in the tissues and blood, forming bubbles that may cause pain by tearing tissues or blocking small vessels. *Acute decompression sickness* causes peripheral or central effects. Peripheral effects may range from mild pains in limbs ('niggles'), itching and a blotchy rash to severe joint pains ('the bends'). Central effects either involve the nervous system, giving paralysis of limbs from spinal cord lesions or cerebral damage causing aphasia or convulsions, or else they involve the lungs, producing acute dyspnoea, cough, chest pain and shock. *Chronic decompression sickness* is most often seen in tunnel workers. Gas bubbles block end-arteries to bones, causing *aseptic necrosis*. The prevention of decompression sickness is very slow, controlled decompression. The treatment is recompression, followed by careful decompression The effects may, however, be permanent.

Saturation diving. Prolonged decompression limits the length and depth of dives. *Saturation diving* involves the saturation of the tissues with a gas mixture that avoids the risk of O_2 poisoning, N_2 narcosis or hypercapnia. Ideally, the P_{N_2} and Po_2 of the gas mixture should be the same as at the surface and the extra pressure is achieved by adding helium. Once 'saturated', divers can remain at considerable depths for long periods.

REFERENCES

Abbott C P, de Burgh Daly M, Home A 1972 Early ultrastructural changes in the carotid body after degenerative section of the carotid sinus nerve in the cat. Acta anatomica 83: 161–185

Astrup P 1972 Some physiological and pathological effects of moderate carbon monoxide exposure. British Medical Journal ii: 447–452

Bhattacharjya B 1964 Mountain sickness. Wright, Bristol

Brooks C M, Kao F F, Lloyd B B 1965 Cerebrospinal fluid and the regulation of ventilation. Blackwell, Oxford

Cotes J E 1979 Lung functions: assessment and application in medicine, 4th edn. Blackwell, Oxford

Elliott D H, Hallenbeck J M, Bove A A 1974 Acute decompression sickness. Lancet, 2: 1193–1199

Ernsting J 1966 Some effects of raised intrapulmonary pressure in man. Technavision, Maidenhead

Gillies J A (ed) 1965 A textbook of aviation physiology. Pergamon, Oxford

Hackett P H, Rennie D, Levine H D 1976 The incidence, the importance and prophylaxis of acute mountain sickness. Lancet 2: 1149–1155

Haugaard N 1968 Cellular mechanisms of oxygen toxicity. Physiological reviews, 48: 311–373

Heath D, Williams D R 1977 Man at high altitudes. Churchill Livingstone, Edinburgh

Howe A, Neil E 1972 Arterial chemoreceptors. In: Neil E (ed) Handbook of sensory physiology. Springer, Berlin, vol 3: p. 47–80

Kilmartin J V, Rossi-Bernardi L 1973 Interaction of hemoglobin with hydrogen ions, carbon dioxide and organic phosphates. Physiological Reviews, 53: 836–890

Lawther P J 1975 Carbon monoxide. British Medical Bulletin, 31: 256–260

Ledingham I M 1967 Hyperbaric oxygenation. Scientific Basis of Medicine Annual Review, 90–108

Maren T H 1967 Carbonic anhydrase: chemistry, physiology and inhibition. Physiological Reviews, 47: 595–781

Margaria R (ed) 1967 Exercise at altitude. Excerpta Medica Foundation, Amsterdam

Miles S, Mackay D E 1976 Underwater medicine. Adlard Coles, London

Pappenheimer J R 1967 The ionic composition of cerebral extracellular fluid and its relation to control of breathing. The Harvey Lectures 1965–1966, Series 61, pp. 71–94

Perutz M F 1970 Stereochemistry of cooperative effects in haemoglobin. Nature, London, 228: 726–739

Rahn H (ed) 1965 Physiology of breath-hold diving and the Ama of Japan, NAS-NRC, Washington

Roughton F J W 1963 Kinetics of gas transport in blood. British Medical Bulletin, 19: 80–89

Semple S J G 1967 Respiration and the cerebrospinal fluid. Scientific Basis of Medicine Annual Review, 109–127

Shapiro B A 1973 Clinical application of blood gases. Lloyd-Luke, London

Torrance R W (ed) 1968 The arterial chemoreceptors. Pergamon, Oxford

West J B 1976 Ventilation/blood flow and gas exchange, 3rd edn. Blackwell, Oxford

Wyman R J 1977 Neural generation of the breathing rhythm. Annual Review of Physiology 39: 417–48

See also references at the end of Chapter 13

15 The Kidney

The kidneys lie behind the peritoneum on either side of the vertebral column. In the healthy adult each weighs between 115 and 170 g and measures from 11 to 13 cm in length. The left kidney is as a rule the longer and is situated slightly higher than the right. The size and shape of the kidneys in life can be determined from an X-ray film taken after the subject has had an injection of a radio-opaque substance which is concentrated in the kidneys (intravenous pyelogram, Fig. 15.1).

The hilum of the kidney is an indentation on its medial border through which pass the renal arteries, veins, nerves and lymphatics, alongside the renal pelvis, the funnel-shaped upper end of the ureter. The pelvis is formed by the joining together of three or four major calyces, each of which is in turn formed by several short branches or minor calyces.

When cut longitudinally the human kidney is seen to consist of an outer cortex and an inner, paler, medulla made up of pyramids, the apices of which, the papillae, project into the minor calyces. The cortex is demarcated from the medulla by the plane of the arcuate vessels (Fig. 15.5). The medullary pyramids, consisting mainly of collecting ducts, are separated from each other by the renal columns (of Bertin) which are continuous with the cortex.

Microscopic anatomy. The minute anatomy of the kidney is difficult to understand from an ordinary histological section because it is made up of an enormous number of intertwined units. It is possible, however, to separate out each unit, or nephron, by painstaking microdissection (Fig. 15.2).

Each nephron (Fig. 15.3) is a tubule about 6 cm long which

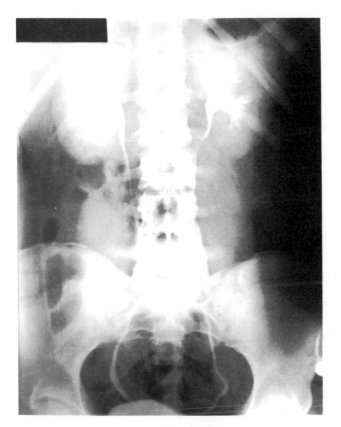

Fig. 15.1 A normal intravenous pyelogram. (*By courtesy of Marjorie Allison*).

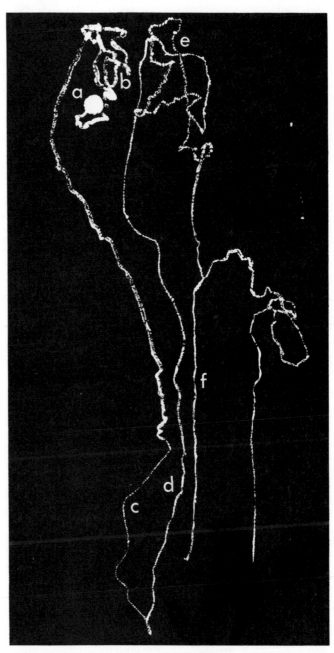

Fig. 15.2 Nephron dissected from a normal human kidney, a: glomerulus, b: proximal convoluted tubule, c and d: thin parts of the loop of Henle, e: distal convoluted tubule, f: collecting duct. × 25 (*By courtesy of J. Oliver.*)

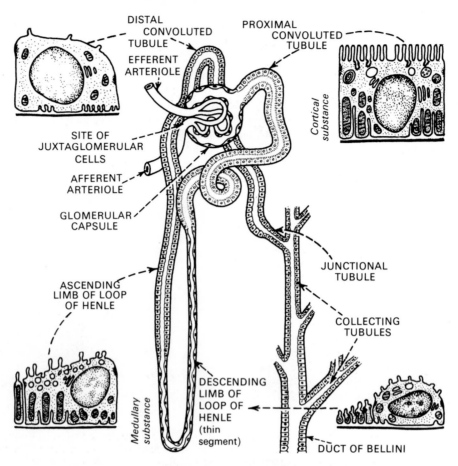

Fig. 15.3 The nephron and collecting tubule diagrammatically represented. (*After* Homer Smith.) The details of the cells given on either side are from J. A. G. Rhodin (1958) *International Review of Cytology*, 7, 485.

begins as a blind dilated end (glomerular or Bowman's capsule) invaginated by a tuft of capillary loops (the glomerulus). These are found only in the cortex. The glomerular capillary tuft surrounded by its capsule is called a renal corpuscle and is about 150 μm in diameter. Each glomerular tuft originates from an afferent arteriole and ends in an efferent arteriole which in turn quickly breaks up to form part of the profuse peritubular capillary network.

From the glomerular capsule issues a tubule which pursues a tortuous course through the cortex and medulla, finally emptying into a collecting duct. These ducts coalesce as they course through the medulla before emptying into the pelvis near the tip of the papillae. The collecting ducts are usually considered to be an integral part of the uriniferous tubule although their embryological origin is different from that of the rest of the nephron. Each adult human kidney contains approximately 1 200 000 nephrons, the total length of all the tubules of both kidneys being approximately 120 km.

The proximal tubule, 12 to 24 mm in length, consists of two parts: a convoluted part which lies near its own glomerular capsule and a straight portion which passes into the descending limb of the loop of Henle. Each loop of Henle penetrates into or towards the medulla for varying depths before forming a U-bend and returning to the cortex, where it lies close to its own renal corpuscle in the space between the afferent and efferent arterioles. Because this part of the tubule

has many prominent nuclei, it has been named the *macula densa*.

The filtering membrane of the renal corpuscle in man consists of three layers: (1) the endothelial lining of the glomerular capillary, (2) a basement membrane and (3) an epithelial layer, the inner wall of the glomerular capsule. The endothelial cells forming the walls of the capillaries are flat and perforated by numerous pores, roughly 50 to 100 nm in diameter occupying approximately 30 per cent of the cell surface (Fig. 15.4). The basement membrane is approximately 300 nm thick and on electron microscopy can be seen to consist of three layers—an inner dense layer bounded on either side by two thinner, less dense layers. The lamina densa consists of a dense meshwork of fine fibrils some 2 to 5 nm in diameter. The basement membrane is composed largely of glycoprotein containing considerable amounts of hydroxylysine and hydroxyproline. Experimental studies with collagenase have shown a collagen-like component but the fibrils lack periodicity. The epithelial cells, or podocytes, are the visceral cells of the glomerular capsule and have long tentacle-like processes (trabeculae) from each of which spring small processes, the pedicels, or foot processes, which surround the capillary and sit upon its basement membrane, frequently interdigitating with each other in a complex fashion (Fig. 15.4). The spaces between the pedicels, each about 20 to 30 nm wide, are known as slit pores. A third cell type, the mesangial cells, is found in

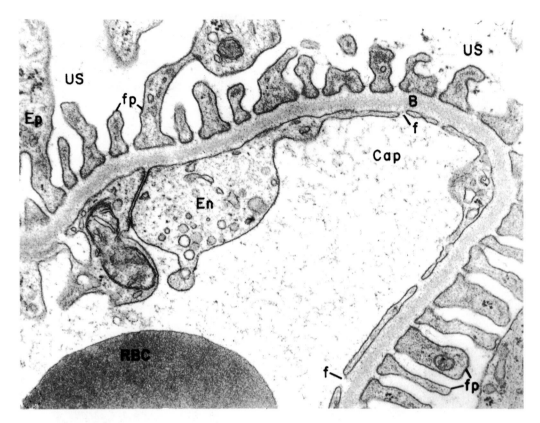

Fig. 15.4 Peripheral area of a glomerular capillary from a normal rat. The capillary wall has three distinct layers: the endothelium (En) with its periodic interruptions or fenestrae (f), the basement membrane (B) and the foot processes (fp) of the epithelium (Ep). Cap = capillary lumen, US = urinary spaces, RBC = red blood cell × 32 000. (*By courtesy of Marilyn G. Farquhar.*)

the centre or stalk region of the capillary tuft. They have phagocytic properties which may be important in glomerular disease.

The cell types found in the different regions of the tubule are shown in Figure 15.3. Proximal convoluted tubule cells are large, columnar type cells with a well marked brush border which consists of thin microvilli (varying in length from 1 to 4 μm), approximately 100 per μm^2 of luminal surface; they greatly increase the surface area of the luminal membrane in contact with tubular fluid. The apical portion of the cytoplasm contains numerous small and large vesicles and vacuoles, while the basal part has many large mitochondria. The cell membrane at the base of each cell is deeply invaginated in a complex fashion, adjacent cells interlocking laterally with each other. The lateral surfaces of adjacent cells are separated by an extracellular space, closed at the luminal margin by a tight junction (Fig. 15.23).

The loop of Henle consists of a thin descending limb and a thick ascending limb; however, if the loop is a long one and dips into the inner medulla, it also has a thin ascending limb. The thin descending limb begins close to the cortico-medullary boundary. The cells are flat with few microvilli or mitochondria. The cells of the thick ascending limb are elaborately interwoven with each other and contain many mitochondria. The cells of the distal convoluted tubule have fewer microvilli than those of the proximal tubule and longer tight junctions between adjacent cells.

Renal Blood Vessels

Blood is supplied to the kidneys by the two renal arteries which arise directly from the abdominal aorta. Upon entering the kidney each divides into a number of major branches called interlobar arteries. Each of these is functionally an end-artery, that is it does not anastomose with any other vessel. Hence blockage of one results in the death of the tissue supplied.

At the junction between cortex and outer medulla each interlobar artery divides into arcuate arteries which run between the cortex and medulla parallel to the surface of the organ (Fig. 15.5). Frequent branches (interlobular arteries) arise from them and run in the cortex at right angles to the surface. From each of these vessels numerous afferent arterioles arise which break up almost at once into the capillaries of the glomerular tuft. The afferent arteriole has a thick muscular coat; blood is thus supplied to the glomeruli at a high but controlled hydrostatic pressure. Blood leaves the glomerulus by the efferent glomerular arteriole which, in cortical nephrons, immediately breaks up into a profuse peritubular capillary network with low hydrostatic pressure which facilitates its function as a reabsorptive vascular bed. The walls of the peritubular capillaries consist of a very thin fenestrated endothelium resting on a basal lamina. From this network blood flows into the renal veins. Renal venous blood thus has perfused two capillary beds, namely the high pressure glomerular tuft and the low pressure peritubular capillaries.

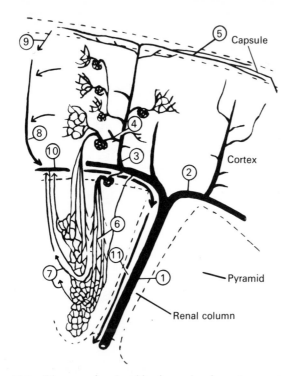

Fig. 15.5 Diagram showing blood supply of renal parenchyma. Veins indicated by arrows. (1) Interlobar artery, (2) Arcuate artery, (3) Interlobular artery, (4) Intralobular artery, (5) Capsular plexus, (6) Arteriolae rectae spuriae, (7) Venae rectae, (8) Interlobular vein, (9) Stellate vein, (10) Arcuate vein, (11) Interlobar vein. (*From* R. E. Coupland in D. A. K. Black (1967) *Renal Disease.* 2nd edition. Oxford: Blackwell.)

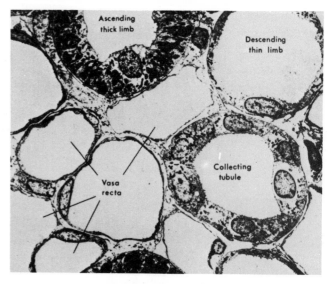

Fig. 15.6 Electron micrograph of part of the outer zone of the rat kidney medulla to show ascending thick limb, descending thin limb, collecting tubule and the vasa recta. × 2100 (*After* A. Maunsbach. (1966) *Journal of Ultrastructure Research*, 15, 242.)

The tubules receive little blood directly from the renal arteries.

The glomeruli are not all identical. The description given earlier applies to the more superficial or cortical nephrons. *Juxtamedullary nephrons*, situated in the deeper layers of the cortex (about 10 to 20 per cent of the total) are larger and have larger glomeruli. Their proximal tubules are longer and the efferent arterioles are at least as wide as the afferent vessels. After a short, straight course towards the medulla the efferent arteriole breaks up into a number of long thin vessels, the descending vasa recta which follow the course of the loops of Henle. Not all vasa recta originate from efferent arterioles, aglomerular branches from acruate and interlobular arteries being found, particularly in old age and hypertension. All end in a capillary plexus around the loops of Henle in the medulla. From this network fenestrated ascending vasa recta originate and run back towards the cortex to drain into the arcuate veins. In the outer medulla ascending and descending vasa recta and loops of Henle run together in vascular bundles (Fig. 15.6). Juxtamedullary glomeruli have very long loops of Henle which penetrate the inner medulla and have thin ascending as well as thin descending limbs. These nephrons seem to be functionally different from cortical nephrons. Micropuncture and isolated tubule studies have shown that the juxtamedullary glomeruli have a higher filtration rate than the smaller glomeruli nearer the surface; they may play an important role in sodium retention (p. 246).

Juxtaglomerular apparatus. This is situated at the hilum of each glomerulus and consists of three parts (Fig. 15.7): (1) the

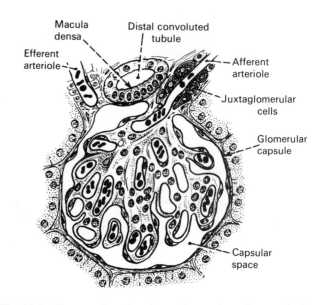

Fig. 15.7 Cross-section of a glomerulus to show the macula densa and the juxtaglomerular cells.

granular epithelioid cells, found mainly in the terminal part of the afferent arteriole but also in the efferent arteriole wall; (2) the macula densa of the distal convoluted tubule; and (3) the lacis cells which fill up the space between the other components. The granular epithelioid cells produce renin (p. 256).

Renal Nerves

The kidneys are abundantly supplied with sympathetic (adrenergic) nerves but only a sparse parasympathetic innervation. Adrenergic fibres are found in association with all muscle-containing arterioles and also in the juxtaglomerular apparatus and vasa recta of the outer medulla. Their physiological function is still disputed.

Both α- and β-adrenergic effects can be demonstrated in the kidney (Chap. 25), of which the α-adrenergic effects seem to be the more important. Thus renal nerve stimulation has an antidiuretic and antinatriuretic effect, associated with a fall in total renal blood flow due to increased renal vascular resistance and possibly also intrarenal redistribution of blood flow from cortex to medulla. Adrenergic stimulation increases renin production. Excess adrenergic activity may be important in the pathophysiology of some salt retaining disease states such as heart failure and cirrhosis of the liver.

RENAL FUNCTION

Each day approximately 180 litres of water, containing more than 1 kg of sodium chloride, 500 g of sodium bicarbonate, 250 g of glucose, 100 g of free amino acids, 4 g of vitamin C and significant quantities of many other important constituents, are filtered through the glomeruli of the human kidney. Excretion of quite small fractions of these filtered quantities, however, is sufficient to balance daily intake. The magnitude of the daily task of the kidneys in filtration, reabsorption and excretion is expressed quantitatively in Table 15.8.

The volume and composition of the urine vary widely from day to day, depending on the type of food consumed, the volume of fluid taken and the amount of fluid lost by other routes which is related to environmental temperature and humidity, exercise and sweating (p. 413). The usual daily volume is between 1000 and 1500 ml.

The yellow colour of normal urine is due mainly to the pigment urochrome. The chemical nature and source of this substance are unknown, but it is probably formed endogenously since its output increases with destruction of tissue protein or increase in metabolism. Traces of other pigments, such as urobilin and uroerythrin, are also normally present. Freshly passed urine has hardly any smell unless it contains derivatives of certain food stuffs but, when it is allowed to stand, it develops an ammoniacal odour owing to the conversion by bacteria of urea to ammonia.

The urine normally contains only very small amounts of protein, 0 to 90 mg per day, too little to be detected by the usual clinical tests. After severe exercise proteinuria can be transiently increased and occasional red cell casts are present. Gross proteinuria can occur in some glomerular diseases; the loss of up to 10 to 15 g of protein in the urine per day results in hypoproteinaemia and oedema (nephrotic syndrome).

Urine from normal persons contains some leucocytes and

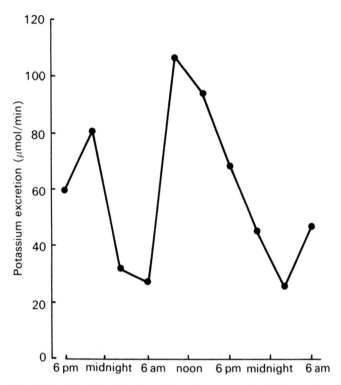

Fig. 15.9 Circadian rhythm of the urinary excretion of potassium. The results are mean values for six male medical students, aged 19 to 22 years, whose only intake was 568 ml milk every 4 hours, day and night. (*By courtesy of H. Simpson.*)

non-squamous epithelial cells, the combined output being between 20 000 and 200 000 per hour, a smaller number of red cells, and some hyaline casts. These casts are formed by precipitation of a mucoprotein secreted by the tubule and are of no clinical importance. In certain pathological states, however, the hyaline matrix can become coated with red blood cells, leucocytes or degenerated tubular cells (cellular and granular casts) and hence their detection can be helpful in diagnosis.

To maintain homeostasis the rate of excretion of a substance must equal the rate of its intake or production. For many substances the urine is the principal route of excretion; for these the urinary excretion each day is determined largely by intake and production in the body. The rate of excretion varies greatly within a 24 hour period. The cause of this *circadian rhythm* is not yet known but probably includes variations in salt and water intake and in hormonal factors. Figure 15.9 shows the circadian rhythm for potassium excretion.

Table 15.8 Filtration, reabsorption and excretion of ions and water by an adult man, with a glomerular filtration rate of 180 l/24 h. One litre of plasma normally contains about 0·93 kg (51·8 mol) of water equivalent to 0·94 l.

	Plasma concentration	Amount filtered	Amount excreted	Amount reabsorbed	Per cent reabsorbed
	(mmol/l)	(mmol/24 h)	(mmol/24 h)	(mmol/24 h)	
Sodium	142	25560	250	25310	99·0
Chloride	100	18000	250	17750	98·6
Bicarbonate	28	5040	2	5038	>99·9
Potassium	4	720	120	600	83
	kg/l	*kg/24 h*	*kg/24 h*	*kg/24 h*	
Water	0·93	167·4	1·5	165·9	99·1

Glomerular Function

The first step in the formation of urine is the ultrafiltration of plasma through the glomerular capillaries. Analysis of fluid in the capsular space obtained by micropuncture techniques shows that the filtrate contains all the constituents of plasma, with the exception of protein, in concentrations almost identical with those in blood plasma.

The polysaccharide inulin, after injection into the frog's circulation, is found in the same concentration in the glomerular filtrate as in plasma. This relatively large molecule (molecular weight 5000) must therefore be transferred across the glomerular membrane in the same way as the much smaller urea and chloride molecules. Since large molecules pass as quickly across the membrane as small molecules, the transference cannot be a process of diffusion but must be one of filtration in which all molecules smaller than the pores of the filter can pass through, the only difference between fluid to be filtered and the filtrate itself being the absence in the latter of substances of large molecular size. Experiments with dextran, another polysaccharide of which suspensions can be prepared containing molecules of different sizes, have shown that the 'pores' of the glomerular membrane are not of equal size. All are permeable to dextran molecules of molecular weight 10000 which pass just as freely as water molecules across the glomerular membrane. Larger molecules have a progressively lower clearance, those of molecular weight greater than 50000 being almost entirely absent from the glomerular filtrate. Similar studies with proteins of various molecular weights have shown that those with low molecular weight are readily excreted, while haemoglobin and albumin with a molecular weight of approximately 68000 are filtered in only very small amounts. The sieving characteristics of proteins and dextrans of various molecular weights have led to the concept that the filtering membrane has pores 7·5 to 10·0 nm in diamter, and 40 to 60 nm in length. The site of the 'pores' still disputed, but it is now widely accepted that the basement membrane itself forms the molecular sieve. Pores of the size indicated from functional studies cannot be demonstrated by electronmicroscopy.

Glomerular filtration rate (GFR). About 125 ml of fluid are filtered through the glomerular membranes of the two kidneys of man per minute. In normal mammals all glomeruli are believed to be functional at all times, and the total glomerular capillary area in man has been estimated to be more than 1·5 m².

Since there are about $2\cdot4 \times 10^6$ glomeruli, about 40 nl must be filtered through each per minute. Direct measurement of the filtration rate of a single glomerulus is possible by micropuncture techniques in experimental animals. Most measurements have been made in the rat where filtration rates in superficial glomeruli have been found to be 20 to 30 nl/min. Filtration rates in juxtamedullary glomeruli in rats with a normal or low salt intake have been found to be approximately twice this value. Thus there are at least two functionally different populations of nephrons in the kidney. Variation in glomerular filtration rate in these two populations of nephrons is now believed to be concerned in the renal regulation of sodium balance, increased salt intake resulting in increased filtration particularly in the superficial nephrons.

The rate of glomerular capillary filtration is determined by the physical forces involved in the transport of fluid across the capillary walls in accordance with the Starling hypothesis. Thus the chief driving force for filtration is the glomerular capillary hydrostatic pressure (Pg). Opposing this is the hydrostatic pressure in Bowman's space (Pbs) and the colloid osmotic pressure of the glomerular capillary blood (COP). These in turn may be affected by the permeability (K) of the filtration membrane. Thus:

$$GFR = K[Pg - (Pbs + COP)]$$

Filtration pressure. Recently advances in micropuncture techniques and the finding of a strain of rats whose glomeruli are visible on the kidney surface have allowed the direct measurement of the hydrostatic pressure within the glomerular capillaries. In the water-depleted rat average values are 44 to 48 mm Hg. This is about half of the renal artery pressure due to the drop in pressure across the resistance of the afferent arteriole. A further fall in pressure also occurs across the efferent arteriole, so that the pressure within the peritubular capillaries is only 8 to 15 mm Hg. Variations in both afferent and efferent arteriolar resistance could be expected to affect the glomerular capillary pressure. Normally, however, this pressure remains relatively constant since afferent arteriolar resistance varies inversely with the arterial pressure (p. 249).

The hydrostatic pressure of the fluid within Bowman's space is about 10 mm Hg and the colloid osmotic pressure (COP) at the afferent end of the capillary bed may be assumed to be equal to that in the systemic circulation, or 15 to 20 mm Hg in the rat (equivalent to a plasma protein concentration of 50 to 60 g/l). At this point the effective filtration pressure must be about

$$48 - (10 + 18) \text{ mm Hg} = 20 \text{ mm Hg}$$

As filtration proceeds along the length of the capillary, the colloid osmotic pressure rises since the plasma protein concentration rises as water is removed by filtration. Measurements of the protein concentrations have indicated that before the end of the capillary is reached COP rises so much that the effective filtration pressure may become zero (Pg = Pbs + COP). Indeed this 'filtration equilibrium' may be reached fairly early in the flow through the glomerular capillary so that a substantial proportion of the length of capillary is not in use as a filter (Fig. 15.10). One consequence of this is that the glomerular filtration rate depends on plasma flow; the greater the plasma flow the greater the length of capillary involved in filtration and the greater the filtration rate. In some diseases, such as glomerulonephritis, the surface area and permeability of the glomerular capillary bed are reduced and filtration equilibrium may never be reached.

Measurement of glomerular filtration rate (GFR). It is clearly not possible to measure single nephron filtration rates in human subjects by micropuncture techniques. An estimate of whole kidney filtration rates can, however, be obtained. Consider a biologically inert substance circulating in the bloodstream, unattached to plasma proteins, small enough to be freely filterable through the glomerulus and neither reabsorbed from, nor secreted into, the tubular fluid (Fig. 15.11). In these circumstances the amount filtered at the glomerulus (GFR×P) must equal the amount secreted (U×V) or

$$GFR = \frac{U \times V}{P}$$

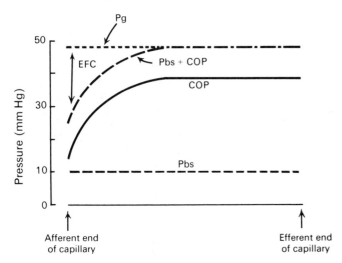

Fig. 15.10 The effective filtration pressure across the glomerular capillary bed (EFC) is the difference between the hydrostatic pressure in the glomeruli (Pg) and the sum of the pressure in Bowman's (capsular) space (Pbs) and the colloid osmotic pressure (COP). As filtration proceeds, COP rises and the effective filtration pressure falls to zero.

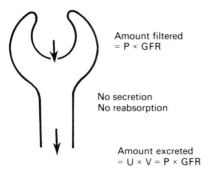

Fig. 15.11 If a substance is filtered by the glomerulus but neither reabsorbed nor secreted by the tubule, the urinary excretion (U × V) is equal to the amount filtered (P × GFR), where P and U are the concentrations of the substance in plasma and urine respectively and V is the urinary output. The glomerular filtration rate is therefore
$$\frac{U \times V}{P}$$

where P and U are the concentration of the substance in the plasma and urine respectively and V is the urine flow rate.

The fructose polysaccharide, inulin, was believed to be such a substance by Homer Smith and Richards about 1935 and it has since been proved by micropuncture techniques that it is indeed freely filtered and is neither secreted nor reabsorbed during its passage down the nephron. To measure the glomerular filtration rate inulin must be given by intravenous infusion since it is hydrolysed in the gastrointestinal tract and is poorly absorbed if it is injected intramuscularly. Accurately timed urine and blood samples are taken and the inulin concentration in each is measured. In normal young men the glomerular filtration rate (GFR) has been found to average 125± 15 ml/min/1·73 m² while that of normal young females is about 10 per cent less. Since the filtration rate varies with body size it is usual to relate the value to that of an ideal subject with a body surface area of 1·73 m².

Inulin is the most satisfactory substance yet found for the

measurement of GFR but other substances which occur normally in man can also be used. Thus creatinine, a substance whose rate of production from the muscles is relatively constant, is readily filtered and is not reabsorbed from the tubular fluid. The fact that small amounts of creatinine are secreted by the tubules in man results in a small apparent increase in the filtration rate. However, the chemical methods used to measure creatinine in plasma often do not differentiate non-creatinine from creatinine chromogens; the falsely high values for plasma creatinine cancel out the effects of creatinine secretion. In practice an accurate 24 hour urine specimen is collected and a blood sample is taken at any time during the period of collection. No restrictions on diet, fluid intake or activity are necessary.

The rate of creatinine production in the body is relatively constant and unaffected by dietary protein intake. Daily excretion equals production rate and overall balance is maintained. As the glomerular filtration rate falls, therefore, the plasma concentration of creatinine must rise to keep the excretion rate constant and equal to the rate of production in the muscles (Fig. 15.12). For the day to day monitoring of renal function in patients with renal disease, serial determinations of the plasma creatinine concentration are very useful and accurately reflect GFR.

Recently radioactive compounds such as cyanocobalamin labelled with ^{57}Co and EDTA labelled with ^{51}Cr have been used to measure GFR because they are easily detected. The accuracy of the results, however, is still uncertain because these substances may be bound to plasma protein.

Concept of 'clearance'. The rate of urinary excretion of a substance (U × V) divided by the plasma concentration (P) is a measure of the minimal volume of plasma required to supply the amount of the substance excreted in the urine in a given period of time. This is termed the *clearance* of a substance and is expressed as

$$C = \frac{U \times V}{P}$$

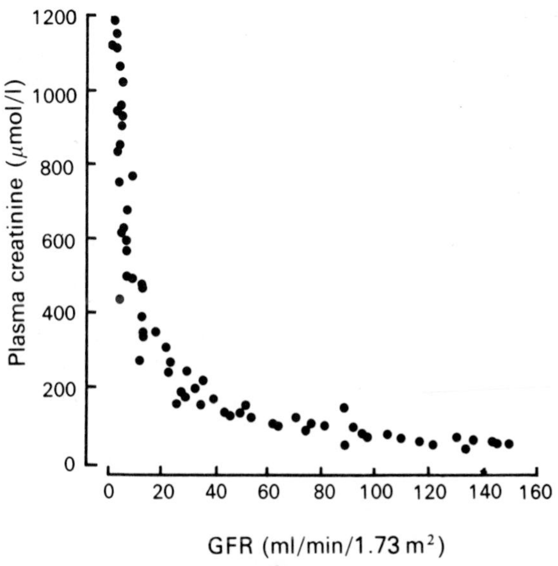

Fig. 15.12 Plasma creatinine levels in relation to glomerular filtration rate in normal persons and in patients with chronic renal disease. (*By courtesy of Marjorie Allison.*)

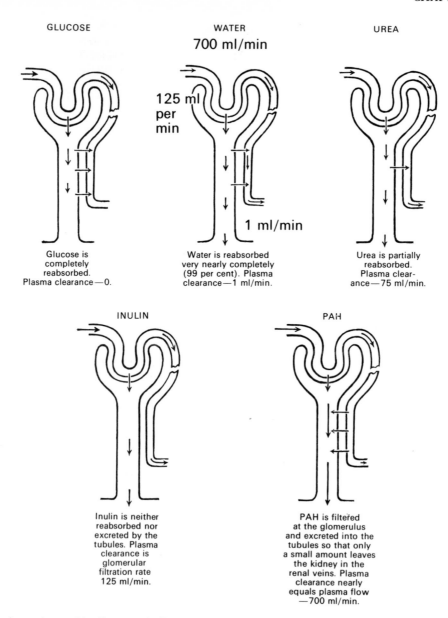

Fig. 15.13 Diagram of a nephron with afferent and efferent glomerular vessels and a tubular capillary. The arrows show the direction of movement of the substance under discussion and their length indicates the amount which is moving. The middle diagram above shows the amount of fluid passing into the kidney (700 ml per min), the amount filtered at the glomerulus (125 ml per min) and the amount eliminated as urine (1 ml per min). Since the 700 ml of plasma flowing through the glomerulus per min carries the red cells the volume of blood flowing through the kidneys is 1200 ml/min.

The clearance of any solute that appears in the urine can be calculated from this formula. As shown above, the clearance of inulin gives a measure of the total glomerular filtration rate. Therefore by comparing the clearance of any substance with that of inulin, some idea can be obtained of the net processes occurring in the passage of that substance down the nephrons. If the clearance is less than that of inulin (for example, urea, sodium, glucose, water), the substance must undergo a net reabsorption in the tubules. If, on the other hand, the clearance of a substance is greater than that of inulin (for example, PAH) excretion must involve tubular secretion (Fig. 15.13).

It should be pointed out that the volume of plasma cleared of a substance is a theoretical concept; no single millilitre of blood actually has all its inulin or creatinine removed in one transit

through the kidneys. Instead, each of many millilitres perfusing the kidneys has a little removed.

Measurement of renal blood flow by clearance methods. Para-aminohippuric acid (PAH) has been used to estimate renal plasma flow (RPF) in animals and man. A large dose given intravenously is followed by a constant infusion to make up for the loss of PAH in the urine. If the plasma concentration is lower than 0·5 mmol/l, some 90 per cent of the PAH is excreted by proximal tubular secretion in one passage through the kidney. The PAH clearance thus provides an estimate of the renal plasma flow;

$$RPF = \frac{U_{PAH} \times V}{P_{PAH}}$$

where U_{PAH} is the concentration of PAH in the urine, V is the urine flow rate in ml/min and P_{PAH} is the concentration of PAH in the peripheral venous blood. In normal males the renal plasma flow thus calculated is 660 ml/min/1·73 m², while that of females is approximately 10 per cent less. This value has been termed the 'effective' renal plasma flow since only about 90 per cent of PAH is extracted in one passage through the kidneys, the remaining 10 per cent probably being accounted for by blood flowing through the fibrous capsule and medulla which does not come in contact with proximal tubular cells for secretion. In kidney disease the extraction of PAH may fall below 90 per cent and it becomes necessary to measure this reduced extraction and to make appropriate correction for it in the clearance equation. This requires catheterization of the renal vein and obviously has limited application in clinical practice.

The 'effective' renal blood flow (RBF) can be calculated from the 'effective' RPF and systemic haematocrit (normally about 45 per cent);

$$RBF = RPF\left(\frac{1}{1 - \text{haematocrit}}\right)$$

$$= 660\left(\frac{1}{1 - 0·45}\right)$$

$$= 1\,200 \text{ ml/min.}$$

The ratio of inulin clearance to PAH clearance, GFR/RPF, is called the *filtration fraction*. In health it amounts to some 20 per cent of the renal plasma flow and represents the proportion of the latter which is filtered.

These calculations show that the kidneys receive approximately one-fifth of the cardiac output. This large blood flow, high in comparison with that in other organs, is not brought about by high metabolic demands but is rather an expression of the fundamental role of the kidney in regulating the composition of extracellular fluid. The renal arterio-venous oxygen difference is small and oxygen is available in abundance to the renal cortical tissues. The kidneys of man consume some 8 per cent of the total oxygen utilized at rest, consumption being directly related to the extent of sodium reabsorption.

Hippuran (iodohippuric acid labelled with ¹³¹I) is used to determine effective renal plasma flow; it is handled like PAH by the kidney but, because of its radioactive label, it is simpler to estimate. Hippuran can also be used to obtain an *isotope renogram*. After a small intravenous dose of Hippuran, radioactivity is measured over each kidney by means of a scintillation counter and the result is displayed graphically against time (Fig. 15.14). The results are thus dependent on a number of factors other than renal blood flow but can be useful in assessing renal abnormalities, such as narrowing of a renal artery, obstruction of a ureter or asymmetric renal disease.

Distribution of renal blood flow. Total renal blood flow amounts to some 1200 ml/min; its distribution within the kidney, however, is not uniform; approximately 90 per cent perfuses the renal cortex while only some 10 per cent perfuses the medulla. The pattern of renal blood flow in man is usually obtained by the inert gas 'wash-out' technique in which radioactive krypton or xenon is injected into the renal artery and its disappearance monitored with an external detector. By graphical or computer analysis four component disappearance

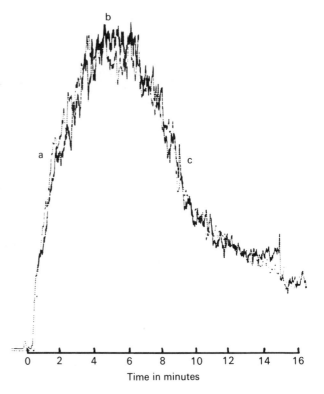

Fig. 15.14 Tracing of a normal isotope renogram during a period of 16 minutes after the intravenous injection of radioactively-labelled Hippuran. Three phases are described: a vascular phase (a), a tissue phase (b), when the isotope is mainly within the cells of the proximal tubule and an excretory phase (c), due to the passage of the Hippuran down the ureter. (*By courtesy of Marjorie Allison.*)

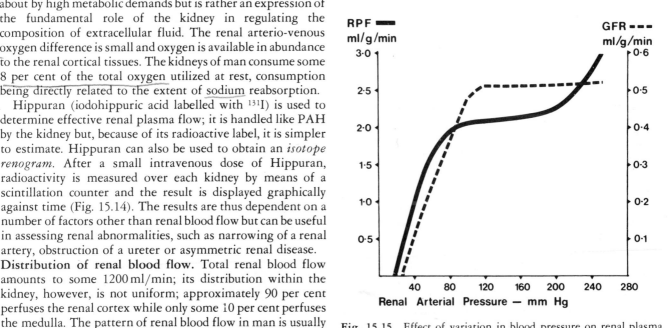

Fig. 15.15 Effect of variation in blood pressure on renal plasma flow (RPF) and glomerular filtration rate (GFR) in the dog, to show autoregulation over the range of perfusion pressure from 80 to 180 mm Hg. (*After R. F. Pitts (1968) Physiology of the Kidney and Body Fluids. 2nd edition. London: Lloyd-Luke.*)

curves can be identified and are believed to represent rates of flow through (a) cortex, (b) inner or juxtamedullary cortex and outer medulla, (c) vasa recta and inner medulla and (d) perirenal tissue. The disappearance of radioactivity is slowest from the inner medulla; the slow rate of flow in the vasa recta enables a high concentration of solute to be maintained in this area (p. 252).

Autoregulation of Renal Circulation

Figure 15.15 illustrates the fact that renal blood flow and glomerular filtration rate change little as arterial pressure changes over a range of 80 to 180 mm Hg. Since this is so in denervated, isolated perfused kidneys, control must reside within the kidney itself and is therefore termed autoregulation. As a result renal blood flow and filtration are stabilized. Autoregulation, however, can be overcome by administration of vasoactive drugs, by stimulation of the afferent renal nerves and breaks down during haemorrhagic or endotoxic shock.

The most widely discussed theory of the mechanism of autoregulation concerns changes in intrarenal vascular tone, perhaps under control of the renin-angiotensin mechanism. According to this theory, an increase in blood pressure (and hence in filtration pressure) increases the glomerular filtration rate. The more rapid flow through the proximal tubule and ascending limb of the loop of Henle provides less time for the reabsorption of sodium. This increased concentration of sodium in the tubular fluid is detected by the cells of the macula densa in the distal tubule. Renin is then released from the cells of the juxtaglomerular apparatus and angiotensin is formed (p. 256). This results in constriction of the afferent arterioles and the filtration rate returns to normal. A fall in blood pressure would be expected to produce the opposite effect.

Tubular Function

Since the concentrations of substances in the glomerular filtrate are very different from their concentrations in the final urine, the composition of the fluid must be altered considerably during its passage down the tubule to the renal pelvis. Micropuncture techniques have been used to study the changes in tubular fluid composition in small mammals and amphibia. After intravenous injection of lissamine green, proximal convoluted tubules, distal tubules and collecting ducts, lying on the surface of the living kidney, can be identified by observing the flow of the dye down the nephron. Glass micropipettes can be inserted into the nephron and minute volumes of tubular fluid (0·5 to 50 nl) can be removed and the concentrations of inulin, sodium, potassium, calcium, phosphate and the osmolality are measured by microtechniques.

Two mechanisms have been found to account for the tubular handling of substances, namely reabsorption and secretion. Each may be either active or passive. Active reabsorption is defined as reabsorption that cannot be explained by the existing electrochemical gradients; it requires the expenditure of metabolic energy. Examples of substances actively reabsorbed in the tubules are sodium and glucose. Similarly, active tubular secretion, transtubular transport from blood to lumen, requires energy expenditure. Examples of substances

secreted in this fashion are a variety of organic acids including phenol red, PAH, penicillin and sulphonamides. Tubular transport along an existing electrochemical gradient is considered to be passive. Thus water and urea are passively reabsorbed from the tubular fluid along gradients created by the active reabsorption of sodium. The tubular handling of water, sodium, potassium, glucose, calcium and phosphate will now be considered in greater detail. The role of the renal tubule in acid-base balance is discussed on page 268.

The excretion of water. One hundred and twenty-five ml of glomerular filtrate are produced each minute. Since the total volume of extracellular fluid in the body is about 15 litres, the equivalent of the whole of this volume passes through the kidneys every 2 hours. Of the 125 ml of glomerular filtrate, however, only about 1 ml appears as urine; in other words, 99 per cent of the fluid passed into the renal tubules is reabsorbed on its way through the kidney.

In the basal state the rate of urine flow is low, perhaps 1 ml per minute, and the urine is moderately concentrated. If a healthy person drinks rapidly a large volume of water the urine volume quickly increases and a water diuresis results (Fig. 15.16). In about 1 hour urine flow reaches a maximum rate of approximately 12 to 15 per cent of the glomerular filtration rate, its osmolality falls to about 85 mmol/kg and the water load is eliminated in 2 to 4 hours. The rate of solute excretion and GFR are unchanged. On the other hand, if a healthy subject is deprived of fluid for over 12 hours, urine output falls below 1 ml/min and the osmolality rises to exceed 800 mmol/kg. Thus the osmolality of the body fluids is kept virtually constant, around 285 mmol/kg, by variation in urine osmolality.

The mechanism that best explains these changes in urine osmolality is the countercurrent system. Among the vertebrates only mammals, and to some extent birds, are able to produce a hypertonic urine. Only these species have thin segments of the loop of Henle. In addition, the maximum extent to which different animals are able to concentrate the urine increases with the thickness of the medulla relative to the cortex. For example, the desert rat, which depends for its existence on its remarkable ability to conserve water, has a

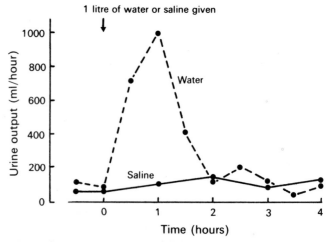

Fig. 15.16 Urine volume after drinking 1 litre of water and, on the following day, 1 litre of sodium chloride solution (154 mmol/l) by a healthy man. At the end of 2 hours all the water volume but little of the saline volume had been eliminated.

also a myogenic control

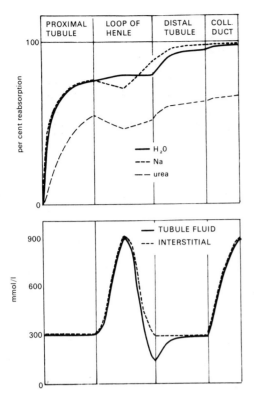

Fig. 15.17 This diagram shows above the amount of reabsorption of several constituents of the glomerular filtrate in the different parts of the nephron. The lower diagram shows the osmolality of the tubular fluid in the different parts of the nephron. (J. N. Barker (1963) *Medical Clinics of North America*, 47, 883.)

particularly long loop of Henle and a thick medulla, while the aquatic beaver has a relatively thin medulla and a much lower maximum urine osmolality. It is now known that the production of a concentrated urine is due to passive water reabsorption, under the influence of antidiuretic hormone, out of the collecting ducts into the hypertonic interstitium of the medulla. The hypertonicity of this area is the result of the activity of the loops of Henle which act as a countercurrent multiplier system and the vasa recta which act as counter-current exchangers.

Experimental evidence for the countercurrent hypothesis was obtained by measuring the osmolality of tubular fluid and of cortical and medullary tissue slices. In the proximal tubule about two thirds of the water, sodium and chloride are reabsorbed from the glomerular filtrate in such a way that the fluid remaining in the lumen of the tubule remains isotonic to plasma (Fig. 15.17). Tubular fluid collected from the tip of the loop of Henle is always markedly hypertonic as are slices of medullary tissue from this area. Fluid entering the distal convoluted tubule is invariably hypotonic. When a concentrated urine is being produced the fluid becomes isotonic in the distal convoluted tubule and later hypertonic in the collecting duct. When a dilute urine is being produced there is little change in osmolality of the tubular fluid as it passes through the distal tubule and cortical collecting duct.

The countercurrent multiplier system operates in the loops of Henle to produce a hypertonic medulla as follows. In Figure 15.18 the density of shading represents the osmotic pressure in the descending limb (D) and the ascending limb (A) of a simplified loop of Henle. (D) and (A) are separated by a membrane (S) impermeable to water but with the ability to

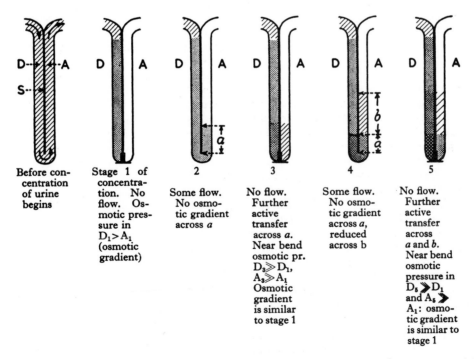

Before concentration of urine begins

Stage 1 of concentration. No flow. Osmotic pressure in $D_1 > A_1$ (osmotic gradient)

2
Some flow. No osmotic gradient across a

3
No flow. Further active transfer across a. Near bend osmotic pr. $D_3 \gg D_1$, $A_3 \gg A_1$ Osmotic gradient is similar to stage 1

4
Some flow. No osmotic gradient across a, reduced across b

5
No flow. Further active transfer across a and b. Near bend osmotic pressure in $D_5 \gg D_1$ and $A_5 \gg A_1$: osmotic gradient is similar to stage 1

Fig. 15.18 A simplified scheme of the countercurrent process. The depth of shading indicates the relative tonicity of the fluid in the loop of Henle. At stages 1, 3 and 5 the flow is supposed to be stopped (by a tap at the end of the loop) while ions are actively transferred from the ascending limb A to the descending limb D of the loop of Henle. Note that the maximum tonicity occurs at the tip of the loop. (*After* P. Wirz.) (*By courtesy of P. Antonis.*)

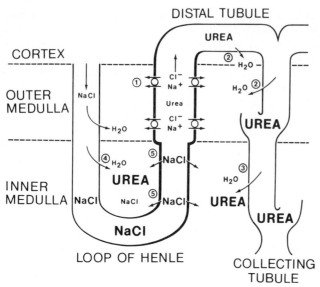

Fig. 15.19 Summary of the principal active transport steps which contribute to the development of a high osmolality in the renal medulla. The size of the lettering used is intended to give an indication of the concentrations of the various solutes. (*From* R. L. Jamieson and R. H. Maffly (1976) *New England Journal of Medicine*, **295**, 1062.)

transport solute actively from ascending to descending limb, thereby creating a concentration gradient across the membrane of approximately 200 mmol/kg. Suppose this simplified loop of Henle to be filled initially with a fluid of approximately 285 mmol/kg and suppose that there is no flow through the tube. Chloride ions are then actively transported from (A) to (D), sodium following passively, the fluid in (D) becomes hypertonic, that in (A) hypotonic (stage 1). If a small amount of fluid is now allowed to flow (stage 2) the osmotic gradient at the lower end of the loop disappears and if the flow is stopped again (stage 3) further transfer of chloride ions from (A) to (D) makes the fluid at the lower end of (D) even more hypertonic. Repetition of this multiplier process (stages 4 and 5) increases the hypertonicity at the lower end of the loop of Henle. This effect is achieved without producing a large osmotic difference at any level between the fluid in the two adjacent limbs of the loop, but results in a high solute concentration at the bend of the loop (Fig. 15.19).

In living kidneys the limbs of the loop are not in direct contact and the exchanges occur between the limbs of the loop and the surrounding interstitial fluid (Fig. 15.6). The countercurrent mechanism depends on the fact that the ascending limb of the loop of Henle, which has a thicker wall than the descending limb, is impermeable to water so that when chloride is actively transferred from it to the interstitium, water does not move with the chloride. It was at first believed that sodium was the ion actively transported out of the ascending limb of the loop of Henle. However, microperfusion studies indicate that it is chloride rather than sodium which is actively transported in this part of the tubule; sodium movement is largely passive. The countercurrent multiplier system of the loops of Henle thus provides a means whereby the inner medulla can develop a high osmolality without subjecting any single part of the loop to a high transtubular osmotic gradient.

The collecting tubule and collecting duct produce a concentration of urine appropriate to the needs of the body by acting as osmotic exchangers under the influence of antidiuretic hormone (ADH, p. 471). When ADH is present, water is reabsorbed in the distal tubule and, at least in the rat, the fluid becomes approximately isotonic by the time it enters the cortical collecting duct. As the collecting ducts pass through the increasingly hypertonic environment of the medulla the fluid within them loses water passively, because of the increased permeability due to ADH, until it reaches the renal pelvis as concentrated urine. During a water diuresis a dilute urine is produced because ADH is absent and the collecting ducts are relatively impermeable to water; the fluid within them remains dilute in spite of the high osmolality of the surrounding medulla.

Specialized blood vessels in the medulla, the vasa recta (Fig. 15.6), also participate in the countercurrent mechanism. These vessels act as countercurrent diffusion exchangers removing water from the medullary interstitium and minimizing the loss of solute in the blood flowing out of the medulla. These blood vessels run alongside the loops of Henle, so that blood flows in a countercurrent fashion towards the tips of the papillae and back again to the vessels running between the cortex and the medulla (Fig. 15.5). The blood flow in these vessels is comparatively slow and their walls are of capillary thickness (Fig. 15.6). Blood flowing down the descending vasa recta becomes, therefore, osmotically more concentrated because of the inward diffusion of solutes from the interstitium and the outward diffusion of water. The reverse occurs in the ascending vasa recta. Diffusible substances, such as sodium and urea, are therefore trapped in the medullary interstitium, while excess water, removed during urinary concentration from the collecting ducts, can be removed. Increased medullary blood flow, such as occurs in haemorrhagic shock and after the administration of certain drugs, results in increased 'washout' of medullary solutes and hence decreased urinary concentrating ability.

The principal factor affecting water excretion is the plasma concentration of antidiuretic hormone (ADH) (Chap. 28) which is released from the posterior pituitary in response to stimuli, such as dehydration, pain, diminished cardiac output and cigarette smoking. These stimuli affect either osmoreceptors in the hypothalmus or baroreceptors in the carotid sinus, left atrium, great pulmonary veins, aortic arch and right subclavian artery.

The osmotic control of ADH release was demonstrated by Verney. He injected solutions of different osmolality into the internal carotid artery, which supplies the supraoptic nucleus and adjacent areas of the hypothalmus. His experiments in dogs (Fig. 15.20) showed that the osmoreceptors respond in a varying fashion depending on the nature of the hypertonic solution injected. If a hypertonic solution of urea is injected rapidly (over a period of 10 seconds) into the carotid artery, the flow of urine does not alter. While a rapid injection of hypertonic glucose is effective in reducing urine flow, a long continued infusion of glucose sufficient to produce a rise of 4·4 mmol/l in the carotid blood sugar concentration has no effect on water elimination. The slow injection of sucrose produces the same secretion of ADH as a prolonged injection of sodium chloride of the same tonicity. To explain these findings Verney suggested that the osmoreceptors are freely

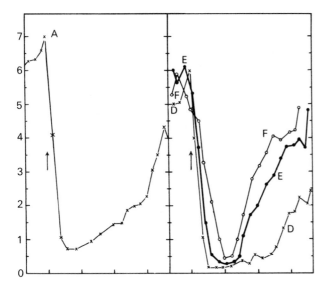

Fig. 15.20   The inhibition of water diuresis by a rise of osmotic pressure in the carotid artery. At A 10 ml of 428 mmol/l sodium chloride was injected into the right carotid artery in 12 seconds. Injection of 10 ml of 856 mmol/l glucose in 11 seconds had almost the same effect. On the right an attempt is made to imitate the antidiuretic effect of the hypertonic solution by injecting at the arrow, D, 3 m-u.; E, 2 m-u, and F, 1 m-u. of posterior lobe extract into the malleolar vein (1 m-u. = 1 milli-unit). (E. B. Verney (1947) *Proceedings of the Royal Society* B, 135, 67.)

permeable to urea, less freely permeable to glucose and relatively impermeable to sodium and sucrose. It is now possible to measure circulating ADH levels by radio-immuno-assay. This technique has shown that the threshold for ADH production is a plasma osmolality of 280 mmol/kg and that when osmolality exceeds 294 mmol/kg ADH production rises steeply. A decrease in arterial blood volume of more than 8 per cent also results in ADH release.

The chief action of ADH is to increase the permeability of the luminal membrane of the collecting tubule and collecting duct to water. Immediately after release the hormone is bound reversibly to the basolateral surface of the target cell. Thereafter it activates adenylate cyclase, accelerating intra-cellular production of cyclic AMP from ATP, an effect that is inhibited by prostaglandin E_1 and calcium. The mechanism by which cyclic AMP increases the permeability to water of the luminal cell membrane is unknown. In addition to its effect on water transport, ADH also increases sodium permeability. Very large doses of ADH result in a marked diuresis in water-depleted animals with an increase in sodium, potassium, chloride and phosphate excretion as well as an increase in urine flow rate. These pharmacological effects have been shown to be due to inhibition of proximal tubular re-absorption.

Factors other than ADH levels also influence urinary concentrating ability. A fall in glomerular filtration rate with enhanced proximal tubular reabsorption results in a dimin-ished sodium load and a slow flow rate through the distal nephron and collecting tubule; a small volume of highly concentrated urine is formed even in the absence of significant quantities of ADH. Concentrating ability also depends on the structural integrity of the loops of Henle and the counter-

current multiplier system, the slow medullary blood flow via a countercurrent exchange system and the protein intake. A low protein intake limits urine concentrating ability while the ingestion of urea restores it.

In clinical practice, urinary concentrating ability is measured by a standard test involving dehydration and the administra-tion of ADH. For example, the patient may be asked to take no fluid or food by mouth from 8 p.m. After 12 hours the osmolality of the urine is measured, ADH is administered as *vasopressin tannate* intramuscularly and fluid is withheld for a further 6 hours. In the young adult normal urinary concentrat-ing ability is indicated by urine osmolality in excess of 900 mmol/kg. This maximum figure decreases with advancing age. The administration of ADH enables the distinction to be made between true diabetes insipidus (caused by ADH lack) and *nephrogenic diabetes insipidus* in which the cells of the distal tubule do not respond to ADH, perhaps because of a defect in ADH-induced production of cyclic AMP. Fluid deprivation in diabetes insipidus can quickly result in a dangerous degree of dehydration. For this reason the patient should be weighed initially and dehydration stopped when weight loss reaches 3 per cent.

A reduction in maximum urinary concentrating ability may be due to ADH deficiency (Fig. 15.21), nephrogenic diabetes insipidus or structural damage to the renal medulla and loops of Henle. This may result from repeated infections, or renal damage due to phenacetin, hypokalaemia or hypercalcaemia.

Excessive and inappropriate secretion of ADH can occur in malignant tumours, particularly of the lung or pancreas, brain disease or in pulmonary disorders. Inappropriate ADH production results in water retention with hypotonicity of the body fluids and a normal or expanded effective arterial blood volume. This volume expansion results in excessive salt excretion and a further fall in the plasma sodium level. Urine osmolality is high despite a low plasma osmolality. Treatment is directed towards making the high ADH level more appropriate to the patient's needs by restricting water intake.

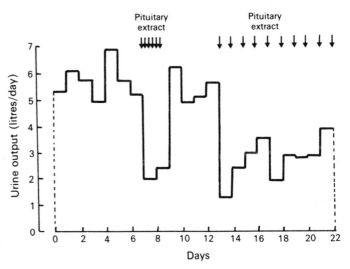

Fig. 15.21   The effect of pituitary extract on the daily output of urine of a male patient, aged 24, with diabetes insipidus. Before treatment he passed large amounts of dilute urine. The pituitary extract was administered by subcutaneous injection and caused a rapid fall in the urine volume.

Sodium reabsorption. Sodium is the principal cation in the extracellular fluid and its urinary excretion is precisely regulated. The amount of sodium excreted is the difference between the filtered load (GFR × plasma sodium concentration) and tubular reabsorption; normally about 99 per cent of the filtered load of sodium is reabsorbed. The remaining 1 per cent amounts to 100 to 250 mmol of sodium per day in a healthy adult with an average salt intake (Table 15.8)

In the proximal convoluted tubule approximately two-thirds of the filtered load of sodium is reabsorbed. As already mentioned, proximal tubular reabsorption is isosmotic since active sodium reabsorption creates an osmotic and electro-chemical gradient favouring equal passive water and anion reabsorption. Active sodium reabsorption represents the greatest expenditure of energy by the kidney, renal oxygen consumption being directly proportional to this activity.

Figure 15.22 illustrates the current views on proximal tubular sodium and water reabsorption. Two pathways are believed to exist, a transcellular pathway and a low resistance 'shunt' pathway in parallel with this and believed to consist of the intercellular space and tight junction. Each proximal tubule cell has a luminal and a peritubular cell membrane and is linked at the luminal border to the next cell by a tight junction. A basement membrane separates the tubular cell from the peritubular capillary. Sodium diffuses down an electrochemical gradient into the proximal tubular cell and is then actively pumped out into the intercellular space; this results in a localized increase in osmotic pressure. Water then follows passively and the hydrostatic pressure in the intercellular space rises, driving the reabsorbate towards the capillary. Uptake from the interstitial space into the peritubular capillary is determined by the balance of hydrostatic and osmotic pressure forces (Starling forces) acting across the capillary, together with the permeability of the capillary wall. Early in the proximal convolution the anion bicarbonate accompanies sodium

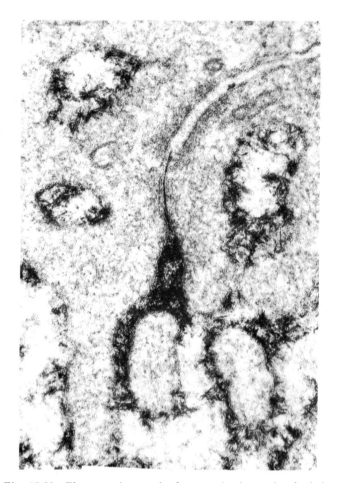

Fig. 15.23 Electron micrograph of rat proximal convoluted tubule to show lanthanum (electron dense) perfused into the lumen (bottom) penetrating the intercellular spaces. (*By courtesy of C. C. Tisher.*)

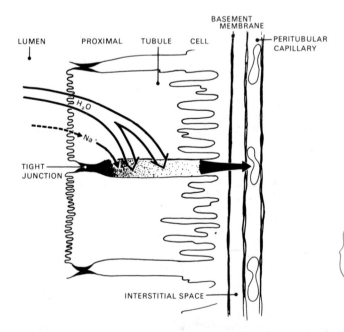

Fig. 15.22 Mechanism of reabsorption of sodium and water by the cells of the proximal tubule. The cell interior is 70 to 80 mV negative to the extracellular fluid. (*By courtesy of Marjorie Allison.*)

and proximal tubular fluid chloride concentration rises, creating a gradient favouring the passive reabsorption of chloride.

The evidence for this hypothesis of proximal tubular transport comes from electrophysiological studies and from electronmicroscopic observations. The intercellular spaces provide a low resistance shunt pathway in parallel with cell membrane resistances. Electron-dense ionic lanthanum perfused through the tubular lumen penetrates the tight junction (Fig. 15.23).

In the distal tubule under normal conditions of hydration approximately 10 per cent of the filtered load of sodium is reabsorbed by a process which also results in the secretion of potassium or of hydrogen ions. The tubular sodium load determines the degree of negativity of the luminal membrane and hence the gradient for passive potassium secretion. Some of this sodium transport (approximately 2 per cent of the total) is under the control of the hormone aldosterone.

The principal factors influencing sodium excretion are the glomerular filtration rate and the hormone aldosterone; other factors which may be important are the natriuretic hormone, physical factors around the tubule, the distribution of glomerular filtration and the adrenergic nerves.

Sodium loading has long been known to be associated with a rise in *glomerular filtration rate*, and some of the increase in

angiotensin = vasoconstrictor → BP (not sustained)
But → aldosterone prod also

sodium excretion that results may indeed be due to a rise in the filtered load of sodium. In the mammalian nephron, however, a rise in the filtered load of sodium, produced by a rise in glomerular filtration rate, is offset by a simultaneous rise in the rate of sodium reabsorption from the proximal convoluted tubule. This combination of circumstances is referred to as glomerulo-tubular balance and its control is one of the unsolved mysteries of renal physiology.

Aldosterone, producd by the adrenal cortex (Chap. 28), is responsible for the overall adjustments in distal tubular sodium reabsorption necessary to maintain sodium balance. Salt loss in the adrenalectomized animal or human being maintained on replacement doses of glucocorticoid together with a liberal salt intake, amounts to approximately 2 per cent of the filtered load of sodium or about 500 mmol sodium per day in the adult human. It is this fraction that is regulated by aldosterone acting to increase sodium reabsorption and potassium excretion in the distal convoluted tubule and collecting duct. There is no evidence that aldosterone affects sodium handling in the proximal convoluted tubule or loop of Henle.

Thirty to forty minutes after the intravenous injection of aldosterone there is a fall in urinary sodium excretion and a rise in urinary potassium loss; the urinary sodium concentration may fall to less than 1 mmol/l. The reason for the time lag is not yet understood. Potassium secretion in the distal tubule depends on an electrochemical gradient established primarily by sodium reabsorption, so that the increase in potassium excretion is secondary to the increase in sodium reabsorption.

Two main factors influence aldosterone secretion rate: sodium balance and body fluid volume. Thus aldosterone secretion rate may vary from 39 μg per day with a high intake of sodium to 1000 μg per day when the intake is low and sodium must be conserved. A decrease in circulating blood volume (hypovolaemia), as for example after a sudden haemorrhage, is associated with increased aldosterone secretion and sodium retention. How these responses are brought about is not entirely certain but three mechanisms appear to control aldosterone secretion: the renin-angiotensin system, plasma potassium concentration and ACTH. The renin-angiotensin system controls body fluid volume by regulating aldosterone secretion (p. 257). Aldosterone secretion can also be regulated by the level of potassium in the plasma. When the plasma potassium is increased the increased influx of potassium to the zona glomerulosa cells results in aldosterone release. A rise of 1 to 2 mmol/l in plasma potassium is sufficient to elicit a response. This forms a protective mechanism against the dangerous effects of potassium excess. Lastly, ACTH is required for optimal aldosterone response to sodium restriction, but is not essential, for hypophysectomized subjects with a moderate salt intake have a normal aldosterone production.

A third factor, *natriuretic factor,* affecting sodium excretion has been proposed because of the observation that dogs given isotonic saline intravenously had a saline diuresis in the absence of any increase in GFR and in the presence of a high concentration of exogenous aldosterone. Subsequent cross-circulation studies suggested that this factor might be a hormone and numerous techniques have been devised in attempts to assay it. Natriuretic hormone is thought to be released in response to an increase in blood volume and to

Slow diuresis

produce its effect by diminishing sodium reabsorption in the proximal tubule. The chemical structure of this substance has not yet been determined.

Sodium reabsorption is also affected by *physical factors* which affect transport across all capillary beds notably hydrostatic pressure and colloid osmotic pressure (Fig. 15.24). Alterations in the intrarenal distribution of glomerular filtration are also probably important in the control of sodium reabsorption. It is suggested that the superficial nephrons are 'salt-losing' while the juxtamedullary nephrons are 'salt-retaining' and that the adrenergic nerves (p. 244) control the intrarenal distribution of blood between these two groups of nephrons. A number of hormones, such as the prostaglandins, bradykinin, the glucocorticoids, thyroxine, insulin, growth hormone and prolactin are thought to affect sodium transport.

Potassium excretion. The amount of potassium excreted per day is about 7 per cent of the filtered load but most of this comes from secretion in the distal tubule. Almost all the filtered potassium is reabsorbed in the proximal tubule by an active transport process; the concentration of potassium is about 5 mmol/l in the proximal tubular fluid and about 140 mmol/l in the cells.

In the distal tubule potassium is secreted passively down an electrochemical gradient established by *active* sodium reabsorption which renders the distal tubular fluid electronegative relative to the cell. Any procedure which increases this electronegativity causes increased potassium secretion. One such mechanism is the level of aldosterone. Another is the intravenous infusion of the sodium salt of a poorly reabsorbed anion, such as sodium sulphate. Distal potassium secretion is also determined by the intracellular concentration of potassium. Potassium and hydrogen behave as if they were

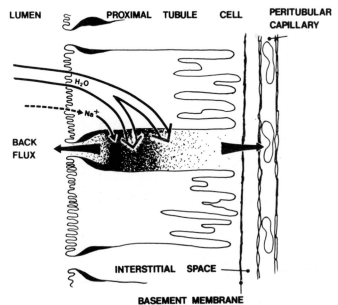

Fig. 15.24 Expansion of the blood volume with an infusion of isotonic saline leads to a rise in the hydrostatic pressure in the capillary lumen and a fall in the colloid osmotic pressure of the plasma. As a result, the flow into the capillary is reduced, the pressure within the intercellular space rises and water and salt diffuse backward into the lumen through the tight junction. (*By courtesy of Marjorie Allison.*)

competing with each other for secretion into the distal tubular fluid. In potassium deficiency, when intracellular potassium concentration is low, hydrogen ion is excreted instead. Hence hypokalaemia generally results in alkalosis. There is a lower limit to urinary potassium conservation; even on a zero potassium intake approximately 15 mmol is lost in the urine per day. Thus dietary deficiency of potassium can lead to severe depletion of body stores.

Glucose excretion. Normally all the glucose filtered by the glomeruli is re-absorbed by the proximal tubules; if, however, in the healthy adult the plasma concentration of glucose is gradually raised by intravenous infusion to about 10 mmol/l, the tubular cells are presented with glucose faster than they can absorb it. Glucose then begins to appear in the urine. This limiting concentration of glucose in the blood is known as the *renal threshold for glucose*, and the maximum amount of glucose that can be reabsorbed per minute is termed the *transfer maximum* or Tm.

Glucose Tm may be determined by measuring plasma and urine glucose levels after raising the plasma glucose to a high level by intravenous injection. The inulin or creatinine clearance, as a measure of GFR, is determined and also the glucose excretion in the urine. The amount of glucose filtered per unit time equals the GFR multiplied by the plasma glucose concentration; the amount excreted equals the urine glucose concentration multiplied by the urine flow rate; the amount reabsorbed by the tubules is the difference between these two quantities. If the GFR is 125 ml/min when the plasma glucose is 22 mmol/l, then $125 \times 22/1000 = 2.75$ mmol/l of glucose is filtered per minute at the glomeruli. If 0.75 mmol of glucose is found in the urine per minute, the maximum tubular reabsorption of glucose (TmG) is 2.0 mmol/min.

It is now realized that glucose Tm is influenced by changes in the rate of proximal salt and water reabsorption and by GFR. When the GFR is low, as for example in advanced diabetes mellitus with renal damage, the tubule cells may be able to reabsorb all the filtered glucose even although the blood glucose is very high; this gives rise to the apparent paradox of hyperglycaemia without glycosuria.

Glucose is carried across the membrane by a transport system of limited capacity. Glucose combines with the carrier at the luminal side of the cell and is transported to the outer side where the glucose separates from the carrier leaving it available to transport more glucose. This transport mechanism, like any other, can carry only a limited number of passengers in a given time, that is it can become saturated. In *renal glycosuria* (p. 92) the capacity of the transport mechanism is greatly reduced. Phlorizin inhibits glucose reabsorption, presumably by binding to the membrane carriers.

Calcium excretion. Approximately 1.5 to 7.5 mmol of calcium is excreted in the urine per day, representing less than one per cent of the filtered load. Calcium is reabsorbed both in the proximal and distal nephron, roughly in parallel with sodium, but the mechanisms are not yet fully understood. Changes that inhibit sodium reabsorption, such as volume expansion, cause parallel changes in calcium transport in the proximal tubule. Calcium excretion, however, seems to be regulated in the distal nephron and here the transport of sodium and calcium are not interdependent. Renal tubular handling of calcium is determined primarily by the plasma levels of calcium and parathyroid hormone (Chap. 18), but also by calcitonin, thyroid hormone and by the factors which affect sodium reabsorption. Parathyroid hormone increases calcium reabsorption by the tubules.

Phosphate excretion. The reabsorption of inorganic phosphate resembles that of glucose, involving an active transport mechanism with a maximum capacity. In contrast to glucose, however, appreciable quantities of phosphate are normally present in the urine. The amount reabsorbed depends upon the concentration of phosphate in the plasma, and on the plasma levels of parathyroid hormone and calcitonin (Chap. 18). When the plasma concentration of phosphate is low, the phosphate in the glomerular filtrate is almost completely reabsorbed. An excess of parathyroid hormone, as in hyperparathyroidism, causes an increased urinary loss of phosphate due to inhibition of proximal tubular reabsorption. A fall in GFR, as in chronic renal failure (p. 259) results in a fall in the filtered load of phosphate and a rise in the level of phosphate in the plasma.

THE RENIN-ANGIOTENSIN-ALDOSTERONE SYSTEM

In 1898 Tigerstedt and Bergman observed a prolonged rise in blood pressure in the unanaesthetized rabbit after intravenous injection of extracts of normal renal cortex. They named the active principle in these extracts renin. However, renin is not itself a pressor substance; it is a proteolytic enzyme, with a molecular weight of 41 000, which hydrolyses *angiotensinogen*, an α_2-globulin in the plasma produced in the liver, to give a vasoconstrictor substance called angiotensin. The steps in its production appear to be as follows:

$$\alpha_2\text{-globulin} \xrightarrow{renin} \text{angiotensin I (decapeptide)}$$

$$\text{angiotensin I} \xrightarrow[enzyme]{hydrolysing} \text{angiotensin II (octapeptide)} + \\ \text{histidyl-leucine.}$$

The second step occurs in the lungs and kidneys. Angiotensin I is only a weak vasoconstrictor but it is active in the release of aldosterone. Angiotensin is destroyed by the enzyme angiotensinase.

The structure of human angiotensin II is Asp-Arg-Val-Tyr-Ile-His-Pro-Phe. When infused intravenously in man synthetic angiotensin octapeptide is, molecule for molecule, 40 to 50 times as potent as noradrenaline in raising arterial pressure; it is the most powerful vasopressor agent known. The rise in pressure begins immediately the infusion (2 to 3 µg/min) is started and continues for about 20 minutes after the infusion is stopped (Fig. 15.25). However, prolonged infusion of angiotensin in man does not produce a sustained rise of blood pressure.

The granular epithelioid cells of the juxta-glomerular apparatus (Fig. 15.7) are believed to be the sole source of renin. Techniques have been developed enabling the measurement of both tissue renin activity and plasma renin concentration. These have shown that the granularity of the juxtaglomerular cells is proportional to the renin content of the kidney. The large refractile granules from individual juxtaglomerular cells of the mouse kidney have been obtained by micromanipulation (Fig. 15.26), and assayed for pressor activity in rats.

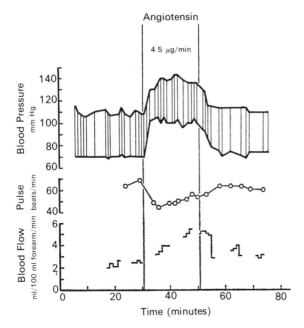

Fig. 15.25 Arterial pressure, pulse rate and forearm blood flow before, during and after an infusion of angiotensin into a foot vein of a healthy man of 24. (E. de Bono, G. de J. Lee, F. R. Mottram, G. W. Pickering, J. J. Brown, H. Keen, W. S. Peart & P. H. Sanderson (1963). *Clinical Science*, **25**, 123–157.)

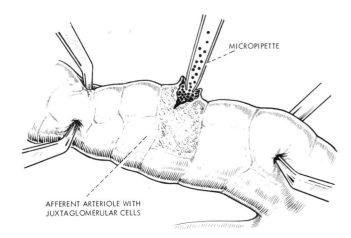

Fig. 15.26 Sampling granules in individual juxtaglomerular cells. The afferent arteriole of an isolated mouse glomerulus held with microforceps. Some of the granules in the juxtaglomerular cells can be taken up by micropipette when the cell membrane is broken. (*By courtesy of W. F. Cook.*)

The physiological role of the renin-angiotensin system is complex. Many different stimuli can release renin, including a decrease in renal perfusion pressure (due for example to haemorrhage), adrenergic nerve stimulation or infusion of exogenous catecholamines, hypoglycaemia, alterations in sodium concentration at the macula densa and alterations in plasma sodium and potassium concentration. The nature of the receptor for these stimuli is controversial. One hypothesis is that a pressure-sensing mechanism in the afferent arteriole responds to a decrease in renal perfusion pressure by increased renin production. Another suggestion is that renin release is determined by changes in sodium concentration at the macula

densa. In addition, adrenergic stimulation may modify renin production.

The physiological effects of angiotensin are both systemic and local. The main *systemic* role of angiotensin is not to raise the blood pressure but to control the output of aldosterone from the adrenal cortex, and so to control body fluid volume (Fig. 15.27). The main stimulus for the production of renin is a change in blood volume which is apparently detected by baroreceptors in the afferent arteriole. Simultaneous adrenergic nerve stimulation increases renin production still further; renal nerves are not essential for renin release since the denervated human kidney is capable of adaptation to changes in salt intake. In the absence of the renin-angiotensin system, for example after bilateral nephrectomy, control of the blood volume is poor and the blood pressure may fluctuate widely.

On a normal sodium intake the plasma renin activity of a recumbent subject on waking is about $1 \cdot 0 \, \mu g/l$. Four hours later after walking quietly the level rises to $2 \cdot 7 \, \mu g/l$. Both values are higher, and aldosterone excretion is greater, if the subject is on a low sodium diet. It seems that in the upright position the blood pools in the legs and the reduction in effective blood volume causes a fall in renal blood flow and perfusion pressure, with increased renin and aldosterone production leading to retention of sodium. Retention of sodium re-expands the blood volume and so counteracts the effect of upright posture. If the lower limbs and the abdomen are firmly bound before the subject stands upright no rise in plasma renin is observed.

The role of the renin-angiotensin-aldosterone system in the pathogenesis of high blood pressure in man is still obscure, partly because it is difficult to measure all the components of the system. The following points appear to have been reasonably established. In the great majority of patients with hypertension no demonstrable abnormality of the system is found (essential hypertension). In patients with severe

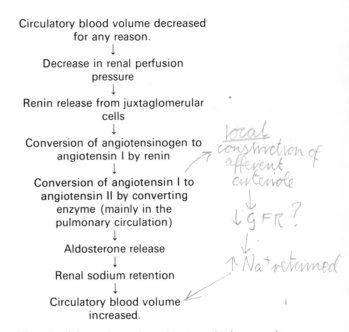

Fig. 15.27 The role of the renin-angiotensin system in the control of blood volume.

hypertension (malignant hypertension) there is an excess of renin and aldosterone but this excess may be the result of the hypertension and not the cause of it (secondary hyper-aldosteronism). In a small proportion of patients with hypertension the cause is a primary excess of aldosterone due to overactivity of the zona glomerulosa of the adrenal gland (Chap. 28). A rare cause of hypertension in man is renal artery stenosis producing renal ischaemia. In this form of hyper-tension there is an excess of renin in the plasma and an increase in aldosterone secretion rate. Correction of the vascular abnormality either by reconstructive surgery or by nephrectomy, if the condition is unilateral, may be followed by cure of the hypertension and a return of renin and aldosterone values to normal.

The *local* effects of angiotensin within the kidney are primarily related to its action as a vasoconstrictor. While its precise role remains controversial it now seems clear that renin is released into the interstitial fluid rather than directly into the efferent arteriole. Renin release could therefore lead to constriction of the afferent arteriole, and thus a fall in the glomerular filtration rate and in the filtered load of sodium. Renin release may also lead to redistribution of blood from cortical to juxtamedullary nephrons such as occurs in sodium depletion or adrenergic nerve stimulation.

Endocrine Activities of the Kidney

Since renin was isolated in 1898 four other hormones have been discovered. First, *erythropoietin*, produced either directly in the kidney itself or indirectly by the interaction of a kidney precursor, erythrogenin, and a plasma factor, stimulates red cell production (p. 109). Erythropoietin is released in response to hypoxia, anaemia or the administration of androgens. Although the hormone is also produced by other organs such as the liver, chronic kidney damage is generally associated with progressive anaemia. Renal tumours may result in a rise in erythropoietin production and increased red cell mass.

Second, the kidneys are the site of production of the active metabolite of Vitamin D, *1,25-dihydroxycholecalciferol* (p. 287). The impaired calcium absorption and osteomalacia of chronic renal disease are due primarily to a deficiency of this hormone.

Last, the kidneys are the source of potent vasodilator and natriuretic substances. The *prostaglandins* PGA_2 and PGE_2, isolated from the medulla, are powerful vasodilator and antihypertensive agents. They are thought to originate in the interstitial cells, particularly in the renal papilla, being released in response to a rise in medullary blood flow and pressure. PGA_2 circulates in the plasma and causes peripheral vaso-dilatation. When injected into the renal artery both result in diuresis and natriuresis. Their production can be blocked by the anti-inflammatory agent indomethacin. A second vasodilator system is the *kallikrein-bradykinin* mechanism. Renal kalli-krein is one of a number of kallikrein enzymes found in plasma and tissues; they act upon plasma proteins called kininogens, releasing peptides known as kinins:

$$\text{Kininogen globulin} \xrightarrow[\substack{\textit{kallikrein}}]{\textit{renal}} \text{Bradykinin}$$

Bradykinin is a potent vasodilator, ten times as powerful as histamine. It is also a potent diuretic and natriuretic substance, but its exact intrarenal mode of action is still disputed. In many respects the kallikrein-bradykinin system acts in opposition to the renin-angiotensin system. Both prostaglandins and brady-kinin have been suggested as candidates for the role of natriuretic hormone.

Renal Function in the New-born

The steady rise of urea and uric acid in the amniotic fluid during pregnancy suggests that normally the kidneys begin to function before birth. The urine of babies examined im-mediately after birth is generally acid with a small amount of urea and a low osmotic pressure and proteinuria lasting a few days is not uncommon.

The neonatal kidney is functionally inferior to the adult kidney but immediately after birth the body is dependent on it for elimination of nitrogenous end-products of metabolism and for the regulation of its internal environment. The limited renal function of the new-born accounts for the sudden fluctuations in the chemical composition of the plasma which may occur in disease.

In babies a few days old the GFR measured by inulin clearance is only about $30 \, \text{ml/min/m}^2$ compared with about $75 \, \text{ml/min/m}^2$ in the adult. Recent micropuncture studies in new-born guinea pigs, rats and puppies have shown that the steady rise in the filtration rate of superficial nephrons occurring after birth is due partly to a steady rise in the pressure in the glomerular capillaries occurring at the same time as the rise in arterial pressure and fall in intrarenal vascular resistance. A simultaneous increase in glomerular capillary permeability has been demonstrated by studying the filtration of dextrans of varying molecular size.

The renal cortex in most neonates is relatively under-developed, filtration rate and blood flow in juxtamedullary nephrons being significantly greater than those in the cortical nephrons. This may explain many of the functional character-istics of the developing kidney. Thus the neonate is less able to excrete a saline load but has a relatively high capacity to retain sodium and water under conditions of deprivation. This is in keeping with the earlier account of two distinct populations of nephrons in the adult kidney, a juxtamedullary group referred to as salt retainers and a more cortical group referred to as salt losers. The more mature juxtamedullary nephrons of the neonatal kidney provide better for sodium retention than the underdeveloped cortex provides for sodium elimination. Infants between 5 and 7 months of age retain sodium when the intake exceeds 50 mmol/day.

Tubular function is also much less efficient in infants than in adults, the extraction of PAH, for example, being only about one-tenth of the adult value. The site of PAH transport is in the proximal tubule, and its low extraction in early infancy is attributed mainly to the relative underdevelopment of the cortex and the probable immaturity in the renal transfer mechanism for organic ions. Adult levels are attained towards the end of the first year.

Peritubular physical factors are also different in the neonatal kidney. The plasma protein level is low in infancy and, therefore, the colloid osmotic pressure of the plasma is lower than in the adult. Both oncotic pressure and hydrostatic pressure are reduced in the peritubular capillary network initially, in association with low proximal tubular reabsorption. Oncotic pressure increases progressively with age in association with increased absolute absorptive rates. The anatomy of the intercellular spaces in the developing kidney is also different from that in the adult kidney, the spaces being smaller and the tight junctions less tight. How these findings relate to proximal tubular function in the immature kidney remains speculative.

In new-born children the volume of urine passed per day is about 20 ml. Water given to babies up to 3 months of age is excreted very slowly, the rate of water excretion being limited by the low GFR. The ability to concentrate urine and to conserve water is severely limited, the maximum osmolality in response to dehydration in the newborn being approximately 700 mmol/l. One factor is the relative lack of urea in the inner medulla due to the intense anabolism of infancy. A further factor is the relatively high blood flow through the juxtamedullary nephrons and vasa recta which results in a wash-out of medullary osmotic gradients. Infants fed urea or a high protein diet show a marked increase in their concentrating abilities. There is no evidence that lack of ADH is involved. Thus infants can easily become dehydrated and conversely the administration of fluids can readily result in oedema because of low plasma concentrations and decreased ability to excrete a water load.

Renal Function in the Elderly

Renal function deteriorates progressively after the fourth or fifth decade of life. The GFR commonly falls to 40 to 70 per cent of that found in early adult life and renal blood flow also falls. The maximal urinary concentrating capacity is significantly reduced. Despite the decrease in creatinine clearance, plasma creatinine levels do not increase because a diminished muscle mass produces less creatinine. The changes in renal function can be explained partly by obstructive vascular disease resulting in atrophy of afferent arterioles. The number of glomeruli in each kidney at birth is about $2 \cdot 1 \times 10^6$, falling to less than $1 \cdot 0 \times 10^6$ in old age.

DISORDERS OF RENAL FUNCTION

Acute renal failure. The kidneys may suddenly become unable to excrete sufficient fluid, electrolytes and waste products of metabolism to maintain homeostasis. The volume of urine is generally less than 500 ml per day and plasma urea and creatinine levels rise, because of the fall in GFR. Fatal hyperkalaemia may result. Three basic causes are described. First, 'pre-renal' causes associated with a fall in blood pressure, due for example to haemorrhage or dehydration resulting in a fall in renal blood flow, and in the effective filtration pressure. ADH levels are high and the kidney initially produces a concentrated urine. At this stage the situation can be remedied by correcting the cause, for example by fluid replacement.

Second, if pre-renal factors are not corrected, the tubules may suffer damage, known as acute tubular necrosis. This is usually caused by prolonged circulatory shock but may result

from the administration of substances toxic to the tubules. In each nephron the low urine flow rate is due to a combination of three factors: a profound fall in filtration rate, blockage of nephrons by intratubular casts and cell debris and perhaps back diffusion of tubular fluid leaking through damaged tubule walls. The fall in GFR may be due to excessive stimulation of the juxtaglomerular apparatus with increased renin and angiotensin production resulting in constriction of the afferent arterioles.

Third, complete absence of urine (*anuria*) may be due to blockage of both ureters or the urethra, by calculi or by malignant tumours.

Chronic renal failure. Chronic renal failure develops gradually over a number of months or years and is the result of widespread disease of both kidneys, for example chronic infection. Microdissection of such diseased kidneys shows that all the nephrons are damaged. Despite gross structural damage, however, the kidney adapts remarkably well and maintains overall homeostasis until late in the disease. Thus the chronically diseased kidney can daily eliminate in the urine an amount of sodium, potassium, urea and creatinine equal to that eliminated by the normal kidney of a subject eating a similar diet. The way in which this is achieved varies for different substances. In the case of creatinine and urea the falling GFR is accompanied by a rise in the plasma level of these substances so that the amount filtered by the kidney per day remains constant. The relationship of GFR to plasma creatinine is illustrated in Figure 15.12. A 50 per cent reduction in GFR is associated with a doubling of the plasma creatinine level.

The plasma levels of sodium and potassium often remain constant in chronic kidney disease. This is because the fractional excretion of electrolytes as well as of water is increased as the GFR falls. Thus at a GFR of $3 \cdot 0$ ml/min some 80 per cent of the fluid filtered and 50 to 60 per cent of the filtered load of sodium and chloride may be excreted. This increased fractional excretion of sodium may be due to natriuretic hormone. Potassium secretion by the distal nephron increases and figures as high as 700 per cent of the filtered load have been recorded.

Finally as the number of functioning nephrons falls still further the volume of urine diminishes, homeostasis can no longer be maintained and death occurs from 'uraemia'. The main features of uraemia are nausea and vomiting, pigmentation of the skin, drowsiness, stupor and coma. The biochemical disturbance in uraemia is complex including acidaemia, retention of many nitrogenous end-products (of which urea is probably the least harmful) and changes in the metabolism of calcium, magnesium, potassium and other substances.

Patients with severe acute renal failure or with chronic renal failure may now be treated by *dialysis*, a procedure which replaces temporarily some of the functions of the patient's kidneys. In haemodialysis this is done by connecting one of the patient's arteries to a cellophane tube immersed in a dialysing solution, isotonic with blood, containing physiological concentrations of electrolytes but without urea. The other end of the cellophane tube is connected to a vein and during dialysis urea and other nitrogenous substances diffuse from the blood into the dialysing fluid. Alternatively the peritoneal membrane can be used as a dialysing surface (peritoneal dialysis). A small tube is placed in the peritoneal cavity and about 2 litres dialysing fluid are inserted over twenty minutes and then allowed to drain out. The process is repeated many times; nitrogenous substances diffuse into the dialysing fluid and are removed from the body.

Hyperaldosteronism. Primary hyperaldosteronism or Conn's syndrome, a rare cause of hypertension, is due to excessive secretion of aldosterone by the adrenal gland. This results initially in retention of salt and water. Were this to continue the patient would become oedematous. However, the body quickly 'escapes' from the sodium-retaining effects of aldosterone probably by diminished reabsorption of sodium in the proximal tubule. Distal potassium loss continues; the resulting hypokalaemia leads to impaired concentrating ability, to excessive loss of hydrogen ions and a metabolic alkalosis.

Secondary hyperaldosteronism is more common and occurs in a wide variety of situations associated with oedema and severe hypertension.

Tubular disorders. Disorders of tubular function may be the principal abnormality in a number of diseases which may be inherited (such as *cystinosis*) or acquired as a result, for example, of poisoning with heavy metals. A wide variety of tubular defects can be identified including a failure of urinary acidification and defective reabsorption of glucose, phosphate, potassium and amino acids. In others the tubular defect is more specific. *Familial hypophosphataemia* is caused by defective phosphate reabsorption and characterized by phosphorus depletion and a bone disease resembling vitamin D deficiency rickets. *Renal tubular acidosis* is the term used to describe a number of disorders characterized predominantly by defective acidification of the urine.

MICTURITION

The urine passes into the pelvis of the kidney and is carried by peristaltic waves down the ureter so that the pressure in the pelvis is kept low. These waves occur every 10 seconds or so and travel at 2 or 3 cm per sec, each wave sending a little spurt of urine into the bladder. These can be seen in man by injecting intravenously a dye which is excreted by the kidney and observing the ureteric orifices through a cystoscope inserted along the urethra into the bladder.

The waves originate in a pace-maker in the minor calyces, the smooth muscle of which possesses excitatory α-adrenoceptors, and pass down the pelvis to the ureter. The ureteric muscle is fairly powerful since if the ureter is obstructed the ureteric pressure may rise to 7 kPa (50 mm Hg). When urine formation is active the cross-sectional of the lumen enlarges up to 20 times by changing its stellate shape to circular. The ureters pass obliquely through the thick muscular wall of the bladder forming a valvular opening so that urine is prevented from regurgitating into the ureter when the pressure within the bladder is raised during micturition.

The bladder is lined by transitional epithelium, the cells of which are seen by the electron microscope to have scalloped margins with complex interdigitations between adjacent cells. When the bladder is full the surface of the epithelium is smooth but when it is 'empty' the thin margins of the cells become buckled and infolded. The luminal surfaces of the cells

of the transitional epithelium have a thick membrane which presumably provides the barrier between the hypertonic urine within the bladder and the blood only a few μm away in the capillaries supplying the epithelium. This barrier prevents the uptake of water by osmosis from the capillaries and the leak of solutes into the capillaries.

The transitional epithelium is firmly adherent to the wall of smooth muscle fibres, the *detrusor* muscle, which is supplied by the hypogastric nerves and by the pelvic splanchnic nerves (Fig. 15.28). At the base of the bladder the smooth muscle fibres pass around the urethral opening loopwise to form the *internal sphincter.* Dissection of this region does not, however, show a definite anatomical sphincter in either male or female; it may be that the sphincteric region is merely an extension of the bladder muscle which is stretched and therefore closed as the bladder fills; according to this interpretation when the detrusor muscle contracts at micturition the sphincteric region also contracts and the urethra is shortened and opened up. The *external sphincter* surrounding the membranous urethra is composed of two striated muscles, the compressor urethrae and the bulbocavernosus; it is under voluntary control through the pudendal nerves. In males the external sphincter is able to maintain continence even when the internal sphincter is damaged.

The mucosa of the human bladder is insensitive to light touch but vigorous pressure causes pain; it is sensitive to large changes in temperature. Nerve fibres from the muscle wall

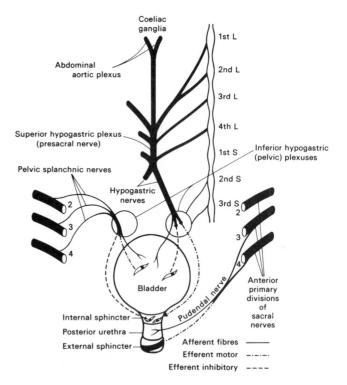

Fig. 15.28 Diagram of innervation of the bladder and sphincters in man (*after J. R. Learmouth*). The pelvic nerves are parasympathetic. The hypogastric nerves are sympathetic. The pudendal nerves are somatic nerves. Some hypogastric fibres synapse with short adrenergic neurones originating in intramuscular ganglia in the base of the bladder, others synapse with short adrenergic neurones in the prostate and vas deferens and seminal vesicles. (See also G. Genser, C. Owman and L. Wehlin (1969) *Lancet*, **i**, 154.)

give information about fullness. Most of these sensory fibres must travel in the parasympathetic nerves since sympathectomy does not affect these sensations. Sensory fibres subserving pain run in the sympathetic. The mucosa of the urethra is sensitive to painful and thermal stimuli.

When the 'empty' bladder is at rest the sphincters are tonically contracted so that the urine gradually expands the bladder without causing the pressure to rise very much (Fig. 15.29). This may be explained by supposing that the detrusor muscle relaxes as the bladder expands; the small rise in pressure in the bladder is probably due to the elastic properties of the bladder wall. The pressure within the bladder with the subject lying is about 2 kPa (20 cm of water); on standing it rises to 4 kPa and when the abdominal pressure is increased by the downward movement of the diaphragm as in coughing or running the pressure may rise to 15 kPa. Normally the sphincters remain closed and urine does not leak out into the urethra. During micturition when the sphincters are relaxed the pressure rises to 5 kPa and falls slowly to its base line.

If the intravesical pressure is increased suddenly by introducing, say, 200 ml of fluid through a catheter into the bladder, rhythmic contractions are set up, but quickly die out. Bladder distension insufficient to produce a sensation of fullness produces cutaneous vasoconstriction; if the pressure is sufficient to cause discomfort the blood pressure may increase by 20 or 30 mm Hg. Normally a person becomes aware of bladder fullness when about 150 ml of urine has accumulated. The bladder is often allowed to fill until it contains nearly 300 ml. If more urine accumulates a feeling of 'urgency' arises and when the bladder contains over 600 ml the contractions

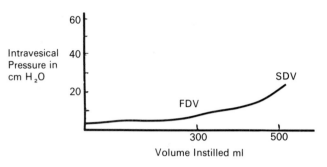

Fig. 15.30 Cystometrogram of adult man. The bladder is filled through a urethral catheter at a rate of 20 ml per minute. FDV: first desire to void, usually about 300 ml in relaxed adult. SDV: strong desire to void, usually about 500 ml. Filling by continuous flow is recommended as giving a more 'physiological' record than the incremental filling of Fig. 15.29 (*By Courtesy of E. S. Glen.*)

become powerful enough to raise the pressure to 10 kPa and cause pain. If voluntary efforts at restraint are made the pressure may fall for a short time but when the pressure exceeds 10 kPa again discomfort becomes acute and micturition becomes inevitable. In pregnancy the bladder has less tone and may increase in capacity up to 1500 ml and may not be completely 'emptied' at micturition, that is there is a considerable amount of residual urine.

The pressure at which the desire to micturate occurs depends partly on the rate of filling—if it is slow the bladder can accommodate more fluid—and partly on the irritability of the nerve endings in the bladder and their central connexions. For example when the bladder mucosa is inflamed (cystitis) the volume at which micturition occurs is much reduced. Afferent impulses travel to the spinal cord in the pelvic splanchnic nerves and impulses passing down the same nerves cause the detrusor muscle to contract and open the 'internal sphincter' so that the bladder is emptied.

The external sphincter, although it is a striated muscle, cannot be relaxed voluntarily but it may be consciously contracted. Efforts to micturate do not produce a relaxation of the external sphincter unless the intravesical pressure is above a threshold value of from 2 to 4 kPa. Inhibition of the sphincters occurs only when the detrusor muscle is contracting, the internal sphincter relaxing a little before the external. The stream of urine can, however, be stopped by a voluntary contraction of the external sphincter.

The afferent impulses play an important part in the initiation and control of micturition. Their significance is shown by the fact that, after section of the dorsal sacral roots in cats, the bladder may enlarge up to ten times its normal size. In the cat stimulation of vesical and also of colonic afferents causes depression of detrusor activity and closure of the internal urethral sphincter. This reflex is presumably responsible for the maintenance of urinary continence. Above a certain bladder pressure the afferent discharge increases sufficiently to overcome the maintenance reflex and to produce reflex discharge of the parasympathetic neurone causing a contraction of the bladder which leads in turn to the opening of the proximal urethra. Simultaneously the external urethra relaxes by a spinal visceral somatic inhibitory reflex. The passage of urine through the external urethra causes a discharge of afferent fibres in the pudendal nerve which, by a

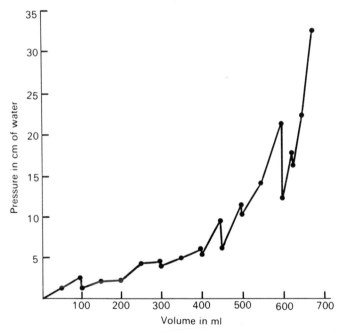

Fig. 15.29 Graph (cystometrogram) of the relationship of the volume of the vesical contents to their pressure in the course of distension of the human bladder. Each vertical fall of pressure indicates the degree of adaptation at a constant volume. (D. Denny-Brown & E. Graeme Robertson (1933) *Brain*, 56, 158.) If for any reason the bladder is overdistended the micturition reflex is absent and the cystometrogram shows no terminal rise.

supraspinal mechanism, reinforces the excitation of the parasympathetic neurones. The increase in bladder pressure brought about by the reflex autonomic discharge leads to an increase in the discharge from tension receptors and a continued discharge of the parasympathetic neurones. There is thus a progressive and self-reinforcing cycle which increases and maintains the contraction of the vesical musculature during micturition.

Although these reflexes are present after transection of the spinal cord, the bladder and its sphincters are normally under voluntary control. An effort to micturate evokes powerful contractions of the bladder after a short latent period and voluntary restraint of micturition results in an inhibition of these contraction waves. Normal micturition depends entirely on active contraction of the bladder; voluntary control, that is the ability to delay or start micturition when desired, should be thought of as inhibition or removal of inhibition respectively of the normal reflex response to distension which depends on the lower parts of the spinal cord. According to this view the infant develops voluntary control of micturition by acquiring the power to inhibit the spinal reflexes.

Certain associated movements occur in micturition which are not regarded as essential parts of the process. An attempt to micturate may be accompanied by relaxation of the perineal muscles, contraction of the abdominal muscles and occasionally movements of the lower colon and rectum. Voluntary restraint is associated with a contraction of the perineal muscles and closure of the external sphincter. After surgical removal of an enlarged prostate (prostatectomy) development by exercises of these associated muscles is important.

Disorders of micturition. The effect of spinal anaesthesia in man is to relax slightly the internal sphincter and the ureteric orifices; the external sphincter remains closed; the subject cannot initiate micturition. In transverse lesions of the spinal cord in man causing paraplegia (pp. 371–2) reflex micturition is at first abolished, the detrusor is relaxed and the bladder distends greatly as urine accumulates; eventually the pressure rises high enough to force some urine through the sphincter. After small amounts of urine have been voided the pressure is somewhat reduced and urine accumulates again in the bladder until the process repeats itself. This is *overflow incontinence*. In treatment of this condition it is important to catheterize the bladder to prevent overdistension. After some months micturition begins to occur automatically, usually at hourly intervals, by contraction of the detrusor muscle. The capacity of the bladder is then smaller than normal and a small increase in its contents causes a considerable rise of pressure. Provided that the sacral cord and its nerve connexions with the bladder are intact the bladder reflexes in man with a transverse lesion of the spinal cord eventually occur in the usual way, except that they are not under restraint from the higher centres which normally exercise a constant inhibition on the detrusor muscle. Destruction of the cauda equina in man leaves the external sphincter flaccid. The internal sphincter gives way at much lower pressure than normal when spontaneous contractions of the bladder occur. A rudimentary micturition mechanism is supplied by voluntary contractions of the abdominal muscles which reinforce the weak contractions of the detrusor.

The bladder is apt to be invaded by organisms passing backwards from the urethra; this invasion is easier through the short female urethra. Serious infection is often prevented partly by the washing out of organisms at micturition, partly by the bactericidal activity of normal bladder mucosa and partly, in the male, by the antibacterial properties of prostatic secretion.

REFERENCES

Allison M E M, Kennedy A C 1971 Diuretics in chronic renal disease: a study of high dosage frusemide. Clinical Science 41: 171–187
Baroch S B (ed) 1975 Symposium on renal metabolism. Medical Clinics of North America 59: 505–790
Brenner B M, Stein J H (ed) 1978 Sodium and water homeostasis. Contemporary issues in Nephology, vol I
Burg M, Green N 1973 Effect of diuretics on the thick ascending limb of Henle's loop. Journal of Clinical Investigation 52: 15a
Davis J O, Freeman R H 1976 Mechanisms regulating renin release. Physiological Reviews 56: 1–56
De Wardener H E 1973 The kidney: An outline of normal and abnormal structure and function, 4th edn. Churchill Livingstone, Edinburgh
Frömter E 1979 Solute transport across epithelia: what can we learn from micropuncture studies on kidney tubules? The Feldberg lecture 1976. Journal of Physiology 288: 1–31
Giebisch G (ed) 1976 Renal physiology. Annual Review of Physiology 38: 7–68
Harrison N 1976 Mechanisms of micturition. British Journal of Hospital Medicine 16: 454–461
Hays R M, Levine S D 1974 Vasopressin. Kidney International 6: 307–322
Jamison R L 1973 Intrarenal heterogeneity. The case for two functionally dissimilar populations of nephrons in the mammalian kidney. American Journal of Medicine 54: 281–289
Jamison R L, Maffly R H 1976 The urinary concentrating mechamism. New England Journal of Medicine 295: 1059–1067
Knox F G, Davis B B 1974 Role of physical and neuroendocrine factors in proximal electrolyte reabsorption. Metabolism 23: 793–803
Leaf A, Cotran R 1977 Renal pathophysiology. University Press, Oxford
Massry S G (ed) 1975 Kidney and hormones. Nephron 15: 165–396
Moffat D B 1975 The mammalian kidney. Cambridge University Press
Nashat F S 1974 Topics in renal physiology. In: Linden R J (ed), Recent advances in physiology 9th edn. Churchill Livingstone, Edinburgh
Peach M J 1977 Renin-angiotensin system. Physiological Reviews 57: 313–370
Peart W S 1977 The kidney as an endocrine organ. British Medical Journal ii: 543–548
Pitts R F 1974 Physiology of the kidney and body fluids, 3rd edn. Lloyd-Luke, London
Schrier R W (ed) 1976 Renal and Electrolyte disorders. Little, Brown and Company, Boston
Sullivan L P 1974 Physiology of the kidney. Lea and Febiger, Philadelphia
Smith H W 1951 The kidney: Structure and function in health and disease. Oxford University Press
Wright F 1974 Intrarenal regulation of glomerular filtration rate. New England Journal of Medicine 286: 135–141

16 Water, Electrolyte and Acid-Base Balance

The cells of the body consist largely of water and are embedded in a matrix containing water. The water of the body may be thought of as being in two compartments or spaces comprising the intracellular fluid (ICF) and the extracellular fluid (ECF). The ECF may be further subdivided into the interstitial fluid, lymph and the blood plasma (Fig. 16.1). Water diffuses freely between the compartments but the movement of most other substances is controlled in various ways.

The distribution of the total body water (TBW) in the average man is shown in Table 16.2. Because adipose tissue has a low water content, the proportion of water in a tissue, or in the body as a whole, depends largely on the proportion of fat (Table 16.3). It is usual, therefore, to relate measurements of TBW to the weight of lean tissue (the *fat-free mass*) rather than the total body weight. When this is done, the proportion of water in the fat-free mass of an adult is remarkably constant at around 75 per cent.

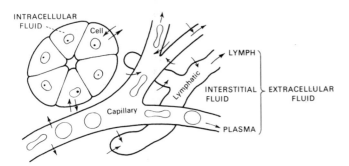

Fig. 16.1 The main subdivisions of the body fluid. The term extracellular fluid includes interstitial fluid, lymph and the protein-free fraction of plasma.

Estimation of total body water. In an animal, TBW can be measured directly by drying the carcass completely and measuring the weight loss. In man indirect methods which use the principle of dilution must be employed. In this type of method a known amount of a substance is injected into the compartment of interest and, once sufficient time has elapsed to allow mixing, its final concentration is measured.

To measure *total body water* the substance used must be freely diffusible throughout the body. Deuterium oxide, tritium oxide and antipyrine have been used but care must be taken with the last of these in view of the possibility of severe reactions.

Table 16.2 Distribution of body water in a man of average build.

	Volume (litres)	Percentage of body weight
Plasma	3·5	5
Interstitial fluid	12	17
Extracellular fluid (ECF)	15·5	22
Intracellular fluid (ICF)	26·5	38
Total body water (TBW)	42	60

Table 16.3 Examples of the relationship between body water and fat content at different body weights

	Wasted	Average	Obese
Body weight (kg)	33	60	90
Fat (kg)	3·5	18·5	40·5
Fat-free mass (kg)	29·5	41·5	49·5
Total body water (kg)	23	31	36
Body water as percentage of body weight	70	52	40
Body water as percentage of fat-free mass	80	75	73

Values for the total body water at different ages are given in Table 16.4. In adult life females have lower values than males because they generally have more adipose tissue.

Measurement of the *extracellular fluid volume* (ECF) requires a substance which cannot enter cells but is otherwise freely distributed. Examples are inulin, bromide, thiosulphate and thiocyanate. The plasma volume can be measured with a marker substance such as labelled albumin which is retained in the blood after injection. The volume of the intracellular fluid cannot be measured directly; it can be obtained by subtracting

Table 16.4 Typical figures for the total body water at various ages, measured by dilution

Age	Percentage of body weight
0– 6 months	72·2
½– 2 years	69·5
2– 7 years	63·1
7–16 years	58·4
22–58 years	51·7
71–84 years	50·8

the volume of the ECF from that of the TBW. The volume of the interstial fluid is obtained by subtracting the plasma volume from that of the ECF.

Composition of the Body Fluids

Table 16.5 shows that sodium is the principal cation in the ECF, whereas potassium predominates in the ICF. While chloride is an important anion in the ECF, phosphate and sulphate predominate within the cells. Protein contributes significantly to the anion content of the ICF, but in the ECF is largely restricted to the plasma.

It is not yet easy to measure the concentration of intracellular electrolytes but the composition of the ECF may be studied by using plasma, which is readily available, to provide a guide to the composition of ECF. In practice the concentrations of all the cations and anions are seldom

Table 16.5 Typical concentrations of the principle anions and cations in plasma, interstitial fluid and intracellular fluid (mmol/l)

	Plasma	Interstitial fluid	Intracellular fluid
Cations			
Sodium	142	145	10
Potassium	4	4	160
Calcium	2	1	1
Magnesium	1	1	13
Anions			
Chloride	101	114	3
Bicarbonate	27	31	10
Phosphate (HPO_4^{2-})	1	1	50
Sulphate	0·5	0·5	10
Organic anions	6	7	
Protein	2	<0·1	8

By expressing the concentrations in milli-equivalents per litre it can be shown that the total anions are equivalent to the total cations.

measured. There is a discrepancy between the sum of the measured cations (sodium and potassium) and the sum of the measured anions (chloride and bicarbonate). This difference is known as the *anion gap* and is usually between 10 and 15 mmol/l. In some diseases alterations in the anion gap may indicate biochemical abnormalities. For example in patients with excessive quantities of lactate the anion gap is greater than normal.

The differences in ionic composition between the ICF and ECF depend on two main mechanisms: the inability of large molecules to pass freely through cell membranes and the active transport of substances across cell membranes. These transport mechanisms, for example the sodium pump, require the expenditure of energy. The differences in composition therefore depend on the integrity of cell membranes and a sufficient supply of energy. In disease these conditions may not be fulfilled and ions may leak into and out of cells. For example in stored blood potassium leaks out of the erythrocytes into the plasma.

Measurement of sodium and potassium. The total amounts of sodium and potassium in the body may be estimated by chemical analysis of cadavers or by dilution techniques with the radioactive isotopes ^{22}Na and ^{40}K. Since the latter isotope occurs naturally as a constant proportion of the total potassium, the body potassium may be estimated by total body scanning. The estimation of total body sodium by dilution gives a figure 17 per cent lower than that obtained by chemical analysis because some sodium is fixed in bone and not immediately exchangeable.

Measurement of sodium and potassium levels in the plasma is a simple routine procedure by flame emission spectrophotometry or other techniques.

Osmolality. Just as the concentration of individual ions needs to be mentioned, so too does the overall concentration of solutes, for an excess leads to interactions between molecules as well as serious practical problems such as increased viscosity. The overall concentration of solutes can be expressed as *osmolality*. One fundamental particle of any substance has unit effect on the depression of freezing point of the solvent or on the osmotic pressure exerted by that solution. Despite their differences in size and weight a sodium ion, a glucose molecule and an albumin molecule all have the same effect on osmotic pressure.

While the physiological importance of solute concentration is related to its effect on osmotic pressure, the easiest method for measuring solute concentration is by measurement of freezing-point depression. Instruments for this purpose are available commercially and give accurate readings of osmolality in mmol per kilogram of water on a sample within a few minutes. There are no direct methods for the measurement of osmolarity which is expressed in mmol/litre. In normal subjects the osmolality of plasma is between 281 and 297 mmol/kg.

While the theoretical osmolality of plasma, calculated from its known constituents, is about 325 mmol/kg water (equivalent to 305 mmol/l) the difference between this value and the actual plasma osmolality of about 291 mmol/kg is due to the facts that electrolytes are not completely dissociated in solution and that some substances are partly bound to protein.

DAILY TURNOVER OF WATER AND ELECTROLYTES

The amount of water in the body at any time is the resultant of input and output. The distribution of the water between the compartments depends on the total amounts of solutes in the compartments as water always follows an osmotic gradient. Table 16.6 shows typical values for the daily gains and losses of water in a temperate climate.

Water Balance

Gains. A healthy man in a temperate climate can maintain his body water by drinking as little as 650 ml per day. He also

Table 16.6 Typical values for the daily intake and output of water by an adult man in a temperate climate, together with values for the daily production of secretions into the alimentary tract.

	ml/day
Intake	
Drink	1 300
Food	850
Metabolic water	350
Total	2 500
Output	
Urine	1 500
Expired air	400
Skin	500
Faeces	100
Total	2 500
Alimentary secretions (almost all reabsorbed)	
Saliva	500 to 1 500
Gastric juice	2 000 to 3 000
Pancreatic juice	300 to 1 500
Bile	250 to 1 100
Intestinal secretions	about 3 000
Total	6 050 to 10 100

angiotensin II → aldosterone release

constriction afferent arteriole

↓ GFR

Na⁺ retention

↓

↑ TBW

gains water from food, either as water contained as such in foodstuffs or as water produced by the metabolism of carbohydrate, fat and protein. It should be noted that urea, the end-product of protein catabolism, requires water for its excretion by the kidneys so that the metabolism of protein is of limited value as a source of water.

Losses. A minimum amount of water must be passed in the urine each day to carry in solution the end-products of metabolism. This volume depends on the diet but is of the order of 500 to 700 ml/day. A further 100 to 200 ml water are lost each day in the faeces.

Water is continually lost through the skin by evaporation even when sweating is not obvious. In a temperate climate this 'insensible loss' amounts to about 500 ml/day. Sweating can increase this amount considerably; up to 10 litres of water per day may be lost by this route. Small children lose relatively more water because of their higher ratio of surface area to body weight.

Water loss by all these routes is associated with a simultaneous loss of sodium and other solutes. Pure water, however, is lost from the lungs and the amount may be greatly increased by over-breathing.

The minimum loss of water in urine, faeces, expired air and sweat is about 1600 ml daily and therefore the daily intake of water (including water of metabolism) must at least equal this total. In practice the intake is usually much greater.

Electrolyte Balance

Gains. All electrolytes are obtained from the diet, principally from food, but drinking water may supply small amounts of some ions. The average daily intake is shown in Table 16.7.

Losses. The average daily losses of electrolytes in a temperate climate are shown in Table 16.7. Apart from a small amount in the faeces, and obligatory sodium and chloride losses in the sweat, most electrolytes are excreted by the kidney. In a hot, dry climate up to 900 mmol of sodium and 50 mmol of potassium may be lost daily in the sweat.

About 8 litres of electrolyte-rich fluid are secreted into the small intestine by the liver, the pancreas and the intestinal mucosa. Most of this is reabsorbed. Table 16.7 shows that almost 20 per cent of the total sodium and water in the body is cycled in this way each day. It follows that a patient with severe fluid loss from the gut, due to vomiting or diarrhoea, can incur serious losses of water and electrolytes in a short time.

Table 16.7 Typical figures for the daily balance of sodium and potassium in a normal adult in a temperate climate

	Sodium (mmol/day)	Potassium (mmol/day)
Intake		
Food	150	100
Output		
Urine	100–250	40–120
Sweat	4	5
Faeces	1·5	4
Turnover in alimentary tract	600	50

Control of ECF Volume and Electrolyte Concentration

A complex set of interlocking mechanisms controls both the volume and the concentration of the ECF. In outline these are: (1) control of water intake (thirst), (2) control of losses via the skin (sweating), (3) renal regulation of ECF volume and (4) renal regulation of ECF composition.

Thirst. Shortage of water causes more immediate and more intolerable distress than shortage of food. A person completely deprived of water soon feels his mouth dry, he complains of thirst and the craving for fluid rapidly becomes compelling. As time goes on the dryness of the mouth increases, the production of saliva ceases and swallowing of food becomes impossible. Finally, when the water loss is about 8 litres, delirium is followed by death.

The sensation of thirst is produced by a general bodily need for water. It is not the result merely of a dry mouth because water deprivation produces thirst long before the mouth becomes dry. Furthermore patients who have a dry mouth as a result of disease or of absence of the salivary glands do not complain of thirst. An injection of atropine, sufficient to stop the secretion of saliva produces a dry mouth but does not make a person thirsty.

On the other hand, the intravenous injection of hypertonic solutions regularly produces thirst. Such solutions increase the osmotic pressure of the extracellular fluid and bring about a movement of water out of the cells, so that the osmolality of the ICF also rises. The mechanism of the thirst response to rises in osmotic pressure is not known. ADH itself does not seem to be involved and the receptors concerned are not the same as the osmoreceptors responsible for ADH release.

The sensation of thirst is not only stimulated by increased plasma osmolality but also by a decreased blood volume. The role of renin and angiotensin in the control of plasma volume was described in the previous chapter. It is now clear that angiotensin II has a direct action on a specialized part of the *sub-fornical organ* a vascular part of the fore-brain adjacent to the third ventricle. In rats direct injection of minute amounts of angiotensin II into this area stimulated drinking while ablation of this structure prevented the drinking response to intravenous angiotensin. However the response to hypertonic solutions remains intact so that there are at least two separate mechanisms for producing thirst.

Sweating. Evaporation of water from the skin allows the body to dispose of a large amount of heat in hot climates. Sweat normally contains sodium and chloride at concentrations up to 50 mmol/l, so that the loss of water is accompanied by loss of salt. After acclimatization to a hot climate the sodium content of the sweat falls and requirement for salt replacement is reduced.

Renal control of ECF volume. The mechanism for the maintenance of plasma volume relies on the detection of low volume by the pressure receptors in the carotid artery. These trigger the renin-angiotensin-aldosterone mechanism described on page 257. The production of aldosterone may also be increased by the presence of a high level of potassium in the ECF. In both cases, increased sodium reabsorption occurs in the distal renal tubule and, with water passively accompanying the sodium, the ECF volume is restored. The loss of fluid from the body leads to a reduction in plasma volume which in turn causes a lowered cardiac output and a lowered renal plasma flow.

The aldosterone mechanism, stimulated by reduced intravascular pressure, leads to increased reabsorption of saline which increases the volume of the ECF. The ADH mechanism complements this system by reducing the amount of water lost in the urine and contributing to the increase in ECF volume (p. 253).

Once the volume of the ECF is restored, the concentration of sodium is adjusted by alteration of the reabsorption of water under the influence of ADH.

Control of ECF composition. The concentration of solutes in the ECF is monitored by the osmoreceptors which control the production of antidiuretic hormone by the pituitary gland. The ADH acts on the distal tubule and the collecting ducts to control the amount of water reabsorbed from the urine (Chap. 15).

The mechanism exists primarily to adjust the concentration of the ECF by controlling the amount of diluent water available. The limiting factor in this process is the osmotic gradient which exists in the renal papillae. When the urine has a specific gravity of 1·036, the osmotic pressure gradient between the urine and the interstitial fluid in the renal papillae is effectively abolished and further water reabsorption cannot take place.

When fluid is lost from the body, for example by loss of alimentary secretions, the volume and concentration of the ECF are adjusted simultaneously. It is an oversimplification to regard either mechanism as acting alone, or as affecting *solely* volume *or* concentration adjustment. In addition, other factors as yet incompletely understood affect sodium reabsorption in the proximal renal tubule.

The control of the body potassium is carried out almost exclusively by the distal renal tubule. Potassium, almost completely reabsorbed in the proximal tubule, is secreted in the distal tubule in exchange for sodium under the control of aldosterone. Despite the fact that such a small proportion of the total body potassium is contained in the ECF, the proportions are constant in the absence of acid-base disturbance, and in these circumstances ECF potassium levels reflect the total body potassium.

Derangements of Salt and Water Balance

The balance of water and electrolytes can be upset by a variety of disease states. The examples which follow are 'pure' disorders but most clinical disorders are mixed disturbances. In general these conditions, involving losses or gains of saline, are more common than conditions in which salt and water are affected independently.

Saline depletion. This is caused by loss of salt and water in approximately physiological concentrations, commonly from the alimentary tract, but also by the kidneys. Saline may also be lost from the body surface after severe burns. Saline depletion due to reduced salt intake alone is rare.

Saline depletion causes a gradual redistribution of fluid between the cells and the ECF but because the cells contain little sodium the loss is borne mainly by the extracellular fluid. The clinical signs are weight loss, diminished skin turgor, dry tongue, muscle cramps, postural hypotension and eventually

circulatory failure. The disorder is corrected by replacement of both salt and water.

It should be noted that although sodium has been lost from the body, the loss of a corresponding amount of water means that the plasma sodium concentration may be within normal limits.

Saline overload. This is most commonly due to failure to excrete the daily salt load and occurs particularly in patients with diseases of the heart or kidneys. Occasionally it may be due to overtreatment with intravenous saline.

Saline overload increases the volume of the ECF and in turn leads to oedema (p. 267). Treatment ordinarily consists of increasing renal losses by the use of diuretics.

Water depletion. This condition is usually the result of an inadequate water intake, especially after losses of fluids with a low sodium content, such as sweat, or of pure water due to hyperventilation. In diabetes insipidus proportionately more water is lost than sodium.

These patients do not necessarily appear dehydrated as the ECF volume may be within normal limits; since the deficiency is of water alone, water moves out of the cells to dilute the concentrated ECF. The water loss is thus spread throughout the body, and the shrinking of the cells causes changes in intracellular metabolism, particularly in the brain where it is declared as thirst by the conscious patient. Except in diabetes insipidus and nephrogenic diabetes insipidus the urine in patients with water depletion is concentrated relative to the plasma.

Water excess. In severe cases this disorder is referred to as 'water intoxication'. It occurs when the intake of water exceeds the excretory capacity of the kidney; this never happens in normal people who can drink up to 20 litres per day without ill effects other than excessive urination. Water excess occurs in patients with a variety of disorders such as chest infections, liver disease and after surgery. The mechanism is not yet understood but in some patients with tumours production of ADH by the tumour is the cause.

The excess water diffuses rapidly into the cells, thus spreading the load throughout the body. The cells swell and the swelling of cells of the central nervous system causes nausea, vomiting, confusion, fits and finally death. The concentration of solutes (particularly sodium) in the plasma is low.

Potassium deficiency. This can be due to an inadequate intake of potassium, especially in the elderly, but is more commonly due to excessive losses of potassium such as occur in repeated vomiting or chronic diarrhoea. Severe potassium loss may occur in the urine of patients with an excess of mineralocorticoids or on treatment with diuretic drugs. A low sodium diet may also lead to potassium losses due to reabsorption of sodium in exchange for potassium. The first clinical sign of a low potassium level may be weakness of the muscles.

Potassium excess. A true increase in total body potassium seldom occurs except in severe renal disease or after excessive oral or intravenous potassium administration. *Hyperkalaemia* (a raised plasma potassium level) can also occur in the presence of normal total body potassium when potassium moves out of the cells as in acidosis, particularly diabetic acidosis. High plasma potassium levels are dangerous in that they interfere with muscle action, notably that of heart muscle, so that hyperkalaemia calls for urgent treatment.

FLUID EXCHANGE IN THE TISSUES

We must now consider the exchange of water and dissolved substances through the capillary endothelium, that is to say between the blood and the interstitial (intercellular) fluid. Quantitatively this exchange is very large; it has been calculated that as much as three-quarters of the plasma water is exchanged with interstitial fluid every minute.

When a solution containing protein and salt is separated from an electrolyte solution of the same concentration by a semi-permeable membrane through which sodium, chloride and water may diffuse, but protein may not, then the protein produces an osmotic pressure effect known as its colloid osmotic pressure. Starling pointed out that a similar situation exists in the capillaries of the vascular system where blood plasma is separated from interstitial fluid by a capillary membrane. In the capillaries, however, the additional factor of the blood pressure must be considered.

There are therefore four pressures which control the flow of water between the plasma and the interstitial fluid: the hydrostatic pressure in each and the colloid osmotic pressure in each. The colloid osmotic pressure in the plasma is about 30 mm Hg while the hydrostatic pressure in the capillaries varies with the arterial pressure, the arteriolar tone, the venous pressure and the height above or below the heart (page 185). In warm fingers for example the capillary pressure is higher than the colloid osmotic pressure throughout the length of the capillary and fluid is filtered out of the capillaries. In cold hands the hydrostatic pressure at the venular end of the capillary is lower than the colloid osmotic pressure so that some fluid is reabsorbed from the interstitial space. After loss of blood, the arterial pressure falls, capillary pressures fall and similarly fluid is withdrawn from the interstitial space into the plasma.

The capillary membrane is not, as in Starling's original hypothesis, completely impermeable to proteins since plasma proteins labelled with ^{131}I, injected intravenously, have been shown to pass into the interstitial fluid, the overall exchange rate being about 140 per cent of the total plasma albumin per day. The total amount of albumin in the extravasular pool is greater than the total amount in the blood plasma. This 'leakage' of protein from the circulation may be useful in carrying antibodies and protein-bound hormones to the tissues. The rate of leakage depends on the size of the molecule and on the size of the 'pores'. The capillary 'pores' in the skeletal muscles are very small but so large in the liver that red cells and lymphocytes may pass from the hepatic vessels to the lymphatics. Attempts to find the size of the 'pores' through which proteins escape by introducing proteins or dextrans of various sizes labelled with a fluorescent dye or with ^{131}I have given conflicting results. The anatomical location of the filtering membrane is also uncertain (p. 185).

The lymphatics. The distal lymphatics form a closed system of tubes (Fig. 16.1) consisting of an endothelial lining supported by fibrous tissue. It is difficult to measure the near atmospheric pressure of the tissue fluid and in the terminal lymphatics. No satisfactory explanation of the movement of fluid into the terminal lymphatics has yet appeared. The tissue fluid taken up by lymphatics includes also large molecules such as hormones, enzymes and other proteins such as lipoproteins, including chylomicrons. The larger vessels have muscle fibres in their walls. The lymphatic vessels possess numerous valves and the flow of lymph from the periphery to the thoracic duct is brought about by muscular and respiratory movements in the same way as the flow of blood in the veins. The lymphatics of the intestine (lacteals) shows rhythmic contractions which, because of the numerous valves in these vessels, propel the lymph on to the thoracic duct. This contractile activity is an intrinsic property of the lymphatics and is not co-ordinated by the nervous system.

Lymph has the same concentrations of salts as interstitial fluids and plasma, a lower concentration of protein than plasma and a slightly higher concentration of protein than interstitial fluid (Table 16.8). Complete obstruction of the lymphatic vessels draining a part of the body leads to oedema of the area (*lymphoedema*). This oedema fluid has a protein concentration similar to that of plasma. Some indication of the daily volume of lymph is given by the fact that after severence of the thoracic duct, fat-laden lymph initially accumulates in the thorax (chylothorax) at a rate of about 3 litres per day.

Table 16.8 Chemical composition of lymph compared with that of plasma and interstitial fluid

	Lymph	Interstitial fluid	Plasma
Protein (g/l)	26	1	71
Chloride (mmol/l)	116	104	101
Calcium (mmol/l)	1·7	1·3	2·4
Urea (mmol/l)	5·0	5·0	5·0

Before reaching the blood lymph passes through at least one or, more usually, 8 to 10 lymph nodes whose structure and function were described in Chapter 9. During its passage through a lymph node, the lymph is altered in composition. Small molecules pass into the blood while large molecules are retained and newly-formed antibodies (immunoglobulins) are added.

Oedema

The Starling hypothesis is helpful in explaining the occurence of oedema, that is the accumulation of excessive amounts of salt and water in the interstitial space. In this condition the tissues, usually in the dependent parts of the body, become swollen with fluid which resembles plasma but has a low protein content.

Oedema may accumulate when the hydrostatic pressure in the veins is increased, as in congestive heart failure (p. 172), or when the colloid osmotic pressure of the plasma is reduced because the albumin level is low. The latter situation arises in protein malnutrition ('famine oedema') and in chronic liver disease (cirrhosis) when albumin synthesis is diminished and in the nephrotic syndrome in which excessive amounts of albumen are lost in the urine. Whatever the cause of the oedema, the kidney retains sodium. The cause of the sodium retention is not always clear but in some cases the output of aldosterone is excessive.

ACID-BASE BALANCE

Since the conformation, and thus the function, of many proteins is very sensitive to hydrogen ion concentration, the pH of body fluids is maintained within very narrow limits. The pH of arterial blood is normally 7.36 to 7.44 (approximately 44 to 36 nmol/l respectively) but in disease this range extends from 6.85 to 7.65 (141 to 22 nmol/l). Such extreme values, if sustained, are associated with a high mortality.

The metabolism of food to produce energy yields carbon dioxide equivalent to about 13 moles of H^+ per day. In addition phosphoric and sulphuric acids, known as fixed acids, are produced to the extent of approximately 70 millimoles H^+ per day. This hydrogen ion is mostly produced within cells, but is carried in the ECF to the sites of excretion.

Buffering. The harmful effect of excess hydrogen ions is minimized by buffers which are present both in the ICF and in the ECF. These buffers are weak acids and their respective anions. Combination of the anions with free hydrogen ions produces minor changes in the equilibrium between acid and anion. By far the most important buffers quantitatively are the proteins, especially within the cells. However the phosphate/phosphoric acid and bicarbonate/carbonic acid systems are also important. The latter is particularly important in the ECF and is of special value in that its total amount is variable, since the amount of ECF bicarbonate lost in the urine and the amount of carbon dioxide lost during breathing are both adjustable to meet abnormal fluctuations in the ECF hydrogen ion concentration. In contrast most of the other buffer systems have a rather fixed capacity.

Respiratory excretion of hydrogen ions. Metabolically generated CO_2 takes part in the following reactions:

$$CO_2 + H_2O \rightleftharpoons H_2CO_3 \rightleftharpoons H^+ + HCO_3^-$$

At the lungs gaseous exchange with alveolar air leads to a loss of CO_2 from the body and a shift of the equilibrium to the left. The reduced hydrogen ion concentration so achieved is equivalent to the excretion of hydrogen ion, but it also results in a simultaneous depletion of bicarbonate/carbonic acid buffer. The rate of excretion of hydrogen ion by this route is determined by the rate of gaseous exchange and thus by the depth and rate of respiration. Changes in pH affect the respiratory centre to alter these and such changes can be achieved very rapidly; the lungs thus provide a rapid-response system to minimize change in ECF hydrogen ion concentration. In normal subjects this mechanism is used for controlling minor fluctuations in hydrogen ion production but in disease additional methods for controlling fluctuations in hydrogen ion concentration may be needed.

Renal excretion of hydrogen ion. Man's ability to compensate for larger fluctuations of hydrogen ion concentration depends on his renal tubular cells. This system has a much slower response than the lungs, taking hours rather than minutes to be effective.

The pH of glomerular filtrate reflects the hydrogen ion concentration of the ECF, but the urine is usually more acidic (pH 5·0 to 6·5 or 10000 to 316 nmol/l). This change is achieved by the secretion of between 40 and 70 mmol of hydrogen ion per day throughout the length of the nephron. The reason the urine is not more acidic is that many of these hydrogen ions are buffered by bicarbonate, phosphate and

other less capacious systems in the urine. Thus, in effect, much of the excreted hydrogen ion is passed from one buffer system in the ECF to another in the tubular lumen. The hydrogen ions are secreted into the tubular lumen in exchange for sodium reabsorption and the process is an active one. These hydrogen ions then combine with bicarbonate and phosphate in the lumen as follows:

$$HCO_3^- + H^+ \rightleftharpoons H_2CO_3$$
$$HPO_4^{2-} + H^+ \rightleftharpoons H_2PO_4^-$$

In the case of bicarbonate this is not the end of the process since the carbonic acid is converted to water and carbon dioxide by the enzyme carbonic anhydrase present in the brush border of the proximal tubule. The carbon dioxide can diffuse back through the tubular cell, since it is soluble in the lipid of the plasma membrane, so leaving the H^+ as water in the lumen.

Another means of trapping secreted H^+ in the lumen is provided by ammonia. This is generated within the tubular cell as shown in Figure 16.9

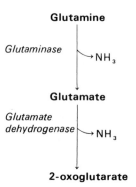

Fig. 16.9   Source of ammonia in the renal tubule.

Some 30 to 50 mmols of ammonia usually diffuse daily into the tubular fluid where combination with H^+ yields the ammonium ion; as this is a charged ion it cannot make the return journey and is excreted in the urine. In exceptional circumstances, this mechanism can allow the excretion of up to 500 mmol H^+ per day. However induction of the enzymes involved takes time so that the renal response to pH changes is very much slower than that of the respiratory centre. The maximum hydrogen ion concentration which can be achieved in urine by man is 40 μmol/l (pH 4·4). The ability to acidify urine normally is tested in clinical practice by administering ammonium chloride which is metabolized to yield H^+.

Assessment of Acid-Base State

With the development of selective electrode technology the measurement of pH and of the partial pressure of CO_2 (P_{CO_2}) have been greatly facilitated. It is now possible to make these determinations on about 100 μl of blood in less than 5 minutes, and then to use the results to calculate other quantities which are helpful in defining the balance between H^+ concentration and the state of the carbonic acid/bicarbonate buffer system. It is then assumed that the findings on plasma are representative of the subjects total H^+ homeostasis in the ECF. At present it is difficult to make any assessment of acid-base balance in the

ICF, but small electrodes capable of being placed within cells are being developed.

The sample used is either an arterial sample taken anaerobically or a capillary sample taken from a warm extremity so that, because of the hyperaemia, its composition is largely that of arterial blood (an 'arterialized' sample). The second method is often used in babies; the area from which the sample is to be taken is warmed with a warm wet flannel or sponge in a polythene bag.

The pH is a measure of the result of the interaction between free hydrogen ions and the buffer systems. It may be within the reference range or on the acid or alkaline side of this. It is important to recognize that pH is a means of stating the *activity* of H$^+$ ions as detected by a standardized measurement system under defined conditions; since activity varies rather unpredictably in complex biological mixtures such as blood, there is no clear relationship between the H$^+$ ion concentration and pH. At present there is no way of measuring H$^+$ ion concentration directly and thus pH is a more realistic statement of the measurement than the molar concentration which is widely recommended. However the fact that pH is a logarithmic scale may mislead the inexperienced into believing that a pH change of 0·5 units on the acid side of 7·40 is of the same significance as 0·5 units in the other direction. In fact if we assume that the activity factor is unity, these changes in H$^+$ ion concentration are 86 and 27 nmol/l respectively (Fig. 16.10). Since the intracellular proteins are sensitive to the true concentration of free hydrogen ions this significant difference in physiological effect is made evident by expression in molar concentration.

The pH tells immediately whether a patient has an excess or deficit of free H$^+$ ions, termed respectively *acidaemia* or *alkalaemia*. A normal value of pH indicates either that the subject is normal or that he has had to alter his buffering systems capacity to *compensate* for a change.

The P_{CO_2} level in arterial blood is a measure of the *respiratory* component of the carbonic acid/bicarbonate buffer system. This is so because, in the reactions below, a is slow in blood and thus the measured P_{CO_2} is closely related to the clearance or retention of CO_2 by the lungs.

$$H_2O + CO_2 \overset{a}{\rightleftharpoons} H_2CO_3 \rightleftharpoons HCO_3^- + H^+,$$

The P_{CO_2} is normally between 4·7 and 6 kPa (35–45 mm Hg), but may be reduced by overbreathing to below 4 kPa (30 mm Hg). While it is almost impossible to lower it by voluntary hyperventilation to below 2·7 kPa (20 mm Hg), such levels can be reached in patients with disorders which affect the respiratory centre. High plasma levels of P_{CO_2} (hypercapnia) occur in some common lung disorders and conditions affecting the respiratory musculature, so that under-ventilation results in the accumulation of CO_2. It is evident, therefore, that an increase in P_{CO_2} tends to increase the amount of carbonic acid and thus the supply of free H$^+$ ions. If these are not buffered or eliminated in some other way, the resultant disorder is known as a *respiratory acidaemia*. Such a disturbance can develop within a minute of the start of the accumulation of CO_2, because if the buffer system is overloaded the only possible compensatory response is in the slow renal tubular mechanism. However, it is possible in time to accumulate sufficient buffers to achieve a normal pH despite P_{CO_2} levels in excess of 13·3 kPa (100 mm Hg) as may occur in obstructive disease of the airways.

The *metabolic* component of the buffers system is related to the molar concentration of bicarbonate, which from the above equilibrium reactions can be seen to be related to the CO_2 concentration. It can be measured by chemical means but since the P_{CO_2} level may change while the sample is being handled misleading results may be obtained.

It is preferable to calculate the *actual bicarbonate*, as it is termed, from the measurements of pH and P_{CO_2} on an arterial sample by use of this formula:

Bicarbonate concentration (mmol/l) $= 0·031 \times P_{CO_2} \times 10^{pH-6.1}$

where P_{CO_2} is measured in mm Hg. This formula is a version of the Henderson-Hasselbalch equation and the components 6·1 and 0·031 are the pK for 'normal' plasma, and the conversion factor for changing P_{CO_2} to CO_2 concentration respectively. It is evident that the use of this formula makes assumptions about the nature of the specimens and the conditions under which it is measured. The calculation is often performed automatically by a microprocessor in the measuring equipment. The actual bicarbonate is normally 21 to 28 mmol/l and departures from this range are termed *metabolic* disturbances.

Some instruments also produce calculated 'metabolic' parameters such as *base excess, buffer base* and *standard bicarbonate* (which is peculiar to the 'Astrup' type of analysis). While 'base excess' does provide a measure of the metabolic disturbance independent of any change in P_{CO_2} it is possible to make a full assessment of an acid base disorder with only P_{CO_2}, pH and actual bicarbonate. Normal values for these determinations are given in Table 16.11.

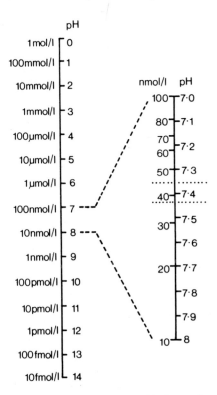

Fig. 16.10 Comparison between pH and hydrogen in concentration in aqueous solutions. The dotted lines indicate the normal range for arterial blood plasma.

Table 16.11 Normal values for arterial blood for the quantities used in the assessment of acid-base balance. In children and pregnant women PCO_2 can be as low as 30 mm Hg (4·0 kPa).

Hydrogen ion concentration	36 to 44 nmol
pH	7·36 to 7·44
PCO_2	35 to 48 mm Hg
	(4·7 to 6·4 kPa)
Actual bicarbonate	22 to 28 mmol/l
Base excess	−2 to +2 mmol/l

Disorders of Acid-Base Balance

Departure from normal control is associated with excess or deficit of acid or of base. If no compensation takes place the pH changes. A knowledge of the type of conditions leading to the various abnormal states may help to identify the cause of a particular patient's disorder.

Metabolic acidaemia. This may be due to an increase in circulating H^+ ion, or to reduced amount of base. The former is the more common and may be due to excessive production of hydrogen ions, as in diabetic ketosis or hypoxic lactic acidosis, or to decreased excretion as in renal failure. Acidaemia due to reduced base is most commonly seen in patients with excessive losses of fluid from the small intestine since this fluid is rich in bicarbonate. Such losses occur in diarrhoea or when intestinal contents are lost through aspiration tubes or fistulae. It is also possible to lose base because of a defect in the reabsorption of bicarbonate in the renal tubules but this is rare. The typical changes in the arterial blood chemistry in metabolic acidaemia are summarized in Table 16.12.

Table 16.12 Chemical changes in the blood in uncompensated and partially compensated metabolic acidaemia. Uncompensated metabolic acidaemia is seldom seen because respiratory compensation takes place very rapidly. N = normal.

	Metabolic acidaemia	
	Uncompensated	Partially compensated
pH	↓↓	↓
PCO_2	N	↓
Actual bicarbonate	↓↓	↓↓
Base	↓↓	↓↓

Metabolic alkalaemia. This may be due to increased amounts of base or to a reduced H^+ ion concentration. The former can occur when the patient's intake of bicarbonate is high, either when bicarbonate is taken by mouth in the treatment of peptic ulceration or when excessive amounts of bicarbonate are administered intravenously in the treatment of a metabolic acidaemia. The hydrogen ion level may be reduced by loss of acidic fluids in vomiting or by repeated aspiration of gastric contents. An interesting type of metabolic alkalaemia occurs in potassium depletion when H^+ ions move into cells to replace the potassium ions so causing a hydrogen ion depletion in the ECF. In this disorder the ECF has a high pH while the ICF has a low pH. The typical changes in arterial blood chemistry in metabolic alkalaemia are shown in Table 16.13.

Respiratory acidaemia. Here the PCO_2 and thus the H^+ ion derived from carbonic acid is increased. It is associated with conditions which impair the efficiency of gaseous exchange in the lungs. These are obstruction of the airways, pneumonia,

Table 16.13 Chemical changes in the blood in uncompensated and partially compensated metabolic alkalaemia. Uncompensated metabolic alkalaemia is seldom seen because of the rapidity of the adjustment of ventilation.

	Metabolic alkalaemia	
	Uncompensated	Partially compensated
pH	↑↑	↑
PCO_2	N	↑
Actual bicarbonate	↑↑	↑↑
Base	↑↑	↑↑

respiratory depression, paralysis of respiratory muscles, and suppression of the respiratory centres by neurological disorders or by toxic substances. Only in acute respiratory obstruction (*asphyxia*) is a pure uncompensated respiratory acidaemia observed. Table 16.14 summarizes the typical changes in arterial blood chemistry in respiratory acidaemia.

Table 16.14 Chemical changes in the blood in respiratory acidaemia

	Respiratory acidaemia		
	Uncompensated	Partially compensated	Fully compensated
pH	↓↓	↓	N
PCO_2	↑↑	↑↑	↑↑
Actual bicarbonate	↑	↑↑	↑↑
Base	N	↑	↑↑

Respiratory alkalaemia. In this disorder the PCO_2 is reduced and the H^+ derived from carbonic acid is reduced. It results from overbreathing (hyperventilation) due either to hysterical behaviour or to a disorder of the respiratory centre. This occurs in aspirin poisoning, cerebral diseases such as viral infections (encephalitis) or head injuries. The pattern can also be seen in patients on artificial ventilators or under general anaesthesia. The typical changes in arterial blood chemistry are shown in Table 16.15.

Table 16.15 Chemical changes in the blood in respiratory alkalaemia.

	Respiratory alkalaemia	
	Uncompensated	Partially compensated
pH	↑↑	↑
PCO_2	↓↓	↓↓
Actual bicarbonate	↓	↓↓
Base	N	↓

Mixed metabolic and respiratory conditions. These occur quite commonly in practice; instead of observing a reciprocal change in the respiratory and metabolic components as in compensation, the two measurements are altered in the same direction to give a compound effect. The most common example in clinical practice is the mixed respiratory and metabolic acidaemia which occurs as a result of cardiac and respiratory arrest. Here the respiratory component is due to the severe retention of CO_2 while the anoxia favours anaerobic glycolysis and so the accumulation of metabolic acids particularly lactic acid. Urgent corrective treatment is required if the patient is to be successfully resuscitated.

REFERENCES

Anderson B 1978 Regulation of water intake. Physiological Reviews 58: 582–603

Barcroft H 1976 Lymph formation by secretion or filtration? Journal of Physiology 260: 1–20

Baron D N, Levin G E 1978 Intracellular chemical pathology. In: Alberti K G M M (ed) Recent advances in clinical biochemistry, No 1. Churchill Livingstone, Edinburgh, pp. 153–174

Epstein A N 1978 The neuroendocrinology of thirst and salt appetite. In: Ganong W F, Martini L (ed) Frontiers of Neuroendocrinology, 5th edn. Raven Press, New York, pp 101–134

Fitzsimons J T 1979 The physiology of thirst and sodium appetite. Monograph No 35 of the Physiological Society. Cambridge University Press

Gardner M L G 1978 Medical acid-base balance. Ballière Tindall, London

House C R 1974 Water transport in cells and tissues. Physiological Society Monograph 24. Arnold, London

Massry S G (ed) 1977 Clinical pathophysiology of electrolyte and acid-base metabolism. Clinical Nephrology 7: 129–240

Nicoll P A, Taylor A E 1977 Lymph formation and flow. Annual Review of Physiology 39: 73–95

Papper S 1976 Sodium and water: an overview. American Journal of the Medical Sciences 272: 43–52

Peach M J 1977 Renin-angiotensin system. Physiological Reviews 57: 313–370

Schwartz A B, Lyons H 1977 Acid-base and electrolyte balance. Grune & Stratton, New York

Swales J D 1975 Sodium metabolism in disease. Lloyd-Luke, London

17 Connective Tissue and Skin

The term connective tissue is used to denote the material that joins together the three primary tissues, epithelial, muscle and nervous. Some kinds of connective tissue cells secrete solid intercellular substances, such as cartilage and bone, which provide protection and support. Other kinds form loose or dense fibrous tissue, tendons, blood vessels, adipose tissues and possibly also the blood cells. As well as cells most connective tissues contain extracellular proteins such as collagen and elastin, proteoglycans and, in the case of bone and teeth, inorganic salts.

Organic Constituents of Connective Tissue

Collagen. Collagen is a fibrous protein, found predominantly in the extracellular phase of many connective tissues. Its functions include the resistance of tensile stress in ligaments and tendons and the fixation of other physiologically important components in cartilage and bone.

Most tissue collagen is insoluble in water but a small proportion can be extracted, by neutral salts or dilute organic acids, as soluble rod-like molecules (tropocollagen) 280 nm long and 1·4 nm in diameter with a molecular weight of 300 000. On denaturation, such molecules are split into three linear chains, each consisting of about 1000 amino acids. In most collagens two of these chains are identical (α_1 *chains*) while the third chain (α_2) has a different amino acid composition. Collagen is characterized by a high content of glycine and by the presence of two amino acids, hydroxyproline and hydroxylysine. Within the chains some hexoses, notably glucose and galactose, are covalently bound to hydroxylysine. In the collagens of most tissues the amount of carbohydrate is small but in that of basement membranes it is high and, like polysaccharides, this tissue stains with PAS (periodic acid—Schiff) in histological preparations.

Within the tropocollagen molecule the α chains form left-handed helices wound round each other as a right-handed triple helix (Fig. 17.1). The triple helix is stabilized by hydrogen bonds between the adjacent α chains and by a single covalent cross-link involving lysine residues in the amino terminal regions of two α chains.

The α-chains are synthesized within fibroblasts or, in bone,

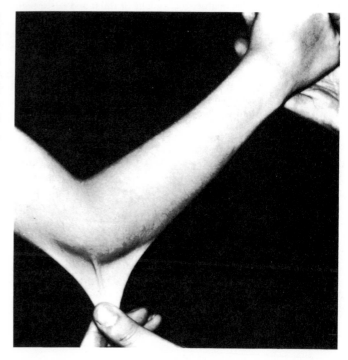

Fig. 17.2 Hyperextensible skin in a 6-year-old boy with Ehlers–Danlos syndrome Type I (*By courtesy of* D. W. Hollister. *Pediatric Clinics of North America* 25 (1978) 575.)

by osteoblasts. Hydroxyproline and hydroxylysine are not incorporated into the original peptide chain as are other amino acids with individual codons and transfer RNA molecules. These amino acids are formed by the hydroxylation, in the microsomes, of certain proline and lysine residues in the newly formed peptide chains. It seems likely that vitamin C has a role in this hydroxylation: in its absence collagen formation is defective. Since 14 per cent of collagen is hydroxyproline, the collagen content of a tissue can be inferred from its hydroxyproline content. Similarly the urinary excretion of hydroxyproline provides a measure of the rate of collagen turnover in the body; high values are found in growing children and in some patients with bone disease.

Each triple helix formed within a cell includes a globular component at one end and is known as *procollagen*. Before the molecule is extruded from the cell, the globular component is split off to give *tropocollagen* by the enzyme procollagen peptidase which is probably in or near the cell membrane. A deficiency of this enzyme is one cause of *Ehlers Danlos disease* in which the collagen in many parts of the body is abnormal so that, for example, the skin is lax (Fig. 17.2) and overextension of the joints can occur. After the tropocollagen molecules are extruded from the cell further maturation takes place (Fig. 17.3). Additional cross-links are formed between tropocollagen molecules; with increasing perfection of packing the collagen microfibrils show a periodic structure which can be demonstrated by electron microscopy (Fig. 17.4). Further links

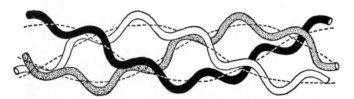

Fig. 17.1 The triple helix of collagen showing the three α-chains (left-handed helices) wound round each other to form a right-handed super helix. The interrupted lines indicate the long axes of the three α-chains. (*From* Serafini-Fracassini and Smith (1974) *The Structure and Biochemistry of Cartilage.* Edinburgh: Churchill Livingstone.)

are formed between individual fibrils so that a tough 'meshwork' of linked collagen fibres is found in many tissues (Fig. 17.5).

Proteoglycans. Most connective tissues contain in addition to proteins glycosaminoglycans which are repeating disaccharide units linked together as long unbranched chains. Glycosaminoglycans are covalently linked to proteins in the form of complex macromolecules known as proteoglycans. Many of these proteoglycans are attached to collagen fibrils at regular intervals; indeed the function of collagen in tissues such as cartilage and the vitreous body of the eye appears to be to provide this anchorage. The principal glycosaminoglycans found in human tissues are hyaluronic acid, the chondroitin sulphates, keratan sulphate, dermatan sulphate and heparin.

Hyaluronic Acid occurs in many tissues, including the vitreous body, the umbilical cord, synovial fluid and skin. The disaccharide unit consists of N-acetyl glucosamine and glucuronic acid. In the *chondroitin sulphates* the disaccharide unit consists of N-acetyl galactosamine and glucuronic acid. The hexosamine is sulphated. The repeating unit in *keratan sulphate* is N-acetyl glucosamine and galactose; the hexose or the hexosamine or both may be sulphated. These sulphated glycosaminoglycans are found particularly in cartilage, the cornea and the nucleus pulposus of intervertebral discs. The glycosaminoglycans are probably bound covalently, in varying proportions, at regular intervals along the same linear protein core, producing a proteoglycan macromolecule with a molecular weight of the order of 2×10^6 and a protein content of about 10 per cent.

Other glycosaminoglycans found in connective tissues are *dermatan sulphate* in skin and elastic ligaments, and *heparin* found in granules in the mast cells of loose connective tissue. Heparin is a polymer of glucuronic acid and sulphated N-acetyl glucosamine; it prevents the clotting of blood (p. 118).

Elastic fibres. This type of fibre is found in loose connective tissue, in elastic cartilages, as in the epiglottis or the external ear, and is a major constituent of the tunica media of large arteries and elastic ligaments such as the ligamentum nuchae. In many situations the fibres are 4 to 7 μm in diameter and form an open three-dimensional network, preferentially orientated in directions of tensile stress, while in others they are closely packed in the form of fenestrated sheets (Fig. 17.6).

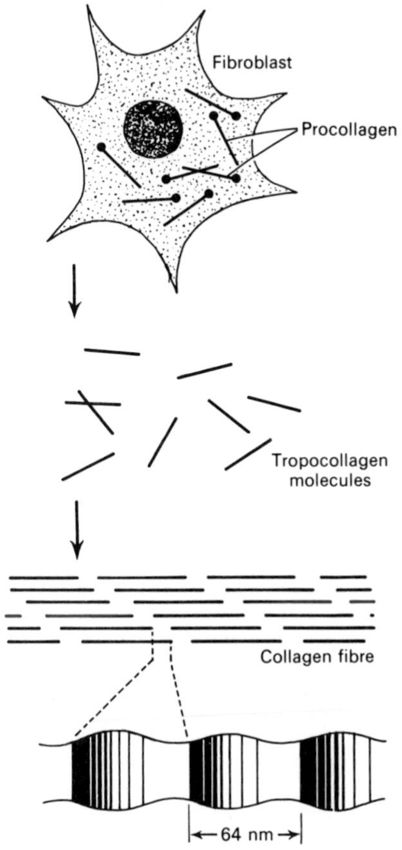

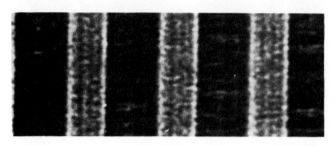

Fig. 17.4 Electron micrograph of a negatively stained collagen fibril ($\times 400\,000$). With this technique the 'stain' passively occupies the spaces between the material elements of the structure and each 64 nm period consists of a light zone and a dark zone. (*By courtesy of J. W. Smith.*)

Fibroblast

Procollagen

Tropocollagen molecules

Collagen fibre

|← 64 nm →|

Fig. 17.3 Tropocollagen molecules are extruded from fibroblast (or osteoblast) and aggregate extracellularly to give collagen fibres with the regular banding which may be detected by electron microscopy.

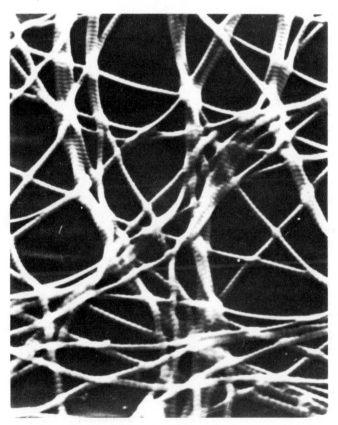

Fig. 17.5 Electronmicrograph of collagen fibres in connective tissue ($\times 1500$). (*By Courtesy of D. A. Hall.*)

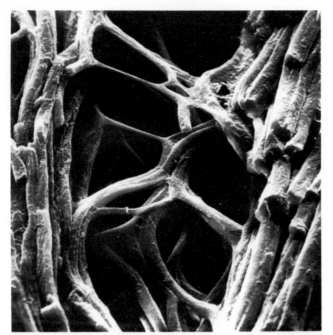

Fig. 17.6 Elastin fibrils as seen by the scanning electron microscope (×1000). (*By courtesy of L. Gotte.*)

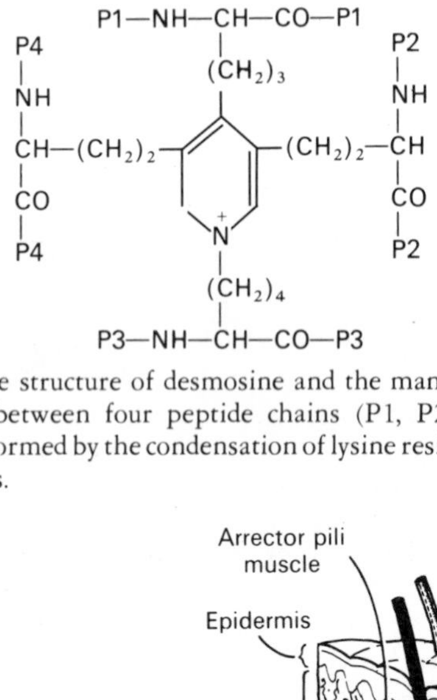

Fig. 17.7 The structure of desmosine and the manner in which it forms a link between four peptide chains (P1, P2, P3 and P4). Desmosine is formed by the condensation of lysine residues located on the four chains.

Elastic fibres respond to external tensile forces by large temporary elongation, provided they have a normal water content. Elastic tissues such as the ligamentum nuchae appear to obey Hooke's law up to an elongation of about 70 per cent and have a Young's modulus of about 10^6 N/m which is similar to that of rubber.

Elastin has an unusually high content of non-polar amino acids, particularly glycine, alanine, valine and proline, and is characterized by polyfunctional amino acids such as desmosine (Fig. 17.7) which link the constituent polypeptide chains.

Keratin. Keratin is a fibrous protein with a high content of the basic amino acids, arginine, lysine and histidine and the sulphur-containing amino acid cysteine. The protein exists in two molecular forms: a pleated sheet (β-keratin) and an α-helix (α-keratin); the keratin of human hair or nails is α-keratin. The structure of the helix of α-keratin is stabilized by the formation of disulphide bonds between adjacent polypeptide chains. This change probably occurs in the epidermis as the epidermal cells pass from the granular layer to the horny layer; at the same time the protein fibrils are coated by a thin layer of lipid.

THE SKIN

In man the chief functions of the skin are to provide an effective barrier to a wide variety of substances, to regulate heat loss, and to mediate sensation (Chap. 22). The skin is divided into three distinct tissue layers—the epidermis, the dermis (corium) and the subcutaneous fatty layer (Fig. 17.8).

Epidermis. The epidermis in the early embryo consists of a single layer of cells; it soon thickens and two main layers—the horny layer on the surface and below it the basal layer—can be distinguished. The basal layer shows mitotic activity which in the adult is greatest between midnight and 4 a.m. The cells so produced are displaced outwards to end in the most superficial layer of the horny layer as dead cells which have lost their nuclei (Fig. 17.9). Nearly 1 g of these cells is shed per day as surface scales; the thickness of this horny layer is, however,

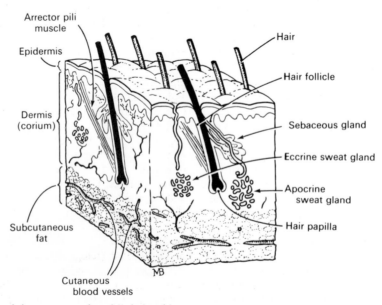

Fig. 17.8 Low power view of the structures found in hairy skin.

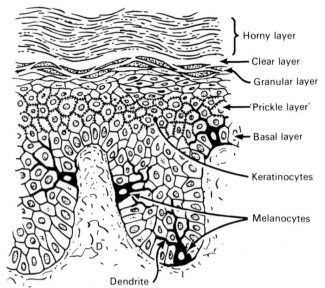

Horny layer

Clear layer

Granular layer

'Prickle layer'

Basal layer

Keratinocytes

Melanocytes

Dendrite

Fig. 17.9 Microscopic appearance of epidermis of the sole or palm. In other parts of the skin the horny layer is thinner and no clear layer is seen. Horny layer = stratum corneum. Clear layer = stratum lucidum. Granular layer = stratum granulosum. D = dermis.

maintained by new cells produced by the basal layer. The horny layer can be stained with a fluorescent dye which binds only to cornified cells. In the forearm the fluorescence disappears after two weeks; this must be the transit time of cornified cells. Below the horny layer is a layer of granular cells (stratum granulosum) which are responsible for the synthesis of the insoluble protein keratin; the granules are precursors of keratin. When the granules are converted into keratin the cells assume a homogeneous appearance and are recognizable, especially if the skin is thick, as the clear layer, a layer of cells lying between the granular layer and the most superficial horny layer.

The horny layer is an effective barrier against external noxious agents and also against water loss from within the body. If this main barrier layer is stripped off the water loss from the underlying tissues can increase 10 to 20 times. Within the stratum corneum hygroscopic water-soluble substances are responsible for much of the water-binding capacity of the horny layer and thus for its extensibility. Their removal by excessive exposure to water, or by increased permeability as a result of extraction of lipids by detergent solutions, results in drying and cracking of the protective horny layer and exposure of the epidermal cells. Free amino acids in the horny layer act as buffers and protect the skin from the action of acids and alkalis.

Projections from the basal layer cells extending down into the dermis are thought to have anchoring and nutritional functions. The cells of the epidermis (keratinocytes, Fig. 17.9) are joined together by 'prickles' or *desmosomes*. An interlocking system of fine filaments attached at the desmosomes criss-crosses the cells and gives the epidermis mechanical stability. The function of the basement membrane lying between the basal layer and the dermis is uncertain but there is no doubt that the dermis influences the cells of the epidermis; separated epidermis when grown as a graft on dermis at a different site takes on the features of the skin at the receptor site.

The thickness of the epidermis varies in different areas of the body; it is thin in the flexures and thick and compact on the palms, soles, and at sites of friction.

The colour of the skin depends on four pigments—oxyhaemoglobin, reduced haemoglobin, carotene, melanin—and on the scattering of light. Melanin is responsible for the dark pigmentation of the skin of the nipple, mammary areola, the margins of the anus, and sites exposed to sunshine and friction. It is formed by special cells, melanocytes, found mainly in the basal layer of the epidermis. These cells inject melanin granules through their dendrites into the keratinocytes of the basal layer. The dark colour of certain races is due, not to a greater number of melanocytes, but to a greater amount of melanin in the epidermis than is found in pale-skinned races. All races have some melanin in the skin. The function of melanin in the protection of the skin against injury by ultraviolet light is described below (p. 277).

Dermis (Corium). The electron microscope shows that the dermis is made up of a network of robust collagen fibres. The network is responsible for the elastic properties of the skin since comparatively few elastic fibres are to be found. The ability of the skin to hold water is attributed to the hydrophilic properties of dermal collagen and glycosaminoglycans. Collagenases are important in wound healing and in the remodelling of injured dermis. The surface of the dermis is formed into ridges or papillae projecting into the epidermis. These papillae contain blood vessels, lymphatics and nerve endings. Although the terminal capillaries of the blood vessels do not enter the epidermis they do nourish the epidermal cells. Beneath the dermis the fibrous tissue opens out and merges with the fat-containing subcutaneous tissue which insulates underlying structures from excessive heat and reduces heat loss in cold climates. Collagen bundles are distributed around the fat cells and in this way a flexible linkage is produced between the skin and the underlying structures. The subcutaneous fat acts as a cushion for the dermis and epidermis and allows lateral displacement.

Hair. Hair, nails, sweat glands and sebaceous glands are all formed by downward growth of the epidermis in the embryo. The fine soft 'lanugo' hair of the human fetus is replaced before birth by (a) vellus hair which is soft, occasionally pigmented and usually not more than 2 cm long—this is the characteristic body hair of the child and the facial hair of the adult woman; and (b) terminal hair which is longer, coarser and often pigmented. Genetic constitution, age and the plasma level of androgens all play a part in determining hair pattern. At puberty (Chap. 30) terminal hair progressively replaces vellus hair and continues to do so up to about the fourth decade. It appears on the pubis, upper lip, axilla, beard, trunk and limbs. The difference between male and female patterns is only one of degree, and some terminal hair is found on the face in at least 40 per cent of Caucasian women over the age of 50.

At the end of the active growing period (anagen) there is a short transition phase (catagen) during which there is a gradual involution of the follicles which lasts approximately two weeks in the human scalp. The hair is then retained for a resting period (telogen) without further growth and is then shed. The rate of hair growth varies between 1 and 3 mm per week according to age, sex and the region of the skin; with increasing age the number of hair follicles gradually declines. In man each follicle acts independently of the others.

Temporary hair loss can be precipitated by physical and mental stresses, most commonly after febrile illness or after childbirth.

In genetically predisposed males baldness develops. Anagen is reduced and an increased percentage of follicles is found in the telogen phase; terminal hairs are gradually replaced by vellus hairs and ultimately the vellus follicles disappear. By the age of 50, 60 per cent of Caucasian males have some degree of baldness of the temples and vertex.

Nails. Unlike hair, the nails grow continuously throughout life and are not normally shed. Growth is greatest in childhood and decreases slowly with age, the normal rate of growth of finger nails being between 0·5 and 1·2 mm per week. A temporary slowing of the growth may follow general body disorders. Nail growth is also affected by local disturbances in the nail fold or by abnormal keratinization of the nail plate. General or local factors may cause thickening, ridging, pitting, discoloration, brittleness and splitting of the nail and even separation of the nail from its bed (onycholysis). The nail may change in colour for a variety of reasons; white spots in the nail plate, which are seen in many normal people, are due to imperfect keratinization with retention of nuclear material.

Sweat glands. In man there are two different types of sweat glands—eccrine and apocrine. The ordinary or eccrine sweat glands (Fig. 17.10) are simple tubular glands found all over the skin, being especially numerous in thick skin. The secretory part of the tubule, about 0·1 mm in diameter, lying deep in the dermis, is coiled and twisted on itself. The initial coiled portion of the tubule is composed of a single layer of epithelial cells surrounded by a layer of myoepithelial cells, whose function is not yet known. The epithelial cells are classified as 'dark' (basophilic) cells and 'clear' cells in about equal numbers, the latter being responsible for the secretion of sweat. The clear cells have many mitochondria and are presumably capable of intense metabolic activity; intercellular canaliculi empty into the lumen of the tube. The function of the smaller dark cells is not known; they contain mucoid substances and nucleic acids but relatively few mitochondria. Further on in the coil, ductal cells appear mixed up with secretory cells. The duct itself has two layers of cuboidal epithelium, the outer layer possessing numerous mitochondria. Micropuncture studies in man have shown that the fluid in the secretory coil is isotonic and that sodium is abstracted from it by the cells of the ducts as the sweat passes to the exterior. The duct pursues a spiral course through the corium and epidermis to open on the surface of a dermal ridge. The control of the sweat glands is discussed on page 413.

Apocrine glands, about 1 mm in diameter, are found in the axilla, the pubic region, in the areola of the breast and as modified glands in the eyelid and external auditory meatus; the mammary gland itself is a modified apocrine gland. An apocrine gland consists of a coiled tube lying in the deepest part of the dermis or in the subcutaneous tissue with a duct opening into a hair follicle above the sebaceous gland (Fig. 17.8). These glands do not become active until puberty and their secretion diminishes in old age. They secrete continuously apparently independently of any nervous control but the delivery of the secretion on to the skin surface, which is intermittent, may be provoked either by the sympathetic nerve supply or by circulating adrenaline. The gland has a single layer of cuboidal or columnar cells resting on a basement membrane

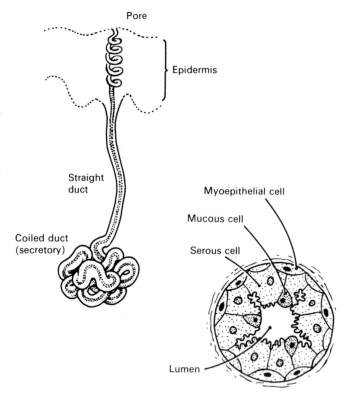

Fig. 17.10 The eccrine sweat gland. On the right is shown a diagrammatic cross-section of the secretory segment. *After* K. Hashimoto (1978). The eccrine gland in *The Physiology and Pathology of Skin*, ed. A. Jarrett. London: Academic Press.

surrounded by myoepithelial cells similar to those seen in eccrine glands. Apocrine secretion results from pinching off part of the cytoplasm of the cells but also from release of vacuoles and from the disruption of the cell-membrane over part of the cell. The axillary apocrine glands produce a viscid milky fluid which is odourless when fresh but decomposition by the bacteria of the skin produces the characteristic unpleasant axillary odour of the human adult. The function of apocrine sweat is not known.

Sebaceous glands. Each sebaceous gland consists of a series of lobes or acini which lead into a short duct. This usually opens into a hair follicle but may also open directly onto the skin surface, particularly in the face. There are about 900 sebaceous glands per cm² on the face and scalp but only about 100 per cm² elsewhere; they are not found on the palms, soles and lower lip. In the eyelid sebaceous glands (tarsal glands) open directly on the skin surface.

The secretion of the sebaceous gland, sebum, is holocrine, being formed by the complete disintegration of the glandular cells. Sebum can be obtained by immersing a limb in acetone and recovering the extracted material. It is a mixture of triglycerides, wax esters and squalene with some sterols derived from epidermal lipids. The water-holding power of the stratum corneum depends in part on this lipid film; it may also help to protect the skin from fungal and bacterial infection. The sebaceous glands are under the control of the sex hormones and their activity increases after puberty. Their secretion is increased by androgens and inhibited by oestrogens, mainly by affecting the rate of cell division. Acne, a common skin disorder in Caucasians, is caused by retention of sebum behind a blocked hair follicle.

Protective Function of the Skin

Many substances applied to the skin are unable to penetrate further than the stratum corneum; some, however, pass through the skin without causing a reaction whereas others produce systemic effects once they have reached the blood. The rate of penetration varies for different substances and different sites; it can be altered by changes in temperature or by abrasion or inflammation of the skin. The physicochemical characteristics of the penetrant, for example solubility, molecular size and particle size, are important; small molecules penetrate faster than large ones. If the stratum corneum is made moist by covering it with a waterproof dressing penetration is increased and corticosteroids applied to it may accumulate in the stratum corneum with advantages in the treatment of certain skin diseases.

Substances enter the skin either by diffusion directly through the horny layer or by way of the appendages, in particular the hair follicles and sebaceous glands (Fig. 17.11). The cells of the sebaceous glands are more permeable than the keratinocytes of the epidermis and thus substances can reach the dermis by passing through the sebaceous glands from the hair follicles and also through the epithelium of the follicular root sheath. Many drugs applied locally to the skin may be absorbed and exert effects elsewhere in the body. Phenolic compounds and steroid drugs are particularly liable to be absorbed in large amounts especially in patients whose skin is abnormal.

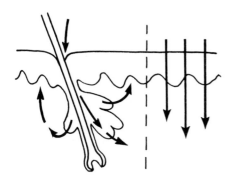

Fig. 17.11   Routes of penetration of the skin.

Protection against ultraviolet light. Ultraviolet light causes cellular damage in the epidermis by inducing the formation of dimers of thymine, by causing other reparable lesions in nuclear DNA and by membrane effects, particularly the effects on lyzosomes. Although there is considerable absorption of radiation in the horny layer and in the living cells of epidermis by protein, by urocanic acid and by melanin, sufficient radiation penetrates to the dermis to have direct effects on blood vessels and on collagen. Ultraviolet light causes an increase in the prostaglandin (notably PGE) content of human skin. This may have a local effect on the underlying blood vessels.

Exposure to ultraviolet rays increases the amount of melanin in the skin and also increases the thickness of the stratum corneum. In these ways the skin is protected from damage; the melanin acts by absorbing light of all wave-lengths while the thickened stratum corneum absorbs most of the carcinogenic wavelengths which are less than 320 nm. The mechanism of sunburn, that is the effect of solar radiation between 290 and 320 nm, is only partly understood. When the skin is exposed to ultraviolet light it becomes red after 7 to 12 hours because of the dilatation of the papillary venous complexes. This erythema may persist from 24 hours to 7 days depending on the dose; with higher doses it may be accompanied by pain, oedema, and even blistering, with systemic effects in the form of nausea or fainting. Mild reactions are followed by increased pigmentation and desquamation of the horny layer.

During exposure to ultraviolet light a colourless melanin precursor is oxidized to melanin and is transferred from the melanocytes to keratinocytes. An inhibitor of tyrosinase is inactivated by exposure so that melanin synthesis is increased after a latent period of a day or so. No doubt the increased pigmentation after exposure affords protection against further insult but thickening of the horny layer and increased amounts of urocanic acid within this layer also give protection.

The bacterial flora of the skin. It is not always appreciated that far from being sterile the skin has a resident flora of yeasts and bacteria, mainly staphylococci and corynebacteria. These are found in small colonies on the surface, in the hair follicles and possibly in the sweat glands. Other environmental bacteria may be transient members of the flora of the skin surface. The resident bacteria do not cause infections in healthy people and may play a useful role in preventing infections by other, more pathogenic, organisms.

REFERENCES

Andrews M L A 1976 The life that lives on man. Faber, London

Bornstein P 1974 Disorders of connective tissues. In: Bondy P K, Rosenberg L E (eds) Duncan's diseases of metabolism, 7th edn. Saunders, Philadelphia, pp. 881–948

Gotte L, Giro M G, Volpin D, Horne R W 1974 The ultrastructural organization of elastin. Journal of Ultrastructure Research 46: 22–33

Hollister D W 1978 Heritable disorders of connective tissue: Ehlers–Danlos syndrome. Pediatric Clinics of North America 25: 575–591

Jarrett A (ed) 1973–1978 vol 1–5 The physiology and pathophysiology of the skin. Academic Press, London

Lancet 1978 Collagen in health and disease. Lancet 1: 1077–1079

Mier P D, Cotton D W K 1976 The molecular biology of the skin. Blackwell, Oxford

Montagna W, Parakkal P F 1974 The structure and function of skin, 3rd edn. Academic Press, New York

Noble W C, Somerville D A 1974 Microbiology of human skin. Saunders, London

Perez-Tamayo R, Rojkind M (ed) 1973 Molecular pathology of connective tissue. Marcel Dekker, New York

Rook A, Wilkinson D S, Ebling F J G (eds) 1972 Textbook of dermatology, 2nd edn. Blackwell, Oxford

Ryder M L 1973 Hair. Arnold, London

Samman P D 1978 The nail in disease, 3rd edn. Heinemann, London

18 Bone and the Metabolism of Calcium and Phosphorus

The skeleton is composed of bone, a living tissue with remarkable properties. It gives support and protection to the softer parts of the body; it is both strong and light and it can grow and remodel itself to withstand normal or new stresses. Bone is also a store for calcium and phosphorus which play an important part in the function of all tissues.

THE TISSUES OF THE SKELETON

Bone

The shafts of long bones are made of a hollow cylinder of hard compact bone containing marrow (p. 108). The ends of long bones and also the vertebrae and flat bones are supported internally by spongy bone (Fig. 18.1) arranged in a pattern of trabeculae which is apparently determined by the load carried by the bone. Compact bone is nearly as strong as cast iron but much more flexible.

Dried cortical bone contains about 25 per cent of organic matter and about 75 per cent of inorganic material. Collagen (p. 272) accounts for 90 per cent of the organic matter (*matrix*), the remainder being glycosaminoglycans, glycoproteins, lipids and peptides.

The mineral of bone, to which its hardness and rigidity are due, can be shown by X-ray crystallography to have a lattice structure similar to that of the natural mineral apatite, $Ca_{10}(PO_4)_6(OH)_2$. The Ca/P ratio in bone is 1·5 which is lower than that of apatite, namely 1·67, but this slight difference can be accounted for by various substitutions in the lattice which has small amounts of Na, Mg, Sr, K, Cl and F together with bicarbonate, citrate and water. About 60 per cent of the apatite is crystalline in form and the surface area presented by the

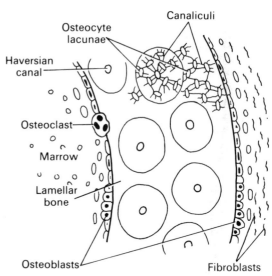

Fig. 18.2 Diagram of cross-section of adult cortical bone to indicate the arrangement of Haversian canals, the osteocytes with their canaliculi, and the cells lining the bone surfaces. The periosteal surface is on the right, the endosteal surface on the left. (*After* Vaughan, 1975.)

small crystals must be very large. About 40 per cent of adult bone mineral is not crystalline but is an amorphous tricalcium phosphate which has a distinct appearance (doughnut) on electron microscopy. The amorphous material seems to be converted *in vivo* to crystalline apatite; the proportion of crystalline material increases with age.

The bones contain 99 per cent of the body's calcium, 88 per cent of the phosphorus, 50 per cent of the magnesium, 35 per cent of the sodium and 9 per cent of the water.

Bone cells. Four main types of cell are associated with bone: osteoblasts, osteocytes, osteoclasts and fibroblasts (Fig. 18.2). All are derived embryologically from primitive mesenchymal reticulum cells.

Osteoblasts line all bone surfaces except those undergoing active osteoclastic resorption and a few bone surfaces in the skull sinuses which are lined with epithelium. Histologically some osteoblasts appear to be extremely thin with flattened nuclei ('lining cells') while others are larger and appear to be more active. However all osteoblasts are able to respond to stimuli such as changes in the levels of parathyroid hormone or of calcitonin in the circulation. Moreover the osteoblasts, together, form a membrane (Fig. 18.3) which appears to have the properties of an epithelial membrane. This is indicated by the differences in the composition of the extracellular fluid on either side of the membrane, by the secretion of collagen on one side only and by the remarkable differences between the ion-exchange activity of living and dead bone.

Osteoclasts are responsible for bone resorption. They are large or very large multinucleate cells. Most have 10 to 20 nuclei, but osteoclasts with several hundreds have been described.

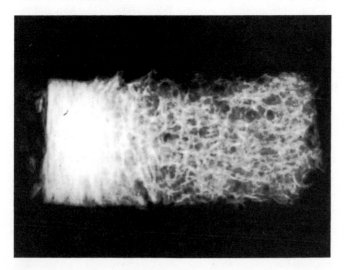

Fig. 18.1 Enlarged radiograph of a sample of bone taken from the iliac crest of an adult. On the left is the compact bone, on the right is the spongy bone (trabecular bone). The whole sample is 12 mm in length. (*Courtesy of C. G. Woods*).

Osteocytes are derived from osteoblasts during bone formation; as they mature they lose some of their cytoplasm. Each osteocyte occupies a lacuna in the bone and gives out cytoplasmic processes of the order of 100 μm in diameter which reach out to a bone territory and also communicate with similar processes derived from osteoblasts (Fig. 18.4). The role of the osteocyte is not yet entirely clear but it is a metabolically active cell and probably responsible for rapid exchanges of calcium between bone and extracellular fluid. It is likely that the osteocyte, rather than the osteoclast, has the major role in the response of the bone to parathyroid hormone.

Fibroblasts are found on the surface of bone outside the layer of osteoblasts and pre-osteoblasts. They seem to be relatively inactive except perhaps after fractures but there is no evidence that they turn into osteoblasts.

Bone growth. Bones develop in two different ways. Some, notably the long bones, appear in the fetus as cartilaginous models and are replaced by bone as shown in Figure 18.5. Others, such as the flat bones of the skull, are formed directly by bone formation within connective tissue membranes without an intermediate stage as cartilage.

A long bone grows in length by the interstitial growth of the epiphyseal cartilage in which the cells are arranged in regular longitudinal columns produced by repeated cell division (Fig. 18.6). Each row of cells is enclosed in a tunnel of cartilage with

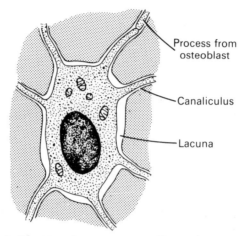

Process from osteoblast

Canaliculus

Lacuna

Fig. 18.4 Diagram of an osteocyte to illustrate manner in which cytoplasmic processes communicate with similar processes from other osteocytes and from osteoblasts on the bone surface.

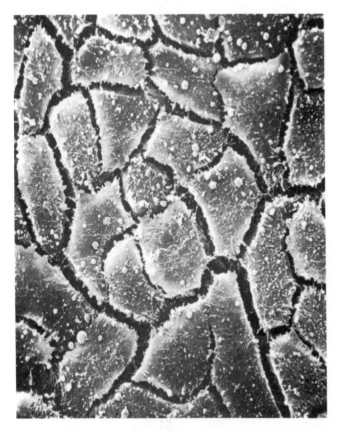

Fig. 18.3 Scanning electron micrograph of bone endosteum (× 1850). The osteoblasts are closely approximated and their surfaces show microvilli. (*From* W. L. Davis, J. L. Matthews, J. H. Martin, J. W. Kennedy & R. V. Talmage (1975) The endosteum as a functional membrane. In *Calcium-Regulating Hormones*, ed. R. V. Talmage, M. Owen & J. A. Parsons. Amsterdam: Excerpta Medica.)

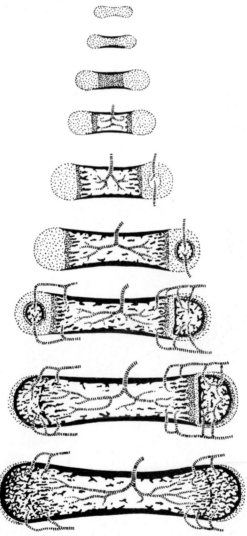

Fig. 18.5 The development of a long bone from a cartilage precursor as seen in longitudinal section. Light stipple: cartilage; heavy stipple: calcified cartilage; black: bone; cross-hatching: arteries. (*After* W. Bloom & D. W. Fawcett (1968) *Textbook of Histology*. 9th edition. Philadelphia: Saunders.)

thin partitions between the cells. As the cells approach the diaphyseal (shaft) side of the epiphyseal plate they enlarge and the cartilage around them becomes calcified. The cells next to the marrow cavity die and the thin transverse partitions of cartilage disappear leaving tunnels which are invaded by capillaries and by osteoblasts. The osteoblasts put down several layers of bone on the inner walls of the tunnels, and this process is repeated. In this way only a narrow channel containing a blood vessel and some cells remains. This concentric arrangement is called a Haversian system. Narrow canaliculi pass radially and circumferentially in the Haversian systems to convey nutrients to the enclosed osteocytes. During the growing period the interstitial growth of epiphyseal cartilage keeps pace with its replacement by bone so the

epiphyseal plate of cartilage is always present as a thin and regular zone. It is important to realize that calcification of cartilage is not ossification; cartilage is not *transformed* into bone—it is *replaced* by it. Calcification of cartilage is defective in vitamin D deficiency, so that the epiphyseal cartilage is much wider than normal.

Because bone is rigid it cannot increase in size by interstitial growth. Growth in width by long bones, and all growth by other bones, is achieved by the deposition of new bone on the surface of exisiting bone. As a child grows not only must new bone be laid down on the surface of a bone but also bone must be removed from the centre. At such sites of remodelling osteoclasts are found.

Bone remodelling and turnover. Even in the adult, bone is

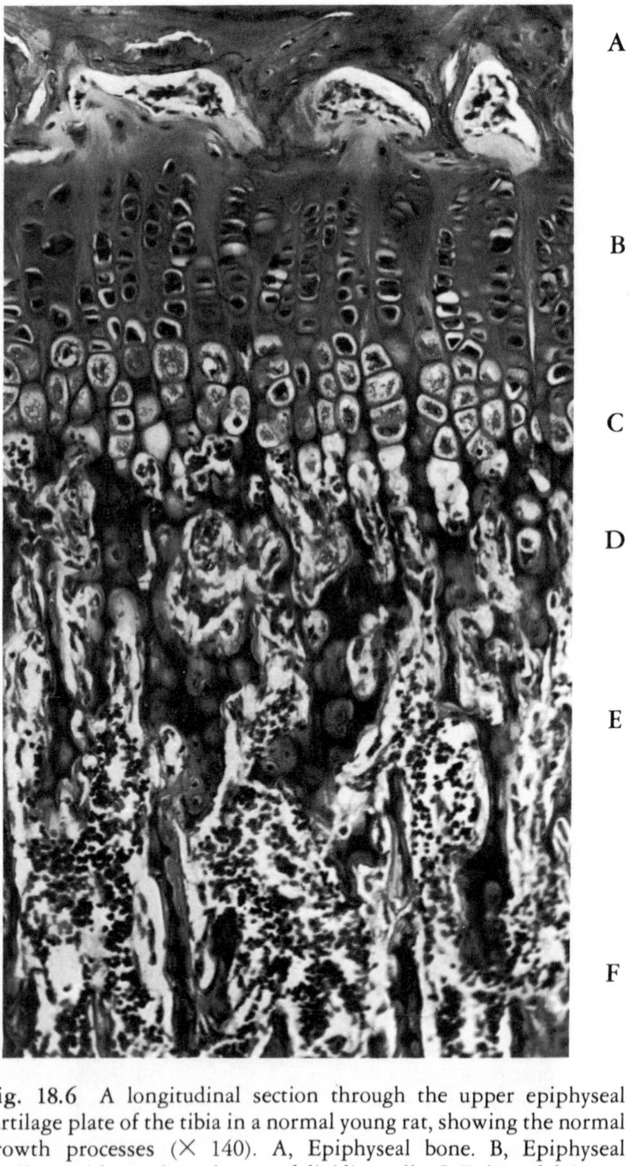

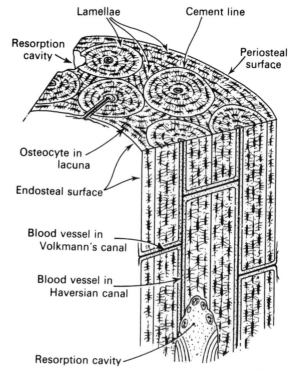

Fig. 18.7 The cortex of the shaft of a long bone to show osteoclastic resorption and the formation of new Haversian systems. (*After* W. H. Harris & R. P. Heaney (1970) *Skeletal Renewal and Metabolic Bone Disease*. Boston: Little Brown.)

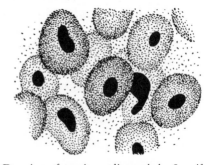

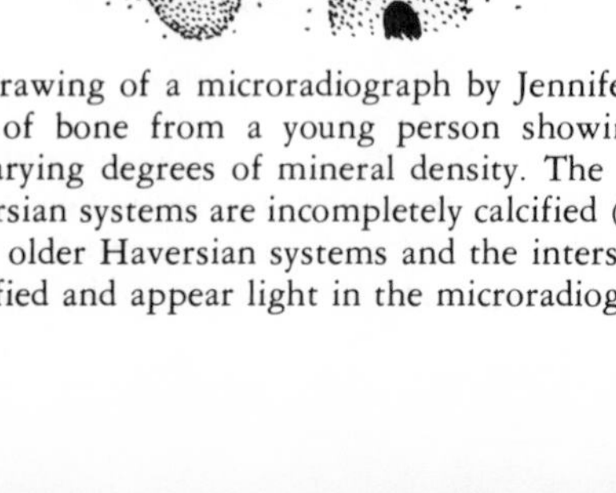

Fig. 18.8 Drawing of a microradiograph by Jennifer Jowsey of a cross-section of bone from a young person showing Haversian systems of varying degrees of mineral density. The most recently formed Haversian systems are incompletely calcified (and therefore darker) while older Haversian systems and the interstitial lamellae are fully calcified and appear light in the microradiograph.

Fig. 18.6 A longitudinal section through the upper epiphyseal cartilage plate of the tibia in a normal young rat, showing the normal growth processes (× 140). A, Epiphyseal bone. B, Epiphyseal cartilage with regular columns of dividing cells. C, Enlarged dying or dead cells surrounded by calcified cartilage. D, Transverse cartilage partitions have disappeared. The tunnels are invaded by capillaries and osteoblasts. E, Bone is being laid down on cartilage and removed and bony trabeculae are laid down. F, Marrow cavity containing blood vessels and bone cells. (*By courtesy of H. A. Sissons.*)

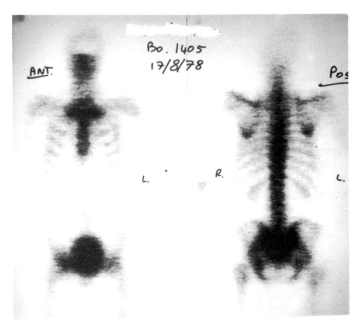

Fig. 18.9 Radioisotope bone scan in a normal adult. A dose of polyphosphate linked to ^{99}technetium is administered intravenously. Two hours later the patient is scanned with a gamma-detecting system and the anterior and posterior views of the skeleton are obtained. Much of the dose not taken up by the skeleton has been eliminated through the kidneys and the isotope can be seen in the residual urine in the bladder. (*Courtesy of F. Hutchinson*).

continually being remodelled. Both the laying down of new bone (*accretion*) and the removal (*resorption*) of bone occur simultaneously; each amounts to about 500 mg calcium daily. The cellular basis of this exchange is shown in Figure 18.7. The new Haversian systems initially contain less calcium than those they replace (Fig. 18.8).

Kinetic studies with radioactive isotopes have also shown that there is a pool of readily exchangeable calcium within the bone. The anatomical site of this pool is not clear but it has been estimated that bone crystal surfaces exposed to extracellular fluid on the walls of the lacunae, canaliculi and Haversian canals amount to 1500 to 5000 square metres in the average man. The continual exchange of the mineral between bone and the extracellular fluid is illustrated by the use of radioisotope bone scans in medicine (Fig. 18.9). These are used to indicate areas of the skeleton with increased turnover such as the sites of bony secondaries in malignant disease; increased turnover is also seen where there are healing fractures or at the growing ends of bone in normal children.

Bone has a remarkable capacity for remodelling. For example, in a child with a fracture that has healed with deformity, the deformity gradually diminishes. Little is known about the control of this process but it seems likely that small electrical currents are involved. In the absence of stress on the skeleton, in immobilized patients for example, bone resorption is greatly increased presumably as a result of the lack of these electrical stimuli. Conversely direct application of small electrical currents may be used to stimulate bone growth.

Calcification. The process of calcification of bone matrix to give bone is still not fully understood. Electron microscope studies show that collagen fibrils play an important part; the earliest deposits of calcium salts are seen in or between the fibres. Moreover it seems that collagen must be of the native type with a 64 nm repeating pattern (p. 273) to be effective in initiating calcification.

The osteoblasts play an important role in mineralization perhaps by increasing the local concentration of calcium and phosphate ions or by producing vesicles, derived from mitochondria, laden with calcium phosphate. It is likely that the first mineral to form is an amorphous calcium phosphate and that this is then converted into apatite.

There are several known inhibitors of calcification. The most extensively studied is pyrophosphate (H_2PO_3—O—H_2PO_3) which is present in many tissues including bone and probably prevents inappropriate calcification. It is broken down to two phosphate residues by alkaline phosphatases which also act as pyrophosphatases. In a rare inherited disorder known as hypophosphatasia the alkaline phosphatase activity in the plasma is low, the levels of pyrophosphate in plasma and urine are increased, and bone mineralization is defective. As a result these patients have bone changes not unlike those of rickets. Pyrophosphate itself is too unstable to be useful in therapy but chemical analogues known as diphosphonates, with a —P—C—P— core instead of —P—O—P—, have been useful in the treatment of patients with diseases, such as Paget's disease of bone, characterized by excessive bone turnover.

Blood flow. At rest the skeleton receives about 5 per cent of the blood volume per minute. The amount does not increase in response to exercise.

Cartilage

Cartilage contains cells known as chondrocytes embedded in a matrix which consists mainly of collagen and a proteoglycan containing the glycosaminoglycans, chondroitin-4-sulphate, chondroitin-6-sulphate and keratan sulphate in varying proportions. Three types of cartilage are recognized. In *hyaline* cartilage about 75 per cent of the material is water; collagen forms 25 to 70 per cent and glycosaminoglycans 14 to 40 per cent of the dry weight. In *fibrocartilage* collagen fibres constitute the greatest proportion of the organic matter with only about 2 per cent of glycosaminoglycans. *Elastic cartilage* occurs in the external ear and in parts of the larynx; it contains about 20 per cent of elastin.

Mature hyaline cartilage is avascular and contains no nervous tissue or lymphatic vessels. The chondrocytes are metabolically active cells and their principal function appears to be the synthesis of matrix. They have several anaerobic metabolic pathways and nutrients reach the cells by diffusion through the matrix.

Cartilage grows in volume interstitially when the chondrocytes it contains multiply and produce more matrix. It also grows by apposition as a result of matrix synthesis by the cells on the surface, collectively known as the perichondrium.

Joints

Adjacent bones in the skeleton may be joined to one another simply by fibrous tissue (*fibrous joint*) as in the skull, or by cartilage (*cartilaginous joint*). But where an appreciable

Fig. 18.10 Appearance of normal articular surface from the hamate bone, as seen by the scanning electron microscope (×890). The 'chicken wire' appearance is due to a network of fine fibrils in the surface matrix. (*Courtesy of I. Redler.* From *Clinical Orthopaedics,* 103, 262–268.)

amount of movement between the bones is necessary they articulate by a *synovial joint* at which the bone ends are coated by a thin layer of hyaline cartilage (*articular cartilage*) and joined by a fibrous tube (*fibrous capsule*), lined by a *synovial membrane.* The cavity of the joint is occupied by *synovial fluid.*

The scanning electron microscope has shown that the apparently smooth surface of articular cartilage is in fact gently undulating and is many times 'rougher' than engineering bearings (Fig. 18.10). The peak to peak distance of the undulations is about 5 μm and the depressions are about 2·5 μm deep. The superficial zone of the cartilage matrix contains tightly packed small collagen fibres lying parallel to the surface forming a 'skin'. The deeper fibres are longer and form an open meshwork; the fibres next to the bone are disposed radially towards the joint surface. The glycosaminoglycan content varies inversely with that of collagen, being as low as 3 per cent of dry weight superficially and much higher towards the cartilage/bone interface. The composition of articular cartilage also changes with age. In fetal life it contains chondroitin-4-sulphate and chondroitin-6-sulphate but little or no keratan sulphate. After birth chondroitin-4-sulphate is progressively replaced by keratan sulphate and this exchange continues throughout life.

Synovial membrane. The fibrous capsule of a joint passes from one bone to the other to form a closed cavity. It is lined internally by the synovial membrane, a connective tissue membrane two or three cells thick containing a rich capillary network.

Two types of cell can be distinguished by electron microscopy in synovial membranes. Type A cells appear to be phagocytic and can be shown to take up particulate matter which has been injected into joints. Type B cells are less numerous and probably synthesize hyaluronic acid.

Synovial fluid. The cavity of a joint contains straw-coloured viscous synovial fluid. Its viscosity is due to the presence of hyaluronic acid secreted by the B cells of the synovial membrane. In other respects the composition of synovial fluid

resembles that of plasma except that the protein concentration is 10 to 20 g/litre. The volume of synovial fluid in a normal joint is quite small: in the human knee, for instance, it is between 0·5 ml and 2·0 ml.

Mechanism of joint action. By sliding the femoral condyles of an amputated human knee joint against the corresponding articular surface of the tibia it has been found that the coefficient of friction is about 0·01 which is three times better than the coefficient of ice sliding on ice and more than 10 times better than the value found in a plain lubricated bearing.

A complete explanation of this very successful form of lubrication has not been found. Since the viscosity of the lubricating film is increased as the articulating surfaces approach under load it is likely that the liquid phase of the synovial fluid, trapped in the undulations of the cartilage, is squeezed away and a thickened gel remains.

CALCIUM METABOLISM

The skeleton contains at least 99 per cent of the total body calcium which in a young adult is about 1.2 kg. After the third decade of life bone resorption exceeds bone accretion and there is a slow but progressive loss of bone which is greater in women than in men.

Dietary Calcium

In Europe and the U.S.A. the average daily calcium intake in adults is 800 to 1000 mg. In developing countries the intake is often considerably less (200 to 400 mg/day). The main sources of calcium are milk and cheese, green vegetables and, in Britain and the United States, artificially enriched bread.

Many attempts have been made by nutrition experts to define a minimum requirement for calcium; typical recommendations have been 400 mg/day for adults, with greater amounts in childhood, pregnancy and lactation. However, there is little evidence that a low calcium intake does any harm in otherwise healthy people or that calcium supplements have any value in people with a low intake. The intestine has a remarkable facility for adapting to a low calcium diet; within a week of the change in the diet, the proportion of the dietary calcium which is absorbed increases. For example in 1952 Hegsted and others, using volunteers from a Peruvian prison, showed that calcium balance can be achieved with a dietary calcium as low as 100 mg daily. During starvation, however, a negative calcium balance occurs because calcium continues to be lost in the urine and in the intestinal secretions.

Intestinal Absorption

In an adult in calcium balance, and on a diet containing 1000 mg/day, the faeces contain about 850 mg/day and the urine about 150 mg/day. Thus the absorption from the diet appears to be 150 mg/day. In fact the true intestinal absorption is about 350 mg/day since about 200 mg/day enters the gut with the intestinal secretions (Fig. 18.11).

Calcium can be absorbed from all parts of the small intestine by an active transport mechanism. The greatest calcium absorbing capacity is in the duodenum where there is an active transport mechanism controlled by the hormone 1,25-dihydroxy-cholecalciferol (p. 31). In the jejunum and ileum calcium absorption takes place by passive diffusion or facilitated diffusion. In normal subjects the proportion of dietary calcium absorbed is greatly increased after a period on a low calcium diet. This 'adaptation' is not seen in the absence of vitamin D so that it seems likely that 1,25-dihydroxy-cholecalciferol is involved.

Many factors affect calcium absorption in man. It is greatly reduced in vitamin D deficiency, renal failure and in intestinal malabsorption. It is also reduced by the administration of phytic acid, phosphate or steroids or the presence of excess unabsorbed fatty acids in the intestine. Calcium absorption diminishes with advancing age. It is increased by parathyroid hormone or vitamin D in excess.

Plasma Calcium

Calcium is constantly entering the plasma from bone and gut and leaving it for bone, gut or urine. Nevertheless the plasma calcium is maintained within narrow limits, a constant concentration of ionized calcium being necessary for the normal function of muscles and nerves.

The normal range for total plasma calcium is 2·2 to 2·6 mmol/l. Just under half of this is bound to plasma proteins, particularly albumin, a small proportion is complexed with citrate and phosphate and the remainder circulates as ionized calcium (Table 18.12). The complexed and ionized calcium are together known as the *ultrafiltrable fraction* or *diffusible fraction*. While it is the level of ionized calcium in the plasma that is physiologically important, the methods available for its measurement are not suitable for routine use. In clinical practice, the total plasma calcium is measured and appropriate allowances are made in patients with abnormalities of the plasma albumin.

Table 18.12 State of calcium in normal human plasma (data of A. Raman (1971) *Clinical Biochemistry*, 4, 141–146). The figures given represent the mean values from 20 normal subjects.

	mmol/l	% of total
Ionic calcium	1·16	44·6
Protein bound calcium	1·07	41·2
Complexed calcium (CaHPO$_4$, calcium citrate, and unidentified fractions)	0·37	14·2
TOTAL	2·60	100

The binding of calcium to protein is affected by pH; it is reduced in acidosis and increased in alkalosis. Because calcium is bound to protein, changes in the total plasma calcium, without any change in the level of ionized calcium, follow changes in the plasma proteins. Thus a low plasma calcium is found with a low plasma albumin in cirrhosis of the liver or in the nephrotic syndrome.

Two consequences of the protein-binding of plasma calcium are of practical importance. If a tourniquet is applied to the arm in order to take a venous blood sample, the pressure within the vein rises and so does the pressure within the capillaries which supply it. Fluid is lost into the interstitial space but blood cells and large molecules, such as proteins, cannot escape and their concentration rises. Since calcium is partly bound to albumin its concentration also rises and

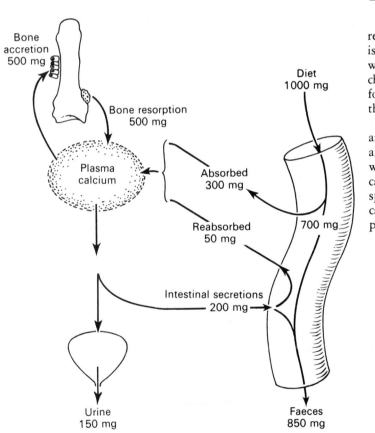

Fig. 18.11 Calcium turnover in man. The figures (mg/day) have been rounded off and show that in health the urinary and faecal calcium excretion together equal the dietary calcium while bone resorption and bone accretion are equal. In developing countries typical figures for dietary calcium and faecal calcium are 500 mg and 380 mg, respectively, but in other respects figures for developing countries are similar to those shown. (*From* Paterson, 1975.)

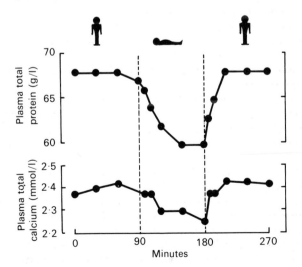

Fig. 18.13 Effect of changes in posture on plasma levels of protein and calcium. (*From* Paterson, 1975.)

misleading results may be obtained. This effect is minimized by taking a blood sample as quickly as possible after a tourniquet has been applied. The effect of posture on plasma calcium has a similar mechanism (Fig. 18.13).

Urinary Excretion of Calcium

About 9 g calcium passes daily into the glomerular filtrate from the diffusible fractions of the plasma calcium. Most of this is reabsorbed by the tubules and in normal people the urinary excretion is 2 to 10 mmol/day (80 to 400 mg/day). Calcium reabsorption is increased in hyperparathyroidism and decreased in hypoparathyroidism and in the presence of a sodium diuresis.

Calcium in Sweat

The loss of calcium in the sweat is very variable between 0·5 and 9·0 mmol/day (20 to 360 mg/day). This limits the accuracy of calcium balance studies.

PHOSPHORUS METABOLISM

The phosphorus content of an adult man is about 800 g; four-fifths of this is in the bones, the remainder being in the cells as organic phosphates, phospholipids or nucleic acids. The inorganic phosphorus concentration in the plasma in fasting adults is between 0·8 and 1·4 mmol/l (2·5 to 4·5 mg/100 ml). Higher values are found in infants. Almost all the inorganic phosphate is diffusible, only 12 per cent being protein-bound. Not all the diffusible phosphate is ionized; some is bound to calcium and magnesium so that the true plasma concentration of inorganic phosphate ions is uncertain. At a normal blood pH 85 per cent of the ionized inorganic phosphate is present as HPO_4^{2-} and 15 per cent as $H_2PO_4^-$.

Since phosphorus is present in all animal and plant cells dietary deficiency never occurs in man. Phosphate depletion may occur as a result of renal tubular disorders (see below) and, very rarely, in patients who consume excessive quantities of aluminium hydroxide, an antacid which binds phosphate in the gut.

Phosphate is excreted by the kidney, and in the steady state the amount excreted is equal to that which the gut absorbs. Ninety per cent of the phosphate filtered at the glomerulus is reabsorbed in the tubule; there is no good evidence for tubular secretion. Defects in phosphate reabsorption occur in patients with parathyroid overactivity and in patients with inherited disorders of the renal tubules. In these conditions the plasma phosphate level tends to be low. A high plasma phosphate is found in renal failure.

HOMEOSTASIS OF CALCIUM AND PHOSPHORUS

A constant and normal concentration of ionized calcium in the extracellular fluid is of great importance in, among other things, muscular contraction, neural and neuromuscular transmission and the activity of several enzymes. If the ionized

calcium is low tetanic spasms or convulsions may occur and may be fatal. If the plasma ionized calcium is high cardiac function is disturbed and calcium may be deposited in the kidney or other tissues.

Physico-chemical Factors

If EDTA (ethylene-diamine tetra-acetate, a calcium-complexing agent) is injected intravenously into man or the dog the plasma calcium falls rapidly but returns to a normal value within a few hours. If EDTA is given after removal of the parathyroid glands the plasma calcium again returns to the preinfusion value but not so rapidly (Fig. 18.14). Thus chemical equilibrium between the labile part of the bone mineral and the interstitial fluid, quite independent of the parathyroid glands, keeps the plasma calcium up to 1·7 to 2·0 mmol/l. In intact animals parathyroid hormone is responsible for maintaining the normal serum calcium level of around 2·5 mmol/l.

Parathyroid Hormone (PTH)

Source. The parathyroid glands develop from the third and fourth pharyngeal pouches of the embryo. They usually lie in the neck adjacent to the posterior surface of the thyroid gland. As a rule they consist of four oval bodies about 6 mm long each weighing 20 to 50 mg, but they are variable in number, size and

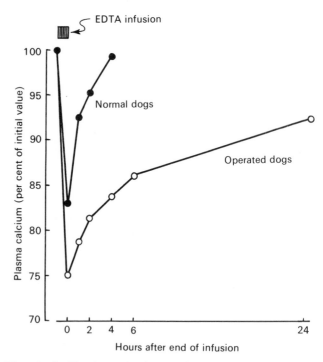

Fig. 18.14 The change in plasma calcium concentration induced by one-hour infusions of EDTA into normal dogs (●) and dogs whose thyroid and parathyroid glands had been removed (○). The intact animal restores its plasma calcium to normal very quickly but the plasma calcium in the operated animal returns only slowly to the base line figures. (Data of P. H. Sanderson *et al.* (1960) *Journal of Clinical Investigation*, 39, 662–670.)

position; accessory parathyroid tissue is not uncommon lower in the neck or even in the thorax. The secretory cells are of two types, the *chief cells* with large nuclei nearly filling the cell and *oxyntic cells* with small nuclei and acidophil granules in the cytoplasm. The function of the oxyntic cells is not known. Normal glands also contain a substantial proportion of fat cells.

The vascular supply is rich but the nervous connexions are scanty. Secretory nerve fibres have never been demonstrated and transplanted glands can function in the absence of all nervous connexions.

H₂N—Ala—Val—Ser—Glu—Ile—Gln—Phe—Met—

His—Asn—Leu—Gly—Lys—His—Leu—Ser—Ser—Met—

Glu—Arg—Val—Glu—Trp—Leu—Arg—Lys—Lys—Leu—

Gln—Asp—Val—His—Asn—Phe—Val—Ala—Leu—Gly—Ala—

Ser—Ile—Ala—Tyr—Arg—Asp—Gly—Ser—Ser—Gln—Arg—Pro—

Arg—Lys—Lys—Glu—Asp—Asn—Val—Leu—Val—Glu—Ser—His—

Gln—Lys—Ser—Leu—Gly—Glu—Ala—Asp—Lys—Ala—Asp—Val—

Asp—Val—Leu—Ile—Lys—Ala—Lys—Pro—Gln—COOH

Fig. 18.15 Amino acid sequence of bovine PTH. The fragment 1 to 34 (heavy type) is biologically active, *in vivo* and *in vitro*, on both bone and kidney receptors (J. T. Potts *et al.* (1971) *American Journal of Medicine*, 50, 639–649).

Chemistry. Bovine PTH is a single-chain polypeptide, containing 84 amino acids (Fig. 18.15); it has a molecular weight of about 8500. Human parathyroid hormone has a similar structure but its full sequence has not yet been determined. PTH (like insulin) is formed as a larger precursor molecule, PrePTH, a peptide with 115 amino acid residues. This is split to give first ProPTH with 90 residues and then PTH itself with 84. In the tissues PTH is broken down to smaller polypeptide fragments, some of which are biologically

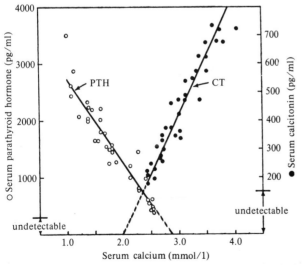

Fig. 18.16 Serum levels of immunoreactive calcitonin and para-thyroid hormone in relation to the plasma calcium in a pig. (*After* C. D. Arnaud *et al.* (1970), pp. 95–101, in *Calcitonin 1969* ed. S. Taylor. London: Heinemann.)

active; these can be found in the plasma and make assays for plasma PTH difficult.

Secretion. Assay of PTH by radioimmunoassay has demonstrated that the secretion of PTH increases linearly with the fall in the plasma calcium (Fig. 18.16). PTH secretion apparently ceases when the plasma calcium exceeds 3·0 mmol/1. Plasma ionized calcium appears to be the sole stimulus for PTH secretion. Since the half-life of the hormone in the blood is about 20 minutes, changes in hormone secretion may play an important part in the minute to minute regulation of the plasma calcium.

Actions. The principal action of parathyroid hormone in physiological concentrations is to increase calcium reabsorption in the renal tubule. Higher concentrations of PTH in the plasma are associated with increased bone resorption by osteoclasts and osteocytes, increased calcium absorption in the intestine and reduced phosphate reabsorption by the renal tubule. The action on the intestine is not a direct action of PTH, but is mediated by 1,25-dihydroxycholecalciferol whose production by kidney is promoted by PTH (see below). PTH operates through adenyl cyclase and cyclic AMP (Chap. 28).

Disorders of PTH secretion. Excessive or deficient secretion of PTH produces well-recognized clinical disorders.

An excess of PTH (*hyperparathyroidism*) results in hypercalcaemia, because of increased calcium reabsorption in the renal tubule, increased calcium absorption in the intestine and, in some patients, increased bone resorption. In a few cases the patient is severely ill with confusion, drowsiness and eventually coma with plasma calcium values as high as 5·0 mmol/1. More often the plasma calcium is lower; the condition may be diagnosed when the patient has developed urinary calculi, or be found 'by accident' in a screening procedure. A few patients complain of bone pains and fractures, the results of the bone demineralization. Figure 18.17 shows the characteristic radiological abnormality seen in such patients.

Hyperparathyroidism is not the only cause of hyper-calcaemia. Other frequent causes include neoplasms with secondary deposits in bone, neoplasms secreting a PTH-like substance and an excessive intake of vitamin D. Hyper-calcaemia of any cause is characterized by thirst, tiredness, weakness and, if severe, coma and death. Untreated hyper-calcaemia causes renal damage.

Deficient parathyroid activity (*hypoparathyroidism*) is uncommon but most cases result from removal of the parathyroid glands, or damage to their blood supply, during surgical operations on the thyroid. Hypoparathyroidism is characterized by hypocalcaemia; some patients may have no symptoms, others may be depressed or may develop muscular spasms in the hands and feet known as *carpo-pedal spasm* or *tetany* (Fig. 18.18). A few patients, notably children, may have generalized convulsions, and occasionally infants with tetany get a spasm of the laryngeal muscles leading to difficulty in breathing (*laryngismus stridulus*). In the early stages of tetany sensory phenomena are present, such as widespread tingling feelings and sensations of heat and flushing (*paraesthesiae*). Two tests can be used to demonstrate the neuromuscular hyperexcitability before tetany occurs (*latent tetany*). In Chvostek's test tapping over the facial nerve in front of the ear produces twitching of the facial muscles. In Trousseau's test carpal spasm is induced by inflating a sphygmomanometer cuff round the upper arm to a pressure exceeding the systolic blood pressure and maintaining the occlusion for 2 minutes. Ischaemia of nerve trunks increases their excitability and reinforces the effect of a low concentration of calcium in the plasma.

The factor most closely related to the onset of tetany is a reduction in the plasma concentration of ionized calcium. This may be caused by a reduced total plasma calcium or by a reduced proportion of ionized calcium due to alkalosis caused by vomiting or by over-ventilation.

Apart from hypoparathyroidism hypocalcaemia may be caused by vitamin D deficiency (rickets in children and osteomalacia in adults), by renal failure and by a rare inherited disorder, *pseudohypoparathyroidism*, in which there is a defect in the cyclic AMP-mediated response of the tissues to PTH.

Calcitonin

In 1962 Copp and his colleagues produced evidence for the existence of a hormone which lowered the plasma calcium. He called it calcitonin. Subsequent work has not only confirmed that the hormone exists but also led to the determination of its chemical structure. The hormone is a lipophilic single chain polypeptide of 32 amino acids (Fig. 18.19).

$$\text{S} \underline{\hspace{8em}} \text{S}$$
$$\text{NH}_2\text{—Cys—Gly—Asn—Leu—Ser—Thr—Cys—Met—Leu—Gly—}$$
$$\text{Thr—Tyr—Thr—Gln—Asp—Phe—Asn—Lys—Phe—His—Thr—Phe—}$$
$$\text{Pro—Gln—Thr—Ala—Leu—Gly—Val—Gly—Ala—Pro—CONH}_2$$

Fig. 18.19 Amino acid sequence of human calcitonin.

In mammals calcitonin is secreted by the parafollicular cells (C cells) of the thyroid gland (Fig. 18.20). These cells contain granules which increase in number during a period of prolonged hypocalcaemia and calcitonin has been identified within them by the fluorescent antibody technique.

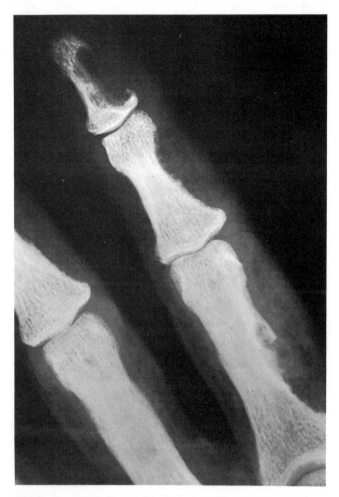

Fig. 18.17 Bone resorption (*subperiosteal erosions*) in the phalanges of the hand in a patient with severe hyperparathyroidism. (*Courtesy of O. L. M. Bijvoet.*)

Fig. 18.18 Position of the hand in tetany. (*From* Paterson, 1975)

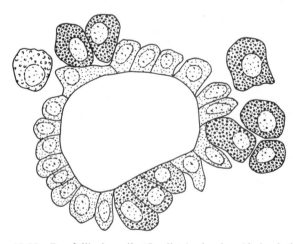

Fig. 18.20 Parafollicular cells (C-cells) in the thyroid gland of a 35 day-old puppy. The parafollicular cells are larger than the follicular cells and, with a silver nitrate stain, are seen to have many argentaffin granules. Some parafollicular cells lie in the follicular walls but most form clusters in the interfollicular spaces. Human parafollicular cells are less readily demonstrated. (*After* J. F. Nonidez (1932) *American Journal of Anatomy*, 49, 479–505.)

Calcitonin secretion is stimulated by hypercalcaemia (Fig. 18.16) and its best documented action is the inhibition of PTH-induced bone resorption (Fig. 18.21). Calcitonin also reduces bone resorption even in the absence of PTH, and reduces the reabsorption of calcium, phosphate and sodium in the renal tubules. Recently calcitonin release has also been shown to be stimulated by gastrin, cholecystokinin-pancreozymin and glucagon. Thus as calcium is absorbed from a meal, there is little or no rise in serum calcium.

Calcitonin excess has been described in patients with medullary carcinomas of the thyroid. Surprisingly these patients seldom have hypocalcaemia probably because of compensatory action of the parathyroid glands. There is as yet no evidence of a syndrome due to calcitonin deficiency.

1,25-Dihydroxycholecalciferol

This hormone is a metabolite of vitamin D_3 (p. 31) and it is now clear that the physiological actions of vitamin D result from its conversion to 1,25-dihydroxycholecalciferol (1,25-DHCC) and perhaps other metabolites.

Secretion. 1,25-DHCC is produced by the renal tubules and its output is regulated by the plasma calcium. When the plasma calcium is low 1,25-DHCC is the principal vitamin D metabolite produced. When the plasma calcium is high the principal metabolite is 24,25-dihydroxycholecalciferol (24,25-DHCC) which has little influence on calcium absorption in the intestine (Fig. 18.22). The production of 1,25-DHCC is promoted by parathyroid hormone, by low levels of phosphate in the plasma and by growth hormone and prolactin from the pituitary gland (Chap. 28). The interrelationship of PTH and vitamin D metabolism is illustrated by the fact that in hypoparathyroidism large doses of vitamin D (1 to 3 mg daily) are needed to raise the plasma calcium but the same effect can be achieved with 2 to 4 μg 1,25-DHCC daily.

Actions. The best known site of action of 1,25-DHCC is on the small intestine where it promotes active absorption of calcium. It is likely that it is responsible for the intestinal adaptation to a low calcium diet (p. 282). The mechanism of action of 1,25-DHCC on the mucosal cell is not yet clear; it enters the cell and binds to a protein receptor within the cytoplasm in the same way as do steroid hormones (Chap. 28). The hormone-receptor complex is taken up by the cell nucleus and promotes the synthesis of a calcium-binding protein.

1,25-DHCC probably also has actions on bone, to stimulate osteoclasts, on the proximal convoluted tubules of the kidney, on the parathyroid glands and on muscle cells. The physiological role of 24,25-DHCC is not yet understood but it probably plays a part in the normal mineralization of bone.

An adequate supply of growth hormone (Chap. 28) from the anterior pituitary is necessary for proliferation of the cells of the epiphyseal cartilage and, therefore, for the growth in length of a long bone. In hypophysectomized animals epiphyseal activity is much reduced or even absent; it can be restored by administration of growth hormone. There is no evidence that this hormone influences the time of closure of the epiphyses. Excessive activity of the thyroid gland is associated with loss of bone; the rate of bone formation is increased but the rate of bone resorption is increased to a greater extent. Increased loss of bone is a feature of mineralocorticoid excess whether due to excessive activity of the adrenal cortex or to steroid therapy.

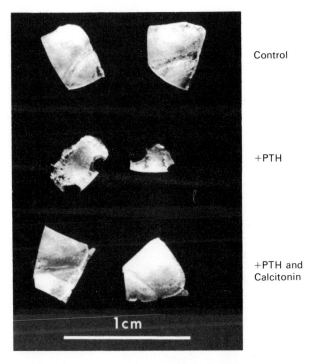

Control

+PTH

+PTH and Calcitonin

Fig. 18.21 Mouse calvaria in tissue culture to show the effect of calcitonin on the bone resorption induced by parathyroid hormone. (*Courtesy of Jennifer Nisbet.*)

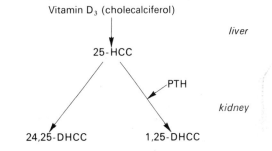

Fig. 18.22 Pathways of vitamin D_3 metabolism to show the renal conversion of 25-hydroxycholecalciferol (25-HCC) either to 1,25-dihydroxycholecalciferol (1,25-DHCC) or to 24,25-dihdroxycholecalciferol (24,25-DHCC).

REFERENCES

Ascenzi A, Bell G H 1972 Bone as a mechanical engineering problem. In: Bourne G H (ed) The biochemistry and physiology of bone, 2nd edn. Academic Press, New York, vol 1, pp. 311–352
Avioli L V, Krane S M (eds) 1977–1978 Metabolic bone disease. Academic Press, New York

Bourne G H (ed) 1972–1976. The biochemistry and physiology of bone, 2nd edn. Academic Press, New York
Boyle J A, Buchanan W W 1971 Clinical rheumatology. Blackwell, Oxford
Brookes M 1971 The blood supply of bone. Butterworths, London
Duncan C J (ed) 1976 Calcium in biological systems. University Press, Cambridge
Lawson D E M (ed) 1978 Vitamin D. Academic Press, London
Nordin B E C (ed) 1976 Calcium, phosphate and magnesium metabolism: clinical physiology and diagnostic procedures. Churchill Livingstone, Edinburgh
Paterson C R 1975 Metabolic disorders of bone. Blackwell, Oxford
Rasmussen H, Bordier P 1974 The physiological and cellular basis of metabolic bone disease. Williams & Wilkins, Baltimore
Serafini-Fracassini A, Smith J W 1974 The structure and biochemistry of cartilage. Churchill Livingstone, Edinburgh
Sokoloff L (ed) 1978 The joints and synovial fluid. Academic Press, New York
Talmage R V, Owen M, Parsons J A (eds) 1975 Calcium regulating hormones. Excerpta Medica, Amsterdam
Vaughan J M 1975 The physiology of bone, 2nd edn. Oxford University Press, London
Wadkins C L, Luben R, Thomas M, Humphreys R 1974 Physical biochemistry of calcification. Clinical orthopaedics 99: 246–266

19 The Nervous System

The nervous system can be divided into *central* and *peripheral* portions. The central nervous system consists of the brain and the spinal cord. The peripheral part has 43 pairs of nerves which leave the cerebrospinal axis and pass to the various organs of the body. The peripheral nerves contain fibres of two kinds, *afferent* or *sensory* fibres carrying nerve impulses from the periphery to the central nervous system and *efferent* or *motor* fibres carrying impulses from the central nervous system to muscles and glands and other organs.

The nervous system is the main co-ordinator of the activities of the body. The afferent nerves bring to the central nervous system information about the external world from receptors which are sensitive to stimuli such as light, sound, temperature, or pressure, and also information about the internal state of the body, for example tension in muscles or distension in viscera. As a consequence of the arrival of these impulses the central nervous system sends impulses along the efferent nerves to produce appropriate movements of muscles or secretion of glands. The pathways taken by impulses after they arrive at the central nervous system are very complex but the basic principle is that impulses are handed on from nerve cell to nerve cell until finally they emerge in an efferent nerve to produce a response in an effector organ such as a muscle or a gland. Sometimes this process rises to conscious levels but many of the activities of the body are regulated without our being aware of them. These activities controlled by the nervous system are called *reflex actions*, or simply *reflexes*, and the pathways followed in the nervous system along afferent, junctional and efferent neurones are called *reflex arcs*.

In man the central nervous system contains 10 000 million neurones, all formed by the sixth month of intrauterine life; no mitotic figures can be found after birth. If tritiated thymidine, which is incorporated into the DNA of cells about to divide, is given intracerebrally to rats a few neurones are labelled. But this small production of neurones—if it does occur in man as well as the rat—is too small to be of importance in recovery from cerebral injuries. Neurones are described further in Chapter 20.

The neuroglia. Each neurone of the central nervous system in man is surrounded by about ten glial cells, their delicately folded membranes covering the neurone except at the synaptic knobs. Neuroglial cells make up a quarter to one-half of the volume of brain tissue. When the adult number of neurones is reached the glial cells multiply rapidly especially in the last months of intrauterine life and the first 18 months of extrauterine life. If the diet of the infant rat is deficient during the period of glial multiplication its brain may be permanently

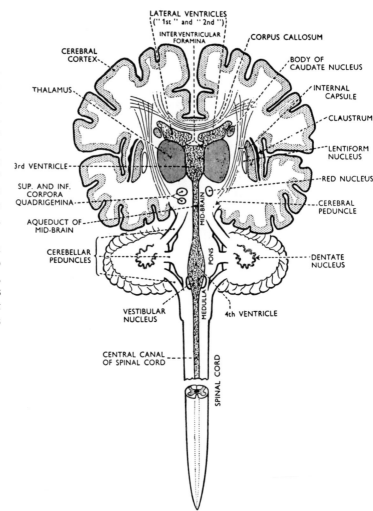

Fig. 19.2 Diagrammatic section through the cerebral hemispheres, brain-stem and spinal cord to show the approximate relationships of the more important parts. Some of the structures are shown on one side only and the two halves of the cerebellum have been separated as they were in early development. The caudate and lentiform nuclei together form the corpus striatum. (*By courtesy of J. D. B. MacDougall.*)

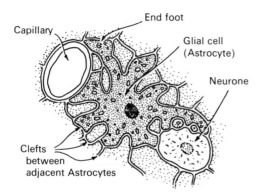

Fig. 19.1 Sketch of neurone-glial-capillary arrangement as shown by the electron microscope. An astrocyte is interposed between the endothelium of the capillary and the neurone. The cells, axons, dendrites and astrocytes are tightly packed, with narrow clefts (greatly exaggerated here) of about 15 nm between them. (*From* S. W. Kuffler (1967) *Proceedings of the Royal Society* B, **168**, 8.)

damaged. In spite of much research it is not possible to state definitely that undernutrition of human infants results in low intelligence but some low birth-weight babies have poor intelligence in later life. It is probable that substances are transferred from blood to neurone through the glial cells, particularly the astrocytes (Fig. 19.1). In tissue culture, only those neurones surrounded by glia survive for any length of time. Glial cells are rich in glycogen, contain only a tenth of the RNA of the neurones but have more lipid and very much more carbonic anhydrase.

Glial cells, unlike neurones, can multiply throughout life. The oligodendrocytes form myelin like the Schwann cells in the peripheral nerves; the microglia (p. 128) phagocytose degenerating neurones. The membrane potential of glial cells, about 90 mV, is due to the difference in potassium concentration between the interior of the cell and that in the narrow clefts between them. Depolarizing currents passed through glial cells do not make them discharge.

Cerebral Circulation

The importance of an adequate blood supply to the brain scarcely needs stressing. Arrest of the cerebral circulation for more than about 5 seconds is followed by unconsciousness, and

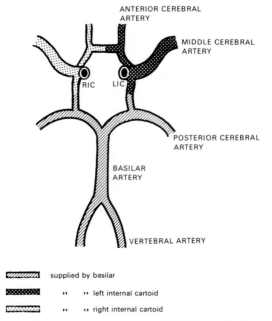

ANTERIOR CEREBRAL ARTERY

MIDDLE CEREBRAL ARTERY

RIC   LIC

POSTERIOR CEREBRAL ARTERY

BASILAR ARTERY

VERTEBRAL ARTERY

⬜ supplied by basilar

⬛ ,, ,, left internal cartoid

⬚ ,, ,, right internal cartoid

Fig. 19.3 The arterial circle (circle of Willis) at the base of the human brain. The internal carotid arteries, LIC and RIC, supply a larger volume of the brain than do the vertebral arteries. In normal persons the left vertebral artery is often larger than the right which may be very small; one or other posterior communicating artery may be narrow or absent. In fact in only 50 per cent of normal persons is the arterial circle present as in the diagram. Movements of the head and neck cause considerable changes in blood flow in the vertebral arteries because they pass through the transverse processes of the atlas and because they are relatively fixed as they enter the foramen magnum. Since the lumen of the internal carotid artery can be constricted from 30 mm² to 5 mm² with only an insignificant reduction in the flow, this important artery could be said to be much larger than is haemodynamically necessary. (*After* R. Brain (1957) *Lancet*, ii, 857–862.)

cerebral ischaemia of longer than 3 minutes causes irreparable damage to the grey matter of the cortex, the Purkinje cells of the cerebellum and the cells of the basal nuclei.

Since, in man, there are almost no anastomoses between the branches of the internal and external carotid arteries, the blood supply to the brain depends on the arterial circle at the base of the brain within the cranial cavity, into which blood is brought by the two internal carotid arteries and by the two vertebral arteries (Fig. 19.3). Studies in rabbits, in which the arrangement of these vessels resembles that in man, have shown that the internal carotid artery and the basilar artery share the blood supply to each cerebral hemisphere in such a way that there is normally, in a steady state, no interchange of blood between them.

The arterial circle clearly provides for continued perfusion of all parts of the brain even if a large vessel should become blocked. Digital compression of one common carotid artery in man normally causes a fall in intraocular tension on the same side. If it does not the blood flow in the artery is deficient and the eye and the brain must be supplied through an anastomotic channel. In the arterial circle, 'the tides of the blood ebb and flow from moment to moment to achieve the sovereign purpose of making available a constant supply of blood to every part of the brain' (R. Brain). Further, the branches of the arterial circle, that is the anterior, middle and posterior cerebral arteries, intercommunicate through their small ramifications over the cortex. The cerebral vascular system can be outlined in man by injecting a radio-opaque solution into a carotid artery.

The cerebral vessels have a prominent internal elastic lamina but their muscle coat is less well-developed than that of arteries of comparable size elsewhere in the body. The grey matter is richly supplied with capillaries but the white matter is less vascular. The venous sinuses of the dura carry away blood from the brain; in addition they also receive cerebrospinal fluid through the arachnoid villi (p. 292).

Cerebral blood flow. The rate of blood flow through the brain can be measured in man by causing the subject to breathe nitrous oxide and measuring the concentration of the gas in samples of blood taken from the internal carotid artery and the jugular bulb over a period of 10 minutes. Application of Fick's principle (p. 161) shows that approximately 55 ml of blood flows through 100 g brain per minute. If the weight of the adult brain is 1400 g the total flow is about 770 ml per min or 15 per cent of the cardiac output. The carotid-venous oxygen difference is about 6 ml per 100 ml of blood. The oxygen consumption is therefore $(55/100) \times 6$ or 3·3 ml oxygen per 100 g per minute, which is not very different from the requirement of muscles during active work. The whole brain therefore consumes about 46 ml oxygen per minute, equivalent to an energy utilization of about 20 W. The oxygen consumption varies relatively little over a wide range of arterial P_{CO_2} and P_{O_2}. Infants with their large brains require a relatively large proportion of the total oxygen consumption. Cerebral blood flow is reduced in the elderly.

It is, of course, likely that even if the total blood flow remains constant there may be considerable regional differences in blood flow through different parts of the brain. The blood flow through the baboon's cerebral cortex can be measured through the intact skull by injecting the γ-emitter ^{133}Xe in saline into the internal carotid artery and determining its clearance rate

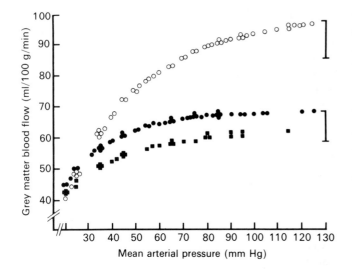

Fig. 19.4 The black circles show the relationship in the baboon between mean arterial pressure and blood flow in the grey matter when the nerves are intact and when the P_{CO_2} and P_{O_2} are kept constant. The curve of flow is nearly flat between 60 and 130 mm Hg—this is the range of autoregulation. The open circles show the effect of sympathectomy; there is no flat region of this curve. Stimulation of the sympathetic (black squares) brought the relationship back to normal. (I. M. James, R. A. Millar & M. J. Purves (1969) *Circulation Research*, 25, 80.)

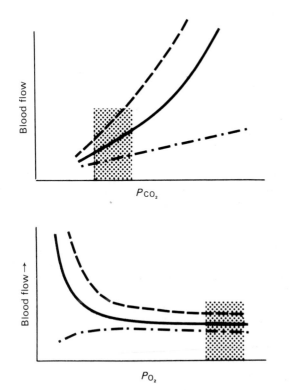

Fig. 19.5 Changes in the cerebral blood flow in response to changes in P_{CO_2} and P_{O_2}. The dotted area indicates the normal values in each case. The continuous line shows the responses with all nerves intact. Interrupted lines (— — —) indicate changes seen when the constrictor pathway is cut and —•—•— indicates the changes seen when the dilator fibres are cut. (*By courtesy of M. J. Purves.*)

with scintillation counters placed over the skull. The decay curve shows a fast component and a slow component representing respectively the flow through grey and white matter. When the P_{O_2} and arterial blood pressure are within the normal range the mean cerebral blood flow is 52 ml per 100 g per min; the flow in the grey matter is 72 ml per 100 g per min and in the white matter 19 ml per 100 g per min.

Mental activity does not increase the cerebral oxygen consumption or blood flow as estimated by the nitrous oxide method. This technique gives the sum of the flow in all regions of the brain. However if ^{133}Xe injected into the carotid artery is used local blood flow can be estimated by means of collimeters at different sites on the skull. In this way Ingvar and his colleagues have measured the flow in 32 regions of one human hemisphere. In normal subjects a verbal test gave an increase in blood flow up to 25 per cent in the frontal region; a visual task increased the blood flow in the occipital, frontal and parietal regions; reading caused an increase in blood flow in the post-central and other areas.

The skull of the human baby is not completely ossified and at each beat of the heart the pulsations of the brain are transmitted to the anterior fontanelle. When he cries the venous pressure rises and the increase of intracerebral pressure bulges the anterior fontanelle. In the adult, just as in the child, the intracranial pressure rises when violent expiratory efforts are made. It falls in the standing position because the pressure in the veins falls (to negative values) and venous drainage is facilitated. Blood entering the skull at each systole displaces a similar amount of blood from the veins, but if there is a prolonged increase of arterial pressure cerebro-spinal fluid may also be forced out of the skull.

Control of cerebral blood flow. Cerebral blood flow remains remarkably constant even when the mean arterial pressure varies over the range 60 to 130 mm Hg (Fig. 19.4). Only when the arterial or, more strictly, the difference between arterial and venous pressure (perfusion pressure) falls below 60 mm Hg or when the cardiac output falls below 3 litres per minute does the cerebral circulation become insufficient. The process whereby a relatively high blood flow is maintained as pressure is reduced from physiological levels to about 60 mm Hg is known as *autoregulation* and appears to depend upon two factors; one, an intrinsic factor which probably represents a response of vascular smooth muscle, is comparatively slow being complete in 30 to 40 seconds. The other is neural and is mediated by the dilator pathway carried for part of its length by the VIIth cranial nerve. If this pathway is interrupted or if atropine is given, there is no longer vasodilatation and blood flow falls to low levels when the animal becomes hypotensive. The constancy of flow at high pressure (> 130 mm Hg) appears to depend largely upon an intact sympathetic pathway (Fig. 19.4).

The cerebral vascular responses to hypoxia and hypercapnia also depend upon intrinsic and neural factors. If the constrictor fibres are cut, the flow response to both hypoxia and hypercapnia is enhanced. If the dilator pathway is cut, the response to hypercapnia is markedly reduced and the response to hypoxia is largely abolished. If both pathways are cut, or if all the peripheral arterial chemoreceptors are denervated, blood flow may actually fall in response to hypoxia but there is evidence of a slow residual intrinsic response to CO_2 (Fig. 19.5).

From this we may deduce that in the intact animal the

vascular response to changes in arterial pressure and P_{CO_2} is determined by alterations in the balance of constrictor and dilator neural activity superimposed upon an intrinsic smooth muscle response.

Metabolism of the Nervous System

By comparing the arterio-venous differences in oxygen, carbon dioxide and glucose it has been found that the RQ of the brain is very nearly 1 and that the oxygen utilized is equivalent to the amount of glucose which disappears, that is 4·9 mg per 100 g per min. Brain tissue uses glucose almost exclusively as a source of energy, the glycogen content being too low, about 0·1 per cent, to make an important contribution. The brain also uses small quantities of two ketones, 3-hydroxybutyrate and acetoacetate.

In some conditions in which consciousness is depressed the oxygen consumption of the brain is reduced; for example, hypoglycaemia reduces it by 20 per cent, diabetic coma by 50 per cent and surgical anaesthesia by 40 per cent. But sleep reduces consumption by only 3 per cent. Conversely, in experiments on cats it was found that oxygen consumption by the cerebral cortex increases by as much as 80 per cent when the cortex is stimulated electrically.

In the fetus and infant the synthesis of new proteins in the brain is quite rapid as might be expected from the rapid growth of the brain. Synthesis slows down gradually and in adult life it is much the same as in other tissues.

The water-soluble proteins of brain tissue are similar to those in other tissues and have a comparable turnover but the lipoproteins of the myelin sheath contain protein with a turnover rate so low that they can be regarded as almost metabolically inert.

Nervous tissue is peculiar in being relatively isolated from the rest of the body because of the difficulty with which many substances, including amino acids, pass into it from the blood, and in its very limited ability to store carbohydrate in the form of glycogen. The brain's dependence on glucose makes it very sensitive to hypoglycaemia. Utilization of glucose for energy production in the brain follows the tricarboxylic acid cycle but only about 25 per cent of the glucose used by the brain is oxidized in this way. The remaining 75 per cent is used for the formation of amino acids, chiefly glutamic acid and aspartic acid, which are used partly for protein synthesis but mainly for oxidation by pathways which exist in the nerve cell for the production of energy.

The concentration of free amino acids in brain tissue is very high, eight times higher than in blood plasma. Of this pool of amino acids about 15 per cent consists of γ-amino butyric acid (GABA) formed by decarboxylation of glutamate. GABA is important as an inhibitory transmitter (p. 323).

Brain tissue has the greatest capability for cyclic AMP synthesis of any tissue and adenyl cyclase is stimulated by transmitters such as noradrenaline and dopamine. In addition cyclic AMP formation can be stimulated by histamine, 5-hydroxytryptamine, drugs such as ouabain and by high plasma potassium levels. The precise role of cyclic AMP at nerve endings is not known but it is likely to be involved in the stimulation of protein phosphokinases and so in the turnover of phosphoproteins in cell membranes.

CEREBROSPINAL FLUID

The central nervous system is covered by three membranes or meninges (Fig. 19.6). Beneath the tough *dura mater* is the narrow *subdural space*, containing a very small amount of tissue fluid. This space is bounded internally by the *arachnoid mater* which is separated from the *pia mater* by the *subarachnoid space* containing cerebrospinal fluid (CSF). The subarachnoid space does not communicate with the subdural space but is continuous with the ventricular system of the brain through medial and lateral apertures in the roof of the fourth ventricle. The arachnoid and pia covering the brain and spinal cord are connected by strands of arachnoid tissue; the pia closely invests the surface of the brain and dips down into the fissures and sulci. At the base of the brain the two membranes are widely separated and form large spaces known as cisterns, the largest being the *cerebello-medullary cistern* or *cisterna magna* (Fig. 19.7).

The cerebral blood vessels passing through the subarachnoid space are invested with two layers of arachnoid. The branches that penetrate into the brain are accompanied by extensions of the subarachnoid space. There are similar extensions of the subarachnoid space along the cranial and spinal nerve roots.

A sample of CSF can be obtained in man by passing a long needle between the third and fourth lumbar spinous processes into the spinal subarachnoid space (*lumbar puncture*) (Fig. 19.8). The subarachnoid space may also be entered by passing a needle through the atlanto-occipital membrane into the

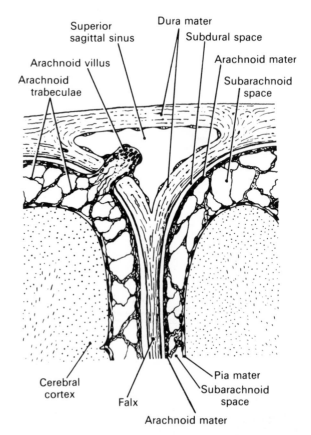

Fig. 19.6 Coronal section through the vertex to show the meninges. (*After* L. H. Weed (1923) *American Journal of Anatomy*, 21, 191.)

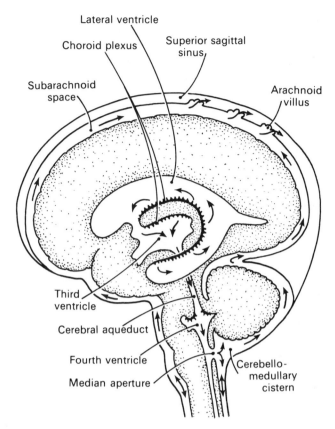

Fig. 19.7   The circulation of the cerebrospinal fluid. (*After* A. J. Gatz (1970) *Manter's Essentials of Clinical Neuroanatomy and Neurophysiology*. Philadelphia: Davis.)

cisterna magna (*cisternal puncture*). This procedure is seldom used to obtain CSF because it is less safe than lumbar puncture.

Formation. Most, but probably not all, of the cerebrospinal fluid is formed by the secretory activity of the cells of the choroid plexuses. These are rich networks of blood vessels projecting into the cavities of the lateral ventricles and third ventricle which are covered only by the pia mater and ependyma. The choroid plexuses are supplied with blood by anterior and posterior choroidal arteries which arise from the internal carotid and posterior cerebral arteries. It is possible that a small quantity of CSF is normally formed by ultrafiltration from brain parenchyma.

The CSF formed in the lateral ventricles passes into the third ventricle by the inter-ventricular foramina and then by the cerebral aqueduct to the fourth ventricle, from which it escapes by three foramina into the subarachnoid space round the brain and spinal cord (Fig. 19.7). Blockage of any of the foramina causes the ventricles upstream to dilate. Blockage of the cerebral aqueduct, for example, causes distension of the third ventricle and the two lateral ventricles (*internal hydrocephalus*). Cerebrospinal fluid is produced continuously at a rate of 0·5 ml per minute (720 ml per 24 h). Since the total volume of CSF is 120 ml the whole of the CSF must be exchanged every four hours or so. Further, since the pressure of the CSF remains relatively constant the production must be balanced by an equal absorption of fluid. The movement of CSF from the lateral ventricles into the ventricular system and subarachnoid space is no doubt helped by the pulsations of the

choroid plexuses and is maintained by its continuous absorption as it passes over the cortex and down the spinal cord.

Reabsorption. Cerebrospinal fluid is absorbed mainly into the venous system through the arachnoid villi, invaginations of the subarachnoid space into the large venous sinuses of the cranium (Fig. 19.6). The arachnoid villi contain a labyrinth of cells separating CSF and blood. The electron microscope has shown that these cells contain large vacuoles opening into the CSF (Fig. 19.9). When the pressure in the subarachnoid space is greater than the pressure in the superior sagittal sinus, the vacuoles open into the blood and CSF passes down the pressure gradient through the vacuoles into the blood. When the subarachnoid pressure is lower than that in the sinus, reflux of blood is prevented by collapse of the vacuoles. It is likely that a rise in CSF pressure sufficient to operate this mechanism occurs at each arterial pulse. The venous sinuses remain patent in spite of the low hydrostatic pressure within them because they are enclosed between layers of tough dural membrane.

Some CSF must be absorbed elsewhere because in chronic obstructive hydrocephalus the increase in brain size per day is only 2 per cent of the amount of fluid formed per day. CSF is probably absorbed into the venous system in the extensions of the subarachnoid space along the roots of the spinal nerves, into the spinal veins and through the ependymal linings of the ventricles. Absorption of CSF into the blood is favoured by the colloid osmotic pressure of the plasma protein, since CSF normally contains very little protein.

Composition. Normal CSF is a clear colourless fluid, of specific gravity 1005, containing not more than 5 lymphocytes per mm³. The pH, about 7·33, remains nearly constant in the presence of large changes of plasma pH. There is a potential difference of about +5 mV between CSF and blood; the maintenance of this difference must involve an active transport mechanism. The chemical composition of CSF is shown in Table 19.10. The protein content in the lumbar region (400 mg/litre) is greater than in the ventricles (100 mg/litre) or in the cisterna magna (200 mg/litre).

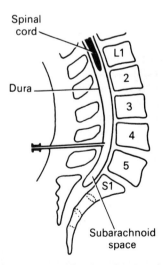

Fig. 19.8   Lumbar puncture. The space between lumbar vertebrae 3 and 4 is most commonly used but an alternative is the space between 4 and 5. The cord is out of danger but the nerves of the cauda equina are sometimes encountered.

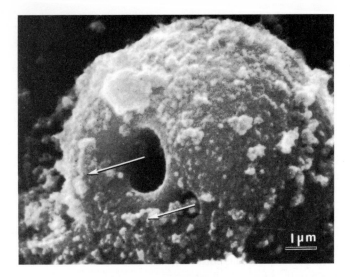

Fig. 19.9 Scanning electron micrograph of a giant vacuole in a mesothelial cell of an arachnoid villus. Two openings are seen through which tracer material (colloidally suspended Thorotrast) is passing. (*From* Tripathi, R. 1974 Brain Research, **80**, 503–506.

Table 19.10 Comparison of the chemical composition of blood plasma and cerebrospinal fluid.

	Blood plasma	Cerebrospinal fluid
Protein	60–80 g/l	200–400 mg/l
Urea	2·5–6·5 mmol/l	2·0–7·0 mmol/l
Glucose (fasting)	3·0–5·0 mmol/l	2·5–4·5 mmol/l
Sodium	136–148 mmol/l	144–152 mmol/l
Potassium	3·8–5·0 mmol/l	2·0–3·0 mmol/l
Calcium	2·2–2·6 mmol/l	1·1–1·3 mmol/l
Chloride	95–105 mmol/l	123–128 mmol/l
Bicarbonate	24–32 mmol/l	24–32 mmol/l

Note the higher chloride and lower glucose content of CSF as compared with blood plasma. CSF glucose levels vary with the plasma glucose and are about 70 per cent of the latter. The concentration of calcium in the CSF is similar to that of ionized calcium in plasma.

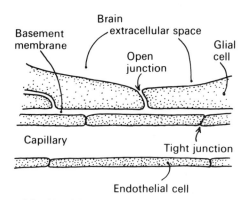

Fig. 19.11 The blood-brain barrier. There is a continuous band of tight junctions between the endothelial cells of the capillaries. The basement membrane does not seem to be a barrier. (*After* Rall, D. P. (1971) In Fundamentals of Drug Metabolism and Drug Disposition ed LaDu, B. N., Mandel, H. G., Way E. I. pp 76–87. Williams & Wilkins, Baltimore.)

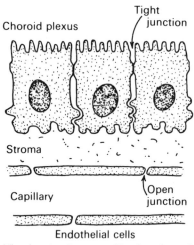

Fig. 19.12 The barrier between blood and cerebrospinal fluid. Drugs and other substances cannot enter the CSF without passing through the cells of the choroid plexus. (*After* Rall, 1971 as in Fig. 19.11.)

The cells of the choroid plexuses seem to exert a selective action on the substances passing through them because the composition of CSF is not exactly that which would be expected for an ultrafiltrate of plasma. Isotope studies suggest that CSF is formed from blood plasma both by secretion and by ultrafiltration. The high chloride content of the CSF can be accounted for by assuming that carbon dioxide enters the glial cells, which are rich in carbonic anhydrase, and produces carbonic acid. The resulting bicarbonate ions are exchanged for chloride ions which then pass into the CSF against a chemical gradient. The greater content of Na^+ and Cl^- makes the CSF slightly hypertonic to blood plasma so that water passes out of the choroid plexuses into the CSF. Both Na^+ and Mg^{2+} seem to be transported actively from blood to CSF.

The composition of the CSF and of the fluid of the extracellular space of the brain is to some extent independent of the composition of the plasma. For example, the plasma K^+ can vary between 2·5 and 8·0 mmol/l with little change in the K^+ concentration in the CSF. Radioisotope investigations show that oxygen, carbon dioxide, alcohol, barbiturates, glucose and lipophilic substances pass quickly into the brain from the blood. Inorganic ions and most highly dissociated compounds, amino acids and sucrose pass very slowly into the brain.

These facts have suggested that there is a barrier composed of a lipid membrane separating the blood from the CSF and the extracellular fluid of the brain. The anatomical basis of the *blood-brain barrier* is shown in Figures 19.11 and 19.12. In the brain the capillaries differ from those elsewhere in the body in that the endothelial cells are joined by tight junctions about the entire periphery of each cell. In other words they are bound together by a 'strip weld' unlike the 'spot welds' of the endothelia of other capillaries. This means that lipophobic substances which do not readily penetrate cell membranes are excluded from the brain unless actively transported through cells. The cells of the choroid plexus also have tight junctions which prevent the passage of substances between cells (Fig. 19.12).

Pressure. If a vertical tube is attached to the lumbar puncture needle the CSF rises about 10 cm when the patient is lying on his side and about 30 cm when he is sitting. A rise of intracranial venous pressure produced by coughing or by digital compression of the internal jugular veins causes the CSF pressure to rise rapidly above these values and the pressure falls rapidly when the compression is removed. The pressure of the CSF in the ventricles may be measured by inserting a catheter attached to a transducer.

Functions. Cerebrospinal fluid acts as a cushion between the soft and delicate brain substance and the rigid cranium. It supports the weight of the brain and distributes the force of blows on the head. The volume of the brain and its blood vessels changes from time to time and such changes take place at the expense of the volume of CSF; when the volume of blood in the brain is increased the volume of CSF is diminished and when the brain degenerates or atrophies there is an increase in the volume of CSF.

Cerebrospinal fluid also acts as a 'sink' in that any solutes which are at a higher concentration in the extracellular fluid of the brain diffuse into the CSF and are carried into the blood at the arachnoid villi. Some substances are transported actively by the cells of the choroid plexus from CSF into the blood. These include 5-hydroxytryptamine, adrenaline and certain drugs such as penicillin.

REFERENCES

Bannister R 1973 Brain's clinical neurology. Oxford University Press

Bito L Z, Davson H, Fenstermacher J D (eds) 1978 The ocular and cerebrospinal fluids. Academic Press, London

Bradbury M 1979 The concept of a blood-brain barrier. Wiley, Chichester

Bray D 1974 The fibrillar proteins of nerve cells. Endeavour 33: 131–136

Brazier M A B 1977 The electrical activity of the nervous system, 4th edn. Pitman, London

Davison A N (ed) 1977 Biochemical correlates of brain structure and function. Academic Press, London

Davidson N (ed) 1976 Neuro-transmitter amino acids. Academic Press, London

Davson H 1976 Review lecture: the blood-brain barrier. Journal of Physiology 255: 1–28

Guyton A C 1977 Structure and function of the nervous system, 2nd edn. Saunders, Eastbourne

Hanley T 1974 'Neuronal fall-out' in the ageing brain: a critical review of the quantitative data. Age and Ageing 3: 133–151

Harper A M 1969 Regulation of cerebral circulation. Scientific Basis of Medicine Annual Review, 60–81

Kuffler S W, Nicholls J G 1976 From neurone to brain: a cellular approach to the function of the nervous system. Freeman, Reading

Legg N J (ed) 1979 Neurotransmitter systems and their clinical disorders. Academic Press, London

Lenman J A R 1975 Clinical neurophysiology. Blackwell, Oxford

Lewin R 1976 The brain's own opiate. New Scientist 69: 13

Lundberg N 1972 Monitoring of the intracranial pressure. In: Critchley M, O'Leary J L, Jennett B (eds) Scientific foundations of neurology. Heinemann, London, p 356–371

Matthews W B, Miller H 1975 Diseases of the nervous system, 2nd edn. Blackwell, Oxford

Oldendorf W H 1974 Blood-brain barrier: permeability to drugs. Annual Review of Pharmacology 14: 239–248

Pasternak T 1974 Cyclic AMP and cyclic GMP. Annual Review of Pharmacology 14: 23–33

Ponte J, Purves M J 1974 The role of the carotid body chemoreceptors and carotid sinus baroreceptors in the control of cerebral blood vessels. Journal of Physiology 237: 315–340

Purves M J 1972 The physiology of the cerebral circulation. Cambridge University Press

Rall D P 1971 Drug entry into brain and cerebrospinal fluid. In: La Du B N, Mandel H G, Way E L (eds) Fundamentals of drug metabolism and drug disposition. Williams & Wilkins, Baltimore, Ch 5, p 76–87

Risberg J, Ingvar D H 1971 Increase in blood flow in cortical association areas during memorization and abstract thinking. European Neurology 6: 236–241

Ryall R W 1979 Mechanisms of drug action on the nervous system. Cambridge texts in the physiological sciences. Cambridge University Press, vol 1

Sokoloff L 1973 Metabolism of ketone bodies by the brain. Annual Review of Medicine 24: 271–279

Tripathi R 1974 Tracing the bulk outflow route of cerebrospinal fluid by transmission and scanning electron microscopy. Brain Research 80: 503–506

Walshe F 1965 Further critical studies in neurology and other essays and addresses. Livingstone, Edinburgh

Watson W E 1974 Physiology of neuroglia. Physiological Reviews 54: 245–271

Watson W E 1976 Cell biology of the brain. Chapman & Hall, London

20 Neurone and Synapse

The nervous system is composed of an enormous number of nerve cells, or *neurones*, which are specially adapted for the handling of information in the form of *nerve impulses*. These impulses pass on from one neurone to another at junctions known as *synapses*. The processes involved in the passage of impulses along peripheral nerves or the fibre tracts of the central nervous system will be considered in the first part of this chapter, and the remainder of the chapter will be devoted to junctional transmission.

The Structure of Nerve Fibres

Each neurone comprises a cell body and a number of attached processes, one of which, usually much longer than the rest, is the *axon* or nerve fibre. No axon can continue to function for more than a short while after being severed from its cell body but nevertheless the cell body does not appear to play a direct role in conduction of the nerve impulse. Vertebrates have two main types of nerve fibre, the larger axons, 1 to 25 μm in diameter being *myelinated* and the smaller ones (under 1 μm) *non-myelinated*. The great size of certain invertebrate (non-myelinated) axons has been extensively exploited by physiologists studying the propagation of nerve impulses. Vertebrate skeletal muscle fibres (10 to 120 μm) have much in common, as far as the spread of electrical activity along them is concerned, with non-myelinated invertebrate nerve fibres.

All nerve fibres consist of a long cylinder of cytoplasm, the *axoplasm*, surrounded by an electrically excitable *nerve membrane*. Since the electrical resistance of the axoplasm is fairly low, by virtue of its content of K^+ and other ions, while

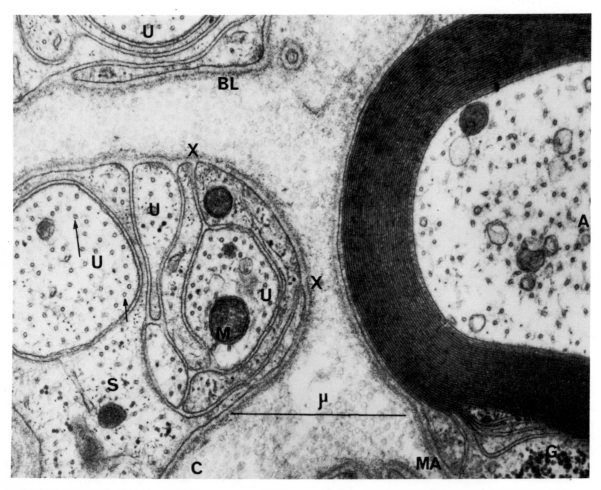

Fig. 20.1 Electronmicrograph of a cross section of a human peripheral nerve. Magnification × 40 000. Part of a myelinated nerve fibre is seen on the right. On the left a Schwann cell surrounds unmyelinated axons. A, Myelinated axon. BL, External or basal lamina. C, Cross-sectioned collagen fibres. G, Glycogen. M, Mitochondrion. MA, Outer mesaxon of myelinated nerve. S, Schwann cell cytoplasm. U, Unmyelinated axon. X, Mesaxons of unmyelinated nerves. Arrows indicate cross-sectioned neurotubules. (Plate 52a of *Cell Structure* by P. G. Toner and Katherine E. Carr, 2nd edition, 1971. Edinburgh: Churchill Livingstone.)

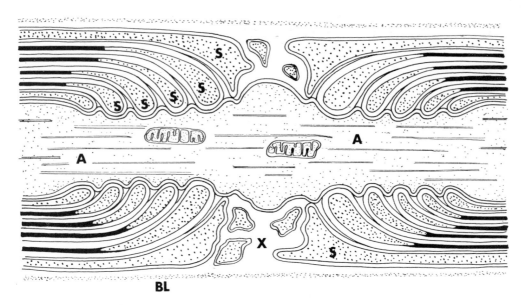

Fig. 20.2 Drawing of a node of Ranvier made from an electromicrograph. The axon, A, is continuous through the node. The myelin sheath, however, terminates on either side, since the node represents the point at which two Schwann cells meet. A narrow gap exists, X, into which small tongues of Schwann cell cytoplasm project. Here the axon is bathed in extracellular fluid, whereas elsewhere it is protected by the Schwann cell and the myelin sheath. The areas of Schwann cell cytoplasm, S, appear in this pattern owing to the termination of successive layers of the myelin sheath as the node is approached. A continuous external or basal lamina, BL, surrounds the entire structure. (Fig. 24 of *Cell Structure* by P. G. Toner and Katharine E. Carr, 2nd edition, 1971. Edinburgh: Churchill Livingstone.)

that of the membrane is relatively high and, since the salt-containing body fluids outside the membrane are again good conductors of electricity, nerve fibres have a structure analogous to that of a shielded electric cable, with a central conducting core surrounded by insulation, outside which is another conducting layer. Many features of the behaviour of nerve fibres depend intimately on their *cable structure*. The layer analogous with the insulation of the cable does not, however, consist solely of the high-resistance nerve membrane, owing to the presence of *Schwann cells*, which are wrapped around the *axis cylinder* in a manner which varies in the different types of nerve fibre. Details of the arrangement of the Schwann cells have become clear with the advent of the electron microscope. The membrane surrounding most types of cell is about 7·5 nm thick, consisting of a pair of dark lines 2·5 nm across separated by a 2·5 nm gap; the membranes of both Schwann cells and nerve axons can readily be made out in electron micrographs. In the non-myelinated fibres of vertebrates the picture is somewhat variable. In some cases (Fig. 20.1) a single Schwann cell may serve as a multi-channel supporting structure partly enveloping a short stretch of a dozen or more tiny axons. Elsewhere, each axon may be more or less closely associated with a Schwann cell of its own, some being deeply embedded within the Schwann cell, and others almost uncovered. In non-myelinated fibres the 10 nm spaces between the Schwann cell membranes and the axon membranes communicate all along the length of the fibres with the extracellular space of the tissue, providing a relatively uniform pathway for the electric current which flows during the passage of an impulse. This pathway can be sufficiently tortuous to prevent ions which move out through the axon membrane in the course of the impulse from mixing quickly with extracellular ions, and an effect of this kind may be important in mammalian C fibres (see p. 300) in the

mechanism of production of after-potentials (see p. 999). However, non-myelinated fibres may be treated as if the external electrical resistance between different points on the outside of the membrane were uniformly low.

In the myelinated nerve fibres of vertebrates, each Schwann cell is responsible for laying down a section of the myelin sheath, by repeatedly enveloping the axis cylinder with many concentric layers of Schwann cell membrane. In an adult myelinated fibre, neighbouring layers of Schwann cell membrane appear to be partly fused together, making a structure whose radial repeat distance is of the order of 17 nm as seen in the electron microscope or as determined by X-ray diffraction studies. Since myelin has a much higher lipid content than cytoplasm, it has a relatively high refractive index, and in unstained preparations has a characteristic glistening white appearance. This accounts for the different appearances of the grey matter of the spinal cord, consisting mainly of nerve cell bodies and supporting tissue, and of the white matter, which is mainly tracts of myelinated nerve fibres; it also accounts for the difference between the white and grey rami of the autonomic nervous system (see p. 400), containing respectively myelinated and non-myelinated nerve fibres.

In a nerve fibre whose outside diameter is 10 μm, each stretch of myelin is about 1000 μm long and 1·3 μm thick, so that the myelin is built up of some 80 double layers of Schwann cell membrane. In larger fibres, the thickness of the myelin and the length of each segment of myelin, are proportionately greater. Between neighbouring segments of myelin there is a very narrow gap, the *node of Ranvier*, under 1 μm in width, where there is no obstacle between the axon membrane and the extracellular fluid (see Figs 20.2 and 20.3). The external electrical resistance between neighbouring nodes of Ranvier is therefore relatively low, whereas the external resistance between any two points on the internodal stretch of membrane

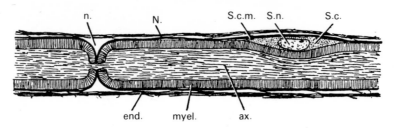

Fig. 20.3 Part of a normal vertebrate nerve fibre. The Schwann nucleus (S.n.) lies much nearer to the node of Ranvier (n.) than it would usually do, but otherwise the proportions are roughly correct. ax., axis cylinder: end., endoneurium; myel., myelin sheath, formed of multiple layers of Schwann cell membrane (S.c.m.); S.c., cytoplasm of Schwann cell; N., neurilemma. (*From* W. Holmes & J. Z. Young (1942) *Journal of Anatomy*, 77, 67.)

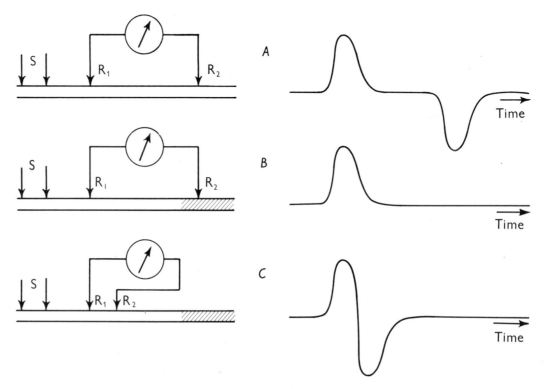

Fig. 20.4 The electrical changes accompanying the passage of a nerve impulse as seen on an oscilloscope connected to external recording electrodes R_1 and R_2. S, stimulating electrodes. An upward deflexion is obtained when R_1 is negative relative to R_2. A, diphasic recording when R_1 and R_2 are both on intact part of nerve and separated by an appreciable distance. B, monophasic recording when nerve is cut or crushed under R_2. C, diphasic recording with R_2 moved on to intact nerve again, much closer to R_1.

is high because of the insulating effect of the myelin. The difference between the nodes and the internodes in accessibility to the external medium is the basis for the *saltatory* mechanism of conduction in myelinated nerve fibres. Nerves may branch many times before terminating and the branches always arise at nodes.

In peripheral myelinated nerves the whole axon is usually described as being covered by a thin, apparently structureless basement membrane, the *neurilemma*. The nuclei of the Schwann cells are to be found just beneath the neurilemma, at the midpoint of each internode. The fibrous connective tissue which separates individual fibres is known as the *endoneurium*: the fibres are bound together in bundles by the *perineurium*, and the several bundles which in turn form a whole nerve trunk are surrounded by the *epineurium*. The connective tissue sheaths in which the bundles of nerve fibres

are wrapped also contain continuous sheets of cells, the perineural epithelium, which prevent extracellular ions in the spaces between the fibres from mixing freely with those outside the nerve trunk. The nerve fibres within the brain and spinal cord are packed together very closely, and are usually said to lack a neurilemma. Their myelin sheaths are laid down by oligodendroglial cells which seem to play a part similar to that of the Schwann cells in peripheral nerves. The myelin is also interrupted at nodes of Ranvier but, since the individual fibres are difficult to tease apart, the nodes are not easily demonstrated by histological techniques.

CHARACTERISTICS OF THE NERVE IMPULSE

As observed with a pair of recording electrodes in contact with the outside of a nerve, the impulse consists of the passage

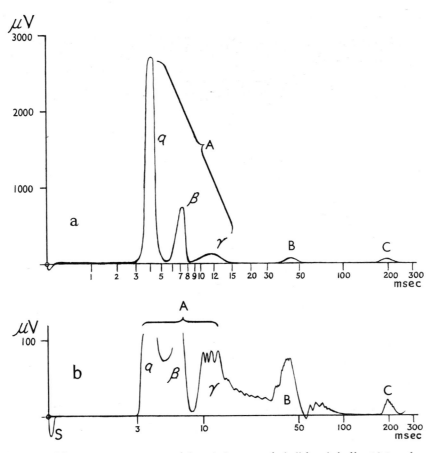

Fig. 20.5 Complex action potential at room temperature of the sciatic nerve of a bull frog led off at 13·1 cm from point of stimulation. The time is in milliseconds (logarithmic scale). Figure b is at ten times the amplification of Figure a. S = stimulus artifact, marking the zero point. (Drawn from diagrams given by J. Erlanger & H. S. Gasser (1937) *Electrical Signs of Nervous Activity*. Philadelphia: University of Pennsylvania Press.)

along the nerve at a constant velocity of a short region which is electrically negative relative to the rest of the nerve. If both electrodes are on an intact part of the nerve, and if they are separated by a great enough distance, a *diphasic* recording of the type shown in Figure 20.4A, is obtained. Here the active region first appears under the left-hand electrode, then traverses the stretch between the electrodes, and finally reaches the right-hand electrode where it gives rise to a mirror-image deflexion on the recording instrument. If the nerve is crushed or cut under the right-hand electrode, the impulse never reaches this point, and a *monophasic* recording of the *action potential* is obtained (Fig. 20.4B). Under many experimental conditions it is difficult to demonstrate the classical diphasic picture of Figure 20.4A because of the impossibility of adequately separating the two electrodes. Thus in a frog nerve at room temperature the duration of the action potential is of the order of 1·5 msec, and the conduction velocity is about 20 m/sec; the length of the active region is therefore 30 mm, which is often as great as the maximum separation of the electrodes. The two phases of the recording then overlap one another to some extent, so that although the record is still diphasic there is no longer a flat portion between the phases (Fig. 20.4C).

When a frog's sciatic nerve is very strongly stimulated (see below) all the nerve fibres in it are excited. A monophasic

recording with an electrode placed near the point of stimulation shows the action potential as a single wave, but a similar recording made at some distance from the stimulating electrodes gives a complicated wave form (Fig. 20.5a) in which three groups of waves (spikes) can be distinguished. These are usually labelled A, B and C; A is further subdivided into α, β and γ. Each part of the complex wave of Figure 20.5a is contributed by a different group of nerve fibres; the action potentials all start from the point of stimulation at the same time, but travel toward the recording electrode at different rates. Such a set of impulses, initiated at the same instant, is called a *volley*. In the experiment Figure 20.5, the distance from the stimulating to the recording electrode was 13·1 cm. If the time for the foot of the wave to reach the recording electrode is read off the logarithmic abscissa of Figure 20.5a, it is easy to calculate that the rate of conduction was 41 metres/second for α, 22 for β, 14 for γ, 4 for B and 0·7 for C. The conduction velocities in mammalian nerves are somewhat greater (100 for α, 60 for β, 40 for γ, 10 for B and 2 for C), partly because body temperature is appreciably higher and partly because the fibres are larger.

The distribution of conduction velocities over such a wide range results from a variation in fibre diameter over an equally wide range. A large nerve fibre conducts impulses faster than a small one. Smaller fibres require stronger shocks to excite them, so that the form of the volley in a mixed nerve is affected by the strength of the stimulus. If the stimulus is weak only the α wave appears; if it is stronger then both α and β waves are seen, and so on. The size of the voltage change picked up by an external recording electrode also varies with fibre diameter; on theoretical grounds it would be expected to vary with (diameter)^2, but the relationship may be a linear one. The consequence is that records of electrical activity in sensory nerves *in situ* show mainly the activity of the largest fibres and it is, indeed, difficult to see at all the action potentials of the smallest non-myelinated fibres.

It has proved hard to assign with confidence particular functions to particular sizes of fibres. The sensory root of the spinal cord contains fibres giving A (that is α, β and γ) and C waves; the motor root yields α, γ and B waves, the latter going into the white ramus. It is now generally believed that B fibres occur only in the preganglionic autonomic nerves so that the elevation labelled B in Figure 20.5 might be better reclassified as subdivision δ of Group A. The grey ramus, containing fibres passing from the sympathetic system, shows mainly C waves. The fastest fibres (α) are either motor fibres activating voluntary muscles or afferent fibres conveying impulses from sensory receptors in the muscles. The γ motor fibres are connected in mammals to intrafusal muscle fibres (see p. 343) and in amphibia to 'slow' (as opposed to 'twitch') muscle fibres. At least some of the fibres of the C group convey pain impulses. The C fibres are probably non-myelinated: they are found especially in autonomic post-ganglionic trunks. Myelinated sensory fibres in peripheral nerves have also been classified according to their diameters into Group I (20 to 12 μm), Group II (12 to 4 μm), and Group III (4 μm and under), with corresponding conduction velocities. The Group I fibres, which conduct impulses most quickly, are found only in nerves from muscles. They have been subdivided into Group I A, connected with annulo-spiral endings of muscle spindles, and the somewhat slower Group I B, carrying impulses from Golgi tendon organs. The slower fibres of Groups II and III transmit other modes of sensation in both muscle and skin nerves.

Resting Potential and Action Potential

In a resting nerve fibre there is a steady electric potential difference between the inside of the cell and the outside, the inside being relatively negative. This so-called *resting potential* gives rise to the *injury potential* recorded when one electrode is in contact with an uninjured part of the nerve and the other is in contact with a cut or crushed point (that is the condition for a normal monophasic recording with external electrodes). Bernstein suggested many years ago that electrical activity in nerve fibres consisted in a temporary collapse of the membrane potential towards zero. Bernstein's hypothesis could not be adequately investigated until 1939, when Hodgkin and Huxley in England and Curtis and Cole in the United States, first devised a technique for introducing an electrode inside a nerve fibre, and so measuring directly the potential difference across the resting and active nerve membrane.

Figure 20.6A shows the type of electrode used to record the internal potential in a squid axon. A 50 or 100 μm electrode of this kind can be used only with an axon as large (500 to 1000 μm diameter) as that of the squid, but glass micropipettes with a tip diameter of 0.5 μm, filled with KCl solution, can be thrust transversely into many excitable tissues without tearing too large a hole at the point of entry, and so used for direct measurement of internal potential (see Fig. 20.6B). Figure 20.7 shows some typical records, from which the following generalizations may be made:

1. There is a resting potential (inside negative) whose size ranges from 60 to 95 millivolts.

2. During the passage of an impulse the membrane potential is reversed for a short while; the size of this overshoot is of the order of 30 to 60 millivolts.

3. Although the sizes of the resting and action potentials thus vary remarkably little from tissue to tissue, the duration of the action potential (spike) shows considerable variation. In mammalian nerves the duration is under 1 millisecond, whereas in amphibian cardiac muscle fibres it is of the order of half a second.

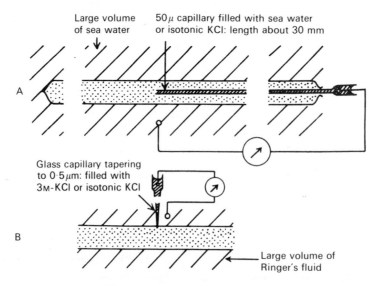

Fig. 20.6 Methods for obtaining absolute values of resting potential and action potential. A, longitudinal insertion of internal electrode used for giant axon of the squid, *Loligo*. B, transverse insertion of internal electrode used for muscle fibres and other cells. (A. L. Hodgkin (1951) *Biological Reviews*, **26**, 342.)

4. There is also some variation in the shape of the spike. Thus the undershoot (positive phase) at the tail end of the spike is always present in isolated squid axons, though it is probably absent in the living animal. In frog muscle fibres the spike is characteristically followed by a relatively long-lasting negative phase, which may be related to the mechanism by which the contractile machinery is activated. In cardiac muscle fibres there is always a long plateau after the peak of the spike; the complicated shape of the spike recorded in the conducting (Purkinje) fibres of the sheep's heart (Fig. 20.7F) is typical.

The first and most important conclusion to be drawn from micro-electrode studies is that Bernstein's hypothesis is only in part correct. The membrane potential at the peak of the spike does not merely collapse towards zero, but is reversed by a substantial number of millivolts.

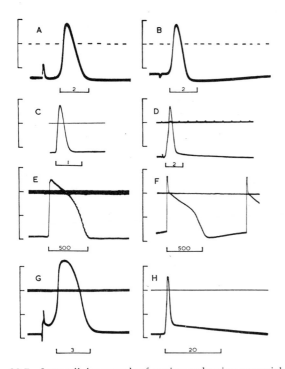

Fig. 20.7 Intracellular records of resting and action potentials. The horizontal lines (dashed in A and B) indicate zero potential level; negative downwards. Marks on voltage scales are 50 millivolts apart in every case. The number against each time scale gives the distance between the marks in milliseconds. In some cases the action potential is preceded by a stimulus artifact. The part of the action potential (usually about 40 mV) above the zero line is referred to as the overshoot. A, squid axon *in situ* at 8·5°C, using 0·5 μm micro-electrode. B, squid axon isolated by dissection, at 12·5°C, using 100 μm longitudinal electrode. C, myelinated fibre from dorsal root of cat. D, cell body of motoneurone in spinal cord of cat. E, fibre in frog's heart. F. Purkinje fibre in sheep's heart. G, electroplate in electric organ of *Electrophorus electricus*. H, isolated fibre from frog's sartorius muscle. (A and B recorded by A. L. Hodgkin and R. D. Keynes, *from* A. L. Hodgkin (1958) *Proceedings of the Royal Society* B, 148, 5; C recorded by K. Krnjevic; D *from* L. G. Brock, J. S. Coombs & J. C. Eccles (1952) *Journal of Physiology*, 117, 439; E recorded by B. F. Hoffman, F by S. Weidmann, *from* S. Weidmann (1956) *Elektrophysiologie der Herzmuskelfaser*, p. 20. Bern: Huber; G *from* R. D. Keynes & Martins-Ferreira (1953) *Journal of Physiology*, 119, 323; H *from* A. L. Hodgkin & P. Horowicz (1957) *Journal of Physiology*, 136, 17P.)

Excitation and the Local-circuit Theory

Although a nerve can be stimulated by the local application of a number of agents—for example, electric current, pressure, heat, or chemical solutions such as KCl— it is most easily and conveniently stimulated by applying electric shocks. The most effective electric current is one which *depolarizes* the nerve membrane, that is to say which reduces the size of the electric potential across the membrane. The other agents listed above also produce their effect by causing a depolarization; pressure and heat do so by damaging the nerve membrane. It was suggested long ago that propagation of an impulse depends essentially on the flow of current in *local circuits* ahead of the active region which depolarizes the resting membrane, and causes it in turn to become active. This local circuit theory is illustrated in Figure 20.8; here it is the flow of current from region A to region B which results in movement of the active region towards the right. There are important differences between the current pathways in non-myelinated nerves (upper diagram) and in myelinated nerves (lower diagram), which will be dealt with later, but the principle is the same for both types of fibre in that the active region triggers the resting region ahead of it by causing an outward (depolarizing) flow of electric current. The local circuit theory has been universally accepted for some time, and is mentioned at this point in order to emphasize that in studying the effect of applied electric currents we are not concerned with a non-physiological and purely artificial way of setting up a nerve impulse, but are examining a process which forms an integral part of the normal mechanism of propagation.

The first concept that must be established is that of a *threshold* stimulus. The smallest voltage which gives a just perceptible muscle twitch is the minimal or threshold stimulus. It is the voltage which is just sufficiently large to stimulate one of the nerve fibres, and hence to cause contraction of the muscle fibres to which it is connected. If the nerve consisted only of a single fibre, it would be found that a further increase in the applied voltage would not increase the size of the twitch. This is because conduction is an *all-or-none* phenomenon; the stimulus either (if it is subthreshold) fails to set up an impulse, or (if it is threshold or above) sets up a full-sized impulse. No intermediate-sized response can be obtained by varying the stimulus strength, though of course the response will change if certain external conditions (for example temperature or ionic environment) are changed. In a multi-fibre preparation like the sciatic nerve there are hundreds of fibres whose thresholds are spread over a wide

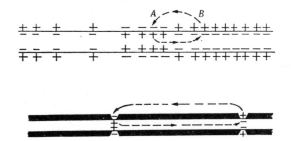

Fig. 20.8 A diagram illustrating the local circuit theory. The upper sketch represents a non-myelinated fibre and the lower sketch a myelinated fibre. (A. L. Hodgkin (1957) *Proceedings of the Royal Society* B, 148, 1.)

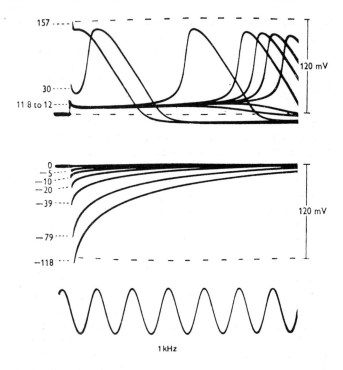

Fig. 20.9 Threshold behaviour of the membrane potential in a squid giant axon at 6°C. Shocks, whose strengths in nanocoulomb/cm² are shown against each curve, were applied to an internal wire electrode with a bare portion 15 mm long. Internal potential was recorded between a second wire 7 mm long opposite the centre of the stimulating wire and an electrode in the sea water outside. Depolarization shown upwards (A. L. Hodgkin, A. F. Huxley & B. Katz (1952) *Journal of Physiology*, 116, 424).

range of voltages. Hence an increase in stimulus strength above that which just excites the fibre with the lowest threshold results in excitation of more and more fibres, with a corresponding increase in the size of the muscle twitch. When the point is reached where the twitch ceases to increase further, it can be taken that all the fibres in this nerve trunk are being triggered; this requires a *maximal* stimulus. A still larger (supra-maximal) shock does not produce a larger twitch.

A particularly clear example of the threshold behaviour of a nerve fibre is provided by the experiment shown in Figure 20.9. Here an isolated squid axon was being stimulated by applying brief shocks between a long wire inserted longitudinally into it and an external electrode; there was an internal recording electrode alongside the stimulating wire. Threshold for excitation was found to occur when a depolarizing shock of 12 nanocoulombs/cm² membrane was applied; at this shock strength the response was delayed for several milliseconds during which period the membrane was in a 'meta-stable' state, depolarized by about 10 mV, sometimes giving a spike and sometimes reverting to its resting state. The effect of increasing the shock strength was to reduce the waiting period but the size of the spike was not changed appreciably. The figure also shows the effect of applying inward (polarizing) currents; it will be seen that these had the effect of temporarily displacing the membrane potential, which then decayed exponentially back to its resting value. But no spikes were generated.

An important variable in investigating the excitability of a nerve is the duration of the shock. If the threshold is determined, it is found that for long shocks the applied current reaches an irreducible minimum; the threshold for a shock of infinite duration is known as the *rheobase*. When the duration

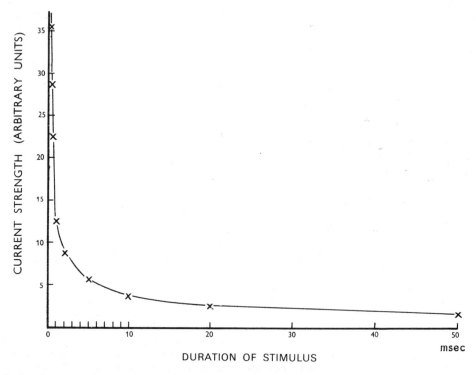

Fig. 20.10 Strength–duration curve showing threshold conditions for direct stimulation of sartorius muscle of the frog. The rheobase in this experiment is 2 and since a current of twice this value must last 9 msec to be effective the chronaxie, as defined by Lapique, is 9 msec. (W. A. Rushton (1933) *Journal of Physiology*, 77, 345.)

is reduced, a stronger shock is needed, so that the curve relating shock strength to shock duration, which is known as the *strength-duration curve*, takes the form shown in Figure 20.10. It may be noted that the essential requirement to stimulate a nerve is that the membrane should be depolarized to a certain critical level whose existence is shown clearly by Figure 20.9. This critical level is, in effect, the rheobase. When the shock duration is reduced, a larger current needs to flow if the membrane potential is to reach the critical level before the end of the shock. This means that for short shocks an approximately constant total quantity of electricity needs to be applied; in Figure 20.9 the shock strength was therefore expressed in nanocoulombs/cm^2 membrane.

The refractory period. If a nerve is stimulated twice in quick succession, it may not respond to the second stimulus. In the period following a spike during which the excitability of the nerve is abolished or reduced, the nerve is said to be in a refractory state. The *absolute refractory period* is the brief interval after a successful stimulus when no second shock, *however large*, can elicit another spike. Its duration is roughly equal to the duration of the spike, which in mammalian A fibres at body temperature is of the order of 0·4 msec (see Fig.

20.11). In frog nerve at 15°C it lasts for about 2 msec (Fig. 20.12). It is succeeded by the *relative refractory period* during which a second response can be obtained if a large enough stimulus is used. After the relative refractory period a supernormal phase can often be detected, when excitability is slightly greater than normal; this is correlated with the occurrence of an afterpotential (see p. 313). The experiment on a mammalian nerve illustrated in Figure 20.11 shows the recovery after an impulse in a somewhat different way from the excitability curve plotted in Figure 20.12. In Figure 20.12 the second (testing) shock was supramaximal throughout. When it fell within 0·4 msec of the conditioning shock there was no response [Fig. 20.11 (1)] but when the interval between the two shocks was gradually lengthened [Fig. 20.11 (2 to 5)] the second shock came within the relative refractory period of more and more of the fibres, and the second response progressively increased.

During the relative refractory period the spike size and conduction velocity are both subnormal as well as the excitability. Therefore, two full-sized impulses travelling down a long length of nerve must be separated by a minimum interval; if the interval is less the second one decreases. A mammalian A fibre can respond at a frequency of over 1000 impulses/second, but the spikes after the first one would be small, and would tend to decline during sustained stimulation. Recovery in such fibres is complete after about 3 msec, so that full-sized impulses can be carried at repetition frequencies of over 300/sec. However this frequency is not often reached in the living animal, though a few sensory nerves may sometimes exceed it for short bursts of impulses.

Figure 20.9 shows that in order to stimulate a nerve fibre it is necessary to depolarize the membrane by causing current to flow outwards. If the current is carried mainly by positively-charged cations, K$^+$ inside the fibre and Na$^+$ outside, then the direction of movement of these ions will be the same as the

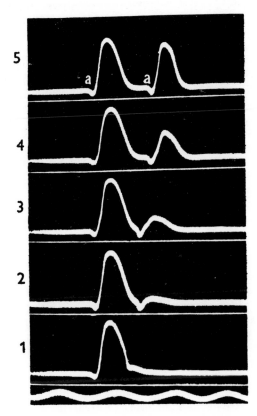

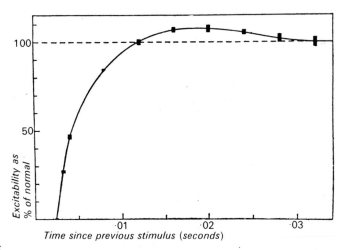

Fig. 20.11 Relative refractory period of A fibres of the phrenic nerve mapped in terms of the height of the response evoked by a supramaximal testing shock. The separation of the conditioning and testing shocks can be determined from the shock artifacts, a, a. At the interval of the lowermost record (about 0·5 msec) the nerve is completely refractory, but a small response is present in the next record. Conduction distance, 8 mm. Temperature, 38°C. The sine wave at the bottom of the figure gives time in msec. (J. Erlanger & H. S. Gasser (1937) *Electrical Signs of Nervous Activity*, p. 172. Philadelphia: University of Pennsylvania Press.)

Fig. 20.12 Time course of the recovery of excitability (reciprocal of threshold) in a frog sciatic nerve after passage of an impulse. Temperature 15°C. The conditioning stimulus and the test stimulus were applied at electrodes 15 mm apart, so that about 0·5 msec should be subtracted from each reading to obtain the course of recovery under the test electrode. The absolute refractory period lasted 2 msec, and the relative refractory period 10 msec; they were succeeded by a supernormal period lasting for 20 msec. (*From* E. D. Adrian & K. Lucas (1912) *Journal of Physiology*, 44, 114.)

direction of the current (when current flows in a wire, the electrons which carry it are actually moving in the opposite direction to the current, since they are negatively charged). If the outward flow of current is to be brought about by the application of an external electrode, then the electrode must be a cathode. Note that *outward* current supplied from an *external* source reduces the membrane potential because it produces a voltage drop across the membrane resistance which opposes the resting potential. When the active process described in the next section has been initiated, further depolarization is caused by an *inward* current; the apparent contradiction arises because the source of the current is now the *internal* sodium battery (E_{Na} in Fig. 20.17). The simplest way of verifying that excitation takes place at a cathode is to arrange a nerve with one of the stimulating electrodes on the cut end. It will be found that the threshold for stimulation is lower when the electrode on the intact part of the nerve is a cathode than when it is an anode. Under some conditions, excitation will take place at an anode when the applied current is switched off; an explanation for such *anode break excitation* is given on page 312. The experiment illustrated in Figure 20.13 shows another way of demonstrating that excitation normally occurs under a cathode. The shortest conduction time (record 1) occurred when electrode C was the cathode and B the anode, the longest (4) when A was the cathode and B still the anode. When B was the cathode there was an intermediate conduction time, which did not change much (records 2 and 3) when the anode was moved from A to C.

Nerve impulses can travel equally well in either direction. If a cathodal shock is applied at the midpoint of a nerve, impulses are propagated away from the stimulating electrode in both directions. In the living animal a given nerve fibre normally conducts impulses in one direction only, but this is because it is always stimulated at the same end—the peripheral end in sensory nerves and the central end in motor nerves. An impulse travelling in the abnormal direction is termed *antidromic*.

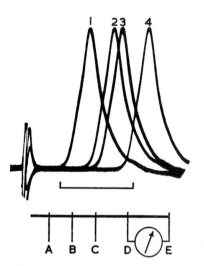

Fig. 20.13   Variation in conduction time with polarity and position of stimulus. Monophasic recordings of an earthworm giant fibre; time scale 1 msec. Shock strength just above threshold. Record 1, B+C—; 2, A+B—; 3, C+B—; 4, B+A—. Distances between electrodes were: AB, 10 mm; BC, 10 mm; CD, 14 mm. (*By courtesy of K. Krnjevic.*)

The ionic basis of resting and action potentials. As has already been seen, the interior of all nerve and skeletal muscle fibres is 69 to 95 mV negative with respect to the outside. It was suggested by Bernstein that the resting potential in nerve fibres arose from the existence of a concentration gradient for potassium (high concentration inside, low outside), allied with a selective permeability of the cell membrane towards K^+ ions.

In a system of this type, where the membrane separating two solutions is permeable to only one species of ion, a potential difference is set up across the membrane whose magnitude is given by the Nernst diffusion equation:

$$E_m = \frac{RT}{F} \log_e \frac{[\text{penetrating ion outside}]}{[\text{penetrating ion inside}]}$$

$$= 58 \log_{10} \frac{[\text{penetrating ion outside}]}{[\text{penetrating ion inside}]} \text{ mV.}$$

E_m can be regarded as the equilibrium potential at which the force exerted by the concentration gradient tending to make the ions move into the weaker solution is exactly balanced by the force exerted by the voltage gradient tending to move them in the opposite direction. Strictly, the equation should be written with chemical activities instead of concentrations on the right-hand side; but for the present arguments it can be assumed that the activity coefficients are equal on the two sides. For a positively-charged cation, E_m is the inside potential with respect to the outside, so that if the concentration ratio is less than 1, E_m is negative. For K^+ ions, E_m will be written as E_K; for Na^+ as E_{Na}, and so on. The resting membranes of the nerve and muscle fibres are not in fact solely permeable to K^+ ions; they are also permeable to Cl^- ions, and are not totally impermeable to Na^+ ions. The potential developed across a membrane permeable to all these ions was calculated by Goldman on the assumption that the voltage gradient was uniform throughout the membrane. His 'constant field' equation can be written thus:

$$E_m = \frac{RT}{F} \log_e \frac{P_K[K]_o + P_{Na}[Na]_o + P_{Cl}[Cl]_i}{P_K[K]_i + P_{Na}[Na]_i + P_{Cl}[Cl]_o}$$

where the subscripts i and o refer to inside and outside respectively, and the Ps are permeability coefficients.

The best evidence for the internal composition of excitable tissues has been obtained for frog muscle and for squid axons whose axoplasm can be squeezed out like tooth-paste and analysed with a minimum of contamination by extracellular fluid. Table 20.14 shows some values for the concentrations in the tissue water of K^+, Na^+ and Cl^- ions in freshly dissected squid axons and frog muscle, and the corresponding plasma concentrations. It will be seen that the concentration ratios for K^+ and Cl^- are of the same order (5 to 40 times) in the two tissues, although the actual concentration of ions is substantially greater in the marine invertebrate (squid) than in the fresh water vertebrate (frog). The reader may wonder how a balance between anions and cations is achieved on each side of the membrane, since the total numbers of negative and positive charges must be almost equal; the numbers will not be *exactly* equal, because of the displacement of a few ions to set up the membrane potential; in a very large cell like a squid axon it is only necessary to displace about 1 in 10^7 of the internal K^+ ions in order to give rise to the observed resting potential, so that for practical purposes equality can be assumed. In the plasma the predominant cation is Na^+, and there are also small concentrations of K^+, Ca^{2+} and Mg^{2+}. The principal anion is Cl^- but there is also a fair amount of HCO_3^- while negatively charged phosphate ions and plasma proteins make a small contribution to the balance. In the cytoplasm, there is more difficulty in drawing up a complete balance sheet. On the cation side, K^+ predominates, with low concentrations of Na^+ and Mg^{2+} and smaller amounts still of Ca^{2+}; there may also be some amino acids with a net positive charge. As far as anions are concerned, the concentration of Cl^- is low, at least in muscle, and the organic anions which make up the deficit in negative charge have not all been identified with certainty. In muscle the main contributions are probably made by phosphocreatine, ATP, hexosemonophosphate and proteins; in squid axoplasm the chief anions are isethionate (CH_2OH. $CH_2SO_3^-$) and the dicarboxylic amino acids, aspartic and glutamic. The important fact about all the intracellular anions except Cl^- is that they are relatively large molecules, to which the cell membrane can be regarded as being impermeable.

Comparison of the resting potentials seen in Figure 20.7 with the theoretical potentials shown in Table 20.14 shows that the agreement is reasonably good. It will be seen that the Nernst potential for Cl^- is also of the same order as the resting potential, confirming that the membranes are permeable to

this ion as well. Another test of the role of K^+ in determining the resting potential is to investigate the effect of varying external $[K^+]$. As Figure 20.15 shows, the membrane potential varies in the expected fashion with large $[K]_o$s, but when $[K]_o$ is lowered below normal the potential flattens off. This flattening is exactly what would be predicted by the constant field equation, since when $[K]_o$ is very low the contributions to

Table 20.14   Concentrations of ions in the cytoplasm and in the blood plasma of squid axons and frog muscle, and the equilibrium potentials calculated from the Nernst equation (inside relative to outside)

	Squid axon	Frog muscle	
$[K^+]$ inside	410	125	mmol/kg H_2O
$[K^+]$ outside	22	2·6	mmol/kg H_2O
E_K	−74	−98	mV
$[Na^+]$ inside	49	15	mmol/kg H_2O
$[Na^+]$ outside	460	110	mmol/kg H_2O
E_{Na}	+56	+50	mV
$[Cl^-]$ inside	123	1·2	mmol/kg H_2O
$[Cl^-]$ outside	560	77	mmol/kg H_2O
E_{Cl}	−38	−104	mV

From A. L. Hodgkin (1951) *Biological Reviews*, **26**, 339–409; R. D. Keynes (1964) *Journal of Physiology*, **169**, 690–705.

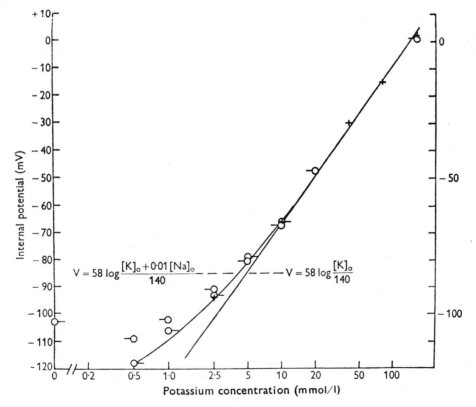

Fig. 20.15   Variation in resting potential of frog muscle fibres with external potassium concentration, $[K]_o$. The measurements were made in a chloride-free sulphate-Ringer's solution containing 8 mmol/l-$CaSO_2$. Crosses are potentials measured after equilibrating for 10 to 60 min; circles are potentials measured 20 to 60 sec after a sudden change in concentration, −O after increase in $[K]_o$, O− after decrease in $[K]_o$. Note that for large $[K]_o$s the measured potentials agree well with the Nernst equation if $[K]_i$ is taken as 140 mmol/l, and that the deviations at low $[K]_i$s can partly be explained by taking sodium permeability into account. (*From* A. L. Hodgkin & P. Horowicz (1959) *Journal of Physiology*, **148**, 135.)

the resting potential of Na$^+$ and Cl$^-$ permeabilities becomes relatively important. A further test of these ideas is to examine the rate of passage of radioactive potassium ions through the resting membrane since it should be appreciated that, although at equilibrium there is no net transfer of K$^+$ through the membrane, the equilibrium is a dynamic one, with equal and opposite fluxes of ions moving through the membrane all the time. Again there is tolerable agreement between theory and experiment, and there is no doubt that the resting membranes of nerve and muscle are permeable to labelled K$^+$ and Cl$^-$ ions.

The basis for the theory of nervous conduction developed by Hodgkin, Huxley and Katz is that the concentration of Na$^+$ ions inside excitable cells is much lower than that in the body fluids outside. If one supposes that the permeability of the nerve membrane can change from its resting state, in which it is relatively permeable to K$^+$ and Cl$^-$ but impermeable to Na$^+$, to an active state in which it becomes temporarily much more permeable to Na$^+$ than to any other ions, one can explain why the membrane potential should change from a value close to E_K (see Table 20.14) to a reversed potential which approaches E_{Na} (compare the values in the table with the overshoots seen in Fig. 20.7). The mechanism can be summarized as follows: when the membrane is depolarized by an outward flow of current, caused either by an applied cathode or by the proximity of an active region where the membrane potential is already reversed, its sodium permeability immediately rises, and there is a net inward movement of Na$^+$ ions, flowing down the sodium concentration gradient. If the initial depolarization is large enough, Na$^+$ enters faster than K$^+$ can leave, and this causes the membrane potential to drop still further; this extra depolarization increases the sodium permeability even more, accelerating the change of membrane potential in a regenerative fashion. The linkage between sodium permeability and membrane potential forms, as shown in Figure 20.16, a 'positive feed-back' mechanism. The entry of Na$^+$ does not continue indefinitely, being halted partly because the membrane potential soon reaches a level close to E_{Na}, where the net inward driving force acting on Na$^+$ ions becomes zero, and partly because the rise in sodium permeability decays inexorably with time from the moment when it is first triggered, this process being termed 'inactivation'. After the peak of the spike has been reached, therefore, the sodium permeability is rapidly reduced (inactivated); at the same time, the potassium permeability of the membrane rises well above its resting value, and an outward movement of K$^+$ takes place, eventually restoring the membrane potential to its original

level. It may be noted that the membrane potential would begin to return towards its normal level as soon as the Na$^+$ permeability was sufficiently inactivated, even if there were no delayed rise in K$^+$ permeability; but the rate of return would be slow, and the result of the increase in K$^+$ permeability is to ensure a more rapid restoration towards the resting potential than would otherwise be achieved. At the end of the spike, the membrane is left with the original potential level restored, but with its sodium permeability mechanism still inactivated. Lapse of further time allows the sodium permeability to be 'reactivated' to the quiescent state in which it is still very low, as is characteristic of the resting membrane, but is now ready once more to increase explosively if the membrane is retriggered.

The important features of the concept may be summarized:

1. The resting membrane is relatively permeable to K$^+$ (and Cl$^-$) ions; and impermeable to Na$^+$ ions. The resting potential therefore lies close to E_K.

2. At the peak of the action potential the permeability of the membrane to Na$^+$ has risen so much that the potential approaches E_{Na}, the limiting value for a membrane exclusively permeable to Na$^+$.

3. The sodium permeability of the membrane (P_{Na}) is controlled by the potential across the membrane in such a fashion that a relatively small degree of depolarization (reduction in potential) causes a large rise in permeability.

4. The potassium permeability of the membrane (P_K) is also controlled by the membrane potential, but whereas P_{Na} rises immediately when the potential is lowered and is subsequently inactivated, P_K only rises after a slight time delay, giving a maintained increase which is not inactivated (it is later reduced to normal by the repolarization of the membrane).

5. The separation in time of the permeability changes, P_{Na} rising quickly and then being cut off, P_K rising with a lag, is very important. Simultaneous increases in P_{Na} and P_K would merely result in an energetically wasteful interchange of Na$^+$ and K$^+$ and would not cause the membrane potential to vary in a useful manner.

6. The immediate source of energy for the electric currents which flow, carried by Na$^+$ and K$^+$ ions, during propagation of a nerve impulse, is the pre-existing ionic concentration gradient.

7. After an impulse has passed along an axon, a little sodium has been gained and a little potassium lost. The quantities involved are small compared with the initial contents of the axon, so that in the course of a single impulse the internal ionic concentrations do not change to a measurable extent. It is the permeability of the nerve membrane which alters, not the concentration of ions within the cell.

Perhaps the most obvious prediction that can be made from this hypothesis is that conduction should be impossible in a medium which contains no sodium. Hodgkin and Katz made a preliminary test of the validity of the ionic hypothesis by showing that in squid axons the presence of Na$^+$ ions in the external medium was essential for conduction. In a choline chloride solution, or one in which sugar was substituted for all the NaCl, conduction was immediately blocked; Li$^+$ seemed to be the only cation which could deputize for Na$^+$.

The next predictions that can be made from the ionic hypothesis concern the slope of the rising phase of the spike,

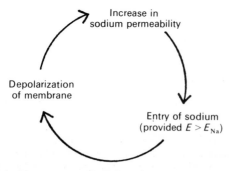

Fig. 20.16 The regenerative linkage between membrane potential and sodium permeability. (*From* A. L. Hodgkin (1951) *Biological Reviews*, **26**, 384.)

and the extent to which the membrane potential is reversed at its peak. If the rising phase is due to an inrush of Na^+ ions, then one would expect its slope to be directly proportional to $[Na]_o$. This was verified by Hodgkin and Katz to be the case in squid axons, and it has since been demonstrated to hold good for various other types of nerve and muscle. If at the peak of the spike the membrane is, as suggested, far more permeable to Na^+ ions than to K^+ or Cl^-, then the potential should approach the Nernst potential for Na^+, E_{Na}, and should vary in a predictable way when either $[Na]_o$ or $[Na]_i$ is changed. This test has also been made successfully on a number of tissues, and the peak potential has generally been found to change by an amount close to the theoretical 17 millivolts calculated from the Nernst equation for a halving of the concentration ratio.

According to the ionic hypothesis, the nerve membrane can be represented electrically by the equivalent circuit shown in Figure 20.17. The membrane has an electrical capacity because of its insulating properties and its ability to keep separate the charged particles on either side; in non-myelinated nerve fibres (and, as a matter of fact, in many other types of living cell) 1 cm² of membrane has a capacity of about 1 microfarad, while in muscle fibres the capacity is somewhat greater. A capacity of this size implies that the insulating layer of the membrane must be exceedingly thin; if a reasonable value for the dielectric constant of lipid material is assumed, a capacity of $1 \mu F/cm^2$ is consistent with the thickness of about 2·5 nm suggested by electron micrographs. The membrane must also be regarded as having an electrically conducting path across it, in parallel with its capacity, because ions are known to be able to move through it, albeit at a rate perhaps $1/10^7$ as great as that at which they would move across a water layer of equal thickness. This conducting path may be represented as three resistances in parallel, one being the channel through which Na^+ ions flow, another being the K^+ channel, and the third being the 'leak' channel for all other ions (probably mainly Cl^-). Each resistance has in series with it an appropriate battery; R_{Na} is pictured in series with E_{Na}, and so on. Re-stated in electrical terms, the mechanism described in the preceding paragraphs involves the following sequence of events:

1. In the resting membrane R_{Na} is much larger than R_K, that is the sodium conductance is much smaller than the potassium conductance. E_M is therefore close to E_K.

2. When a large enough depolarizing (outward) current is applied to the membrane, R_{Na} falls, because its value is controlled by the size of E_M at any instant. Current carried by Na^+ ions flows through the membrane, reversing the charge on the capacity C_M.

3. The flow of Na^+ current slows down when the peak of the spike is reached, partly because C_M is now recharged to a potential close to E_{Na}, and partly because the inactivation process begins to make R_{Na} rise once more.

4. A delayed fall in R_K now takes effect, and current carried by K^+ ions flows outwards through the membrane, recharging C_M to its original potential.

To change the potential across a 1 microfarad capacitance by 120 millivolts requires the transfer of $1·2 \times 10^{-7}$ coulombs. One gram-molecule of a monovalent ion can carry 96 500 coulombs, whence the minimum inward movement of Na^+ ions to produce a 120 mV spike across a squid nerve membrane whose capacity is $1 \mu F/cm^2$ is $1·2 \times 10^{-7}/96\,500 = 1·2 \times 10^{-12}$ mol/cm²; a similar calculation for a frog muscle membrane

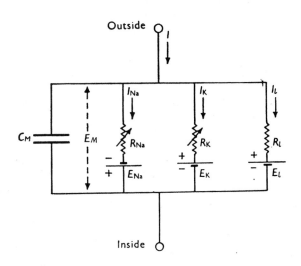

Fig. 20.17 Equivalent circuit for the nerve membrane described on this page. R_{Na} and R_K vary with membrane potential and time; the other components are constant. (*From* A. L. Hodgkin & A. F. Huxley (1952) *Journal of Physiology*, 117, 501.)

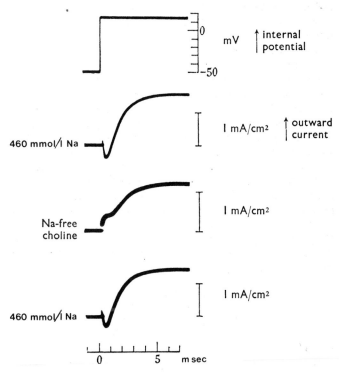

Fig. 20.18 An example of the kind of result obtained when applying the voltage-clamp technique to the squid giant axon. The top record shows the imposed change in membrane potential, a sudden depolarization of 65 mV. The lower three records show the resulting membrane currents in the presence and absence of external Na^+ ions. Temperature 11°C. (*From* A. L. Hodgkin & A. F. Huxley (1952) *Journal of Physiology*, 116, 449.)

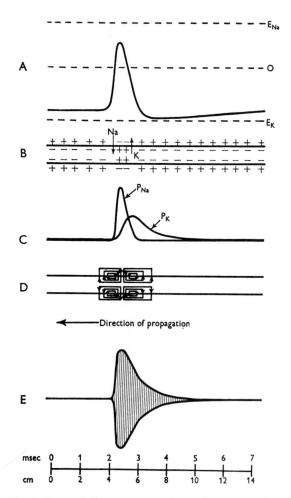

Fig. 20.19 Some of the events occurring during propagation of an impulse along a non-myelinated squid giant axon. The horizontal scale corresponds to a conduction velocity of 20 m/sec, and the diagrams can be considered to represent *either* the events at different points along the axon at the same moment in time, *or* the events at different times for one position. A, change in membrane potential; the dashed lines show zero potential and the Nernst potentials for Na^+ and K^+. B, polarity of potential difference across membrane, and approximate position of ion movements. C, variation in sodium and potassium permeabilities. (*After* A. L. Hodgkin & A. F. Huxley (1952) *Journal of Physiology*, 117, 530.) D, local circuit current flow. E, variation in total membrane conductance, as recorded by Cole and Curtis with an impedance bridge. (*After* K. S. Cole & H. J. Curtis (1939) *Journal of General Physiology*, 22, 649.)

whose capacity is $7.5\,\mu F/cm^2$ gives a minimum inward Na^+ transfer of $9 \times 10^{-12}\,mol/cm^2$. A useful direct check of the validity of the ionic hypothesis is to measure the net entry of Na^+ per unit area of membrane per impulse, to see whether or not it is greater than this figure. By using radioactive isotope and radioactivation analysis techniques it was found that in squid axons each impulse causes a net gain of about 4×10^{-12} mol Na^-/cm^2, and a net loss of an equal quantity of potassium; in frog muscle fibres the net gain of Na^+ was $16 \times 10^{-12}\,mol/cm^2$, and the net loss of K^+ 10×10^{-12}. It is not surprising that the experimental values should be somewhat larger than the calculated minima, this being the expected consequence of some degree of overlap between the changes in P_{Na} and P_K, but it would have raised serious difficulties for the

theory had they been smaller. Measurements by Caldwell and Keynes of the net gain of labelled Cl^- in stimulated squid axons have given much smaller values (about $0.05 \times 10^{-12}\,mol/cm^2$ impulse), but this finding is consistent with the tacit assumption that has been made in this account of the conduction mechanism that the chloride permeability of the membrane does not change during the passage of a nerve impulse.

In order to examine in detail the laws governing the flow of Na^+ and K^+ ions through the nerve membrane, that is to say to measure the variation in P_{Na} and P_K as functions of time and membrane potential, Hodgkin and Huxley used the 'voltage-clamp' technique for studying the membrane of the squid giant axon. Essentially the method involves changing the membrane potential uniformly over a fixed area of membrane in a predetermined fashion, and measuring the resulting current flow through the membrane. The type of record obtained is illustrated in Figure 20.18, which shows how depolarization of the membrane causes a brief phase of inward current flow, identified as carried by Na^+ ions by the effect of substituting choline, followed by a maintained outward current flow carried by K^+ ions. Analysis of a series of records with different imposed voltage steps gave information about the exact relationship between membrane potential and P_{Na} and P_K, and about the time course of the permeability changes, P_{Na} being increased immediately by depolarization but subsequently inactivated, and P_K being increased with a time lag but not inactivated. This analysis was used to construct the curves for the time courses of the separate permeability changes shown in Figure 20.19, which summarizes in pictorial form some of the events taking place during propagation of an impulse.

Saltatory Conduction in Myelinated Nerves

In 1925 Lillie suggested that the function of the myelin sheath in vertebrate nerve fibres might be to restrict the inward and outward passage of local circuit current to the nodes of Ranvier, so causing the nerve impulse to be propagated along myelinated fibres from node to node in a series of discrete jumps. He coined the term 'saltatory conduction' for this kind of process. Physiological experiments on saltatory conduction could not be performed until techniques for dissecting isolated myelinated fibres had been developed. The threshold for electrical stimulation of an isolated fibre is much lower at each node than along the internodal stretches, and also blocking by anodal polarization and by narcotics is more effective at the nodes than elsewhere. A particularly clear demonstration of the validity of the saltatory theory was provided by Huxley and Stämpfli (Fig. 20.20). This involved measurement of the longitudinal and transverse currents flowing at different points during the passage of an impulse along a single myelinated frog fibre. A fibre was pulled through a short glass capillary about $40\,\mu m$ in diameter set in a partition between two troughs of Ringer's solution. The space around the nerve was narrow enough to have a total resistance of about 0.5 megohm, so that current flowing between neighbouring nodes outside the myelin sheath gave rise to a measurable potential difference between the two sides of the partition, which could be recorded on an oscilloscope. The records of longitudinal

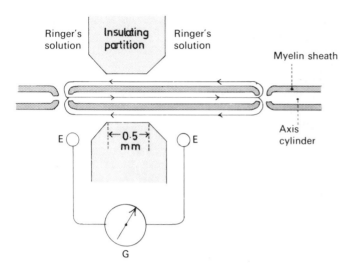

Fig. 20.20 Diagram of the method used by Huxley and Stämpfli to investigate saltatory conduction in nerve. The nerve fibre is drawn through a fine hole about 40 μm in diameter in an insulator by a micromanipulator. The current flows along the axis cylinder out of one node and in the other node as indicated by the arrows. The resistance of the gap between the insulators being about half a megohm, a potential difference set up between the two pools of Ringer's solution is measured by the oscilloscope G connected to the two electrodes, one in each pool of Ringer's solution. The internodal distance in frog's myelinated fibres is 2 mm. (*After* A. F. Huxley & R. Stämpfli (1949) *Journal of Physiology*, **108**, 315.)

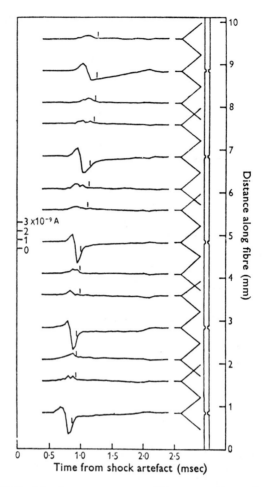

Fig. 20.22 Membrane currents at different positions along an isolated frog fibre. Each curve shows the difference between the longitudinal currents, recorded as in Figure 20.21, at the two points 0·75 mm apart indicated to the right. The vertical mark above each graph shows the time when the change in membrane potential reached its peak at that position on the fibre. Outward current is plotted upwards. (*From* A. F. Huxley & R. Stämpfli (1949) *Journal of Physiology*, **108**, 327.)

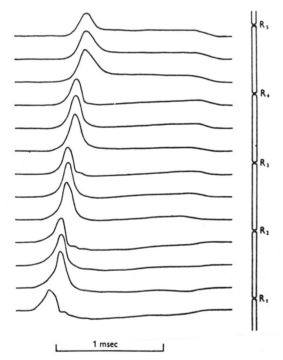

Fig. 20.21 Records obtained by the method shown in Fig. 20.23. Each cathode-ray oscillograph record is shown opposite the position on the fibre which the short glass capillary occupied when the record was obtained. All the records from any one internode are nearly the same and the peak of the disturbance occurs at the same time. R_1, R_2 to R_5 are nodes of Ranvier. (*After* A. F. Huxley & R. Stämpfli (1949) *Journal of Physiology*, **108**, 321.)

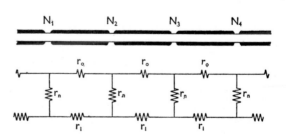

Fig. 20.23 Equivalent circuit for the resistive elements of a myelinated nerve fibre. According to Tasaki (1935), for a toad fibre whose outside diameter is 12 μm and nodal spacing 2 mm, the internal longitudinal resistance r_i is just under 20 MΩ and the resistance across each node r_n is just over 20 MΩ. In a large volume of fluid the external resistance r_o is negligibly small.

current showed (Fig. 20.21) that at all points along the outside of any one internode the current flow was roughly the same, both in magnitude and in timing; but the peaks of current flow were displaced stepwise in time by about one-tenth of a millisecond as successive nodes were passed. To determine transverse current flow, neighbouring pairs of records were subtracted from one another, since the difference between the longitudinal currents at two positions must have arisen from current entering or leaving the axis cylinder transversely between these positions. This procedure gave the results illustrated in Figure 20.22, from which it is seen that over the internodes there was only a small leakage of outward current, but that at each node there was a brief pulse of outward current followed by a substantially larger pulse of inward current.

The equivalent electrical circuit for a short length of a myelinated fibre is shown in Figure 20.23. Owing to the cable structure of the nerve fibre, whenever a change in electric potential is developed across the membrane at a node, its effect spreads nearly instantaneously along the fibre, because of a flow of electric current through the network of resistances. This type of distribution of potential change, which depends only on the passive electrical behaviour of the system, is known as an *electrotonic* spread of potential. The dissimilarity between electric cables and nerve fibres arises because the materials composing the nerve are less suitable for obtaining electrotonic spread over long distances than those used by an electrical engineer; the central conductor, that is to say the axis cylinder, has too high an electrical resistance, and the insulator, that is to say the nerve membrane and myelin sheath, too low a resistance. The values of the resistances shown in Figure 20.23 are approximately such that if a potential change, V, develops across one node, the change at the neighbouring node is 0·4 V, at the next node but one 0·16 V, and so on. In other words, the passive or electrotonic spread of potential decrements rather rapidly. However, the nerve membrane does *not* behave merely as a passive resistance, since the potential across it is capable of altering actively as a result of the sequence of permeability changes already described. Figure 20.22 shows that the myelin sheath exhibits only passive electrical behaviour, but that the membrane at the nodes behaves in a more complicated way. The initial flow of outward current at each node arises from the electrotonic spread of activity from the preceding node; this triggers an active process which then allows current to flow inwards so amplifying the potential change handed on to the next node, and so on.

Experiments by various workers have established that the permeability changes that take place at the nodes of a myelinated fibre are essentially similar to those that take place all along a non-myelinated fibre. Since the size of the fully-developed action potential is of the order of 120 mV, and since it is necessary to depolarize the membrane at the next node by only about 15 mV in order to initiate the active changes, the conduction mechanism embodies a considerable margin of safety. From these figures, and from the fact that the electrotonic potential decrements to about 0·4 from node to node, it can be predicted that the nerve impulse should be capable of being conducted past one or even two inactive nodes without blocking and this is indeed the case.

A simple experiment performed by Huxley and Stämpfli to demonstrate the importance of the external current pathway in propagation along a myelinated nerve fibre is illustrated in

Figure 20.24. The nerve of a nerve-muscle preparation was pared down until only one fibre was left. Stimulation of the nerve at P then caused a visible contraction of a motor unit in the muscle, M. The preparation was now laid in two pools of Ringer's solution on insulated microscope slides A and B in such a position that part of an internode, but not a node, lay across the 1 mm air gap separating the pools. At first, stimulation at P continued to cause a muscle twitch, but soon the layer of fluid outside the myelin sheath in the air gap was dried up by evaporation, and the muscle ceased to twitch. Conduction across the gap could, however, be restored by placing a wet thread, T, between the two pools. This proved that an action potential arriving at the node just to the left of the air gap could only trigger the node on the further side of the gap if there was a reasonably low-resistance electrical connexion between the pools. On reference to Figure 20.23 it will be seen that if r_0 becomes at all large, the potential change at N_2 produced by a spike at N_1 will fall below the threshold for excitation.

Since the electrotonic spread of potential along a nerve fibre is a virtually instantaneous process, it may be asked why the nerve impulse is not propagated more rapidly than it is. The explanation is that there is a definite delay at each node, of the order of 1/10 msec (see Fig. 20.21), which represents the time necessary for the ions to move through the capacitance of the membrane at the node and to reverse the potential across it. The main reason why myelinated fibres conduct impulses more rapidly than non-myelinated ones of equal diameter is that their total membrane capacity is smaller. In a non-myelinated fibre the delay in altering membrane polarization is in effect encountered all along the fibre and not just at the nodes. Conduction velocity is also affected by the longitudinal electric resistance, and is decreased by a rise in either the internal or the external resistance. Thus a large non-myelinated axon conducts faster than a small one because of its lower internal resistance, while Hodgkin showed some years ago that the conduction velocity in a squid axon supported on a series of metal strips was greater if the strips were connected together electrically than if they were insulated from one another. It might be added that an increase of the distance between nodes in a myelinated fibre is not as advantageous as might be supposed, since the greater spacing is offset by an increase in the delay at each node. Huxley and Stämpfli pointed out that there is likely to be an optimum spacing of nodes for

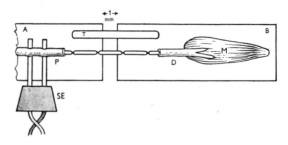

Fig. 20.24   Diagram to illustrate the experiment described by A. F. Huxley & R. Stämpfli (1949) *Journal of Physiology*, **108**, 315, to show the importance for conduction of the nerve impulse of current flowing outside the myelin sheath. A and B, microscope slides; P and D, proximal and distal portions of the nerve to the muscle M; T, wet thread; SE, stimulating electrodes.

maximum conduction velocity, and that the spacing found in normal fibres is probably close to this optimum.

Myelinization not only increases conduction velocity but also, because of the lower total membrane capacity, reduces the exchange of Na^+ and K^+ ions that takes place during the passage of each impulse. It therefore results in considerable economy of energy expenditure. The ionic exchange has not yet been measured very accurately in myelinated fibres, but it is certainly much smaller than in non-myelinated fibres of comparable size.

Nerve Metabolism and Active Transport of Ions

The mechanisms described so far do not require a direct supply of energy from cell metabolism. Energy is certainly dissipated during the passage of a nerve impulse, since electric currents are generated which flow through the surrounding tissue and through the nerve itself; but the *immediate* sources of this energy appear to be the pre-existing concentration gradients for Na^+ and K^+ ions. Nerve metabolism is required to provide the energy to drive an active transport system which builds up the concentration gradients in the first place, and then reverses the loss of K^+ and gain of Na^+ which occur during nervous activity. The clearest evidence for this statement comes from experiments on the squid giant axon, where metabolic inhibitors can be shown to block the active transport mechanism without having any obvious effect on the ability of the axon to conduct impulses. Thus in the experiment illustrated in Figure 20.25, the effect of applying cyanide was to reduce the rate of extrusion of labelled sodium to less than a quarter of its initial value, but the size of the action potential was unchanged in the poisoned axon. This dissociation between the mechanism of the action potential, involving downhill ionic movements, and that of the recovery process, involving uphill movements against the concentration gradients, can be revealed in squid axons because of their exceptional size. The quantity of potassium lost by a squid axon in the course of a single impulse is less than a millionth part of its initial content, so that one would expect such an axon to be capable of conducting a large number of impulses even though its recovery mechanism were totally inoperative. The same argument probably applies to myelinated nerve fibres in which the economy in ionic exchange during the impulse, resulting from the presence of the myelin sheath, again means that many impulses can be conducted without large internal concentration changes; but for these fibres the experimental evidence is less clear cut. The situation where conduction and recovery mechanisms cannot be clearly dissociated is that of excitable cells whose ratio of surface to volume is relatively large, that is to say in non-myelinated C fibres and in the cells of the central nervous system with their innumerable fine dendrites. Here a single impulse might lower the internal potassium concentration by over a thousandth part, so that, if recovery were blocked, the ionic reserves would suffice only for the conduction of a few hundred impulses. In such cells the recovery mechanism has to work continuously even to combat the resting leakage of K^+ and gain of Na^+, and this is an important reason for the dependence of the central nervous system on an adequate supply of both glucose and oxygen in the blood.

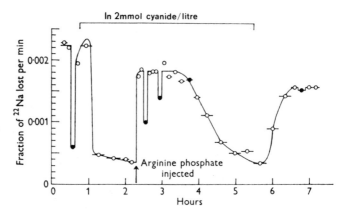

Fig. 20.25 The effect of the efflux of labelled sodium from a squid giant axon of first blocking metabolism with cyanide and then injecting a large quantity of arginine phosphate. Open circles show efflux with $[K]_o = 10\,mmol/l$, filled-in circles show efflux into a K-free solution. Immediately after the injection the mean internal concentration of arginine phosphate was $33\,mmol/l$. Axon diameter 686 μm, temperature 18° C. (*From* P. C. Caldwell, A. L. Hodgkin, R. D. Keynes, & T. I. Shaw (1960). *Journal of Physiology*, **152**, 561.)

In the investigation of the active transport of ions in nerve and muscle, radioactive isotopes have been very useful tools. The experiment of Figure 20.25 provides an example of the kind of approach that has been used. It will be seen that in an unpoisoned squid axon with an external $[K^+]$ of $10\,mmol/l$ the so-called 'sodium pump' operates at such a rate that about 2 parts in 1000 of the internal Na^+ are exchanged per minute. The absolute size of the sodium efflux depends on this 'rate constant' and on the internal $[Na^+]$, so that the system is self-regulating as far as the internal sodium level is concerned. Thus in an axon at rest, the internal $[Na^+]$ settles down at the level which makes the active efflux just balance the resting inward leakage (which is low, because P_{Na} is small, but is not zero). After a burst of impulses the internal $[Na^+]$ will be temporarily raised, so that for a while sodium efflux will be greater than influx, and the internal $[Na^+]$ will slowly fall back towards its steady-state value. Another important feature of the mechanism is that the outward movement of Na^+ is coupled in some way as yet not understood to an inward movement of K^+; the best evidence for the existence of some degree of coupling is that removal of external K^+ immediately reduces the Na^+ efflux, as Figure 20.25 shows. This behaviour is also exhibited by the sodium transport processes in many other tissues, such as muscle fibres and erythrocytes. The other question with which Figure 20.25 is concerned is that of identifying the metabolic intermediate which drives the sodium pump. In the cyanide-poisoned axon it has been found that the concentrations of ATP and arginine phosphate (the counterpart in many invertebrate tissues of the creatine phosphate in vertebrates, whose role, as described on page 340, is to provide a readily available reserve supply of high-energy phosphate bonds) quickly fall to zero; at the same time the sodium efflux drops to a small fraction of its initial value, and the potassium influx is also cut down. As the figure shows, if a quantity of arginine phosphate is injected into the poisoned axon, restoring the concentration of ATP temporarily to its unpoisoned level, the sodium efflux is also restored for a while.

Later, when the injected high-energy phosphate bonds have been used up, the efflux returns to the poisoned level. Finally, when the cyanide is washed away, and oxidative phosphorylation is allowed to start up again, ATP and arginine phosphate reappear in the axoplasm and the sodium efflux recovers.

A. V. Hill and his colleagues, using specially designed thermocouples and galvanometers, first showed more than 50 years ago that the conduction of nerve impulses was accompanied by the liberation of a minute amount of heat; it has also been shown that there is a concomitant increase in oxygen consumption and in the production of carbon dioxide. In the earlier work, it was possible to distinguish between the extra heat production occurring within one second of stimulation, which was termed the *initial heat*, and a slower heat production spread out over the following thirty minutes, termed the *recovery heat*. The initial heat formed a rather variable fraction (usually about one-twentieth) of the total extra heat, and in a *Maia* (spider crab) nerve at 0°C amounted to about 8×10^{-6} joules/g nerve for a single impulse. In a myelinated frog nerve the extra heat production on stimulation was smaller than in crab nerve. The resting heat production of a frog nerve at 20°C was about 300×10^{-6} joules/g nerve per second, while the maximum additional heat production during continuous stimulation was about 170×10^{-6} joules/g nerve per second. The resting oxygen consumption of frog nerve is around 30 mm^3/g per hour, and during maximal stimulation the consumption may be doubled.

The initial heat production in non-myelinated nerve fibres has now been reinvestigated with more rapid recording equipment, and it has become clear that it consists of an evolution of heat during the upstroke of the action potential followed by an absorption of heat during the downstroke. Thus in a single impulse at 0°C in *Maia* nerve, Abbott, Hill and Howarth found that the first thermal event was a temperature rise of about 9×10^{-6}°C; there was then a somewhat more gradual fall averaging 7×10^{-6}°C, leaving the net rise of around 2×10^{-6}°C that had been seen before with slower instruments. In the non-myelinated C fibres of the rabbit's cervical vagus nerve, Howarth, Keynes and Ritchie have estimated the initial positive heat for a single impulse at 5°C as 103×10^{-6} joules/g nerve, and the initial negative heat as 93×10^{-6} joules/g nerve.

Other phenomena observed in stimulated nerves which have not yet been fully explained are the production of small quantities of ammonia, changes in the amount of light scattered and in the optical retardation of the membrane and a very slight swelling.

Other Aspects of Nerve Conduction

Threshold. As may be seen from Figure 20.9, excitation of a nerve fibre involves the rapid depolarization of the membrane to a critical level normally about 15 mV smaller than the resting potential. Depolarization to a lesser extent does not, of course, fail to increase the sodium permeability of the membrane; subthreshold depolarization does increase P_{Na}, but not to the point where Na^+ ions enter faster than K^+ ions can leave, so that at the end of the shock the membrane is merely repolarized. The critical level for excitation is the membrane potential at which the net rate of entry of Na^+ becomes exactly equal to the net rate of exit of K^+ (plus a small contribution from entry of Cl^-). Greater depolarization than this tips the balance in favour of Na^+, and the regenerative process already described takes over and causes a rapidly accelerating inrush of Na^+. After just subthreshold depolarization, when P_{Na} has been raised over an appreciable area of membrane, the repolarization process may be somewhat slow to begin with, and a *local response* may be observed.

Refractory period. At the end of the spike the membrane is left with its sodium permeability mechanism inactivated and its potassium permeability appreciably greater than normal. Both changes help to raise the threshold for re-excitation above normal. The partial inactivation of the sodium permeability means that even to raise inward Na^+ current to the normal critical level requires more depolarization than usual, and the raised potassium permeability means that the critical Na^+ current is actually greater than normal. Until the permeabilities for both ions have returned to their resting values and the sodium mechanism is fully reactivated, the shock necessary to trigger a second spike is above the normal threshold in size.

Accommodation. It has long been known that nerves are not readily stimulated by the application of slowly rising currents, because they tend to 'accommodate' to this type of stimulus. Accommodation arises from two causes:

1. Depolarization brings about a long lasting rise in potassium permeability.

2. Sustained depolarization semi-permanently inactivates the sodium permeability mechanism.

Both changes take place with an appreciable time lag after the membrane potential is lowered, so that they are not effective when a constant current is first applied, but do become important at long times. They also persist for some time after the end of a stimulus, and are thus responsible for the appearance of *post-cathodal depression*, that is to say for a lowering of excitability after application for some while of a weak cathodal current. As a result of accommodation, cathodal currents rising more slowly than a certain limiting value do not stimulate at all, since the rise in threshold keeps pace with the depolarization.

Anode break excitation. Another familiar phenomenon is the occurrence of excitation when an anodal current is switched off. This can readily be demonstrated in isolated squid axons or frog nerves, but is not seen in freshly dissected frog muscle or in nerves stimulated *in situ* in living animals. In general, the conditions which allow anode break excitation to be exhibited seem to be that the resting potential should be rather low, so that there is an appreciable resting leakage of potassium and gain of sodium. The nerve can then be considered to be in a state of mild cathodal depression, with its sodium permeability mechanism partially inactivated, and an abnormally high potassium permeability. The effect of anodal polarization is to reactivate the sodium permeability and to reduce potassium permeability, and this 'improved' state persists for a short while after the applied current is switched off. While it persists, the critical potential at which inward Na^+ current exceeds outward K^+ current may be temporarily above the membrane potential in the absence of external current. Hence when the current is removed, an action potential is initiated.

Stimulation by solutions of high potassium concen-

tration. Application to excitable tissues of solutions containing high concentrations of potassium may have a stimulatory effect. This action is related to the depolarization caused by high external [K$^+$], which is illustrated in Figure 20.15. However, if a solution of high [K$^+$] is applied simultaneously over the whole surface of a fibre, its effect is usually to depress or even to abolish excitability since, as discussed in the two previous paragraphs, a maintained depolarization both inactivates P_{Na} and raises P_K. Thus, although at first sight the uniform depolarization produced by high [K$^+$] might be expected to shift the membrane potential closer to the critical triggering level, and therefore to increase excitability, the critical level is itself altered by the changes in P_{Na} and P_K in such a way that larger currents have to be applied to the nerve in order to reach it. The statement that under these conditions excitability is lowered and not raised does not conflict with the common experimental finding that application of potassium solutions to many excitable cells makes them generate impulses. Stimulatory effects of this kind are apt to arise if the applied solutions do not penetrate uniformly into the tissue, because if one part of a nerve is depolarized much more than another, this is analogous to the application of a local catelectrotonus, and a repetitive discharge may arise at the edge of the depolarized region.

The effect of calcium on excitable tissues. The actions on nerve and muscle fibres of solutions containing less than the normal amounts of Ca^{2+} and Mg^{2+} ions are sometimes dramatic. In squid axons, slight lowering of external [Ca^{2+}] leads to an oscillatory behaviour of the membrane potential, while more drastic reduction of calcium causes a spontaneous discharge of impulses at a high repetition rate. Conversely, a rise in external [Ca^{2+}] tends to stabilize the nerve membrane and to raise the threshold for excitation. Changes in external [Mg^{2+}] have rather similar effects on peripheral nerves. Studies by Hodgkin and Frankenhaeuser with the voltage-clamp technique have shown that the curve relating P_{Na} to membrane potential is shifted in one direction along the voltage axis by lowering [Ca^{2+}], and in the other direction by raising [Ca^{2+}]. However, the resting potential is rather intensitive to changes in [Ca^{2+}]. This readily explains the relationship between [Ca^{2+}] and threshold, since a rise in [Ca^{2+}] moves the critical triggering level away from the resting potential, while a fall in [Ca^{2+}] moves the critical level towards it. If the reduction in external [Ca^{2+}] is large enough, the critical level may even be shifted beyond the resting potential, causing a spontaneous discharge. Although calcium and magnesium have similar actions on the excitability of nerve and muscle fibres, they have antagonistic actions at neuro-muscular junctions and possibly also at synaptic junctions between neurones. Thus calcium appears to increase the amount of acetylcholine released by a motor nerve ending, while magnesium seems to decrease it.

After-potentials. In many types of nerve and muscle fibre the membrane potential does not immediately return to the base-line at the end of the spike, but undergoes further small and relatively slow variations known as 'after-potentials'. The nomenclature of after-potentials dates from the period before the invention of intracellular recording techniques, so that a variation of membrane potential in the same direction as the spike itself is termed a *negative after-potential*, while a

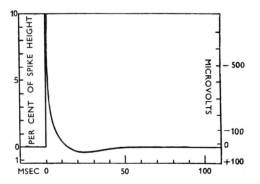

Fig. 20.26 Phrenic nerve at 37°C. The spike, lasting only 0·5 msec, leaves the base-line and goes above the figure; it then returns to the figure and is continued for about 10 msec as the negative after-potential, which is succeeded by a positive phase, the dip below the base line lasting about 50 msec. (J. Erlanger & H. S. Gasser (1937) *Electrical Signs of Nervous Activity*, p. 148 Philadelphia: University of Pennsylvania Press.)

variation in the opposite direction (that is to say, a hyperpolarization relative to the normal resting potential) is termed a *positive after-potential*. As may be seen in Figure 20.7 A and B, isolated squid axons display a characteristic positive phase, which is almost completely absent in the living animal, while frog muscle fibres have a prolonged negative after-potential (Fig. 20.7 H). In some mammalian nerves there is first a negative and then a positive after-potential; these are seen both in myelinated fibres (Fig. 20.26) and in non-myelinated fibres. A related phenomenon, which is most marked in the smallest fibres, is the occurrence after a period of repetitive activity of a prolonged hyperpolarization of the membrane, known as the post-tetanic hyperpolarization.

It seems reasonable to suppose that after-potentials are always connected with changes in membrane permeability towards certain ions, but the precise sequence of changes probably varies with the type of fibre concerned. For example, in the isolated squid axon the positive phase arises because P_K is abnormally high at the end of the spike and P_{Na} very low, so that the membrane potential temporarily comes close to E_K (Fig. 20.19). On the other hand, there is good evidence that production of the post-tetanic hyperpolarization which has been studied in frog nerves by Connelly and in mammalian C fibres by Rang, Ritchie and Straub, depends on an enhanced rate of electrogenic extrusion of Na$^+$ and of reabsorption of K$^+$ after a burst of impulses. There is also evidence that the presence of Schwann cells partially or wholly enveloping certain types of nerve fibre has important effects on the after-potential by slightly restricting the rate of diffusion of ions in the immediate neighbourhood of the nerve membrane.

The mechanism of the permeability changes. It is now clear that the changes in permeability that underlie nervous excitation depend on the presence in the nerve membrane of two sets of ionic channels that open and close appropriately under the influence of membrane potential. The channels selective for Na$^+$ ions can be blocked completely by very low concentrations of the Japanese puffer fish poison tetrodotoxin applied externally, while the K$^+$ channels are best blocked from the inside by tetraethyl ammonium or Cs^+ ions. Since the time and voltage dependence of the K^+ permeability changes is entirely unaffected by total blockage of the Na^+ channels, while the converse is equally true for the Na^+ permeability changes, which remain normal in axons treated with tetraethyl ammonium chloride, there can be no doubt that the Na^+ and K^+ channels operate in parallel and independently of one another, except that the same potential acts on both of them. From studies with tritium-labelled tetrodotoxin by Ritchie and others, the Na^+ channels can be quite accurately counted, the numbers in $1\ \mu m^2$ of membrane ranging from about 3 in the very small fibres of the garfish olfactory nerve and 25 in the C fibres of the rabbit cervical vagus to several hundred in the squid giant axon. Since in the same area there are around 4 million phospholipid molecules, the Na^+ channels are relatively sparsely distributed. It has not yet proved possible to make similar estimates of the density of the K^+ channels, but there are indications that there may be even fewer of them.

The fact that the opening and closing of the Na^+ and K^+ channels is voltage-dependent implies that they must be controlled by some kind of electrically charged gating system. Mobile charged particles or dipoles form an integral part of the structure of the Na^+ channels. The movement of these particles when the potential across the membrane is altered gives rise to a small surge of 'gating current'. Several lines of argument suggest that each Na^+ channel incorporates 3 gating particles; and these evidently function in series with and independently of the filter responsible for the ionic selectivity of the channels.

Regeneration of Peripheral Nerves

When a mixed peripheral nerve is cut across there is paralysis and anaesthesia in the area supplied exclusively by that nerve; because of the wide overlap of sensory innervation, the completely insensitive area is much smaller than the total field supplied by the nerve. The interruption of the efferent fibres also causes sudomotor, pilomotor and vasomotor paralysis (see p. 400). The peripheral part of the nerve, that is the part containing nerve fibres no longer connected to their cell bodies, degenerates, and after a few days the affected muscles show a characteristic change in their strength-duration curve for electrical excitation (Fig. 20.10) and begin to atrophy. Whereas in a normally innervated muscle the strength-duration curve tends to be determined by that for the nerve endings, with greatest excitability at the point of entry of the motor nerve, the denervated muscle gives the curve typical of the muscle fibres themselves, with a much greater chronaxie and an excitability that is almost the same all over the muscle belly. Another change in the denervated muscle fibres is that all parts of the muscle, and not just the region of the nerve endings, become sensitive to the application of acetylcholine (p. 336).

If a nerve is crushed, for example by the end of a fractured bone, the axons may be divided but the nerve trunk may be held together by its fibrous tissue. The paralysis and anaesthesia are then exactly as before, and the peripheral part of the nerve degenerates, but no surgical operation is required to bring the severed ends of the nerve together. Pressure on a nerve by a

tourniquet or by a crutch may cause a predominantly motor paralysis with little muscular wasting and with relatively little sensory loss, affecting chiefly the large myelinated motor nerve fibres. Complete recovery usually occurs within a few days or at most within a few weeks.

In spite of the relatively enormous length of the nerve fibre, its cell body exerts a great influence over even its most distant parts. If a nerve is cut and examined about a day later it is found that material has been extruded from the end of the central stump. Within a few days the myelin sheath in the peripheral stump breaks up into ovoid segments each somewhat shorter than the internodal distance. Phosphatase and esterase concentrations in the tissue are increased, suggesting that autolysis is being carried out by enzymes of the lysosomal system. A week after section the degenerating myelin stains black with osmic acid after treatment with bichromate (Marchi's method). This staining property, which has proved most useful in tracing the conducting tracts within the spinal cord, is then gradually lost. Shortly after nerve section the peripheral parts of the axons also fragment, and they and the myelin are subsequently removed by macrophages. This whole process is often called *Wallerian degeneration* because it was described first by Waller in 1862. In the central stump, where the fibres are still attached to their cell bodies, degeneration is usually confined to the centimetre or so next to the point of section, although a few of the central fibres and even their cell bodies may disappear, especially in very young animals. The cell body itself also shows changes which are known as *chromatolysis*; they are particularly well marked on cutting the nerve close to the cell body. The Nissl granules disappear from the dendrites and later from the main body of the cell, and the nucleus moves to one side of the cell. These changes, which are associated with an alteration in the excitability of the cell, begin on the first day and reach their maximum in the third week, after which the Nissl substance gradually reappears and the cell regains its normal appearance.

While Wallerian degeneration of the peripheral stump is proceeding, regeneration begins at the central end. Large numbers of little branches sprout from the cut fibres in all directions, forming an expanded mass or *neuroma*. Some of these branches enter the peripheral stump, where Schwann cells have proliferated and now form continuous tubes which guide the growing elements towards the periphery. When one branch has found its way satisfactorily into the peripheral stump, the other sprouting branches of that fibre disappear. Denervated organs such as muscle strongly attract new nerve fibres, probably by liberating a chemical factor which promotes their growth. Therefore neighbouring nerves also produce fresh branches. When new fibres reach the muscle, several of them may contact the same muscle fibre, but after the first functional end-plate has been formed, the other nerve branches degenerate.

The randomness in the healing process excludes any regular order in the return of function and makes complete recovery unlikely. However, there is sometimes a surprisingly good restoration of function after nerve section, which has been attributed to 're-education' of the controlling centres, perhaps through rearrangements of the relevant synaptic connexions in the spinal cord or to the existence of a guidance mechanism. The most complete recovery is obtained when the cut ends of the nerve are brought together very soon after the injury. The power of repair in nerves is not lost for many months, but the longer the delay in apposing the ends the poorer is the final result. This is partly due to the atrophy of the end-organs and partly to the atrophy and eventual disappearance of muscle cells. Improvement in muscle power and in sensation often continues for up to three years. Some of the properties of a muscle apparently depend on its particular nerve supply. Thus if a 'slow' muscle such as the soleus is re-innervated by fibres which previously supplied a 'fast' muscle like flexor digitorum longus, soleus becomes relatively fast.

Various methods are available clinically for determining the rate of recovery in a nerve. As regenerating fibres grow down the peripheral stump of a damaged nerve they re-innervate muscles in turn according to the distance to be travelled to each muscle. The time of recovery of motor function is taken as the time at which muscles show the first signs of voluntary contraction. The regenerated fibres are initially very much thinner than normal, and they may not regain their original thickness and conduction velocity for over a year; they probably never do if the nerve has been cut and not merely crushed. From anatomical dissections detailed information has been obtained about the lengths of the nerves to the muscles and, by dividing the distance from the point of section to the point of attachment of the nerve to the muscle cells by the time needed for recovery, it is found that a nerve fibre grows about 1·5 mm per day. Percussion over the non-myelinated tip of the advancing axon produces a tingling sensation which is known as Tinel's sign. This phenomenon advances at an average rate of about 1·7 mm per day, but it is not so satisfactory a method as the previous one for determining the rate of regeneration in a nerve. In calculating the time likely to be taken after nerve suture for the return of function it is well to add 6 or 8 weeks to allow for the possibility of an unusually slow rate of regeneration.

When the spinal cord is cut or the posterior roots are sectioned next to the cord, Wallerian degeneration occurs within the cord; although it may be followed by regeneration of a few new fibres within the central nervous system, restoration of function does not occur. The reason for this failure is not entirely clear, but two important factors seem to be scarring at the site of section, which prevents orderly penetration by regenerating fibres, and the absence of Schwann cell tubes. Unlike spinal neurones, cells in the brain itself usually degenerate irreversibly after section of their axons.

The Afferent Impulse

So far we have considered the nerve impulse produced artificially by electrical stimulation of a nerve. In the living body certain nerve fibres are connected to specialized endings and these, when suitably stimulated, generate continuous trains or phasic discharges of afferent impulses. As Adrian pointed out, the stimulus applied to an end-organ may be compared to the pressure on the trigger of a machine-gun; either it is strong enough to fire the bullets or it is too weak to do anything at all (all-or-nothing relationship). Because of its refractory period the nerve fibre cannot transmit a steady potential but only a series of pulses, so that the message passing along the nerve may be likened to a stream of machine-gun bullets. If the abnormal conditions obtaining during the

relatively refractory period are disregarded, the intensity of each impulse is constant or, to pursue the analogy, all the bullets are of the same size. The magnitude of the impulses cannot be altered by changing the strength of the stimulus. The only way, in fact, in which the message, carried by a given fibre, can be graded to give the central nervous system information of the strength of the stimulus applied to the end-organ is by a variation in the total number of impulses and in the frequency with which they recur. Oscillograph records from even quite small nerves in the body may be too complex for analysis if many fibres are active and the action potentials from individual fibres are superimposed on one another. In the case of cutaneous sensory nerves the record may be simplified by stimulating only a very small area of skin, by cutting away unwanted receptors, or by cutting partly through the nerve. It is also possible to sample the activity of individual nerve fibres by probing the nerve trunk with a micro-electrode. In this way the action potentials resulting from the activity of a single end-organ have been recorded. The form of these endings is very variable and, with the histological methods at present available, gives little clue to the particular stimulus to which the ending is sensitive. However, fibres have been isolated which carry signals from endings specifically sensitive to stretch, the chemical environment, temperature deviation, touch and pressure. The normal stimulus for the stretch sensitive endings is determined by the tissue in which they are deployed. Thus when arranged in the wall of a hollow organ, such as the carotid sinus, they signal fluid pressure (see p. 194 and p. 234), whereas arranged between the fibres of a tendon or linked mechanically to a contractile element composed of the intrafusal fibres of a muscle spindle (see p. 343) they signal longitudinal tension and act as muscle proprioceptors.

Adrian and Zotterman in 1926 first elucidated some of the properties of the muscle spindle by using the small sterno-cutaneous muscle of the frog. When the muscle was partly cut away records of the activity of one spindle were obtained from electrodes placed on the larger nerve trunk which is joined by the tiny nerve from the muscle. Matthews used the flexor digitorum brevis IV of the frog's foot, a muscle in which there is only one muscle spindle. Later in 1933 he recorded impulses from single spindle endings and tendon endings in the cat by cutting down a muscle nerve and leading from a single active nerve fibre. When the muscle is stretched by a weight the endings in a spindle discharge at a rate that depends on the weight used (Fig. 20.28) and continues for long periods with only a small decline in frequency (Fig. 20.27). This slight falling off is known as slow adaptation; it is a decline in excitability produced by the stimulus. Each end-organ has its own rate of adaptation; muscle spindles adapt slowly, pressure organs more quickly and touch and hair endings very rapidly. The nerve fibre itself, in contrast with the nerve ending, adapts most quickly of all, since it responds with only one impulse at the beginning of a constant stimulus. These observations are summarized in Figure 20.29.

By placing electrodes near the muscle spindle in a frog muscle Katz has found that, when the muscle is stretched, there is, in addition to the spikes (nerve impulses) shown in Figure 20.27, a negativity of the spindle. The amount of this electrical potential, the so-called *generator potential*, which gives rise to a train of impulses in the sensory nerve, depends on the amount and rate of stretching. The spikes but not the generator potential are abolished by a local anaesthetic. Katz has tried to account, at least partly, for these findings by supposing that the cell membrane becomes thinner on stretching so that its capacity increases and its potential falls, thus giving rise to the initial portion of the generator potential. In the muscle spindle the stretch stimulus may be produced by activity of the contractile elements within the spindle or stretching of the spindle as a whole if the muscle is stretched; in the living animal both these processes may interact. A fuller description of muscle spindles is given on page 343.

A simpler arrangement is found at the joints where stretch receptors concerned with joint position sense are found in the capsule; these are spray-like nerve terminals (Ruffini organs) several of which may share a single medium-sized (7 to 10 μm) sensory nerve fibre. The endings which, in any given position

of the joint, lie on *stretched* connective tissue, discharge continuously. As parts of the joint are differentially stretched, or compressed, according to the position of the limbs, an individual joint proprioceptor may discharge impulses over a limited area of joint position (Fig. 20.30).

Larger Golgi endings with bunches of nerve sprays are found outside the capsules; each ending has its own nerve fibre (10 to 15 μm). These endings give a slower discharge than Ruffini organs, and may be associated with the joint ligaments. Numerous small Paciniform corpuscles give rapidly adapting responses and are very sensitive to quick movements. The fine free nerve endings probably subserve pain.

Also near the joints, often under the tendons of the muscles, are Pacinian corpuscles which are again sensitive to quick movements and are probably the receptors for recording vibrations. The vibration sense is highly developed in mammals

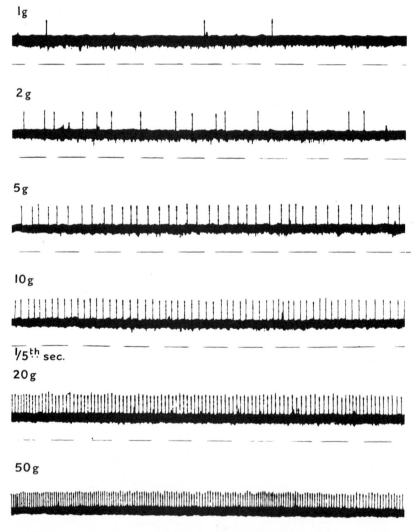

Fig. 20.27 Photographic recordings from a cathode-ray oscilloscope of action potentials in the sciatic nerve from a single stretch-receptor in the gastrocnemius muscle of a frog. Responses in other stretch-receptors had been eliminated by cutting down the sciatic nerve trunk until it contained only one active fibre. The load indicated on the diagram was applied to the tendo calcaneus one second before the beginning of each record. Close inspection of the records, especially those for 20 g and 50 g, shows that the space between individual spikes increases progressively from left to right. This decline in the frequency of discharge of the receptor is called adaptation. It is quite slow in the case of the stretch receptors. Some adaptation had, of course, occurred between the application of the weight and the beginning of the record in each case. Time marks represent 0·2 sec, spike-height approximately 50 μV. (*By courtesy of B. L. Andrew.*)

and its loss is an early sign of sensory deficiency (see p. 370). In structure these corpuscles consist of a single nerve fibre (4 to 7 μm) terminating in a long non-myelinated portion which forms the ending proper. The ending, which contains many mitochondria but has no sheath of Schwann, is enclosed in a thick onion-like connective tissue capsule. These corpuscles have proved useful for the study of the transference of mechanical stimuli into electrical impulses since they have in a simple form the component parts of many of the more complicated receptors. Joint receptors seem to have an important role in motor regulation by their influence on interneurones controlling motoneurones.

An end-organ, such as a tactile end-organ, which adapts quickly cannot give well-graded responses to different strengths of stimulation because the response is over and done with in such a short time. On the hand slowly adapting end-organs, like the muscle spindles, are able to give the central nervous system very accurate information about the intensity of the stimulus. Since a tactile stimulus is usually applied not to a single end-organ but to a fairly large area of skin a large

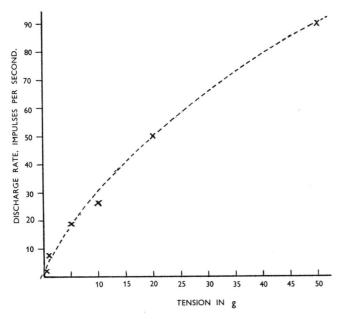

Fig. 20.28 Graph showing the relation between the tension applied to the tendon of a frog's gastrocnemius and the rate of discharge of nerve impulses from a single stretch-receptor within the muscle (calculated from Fig. 20.27).

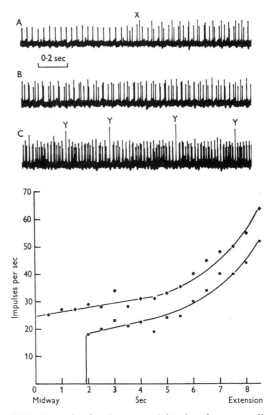

Fig. 20.30 Records of action potentials taken from a small sensory nerve filament arising from sensory endings in the thyroepiglottal joint of the larynx of a rat. The joint was moved slowly to full extension, the whole movement lasting 8 sec. A, B and C are small sections of the original continuous record taken respectively at the beginning of the movement and at 4 and 6·5 sec later. At the beginning of A, a single ending was active and discharged impulses at the rate of 25 per sec. Note that the impulses are of nearly constant size and are regularly spaced. At the point marked X a second ending began to discharge impulses which can be distinguished from those in the fibre connected to the first ending by the difference in the size of the action potential. The progressive addition of new active endings as the stimulus (in this case joint extension) is increased is referred to as recruitment of sensory endings. The large action potentials marked Y are not due to the recruitment of a third ending but to the electrical summation of two impulses which have occurred simultaneously in each of the two active fibres. In the lower figure the frequency of discharge of the two endings has been plotted against time. Apart from the differences of threshold the curves are of similar shape. Since the frequncy of both endings rises as the joint is extended it is easy to see that these endings signal the position of the joint to the central nervous system, that is they act as joint proprioceptors. (B. L. Andrew (1954) *Journal of Physiology*, **126**, 514.)

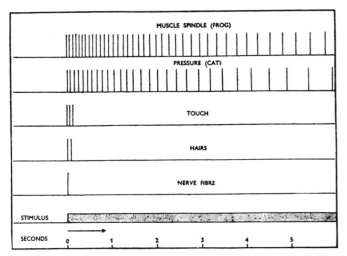

Fig. 20.29 Diagrams to illustrate the effect of applying a constant stimulus to various end-organs and to a nerve fibre. In the case of a nerve fibre a single impulse is aroused but in the end-organs a series of impulses of declining frequency is evoked. (*After* E. D. Adrian.)

number of end-organs is affected and so the information received at the central nervous system may be more complete than would be inferred from our knowledge of the properties of a single end-organ. Moreover when we touch an object we often run the fingers over it. This procedure causes stimulation of a large number of the quickly adapting end-organs and presents each with a rapidly changing stimulus so that each end-organ is continually re-excited. In this way a quickly adapting end-organ may be made to send a large number of impulses to the central nervous system.

THE SYNAPSE

The meeting-place of two neurones is called a synapse; at this point their surface membranes are very close together, but there is never any cytoplasmic continuity between them. The synapses between different types of excitable cell vary in their structure, but have some features in common. In general, the presynaptic fibre divides up into numerous fine branches which then end in greatly expanded terminals, *presynaptic knobs*, which make intimate contact with part of the membrane of the cell body or dendrites of the *post-synaptic* cell. A single anterior horn cell may be invested by as many as 33 000 synaptic knobs (Fig. 20.31) derived from a large number of axons. In the part of the presynaptic knob closest to the postsynaptic cell, there is always a dense assembly of spherical vesicles (synaptic vesicles) about 50 nm in diameter (Fig.

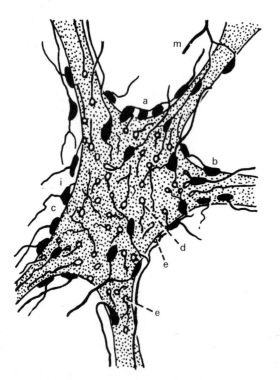

Fig. 20.31 This drawing of a motor cell of the spinal cord shows that it is invested by a large number of synaptic knobs from many neurones. The synaptic density is about 20 per 100 μm^2. The surface area of a motoneurone is on average 165 000 μm^2. This gives about 33 000 synapses. a, b, strong bulbs; c, i, terminal buttons; d, e, fine bulbs; m, terminal nerve fibre. (S. R. Y. Cajal (1933) *Histology*, p. 290. London: Baillière, Tindall & Cox.)

20.32). There are no vesicles in the postsynaptic cell. The width of the extra-cellular space separating the pre- and postsynaptic membranes, the *synaptic cleft*, is another rather constant feature; it is generally about 25 nm.

The electrical resistance of the synaptic cleft is low enough to prevent any appreciable spread through the postsynaptic membrane of the electric current which flows around the presynaptic terminal when an impulse arrives there. Another factor which militates against electric excitation of the postsynaptic membrane by presynaptic action currents is the relatively greater area of the postsynaptic membrane. Except in a few special situations the coupling between the pre- and postsynaptic membranes is chemical rather than electrical. It depends on the release of a chemical transmitter substance from the presynaptic terminal, which then diffuses across the synaptic cleft and interacts with receptor sites on the postsynaptic membrane so as to cause a specific change in its ionic permeability. At some synapses the nature of this change is such as to produce a depolarization and hence an excitatory effect. At others the permeability change may tend to hold the membrane potential at its resting value, or may even cause a hyperpolarization; these synapses are inhibitory.

Some obvious distinctions between transmission of an impulse along a nerve fibre and transmission across a synapse follow directly from this description. In the first place, although the impulse can travel equally well in either direction along a nerve fibre, its passage across a synapse is strictly unidirectional. No chemical transmitter is released when an antidromic impulse arrives at the postsynaptic membrane, so that such an impulse cannot travel backwards any further than the first synapse it reaches. Secondly, passage across a synapse involves a finite time delay, because the release of the transmitter, its diffusion across the synaptic cleft and its action on the postsynaptic membrane are relatively slow processes. In a spinal motoneurone, delay from this source, to which has to be added a smaller contribution from the slowness of conduction in the very fine presynaptic nerve branches, is about 0·4 msec. In autonomic ganglia it may be somewhat longer. As will be seen later (p. 364), a knowledge of the total delay in a complex reflex pathway is valuable in determining the number of synapses involved. Thirdly, the intervention of a chemical transmitter results in a susceptibility of synapses to blocking by a wide variety of drugs which have relatively little effect on conduction in nerve fibres. These may act either by interfering with the synthesis or release of the transmitter, or by changing the sensitivity of the postsynaptic membrane; some specific examples are discussed on page 327. The last distinction, and by no means the least important, is that although some synapses—in particular the neuromuscular junction (p. 325)—operate in such a way that there is a one-to-one correspondence between presynaptic and postsynaptic impulses, the majority do not. In most neurones, a spatial and temporal summation of the several excitatory and inhibitory postsynaptic potentials takes place, and the postsynaptic membrane is triggered only by an appropriate combination of the impulses arriving along the presynaptic pathways. In contrast, therefore, to the all-or-none behaviour of peripheral nerves, synapses operate in a graded fashion, enabling the neurone to carry out an integration and sifting of the incoming information.

Many of our ideas about the mechanism of transmission

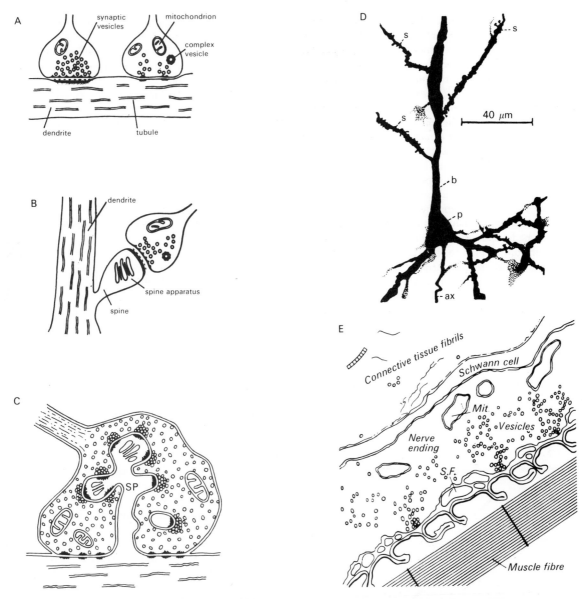

Fig. 20.32 The morphology of some synapses. A, two types of synaptic knob found on the soma and dendrites of cortical neurones. B, a dendritic spine of a neocortical pyramidal cell with its synapse. C, a more complicated synapse found on the spine (sp) of a dendrite of a hippocampal pyramidal cell. D, a Golgi preparation of a neurone from cat cerebral cortex showing spines (s) on its apical and basal dendrites, but not on the soma (p), axon (ax) or dendritic stumps (b) (*after* Whittaker & Gray). E, a frog motor end-plate, showing mitochondria (Mit), the characteristic folding of the synaptic cleft, and a few finger-like extensions of the Schwann cell (SF) beneath the nerve ending. (*After* Birks, Huxley & Katz.) (*From* J. C. Eccles (1964) *The Physiology of Synapses*. Berlin: Springer.)

across excitatory synapses have originated from micro-electrode studies of the neuromuscular junction. It is important to note that there is no doubt as to the identity of the chemical transmitter at the motor end-plate, which is one of the places where acetylcholine exerts its 'nicotinic' effect, to use the term introduced by Dale, as opposed to its 'muscarinic' effect when it acts as a peripheral parasympathetic humoral transmitter. The characteristic action of nicotine in this context is to cause rapid excitation, followed by block; this action is antagonized by substances like curare. Muscarine, on the other hand, has a slower and longer-lasting action, and is antagonized by atropine.

Another relatively simple type of synapse where acetyl-choline is certainly the transmitter is found in the ganglia of the autonomic system. Sympathetic ganglia have in fact provided particularly convenient material for studies on the chemistry of synaptic transmission, since it is not too difficult to perfuse their blood vessels and both to test the perfusate for the appearance of acetylcholine during electrical stimulation of the presynaptic nerve trunk and to see whether perfusion with acetylcholine sets up impulses in the postsynaptic fibres. These ganglia were also used in making some of the earlier electrical recordings of synaptic potentials, the superior cervical ganglion being conveniently accessible to electrodes without interrupting its blood supply. However, the potential changes observed with external electrodes were somewhat complex and as elsewhere internal microelectrodes were needed for a proper examination of the mechanism. Figure 20.33 shows that the spike recorded when the presynaptic nerve is stimulated orthodromically (O) differs from the antidromic spike (A) in being preceded by a small step, the *excitatory post-synaptic potential* (e.p.s.p.), which represents the depolarization of the postsynaptic membrane produced by the acetylcholine liberated from the presynaptic endings. The e.p.s.p. in a spinal motoneurone can be seen in Figure 21.34, and the similar junctional potential at the motor end-plate in Figure 21.2. The third record in Figure 20.33 shows the change in shape resulting from a superimposition of synaptic activity on the peak of an antidromic spike and provides evidence about the equilibrium level towards which the membrane potential drops under the influence of acetylcholine. As Katz had previously found for the frog motor end-plate, this equilibrium level is 10 to 20 mV below zero (that is internal potential still slightly negative); this suggests that the effect of acetylcholine is to cause a short-circuiting of the postsynaptic membrane by increasing its permeability simultaneously to Na^+ and K^+ ions. Another respect in which these

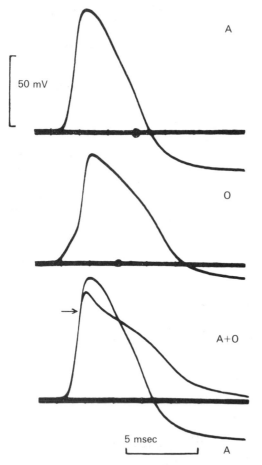

Fig. 20.33 The action potential recorded with an intracellular microelectrode in a frog sympathetic ganglion cell. A, antidromic response produced by stimulation of the postsynaptic nerve, O, orthodromic response produced by stimulation of the presynaptic nerve. A + O, the effect on the antidromic response of initiating synaptic activity at the arrow. (*From* J. G. Blackman, B. L. Ginsborg & C. Ray (1963) *Journal of Physiology*, 167, 355.)

synapses behave similarly to the neuromuscular junction is in the occurrence of spontaneous miniature end-plate potentials (m.e.p.p.s) 1 to 3 mV in amplitude, which are apparently due to the release of small packets of acetylcholine (p. 327). The parallel with the motor end-plate extends to the effects on the m.e.p.p.s of various changes in the ionic concentrations of the external medium, but the number of quanta normally released by each presynaptic impulse has been estimated as only about twenty, as compared with several hundred for the motor end-plate.

Eccles has used multibarrel pipettes to study motoneurones in the mammalian spinal cord. After inserting a double-barrelled micropipette into a motoneurone, one barrel can be used for recording the junctional potentials set up by volleys in excitatory or inhibitory presynaptic pathways, while the other is used to alter the membrane potential in either direction by flowing electric current into or out of the cell. In this way (Fig. 20.34) the equilibrium potential level at which the e.p.s.p. disappears and beyond which it is reversed, was found to be slightly closer to 0 mV than it appears to be at the motor end-plate. The equilibrium potential for inhibitory postsynaptic potentials (i.p.s.p.s) could be determined in a similar way; in the second experiment shown in Figure 20.34 it was about −80 mV. In order to investigate the ionic permeability changes underlying the e.p.s.p. and i.p.s.p. micropipettes can be filled with various salt solutions and the internal ionic concentrations of the motoneurones can then be altered by iontophoretic injection. The tentative conclusion from these studies is that during the e.p.s.p. the membrane becomes highly but unselectively permeable to cations (chiefly Na^+ and K^+), its anion permeability being little changed. During the i.p.s.p. the membrane becomes highly permeable to small anions like chloride but remains relatively impermeable to anions whose hydrated diameter is more than 1·3 times that of the hydrated K^+ ion. There may also be a somewhat smaller rise in K^+ permeability. The inhibitory mechanism in motoneurones would thus involve a combination of a rise in chloride permeability and of a rise in potassium permeability as takes place when acetylcholine acts on cardiac muscle fibres during vagal inhibition.

In the kind of inhibition so far considered there is a direct additon or subtraction of the e.p.s.p.s and i.p.s.p.s, as may be seen in Figure 20.35. A typical inhibitory connexion which operates in this fashion is that between a flexor muscle and its extensor antagonist, and vice versa. Reflex tests show that the latency of inhibition is short, as is consistent with the interpolation of a single interneurone (Fig. 20.36), and that its duration is of the order of 10 msec which fits well with the recorded picture of the i.p.s.p. The time courses of the e.p.s.p. and i.p.s.p. also agree with those postulated by Sherrington for the central excitatory and inhibitory states (p. 320). Other examples of direct inhibition are found in the autogenic inhibition of a muscle by its own Golgi tendon organs, which is responsible for Sherrington's lengthening reaction (p. 368), and in the inhibition of a motoneurone by Renshaw cell axons (see R in Figure 20.36) activated by recurrent collaterals from neighbouring motoneurones. It should not be supposed, however, that this is the only type of inhibition. When, for example, cutaneous afferents are stimulated, reflex activity may be inhibited for several hundred milliseconds, particularly in flexor muscles, without any visible change in the

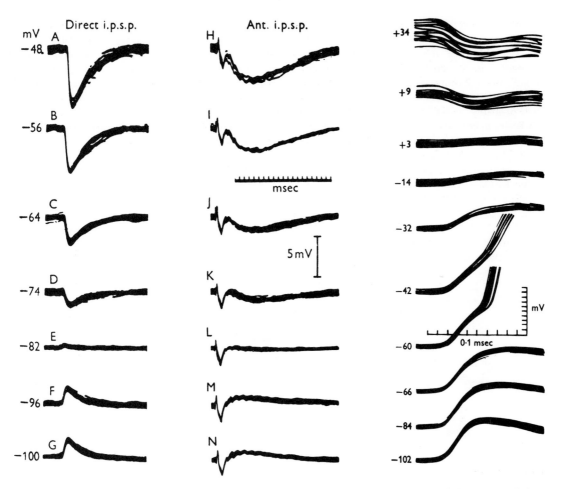

Fig. 20.34 Potentials recorded intracellularly from biceps-semitendinosus motoneurones by means of double-barrelled micropipettes. In each case 15 to 40 traces were superimposed, and the membrane potential was set at the level indicated by passing electric current from one of the barrels. Left-hand column shows the direct inhibitory action of a group Ia volley in the afferent fibres from the antagonist muscle quadriceps; central column shows the i.p.s.p. set up by an antidromic volley in the motor axon collaterals; right-hand column shows the e.p.s.p. elicited by a group Ia volley in the afferent fibres from the synergic muscle group. The reversal potential for the i.p.s.p. was about —80 mV, while for the e.p.s.p. it was close to 0 mV. (*From* J. S. Coombs, J. C. Eccles & P. Fatt (1955) *Journal of Physiology*, 130, 326 and 374.)

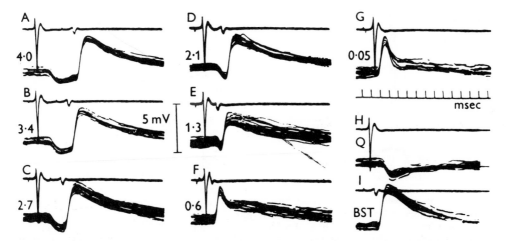

Fig. 20.35 Interaction between the direct i.p.s.p. and the monosynaptic e.p.s.p. recorded from a biceps-semitendinosus motoneurone as in Figure 20.34. The interval between the test volleys is shown against each record, while H and I are the control responses to quadriceps and to biceps-semitendinosus volleys alone. (*From* J. S. Coombs, J. C. Eccles & P. Fatt (1955) *Journal of Physiology*, 130, 396.)

postsynaptic membrane potential of the motoneurones. It is now thought that this so-called presynaptic inhibition is brought about by inhibitory terminals situated on the excitatory presynaptic nerve endings (Fig. 20.36), which reduce the amount of transmitter released. Although presynaptic inhibition does not result in an intracellularly recorded i.p.s.p. it probably gives rise to the long-lasting dorsal root potentials which can be observed with external electrodes.

The diagram in Figure 20.36 summarizes some of the main excitatory and inhibitory connexions to the alpha motoneurones in the spinal cord. One point that it illustrates is a generalization due to Dale that nerve cells of any particular type act at all their synapses by liberating the same chemical transmitter. Thus the only type of synapse within the central nervous system where acetylcholine has been identified with certainty as the transmitter is at the junctions between the Renshaw cells and the recurrent collaterals, which are of

course branches from efferent axons which also release acetylcholine at the motor end-plates. On Dale's principle it is not surprising that it should now have been proved that interneurones intervene in the pathway between Ia afferents from muscle spindles (Fig. 20.36) and the inhibitory connexions on the antagonist motoneurones. Moreover, although the chemical identity of the transmitter involved in direct inhibition is not yet certain, it seems likely to be the same for all the direct inhibitory terminals, since all of them are blocked in a similar fashion by strychnine and tetanus toxin, whereas the most active blocking agent for the presynaptic inhibitory synapses appears to be picrotoxin.

As far as synaptic transmission within the brain itself is concerned, the picture is at present less clear. However, evidence is steadily accumulating that the mechanisms which have been demonstrated in the spinal cord also operate in the brain.

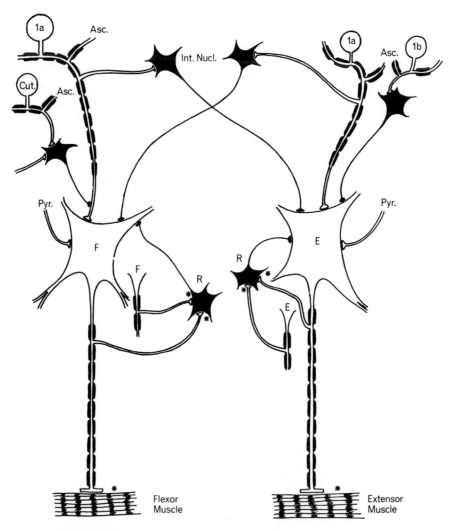

Fig. 20.36 A schematic diagram of some of the interconnexions between two flexor motoneurones (F) and the motoneurones (E) of the antagonist extensor muscle. Inhibitory neurones and their synaptic terminals are shown in black. The recurrent collaterals make cholinergic connexions (*) with Renshaw cells (R). 1a, cell bodies of afferent fibres from annulo-spiral endings on muscle spindles within the corresponding muscles. 1b, cell body of an afferent fibre from a Golgi organ in the tendon of the extensor muscle. Cut., cell body of a cutaneous afferent which is connected to an inhibitory neurone having a presynaptic inhibitory terminal on one of the 1a excitory endings. Int. Nucl., inhibitory neurones in the intermediate nucleus. Pyr., excitory terminals of the descending pyramidal tract. Asc., branches of the afferents joining the ascending sensory fibre tracts. (*By courtesy of R. D. Keynes.*)

We come now to the difficult question of the chemical identity of the transmitters in the central nervous system. The criteria to be satisfied should ideally be as follows: (1) the substance should be known to be present in presynaptic terminals, along with the enzymes necessary for its synthesis; (2) on stimulation of the presynaptic nerves it should be released in adequate quantities; (3) its action on the postsynaptic structures when applied directly should be identical with the normal transmitter action; (4) in some cases at least, an inactivating enzyme should be present in the synaptic cleft; (5) blocking and competitive agents should affect its normal action and the action on direct application in the same way. However, although various substances satisfy one or two of these criteria and are therefore suspected of being transmitters, the only situation where the evidence is reasonably complete is at the excitatory terminals of the recurrent collaterals on the Renshaw cells in the spinal cord, where as has already been mentioned acetylcholine appears definitely to be the transmitter. It has long been known that acetylcholine and the enzyme choline acetylase are present in the brain, that injection of acetylcholine into cerebral arteries gives rise to excitatory effects, and that acetylcholine is released in the cortex on stimulation of afferent tracts, but the complexity of the central nervous system is such that experiments of this type do not readily establish which specific pathways are cholinergic. One technique which has considerable resolving power is a histochemical examination of brain slices for the presence of acetylcholinesterase. Application of acetylcholine from multi-barrelled micropipettes shows that some of the large pyramidal cells in deeper layers of the motor cortex can be activated by the local release of small quantities of acetylcholine. However for technical reasons only some of the cholinergic interconnexions within the brain have been identified with certainty.

There is also strong evidence that certain monoamines, in particular noradrenaline, dopamine and 5-hydroxytryptamine, are central transmitters. The total number of monoaminergic neurones is small, but histochemical studies have shown that those which release noradrenaline radiate widely to supply many areas of the brain. Glutamate and certain other amino acids may also act as central transmitters. They certainly stimulate a high proportion of neurones when applied iontophoretically but they have yet to be shown to satisfy the criteria listed in the previous paragraph. As far as inhibitory transmitters are concerned circumstantial evidence has long pointed to the amino acids glycine and γ-aminobutyric acid (GABA) as possible candidates but attempts to decide between them proved indecisive. It would now appear that both play a part in central inhibitory machanisms, glycine being more important in the spinal chord and GABA in many areas of the brain. Hughes and Kosterlitz in 1975 found two pentapeptides (enkephalins) in the brain with powerful opiate (morphine-like) properties. Larger peptides, endorphins, with similar properties have been found in the pituitary. They are probably neurotransmitters; usually they have a depresssive effect.

In 1931 Gaddum and von Euler found a compound in equine brain with vasodilator properties. They named it substance P (for powder). Forty years later it was found to be an undecapeptide (11 amino acids). It has been detected by immunological methods in many parts of the human nervous system, notably the dorsal horn of the spinal cord where there are many thin unmyelinated C fibres. The physiological significance of these fibres is uncertain but substance P is likely to be a neurotransmitter on the sensory pathway.

Proteins and other macromolecules found in nerve endings are not synthesized there but mainly in the cell body. They then pass down the axon, being guided along microtubules. Some substances move at a rate of only a few mm/day, not much faster than a peripheral nerve can grow during regeneration. Other substances move extemely fast. In a wide range of experiments on both peripheral and central neurones a fast component of axonal flow is consistently found moving at a rate of about 400 mm/day in mammals and at a somewhat slower rate in cold blooded vertebrates. Still other substances are observed to move at an intermediate rate. In general, the substances involved in the synthesis and metabolism of the neurotransmitters move at either the fast or intermediate rate. The phenomenon is not restricted to individual macromolecules; microvesicles, mitochondria and other intracellular organelles are also involved. There is also evidence for a retrograde flow, molecules moving from the nerve endings up to the cell body. This seems to apply to endogenous substances but not to exogenous substances such as tetanus toxin. A considerable traffic of molecules is therefore occurring all the time within the axoplasm.

REFERENCES

Adrian E D 1928 Basis of sensation. Christophers, London
Adrian R H 1974 The nerve impulse. Oxford Biology Readers, no 67. Oxford University Press
Bacq Z M 1975 Chemical transmission of nerve impulses: a historical sketch. Pergamon Press, Oxford
Bowden R E M 1958 Peripheral nerve injuries. Lewis, London
Bradley W G 1974 Disorders of peripheral nerves. Blackwell Scientific Publications, Oxford
Brazier M A B 1976 Electrical activity of the nervous system, 4th edn. Pitman, London
Burnstock G 1975 Purinergic transmission. In: Iversen L, Snyder S (eds) Handbook of Psychopharmacology. Plenum Press, New York
Caldwell P C, Keynes R D 1960 The permeability of the squid giant axon to radioactive potassium and chloride ions. Journal of Physiology 154: 177–189
Cohen L B, Hille B, Keynes R D, Landowne D, Rojas E 1971 Analysis of the potential-dependent changes in optical retardation in the squid giant axon. Journal of Physiology 218: 205–237
Davidson N 1976 Neurotransmitter amino acids. Academic Press, London
Davison A N 1969 Biochemistry and the myelin sheath. Scientific Basis for Medicine Annual Review: 220–235
Eccles J C 1964 The physiology of synapses. Springer, Berlin
Erlanger J, Gasser H S 1937 Electrical signs of nervous activity. Oxford University Press

Gray J A B 1959 Mechanical into electrical energy in certain mechanoreceptors. Progress in Biophysics 9: 285–324

Guth L 1956 Regeneration in mammalian peripheral nervous system. Physiological Reviews 36: 441–479

Hebb Catherine 1972 Biosynthesis of acetylcholine in nervous tissue. Physiological Review 52: 918–957

Hodgkin A L 1963 The conduction of the nervous impulse. Liverpool University Press

Howarth J V, Keynes R D, Ritchie J M 1968 The origin of the initial heat associated with a single impulse in mammalian nonmyelinated nerve fibres. Journal of Physiology 194: 745–793

Hubbard J I 1970 Mechanisms of transmitter release. Progress in Biophysics and Molecular Biology 21: 33–124

Hubbard J I, Llinas R, Quastel D M J 1969 Electrophysiological analysis of synaptic transmission. Monograph No 19 of the Physiological Society. Arnold, London

Katz B 1966 Nerve, muscle and synapse. McGraw Hill, London

Keynes R D 1972 Excitable membranes. Nature 239: 29–32

Keynes R D, Rojas E 1974 Kinetics and steady-state properties of the charged system controlling sodium conductance in the squid giant axon. Journal of Physiology 239: 393–434

Kuffler S W, Nicholls J G 1976 From neuron to brain. Sinauer, USA

Landon D N (ed) 1976 The peripheral nerve. Chapman and Hall, London

Legg N J (ed) 1978 Neurotransmitter systems and their clinical disorders. Academic Press, London

Levi-Montalcini, Rita, Angeletti P U 1968 Nerve growth factor. Physiological Reviews 48: 534–569

Lubińska L 1975 On axoplasmic flow. International Review of Neurobiology 17: 241–296

Ochs S 1975 Retention and redistribution of protein in mammalian nerve fibres by axoplasmic transport. Journal of Physiology 253: 459–475

Rang H P, Ritchie J M 1968 On the electrogenic sodium pump in mammalian non-myelinated nerve fibres and its activation by various external cations. Journal of Physiology 196: 163–221

Robertson J D 1960 The molecular structure and contact relationships of cell membranes. Progress in Biophysics 10: 343–418

Sunderland S 1968 Nerves and nerve injuries. Livingstone, Edinburgh

Thomas R C 1972 Electrogenic sodium pump in nerve and muscle cells. Physiological Reviews 52: 562–594

Triggle D J, Triggle C R 1977 Chemical pharmacology of the synapse. Academic Press, London

Watson W E 1974 Cellular responses to axotomy and to related procedures. British Medical Bulletin 30: 112–115

Whittaker V P 1973 The storage of acetylcholine in presynaptic nerve terminals. The Scientific Basis of Medicine, Annual Reviews: 17–31

Zaimis Eleanor (ed) 1972 Nerve growth factor and its antiserum. Athlone Press, London

21 Skeletal Muscle and Exercise

All the movements of higher animals are accomplished through the contraction of muscles; they are the 'biological motors' that convert chemical energy into mechanical energy and translate the signals from the central nervous system into movements. Muscles consist of large numbers of elongated cells, usually referred to as muscle fibres. When these fibres are suitably activated they develop tension and shorten.

SKELETAL MUSCLE

Most mammalian skeletal muscle is of the twitch type, which is described in detail below. Tonic skeletal muscle occurs in muscles innervated by cranial nerves; it is qualitatively similar to twitch muscle in many respects, and the differences are described later. Skeletal muscle fibres contract only in response to activity in their motor nerve fibres. Action potentials in these motor neurones are conducted down to their terminals, the motor end-plates, where the process of neuromuscular transmission leads to a similar action potential in the corresponding muscle fibre; this then spreads in both directions along the muscle fibre initiating a mechanical contraction in the underlying myofibrils.

Nerve action potential
    ↓   (Neuromuscular transmission)
Muscle action potential
    ↓   (Contraction coupling)
Muscle contraction

Motor nerve fibres usually branch as they approach their termination so that a single nerve fibre supplies a number of muscle fibres, all of which contract in synchrony in response to each nerve impulse. The group of muscle fibres along with the nerve fibre that supplies them is known as a 'motor unit'.

Neuromuscular Transmission

Each adult muscle fibre is innervated by a terminal branch of one motor nerve. At the region of apposition both the nerve and muscle are specialized and form the motor end-plate (Fig. 21.1). When innervation first occurs in late intra-uterine life each muscle fibre receives a number of end-plates ('multi-terminal innervation') derived from several nerves ('poly-neuronal innervation'). During early post-natal development all endings except one are lost. In adult life polyneuronal innervation recurs if reinnervation follows nerve section, and may persist for several months. The membranes of the nerve and muscle fibres are separated by a cleft 50 to 100 nm wide and the folding of the two membranes is such that this close apposition occurs over about 2000 μm^2 of membrane. This structure is analogous to that of a synapse in which two neurones come into close apposition. The motor end-plate, however, differs from synapses elsewhere in that each action potential in the nerve fibres gives rise to a single action potential in the muscle fibre.

When an action potential invades the terminal part of the nerve fibres, acetylcholine (ACh) is released from the nerve terminals. This then diffuses in the cleft that separates the nerve and muscle membranes and acts on the muscle membrane in a way that leads to depolarization and the generation of an action potential in the muscle fibre.

Acetylcholine is formed in the nerve terminal by a process involving the enzyme choline acetyl transferase which, like all neuronal proteins, is synthesized in the cell body and actively transported along the axon at a rate of about 400 mm/day. In the resting fibre ACh remains stored within the nerve terminals in synaptic vesicles (Fig. 20.32). When the fibre is depolarized by an action potential, some acetylcholine is released from the vesicles into the synaptic cleft. This release occurs only if there is an adequate concentration of Ca^{2+} in the extracellular fluid and entry of Ca^{2+} into the nerve terminal during the action potential plays an important part in the releasing mechanism. If the extracellular Ca^{2+} concentration in the end-plate region is reduced the amount of ACh released during each action potential is also reduced. An excess of extracellular Mg^{2+} has a similar effect because it blocks the entry of Ca^{2+}. The intensely poisonous bacterial toxin from Clostridium botulinum inhibits the release of ACh from the nerve endings. It has been used experimentally to block neuromuscular transmission and causes in man the disease 'botulism'.

After its release into the synaptic cleft ACh is rapidly broken down and rendered inactive by the enzyme acetylcholine esterase; under normal conditions, however, the local concentration of ACh persists for long enough to depolarize the muscle membrane and to initiate one action potential. The ACh that is released on nerve stimulation cannot normally be detected in the fluid which has perfused the muscle but, if the acetylcholine esterase is inhibited by eserine (physostigmine), prostigmine, or tensilon, then ACh can be identified and measured in the perfusate. In the presence of these drugs the concentration of ACh in the end-plate region remains high for some time after each action potential and a single nerve impulse may then give rise to more than one action potential in the muscle fibres. Acetylcholine injected experimentally into the blood supply of a muscle is also destroyed by a choline esterase and it is only by injecting it in very large quantities that a muscle contraction can be provoked in this way. Other choline esters such as suxamethonium are not so rapidly inactivated and they produce a prolonged depolarization of the muscle fibre membrane, associated with a brief contraction.

Acetylcholine reacts with 'receptor sites' on the end-plate region of the muscle fibre membrane to cause an increase in the permeability of the membrane to sodium and potassium ions. Sodium ions then enter the cell under the influence of the concentration gradient and electrical gradient and the membrane potential is consequently reduced. The quantity of ACh released during normal neuromuscular transmission increases the membrane permeability to such an extent that the membrane is rapidly depolarized to a level at which an action

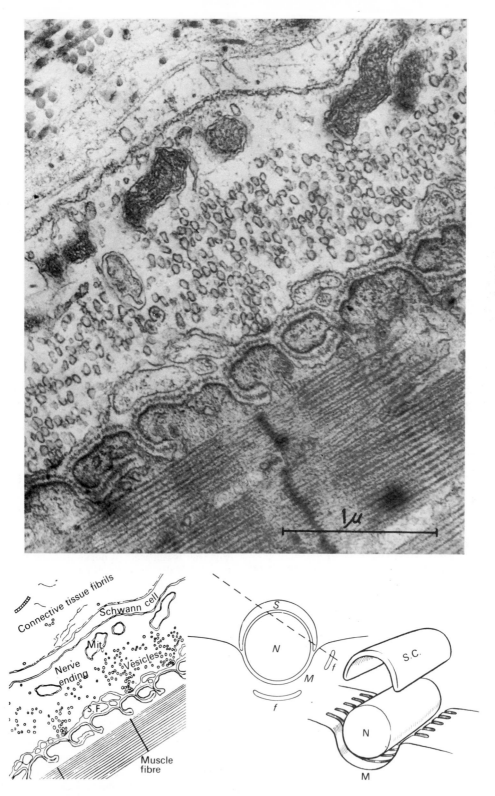

Fig. 21.1 Electron micrograph of a longitudinal section through the neuromuscular junction of the frog. The small diagram on the left below is a reduced tracing of the electron micrograph. Mit., mitochondria (four are shown). S. F. Schwann finger, which extends a little way into the cleft between the nerve terminal and the muscle fibre. The 'exploded' diagram on the right shows the Schwann cell, S. C. lifted off the terminal branch of the motor nerve N which lies in a shallow gutter on the surface of the muscle fibre M. The gutter has semi-circular junctional folds. The small diagram in the centre is a transverse section through the nerve terminal N with the Schwann cell covering it, except for the part in contact with the muscle fibre, M; the junctional folds are cut through at f and f. The plane of the electron micrograph is shown by the dashed line; note that the section passes through the Schwann cell at two places. (R. Birks, H. E. Huxley & B. Katz (1960) The fine structure of the neuromuscular junction of the frog. *Journal of Physiology*, **150**, 134–144.)

potential is generated; this action potential is conducted along the fibre in both directions.

The situation described above is the normal one in which the neuromuscular junction behaves as a 'safe synapse', each nerve action potential giving rise to a corresponding muscle action potential. In the cat the safest end-plates must have 92 per cent of their receptors blocked before neuromuscular conduction fails; 'safe' end-plates fail when at least 74 per cent of receptors are blocked. Care must be taken in extrapolating to man because there are differences between species and muscles. In a number of abnormal and experimental conditions, however, the neuromuscular junction behaves in a different way, and these are important for the light they throw on the general properties of synapses elsewhere. If the amount of ACh released from the nerve terminals is reduced by immersing the end-plate region in a solution containing too few Ca^{2+} ions, then the smaller amounts of ACh released by each nerve impulse may reduce the membrane potential of the muscle fibre by an amount that is insufficient to initiate a muscle action potential; the threshold for stimulation of the muscle fibre is not reached and the only electrical change in the muscle fibre is the local *end-plate potential* which is the direct result of the increase in permeability of the muscle to sodium and potassium ions.

Although the permeability changes are strictly confined to the end-plate region, the current flow in this region causes some depolarization of the immediately adjacent parts of the fibre, and this may be recorded a millimeter or two on either side of the end-plate. The increase in the local concentration of ACh that gives rise to the end-plate potential lasts for a few msec so that each ACh molecule reacts only once with the membrane receptors, but the end-plate potential itself decays much more slowly (Fig. 21.2), and may still be of significant size after 5 msec. If a second nerve action potential arrives during this time the further release of ACh that follows causes a further depolarization which may exceed the response to the first nerve impulse, and may perhaps exceed the threshold of the muscle fibre. The amplitude of the end-plate potential varies in a train of stimuli according to the frequency and duration of stimulation.

It is clear that the end-plate potential differs from the action potential in a number of ways: its time course is longer, it may be graded in its amplitude (though it is always much smaller), it does not leave the membrane in a refractory state, it is a local response which is not conducted along the length of the fibre, and it is associated with a simultaneous increase in permeability to sodium and potassium ions. Although end-plate potentials of this type are not normally seen, they are closely analogous to the *excitatory postsynaptic potentials* that occur in synapses between neurones (Fig. 20.34).

The drugs *tubocurarine (curare)* and *gallamine* compete with ACh for the receptor sites on the muscle membrane and thus render the muscle fibres less sensitive to ACh released during nerve activity. An appropriate amount of one of these drugs can reduce the depolarizing action of ACh to a level at which sub-threshold end-plate potentials may be demonstrated; the results shown in Figure 21.2 were in fact obtained in that way. Some snake venoms contain components which combine irreversibly with the receptors and produce prolonged block. If the animal survives, new receptor molecules are synthesized and neuromuscular transmission is re-established within a week. An example is α-bungarotoxin which may be labelled with a fluorescent dye or with radioactive iodine, and can then be used to examine the ACh receptor site microscopically or to count the number of receptors.

The use of glass capillary micro-electrodes for recording the muscle fibre membrane potentials has permitted a more complete and quantitative investigation of the properties of the neuromuscular junction. This method of recording has also revealed that in addition to the end-plate potentials already described there occur also spontaneous miniature end-plate potentials (m.e.p.p.s); these have the same form as the end-plate potentials that follow activity in the motor nerve fibre, but they occur quite spontaneously at random intervals, and they are very much smaller in amplitude (perhaps 0·5 mV). These spontaneous miniature end-plate potentials are caused by the release of ACh from the nerve terminals. The nerve terminal in fact 'leaks' small amounts of ACh when it is apparently at rest, and this 'leakage' of ACh is in the form of discrete 'quanta'. The amount of transmitter that leaks out in this way is normally much too small (about 10^4 molecules) to have any important effect on the muscle fibre, but when an

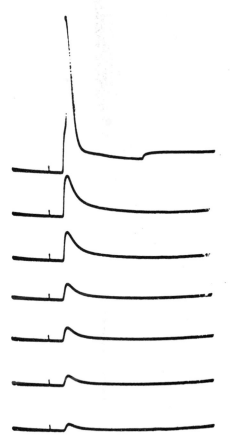

Fig. 21.2 Muscle fibres were immersed in Ringer's solution containing d-tubocurarine. They were then perfused with Ringer's solution to remove the tubocurarine. The effect of nerve stimulation was recorded at 3 sec intervals beginning at the lowest trace. The amplitude of the end-plate potential increased, as this tubocurarine was worked out, until it reached the critical membrane potential when a propagated action potential is generated. (*From* W. L. Nastuk (1955) *American Journal of Medicine*, 19, 663.)

action potential invades the nerve terminal it accelerates the release of these quanta of ACh. The relatively large quantity released by an action potential is merely a much more rapid form of the same process. Recently it has been shown that one molecule of ACh opens a 'gate' in the membrane for a few msec, during this time a current of less than 5pA flows, depolarizing the membrane by about 1 μV.

In the disease *myasthenia gravis* the skeletal muscles are very easily fatigued. In the most severely affected fibres neuromuscular transmission is blocked and in others failure may develop during repetitive stimulation. Labelling with α-bungarotoxin has shown that the end-plates are abnormally large, but contain only 50 per cent to 10 per cent of the normal number of receptors. The loss of receptors may be due to a circulating antibody to the receptor molecules, which is found in nearly 90 per cent of the patients. Miledi has shown that the presynaptic release of ACh is normal. The symptoms of the disease may be alleviated by anticholinesterase drugs, although these can cause depolarizing block due to persistance of ACh. Thymectomy, steroids and plasma exchange transfusion can be effective against the antibody.

The Contractile Mechanism

Most of the space within each muscle fibre is occupied by myofibrils, longitudinal filaments approximately 1 μm in diameter. When examined by light microscopy, the fibres appear to be transversely striated; these striations are due to alternating zones of different refractive index within the myofibrils. The A (anisotropic) bands are birefringent, having a high refractive index, whereas the I (isotropic) bands have a lower refractive index. In most stained preparations of striated muscle tissue the A bands are more deeply coloured. In the centre of each I band is a Z line (Fig. 21.3) which is a disc of material running across the whole muscle fibre and joining the myofibrils to each other. The central region of the A band is paler and is known as the H (Hensen's) band. The region between one Z line and the next is known as a sarcomere. It is the fundamental unit of muscular contraction. The length of a sarcomere varies between 1·5 and 3·0 μm depending on the state of extension of the muscle fibres.

Contractile proteins. Electron microscope photographs (Fig. 21.4) give more information about the structure of myofibrils. Each myofibril contains a system of longitudinal filaments arranged in a regular pattern (Fig. 21.4A). In the I bands there are thin filaments consisting mainly of the protein *actin* arranged spirally along the filamentous protein *tropomyosin*. At regular intervals of nearly 40 nm there is a regulatory protein complex consisting of *troponins-C, -I* and *-T* (Fig. 21.5). The thin filaments are attached to the Z line, or Z disc. The thin filaments extend into the A band where they interdigitate with a system of thicker filaments. The thick filaments consist mainly of the protein *myosin*; these too are arranged in a regular manner; they lie approximately 45 nm apart, each being surrounded by six thin filaments (Figs 21.3 and 21.4A).

As the muscle changes in length, the thick and thin filaments slide over each other; during shortening the thin filaments move progressively further in between the thick filaments, and the I band becomes correspondingly narrower,

though the width of the A band remains the same. At all but the shortest muscle lengths there is a region in the centre of the A band into which the thin filaments do not extend; this is the paler H zone which becomes wider as the muscle fibre length increases.

The myosin molecules that form the thick filaments are arranged as shown in Figure 21.5; the head of each myosin molecule projects out from the thick filament toward an adjacent thin filament. Six such side-chains occur in a helical arrangement over a distance of 43 nm. These side-chains play an important part in the mechanism of muscle contraction; the central part of the thick filament, the H zone, does not have them.

Amongst the myofibrils is a system of fine tubules, the *sarcoplasmic reticulum*, which is important in activating the process of contraction. Transverse tubules extend inward from the surface of the muscle fibre; these are, in fact, inward extensions of the extracellular space within the substance of the fibre. The transverse or T-tubules are situated close to the end of the A bands in mammals. A second system of tubules

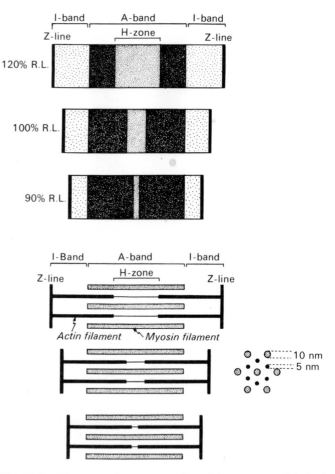

Fig. 21.3 Diagrammatic representation of the structure of skeletal muscle. The three diagrams at the top show the appearances as seen with the phase contrast or with the interference microscope at various percentages of the resting length, R. L. Note that the A band remains constant in length, about 1.5 μm in the rabbit psoas. The diagrams at the bottom show the arrangement of the filaments in muscle in both longitudinal and transverse section; the latter should be compared with the middle portion of Figure 21.4A. (*After* H. E. Huxley (1956) *Endeavour,* 15, 177–188.)

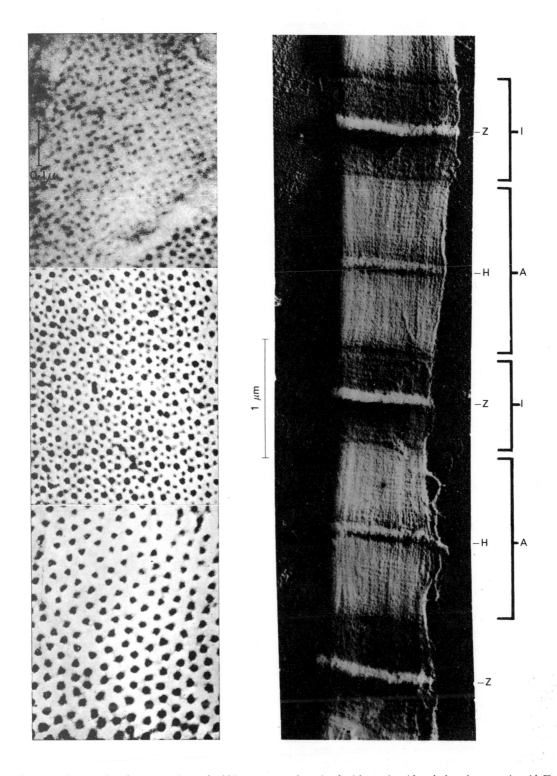

Fig. 21.4A Electron micrographs of cross-sections of rabbit psoas muscle stained with osmic acid and phosphotungstic acid. Top: thin actin filaments in the I band. Middle: double hexagonal array of filaments in the A band. Bottom: simple hexagonal array of myosin filaments in the H zone. (*By courtesy of H. E. Huxley.*)

Fig. 21.4B Electron micrograph of toad muscle, platinum shadowed. I, isotropic band. A, anisotropic band. Z, Dobie's line. H, Hensen's band. (*By courtesy of M. H. Draper and A. J. Hodge.*)

extends longitudinally through the sarcoplasm amongst and around the myofibrils. This longitudinal component of the sarcoplasmic reticulum comes into close contact with the transverse tubules; the junction region is called a *triad* (see also Fig. 10.4).

A. F. Huxley has produced convincing evidence for the view that the forceful contraction of a muscle fibre is the result of a sequence of chemical reactions between the actin molecules and the myosin heads; in the course of this reaction the thin filament is drawn along the thick one. A number of physico-chemical reactions have been postulated; for the sake of simplicity the following description will be based on one of these, though there are some aspects of it that are as yet hypothetical.

In the presence of calcium ions, a chemical bond forms between the thin filament and the myosin head (Fig. 21.6,1) and a cross-bridge is created. At low Ca^{2+} concentrations (less

than 10^{-7}M) the troponin–tropomyosin complex prevents actin-myosin interaction. At higher concentrations Ca^{2+} binds to troponin-C and causes a change of shape in tropomyosin which uncovers active sites on actin at which cross-bridges are formed. Once the first link has been formed there is a strong tendency for a second form of linkage to follow (Fig. 21.6,2), and then a third (Fig. 21.6,3). The changes illustrated in Figure 21.6 can, however, only occur if there is movement of the thick filament by about 12 nm to the right in relation to the thin one, though some movement can occur if the side chain of the myosin molecules becomes extended (as shown in Fig. 21.6) with a consequent increase in the muscle tension. Once the attachment of the myosin head has moved through this sequence of positions (and there may be more than the three shown in Fig. 21.6), it comes under the influence of an enzyme system which de-couples the actin-myosin complex and leaves the side-chain free to reattach to some other site on the thin filament. To break the cross-bridge a small amount of ATP must be split to ADP. Actomyosin is an ATPase which

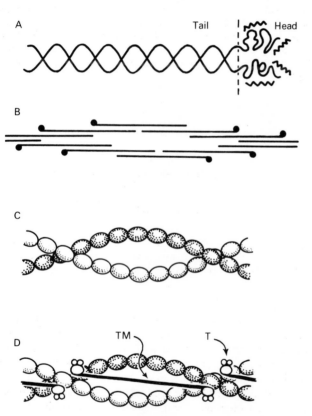

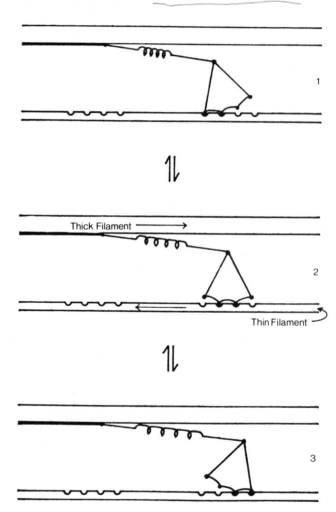

Fig. 21.5   A, myosin molecule. The 'tail', consisting of two coiled α-helical peptide chains (light meromyosin), gives rigidity to the thick filament. The 'head' contains two units of heavy meromyosin and two pairs of light peptide chains. The important cross-linking activity of myosin is related to the head; the light chains are related to ATPase activity. B, in the thick filaments the myosin molecules are arranged with their heads away from the middle of the filament. The heads project out toward the adjacent thin filaments. C, the backbone of the thin filament is a double stranded helix of actin; the two polypeptide chains are joined by disulphide bonds. D, tropomyosin molecules (TM), with double helical structure, lie as discrete filaments in each of the two grooves between the strands of actin. Troponin (T) molecules are bound to TM at intervals; each molecule contains three components, one of which (troponin-C) is a binding site for Ca^{2+}. Adapted from Katz, A. M. (1977). *Physiology of the Heart*, New York: Raven Press.)

Fig. 21.6   Diagram of a possible mode of interaction between a thin (actin) filament and the side-chain of a thick (myosin) filament. The head of the myosin molecule links on to the actin in position 1, but once this linkage has formed there is a strong tendency for it to move into position 2 and then to position 3. Once this third position is reached the linkage may be broken down. (*From* A. F. Huxley (1974) *Journal of Physiology*, 243, 30.)

requires Mg^{2+} for activation; myosin alone has some ATPase activity but some 10^3 times lower.

The behaviour of contracting myofibrils can be examined after destruction of the muscle fibre membranes by immersion in glycerol at low temperatures. In such a preparation chemical agents can be applied directly to the myofibrils. Contraction occurs when ATP is added to glycerinated muscle fibres in the presence of free calcium and magnesium ions; during the course of this contraction ATP is converted to ADP and it is this conversion that provides the energy necessary for the mechanical work done during shortening. If in such a preparation the supply of ATP becomes exhausted, the reaction ceases but the fibres remain stiff, a state that is analogous to the 'rigor mortis' that occurs when ATP disappears after death. This stiffness in the absence of ATP implies that the reaction has ceased with the filaments linked together. ATP is used in the stage of uncoupling the thin filaments from the myosin side chains. The fact that energy is injected into the system by breakdown of ATP when cross links are broken down suggests that at the onset of activity cross links can be formed rapidly and the contraction begun before any ATP is required. In this sense muscle is held 'charged' and ready for immediate release.

Contraction coupling. Contraction of myofibrils is initiated by a release of calcium within the fibre. In the resting muscle calcium is actively pumped into the sarcoplasmic reticulum surrounding the myofibrils so that, although the overall calcium content of the fibre is high, the concentration of Ca^{2+} ions in the fluid that surrounds the actin and myosin filaments is less than 10^{-7}M. As the action potential travels along the surface sarcolemma (at 2 to 6 m/sec) it initiates an action potential in the T-tubules. The *T-tubule potentials* are probably sodium spikes similar to those at the surface, and are responsible for the transfer of activation from the surface towards the centre of a fibre. The T-tubules are about 50 nm in diameter, so inward spread of activation takes several msec but this is much less than the time that would be needed for diffusion of Ca^{2+} from the surface membrane. In mammalian muscle it is possible that the T-tubule activity does not propagate to the centre of the fibre following a single stimulus, so that only the more peripheral myofibrils are activated in a twitch. At the triads the terminal elements of the sarcoplasmic reticulum are stimulated by T-tubule depolarization and release Ca^{2+} into the fluid near the myofibrils. The Ca^{2+} concentration rises to about 5×10^{-6}M, necessary for full activation of cross-bridge formation. The contraction is ended by Ca^{2+} being pumped back into the sarcoplasmic reticulum.

The protein aequorin, obtained from the luminescent jelly fish *Aequorea forskålea*, emits blue light when it is activated by Ca^{2+}. If this is injected into the cytoplasm of a muscle fibre, the Ca^{2+} concentration around the myofibrils may be measured by the light that is emitted. Figure 21.7 shows the rise in Ca^{2+} concentration after a single action potential and twitch contraction of a single muscle fibre.

Mechanical Properties of Muscles

When a muscle is activated its fibres shorten or, if they are restrained from doing so, they exert tension on the tendon to which they are attached. The force that a muscle is able to exert

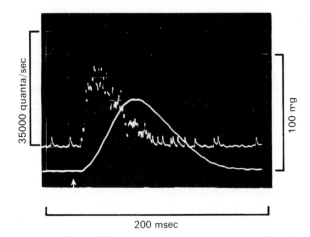

Fig. 21.7 Luminescence and mechanical response during a single isometric twitch. Single twitch muscle fibre dissected from tibialis anterior muscle of a frog. Temperature 15°C. Sarcomere spacing 2·4 μm. Upper tracing: photomultiplier output (luminescence). Lower tracing: force developed. Moment of stimulation indicated by white arrow. (S. R. Taylor, R. Rindel & J. R. Blinks (1975) Calcium transients in amphibian muscle. *Federation Proceedings*, 34, 1380.)

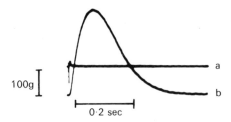

Fig. 21.8 Isometric twitch contraction of cat soleus muscle. (a) The action potential recorded from electrodes placed on the muscle surface; (b) tension measured at the muscle tendon. (*By courtesy of P. M. H. Rack.*)

is by no means constant and depends on the degree of activation, the muscle length, and the rate at which it is shortening (or being lengthened). In the body muscle activity often involves an initial phase without movement during which an opposing force is overcome, followed by a period of acceleration up to a reasonably constant velocity, and ends in controlled deceleration. Lengthening, too, is complex, and may be brought about by the action of antagonists, sometimes against continuing agonist activity. Experimentally *isometric* and *isotonic* contractions have received most attention. The maximum isometric tension developed by mammalian skeletal muscle is about 35 mN per sq. mm.

If a muscle is activated while its ends are rigidly fixed so that no shortening can occur, it is said to contract isometrically. This is the simplest situation and it will be described first.

The isometric twitch. If a muscle fibre is stimulated by a single electrical pulse of adequate amplitude, an action potential passes along it followed by a brief contraction, a muscle twitch. A similar, though much more forcible, muscle twitch may be obtained from the whole muscle after stimulation of its motor nerve; all the fibres in the muscle are then contracting simultaneously. Figure 21.8 shows the tension record during such an isometric twitch contraction. The muscle action potential is over in a few milliseconds but the mechanical contraction lasts much longer.

The twitch of a whole muscle is due to the summed activity of many muscle fibres, and its amplitude therefore varies with the number of fibres stimulated. By varying the strength of an electrical stimulus applied to the motor nerve it is possible to excite different numbers of nerve fibres and therefore different numbers of muscle fibres with corresponding differences in twitch tension, but once the stimulating pulse is made large enough to excite all the nerve fibres a further increase does not lead to a further increase in tension.

If instead of single pulses, pairs of stimuli are delivered to the motor nerve and these are so timed that the second stimulus falls during the twitch contraction that followed the first, a second twitch grows out of the first one (Fig. 21.9), the tension rising to a higher level than in a single twitch. The closer together the two stimuli the higher is the tension so long as the second pulse is outside the refractory period of the nerve and muscle that follows the first pulse. This higher tension may result from the double action potential propagating further along the T-tubule with consequent activation of central myofibrils. Pairs of short interval action potentials occur in natural human contractions.

Tetanus. If a motor nerve is stimulated by a train of pulses the tension in the muscle rises progressively higher with each of the first few pulses until a plateau is reached (Fig. 21.10). If a high rate of stimulation is used the contraction is then continuous and a smooth tension record is obtained; when the stimulus rate is low the tension is not smoothly maintained but fluctuates at the frequency of the stimulating pulses. The tension generated during the smooth 'fused' tetanus (or 'complete' tetanus) that accompanies stimulation at a high rate is considerably larger than the twitch tension of that muscle.

In a living animal muscle fibres are seldom activated at the high rates necessary for a smooth tetanic contraction, but since impulses are normally delivered to different motor units at different times, the whole muscle contracts smoothly, although the rate of stimulation for each muscle fibre may be quite slow. This situation may be reproduced experimentally by subdividing the nerve supplying a muscle and stimulating different groups of fibres asynchronously. Figure 21.11 shows how the force increased with increasing stimulus rate in muscles stimulated in this way. At frequencies higher than those necessary to produce maximal tension, the tetanus still changes in that the tension rises more quickly (compare e with d in Fig. 21.10). Maximum rate of rise of tension is elicited by frequencies some three times higher than those necessary for maximum tension: these frequencies do not occur naturally except possibly in the extra-ocular muscles.

The effect of muscle length on tension. There is a characteristic relationship between muscle length and the tension that develops in an isometric tetanus (Fig. 21.12). The maximum tension develops when the muscle is at a length that usually approaches the maximum that it takes up in the intact animal; at lengths shorter than this the tension is smaller, and

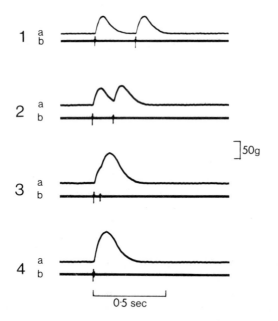

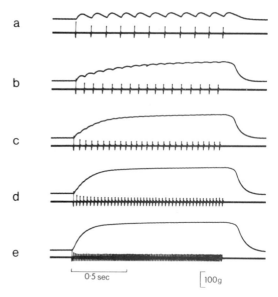

Fig. 21.9 The fusion of the mechanical response in skeletal muscle when the interval between stimuli to the nerve is reduced. Isometric tension is shown on trace (a) of each record and the electromyogram is shown on trace (b). Two maximal stimuli were applied to the motor nerve of the rat soleus muscle and tension recorded from the distal tendon. When the shocks were separated by 0·25 sec as in 1, two identical twitches, each preceded by an electromyogram, were produced. If the intervals between the stimuli were progressively reduced as in 2, 3 and 4 the tension twitches fused to form a smooth record in 4, but note that the tension developed in now larger and the electromyograms are still separate. (*By courtesy of B. L. Andrew.*)

Fig. 21.10 The effect of frequency of nerve stimulation on the mechanical response of a skeletal muscle, in this case the rat soleus. In each pair of records the upper tracing is muscle tension developed at the distal tendon and the lower tracing is the electromyogram. The motor nerve was maximally stimulated at the following frequencies per second (a), 8; (b), 14; (c), 20; (d), 30 and (e), 80. Note that in (a) separate identical twitches occur, in (b) there is a tremor applied to a steadily rising tension, in (c), (d) and (e) the tremor becomes progressively smaller in amplitude and the gradient of increase of tension at the beginning of the tetanus increases. Also note that the tension developed by the twitch responses in (a) is substantially less than that in the tetanic contraction in (e). (*By courtesy of B. L. Andrew.*)

if the muscle is stretched beyond this optimum length the active tension also declines, though at extreme lengths the connective tissue in and around the muscle resists extension with a considerable force and dominates the situation. Figure 21.12 shows the effect of length on one muscle. In other muscles the relative contributions of passive (1) and active (2) tension may be different. Mammalian muscles have more connective tissue which increases the passive tension element, and as a result the total tension (3) does not always show a region of negative slope. Another factor is the extent of activation. Active twitch and tetanic tension are both maximal near the resting length of the muscle in the body. However an unfused (physiological) tetanus is greatest at significantly longer muscle lengths because twitches are prolonged at long muscle lengths and therefore summate more effectively.

A. F. Huxley and his colleagues have shown that the form of the isometric *length-tension curve* can be explained in terms

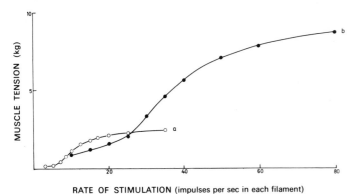

RATE OF STIMULATION (impulses per sec in each filament)

Fig. 21.11 The effect of stimulus rate on muscle tension. (a) Cat soleus; (b) medial head of cat gastrocnemius. In each case five different subdivisions of the motor nerve were stimulated sequentially to obtain a smooth contraction of the muscle at low rates of stimulation. (*By courtesy of P. M. H. Rack.*)

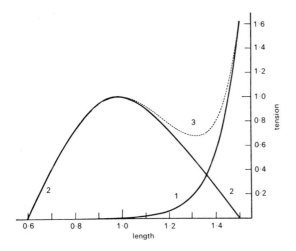

Fig. 21.12 Diagram of tension–length relations of sartorius muscle of frog or toad. (1) At rest passively stretched; (2) extra force developed during maximal tetanus; (3) dotted line, total force in maximal tetanus, sum of (1) and (2). The length is given as a fraction, or multiple, of the standard length in the body; the tension, of the maximum force developed. (*From* A. V. Hill (1953) *Proceedings of the Royal Society* B, 141, 113.)

of the sliding filament theory of muscle contraction. The maximum active tension develops when the sarcomere lengths are such that there is sufficient overlap between thick and thin filaments in the myofibrils for all the side-chains of each thick filament to have access to the thin filament so that a maximum number of cross links can form. When, however, the muscle is extended beyond this optimum length, the thin filaments are pulled out from among the thick ones, the overlap is less, and there are correspondingly fewer possible sites for cross link formation; the greater the extension, the smaller is the overlap and the lower the tension.

When the muscle shortens from the optimal length each thin filament moves further in between the corresponding thick filaments, but this movement is impeded when, at a sarcomere length of $2.2\ \mu m$, each filament meets another one moving in the opposite direction. Some part of the contractile force is then taken up in compressing these filaments against or past each other so that the external force generated by the muscle is correspondingly less at the shorter length. If shortening proceeds further, a point will be reached, at a sarcomere length of $1.5\ \mu m$, at which the ends of the thick filaments become compressed against the Z line; further shortening is impeded and the tension falls.

Although many features of the iosmetric length-tension curve can be explained in terms of the positions of filaments within the myofibrils, it seems likely that there are also other factors operating and, in particular, it is probable that the contractile system within the myofibrils is more completely activated when the muscle fibres are long than when they are short.

The effect of speed of shortening on muscle tension. Muscle develops less tension during shortening than in an isometric contraction at the same length, and the more rapid the shortening the lower is the muscle tension; or conversely, the muscle cannot shorten so quickly against a large force as against a small one.

A. F. Huxley has pointed out that the sliding filament theory of muscle contraction offers an explanation for the *force-velocity relationship* in active muscle. Cross links form between thick and thin filaments in the myofibrils exerting a force that tends to draw the thin filaments along the thick ones. The formation of these links is a chemical process, the rate of which is limited and depends among other things on the availability of calcium ions; once formed, however, the links are broken down at a rate that depends to a large extent on how fast the filaments move and allow rotation of the myosin heads. When the filaments are stationary or movement is slow, the formation of cross links can proceed at a normal rate, and each link may have a long life since the myosin head is unlikely to rotate into the position where enzymic breakdown can occur. A large number of cross links are therefore present and tension is high. When, however, shortening occurs and the filaments move over each other, the actin-myosin linkages can move into the configuration in which enzymatic breakdown may occur; each link has therefore a shorter life, and at any time there are fewer of them with a correspondingly smaller total tension. Men pulling in a rope provide a useful analogy; if the rope is stationary, or moving only slowly, all their hands are on it and the force is maximal. When, however, the rope is being pulled in more quickly there are always a number of hands off the rope preparing to take a new hold, and the force is correspondingly smaller. Velocity of shortening is maximal with zero load and tension is maximal with no shortening. Maximal power is available when the load and the shortening velocity are at about one third of their maximal values. Efficiency of work (external work/energy used) is highest in this region of the force–velocity relationship.

The force developed by a muscle depends on the number of fibres arranged in parallel to pull on the tendon. For maximal tension within a given volume of muscle the fibres will be short and numerous; such muscles are often multipennate, with a central tendon into which fibres are inserted obliquely. In contrast the shortening velocity of a muscle is proportional to the number of sarcomeres in series. Muscles capable of rapid shortening therefore consist of long fibres.

The stiffness of muscle. The length:tension diagram (Fig. 21.12) illustrates a form of negative feedback within muscle. If an extra load is imposed on a steadily contracting muscle, the muscle will be extended and, according to the slope of the total-tension/length curve, it will develop more tension and resist excessive extension. Muscle stiffness may be calculated as change of tension/change of length. This stiffness has an effect similar to that of the stretch reflex (p. 367) but with two differences. First the muscle response is immediate, indeed if rapid stretches are imposed on active muscle, the tension increase is maximal at the end of the change in length. Secondly the muscle stiffness appears to be small if judged from the slope of Figure 21.12. However if the tension is measured immediately at the end of a stretch, much higher values are obtained for stiffness. Stiffness is also higher for small than for large stretches. Maximal muscle stiffness is some ten times greater than the steady state measurements of Figure 21.12. In some muscle contractions it has been demonstrated that the resistance to an unexpected load is due more to muscle stiffness than to the stretch reflex. A further property of the muscle stiffness is that it is directly proportional to the active tension in the muscle, so that stiffness is related to the task being performed. This is a consequence of the fact that much of the stiffness is located in cross-bridges; both tension and stiffness are proportional to the number of cross-bridges formed at any time. The tension excess during stretch is proportional to the velocity of stretch, another point of resemblance to the stretch reflex. However, if velocity is too high the force collapses, possibly providing a protective mechanism.

Fast and Slow Muscle

The preceding description takes little account of differences between muscles. In almost all mammals two types of twitch muscle have been described, fast and slow. Most experiments have been done on muscles of quadrupeds in which some extensors are active in posture to support the weight of the body, and in these mammals the difference between slow postural muscles and fast phasic muscles is clearly seen. In man normal posture depends on continuous but minimal activity of extensors and flexors to maintain the centre of gravity over the joints (the paravertebral muscles and those supporting the head are exceptional). Correspondingly, in man there is not such a clear division into fast and slow muscles. However, large differences do exist between muscles in man; the speed of

contraction may be characterized by measuring the contraction time of an isometric twitch (time from onset to peak of tension). The extra-ocular muscles are the fastest in the body, followed by the muscles of the jaw (40 msec) and those of the hand and foot (50 to 60 msec). The biceps brachii (70 msec) is faster than the muscles of the calf where the gastrocnemius (100 msec) is faster than the soleus (120 msec); in quadrupeds the soleus is a typical slow muscle. Possibly the differences between human muscles are adaptations to the mass of the structure which they have to move. Hill has commented on a similar difference between muscle speeds of different species, fast and slow muscle of the mouse having twitch contraction times of 7 and 20 msec and those of the cat 20 and 70 msec respectively. Hill pointed out that if the muscles of a large animal were to contract as quickly as those of a small one the extra inertial forces could break bone and rupture muscle and tendon.

There are a number of other differences between fast and slow muscle. Fast muscle relaxes faster, needs a higher stimulation frequency for tetanic fusion (Fig. 21.11), has a higher rate of rise of tension and a greater velocity of isotonic shortening. Slow muscle is more efficient for a given work load. The contractile differences are reflexions of biochemical differences. The actomyosin ATPase of fast muscle splits ATP more rapidly, the myosin heads contain different amino acid sequences and, together with other contractile proteins, are different electrophoretically. There is relatively more sarcoplasmic reticulum in fast muscle and it sequesters Ca^{2+} more rapidly. Electrically the fast muscle action potential is briefer and propagates faster, and the resting potential is slightly higher. End-plates are not identical and differ in their sensitivity to neuromuscular blocking agents; fast muscle is more sensitive to tubocurarine and similar competitive inhibitors, but less sensitive to depolarizing agents such as decamethonium. This is particularly important because the muscles of respiration may not have the same sensitivity as those of the limb.

The twitches of fast and slow muscle differ in the way they are affected by a number of factors: three will be considered. Preceding activity, such as a tetanus, increases the twitch of fast muscle without any effect on its time course, possibly by increasing the central propagation into the T-tubules; in contrast a slow muscle twitch become smaller and briefer. Adrenaline, but not noradrenaline, also potentiates fast and depresses slow muscle. Physiological levels of adrenaline produce significant effects only in slow muscle because the threshold of fast muscle is five times higher. An increase of temperature also decreases the twitch of fast muscle and increases the contraction and relaxation phases of both. Rate of rise of tension and shortening velocity of tetanic contractions are also increased by warming. These changes are physiologically important since muscle temperature is a few degrees above 30°C when at rest in a cool environment and rises to above 40°C during exercise, higher than the elevated core temperature.

Differences in contractile properties are accompanied by differences in muscle metabolism. Slow muscle has a greater density of capillaries and a high resting blood flow, being about equal to the flow reached in fast muscle in maximal activity. Slow muscle is red because of a high myoglobin content, but also has more lipid and oxidative enzymes, such as succinic dehydrogenase (SDH). As a result slow muscle is more resistant to fatigue during repetitive stimulation. In the past all fast muscle was considered to be pale, but some fast muscles are red and have the metabolic properties of slow muscle. The commoner white form of fast muscle has low concentrations of myoglobin and oxidative enzymes but large amounts of glycogen and enzymes concerned with glycolysis and anaerobic metabolism such as phosphorylase. Such muscle is capable of short periods of intense activity but fatigues very rapidly with depletion of glycogen stores.

Many of the differences between fast and slow muscle may be seen between muscle fibres, and all muscles in man contain fast and slow fibres in different proportions. The mechanical properties of single fibres from man have not been studied in detail, but evidence can be obtained from histochemistry of muscle biopsy samples. Serial frozen sections are used to estimate the activity of particular enzymes. Myosin ATPase is important and has been correlated with twitch contraction times; examples of oxidative and glycolytic enzymes are commonly used, too. Many systems of nomenclature have been introduced to describe histochemical fibre types but only two systems will be mentioned. Figure 21.13 shows serial sections stained histochemically. Fast contracting fibres have been termed Type II and can be further subdivided on the basis of whether they have high glycolytic and oxidative enzyme concentrations (found in red fast muscles) or only glycolytic enzymes (predominate in white fast muscles). Fibre iv in Figure 21.13 is an example of the first class of fast fibre which

is termed Type IIA or Group C. Fibre i is of Type IIB or Group A. Fibre vi is Type I or Group B and would be expected to be slow contracting. A problem of such rigid classification is illustrated by fibre ii: it has the ATPase and phosphorylase activity typical of Type IIB fibres but reacts positively for SDH.

Motor units. A motoneurone axon, all its branches and the muscle fibres innervated by it are called a *motor unit*. A motor unit is the quantum of motor response: once the motoneurone is excited all the fibres of the motor unit respond in an-all-or-none manner in normal muscle. In man the motor unit contains from some 2000 muscle fibres (in calf muscle) to little more than 100 (lumbrical muscles). Extra-ocular muscle motor units may be even smaller (about 10 fibres suggested) but the presence of tonic muscle (below) makes calculations difficult. The fibres of a motor unit are restricted to a limited region of the large muscles, but within their territory they are completely mixed with fibres of other units. In re-innervated muscle the fibres of one unit are often grouped together and give characteristic electrical responses (compare Fig. 21.14,C). Motor units can be classified as slow contracting with great resistance to fatigue or as fast contracting, easily fatigued, or as fast contracting with high fatigue resistance (labelled as S, FF and FR respectively). Within each group there is variation of twitch contraction times, so a continuous spectrum exists from the fastest to slowest. A wide range exists in each muscle: Twitch contraction times of motor units have been found in human dorsal interosseous muscle from 30 to 100 msec (mean 55 msec) and in the gastrocnemius between 40 and 110 msec.

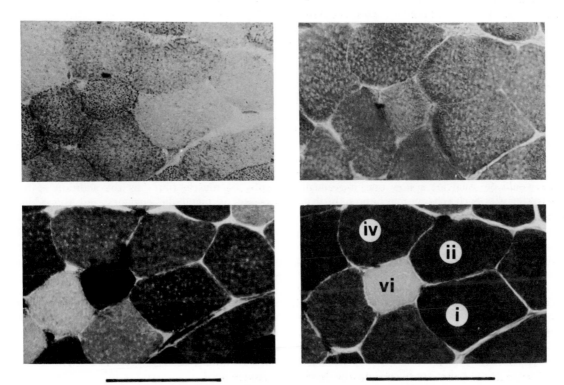

Fig. 21.13 Histochemistry of a cat fast twitch muscle. The muscle was rapidly frozen in liquid nitrogen and sections 15 µm thick were cut in a cryostat. Serial sections were incubated in different substrate media designed so that particular enzymes produce a coloured end product, the density of which indicates enzyme activity. Below: reactions for myosin ATPase with pre-incubation in acid (left) or alkaline (right) medium. Above-right: phosphorylase. Above-left: succinic dehydrogenase. Individual fibres can be identified in each of the four sections, for example the small fibre labelled (vi). Fibre types (labelled i – vi) are described in the text. Calibration bars indicate 100 µm for each column. (After G. D. Edjtehadi, 1974, Ph.D. thesis, University of Bristol.)

Motor unit tensions also vary widely. In the interosseous muscle twitch tension of units range from 1 mN to 100 mN; in gastrocnemius the relative range is slightly higher (10 mN to 2 N), but it is clear that the units are large in the larger muscle. The larger muscles would also contain a greater number of units but fast units tend to be larger than slow ones. The motoneurones of motor units also differ. Fast contracting units have large, fast conducting axons originating from large motoneurones. Slow motor unit neurones and axons are smaller, although still within the α range. Large motoneurones discharge at higher frequencies than the small ones.

Voluntary control of muscle contraction. The force of muscle contraction may be modified by alteration of the number of motor units employed, or by alteration of their rate of activation (Fig. 21.11). The nervous system makes use of both methods. When the force to be exerted is small, only a few of the motor units are active, and these are usually the smaller ones; the activity in the different units is, however, asynchronous so that a smooth contraction of the whole muscle is obtained. For a more powerful contraction larger motor units are also brought into action, and to obtain very large forces all the motor units are activated at higher rates. The use of a number of small motor units for the less forcible movements gives an accuracy of control that is no doubt desirable for the fine movements, and could hardly be achieved by larger motor units. The organization of motor units in size and speed is related to their use in natural contractions. For example, in stereotyped voluntary contractions small motoneurones have lower thresholds than large ones, so small slow motor units are recruited before large fast ones. This regular recruitment order persists in other types of contractions such as very rapid transient (ballistic) ones. However, if the skin near the muscle is stimulated during a contraction the recruitment order may be reversed.

Trophic Effects of Nerve

Although there are clear differences between the fast and slow fibres, either type can be changed into the other experimentally. If a fast muscle is subjected to the pattern of activation that would be usual for a slow one, it gradually changes its characteristics. Such a change may be brought about by implanting the nerve of the (slow) cat soleus muscle into a denervated (fast) flexor hallucis longus; when this re-innervation has occurred, the flexor hallucis is found to have a slower twitch than previously, its enzyme systems, both those concerned directly with contraction and those regulating fibre metabolism, have changed toward the pattern seen in slow muscles, and a number of new capillaries have been generated together with an increase in resting blood flow. The opposite transformation from slow to fast can also be produced by the appropriate nerve transposition. A similar change from fast to slow follows repeated stimulation of the nerve to the (fast) flexor hallucis longus at rates that are normal for the (slow) soleus.

Denervated muscle. Intermittent high frequency stimulation of denervated muscle changes some of the properties of slow muscle. Therefore the pattern of activity of the muscle modifies somewhat the type of proteins that are synthesized.

Some do not believe that activity patterns are the only trophic influence of nerve, but consider that a chemical is released from the nerve which affects gene expression in the muscle. A denervated muscle undergoes a number of changes. The most obvious of these is atrophy of the fibre which, if not re-innervated within a few months, involves degeneration and irreversible loss of fibres. The muscle fibres show spontaneous activity known as *fibrillation*; this is a useful diagnostic finding (Fig. 21.14,E). Fibrillation arises from generator sites in individual fibres which wax and wane over a three-day cycle. The action potential become smaller and prolonged and is resistant to tetrodotoxin unlike normal muscle spikes. The twitch is potentiated and prolonged possibly as a result of changes in the sarcoplasmic reticulum. Finally the whole of the muscle membrane becomes hypersensitive to ACh.

Many of these changes are a consequence of the loss of natural activity in the paralysed muscle and can be reproduced by procedures which block neuromuscular transmission but leave the nerve histologically intact. Crush injuries to a peripheral nerve in man which block conduction without nerve degeneration, produce changes in the muscle. Gilliat and his colleagues have produced pressure block in baboons and confirmed that denervation changes result in the muscle without degeneration of the nerve. In part these changes were due to the reduction in muscle activity but they were quantitatively smaller than those following nerve section; these differences suggest that a chemical trophic factor is released from the intact nerve. It is known that the transport of materials (at 400 mm per day) along the axon from the cell body of the motoneurone may persist after nerve impulse block. Kuho and his colleagues found changes in the motoneurone after denervation, whilst Lewis and his colleagues showed that slow muscle nerve could be modified by cross-innervation. These findings are difficult to explain in terms of activity but they may be trophic effects resulting from the retrograde transport of materials to the body of the nerve cell in which chromatolysis and increased synthesis of protein for nerve regeneration are occurring.

The nature of the supposed trophic factor is unknown but the effects of activity are clear and the consequences may be of use therapeutically.

The increased activity of physical training causes hypertrophy of muscle fibres by the addition of myofibrils, an increase of metabolic enzymes and the addition of new capillaries. Natural activity, in contrast to artificial stimulation, does not seem to influence the contractile proteins. Greyhounds have a larger proportion of Type IIb fibres than other dogs, and they maintain this proportion despite a year of sedentary existence.

Muscle has a limited capacity for repair. After damage it is replaced by fibrous tissue. If cut across, the degenerated fibres induce sprouting of axons nearby and re-innervation occurs; the two halves will be joined by a scar. Axon sprouting and re-innervation also occur if part of a muscle is denervated by motor neurone disease. Experimentally only 20 per cent of the neurones need to survive for full recovery of tension. After extensive muscle damage some recovery can occur by neighbouring fibres extending into the gap but regeneration is probably small.

If a muscle is abnormally stretched new sarcomeres are laid down at the ends of the fibres. This is part of the normal process of growth and occurs even in denervated muscle.

Tonic Muscle

Some skeletal muscle is different from the twitch fibres. It is called *tonic* or slow muscle. Each fibre in tonic muscle is innervated by a number of nerves, so the fibre is covered by many end-plates over its whole length. The fibres cannot generate action potentials but are activated by end-plate potentials that spread only passively and locally. Such fibres do not respond mechanically to a single stimulus. Repetitive stimulation generates a slow-rising smooth tetanus, the tension of which increases with stimulation frequency: several hundred pulses per second are necessary for full activation. Tonic muscles respond to depolarizing neuromuscular blocking agents with a prolonged contracture.

Tonic fibres occur in large proportions in the extra-ocular muscles, but also are found in the muscles of the middle ear and possibly the larynx; all are innervated by cranial nerves of α-diameter. Muscles innervated by spinal nerves have no tonic fibres, but many intrafusal fibres (p. 343) have comparable properties.

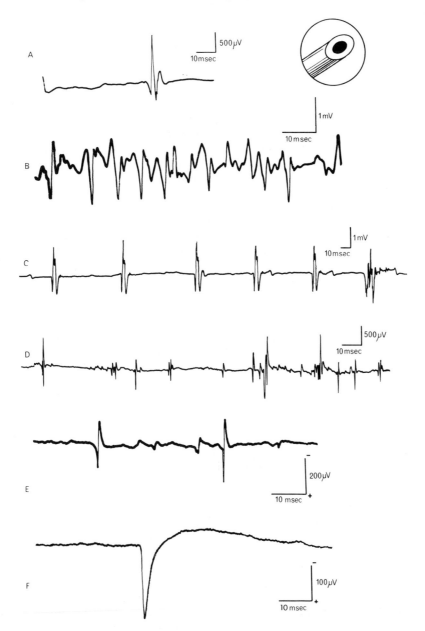

Fig. 21.14 Human electromyogram recorded with a concentric electrode (inset).
   A. Motor unit action potential from healthy subject during weak voluntary contraction.
   B. Interference pattern recorded from healthy muscle during prolonged contraction.
   C. High amplitude long duration action potentials recorded from muscle of patient with disease affecting anterior horn cells.
   D. Short duration polyphasic potentials recorded from muscle of patient with muscular dystrophy.
   E. Fibrillation potentials recorded from denervated muscle.
   F. Positive sharp wave recorded from denervated muscle.

(By courtesy of J. A. R. Lenman.)

Electromyography

When a motor unit is activated, all its constituent muscle fibres carry action potentials at almost the same time. The resulting electrical field is much larger than that generated by a single nerve fibre, and it can be recorded relatively easily in a human subject with fine wires or needle electrodes introduced into muscles.

In healthy muscle no electrical activity is seen when the muscle is relaxed, but during a weak voluntary contraction motor unit action potentials can be recorded which during maximal effort can no longer be distinguished from one another and appear as an 'interference pattern'. In disease affecting the lower motor neurones a reduced number of motor unit potentials may be recorded so that individual units can be recognized even during a strong contraction. Where there is loss of motor neurones, as in poliomyelitis and motor neurone disease, surviving axons send out sprouts to re-innervate denervated muscle fibres and these enlarged units give rise to potentials of high amplitude and long duration. In muscle disease, on the other hand, where there may be little or no loss of motor units but a proportion of the muscle fibres in the units may have degenerated, the number of motor unit potentials is not reduced but individual potentials are of short duration and polyphasic. In denervated muscle apparently spontaneous contraction of muscle fibres takes place which appears as fibrillation potentials. These are short duration low amplitude potentials, which have an initial positive phase unless recorded from the end-plate zone. Positive sharp waves are also recorded from denervated muscle particularly following electrode movement (Fig. 21.14).

Measurement of nerve conduction velocity (Fig. 21.15) has been found to be clinically useful. Nerve conduction may be slowed if there is demyelination along the course of a peripheral nerve as may be the case in certain forms of peripheral neuropathy. In entrapment neuropathies where there is local compression of a peripheral nerve, as for example where the median nerve is compressed in the carpal tunnel, there may be marked slowing of conduction along the affected segment of nerve.

MUSCULAR EXERCISE

Internal energy stores allow very high levels of activity for about 20 sec, reaching nearly 2 horsepower (1.4 kW) in trained men sprinting 200 m. Longer activity depends on chemicals brought to the muscle, and only about a quarter of this output of power can be maintained. Although skeletal muscles are the principal tissues concerned in exercise, many other systems are also involved in the adaptation to physical work.

The initiation and co-ordination of movement depend on the nervous system; the extra fuel and oxygen requirements of the muscles are supplied by appropriate adjustment of the cardiovascular and respiratory systems. These adjustments are initiated by chemical, mechanical and thermal stimuli associated with the neuromuscular activity; they are carried out through the nervous system and the endocrine system. Not

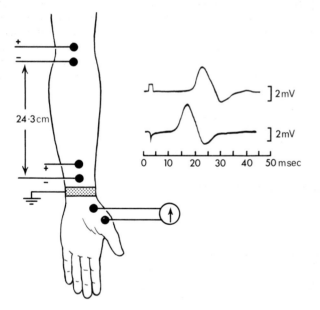

Fig. 21.15 Motor conduction measurement in the median nerve of a diabetic patient with the carpal tunnel syndrome. The latency, 10·0 msec between the stimulus at the wrist and the evoked potential, is greatly increased. Since the latency after stimulation at the elbow is 16·0 msec and the distance between the stimulating cathodes 24.3 cm the conduction velocity elbow to wrist is

$$\frac{24 \cdot 3}{16 - 10} = 40 \text{ m/s. (normal, above 47 m/s)}$$

(J. A. R. Lenman & A. E. Ritchie (1976) 2nd edition *Clinical Electromyography*. Bath: Pitman.)

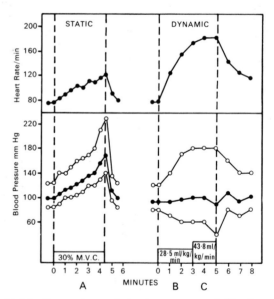

Fig. 21.16 Comparison of the heart rate and blood pressures (systolic, diastolic and estimated mean pressures) in response to a fatiguing, sustained hand-grip contraction at 30 per cent maximum voluntary contraction (MCV), and to an exhausting treadmill-walking test with stages of progressive severity shown as oxygen uptake/kg body weight/min. The results clearly show the great rise of blood pressure, and the small rise of heart rate during the sustained hand-grip, which contrasts with the large rise in heart rate with little change in mean blood pressure during the fatiguing rhythmic exercise. A, 30 per cent MCV; B, 28:5 ml/kg/min oxygen uptake; C, 43:8 ml/kg/min oxygen uptake. (A. R. Lind & G. W. McNicol (1967) *Canadian Medical Association Journal*, 96, 706–713.)

Table 21.17 Approximate figures for the cardiac output and oxygen consumption during exercise of varying severity

Exercise	Cardiac output (l/min)	Total oxygen consumption of body (l/min)	Arterio-venous oxygen difference (ml/100 ml)
Rest	5	0·25	5
Walking 3·2 km/h (2 m.p.h.)	10	0·8	8
Walking 8 km/h (5 m.p.h.)	20	2·5	12
Running 12 km/h (7·5 m.p.h.)	25	3·0	12
Very severe exercise (max. athletic effort)	34	4·0	13

These values apply to calm conditions. Walking or running against a wind increases the oxygen consumption markedly. For example walking at 3·2 km/hr against a gale may cost 2 litres/min. (L. G. C. E. Pugh (1971) *Journal of Physiology*, **213**, 255–276.)

only must an exercising man supply his muscles with metabolic substrates from the liver, intestine and lungs, while transporting metabolites to the lungs and kidneys for excretion, but he must also increase the blood supply to the skin in order to dissipate the extra heat generated.

The adaptation to exercise depends on the type and the severity of the work that is performed and on the state of training of the individual. Muscular work may be thought of in two categories: 'dynamic work' in which muscles contract through some distance against a resisting force (as in running or cycling) and 'static work' in which the muscles contract to support a load, or exert a force without movement. (Some of the differences between the adjustments to static and dynamic work are shown in Figure 21.16.)

In practice the severity of muscular work is usually classified in terms of the energy expenditure or the oxygen uptake (Table 21.17). Work involving an O_2 consumption of up to 3 times the basal level is described as *moderate work*, while 4 to 8 times the basal O_2 consumption implies *hard work*. This method of measurement is less useful for determining the maximum work rate, since it is possible for muscles to incur a metabolic debt, and for short periods to release more energy than could be expected from the O_2 intake. The maximum rate of O_2 consumption during exercise ($\dot{V}o_2$ max) is, however, a useful measurement which depends on age, sex, and state of physical training. A likely value for a 15-year-old boy is 46 ml/kg/min, while for a girl of the same age it would be about 36 ml/kg/min. The value would be rather higher for a young adult, but less in old age. Physical training may increase the $\dot{V}o_2$ max by as much as 80 per cent.

Muscle Metabolism

Muscle obtains the energy for mechanical work from chemicals with an efficiency of about 0.25. The principal fuels used by muscle tissue are carbohydrates and fats. The relative amounts used may be approximately determined from the respiratory quotient (RQ), which is obtained from measurements of inspired and expired gases. The relationship between RQ and metabolic fuels is explained on page 13.

At rest the RQ is usually about 0·85 but it increases during exercise; this indicates that a higher proportion of carbohydrate is then used. During exercise, however, other respiratory and metabolic changes cause fluctuations in the RQ. At the beginning of exercise CO_2 is blown off in excess, partly because stimulation of respiration by higher centres of the brain precedes the major O_2 requirement and partly because, in strenuous exercise, lactic acid produced by muscular

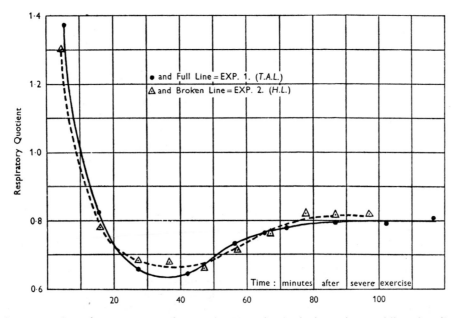

Fig. 21.18 The respiratory quotient after severe muscular exercise. Note that in the later phases, while carbon dioxide is being retained to compensate for that initially driven off, the respiratory quotient falls to a very low level, returning to its final value in about 80 minutes. (A. V. Hill, C. N. H. Long & H. Lupton (1924) *Proceedings of the Royal Society* B, **96**, 472.)

metabolism is liberated into the blood where it is buffered by the bicarbonate (p. 268) with formation of carbonic acid. The latter stimulates respiration and more CO_2 is blown off in the lungs. Since oxygen is involved in neither of these processes the RQ (the ratio CO_2 produced $/O_2$ used) becomes larger and may be greater than 1. After vigorous exercise has ended the oxygen intake remains high for some time because lactic acid and other substances which had accumulated in the muscles must be oxidized. The oxidation of lactate yields relatively small amounts of CO_2 so that during this process the RQ may fall below 0·7 (Fig. 21.18).

A more complete picture of muscle metabolism is obtained from biochemical investigation of muscle biopsies taken at rest and during exercise, and from the examination of aterial and venous blood samples. These methods show that, whereas fatty acids are an important fuel for the metabolism of muscles that are at rest or only mildly active, it is the carbohydrates that provide the major source of energy during exercise. Muscle glycogen is the principal carbohydrate store, and this supplies the extra energy during the first minutes of muscular exercise; as time passes, however, and glycogen stores diminish, the glucose in the circulating blood assumes an increasingly important role. As the muscle glycogen stores become depleted the subject experiences a sensation of fatigue. Subjects in whom the muscle glycogen stores have been increased by a diet rich in carbohydrate can continue to work against a controlled load for longer than similar subjects on a normal diet. During training the muscle glycogen stores increase (though less glycogen is actually used for a given task), the rate of entry of fatty acids into the cells and the rate of triglyceride formation also increase. Highly trained subjects can exercise hard for long periods without accumulation of lactate; they are better able to oxidize fatty acid.

Oxygen debt. The rate at which oxygen can be utilized by the muscles depends on the O_2 transport by the circulation, and on the proportion of that O_2 that is extracted from the circulating blood. During exercise the low O_2 tension in the cells, the increased CO_2 formation, and the presence of acid metabolites all favour an increased uptake of O_2 from the blood. More O_2 is taken out of each ml of blood so that the arteriovenous O_2 difference is greater during exercise than at rest; in strenuously contracting muscles it may increase 2 to 3 times. In trained muscles the oxygen extraction is even higher since training enhances the activity of oxidative enzyme systems.

During short periods of intense exertion, however, the metabolic work done in the muscles is often far greater than one would expect from the O_2 consumption, and the same is true in the early part of more prolonged hard work; the necessary additional energy is then produced by anaerobic metabolism. Figure 21.19 shows the O_2 consumption during 10 minutes steady running on a treadmill at four different speeds. Although the work began quite abruptly, the O_2 consumption took a minute or two to rise to an appropriate steady level, and during these first minutes part of the energy was provided by anaerobic metabolism. After the period of work was over, the O_2 consumption did not at once fall to its previous level, but it declined rather gradually. This additional O_2 consumption after the work had been completed is the *oxygen debt*, it is the amount of O_2 required to restore the energy stores which had been broken down anaerobically during the preceeding exertion. (After prolonged hard work the O_2 consumption may be raised above the normal level for several hours; this is not, however, all due to simple oxygen debt, but represents a prolonged general elevation of the metabolic rate.)

Three reactions are important in the anaerobic metabolism of muscles:

Adenosine triphosphate (ATP)→

Adenosine diphosphate (ADP)+phosphate

Creatine phosphate (CP)→Creatine + phosphate

Glycogen→pyruvate and lactate

The first two reactions involve high energy phosphate links. Magnetic nuclear resonance has been used to monitor such metabolic changes, and has revealed unknown phosphate-containing metabolites. The stores of ATP are sufficient to provide energy for less than 10 twitches. If ATP is completely depleted irreversible rigor occurs. The ATP level falls only in violent exercise but not enough to produce rigor. After exercise ATP and CP levels in the muscles are rapidly restored. The third step in 'repaying' the oxygen debt (the oxidative conversion of lactate or pyruvate to glycogen) is slower than the resynthesis of ATP or CP and may take 15 to 30 minutes (Fig. 21.20).

The maximum oxygen debt that can be incurred is probably related to the maximum tolerable level of lactic acid. The relationship between the O_2 debt and the lactic acid level is not, however, simple, since the outward diffusion of lactate from muscle cells is relatively slow, and lactic acid is taken up by the liver and heart. Some of the chemical changes in the blood during and after exercise are shown in Figure 21.20.

Circulatory Adjustments

With the onset of muscular activity, and perhaps even before it, the blood flow through the active muscles increases dramatically; an increase in flow of more than 10 times is not unusual in fast muscle. The increase in flow is brought about by

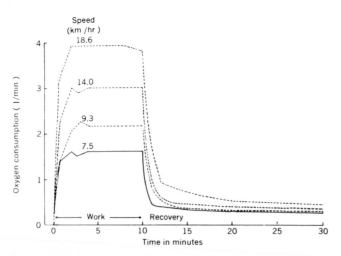

Fig. 21.19 Effects of increasing intensities of work on a treadmill on a man's O_2 consumption. (*After* Margaria.)

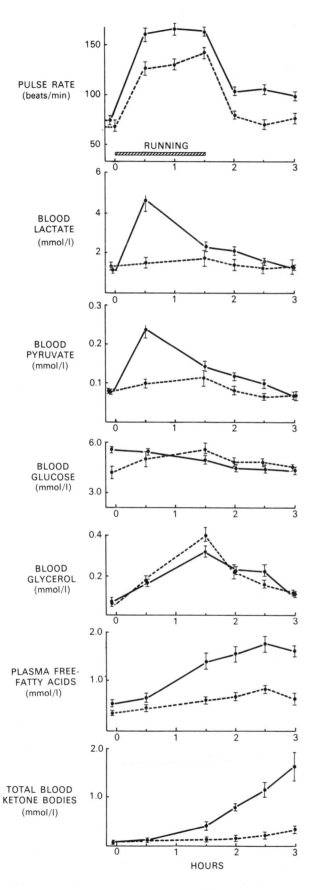

metabolites of active muscle which act on the pre-capillary sphincters. There are a number of candidates which include organic molecules (AMP and ADT), inorganic ions (H^+, K^+ and PO_4^{3-}) and low Po_2, high Pco_2. The effect may well be due to the summation of several factors, and the increase in extracellular fluid osmotic pressure may itself have an effect.

Relaxation of pre-capillary sphincters allows the perfusion of many more capillaries, and not only does the blood flow through the muscle increase but the mean diffusion distance from capillaries to active muscle fibres is reduced so that the gas exchange becomes more efficient. The number of capillaries that can be opened up in this way becomes greater when a muscle is trained. The blood flow through a muscle is also affected by the frequency of contraction of the active muscle fibres; blood cannot flow freely through capillaries and veins that are compressed by the continuous contraction of neighbouring muscle fibres, but intermittently contracting fibres may, by their pumping action, actually enhance the blood flow.

The increase in blood flow through muscles during even moderate exercise is so great that it can be met only by an increase in the cardiac output. It is true that blood flow through the skin and viscera is decreased by local vasoconstriction, but this redistribution of flow can only satisfy a part of the muscles' requirements, and the cutaneous vasoconstriction passes off anyway when the body temperature begins to rise. Table 21.17 shows the increase in cardiac output that may occur during exercise of varying severity.

Cardiac output rises in direct proportion to the increase in oxygen consumption over a wide range of exercise levels. Despite a large increase in the cardiac output, the arterial blood pressure rises less than might be expected during exercise, and may actually fall, since the total peripheral resistance is substantially reduced.

The increase in cardiac output during exercise is due to increases in both heart rate and stroke volume. An average young man with a resting heart rate of 65 beats/minute and a stroke volume of 90 ml, might have a maximal cardiac output during severe exertion of about 25 litres/minute, with a heart rate of up to 190 per minute and a stroke volume of 130 ml. In a trained subject, however, the pulse rate rises less (Fig. 21.20), and more of the increase in cardiac output is obtained by increasing the stroke volume.

The physiological mechanisms that lead to the increase in cardiac stroke volume during exercise are still open to some doubt. The increase in venous return that results from the pumping action of contracting muscles and of increased respiratory movements is undoubtedly important, but during exercise a normal heart does not significantly increase its diastolic volume. The increased stroke volume is due to a more complete emptying, by a more forcible systolic contraction (Fig. 21.21). There is an increase of sympathetic activity very

Fig. 21.20 Mean and standard deviation of the mean of observations in nine athletes (●-----●) and 18 untrained subjects (●———●) before and after running for 1½ hours. The athletes ran much faster than the non-athletes. The athletes had a lower heart rate than the untrained subjects both during and after exercise. (R. H. Johnson, J. L. Walton, H. A. Krebs & D. H. Williamson (1969) *Lancet* ii, 452–455.)

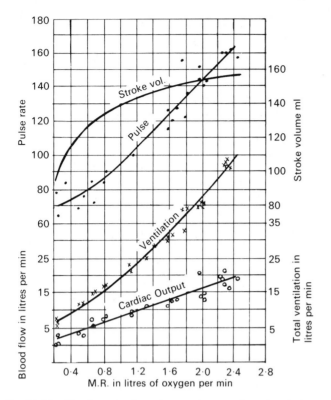

Fig. 21.21 Circulatory and respiratory changes of man in relation to increments O_2 consumption produced in experiments at different intensities of work on bicycle ergometer. (*From* A. V. Bock, C. Vancaulaert, D. B. Dill, A. Fölling & L. M. Hurxthal (1928) *Journal of Physiology*, 66, 141.)

early in exercise. The heart muscle contracts more strongly with an increase in the rate of shortening and relaxation so that the duration of systole is decreased. Increased venous return ensures that filling keeps pace with increasing cardiac output so that the heart muscle remains at an optimal degree of stretch for maximal contraction.

The increase in force of ventricular contraction and the increase in heart rate are both results of reflex control through the autonomic nervous system. At the onset of exercise the main effect is a reduction of the cardio-inhibitory action of the vagus, but within a heart beat or two the increase in heart rate and stroke volume are largely due to increased activity in the cardiac sympathetic nerves and later to circulating adrenaline. The receptors involved in these cardiac reflexes are situated in the muscles and around the joints; their precise nature is not, however, clear, though they are known to be activated to a considerably greater extent by 'static' than by 'dynamic' exercise (Fig. 21.16).

Respiratory Adjustment to Exercise

During exercise respiratory ventilation increases in both rate and depth. The increase in ventilation, like that in cardiac output, is directly proportional to the increase of oxygen consumption. The precision of control is such that the arterial Po_2 and Pco_2 remain almost unchanged except in severe exercise. The stimulus to increase ventilation is therefore not,

at least in any obvious way, a change in the gaseous composition of blood. Other reflex mechanisms summate to stimulate ventilation. Collaterals of descending motor pathways could form one such mechanism. Another could involve limb afferents stimulated by movement. A more precise mechanism has been suggested by Ponte and Purves who found that increased venous return, such as occurs in exercise, stimulates respiration. The mechanism of this stimulation is unknown but it may be indirect; increased venous return increases cardiac output which may be detected by the more rapid flow of blood from peripheral to central chemoreceptors. A further factor may be that peripheral chemoreceptors become more sensitive to changes in Po_2 and Pco_2 during exercise, probably by a neural mechanism. The rise in body temperature that accompanies prolonged hard work (several degrees centigrade) also stimulates respiration, though only after a few minutes; it cannot account for the large rise in ventilation that occurs in the first 2 to 3 minutes.

Second wind. At the beginning of moderately severe exercise, say a long-distance run, the breathing becomes increasingly laboured; after some time the discomfort disappears and the subject says he has his 'second wind'. The phenomena of second wind are variable. In some people the transition from dyspnoea to hypernoea occurs suddenly, while in others the change is quite slow. The rate of transition has little to do with training as the phenomenon is often quite marked in the untrained person. During the dyspnoeic period the alveolar carbon dioxide tension is higher than normal, but when the subject gets his second wind the alveolar carbon dioxide tension falls, the ventilation rate falls and the subject feels more comfortable. At the same time the body temperature may rise and sweating may occur. The RQ usually falls. This phenomenon has not yet been fully explained but it is likely that the early discomfort of heavy exercise is due partly to increase in blood Pco_2.

Hormonal Changes during Exercise

Up to half of the carbohydrate consumed during a period of severe exercise may be mobilized from the liver glycogen stores. This glycogenolysis is enhanced by the increase in circulating adrenaline that accompanies exercise. The fact that the plasma insulin concentration falls and the glucagon level remains unchanged prevents the blood glucose level from falling too low and promotes the mobilization of fats from fat depots (see Fig. 21.20).

Noradrenaline and growth hormone levels increase during exercise and both lead to a mobilization of fat and an increase in the free fatty acid concentration in the plasma. In fit subjects the growth hormone level falls rapidly at the end of exercise, but in the unfit it returns only slowly to its basal value. The adrenal cortex is also activated in exercise. In long-distance swimmers, for example, the output of 17-hydroxysteroids in the urine may increase eightfold—an increase comparable to that occurring after major surgery.

Fatigue

The loss of muscular power that occurs during fatigue may be due to failure at a number of different places including central synapses, the motor end-plates and the contractile machinery. Merton has suggested that in a simple human limb movement it is probably the muscle fibres themselves that become fatigued. If a muscular movement of the hand is carried on to complete fatigue and at this moment the circulation in the arm is arrested by inflating a sphygmomanometer cuff there is no recovery of strength until the cuff is released and the blood flow restored, although muscle action potentials can still be recorded in response to nerve stimulation. Since occlusion of the circulation in the arm does not affect the central nervous system and yet delays recovery, the site of fatigue must be in the muscle fibres themselves. However, Stephens and Taylor have found that when a muscle contracts maximally fatigue may occur at the neuromuscular junction before contractile failure of the muscle fibres develops. The site of fatigue may depend on the nature and severity of the muscle activity. Even when the site is muscular (Merton's experiments) one can speculate that it is conduction within the T-tubules that is blocked rather than depletion of metabolites or other factors directly affecting contractile proteins. The effect would be due to K^+ accumulation and Na^+ depletion within the extracellular space of the T-tubules. Conduction failure at such sites might be regarded as a mechanism protecting the contractile machinery from irreversible damage.

The general fatigue experienced after severe exercise is probably due to events at the synapses in the central nervous system. This may be regarded as a protective mechanism since central fatigue is manifest before there is any block at the neuromuscular junction and long before the muscle itself is incapable of contraction. It should be kept in mind that the word fatigue has also a psychological meaning; fatigue may, for example, arise through lack of interest in a routine and boring task. This is very different from the physiological meaning of fatigue.

Normal active muscle exhibits a slight tremor with a dominant frequency near 10 Hz. The tremor increases in some pathological states and also after strong exercise; this physiological increase may persist for a day or more.

SENSORY INNERVATION OF SKELETAL MUSCLE

Skeletal muscle contains many sense endings. Some of these give rise to sensations of discomfort or pain when the muscle is fatigued; these can be regarded as protective, preventing the individual from overworking his muscles. The remaining sense endings do not give rise to sensations but pass information to the central nervous system about the mechanical events in the muscle. This information is supplied to the motoneurones which control the motor units in the muscle and is used to make adjustments to the discharge of motor impulses. Branches of the afferent fibres carry duplicate information to higher levels of the nervous system, such as the cerebellum.

Two types of sensory nerve ending are present, tension receptors called *Golgi tendon organs* and length receptors called *muscle spindles*.

Golgi tendon organs. The Golgi tendon organs (Fig. 21.22) are mounted on connective tissue lying in series with the muscle fibres. They issue signals when the connective tissue is

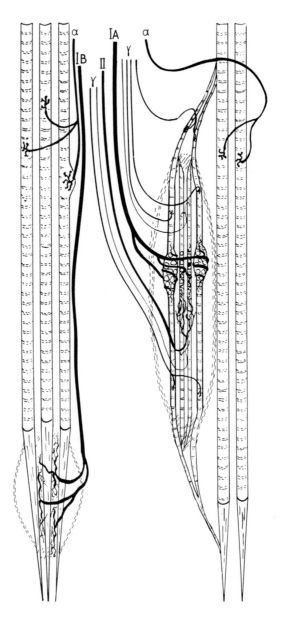

Fig. 21.22 Diagrammatic drawings of a muscle spindle and a tendon organ. The muscle spindle on the right is attached to extrafusal muscle fibres and tendon. It consists of small diameter intrafusal muscle fibres which are largely enclosed in a connective tissue capsule. Longitudinally the drawing is not to scale (the length of a spindle may be fifty times its width). Transversely in the drawing the width of the extrafusal muscle fibres represents a diameter of 40 μm; the intrafusal fibres are drawn to the same scale and represent diameters of about 20 μm for the two long fibres with nuclear bags at the equator of the spindle and about 10 μm for the two short fibres with nuclear chains at the equator. The group of nerve fibres shows the relative diameters of these fibres to each other. The largest nerve fibre, marked IA, supplies the main primary afferent ending lying over the nuclear bags and chains. Fibre II goes to a secondary afferent ending on the nuclear chain fibres adjacent to the primary ending. Six small γ motor fibres of varying sizes supply motor endings on the intrafusal muscle fibres. The motor end-plates on the extrafusal muscle fibres are supplied by larger α nerve fibres. The remaining IB nerve fibre goes to the encapsulated tendon organ on the left; the branches of the afferent nerve ending lie between the tendons of a group of extrafusal muscle fibres. (*By courtesy of Sybil Cooper.*)

stretched by forces produced by the contraction of the muscle. Below a certain value of tension, the threshold, the ending does not discharge nerve impulses, above this value the frequency of discharge rises as the tension rises. Inactive muscle can be extended, within physiological limits with very little rise of tension, so the extension of an inactive muscle by a joint

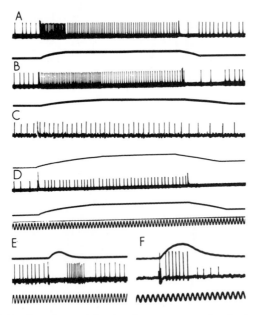

Fig. 21.23 Impulses originating in receptor organs in the soleus muscle of a decerebrate cat and recorded by cathode ray oscilloscope in single nerve fibres in the dorsal spinal roots. The ventral spinal roots were intact so that motor impulses may be travelling in both α and γ motor nerve fibres to the muscle to maintain tone in the extrafusal muscle fibres and to activate the intrafusal muscle fibres. All the other muscles in the limb were denervated.

In A to D the second trace records the application and release of a 4 mm stretch to the muscle. The time signal of 50 Hz is shown below D.

A and B. Responses from the primary ending of a muscle spindle. In A the stretch is applied at 25 mm per sec, and in B at 10 mm per sec. In both cases the discharge rate rises rapidly during the dynamic part of each stretch, reaching 200 per sec in A and 150 per sec in B. The discharge is steady during maintained stretch and slows during release of stretch, after which it returns quickly to the resting rate.

C. Response from a secondary ending of a muscle spindle to a muscle stretch at 10 mm per sec. The increase in discharge rate during the dynamic period is much less marked than in B. The rate is steady during maintained stretch and shows some slowing on release of stretch.

D. Response from a tendon organ to a muscle stretch at 10 mm per sec. Owing to the high threshold of the organ the increase in discharge is slow to start. The discharge continues during the maintained stretch but stops at once when the stretch is released and does not start again.

E and F. Responses of the three kinds of ending to a maximal shock to the muscle nerve. Tension is recorded in the upper traces and 50 Hz is shown below.

E. Primary ending. The discharge stops during the contraction but comes in at an increased rate during relaxation.

F. Secondary ending (small deflexions) and tendon ending (large deflexions). The secondary ending shows no response during contraction but give a discharge during relaxation. The tendon organ discharges during contraction but stops during relaxation. (*By courtesy of Sybil Cooper.*)

movement has little effect on Golgi organs. However, many movements, for example, walking down a flight of stairs, involve elongation of an active muscle; in this example the activity of the thigh extensors acts as a brake opposing the descent. The discharge of a Golgi tendon organ is shown in Figure 21.23F. It can be seen that the ending discharges only during the phase of tension produced by the muscle contraction.

Muscle spindles. The spindle is much more complicated than the tendon organ; the basic element is a small bundle of skeletal muscle fibres a few millimetres long which lies within a fluid-filled capsule (Fig. 21.22). The fibres are unusual because they are much smaller in diameter than the other fibres; they are called *intrafusal fibres* to distinguish them from the large extrafusal fibres which make up the bulk of the muscle. The ends of the intrafusal fibres, which may protrude some distance beyond the poles of the spindle-shaped capsule, are attached to the connective tissue structure of the muscle. The bundle of intrafusal fibres has a motor innervation which is different from that of the extrafusal fibres. The motor fibres are small, and called either γ efferents or small motor fibres (Fig. 21.22). The motoneurones which give rise to these fibres lie scattered in the motoneurone pool supplying the extrafusal fibres but their activity is controlled differently. Each motoneurone controls a group of muscle fibres, called its motor unit; it is able to exercise this multiple control because the motor axon branches many times in the muscle. Extrafusal motor units range from several thousand in the large limb muscles to tens of fibres in small muscles of the hand.

Intrafusal motor units are numerically small and endings from more than one intrafusal motoneurone make contact with an individual intrafusal muscle fibre; this is called polyneural innervation of the muscle fibre. Polyneural innervation is not found in extrafusal muscle. Two types of intrafusal muscle fibres have been indentified their main anatomical difference lies in the arrangement of the cell nuclei. If these are closely packed in a group, they are called *nuclear bag fibres*. If they are arranged in a line they are called *nuclear chain fibres*. The contraction properties of the two types of fibre are different.

The main sensory nerve ending of the intrafusal muscle is found on the mid-capsular region called the equatorial zone. The contractile apparatus of the intrafusal muscle fibre is weakened at the equator, the cross-striation being very faint. The main sensory ending, the primary ending, consists of unmyelinated nerve terminals with many small swellings wrapped around the equatorial zone. It is sometimes called an annulo-spiral ending and is the terminal of a large myelinated afferent fibre. In some spindles there are in addition sensory endings called secondary endings which lie a small distance away from the primary ending on the intrafusal muscle fibres. There is a great range of complexity in muscle spindles both in the number of intrafusal muscle fibres and the number of sensory endings.

The sensory nerves which form the primary endings are of large diameter, usually the largest in the muscle nerve, slightly larger than the fibres serving the Golgi tendon organs and about twice as large as the fibres serving the secondary endings. It is not possible to generalize about the sizes of these nerves since the spectrum of fibre sizes varies with different muscles and with different animals but the spindle primary afferents are described as group IA, the Golgi tendon organ afferents as group IB and the secondary ending afferents as group II (see Fig. 21.22).

If an isolated spindle is held in a slightly stretched position the sensory endings discharge nerve impulses steadily; if the length of the spindle is increased the frequency rises during the time of stretching and declines to a steady value which may be only slightly different from the initial frequency. The period during which the increase in length occurs is called the dynamic phase, and the increase in frequency during this phase is called the dynamic response. There is a marked difference in the behaviour of the primary and secondary endings during the dynamic phase. The primary endings have a noticeable dynamic response, the secondaries have little or none. This difference is illustrated in Figure 21.23A, B and C. Thus a nerve centre supplied with the output of both primaries and secondaries from a spindle could calculate the instantaneous length from the secondary discharge and the rate of change of length from the dynamic response of the primary ending.

The spindle intrafusal muscle lies in parallel with the extrafusal muscle, so that changes in length imposed on the muscle when the joints are moved are also equally imposed on the muscle spindles within the muscle. In a passively extended muscle the spindles signal stretch. The situation becomes more complicated when the muscle contracts. If the extrafusal muscle is made to contract, but the intrafusal muscle is inactive, the spindle shortens passively and the sensory discharge declines or stops. If the intrafusal muscle contracts in isolation it cannot, since it is very feeble, move the joints to which the muscle is attached; contraction of the muscular poles of the spindle stretches the equatorial zone of the spindle and leads to a vigorous discharge.

If the intrafusal and extrafusal muscles are stimulated simultaneously the discharge from the spindle varies according to the resistance to shortening experienced by the extrafusal fibres. If the muscle meets little resistance to shortening and so makes an isotonic contraction, it brings together the points of attachment of the two ends of the spindle and thus the tension applied to the equatorial zone is slight and there is little afferent discharge. If the extrafusal contraction is isometric, or nearly so, the intrafusal contraction is concentrated on the equatorial zone and so a vigorous stimulation of the sensory endings occurs. Thus if the motor centres send simultaneous messages to the intra- and extrafusal muscle, the reply from the sense endings will indicate how much muscle shortening has occurred. The spindle discharge is relayed back to the motoneurones of the extrafusal muscle, where by excitatory synaptic action the discharge of the motoneurone tends to increase. Thus if the muscle meets resistance during shortening extra contractile force is called in by way of the spindles. However, this is a simplification because other influences act on the extrafusal motoneurone which can control it independently of its spindle feed-back. Movements are possible even after section of all sensory afferent feed-back from the muscle.

The impulses from the spindle play a part in the nervous control, at the subconscious level, of muscular activity both during movement and during sustained contractions and contribute to position sense as well.

When the skeletal muscles are examined histologically great variation is found in the density of muscle spindles and tendon organs. A few muscles, for example the cricothyroid and the extraocular muscles in many animals, have no spindles at all; some muscles have spindles and no tendon organs; others, like the diaphragm, have few spindles and tendon organs. The highest densities are found in the small muscles of the limbs such as the lumbricals and interosseous muscles. It seems reasonable to suggest that those muscles which take part in delicate movements need a more extensive sensory equipment.

REFERENCES

Bannister R 1972 Sport, physical recreation, and the national health. British Medical Journal ii: 711–715

Bennett M R 1972 Autonomic neuromuscular transmission. Cambridge University Press

Bevegård B S, Shepherd J T 1967 Regulation of the circulation during exercise in man. Physiological Reviews 47: 178–213

Bhattacharyya N K, Cunningham D J C, Goode R C, Howson M G, Lloyd B B 1970 Hypoxia, ventilation, P_{CO_2} and exercise. Respiration Physiology 9: 329–347

Bourne G H (ed) 1972 Structure and function of muscle, 2nd edn 4 vols. Academic Press, New York

Campbell E J M 1967 Exercise tolerance. Scientific Basis of Medicine, Annual Review, 128–144

Carlson F D, Wilkie D R 1974 Muscle physiology. Prentice-Hall, London

Catton W T 1970 Mechanoreceptor function. Physiological Reviews 50: 297–318

Ebashi S, Endo M, Ohtsuki I 1969 Control of muscle contraction. Quarterly Review of Biophysics 2: 351–384

Endo M 1977 Calcium release from the sarcoplasmic reticulum. Physiological Reviews 57: 71–108

Fuchs F 1974 Striated muscle. Annual Reviews of Physiology 36: 461–502

Ginsborg B L, Jenkinson D H 1976 Transmission of impulses from nerve to muscle. In: Zaimis E (ed) Neuromuscular junction. Handbook of experimental pharmacology. Springer, New York, pp 292–364

Gonzales-Serratos H 1971 Inward spread of activation in vertebrate muscle fibres. Journal of Physiology 212: 777–799

Gordon A M, Huxley A F, Julian F J 1966 The variation in isometric tension with sarcomere length in vertebrate muscle fibres. Journal of Physiology 184: 170–192

Havard C W H 1973 Progress in myasthenia gravis. British Medical Journal ii: 437–440

Hill A V 1956 The design of muscles. British Medical Bulletin 12: 165–166

Hudlicka O (ed) 1973 Muscle blood flow. Swets & Zeitlinger, Amsterdam

Hunt C C (ed) 1974 Muscle receptors. Handbook of sensory physiology. Vol III, Part 2. Springer-Verlag, Berlin

Huxley A F 1971 The activation of striated muscle and its mechanical response. Proceedings of the Royal Society B 178: 1–27

Huxley A F 1974 Muscular contraction. Journal of Physiology 243: 1–43

Huxley H E 1971 The structural basis of muscular contraction. Proceedings of the Royal Society B 178: 131–149

Johnson R, Rennie M 1974 Athletic training and metabolism. New Scientist 64: 585–587

Katz B 1966 Nerve, muscle and synapse. McGraw-Hill, New York

Katz B 1969 The release of neural transmitter substances. Liverpool University Press

Keul T (ed) 1973 Limiting factors of physical performance. Thieme, Stuttgart

Lind A R, McNicol G W, Donald K W 1966 Circulatory adjustments to sustained (static) muscular activity. In: Evang K, Andersen K L (eds) Physical activity in health and disease. Universitetsforlager, Oslo, pp 38–63

Margaria R 1976 Biomechanics and energetics of muscular exercise. Clarendon, London

Margaria R (ed) 1967 Exercise at altitude. Exerpta Medica, Amsterdam

McComas A J 1977 Neuromuscular function and disorders. Butterworth, London

Matthews P B C 1972 Mammalian muscle receptors and their central actions. Physiological Society Monograph No 23, Arnold, London

McCloskey D I 1978 Kinesthetic sensibility. Physiological Reviews 58: 763–811

McIntyre A K 1974 Central actions of impulses in muscle afferent fibres. In: Hunt C C (ed) Handbook of Sensory Physiology. Springer-Verlag, Berlin, vol III/2, Ch. 3

Milner-Brown H S, Stein R B, Yemm R 1973 Changes in firing rate of known motor units during linearly changing voluntary contractions. Journal of Physiology 230: 371–390

Pernow B, Saltin B (eds) 1971 Muscle metabolism during exercise. Plenum Press, London

Rack P M H, Westbury D R 1969 The effects of length and stimulus rate on tension in the isometric cat soleus muscle. Journal of Physiology 204: 443–460

Salmons S, Vrbová G 1969 The influence of activity on some contractile characteristics of mammalian fast and slow muscles. Journal of Physiology 201: 535–549

Shephard R J 1977 The fit athlete. Oxford University Press

Simkiss K 1974 Calcium translocation by cells. Endeavour 33: 119–123

Simmons R M, Jewell B R 1974 Mechanics and models of muscular contraction. Recent Advances in Physiology 9: 87–147

Thesleff S (ed) 1977 Motor innervation of muscle. Academic Press, London

Vrbova G et al 1978 Nerve/muscle interaction. Chapman and Hall, London

Zaimis E (ed) 1976 Neuromuscular junction. Handbook of Experimental Pharmacology, vol 42, Springer, Berlin

22 Sensation

The application of a stimulus to the skin can evoke a variety of sensations including touch, cold, warmth and pain. These different modalities of sensation depend on the activation of specific receptors and interactions among their central actions. Vision, hearing, taste and olfaction depend on the stimulation of highly specific sense receptor organs; these specialized forms of sensation, in contrast to the skin senses, are usually referred to as *special senses*.

The sensory processses of an animal may be investigated by training it to respond differentially to two stimuli, and then testing the limits of this discrimination by behavioural trials, including the technique of conditioning (p. 392). Similar methods may be used with human subjects but it is usually more convenient to rely upon previous learning by obtaining verbal reports, provided that suitable precautions are taken to avoid mistaken inferences. Thus a colour-blind person may have learned to call a leaf 'green' and blood 'red', but may fail to distinguish these hues when appropriately tested. When a subject reports that light of a certain wavelength is of one hue rather than another, he is not communicating the essence of his unique experience, and there is no way of determining whether his experience is the same as that of another person. The subject's words merely indicate the ability to discriminate between two stimuli, and thus provide objective evidence from which it may be inferred that the sensory processes aroused by these stimuli differ in some respect.

There is no direct or automatic relationship between a stimulus and the sensory effect that it produces but in ordinary usage the two are often taken to be the same. For instance, a sound may be described as loud, but the word 'loud' properly refers to the psychological effect and not to the stimulus, which is more correctly described as intense or powerful. Indeed, although loudness is determined mainly by the intensity of a sound, it is also a function of its frequency. There is no precise and immutable correspondence between physical and psychological dimensions.

Although end-organs are specialized to be sensitive to different forms of stimulus energy, the quality of a sensation does not depend upon the type of energy which arouses it. A vibrating tuning-fork placed on the lower end of the radius gives rise to a sensation of vibration, whereas the same fork placed on the head or near the ear arouses a sensation of sound. A variety of excitatory stimuli applied to a given end-organ evoke the same kind of sensation. An electric current, pressure and light applied to the eye all evoke sensations of light. This is so even though experiments with single nerve fibres show that all nerve impulses, however they are initiated, are the same. A similar stimulus applied to different end-organs' evokes different sensations: different kinds of stimuli applied to one end-organ all call forth the same sensation. Müller called this the law of specific irritability or the law of specific nerve energy. The quality or modality of the sensation aroused by the stimulation of any end-organ or nerve depends on the central nervous system as well as the end-organ.

It may be asked whether there is any lower limit to the sensitivity of a sensory system. The classical view has been that the subject either experiences a sensation or does not, and that there is some minimal stimulus energy (the *absolute threshold*) below which a sensation cannot be evoked. The concept of a psychological threshold is clearly allied to that of a physiological threshold, such as the minimal energy required to excite a neurone. Such a threshold does not have a constant value, since if we repeatedly present a sound of a given low intensity, and ask the subject whether he can hear it, he will sometimes report that he can, and sometimes that he cannot. This variability means that the threshold can be defined only statistically, by stating the energy required to evoke a positive response with some arbitrary probability (usually 50 per cent).

In any threshold experiment, the experimenter includes blank stimuli, in order to check the reliability of the subject. If a subject reports a significant number of these as perceived, the experimenter may either reject him as unreliable, or inform him, so that he is trained to become reliable in the sense that he has to be reasonably sure before reporting a stimulus as perceived. It is possible to encourage a subject to be more adventurous, for example by giving a large penalty for missing a stimulus which was presented and only a small one for perceiving one which was not in fact presented. In this case his threshold will be lower, but he will be 'unreliable' in the sense that he has reported stimuli which were not there. A complete and accurate definition of threshold should therefore include the proportion of blanks which were reported as peceived. In practice, such a threshold measurement is extremely laborious, requiring to be repeated with different criteria, so that a curve may be drawn, relating threshold to the proportion of blanks perceived. As an example of the relationship, the absolute threshold for vision is about 4 to 6 photons absorbed when 2 per cent or less of blanks are seen, but can be reduced to 1 to 2 photons if 15 to 30 per cent of blanks are seen. In many experiments, such differences are not important, and it is far quicker to adopt a conservative criterion. The complete procedure is of interest in implying that sensitivity is limited by fluctuations of spontaneous activity in sensory pathways.

A related problem is the measurement of differential sensitivity, for example the subject's ability to decide whether one sound is louder than another. The traditional procedure has been to determine a *difference threshold*, estimated as the difference in energy required to produce some arbitrary proportion (usually 75 per cent) of judgements that a variable stimulus is more intense than a standard. Many measures of sensory acuity take this form.

Weber found that as the intensity of the standard stimulus increases, the size of the difference threshold is a constant proportion of the intensity level at which it is measured. The law is valid at intermediate intensities but does not hold at very low intensities where it is difficult to detect the stimuli, and may not hold at very high intensities. Thus although we may be able to distinguish between 20 and 21 g by the sense of touch, we cannot distinguish between 2·0 and 2·1 mg, nor between 200 and 210 kg. Over the major portion of the intensity range the Weber ratio is, however, approximately constant, typical values being for touch $\frac{1}{10}$, for hearing $\frac{1}{5}$, for olfaction $\frac{1}{3}$, and for vision $\frac{1}{100}$ of the magnitude of the stimuli which are being compared.

Fechner, accepting the Weber law as true, derived from it a scale of sensation and related it to the physical size of stimulus intensity. He assumed that all difference thresholds, since they rest upon an equal probability that two stimuli can be discriminated, are subjectively equal. Then by integration he obtained the formula:

$$R = a \log S$$

Sensation intensity (R) = constant (a) × logarithm of the stimulus intensity (log S). A constant ratio of stimulus energies is thus required to produce a constant difference in sensory magnitude.

Such a relationship has been found useful especially in the measurement of sound intensity, where a logarithmic unit, the decibel (p. 455) is in everyday use. However, a decibel scale, though satisfactory for the measurement of sound transmission, is of more doubtful value in psychoacoustics. A tone of 100 decibels, for example, sounds much more than twice as loud as a tone of 50 decibels. This observation implies that a subject can define sensory magnitude introspectively and can assign a numerical value to a given sensation. Extensive experiments involving 'magnitude-naming' have suggested a sensory scale in the form of a power function:

$$R = a.S^b$$

where R is sensation intensity, S is stimulus intensity and a and b are constants. The power function has two arbitrary constants (a and b) which can be selected to give a good fit, whereas the logarithmic function has only one. The former can therefore be more easily adapted to fit a given set of data. Both functions imply that the stimulus scale is compressed at its upper end in relation to the sensation scale. There is no reason why either should represent the truth about sensory magnitude; which gives the better fit may depend primarily on the definition adopted for sensory magnitude. Many sets of published data, from psychology or neurophysiology, fit either function with an equal amount of inaccuracy.

If we are concerned solely with the characteristics of a sense organ, we may correlate stimulus intensity with an electrophysiological measure. In general, while sensory quality is related to the place where afferent fibres terminate, intensity is coded in terms of their discharge frequency. Thus it is known that the rate of firing of receptors in the eye of *Limulus* (king crab) is logarithmically related to the intensity of light; and in the case of a muscle-spindle the frequency of impulses in the afferent nerve is roughly a logarithmic function of the load. However, in the cutaneous system the frequency of impulses in a single afferent nerve fibre approximates to a power function of the degree of indentation of the skin for some mechanoreceptors and to logarithmic function for others.

CUTANEOUS SENSES

Stimulation of the skin gives rise to a sensation of touch, of warmth, of cold, or of pain, and these are described as the four 'modalities' of cutaneous sensation. On the basis of these sensations we attribute properties to external objects.

The Sense of Touch

This sense allows us to distinguish between hard and soft bodies and to judge their shape. In practice, however, muscle-joint sense may also be used to estimate hardness and, although we judge the roughness of a surface by passing the tips of the fingers gently along it, our conclusion may also depend on the auditory stimuli produced at the same time. The threshold of the tactile sense is measured by von Frey's bristles which consist of a series of fibres of different thicknesses mounted on match-sticks by which they can be held between the fingers. Each is calibrated by pressing the end of the bristle on a balance till it just bends. This weight divided by the cross-sectional area of the bristle gives the pressure exerted on the skin. A newer method is to use electromechanical transducers that deliver adjustable mechanical indentation to the skin.

If the skin is explored with a bristle it is found that the tactile sense is distributed in a punctate fashion. The map of the distribution of the touch spots in any given area varies from day to day and this variability makes it difficult to believe that there is a fixed anatomical basis for the touch sense. By means of a large series of bristles von Frey found that the smallest pressure in g/mm^2 required to elicit a sensation of touch varied in different parts of the skin, (Table 22.1.) If these values are converted into lb/in^2 (second column in Table 22.1) quite ridiculous values are obtained; the lips (fourth entry in the table) are certainly sensitive to much less than 3·5 lb on an area of 1 in^2, Thus the adequate stimulus for eliciting a sensation of touch cannot be mere pressure. If a finger is inserted into a bowl of mercury contact is felt only at the air/mercury junction where the skin is deformed by the abrupt change of pressure. Deeper in the mercury at the tip of the finger, although the pressure is actually much greater, there is no deformation. Thus deformation rather than pressure is the effective stimulus.

Touch spots are thickly distributed around hair follicles. The

Table 22.1 Threshold pressure in g/mm^2 required to elicit sensations of touch and of pain on various areas of the skin surface as measured by von Frey. In the second column the values have been converted to lb/in^2 to show that there is a fallacy in expressing the threshold in terms of pressure (see discussion in text)

| Area | Touch | | Pain |
	g/mm^2	lb/in^2	g/mm^2
Cornea			0·2
Conjunctiva			2
Tongue and nose	2	2·8	
Lips	2·5	3·5	
Finger-tip and forehead	3	4·3	300
Back of finger	5	7·1	
Palm, arm, thigh	7	10	
Forearm	8	11	20
Back of hand	12	17	100
Calf, shoulder	16	23	30
Abdomen	26	37	15
Outside of thigh	26	37	
Skin and sole	28	40	
Back of forearm	33	47	30
Loins	48	68	
Thick parts of sole	250	356	200

root of each living hair is surrounded by a network of nerve fibres; the nerve elements become very scanty when the hair is shed. Each hair pivoted at the skin surface acts as a lever to transmit deformation to the nerve-endings in the root round the shaft. When the hairs are removed the sensitivity to touch is greatly reduced.

Afferent fibres which innervate the receptors in hair follicles have, characteristically, a large receptive field (perhaps several centimetres in diameter) but some tactile receptors with a field not more than 0·5 mm in diameter may be supplied by a single nerve fibre (Table 22·5).

The tactile sense can be sub-divided into the categories of touch, which is very short-lasting; flutter-vibration aroused by repetitive mechanical stimulus and pressure which is more persistent. Each sensation last only a very little longer than the stimulus. The sensory mechanisms interact. If a finger is held lightly against a revolving cog wheel each stimulus gives rise to a separate sensation until the contacts follow one another at more than 500 or 600 per second. Above this frequency of stimulation the rotating cog wheel is described as smooth, the separate sensations having fused into a continuous sensation. If, nevertheless, the amplitude of vibration of an object applied to the skin is very high, a sensation of vibration may persist up to 8000 Hz and, with practice, amplified speech vibrations can be felt by the fingers and recognized.

The tactile sense shows adaptation during the continued application of stimuli; it is partly peripheral and partly central. We are aware of the contact of our clothes with the skin when they are first put on but this sensation quickly disappears. It can, however, be brought to consciousness by an act of the will or by a slight movement of the body. In the same way a new denture is very obvious at first but after a time the wearer becomes unconscious of its presence.

Localization. When a blindfolded person is touched not only does he have an impression of the strength of the stimulus but also he can indicate the point touched with considerable accuracy. The power of localization depends partly on the position at which the nerve fibres from the tactile end-organs enter the spinal cord and on their higher connexions and partly on experience. Aristotle's experiment shows the influence of experience. A pencil laid between two crossed fingers of a blind-folded subject gives the sensation of contact by two pencils. Experience also plays a part in visual localization. After removal of a congenital cataract a person blind from birth is not able at first to localize his visual impressions; the power to do so grows as experience of his new sense develops.

Discrimination. If two points on the skin are touched simultaneously and with identical punctate stimuli by means of a pair of dividers (aesthesiometer) the subject reports that two separate points have been touched, provided that the distance exceeds a value depending on the area of skin under test (Table 22.2). If the skin is carefully explored for touch spots it is found that in the area showing the lowest two-point threshold they are less than 1 mm apart but at no part of the body is the distance between these spots more than 6 mm. A low density of touch spots is not the explanation of the poor discrimination shown in Table 22.2.

This two-point threshold is usually three or four times the error of localization in the same region. This apparent anomaly is partly due to the diffuse nature of the stimulus. The blunt point on the skin stretches the surrounding skin and

Table 22.2 The two-point discrimination threshold*

Area	Separation in mm
Tip of tongue	1
Anterior surface of finger-tip	2
Posterior surface of third phalanx	6
Palm of hand	11
Back of hand	32
Back of neck	54
Middle of back	67

*The distance at which two points on the skin touched simultaneously with approximately the same pressure must lie apart to be recognized as separate points of contact.

S Weinstein (1968) in ch 10 of *The Skin Senses* (Ed D R Kenshalo)). Springfield: Thomas.

localization is probably determined by the centre of strongest stimulation; in the case of two-point stimulation the whole stretched area is effective in giving a broad impression and obscuring the presence of the two points. In other words, when the two points of contact are fairly close to one another the stimulus is not very different from that produced by one contact. Convergence of afferent fibres on to neurones in the tactile pathway in the central nervous system determines the size of the receptive fields of neurones in the sensory pathway and is another important factor influencing the accuracy of two-point discrimination.

Projection. This is most highly developed in vision but it occurs also with tactile sensation. If a pudding is stirred with a spoon, lumps may be detected and the bottom of the pan feels hard. The stimuli which originate these sensations are applied to the skin in contact with the upper end of the spoon but the sensations are projected to the lower end of the spoon.

Temperature Sense

Although we are apt to think of the skin as being uniformly sensitive all over its surface, each modality has a punctate distribution. In the case of the temperature sense this can be shown by slowly passing a small warm metal rod over the skin. At some places no sensation of warmth is aroused, while at other places, called 'warm spots', a sensation of warmth is quite distinct. The 'cold spots' can be mapped out by passing a cold metal rod over the skin. The cold spots are more numerous and do not coincide with the warm spots. Furthermore, tests made from day to day show that the distribution of these spots is continually altering (Fig. 22.3). The punctate distribution is lost if the skin becomes red, as in sunburn, in which all parts give rise to a sensation of warmth on being touched with a warm rod. A further observation suggesting that the two receptors are distinct is that a hot rod passed over a cold spot may give rise paradoxically to a sensation of cold. This may be explained by Zotterman's electrophysiological experiments described below.

A piece of cloth and a piece of metal at the same temperature, either high or low, arouse quite different sensations due to the differing thermal conductivities of the stimulus material. The thermal sensations depend in part on the rate of withdrawal or addition of heat. If a finger of one hand is placed in hot water and a finger of the other in cold and after 30 seconds both are placed in water at an intermediate temperature the water feels cold to the former and warm to the latter. It is reasonable to conclude that the cause of the sensation, in this experiment, is a fall or a rise in the temperature of the nerve-endings already adapted to different temperatures. This cannot, however, account for the sensation of cold in the following experiment. If a cold object such as a coin is pressed on the forehead and then removed the sensation of cold persists, although at this time the temperature of the end-organs must be rising.

The experiment with the hot and cold water shows a feature common to all sensations—adaptation. The finger kept in cold water for some time does not feel cold; it becomes adjusted to the new situation which, since it arouses no sensation, becomes a new zero. The finger in the hot water also shows adaptation but in the opposite direction. This experiment also shows that the temperature sense is not to be regarded as a thermometer; with its shifting zero it cannot measure absolute temperature.

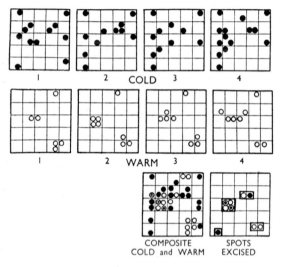

Fig. 22.3 Maps of cold and warm spots on an area of 1 cm² on the upper arm. The successive maps were made at intervals of two days. All the spots are combined in the diagram marked 'Composite Cold and Warm'. The spots in the last diagram were excised but no specialized nerve-endings were found. (K M Dallenbach (1927) American Journal of Psychology 39: 416.)

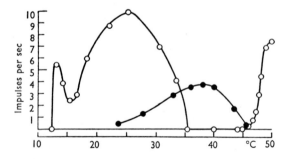

Fig. 22.4 Graph showing the frequency of the steady discharge of a single cold fibre (open circles) and of a single warm fibre (solid circles) when the receptors on the surface of the cat's tongue were exposed to constant temperatures within the range of 10° to 50°C. (Y Zotterman (1953) Special senses: thermal receptors. Annual Review of Physiology 15: 363.)

It can, however, detect quite small temperature differences. The sensitivity of the exposed areas of the skin (face, hands and scalp) is less than that of areas normally covered, such as the arms and forearms. At ordinary skin temperatures differences as small as 0·2°C can be appreciated by the arms whereas differences of 0·5 to 1·0°C are required by the fingers. The mucous membrane of the mouth is relatively insensitive to heat; tea can be drunk at a temperature which is painful to the finger.

Electrophysiological studies can account for the above sensory results. Zotterman and his colleagues have recorded impulses in single nerve fibres coming from the tongue of the cat and have found two sets of thermoreceptors (Fig. 22.4). If the temperature of the surface of the tongue is held steady the 'cold' receptors discharge continuously but the actual rate of discharge depends on the temperature. The discharge begins about 10°C and reaches a maximum of about 10 impulses per second between 20 and 30°C; above 30°C there are very few impulses until the tongue temperature reaches 45 to 50°C when the discharge rate increases again. If cold receptors in man behave similarly it is easy to account for the paradoxical sensation of cold mentioned above. Zotterman found that the 'warm' receptors behave quite differently, discharging when the tongue temperature is in the range 25 to 45°C. The actual rate of discharge, usually less than 3 impulses per sec, depends on the temperature. Both receptors show marked adaptation. A sudden fall of temperature arouses a discharge up to 100 or more impulses per sec from the cold receptors but this quickly falls to the steady value of 10 or less. Similarly, a sudden rise in tongue temperature produces an immediate increase in the discharge from the warm receptors which falls quickly to a new resting value. In the snout of the cat distinctive cold receptor terminals have been seen with the electron microscope. The nerve fibres supplying them are myelinated (Table 22.5).

Iggo has found that the 'cold' receptors of primates have a very restricted receptor field in both hairy and glabrous skin. The speed of conduction of nerve impulses in the nerve trunk remote from the receptors ranged from 0·6 to 15·3 m/sec; the speed of the majority corresponds to myelinated axons 1 to 3μm in diameter. The receptors discharged in bursts which showed adaptation but they continued to discharge at constant thermoneutral temperatures. Electrophysiological experiments on conscious human subjects are now providing confirmation of the results obtained from non-human primates that establish modality-specific thermoreceptors and mechanoreceptors. The anatomical nature of the thermoreceptors in man is not known.

The Pain Sense

In the following paragraphs we are concerned only with pain actually arising in the skin. Pain projected to the surface of the body when internal organs are diseased (referred pain) is discussed later (p. 355).

Pain elicited by stimulation of the skin has a pricking, burning or itching quality and is well localized. The pain threshold may be raised by one-third by distracting the subject's attention but in sunburnt skin it may be lowered by half. If the finger just proximal to the nail-bed is pressed against a hot electric bulb a double pain is produced. The first sensation arises abruptly and is pricking in quality; it is probably carried in moderately large fibres conducting impulses at about 10 metres per second. The second sensation follows a second or more later, has a burning quality but is less abrupt in onset and disappearance; it is carried in non-myelinated fibres. If the circulation through the finger is obstructed by a bandage to produce asphyxia of the skin and nerves distal to the bandage the first pain is abolished more quickly than the second pain; the underlying mechanisms must therefore be different. There is good evidence that the first pain is mediated by myelinated (A) and the second pain by unmyelinated (C) afferent fibres (p. 299).

Quite gentle exploration of the skin surface with a needle produces a painful sensation at certain places. The pain end-organs are distributed in a punctate fashion, independently of the end-organs of touch or temperature. Any given area of skin may show ten-times as many pain spots as touch spots. These pain endings have different characteristics from the tactile end-organs; the threshold stimulus is quite different and the order of increasing sensitivity is completely different from that given for touch (Table 22.1). The pain sense has a relatively slow rate of adaptation. Asphyxia reduces the response of the other senses but may increase the response to painful stimuli. In syringomyelia, a disease of the spinal cord, pain may disappear while the other cutaneous senses remain. Pain is certainly a separate modality and is not due simply to excessive stimulation of nerve-endings.

Pain sensation may be tested by thermal radiation. The threshold temperature of the skin which gives rise to pain lies between $43°$ and $47°C$ with slow or no adaptation. Sudden application of water at $37°C$ to a large area of the skin may cause a sensation of pain which disappears in a few seconds. Pain sensation can also be tested by a pressure algometer which consists of a calibrated spring-loaded metal cylinder $0.5cm$ in diameter. It is applied perpendicularly with gradually increasing force to the body surface until the patient describes the pressure as painful. The threshold of complaint is normally about $2 kg$. At the receptor a painful stimulus depolarizes the nerve-endings and sets up impulses. Mechanical or chemical stimuli could produce the effect directly or indirectly by releasing a chemical substance from damaged cells. Keele and his colleagues have investigated the second possibility by the simple expedient of raising a skin blister with cantharidin and then applying the substances to be tested to the exposed base of the blister. Blood, plasma or inflammatory exudate withdrawn into a siliconed syringe have very little pain-producing activity; on transfer to a glass vessel, pain-producing activity appears in a few minutes but declines and disappears in about an hour. The pain-producing substance (PPS) is a polypeptide with pharmacological properties resembling those of bradykinin (p. 483). Pure bradykinin in a concentration of $0.1 \mu g/ml$ produces pain when applied to a blister base. The skin possesses many proteolytic enzymes which are known to be released when it is damaged. It is therefore reasonable to speculate that tissue injury sets free an enzyme capable of acting on some component of the plasma proteins to give PPS which then produces pain. Haemolysis of red cells (and indeed damage to any cell) releases potassium ions and application of the haemolysate to the base of the blister produces pain. This is, however, somewhat greater than that produced by a solution of potassium chloride, containing the same amount of potassium as the haemolysate, and made isotonic with NaCl. Since 5-hydroxytryptamine (5-HT, p. 482) causes pain when it is placed on the base of a blister it may be that damage to blood platelets by releasing 5-HT also gives rise to pain. 5-HT potentiates the algogenic effect of bradykinin and of potassium. Acetylcholine even in high dilution gives rise to pain immediately. It is not likely that histamine is of any importance in this respect because pain is caused only when high concentrations, unlikely to be produced by injury, are applied. Recent experiments by Keele suggest that the algogenic effect is due mainly to AMP.

Prostaglandin E_2 is produced in inflamed tissue. It does not directly excite the pain-endings but it can potentiate the action of algogens such as 5-HT and bradykinin. Pain can be relieved by non-steroidal anti-inflammatory agents, such as aspirin (acetyl salicylic acid) and indomethacin. Both chemicals block the formation of prostaglandins by inhibiting the enzyme, prostaglandin synthetase. Their analgesic action is probably indirect and due to a fall in tissue prostaglandin concentration, which in turn reduces the potency of the algogens formed during the general inflammatory action.

Pruritus or itching may be defined as 'an unpleasant cutaneous sensation which provokes the desire to scratch'. The sensation may be mild, in which case it is almost pleasurable, and this is quite common in elderly people; sometimes it may be so severe as to cause the sufferer to attempt suicide. Pruritus may be generalized, as in jaundice, or it may be confined to quite a small area of skin or to a particular part of the body such as the perineum or the nostrils. The sensation arises in nerve-endings in the epidermis since pruritus cannot be elicited in areas denuded of epidermis. It can be produced in a sensitive area by chemical, mechanical, thermal or electrical stimuli, and mild forms of such stimuli may elicit itching in a localized area of skin long after the initial pruritus has subsided. Thus, light stroking of an insect bite may produce itching weeks after the local reaction has subsided. In other words, the skin remains in a state of increased excitability. If the itching so produced leads to vigorous scratching, the area of excitable skin enlarges and the threshold is further reduced.

By inserting stinging hairs of a tropical plant *Mucana pruriens* into the skin Shelley and Arthur showed that the most effective site for itch production was the dermo-epidermal junction; they believe that damage to the skin liberates endopeptidases which act on peripheral nerve filaments and produce the sensation of itch. An alternative explanation is that the endopeptides form polypeptides (PPS, see p. 351) and these in turn excite cutaneous receptors. This sensation is carried in the sensory spinal nerves to the spinothalamic tract and then to the thalamus and sensory cortex. Because no itching can be elicited in analgesic skin itching has been thought to be a kind of pain sensation. In syphilitic disease of the posterior roots of the spinal cord (tabes dorsalis) the sense of touch may be lost without loss of the sense of pain; itching can be elicited in the affected areas of skin. On the other hand the fact that removal of the epidermis and the subepidermal nerve network abolishes itch but not pain suggests that itch is a distinct sensory experience. If this is accepted it is easy to understand how it is that itch and pain can be experienced simultaneously and that immersion of the skin in water at $40°$ to $41°C$ quickly abolishes itch but intensifies pain. The itch threshold may be affected by psychological

Table 22.5 Cutaneous receptors

Name	Structure	Location	Receptive field	Effective stimulus	Sensory function
TACTILE RECEPTORS. Rapidly adapting					
Pacinian corpuscle PC		subcutaneous	100 mm²	vibration 40–600 Hz movement	vibration
Krause end bulb RA		dermis of glabrous skin	2 mm²	vibration 10–200 Hz movement	touch spatial analysis intensity
Meissner corpuscle RA		dermis of glabrous skin	12 mm²	low frequency vibration 5–200 Hz movement	flutter spatial analysis intensity
Hair follicle receptors RA		hair follicles	1·5 cm²	hair movement or vibration 5–40 Hz	flutter spatial analysis intensity

Table 22.5   continued

Name	Structure	Location	Receptive field	Effective stimulus	Sensory function
TACTILE RECEPTORS. Slowly-adapting					
Merkel receptor SAI		base of epidermis	11 mm²	indentation and pressure	spatial analysis intensity
Ruffini ending SAII		dermis	60 mm²	stretch of skin pressure	(pressure touch)
C-mechano-receptor		dermo-epidermal boundary	2 mm²	indentation slow movement	(itch)
THERMORECEPTORS					
cold		base of epidermis	1 mm²	steady and falling temperatures 40°–10°C	cold
warm		base of epidermis	1 mm²	steady and rising temperatures 35°–50°C	warmth and heat
NOCICEPTORS					
Mechanical ?		skin	3 mm²	pin-prick squeezing	pain (sharp, first)
Thermomechanical ?		skin	3 mm²	> 42°C severe mechanical algogenic chemicals	pain (dull, second)

Key to diagrams: A, axon; B, capillary; BM, basement membrane; C, capsule; CF, collagen fibres; E, epidermis; F, fibroblast; H, hair shaft; L, laminae; M, Merkel cell; S, Schwann cell; T, nerve terminal. The abbreviations PC, RA, SAI and SAII are used in the text for these receptors.

(*By courtesy of A. Iggo*)

factors. It is not clear why scratching relieves itching but it may do so by disturbing the rhythm of afferent impulses travelling towards the spinal cord, by local depletion of kinins or by afferent inhibition in the central nervous system (central interaction).

Tickle can be demonstrated all over the body by light touch with a wisp of cotton wool. After a tickle stimulus, adjacent areas of skin are more sensitive with the result that a single light touch stimulus applied within them will arouse tickle. The stimulus for tickle is so slight that involvement of an end-organ deeper than the most superficial layer of the skin seems unlikely. It may arise in slowly-adapting mechanoreceptors, particularly the SA II, (Table 22.5) which may continue with a persistent discharge after a brief stimulus.

Anatomo-physiological Basis of Cutaneous Sensations

The experiments just described provide evidence for the hypothesis that there are four 'modalities' of cutaneous sensation, and indeed the punctate distribution of the sensitive areas makes it logical to search for special receptors. The older histologists found many organized (that is elaborate) endings in the skin and, as it appears now, rather rashly labelled them 'pressure' endings, 'cold' endings and so on, simply on the basis of their morphology. Since then many workers have questioned the validity of a simple correlation between cutaneous receptor morphology and sensation.

Exact analysis requires a detailed study of the properties of component elements in the sensory pathways. Combined electrophysiological and morphological studies, principally in laboratory animals and monkeys, have established the existence of several well-defined kinds of afferent units (Table 22.5) with a strict correlation of functional properties and morphology for the encapsulated receptors.

The names given to the sensory receptors in Tables 22.5 and 22.6 are derived from two sources—either based on the morphology of the receptors where this is known (and often given the name of their discoverer) or based on their physiological properties and sensory functions. For these reasons there can be several alternative names in current use.

An important difference in physiological properties is recognized among the cutaneous mechanoreceptors. Some of them are excited only briefly by steady mechanical stimulation of the skin, although they respond very well to an oscillating or repeated on/off indentation of the skin. Because of these properties they are called *rapidly-adapting* (abbreviated to RA). Other tactile receptors continue to discharge impulses during steadily maintained indentation of the skin, as for example by constant pressure on the buttocks when sitting on a chair. For this reason they are called *slowly-adapting* (abbreviated to SA). In Tables 22.5 and 22.6 the tactile receptors comprise the rapidly-adapting group as follows: Pacinian corpuscles (abbreviated PC); Krause end-bulbs and Meissner corpuscles named after their discoverers. Together with the hair-follicle receptors they are put in the rapidly-adapting category on the basis of their functional properties, and given the abbreviation RA (for rapidly-adapting). The Pacinian corpuscles are given a separate abbreviation because of their distinctive properties. In the slowly-adapting group of tactile receptors we find *first* the Merkel receptor, which denotes the slowly-adapting Type I cutaneous receptor and abbreviated SAI, *second* the Ruffini ending, denoting the slowly-adapting Type II receptor and abbreviated SA II and *third*, tactile receptors with non-myelinated afferent axons and which are called C-mechanoreceptors. The Merkel and Ruffini receptors are named eponymously after their discoverers.

Although it has not been possible to make such exact studies similar findings have been made in man (Table 22.6).

The cutaneous sensory pathways in the central nervous system to which the cutaneous afferent fibres project arise in either the dorsal horn of the spinal cord or in the dorsal column nuclei in the medulla oblongata. At each of these places the incoming afferent fibres make both specific and non-specific connexions. That is, there are some neurones excited for example only by particular kinds of mechanoreceptors or thermoreceptors, and others which are excited by the convergence on to them of many kinds of cutaneous receptors. The former provide a specific, modality-defined, sensory pathway, whereas the latter are not specified in the same way. Within each of the possible sensory pathways these afferent fibres may have inhibitory and/or excitatory actions and the interaction of excitation and inhibition decides the degree and kind of sensory pathway activity. For example, nociceptor-excited neurones in the dorsal horn can have their discharge abolished by concurrent excitation of cutaneous mechano-receptors which excite interneurones that inhibit the nocicep-tor neurones and reduce their activity. This kind of action provides a satisfactory explanation of the efficacy of counter-irritation or rubbing the skin to relieve pain or itch, since impulses from the mechanoreceptors inhibit or block the excitatory effect of the nociceptors. In addition there are powerful and selective descending inhibitory mechanisms with an origin in the brain stem and cerebral cortex that shape the sensory inflow to the brain.

Although the idea of exclusive 'modality-specific' pathways must be revised there is now evidence that in animals individual 'modality-specific' afferent fibres enter both 'rela-tively specific' as well as 'non-specific' centripetal pathways. The recently discovered divergence and richness of pathways for afferent units excited by mechanical stimuli (that is within the touch/pressure modality) could provide for two kinds of

		Receptive field characteristics:	
		distinct borders, small size	indistinct borders, large size
Adaptation:	rapid, no static response	**RA** (Meissner endings)	**PC** (Pacinian endings)
	slow, static response present	**SA I** (Merkel endings)	**SA II** (Ruffini endings)

Table 22.6 Properties of cutaneous receptors in glabrous skin of the human hand. Based on single fibre electrophysiological recordings from the median nerve. (*From* A. B. Vallbo & R. S. Johansson. (1978). pp. 29–54 in *Active Touch* (Ed. G. Gordon) Oxford: Pergamon Press.

pathway. Also certain cells in the trigeminal nucleus in monkeys are excited by impulses from thermoreceptors but not by impulses from mechanoreceptor units. Therefore some cells at several levels in the sensory pathway display an input specificity.

Work in progress has established that within the 'tactile' modality several distinct sensations can be recognized in both sensory and behavioural tests. The mechanisms have been analysed to include; (a) specific cutaneous receptors (b) specifically activated neurones in the dorsal horn and dorsal column nuclei and (c) frequency-dependent neurones in the somato-sensory cortex. Detailed frequency analysis (threshold analysis) studies of the elements in the pathway establish a strong correlation between the unit activity and the sensations of flutter (present at 6 to 40 Hz) and of vibration (40 to 500Hz). Mountcastle's work indicates that the sense of vibration arises in Pacinian corpuscles, that flutter is mediated by rapidly-adapting receptors (Meissner's corpuscles in glabrous skin and hair follicle afferents in hairy skin) and that the slowly-adapting mechanoreceptors do not contribute to either sensation. Thus the sensory pathways have the capacity to preserve an input from the 'sub-modality specific' cutaneous receptors.

AFFERENT IMPULSES FROM THE VISCERA

Afferent fibres from the viscera (stomach, intestine and other abdominal organs) are carried alongside the fibres of the sympathetic and parasympathetic systems. Fibres conveying visceral sensation are therefore sometimes spoken of as 'autonomic afferents' although the autonomic system is strictly speaking an efferent system. Many of these viscerosensory fibres form part of visceral reflex arcs. Some mediate the sensation of visceral pain; visceral pain can be relieved by sympathectomy, that is by cutting sympathetic nerves. After section of the splanchnic nerves Pacinian corpuscles in the mesentery degenerate just as those in the skin do when a cutaneous nerve is cut. There is apparently no essential difference except in size between viscerosensory fibres and afferent fibres from the skin. In the cat impulses in the splanchnic nerves have been traced into the cord, up the dorsal columns of white matter on the same side to the nucleus gracilis on the same side and then across the midline to the opposite thalamus; more slowly running impulses project via the spinothalamic tracts to the thalamus on both sides and also to the hypothalamus.

Records of activity in single fibres of the vagus and pelvic nerves show that there are several kinds of visceral receptors. Very slowly-adapting mechanoreceptors are present in the stomach, intestine and urinary bladder. The rate of firing depends on the rate of distension of these viscera, being greater the more sudden the distension. The nerve endings are activated by passive distension and by active contraction. Impulses pass from the receptors along non-myelinated fibres with a conduction velocity of less than 2·5 m/sec. Pacinian corpuscles which are in the mesentery adapt very quickly; they have large myelinated axons (conduction velocity 40 m/sec). Their function is unknown. Other rapidly-adapting receptors exist, for example the receptors in the urethra responding to the flow of urine. Chemoreceptors in the gastrointestinal mucosa are excited by a pH of less than 1·5.

In a conscious unanaesthetized person the abdominal viscera, provided that they are healthy, can be cut or burned without causing pain; that is clearly demonstrated when a knuckle of colon, brought through the abdominal wall by the surgeon, is opened painlessly some days later without any anaesthetic. Wolf and Wolff (p. 60) found that Tom's normal healthy gastric mucosa was not sensitive to pinching or electric stimulation but, if the mucosa became hyperaemic and oedematous, pain was readily evoked by these stimuli. The pain threshold of this viscus is normally high but it may be lowered by inflammatory changes. However, pain arises in the absence of inflammation if the appropriate kind of stimulation is applied. For example, pain is produced if the mesentery is pulled upon or injected with irritant material; since all the nerve fibres from the five metres of gut are crowded into the 15cm long mesentery, traction on this structure must necessarily stimulate a much larger number of nerve fibres than does cutting or pinching of an equal length of the gut. Thus the production of pain by stimulation of visceral nerves depends on (a) the strength of the stimulus, (b) the number of nerve fibres stimulated and (c) the pain threshold at the moment of stimulation.

Pain impulses from the abdominal viscera are conveyed almost entirely in afferents passing in the sympathetic nerves, especially the splanchnic nerves. If a balloon passed into the small intestine is inflated the subject feels pain in the centre of the abdomen but after bilateral section of the splanchnic nerves inflation of the balloon does not cause pain. Vagotomy has no effect on pain produced by distension of the small intestine. Furthermore, patients with a complete transection of the spinal cord at about L1 which renders the abdominal wall anaesthetic can not only experience intestinal colic but localize the pain in the centre of the abdomen. Learmonth reported that a patient who had been given a spinal anaesthetic to anaesthetize the lower part of the body experienced pain which he accurately localized to the bladder when the superior hypogastric plexus was crushed; the afferent fibres must of course have entered the cord above the level of the anaesthetized part of the cord. Pain from pelvic viscera is also mediated by afferent fibres in the pelvic (parasympathetic) nerves.

It is well known that pain arising from a diseased organ may be projected to a definite position on the surface of the body (*referred pain*). A knowledge of the areas of localization of pain is, however, of great service in diagnosis and has been summarized in Table 22.7. The position at which a patient feels pain may coincide with the position of the tissue in which it is produced, or the pain may be felt at a distance from the place of its production. The pain due to pinching the skin on the surface of the body is felt by the subject at the point of stimulation. However, when a transposed pedicle skin graft with intact innervation is pinched, the blindfolded patient experiences the pain in the position from which the graft was taken and not in its new site. Moreover, pain due to heart disease (angina pectoris) may be projected to the left arm even when this has been amputated. Pain is, therefore, projected to a position in the body image and not to any particular tissue. This phenomenon is further illustrated by the fact that pain produced in organs such as the diaphragm and the testis, which have migrated during development, is projected to the primary or embryonic site of the organ. Rubbing the diaphragm at operation, or electrical stimulation of the phrenic nerve, produces pain which is felt at the root of the neck; the diaphragm develops in the neck, acquires its nerve supply there and later moves caudad. The testis develops near the kidney but low in the abdomen, and accordingly testicular pain is felt in the lower abdomen and not in the testis itself. In other words the sensorium seems to make contact with, and to become aware of the position of, the organs in embryonic life and it continues to use the same reference map. The alimentary tract is embryologically a midline organ and pain arising in it or in any other midline organ should, according to this interpretation, be projected to various levels of the midline no matter whether the part concerned had migrated right or left. This is what is actually found. Thus in colic due to violent peristalsis of the intestine, pain is felt in the midline. In disorders of the stomach pain is felt in the midline high up in the abdomen; small-intestine pain is felt in the umbilical region; colon pain is situated in the midline in the lower part of the abdomen. The gall-bladder is embryologically a midline organ and true gall-bladder pain is felt in the epigastrium but, if the inflamed viscus irritates the diaphragm, pain is felt in the neck and right shoulder. It is unlikely that any nerve fibres from the gall-bladder or its peritoneal covering reach the spinal cord by the phrenic nerve, since the gall-bladder can be painlessly removed under spinal anaesthesia in which the phrenic nerves and the diaphragm are functioning normally. Distension of the bile duct usually gives pain in the midline of the abdomen but sometimes in the back. Pain arising in the body and cervix of the uterus is felt in the midline about 4 cm above the symphysis pubis.

Table 22.7 The segmental sensory innervation of the viscera

Organ	Superficial areas to which pain is referred	Segments at which visceral afferent axons enter spinal cord — Sympathetic — Thoracic												Lumbar		Parasympathetic sacral			Afferent pathway from viscus
		1	2	3	4	5	6	7	8	9	10	11	12	1	2	2	3	4	
Heart	Precordium and inner arm	+	+	+	+	?													Middle and inferior cervical and thoracic cardiac nerves
Lung	No referred pain*		+	+	+	+	+	+											Inferior cervical and thoracic nerves (convey reflex impulses)
Liver and gall-bladder	Right upper quadrant and right scapula					+	+	+	+	+									Greater splanchnic nerve
Stomach	Epigastrium						+	+	+	+									Greater splanchnic nerve
Small intestine	Umbilicus									+	+	?							Greater splanchnic nerve
Colon { ascending	Suprapubic											+		+					Lumbar chains and preaortic plexus
Colon { sigmoid and rectum	Deep pelvis and anus															+	+	+	Pelvic nerves and plexuses
Kidney	Loin and groin										+	+		+					Renal plexus via lowest splanchnic nerve and upper lumbar rami
Ureter	Loin and groin											+	+	+	+				Renal plexus and upper lumbar rami
Bladder { fundus	Suprapubic											+	+						Hypogastric plexuses
Bladder { bladder neck	Perineum and penis															+	+	+	Pelvic nerves and plexuses
Uterus { fundus and cervix	Suprapubic region and lower back, perineum										+	+	+	?					Hypogastric plexuses
Testes, vas deferens, seminal vesicles, prostate	Pelvis, perineum										+	+	+	+					Hypogastric plexuses

*Lung parenchyma is insensitive. Pain from larger bronchi is transmitted over somatic vagal axons. When disease spreads to parietal pleura pain is transmitted over intercostal nerves.

(Derived from: J C White, R H Smithwick & F A Simeone (1952) The Autonomic Nervous System 3rd edn, p 136. London: Henry Kimpton; and J J Bonica (1968) Autonomic innervation of the viscera in relation to nerve block. Anesthesiology 29: 793.)

When the parietal peritoneum is irritated as a consequence of visceral disease, pain is sharply localized to the site of irritation and is associated with tenderness and often with spasm (rigidity) of the adjacent skeletal muscles. Thus the pain of early appendicitis is felt in the midline near the umbilicus. Not until the parietal peritoneum, supplied by the somatic nerves, is irritated is the pain felt at the situation of the inflamed appendix, that is, generally, in the right iliac fossa. Similarly, although distension of the gall-bladder produces pain in the centre of the epigastrium, inflammation of the fundus of the gall-bladder is associated with pain in the right hypochondrium in an area overlying the diseased organ.

Visceral pain can be modified by anaesthetization or irritation of the skin area in which the pain is felt. The pain of gastric ulcer is reduced by anaesthetization of the abdominal wall. The pain of angina pectoris can be relieved by anaesthetization of the painful area of the left arm and angina pectoris projected into an amputated limb is relieved by anaesthetization of the brachial plexus. Moreover, if, in a patient in whom angina pectoris is elicited by exercise, an area of skin is blistered by cantharidin the pain induced by the exercise may be felt in the blistered area. Even after complete cutaneous anaesthesia intended to relieve abdominal pain the patient may complain of a dull, aching, deep form of pain which is usually localized in or near to, the diseased organ itself. This pain is similar to that produced by stimulation of the coeliac ganglion and is relieved only by section of sympathetic nerves.

The probable 'explanation' of the results of experiments on diaphragmatic pain is as follows. Nerve impulses from the diaphragm and from the skin of the shoulder reach and synapse with common neurones in the same segment of the spinal cord (Fig. 22.8). These neurones are normally associated in sensation with impulses coming from the cutaneous sensory field. The impulses from the viscera increase the excitability of the neurones, which then become more readily excited by the cutaneous input. Figure 22.8 illustrates the mode of action. The normal threshold for pain is at the level represented at (a) in Figure 22.8. Anaesthetization of the shoulder area reduces the number of impulses reaching the cord from the shoulder and so raises the threshold as shown at (b) and (c). Irritation of the diaphragm to a degree represented by the height of the triangle at (a) normally produces a shower of impulses which reach the threshold and pain is felt. After anaesthetization of the shoulder, however, a similar degree of irritation of the diaphragm represented by (b) now falls short of the threshold and there is no pain. A larger stimulus (large triangle at (c)) such as could be produced by a phrenic nerve crush can, however, reach the threshold and cause pain. The observations on angina pectoris already mentioned may also be explained on this theory, if we postulate that blistering increases the number of afferent impulses arriving at the central nervous system and so lowers the threshold for pain.

SENSORY PATHWAYS IN THE CENTRAL NERVOUS SYSTEM

The nerve impulses that enter the central nervous system in cutaneous afferent fibres all make synaptic connexions in the spinal cord (for dorsal root afferents) or the brain stem (for cranial nerve afferents). Onward transmission of the information is from the neurones with which the afferents make synaptic contact. Several major pathways exist (Fig. 22.9). They are:

1. The dorsal column—dorsal column nuclei—lemniscothalamo cortical system (dorsal column system).

2. The spinocervico-lemnisco-thalamic system (spinocervical system, SCT).

3. The spinothalamic system (STT).

Each of these pathways occupies a different region of the spinal cord, but they all eventually enter the thalamus and go from there to the somato-sensory cortex (Fig. 22.9) (see p. 359). The dorsal column system occupies the ipsilateral dorsal column and is a pathway from the large cutaneous tactile receptors (Meissner (RA), Pacinian (PC) and hair follicle (RA) receptors). The spinocervical tract, which has an ipsilateral dorsolateral location in the spinal cord, is also a tactile pathway, particularly from hair follicle receptors. The slow adapting receptors (SAI and SAII) also project through the dorsal column system but the spinal pathways may be less direct than for the PC and RA receptors. The spinothalamic tract has a crossed anterolateral position, and is a pathway for thermal and for noxious sensations, as well as for tactile inputs. It is sectioned in the surgical operation of anterolateral cordotomy to relieve chronic pain.

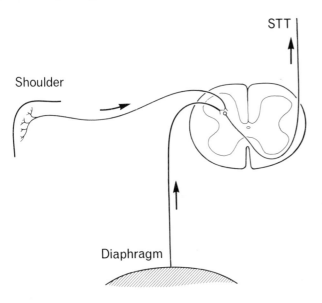

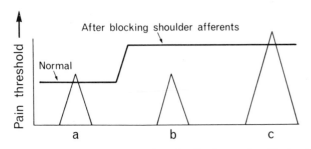

Fig 22.8 Visceral pain. (a) When the diaphragm is rubbed pain is felt in the shoulder. (b) When the diaphragm is rubbed after anaesthetization of the shoulder no pain is felt. (c) Crushing the phrenic nerve after anaesthetization of the shoulder is painful. (after F R Brown (1948) Lancet i: 386).

Although these pathways are well-defined none of them provides an exclusive route for any sensation. Thus surgical interruption of any single path, although it may yield temporary relief or interference with a sensation, does not cause permanent sensory impairment.

Descending Control of Sensory Pathways

The cutaneous sensory pathways are not one-way channels, conducting sensory impulses to the brain in an automatic and uncontrolled manner. Instead, the brain imposes a variable degree of control over the conductivity of the various ascending pathways. This central modulation is produced by efferent nerves acting at the various synaptic junctions of the relay nuclei of the ascending pathways. Sites of these synaptic interactions are the dorsal horn of the spinal cord, dorsal column nuclei and thalamic nuclei. The actions can be both facilitatory, enhancing transmission at a synapse, and inhibitory, by depressing synaptic transmission. Often these two effects will be balanced, and inhibition of one sensory channel may be simultaneously accompanied by facilitation of another.

These descending control mechanisms have taken on a renewed importance with the recent discovery of brain-stimulated-analgesia (BSA), (or stimulation-produced-analgesia, SPA) and of the endorphins and enkephalins. Brain stimulated analgesia in both man and animals, can be induced by electrical stimulation of the median raphe nuclei and the peri-aqueductal grey matter in the brain stem through implanted electrodes. During and after stimulation the subject develops an indifference to noxious stimuli that had previously caused severe pain or behavioural activity consistent with a painful state.

Beta-endorphin is a 31 amino acid peptide molecule, produced in the brain and the pituitary gland. The concentration of beta-endorphin in cerebrospinal fluid has been found to increase during brain-stimulated-analgesia. Part of the molecule consists of enkephalin, a pentapeptide, which occurs in two forms as leu-enkephalin (tyrosine-glycine-phenyalanine-leucine) and met-enkephalin (Tyr-Gly-Gly-Phe-methionine). These enkephalins are naturally-occurring and can bind to the same receptor sites in the body with which opiates react. Their actions can be blocked by naloxone, which is a morphine antagonist. It is therefore probable that they have the same pain-reducing properties as morphine. Since brain stimulated analgesia can also be prevented by naloxone it is likely that it may work through the release of an enkephalin. These peptides thus become links at one stage in the descending control mechanisms that can cause analgesia, though the exact sites of action are still under investigation.

THE THALAMUS

The thalami are two large masses of grey matter about 4 cm long placed on either side of the third ventricle and extending posteriorly, as the pulvinar, to overhang the superior colliculi. Each thalamus possesses three main nuclei; the anterior and medial form the *palaeothalamus*, while the lateral nucleus,

which occupies the greater portion of the thalamus including the pulvinar, constitutes the *neothalamus*. The geniculate bodies (the *metathalamus*) lie near the pulvinar, superolateral to the colliculi.

The thalamus can be regarded as a relay station on the ascending sensory pathways (Fig. 22.9). The anterior nucleus receives impulses from the mamillothalamic tract and transmits impulses to the gyrus cinguli. The medial nucleus receives some impulses via the hypothalamus from the viscera; most visceral afferent fibres, however, relay in the lateral nucleus of the thalamus whence fibres pass to the somato-sensory area (SI) of the cerebral cortex (areas 1, 2 and 3 in Fig. 24.4). Impulses can also pass from the frontal cortex to the medial nucleus and from there to the hypothalamus. The ventral portion of the lateral nucleus receives afferents from the medial, spinal and trigeminal lemnisci which carry impulses subserving proprioceptive, tactile, pain and temperature senses, and sends out efferents through the posterior limb of the internal capsule to the postcentral gyrus of the cerebral cortex (C.S. in Fig. 22.9).

Thus the somatic sensory impulses originating in, say, the right side of the body, cross over to the left thalamus which transmits them to the cerebral cortex on the left side only. The lateral nucleus of the thalamus also receives fibres from the dentate nucleus of the cerebellum of the opposite side and relays impulses to the motor cortex (areas 4 and 6). Impulses from the cochlea pass through several synapses before reaching the medial geniculate nucleus from which fresh impulses pass to the auditory cortex in the superior temporal gyrus (p. 447). The lateral geniculate nucleus relays visual impulses from the retinae to the occipital cortex (areas 17, 18 and 19) on the same side (p. 438). These *cortical relay nuclei* do not act in a random way but relay impulses from points on a limb, for example, to specific areas on the cortex; similarly every point on the retina has a corresponding point in each of the areas 17, 18 and 19 in spite of the intervention of the relay in the lateral geniculate nucleus.

In addition to these cortical relay nuclei there are *association nuclei* in the neothalamus which receive impulses from the relay nuclei and project to the association areas of the cerebral cortex, namely the prefrontal, parietal and occipital cortex. The dorsomedial nucleus is the largest of those; it receives fibres from the lateral nucleus of the thalamus and from the hypothalamus and projects largely to the cortex of the frontal lobe. The thalamus also sends impulses to the caudate and lentiform nuclei, and the hypothalamus.

When the thalamogeniculate artery is blocked in man, the caudal portions of the thalamus are destroyed and there is a temporary loss of cutaneous sensation on the contralateral side of the body (a crossed hemianaesthesia) with permanent loss of sense of position of the limbs resulting in ataxia. After the lapse of a few weeks the patient may complain of insufferable pain on the affected side. Stimuli, such as a pinprick, which do not on the normal side give rise to anything more than discomfort, may cause quite severe pain. The threshold for pain is actually raised but the reaction to pain is exaggerated. There are no motor disturbances. This is described as the *thalamic syndrome*. The reason for these overactions is unknown; they do not occur when the sensory cortex alone is removed and cannot be due solely to a release from cortical control.

When the cerebral cortex is removed on one side (hemi-decortication) in man there is, for a few days, anaesthesia in the opposite side, then painful stimuli are appreciated but only poorly localized. Tactile sensation may eventually return but not the position sense. The return of crude sensation is possibly partly due to the ability of the thalamus on the decorticate side to subserve crude sensation and partly to bilateral representation of touch and pain as mentioned above. Position sense is not bilaterally represented in the thalamus.

SENSORY AREAS OF THE CEREBRAL CORTEX

Since little information about sensation can be gained from animal experiments, except perhaps by the study of con-ditioned reflexes, or by behavioural studies and then only by inference, most of our knowledge must come from clinical investigation. For example, a conscious patient may describe his sensations when areas of the cortex exposed at operation are stimulated electrically. Data have also been obtained from the investigation of patients with traumatic or pathological lesions, although in such cases we are dependent on the co-operation of a patient who has a lesion the extent of which may be difficult to judge even at later post-mortem examination. Information obtained in this way is not always entirely satisfactory.

The sensory areas of the cortex are the highest points in the brain reached by the impulses concerned in sensation. Although they are undoubtedly important as relay or

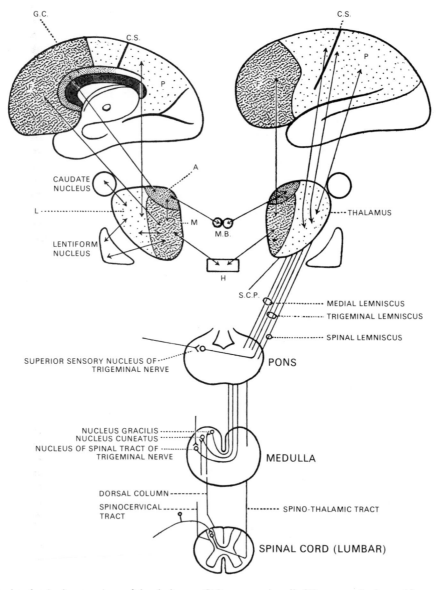

Fig. 22.9 Major cortical and spinal connexions of the thalamus. G.C. = gyrus cinguli; C.S. = central sulcus with motor and somaesthetic areas on each side; F = frontal area; P = parietal area; A = anterior group of thalamic nuclei; M = medial group of thalamic nuclei; L = lateral group of thalamic nuclei; M.B. = mamillary bodies; H = hypothalamus; S.C.P. = superior cerebellar peduncle. On the upper right of the diagram the projections are to the lateral surface of the cerebral hemisphere: on the upper left the projections to the medial surface of the cerebral hemisphere are given. Internuclear connexions of the thalamus are shown only on the left. The lines joining the various parts of the thalamus and cortex have in most cases been given arrows to indicate that impulses may pass in either direction. The metathalamus has been omitted. The pulvinar is included in the lateral nucleus. *(By courtesy of G W Pearce.)*

junctional areas in the complicated pattern of the cerebral neurones, we are not justified in claiming that these areas are the seat of sensations and consciousness (p. 396). The cortical representation of pain is less well-documented but it can be argued that the cerebral cortex is necessary for the full appreciation of pain; after bilateral frontal leucotomy the pain is still felt but the emotional reaction is no longer present.

Cortical injury seldom causes pain but in few patients pain arising from damage to the temporal cortex has been relieved by electrical stimulation of an area in or near the posterior limb of the internal capsule.

The most important part of the brain in relation to tactile and bodily sensation is the parietal lobe and an account of this is given in the following section. The occipital and temporal lobes, which are concerned with the central representation of vision and hearing, are discussed in the chapter on special senses (Chap. 27).

The Parietal Lobes

When the region of the postcentral gyrus in man (areas 3, 1 and 2 of Fig. 24.14) is stimulated electrically, sensations of touch and pressure are aroused. This is the primary somato-sensory area (SI) of the cerebral cortex. Occasionally feelings of warmth are elicited but only rarely is a painful sensation reported, and no muscular movements occur if stimulation of the precentral gyrus is avoided. Sensation of the leg, trunk, arm and face on the opposite side of the body is represented in that order from above downwards (Fig. 22.10) and area representation in the sensory cortex (*somaesthetic area*) is, therefore, very similar to that of the motor cortex (area 4) lying

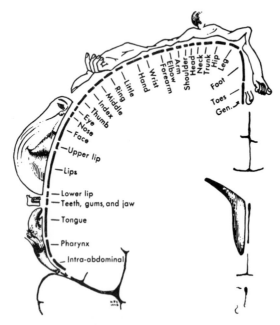

Fig. 22.10   Sensory homunculus. The right side of the figurine is laid upon a cross-section of the hemisphere, drawn somewhat in proportion to the extent of sensory cortex devoted to it. The length of the underlying black lines indicates more accurately the comparative extent of each representation. (W Penfield & T Rasmussen (1950) *The Cerebral Cortex of Man*, p 44. New York: Macmillan.)

immediately in front of it. The postcentral convolution receives impulses via the thalamus from the medial lemnisci and spinothalamic tracts. Stimulation of the posterior lip of the precentral gyrus, which is usually regarded as part of the motor area, also gives rise to sensations similar to those arising on stimulation of the postcentral gyrus.

The sensory areas in animals have been mapped out in conscious animals by inserting recording micro-electrodes into the cortex, connecting them to an amplifier and thence to an oscillograph or a loudspeaker. The experimenter, by touching various parts of the animal's body in turn, finds the area of skin giving a discharge of impulses. In this way the representation of the body surface—leg, arm and one side of the face from above downwards—on the contralateral postcentral gyrus has been confirmed. Stimulation of the skin activates neurones mainly in area 3b while the cells in area 2 just behind 3 are activated by joint movements as well. A small *secondary sensory area* (SII) has been found at the lower end of the postcentral gyrus. There is a bilateral representation of the body. Pain can be elicited by electrical stimulation of SII.

Removal of the postcentral gyrus leads to impairment but not complete abolition of the ability to detect differences in weight and texture and of stereognosis—the ability to recognize objects through touch. The latter implies more than superficial touch perception since temperature and deep pressure sensibilities as well as appreciation of weight (from joint receptors) are all involved. *Tactile agnosia* is the inability to recognize objects through touch when all relevant sensory pathways are intact. It occurs in lesions of the posterior parietal lobe, possibly the supramarginal gyrus, and lesions of this part of the brain on the left side may produce bilateral tactile agnosia. This capacity to recognize, the failure of which gives rise to the different varieties of agnosia, is essentially a function of the cerebral cortex and depends on the ability of sensory perceptions to evoke the neuronal responses necessary to identify the object perceived.

A lesion of the left angular gyrus (Fig. 24.1) in a right-handed person may result in inability to write (*agraphia*). This deficit is sometimes accompanied by inability to distinguish right from left, inability to recognize individual fingers and inability to calculate. Lesions in the parietal area in man may produce a loss of the ability to find the way even in the patient's own house together with the loss of the ability to conceive space even in two dimensions. When we are aware of the position of our body relative to other objects around us the position of its various parts, head, trunk and limbs, to one another, we are also aware of changes in all these relationships. To this sort of awareness the term 'body image' has been assigned. Disturbances of the body image are particularly liable to occur when disease affects the parietal lobe of the right or non-dominant cerebral hemisphere. If this region is damaged there may be total neglect of one half of the body and the patient may have difficulty in carrying out such everyday acts as dressing and sitting down in a chair. Damage to the parietal lobe of the dominant hemisphere may sometimes make it impossible to carry out actions to command or even perform complex actions at all. This inability to perform organized movements in the absence of paralysis is termed *apraxia*.

Taste has been localized in the lowest part of the postcentral gyrus. Lesions in this area cause disturbances of taste on the opposite side of the tongue as well as cutaneous sensory impairment on the face on the opposite side. Electrical stimulation gives rise to taste sensations. Impulses from each side of the tongue cross over almost completely to the opposite side in the medial lemniscus to the thalamus and so on to the cortex.

After removal or destruction of the postcentral gyrus there is a considerable recovery of sensation, a fact which may be explained by ipsilateral representation of sensation or by supposing that representation is not confined to the post-central gyrus as is usually assumed. It is now thought that the sensory paths from the limbs and trunk are bilateral. The second somatic area (SII) containing ipsilateral representation is intermingled with the classical contralateral representation. The lemniscal pathway goes almost exclusively to the contralateral side of the hemisphere; the anterolateral system (spinothalamic system) is probably the main source of ipsilateral representation. Damage to the sensorimotor cortex on one side impairs the touch and pressure sense of the hand on the same side in both man and monkeys and it is no longer realistic to regard the sensory and motor cortical mechanisms as being independent.

REFERENCES

Bonica J J 1968 Autonomic innervation of the viscera in relation to nerve block. Anaesthesiology 29: 793–813
Butler S R 1971 Organization of cerebral cortex for perception. British Medical Journal ii: 544–547
Chrenko F A 1964 Threshold intensities of thermal radiation evoking sensations of warmth. Journal of Physiology 173: 1–12
Daniels F Jr, van der Leun, J C, Johnson, B E 1968 Sunburn. Scientific American 219: 38–46
Gordon G (ed) 1977 Somatic and visceral sensory mechanisms. British Medical Bulletin 33: No 2
Gordon G 1978 Active touch. Pergamon Press, Oxford
Green D M, Swets J A 1966 Signal detection theory and psychophysics. Wiley, London
Hubbard J I 1974 The peripheral nervous system. Plenum Press, New York
Iggo A 1966 Physiology of visceral afferent systems. Acta Neurovegetativa 28: 121–134
Iggo A 1969a Cutaneous thermoreceptors in primates and subprimates. Journal of Physiology 200: 403–409
Iggo A 1969b The structure and function of a slowly adapting touch corpuscle in hairy skin. Journal of Physiology 200: 763–796
Keele C A, Armstrong D 1964 Substances producing pain and itch. Arnold, London
Kerr F W L, Wilson P R 1978 Pain. Annual Review of Neuroscience 1: 83–102
Lynn B 1975 Somatosensory receptors and their CNS connections. Annual Review of Physiology 37: 105–127
Poulton E C 1968 The new psychophysics. Psychological Bulletin 69: 1–19
Stevens S S 1970 Neural events and the psychophysical law. Science, New York 170: 1043–1050
Swets J A 1961 Is there a sensory threshold? Science, New York 134: 168–177
Swets J A, Tanner W P, Birdsall T G 1961 Decision processes in perception. Psychological Reviews 68: 301–340
Thompson R F 1967 Foundations of physiological psychology. Harper & Row, London
Zotterman Y 1976 Sensory functions of the skin in primates. Pergamon Press, Oxford

23 Spinal and Postural Reflexes

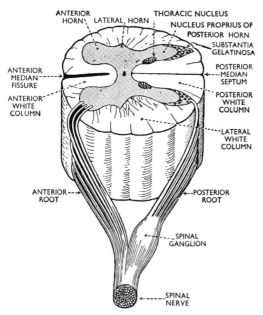

Fig. 23.1 A spinal segment from the thoracic region viewed from the left side.

Structure of the Spinal Cord

The spinal cord extends in adult man from the upper border of the first cervical vertebra to the lower border of the first lumbar vertebra. It is about 1 cm in diameter on average, being a little wider at the cervical and lumbar enlargements where the nerves to the arms and legs arise because of the greater amount of grey matter there. No trace of segmentation can be seen on the surface of the spinal cord but it is convenient to describe it as if it were divided up into 31 segments from each of which arises a pair of *spinal nerves* (Fig. 23.1).

The *posterior root* emerges from the postero-lateral aspect of the segment as a number of rootlets which fuse as they pass laterally to form a single trunk upon which is an enlargement, the *spinal* or *posterior root ganglion*. The *anterior root* is formed by the fusion of a number of rootlets which arise from the antero-lateral aspect of the cord. The anterior root joins the posterior root beyond the ganglion to form the spinal nerve which emerges between the vertebrae.

The interior of the cord around the central canal is occupied by an H-shaped mass of *grey matter* consisting largely of nerve cells (Fig. 23.1). The grey matter shows three main parts, anterior, lateral and posterior columns or horns. From the large motor cells of the anterior horn axons pass in the anterior root to the voluntary muscles. The small lateral horns, seen only in the thoracic and upper lumbar regions of the cord, contain cells of medium size belonging to the sympathetic system, from which axons travel in the anterior roots to the white rami communicantes (Fig. 25.2). The posterior column of grey matter possesses two main collections of small nerve cells, the thoracic nucleus at the base and the substantia gelatinosa at the apex of the horn. Scattered throughout the grey matter of the posterior horn are other cells which form the nucleus proprius and give off fibres to connect neighbouring segments.

The peripheral part of the cord, the *white matter*, consists almost entirely of myelinated nerve fibres supported in a mesh-work of neuroglia. The white matter can be divided into posterior, lateral and anterior columns as shown in Figure 23.1, but these areas are not precisely marked off from one another. In the white matter nerve fibres having similar functions and destinations are grouped together but the various groups cannot be distinguished by their microscopic appearance.

Methods of determining anatomical pathways. The degeneration which is a consequence of the cutting of a peripheral nerve has already been described (p. 314). The mapping out of the degeneration after destruction of a part of the nervous system is an important technique for finding the routes taken by nerve fibres in the central nervous system.

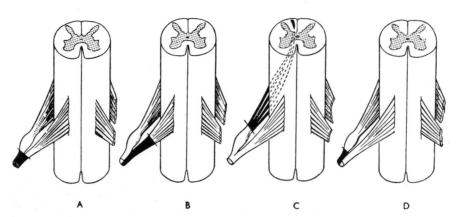

A   B   C   D

Fig. 23.2   The site of degeneration (black) after division of the spinal nerve or its roots. A, division of spinal nerve below ganglion. B, division of anterior root. C, division of posterior root above ganglion. D, division of posterior root below ganglion. (*After* G. F. Yeo (1893) *A Manual of Physiology*, p. 478. London: Churchill.)

Degenerations produced in man by surgical operation or by war wounds have given valuable information.

Further information about the connexions of nerve fibres is given by the study of transneuronal degeneration; a neurone may show chromatolysis and degenerative changes if the nerve fibres sending impulses to it have degenerated, but the only good example of this is the degeneration of certain cells in the lateral geniculate body after section of one optic nerve. Another clue is furnished by observing the myelination of nerve fibres in the embryo, since different groups acquire their myelin sheaths at different times (p. 385). Histochemical tests for adrenaline and cholinesterase are used to show the position of adrenergic and cholinergic nerves. The use of microelectrodes attached to sensitive amplifiers has made it possible to map out the pathways through the brain of nerve impulses started off by physiological stimuli such as sound or light touch or by artificial stimuli such as electrical pulses or the local application of strychnine.

Pathways in the spinal cord. Study of the degeneration after section of the spinal nerves or their roots (Fig. 23.2) allows a number of conclusions. Axons from motor cells situated in the anterior horn of the grey matter run in the anterior root. The fibres of the posterior root either pass a short distance into the cord to terminate around cells in the posterior horn, or pass up the cord in the posterior columns to the caudal part of the medulla oblongata where they end in the gracile and cuneate nuclei. The cell bodies of these posterior root fibres lie in the posterior root (spinal) ganglion. However, a significant number of afferent fibres passes into the spinal cord in the ventral roots.

When the spinal cord is cut across, degeneration occurs below (Fig. 23.3) and above the line of section (Fig. 23.4). That occurring below the section, *descending degeneration*, shows the position of the fibres whose cell bodies are above, that is cranial to, the cut. Conversely the degeneration occurring above the cut, *ascending degeneration*, shows the position of fibres ascending in the cord from cell bodies below the plane of section.

When the posterior root fibres are followed into the spinal ganglion it is found that the fibres have a side branch connecting them with the nerve cells in the ganglion (Fig. 23.6). Counts of microscopic preparations show that the

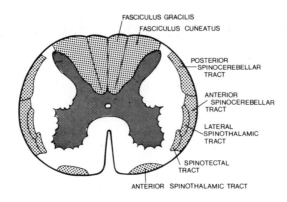

Fig. 23.4 Ascending degeneration showing the position of the ascending tracts in the white matter of the human spinal cord. The position of the spinothalamic tracts in the anterolateral part of the cord may be more correctly given in Figure 23.5. Magnification about ×5½.

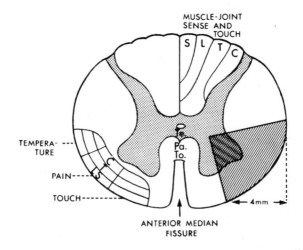

Fig. 23.5 The approximate position of the main sensory paths in a cross-section of the spinal cord. The separation of the various groups of fibres is by no means as sharp as shown. The letters indicate the relative positions of the fibres carrying impulses from C, the cervical; T, thoracic; L, lumbar; S, sacral root areas. Te, Pa, To, indicate place of decussation of the temperature, pain and touch fibres. Some of the touch fibres may decussate just posterior to the central canal. (*After* Foerster). Fibres carrying touch and proprioception are mainly ipsilateral but they are not confined to the posterior columns. The cross-hatched area shows the extent of the incision in the operation of anterolateral chordotomy performed usually in the upper part of the thoracic cord for relief of pain (see p. 372).

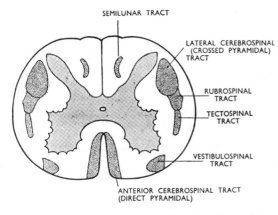

Fig. 23.3 Descending degeneration showing the position of the descending tracts in the human spinal cord. Intersegmental tracts lie between the grey matter and the descending fibres; the semilunar tract is also intersegmental. Magnification about ×5½.

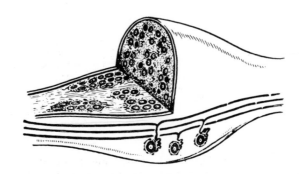

Fig. 23.6 Diagram of spinal root ganglion.

number of cells is very nearly (97 per cent) the same as that of fibres. Presumably, therefore, nearly every fibre has a cell body in the ganglion. As each fibre enters the cord it divides into ascending and descending branches, each branch sending off numerous side branches at different levels in the cord.

The posterior root fibres have three main methods of termination: (1) a few pass to the cells of the anterior horn of grey matter to form a synapse directly with the motor neurones of the same side, the monosynaptic pathway, (2) a large number form synapses with cells at various positions in the grey matter of the posterior horn such as the cells of the nucleus proprius, the thoracic nucleus and the substantia gelatinosa, and from these secondary neurones impulses pass on to other parts of the central nervous system, (3) a large number of fibres pass up the same side in the posterior columns of the white matter of the cord to the cuneate and gracile nuclei in the medulla, sending collateral branches to the grey matter as they ascend. This group includes fibres carrying impulses from the muscles (muscle–joint sense) and a proportion of the fibres subserving touch. The posterior columns, however, are not the sole route for this type of sensory information but may be particularly important in conveying information necessary for co-ordinated movement in space.

The secondary neurones of group (2) have various destinations. Many are simply short interconnecting or internuncial neurones (interneurones) carrying impulses to the motoneurones of the anterior horn of grey matter of the same or adjacent segments of the cord, but other secondary neurones have much longer paths. From the thoracic nucleus (Fig. 23.1) fibres pass to the posterior spinocerebellar tract of the same side; from other cells in the posterior horn fibres go up the anterior spinocerebellar tracts of both sides (Fig. 23.4) carrying impulses from the limb muscles to the cerebellar cortex (mainly ipsilateral). From the nucleus proprius the secondary neurones cross the midline, passing anteriorly or posteriorly to the spinal canal, and ascend in the contralateral cord as the spinothalamic tract (Fig. 23.4), the posterior part of which carries mainly the fibres of pain and temperature while the anterior part contains chiefly touch fibres (Fig. 23.5).

REFLEX ACTION

If the foot of a decapitated frog is pinched the legs move quickly away from the harmful stimulus but, if the spinal cord of this brainless preparation is destroyed by pithing, reflex withdrawal no longer occurs.

Except for the monosynaptic reflex between the annulo-spiral discharge of a muscle spindle and certain motoneurones of the same muscle (p. 343), it is unusual for a reflex to be confined to one segment of the cord. In the withdrawal reflex in the frog just described there is a co-ordinated flexion of the ankle, knee and hip by synergistic groups of muscles innervated by a number of spinal segments.

Since the activities of the spinal cord are greatly modified by the higher parts of the nervous system it is necessary for analysis of spinal reflexes to make a *spinal preparation*. The cat and dog have most frequently been used in such experiments. After the cord has been divided in the neck there is a period of spinal shock (p. 371) but if respiration is maintained by a ventilator the shock passes off and many reflexes can be elicited.

Flexion Reflexes

If an injurious stimulus, one which would be painful if applied to the intact animal, is applied to the foot of a spinal preparation the flexion reflex results in a withdrawal of the foot. Withdrawal also occurs when any sensory nerve in the limb is stimulated electrically and this phenomenon is used in experimental analysis of the properties of the spinal cord. For example, by varying the strength of the stimulus it is easy to demonstrate *irradiation*. A small stimulus causes a small response confined to a few muscles, whereas stronger stimulation involves many muscles in the limb and may cause movements in other limbs.

The *total latent period* of a reflex is the time elapsing between the stimulus and the reflex response. If the time taken for the nerve impulses to pass inward along sensory nerves plus the time taken by the motor impulses to pass from the cord out along the motor nerves is subtracted from the total reflex time, we have the *central reflex time* which in a spinal reflex must be due mainly to synaptic delay. Since the synaptic delay at the motoneurone is about 0·5 msec the central reflex time can never be less than this. For a single volley set up by a single afferent stimulus the central reflex time for a flexion reflex in the cat is about 4 msec. When two subliminal volleys reach the cord with only a short interval, say 7 msec, between them, the central reflex time for the flexion reflex evoked by the second volley is reduced, in some cases to 0·5 msec. The rise in *central excitatory state* produced by the first volley can be quickly enhanced by the second volley to a level at which the motor neurones discharge. A better explanation is that the first volley, although not sufficient to excite the motoneurones, sets chains of internuncial neurones 'reverberating' and in this way the motoneurones are continuously bombarded with impulses which facilitate the action of the next volley. Eccles' explanation is that each excitatory impulse arriving at a motoneurone reduces the potential across the cell membrane by a small amount, the excitatory postsynaptic potential (e.p.s.p., p. 320); if the critical level for depolarization and discharge of a spike is not reached by the arrival of one excitatory impulse a rapid succession of such impulses can reduce the potential sufficiently to make the motoneurone discharge.

When a motor nerve to a muscle is stimulated by a single electrical impulse a single volley travels down to the muscle which shows a sudden abrupt rise of tension followed by a quick relaxation, that is, a twitch. A single volley reaching the cord along an afferent nerve evokes a muscular response which is less abrupt in onset and more sustained than a twitch; the latent period of the reflex contraction is, of course, longer than the latent period when the motor nerve itself is stimulated. The muscle tension may rise relatively slowly if the afferent volley does not bring all the accessible motoneurones into action at the one instant. The reflex contraction lasts somewhat longer and often attains a higher tension than a twitch produced by stimulation of the motor nerve. This is due to irregular repetitive firing of the motoneurones termed

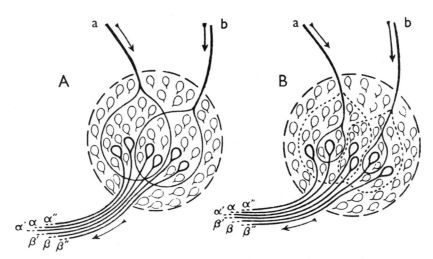

Fig. 23.7 A. Two excitatory afferents, *a* and *b*, with their fields of supraliminal effect in the motoneurone pool of muscle, *a* activates by itself 4 units (α', α, α'' and β'); *b* by itself 4 (β', β, β'' and α'). Concurrently they activate not 8 but 6, that is, give a contraction deficit by occlusion of contraction in α' and β'. B. Weaker stimulation of *a* and *b* restricting their supraliminal fields of effect in the pool as shown by the continuous line limit: *a* by itself activates 1 unit; *b* similarly; concurrently they activate 4 units (α', α, β' and β) owing to summation of subliminal effect in the overlap of the subliminal fields outlined by dots. (Subliminal fields of effect are not indicated in diagram A.) (C. S. Sherrington (1929) *Proceedings of the Royal Society* B, 105, 338.)

after-discharge which can be explained on the basis of the activity of reverberating internuncial neurones. The after-discharge also accounts for the relatively slow relaxation at the end of a reflex contraction.

If two stimuli are applied to an afferent nerve at an interval greater than the refractory period of the nerve two reflex muscle responses are obtained but if the separation between the stimuli is less than the refractory period (say 0·5 msec) the second is ineffective.

The following experiment shows *spatial summation*. The tibialis anterior muscle of a cat is attached to an isometric lever and the medial and lateral branches of the sciatic nerve (an afferent nerve) are dissected out and laid on stimulating electrodes. The strength of stimulus (the threshold) required to be applied to each branch to produce a just perceptible reflex increase of tension in the muscle is found. If two such stimuli are applied simultaneously to the two branches of the sciatic nerve a considerable tension is aroused reflexly. If there is an interval between the stimuli the tension developed is less, but spatial summation is still detectable even when the interval between the stimuli is as long as 15 msec.

Sherrington supposed that the arrival of afferent impulses at the motoneurones increases the *central excitatory state* (c.e.s.) and that when this rises to a certain critical value the motoneurones discharge and a reflex contraction occurs. It is now recognized that postsynaptic potentials (p. 320) underlie excitation and inhibition. If the experiment just described is considered in conjunction with Figure 23.7B, an explanation of spatial summation can be given. When a weak stimulus is sent in at *a*, one motoneurone discharges and a small contraction is obtained; at the same time the excitatory state in the neighbouring motoneurones (within the dotted lines) is raised. This part of the motoneurone pool is described as the *subliminal fringe*. A similar state of affairs occurs when *b* is weakly stimulated but, if both *a* and *b* are stimulated at the same time, the subliminal fringes overlap and the c.e.s. in the area common to both may rise to a value at which a number of

motoneurones discharge and produce a large muscular contraction.

If any afferent nerve of a limb is stimulated by a series of electrical impulses the flexor muscles of the limb show a reflex tetanus. This presumably corresponds, in an animal in a normal situation, to the maintained withdrawal of a limb subjected to a painful stimulus. The tension developed depends on the strength of the afferent stimulation up to a maximum tension which is never as great as in a maximal tetanus obtained by direct stimulation of the motor nerve. No single afferent nerve can reach all the motoneurones of a given muscle; some, however, command a larger fraction than others. Sherrington described this phenomenon as *fractionation*.

The motoneurone is the *final common path* to the muscle and afferents arising in many different parts of the body converge on it. This convergence leads to *occlusion* as explained in Figure 23.7A. Strong stimulation of afferent *a* alone brings four motoneurones into action and stimulation of afferent *b* alone makes four motoneurones discharge; simultaneous stimulation of the two afferents, because of their overlap, brings only six, not eight, motoneurones into action. In fact, in experiments on the flexion reflex in a spinal animal the tension produced by the simultaneous maximal stimulation of two afferents is only a little greater than that obtained if either afferent is stimulated alone.

Motoneurones are not all of the same type; it is possible to distinguish fast and slow (phasic and tonic) motoneurones, the nerve cells concerned supplying a group of muscle fibres which are apparently homogeneous. The phasic motoneurones are now thought to be large motoneurones; they have a high threshold for excitation and are readily fatigued. The tonic motoneurones are presumably small cells which have a low threshold for excitation but do not fatigue easily (see size principle below).

In the flexion reflex the tension of the flexor muscle rises very suddenly (Table 23.9). This suggests that all the motor neurones involved discharge simultaneously and that there is no gradual *recruitment* of neurones. The latent period is very short—of the order of 10 msec. A smooth tetanus (p. 332) is produced only when a high rate of stimulation is used, say 40 per second.

If a reflex is repeatedly elicited the response of the muscle gradually declines and may eventually cease. Since direct stimulation of the motor nerve or the muscle itself is still able to produce a contraction it is evident that the *fatigue* must depend on changes in the central nervous system, probably as the result of changes at the synapses (for a contrary view see p. 343). The scratch reflex in the dog (p. 369), elicited by stimulation of the skin over the thorax, shows a progressive decline in response if the point of stimulation is kept constant but if this is changed the rhythmic scratching movements can be restored and prolonged. This is an example of *habituation* and *dishabituation* and can be readily demonstrated in many reflexes which have a protective role. Reflex fatigue occurs very much later than habituation and reflexes such as the postural reflexes which do not habituate readily can be maintained almost indefinitely.

Extension Reflexes

If in a spinal preparation flexor withdrawal is evoked in one limb by the application of a noxious stimulus extension of the opposite limb takes place (Fig. 23.8). This is a *crossed extension reflex*. The latent period, from 40 to 100 msec, is several times that of a flexor reflex. When this reflex is elicited a single afferent volley produces a succession of volleys from the motoneurones. Thus a slow rate of stimulation of the afferent nerve, say 5 per second, results in a smooth tetanus which could be produced by direct stimulation of the motor

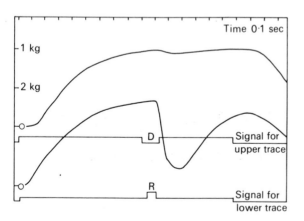

Fig. 23.8 Two records of a reflex tetanus of the vasto-crureus muscle of a decerebrate cat produced by electrical stimulation of the opposite peroneo-popliteal nerve 48 times per second. The same intensity of stimuli was applied in both cases. (The two records were made separately but are placed together in one figure for ease of comparison.) In the the upper trace 6 consecutive stimuli were omitted during the drop in the signal line D. In the lower trace there was no break of the stimulation of the excitatory afferent nerve but the ipsilateral peroneal-popliteal nerve was stimulated during the period marked R. The tension scale applies to both curves. (E. G. T. Liddell & C. S. Sherrington (1924) *Proceedings of the Royal Society* B, **95**, 142.)

nerve only if 40 volleys per second arrived at the muscle. As stimulation of the afferent nerve continues the tension rises slowly as the number of motoneurones involved (or *recruited*) gradually increases. Because after-discharge of motoneurones (Table 23.9) is well marked in extension reflexes the muscle tension falls off more slowly than in a flexion reflex when the stimulation of the afferent nerve ceases.

Table 23.9 Characteristics of flexion and crossed reflexes

	Flexion reflex	Crossed extension reflex
Latent period	Short (10 msec)	Long (40 to 100 msec)
Tension	Rises suddenly	Rises slowly (recruitment)
	Declines quickly	Declines slowly (after-discharge)
Stimulation for complete tetanus	40 per sec to ipsilateral afferent nerve	5 per sec to contralateral afferent nerve
Central excitatory state	Dies away quickly	Dies away slowly

The crossed extension reflex is elicited by stimulation of a *contralateral* afferent nerve. If, during the course of such a reflex, an *ipsilateral* afferent is stimulated there is, after a very short latent period, a large reduction of tension (Fig. 23.8). The amount of this inhibition depends on the strength of the stimulation of the ipsilateral afferent nerve but even a weak stimulus can cause some inhibition. Stimulation of the ipsilateral nerve alone, of course, elicits a flexion reflex; this is an artificial way of producing a flexion reflex which in the intact animal is usually elicited by applying a noxious stimulus to the skin. The flexion reflex, no matter how it is elicited, takes precedence over the extension reflex. During the inhibition of a crossed extension reflex, caused by stimulating an ipsilateral afferent nerve, the tension curve falls as quickly as at the end of a tetanus produced by direct stimulation of the motor nerve. Since an extension reflex dies away quite slowly the inhibitory stimulus must stop the discharge of the motor neurones. Since skeletal muscle has no inhibitory nerve supply inhibition in spinal reflexes must be due to events in the spinal cord.

Sherrington supposed that an afferent impulse which leads to inhibition of a reflex builds up a *central inhibitory state*, or c.i.s., and that this is capable of neutralizing or removing c.e.s. The c.i.s. can last for a considerable time—in some experiments 200 msec or larger (Figs. 23.8 and 23.10). It may be regarded as a process which makes polarized membranes of neurones more stable by increasing the potential difference across them, that is by hyperpolarization.

The Tendon Reflex

By tapping the patellar tendon the muscle spindles within the quadriceps, the extensor muscle of the knee, are stretched and after a very short latent period (about 30 msec) the muscle contracts and the leg is jerked forward (Fig. 23.10). This tendon reflex is an example of a phasic stretch reflex to be distinguished from the tonic stretch reflex which follows sustained stretch of a muscle. It is essential for the eliciting of the reflex that the quadriceps be initially partly stretched. The reduced (central) reflex time, about 2 msec, is so short that the reflex must be purely spinal and involve not more than two neurones. If the muscle tension and the electromyogram are recorded simultaneously a burst of electrical activity is seen before the tension develops and then there is a 'silent period' as the tension develops; this is followed by a further period of muscle contraction. The reflex depends, like any other reflex, on the integrity of the reflex arc which consists of the afferent nerves, spinal cord and the efferent nerves. If the reflex is absent there must be an interruption somewhere in the arc. The jerk may be exaggerated in suprasegmental or upper motor lesions above the level of the spinal arc (Fig. 24.13). In animal experiments the knee jerk is inhibited if a flexion reflex is induced at the same time (Fig. 23.10).

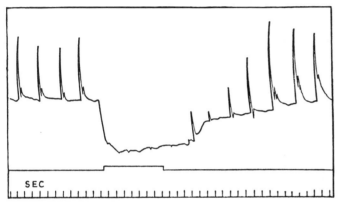

Fig. 23.10   Reflex inhibition of the knee-jerk. Records from above downwards: Tracing from preparation of the extensor muscles of the knee, recording a regular series of knee-jerks. Signal line: weak repetitive stimulation of the central end of the hamstring nerve during the time marked by the rise of the signal. Time in sec. At the onset of stimulation the tonus of the extensor muscles at once fell and the knee-jerk was temporarily abolished. After cessation of the inhibiting stimulus the tonus and the knee-jerk quickly returned, and the latter became more brisk than before the inhibition. (C. S. Sherrington (1947) *The Integrative Action of the Nervous System.* Cambridge University Press.)

In the human subject the knee jerk is markedly depressed if a vibratory stimulus of 100 Hz is applied to the quadriceps muscle. Vibration is a powerful stimulus to the muscle spindles and one explanation of the reflex depression it produces is that by creating a 'busy line' it blocks the flow of afferent impulses. Another explanation is that it brings about presynaptic inhibition of the spindle afferents.

Stretch Reflexes

Quantitative studies of stretch reflexes, sometimes called myotatic reflexes, are most easily made by increasing the length of a muscle attached to a myograph. The rise of tension which occurs on stretching is shown extremely well by the extensor muscles of a decerebrate preparation (p. 374). The rise of tension depends on the integrity of the reflex arc. It is

not abolished by anaesthetization of the tendon or by removal of the skin. These stretch reflexes are responses of muscles to a relatively slow stretch and must be distinguished from the rapid tendon jerks in response to a single afferent volley. Since the tension produced by stretching can be reduced by stimulation of an ipsilateral sensory nerve or by stretching an antagonistic flexor muscle there is no doubt about its reflex origin. After the nerve to the muscle is cut the rise of tension on stretching the muscle is relatively small and can be accounted for by the elastic properties of the muscle itself.

When a muscle is stretched the discharge in the large afferent fibres from its muscle spindles increases and produces, by a pathway which may be monosynaptic, a contraction in the same muscle which resists the applied stretch. The rate of discharge can be increased, even when the length of the muscle is fixed, by stimulating the γ efferents (see p. 345). The increased discharge from the annulospiral endings produces a reflex contraction of the muscle. The discharge in the large afferents, therefore, depends partly on the length of the muscle and partly on the length of the intrafusal fibres (see Fig. 23.11). If a muscle is stretched and potentials are recorded from ventral root filaments it is seen that recruitment of motor units occurs in an orderly manner, the fibres with small action potentials being recruited earlier. Since the larger neurones give rise to larger action potentials it is evident that the threshold for excitation is lower in the smaller neurones—*the size principle.*

When a muscle is contracting the discharge from its spindles declines and the reflex excitation of its α motoneurones

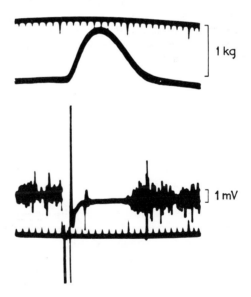

Fig. 23.11   The subject makes a steady voluntary contraction of 1 kg, and the associated action potentials (the electromyogram) are recorded. When the muscle is excited by stimulating the motor nerve with a brief electrical impulse, the electromyogram is 'silent' during the superimposed twitch. This is because impulses from the muscle spindles cease during the twitch and thus excitation is withdrawn from the α motoneurones. The record consists of 10 traces superimposed, to demonstrate the great regularity of the phenomenon. Top and bottom traces: 10 msec and 100 msec. Second trace: twitch tension, roughly 1 kg. Third trace: action potentials recorded with a needle electrode in the muscle. (P. A. Merton (1951) *Journal of Physiology*, 114, 187.)

declines also. As the muscle relaxes when the contraction has ended the spindle discharge increases and the excitation of the α motoneurones increases. Muscular movement is thus prevented from being jerky by a reduction of tension during contraction and by a slowing of the fall of tension in relaxation.

If a quadriceps muscle is divided into four innervated portions which can be separately stretched it is found that the rise of tension is most marked in the part extended and quite small in neighbouring muscles. Presumably the impulses from the muscle spindles excite motor neurones which innervate muscle cells in their immediate vicinity. In this way each part of the muscle contributes its share to resisting elongation.

These stretch reflexes are characteristic of the antigravity extensor muscles and they are especially noticeable in the decerebrate preparation (p. 374) in which the extensor muscles are firmly contracted. This state of contraction of the antigravity muscles is reflex in origin since it is abolished by cutting the anterior or posterior roots or by section of the muscle tendon. The excessive tonus seen in decerebrate rigidity is similar in character to the spasticity which develops in patients with hemiplegia. In a healthy subject fully relaxed skeletal muscle is electrically silent but passive movement evokes a contraction to oppose the stretching force. A lesion affecting the upper motor neurone makes the stretch reflex abnormally excitable and there is an abnormal degree of resistance to passive movement. A characteristic of muscle tonus and of stretch reflexes is that they can be maintained for long periods with only a small expenditure of energy and with, consequently, an absence of fatigue. However, recording from human spindle afferents during voluntary contraction, although it confirms that spindle discharge accompanies voluntary contraction, has failed so far to support the idea that it initiates the α-motoneurone discharge.

The γ efferents, by controlling the tension in the muscle spindles, control their sensitivity. The rate of discharge of the γ efferents can be altered by the 'higher centres' and may rise before the α-motoneurones discharge. This latter finding has suggested that changes in tone could be brought about by an increase or decrease in the γ efferent discharge, the subsequent increase or decrease in the spindle afferent discharge causing through monosynaptic pathways an alteration in the reflex discharge of the α motoneurones. Evidence that this self-regulating mechanism is in action in posture is provided by the 'silent period'. While a steady voluntary contraction is maintained the muscle is made to twitch by applying a brief electrical impulse to it; during the twitch the electromyogram (Fig. 23.11) is reduced to a straight line (that is, is 'silent'). The shortening of the muscle reduces the length of the muscle spindles with a consequent decline in the number of impulses in the large afferents, and this withdrawal of excitation from the α motoneurones makes them silent. This pathway seems, however, hardly suited for carrying out rapid movements because of the slow conduction of the small γ fibres and because of the delay in the reflex circuit. Experiments on animals with deafferented limbs or deafferented respiratory muscles have indicated that voluntary and respiratory α motoneurones can be reached directly by descending pathways; the large calibre, fast conducting, axons of the α motoneurones are eminently suitable for rapid movements.

Stretch reflexes in man can be studied by moving a joint and noting the time taken to produce electrical activity in the muscle being investigated, that is the reflex time. In the case of the long flexor of the thumb the latency is about 45 msec which is double that of a finger jerk and much more than is necessary for a purely spinal reflex. The longer latency suggests that the impulses pass in a transcortical pathway. The afferent limb of the reflex presumably goes to the central sulcus of the cortex; nerve impulses from the muscle spindles have been detected in the cortex of the baboon. The efferent limb is likely to be in the fast-conducting fibres of the corticospinal pathway. The human stretch reflex cannot therefore be exactly comparable to that seen in the decerebrate cat in which there cannot be a transcortical pathway.

A decerebrate preparation (p. 374) with rigidity of the extensor muscles can be used to demonstrate other characteristics of the myotatic reflex. If the experimenter tries to flex the hind-limb at the knee there is first considerable resistance since the myotatic reflex is evoked but, if the force is maintained, the muscle slackens quite suddenly and then can easily be flexed. The sudden loss of resistance is similar to that felt when closing a pocket-knife; hence the name *clasp-knife reaction*. This reaction occurs only when great force is applied to the extensor muscle; it may therefore be regarded as a protective mechanism since the muscle gives way before the force is great enough to produce damage by tearing the fibres. The discharge from the Golgi tendon organs (p. 343) is believed to be the basis of this reaction; the impulses from these organs inhibit the motoneurones of the synergic muscles and perhaps excite the antagonists by a polysynaptic pathway. In this way the extension phase of stepping could be terminated and the flexion phase initiated.

After the limb of a decerebrate preparation is forcibly flexed, as just described, the extensor muscles are lengthened and the new flexed position is maintained (*lengthening reaction*). If the flexed limb is now extended the tension in the extensor muscle is reduced because the ends are brought nearer and, presumably because the γ efferents take up the slack of the intrafusal fibres, the afferent spindle discharge increases; the α motor neurone discharge is then increased reflexly so that the position of the limb is maintained. This is called the *shortening reaction*, since the fibres of the extensor muscle are shortened. These two modifications of the stretch reflex give the limbs plasticity, that is to say they allow the limbs to remain in the position in which they are placed.

Reciprocal Innervation

In addition to these 'static' reflexes, which are responsible for maintenance of posture, the spinal cord is concerned in the 'dynamic' reflexes involved in walking and running. The alternating contractions of the flexors and extensors of the limbs depend on production and inhibition of the appropriate reflexes. At any one instant one muscle group of a limb is contracting and the antagonistic group is relaxing. These movements depend on reciprocal innervation. The nerve pathways involved are described in Figure 20.36. As the limb flexes the extensor muscles are stretched and the extensor muscles contract reflexly with a reflex relaxation of the flexors. The resulting extension stretches the flexor muscles in turn and produces flexion of the limb with an inhibition of the extensor muscles. A rhythmic movement is thus set up in which the flexor and extensor reflexes come into action successively and the final common path is commanded alternately. This rhythmic response is readily evoked because after the occurrence of a reflex of one type it is easier to elicit the antagonistic reflex. Figure 23.12 illustrates how the alternating movements of the limb, the well-known pattern of walking, may be brought about. At the instant represented in Figure 23.12b, a flexion reflex is elicited in the left fore-limb and an extension in the right fore-limb. This can be explained on the basis of the connexions shown in Figure 20.36. By longer connexions in the spinal cord the full walking pattern involving reciprocal activity in all four limbs is obtained.

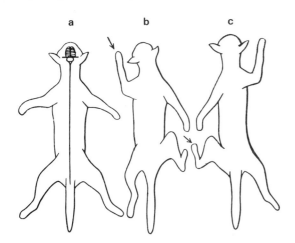

Fig. 23.12 a = Position in decerebrate rigidity (all four limbs extended). b = Change of attitude from a evoked by stimulation of left fore-foot. c = Change of attitude from a evoked by stimulation of left hind-foot. (C. S. Sherrington (1897–98). *Journal of Physiology* 22, 330.)

The pattern of successive flexions and extensions brought about through reciprocal innervation can be overcome in several ways. For example, when the pad of the foot of an intact animal is pressed there is a *positive supporting reaction* in which the extensors and flexors contract simultaneously to convert the limb into a pillar to support the weight of the body. The rhythmic scratch reflex depends on reciprocal innervation. It can be elicited in an intact dog or in one which has been allowed to recover after section of the cervical spinal cord below the level of the phrenic nerves. Stimulation of the skin over the ribs results in rhythmic scratching movements by the hind-limb which appear to the observer to be purposeful. At any rate, the movements are co-ordinated accurately enough to remove the source of irritation. Thus this reflex may be said to possess 'localization'. If a noxious stimulus is applied to the foot during a scratch reflex the latter is completely inhibited. As described already, flexion withdrawal reflexes which take the animal away from danger are prepotent, that is they have precedence over all other reflexes.

The H Response

If the posterior tibial nerve is stimulated electrically while potentials are being recorded by surface electrodes over the soleus, a stimulus too weak to excite the efferent fibres is followed by a late potential. This potential increases in latency as the stimulus is moved distally. As the stimulus intensity is increased the efferent fibres are activated and evoke a direct muscle response. The late potential decreases in amplitude and disappears. This response was first described by Hoffmann in 1918 and so is known as the H response. Normally it can be obtained only in the posterior tibial nerve where it is the electrical homologue of the ankle jerk. It is a monosynaptic reflex and provides a measure of reflex latency in man and its excitability is markedly altered in the presence of suprasegmental lesions (Fig. 23.13).

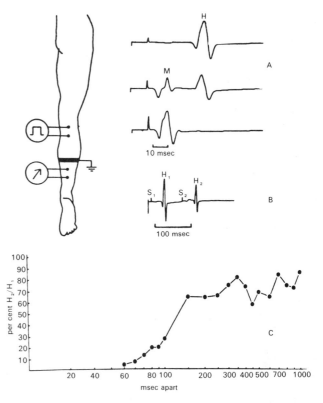

Fig. 23.13 Arrangement for evoking a monosynaptic response (H response) from the posterior tibial nerve in the human subject. In A it is seen that as the stimulus is increased from a weak stimulus in the upper trace to a strong stimulus in the lowest trace the reflex response (H wave) decreases in amplitude as the directly evoked response (M wave) appears. In B, two H responses are evoked by stimuli (S₁ and S₂) 80 msec apart, the second response being smaller than the first. Graph C shows the recovery of excitability of the H reflex when it is evoked by paired stimuli. The shape of the recovery curve is to some extent dependent on the parameters of stimulation and may be modified by suprasegmental lesions. (*From* J. A. R. Lenman, 1975, *Clinical Neurophysiology*, Oxford: Blackwell.)

The Tonic Vibration Reflex

A vibratory stimulus of 100 Hz or more applied to a muscle or its tendon evokes a sustained contraction of the muscle and a relaxation of its antagonist. This tonic vibration reflex (TVR) is due to activation of the muscle spindles and provides a useful method of studying the tonic stretch reflex. It is dependent to some extent on suprasegmental facilitation because it can be abolished in the cat by spinal cord transection and in man it may be markedly depressed by injury to the spinal cord.

Superficial Reflexes

The flexion reflex in which the extremity is withdrawn from a nocuous stimulus is an important example of a cutaneous protective response but there are many local reflexes which provoke localized withdrawal mediated by extensor muscles. The plantar response to stroking the sole of the foot (p. 387) is an example of a local extensor reflex which becomes overridden by a generalized flexor reflex in the presence of a suprasegmental lesion. The abdominal reflex is a local withdrawal response to scratching the skin of the abdomen. Because it may be lost in the presence of suprasegmental lesions it has been thought to be a long loop reflex with a suprasegmental pathway, but latency measurements have shown it to be a spinal reflex. The abdominal response tends to disappear if elicited repeatedly and provides a good example of habituation. Its continued presence seems to depend on supraspinal facilitation which may be lost if there is a suprasegmental lesion. If the abdominal reflexes are absent in a person with a suprasegmental lesion, as is frequently the case in multiple sclerosis, they can still be dishabituated by a strong enough electrical stimulus.

Effects of Section of Roots of Spinal Nerves

For the localization of lesions of the spinal cord it is important to know the area of distribution of the posterior root fibres. The area of skin innervated by each root is called a *dermatome*. When a single posterior root is cut the area of anaesthesia is small because the skin-fields of neighbouring posterior roots overlap considerably, any one patch of skin being supplied by two, or even three, posterior roots. To demonstrate the area of a dermatome the method of *remaining sensibility* was first used by Sherrington (1893) in the monkey and forty years later by Foerster in man. They cut three posterior roots above and three posterior roots below the root to be studied. This root, isolated from its neighbours, is left intact. The skin area which remains sensitive to mechanical stimulation is then marked out. The results of numerous experiments of this kind can be plotted as a map of the dermatomes (Fig. 23.14).

Section of a series of posterior roots, or their destruction by disease, causes, in addition to the cutaneous anaesthesia just described, complete loss in the areas supplied of all forms of sensation whether cutaneous, proprioceptive or visceral. Since the ingoing part of the reflex arc is interrupted, spinal reflexes are abolished and muscle tone is reduced. Loss of the protective pain reflexes frequently results in damage to the skin which may be followed by ulceration. The interruption of the proprioceptive pathway to the cord prevents the patient from knowing, unless visually, the position of the muscles and joints in the affected area. As a result voluntary movements are carried out most inaccurately. Section of posterior roots also interferes with the perception of vibration. When a heavy tuning fork is struck and laid with its base on the skin,

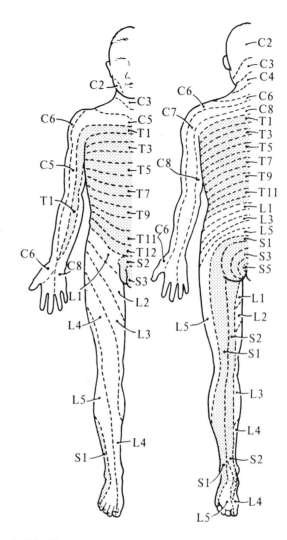

Fig. 23.14 The cutaneous areas supplied by the posterior nerve roots (dermatomes). (J. A. R. Lenman, 1975, *Clinical Neurophysiology*. Oxford: Blackwell.)

Table 23.15 Paralysis due to lesions affecting upper and lower motor neurone

Upper motor neurone	Lower motor neurone
Paralysis extensive or localized	Paralysis localized to segmental or peripheral nerve distribution
Little wasting	Marked wasting
Increase in tone (spasticity or rigidity)	Decrease in tone
Fasciculation absent	Fasciculation may be present
Tendon reflexes increased	Tendon reflexes diminished
Extensor plantar response (Babinski's sign)	Flexor plantar response
Electrophysiological tests normal or non-specific	Electrophysiological evidence of denervation or impaired nerve conduction

(From J. A. R. Lenman (1976) The Nervous System, in Bouchier and Morris, *Clinical Skills*, London: Saunders). *Physiological* 'flexion' is any movement that draws the limb from the ground, so in physiological terms the 'extensor response' is part of the physiological flexor reflex (see p. 387).

especially over a bony prominence, the normal subject has a sensation of vibration which is conveyed by impulses passing along the afferent nerves and their continuations up the ascending columns of the cord. The spinal pathway for vibration sense includes fibres travelling in both the posterior and the lateral columns. Vibration sense is also impaired in thalamic lesions.

Section of the anterior roots causes paralysis of the muscles supplied with complete loss of voluntary and reflex movements. The affected muscles become flaccid, toneless and soon waste. The motor cells in the anterior horn of the grey matter show degenerative changes which prove that they are the cell bodies of the anterior root fibres. Destruction of these cells as in poliomyelitis has the same effect as section of the anterior roots and the results, described as lower motor neurone paralysis, are summarized in Table 23.15. Since the sympathetic fibres also emerge in the anterior roots (Fig. 25.2)

their section causes loss of sweating in the area and dilatation of the skin vessels (see p. 999).

Transection of the Cord and Spinal Shock

After spinal transection the reflexes in the cord caudal to the cut are depressed for a time, those in the cranial part of the nervous system remaining unaffected. In the frog spinal reflexes recover after two or three minutes and in the cat spinal reflexes may be depressed for an hour or more. In man the period of depression, that is total absence of reflexes below the transection, varies from about two days to six weeks or longer.

The state of depression accompanied by flaccidity of the muscles is called *spinal shock*. It is not due to the trauma of section since it occurs if the continuity of the cord is interrupted by cooling or by the injection of local anaesthetic. It

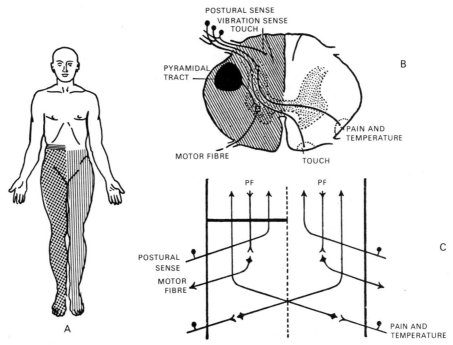

23.16   The Brown-Séquard syndrome arising from a lesion of the right half of the cord. In A the distribution of cutaneous sensory change is indicated by horizontal and vertical shading. The area of spastic paresis is indicated by stippling. In B, the shaded (right) half of the cord is the seat of the lesion. A diagrammatic longitudinal section given in C indicates the pathways which are interrupted. The black line indicates the site of the hemisection. The ascending and descending tracts which are interrupted are labelled. PF, pyramidal fibre. The resulting disorders are given in the table below.

On the Side of the Lesion	On the Opposite Side
Sensory	
At level of lesion. A band of cutaneous hyperaesthesia may be present. Alternatively, but only if three successive spinal segments are involved, there may be a band of impairment of cutaneous sensibility to touch, pain and temperature (horizontal shading).	*At level of lesion.* No abnormality.
Below level of lesion. Tactile, painful and thermal sensibility normal. Postural and vibratory sensibility (p. 370) impaired or lost (stippled area).	*Below level of lesion.* Impairment or loss of painful and thermal sensibility. Tactile, postural and vibratory sensibility normal (vertical shading).
Motor	
Below level of lesion. Spastic paresis of leg, increased tendon jerks, clonus, extensor plantar response (stippled area).	*Below level of lesion.* No abnormality.

(Sir Francis Walshe (1963) *Diseases of the Nervous System.* 10th edition. Edinburgh: Livingstone.)

is probably related to the sudden interruption of impulses from higher parts of the nervous system. This concept explains the fact that, when recovery of reflex function has occurred, a second transection below the level of the original cut does not cause spinal shock in the remaining part of the cord. The reason for the recovery from spinal shock is not known.

Immediately after complete transection of the spinal cord in the thoracic region in man there is a total loss of voluntary movement in both legs (paraplegia) with loss of sensation (anaesthesia) over the lower part of the trunk and legs. At first the leg muscles are flaccid and no reflexes can be elicited. Slight movements of the toes or reflex penile contractions may sometimes be observed a few hours after transection. Reflex activity begins to appear first in the distal part of the limbs, later in the proximal parts, and the first response may be as early as two days or as late as six weeks. A number of cases of transection of the cord in man have been followed by permanent flaccid paraplegia, possibly due to extensive trauma leading to damage to the anterior horn cells below the level of the section. The earliest reflexes to return are the flexor withdrawal movements following plantar stimulation (p. 387). Later the flexor spasms become so pronounced that spread occurs to the autonomic outflow with emptying of the bladder and bowel and sweating. This *mass reflex* is particularly liable to develop in the presence of infection of the bladder and bedsores. In the majority of cases the predominantly flexor activity is followed by a return of extensor reflexes so that the knee-jerk and other reflexes are easily elicited and may be exaggerated. Generally the final outcome is one of predominantly extensor activity, although this is usually less marked than in incomplete sections of the cord. In complete sections of the cord paraplegia and anaesthesia below the line of section are permanent.

Hemisection of Spinal Cord

A hemisection produces paralysis of movement with loss of position sense on the same side below the level of the cut and on the opposite side loss of sensation of pain and temperature without loss of movement. The reason for this characteristic distribution of motor and sensory loss is clear from Figure 23.16. The band of hyperaesthesia on the same side is attributed to irritation of the neurones adjacent to the lesion. If the local lesion destroys at least three segments there may be a band of impaired sensation in the dermatomes corresponding to the level of the lesion. When the anterior horn cells are involved a paralysis of the lower motor neurone type affects the muscles innervated by the corresponding segments. The muscles are represented in the cord by vertical groups of motoneurones extending over several segments; it is therefore difficult to locate the exact level of a lesion by observing the extent of motor paralysis.

Disease in man causes incomplete transections of the cord more commonly than complete transections. Flexor spasms may be a feature of both complete and incomplete lesions; in incomplete lesions extensor spasms, however, generally predominate, and in complete transections although extensor reflexes may be late in appearing they may be dominant in the final state of the patient.

Unilateral chordotomy (see Fig. 23.5) does not make the other side of the body below the lesion permanently analgesic. Even for unilateral pain a bilateral chordotomy is successful only in one half of patients. In fact relatively few of the spinothalamic fibres reach the thalamus and it is likely that the tract consists of a few long fibres but mainly of multisynaptic chains of short fibres of small diameter ending at all levels of the neural axis forming a nerve net, which is very difficult to interrupt effectively.

BODY POSTURE

The maintenance of body posture depends on a complex set of interacting reflexes that are modified and integrated at different levels of the brain. They depend on information reaching the central nervous system from proprioceptors in muscle, from the labyrinthine organs and from the visual system. Many of the simpler reflexes are integrated in the brain stem but those representing more complex forms of postural activity such as the righting reflexes may require the integrity of the cerebral cortex. In this section an account of the anatomy of the brain stem structures is followed by a description of postural reflexes occurring at different levels.

Anatomy of Brain Stem

The spinal cord is continuous with the brain stem which includes the medulla oblongata, the pons and the mid brain. Figure 23.17 shows that the medulla oblongata widens as it passes forward and the spinal canal opens out into the fourth ventricle. On the ventral aspect of the medulla (Fig. 23.18) the pyramids and their decussation are prominent; a little rostral

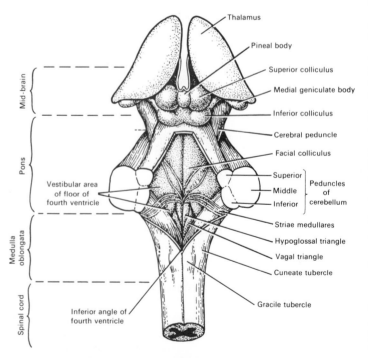

Fig. 23.17 Diagrammatic view of the human brain stem exposed from behind and above (approximately natural size). The cerebellum has been removed by section through the peduncles.

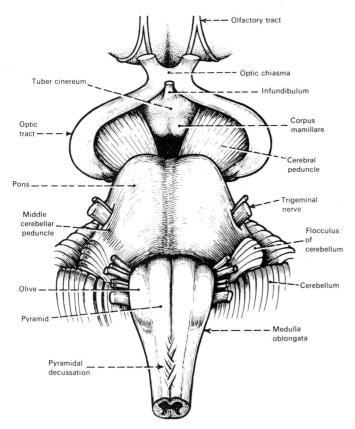

Fig. 23.18 View of ventral (lower) surface of medulla oblongata, pons and mid-brain of man (approximately natural size). The cerebral peduncles pass over the optic tracts and enter the fore-brain.

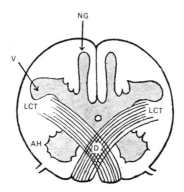

Fig. 23.19 Section through lowest part of the human medulla at the level of the *motor decussation*. AH = most rostral part of the anterior horn; D = decussation of cerebrospinal fibres (decussation of the pyramids); LCT = lateral cerebrospinal tract; V = spinal nucleus of fifth nerve, continuous caudad with the posterior horn of the spinal cord. (About 3 times actual size.)

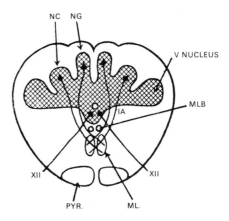

Fig. 23.20 A section somewhat rostral to that in Fig. 23.19 to show the *sensory decussation*. NG = nucleus gracilis; NC = nucleus cuneatus; ML = medial lemniscus; XII = hypoglossal nerve; IA = internal arcuate fibres; PYR = pyramid; MLB = medial longitudinal bundle (fasciculus). (About 3 times actual size.)

to this the pons forms a bridge of decussating transverse fibres gathered together into the two middle cerebellar peduncles which consist of fibres running into the cerebellum. On the dorsal aspect of the medulla (Fig. 23.17) the inferior cerebellar peduncles diverge and pass to the cerebellum. Anterior to the pons is the short mid-brain, the four colliculi lying on its dorsal surface.

A transverse section through the caudal, or lower, part of the medulla (Fig. 23.19) shows that the grey matter is cut across by fibres of the corticospinal tract passing from the pyramids across the midline to run down the cord in the lateral corticospinal or crossed pyramidal tract. These interlacing fibres form the decussation of the pyramids or the *motor decussation*. A section a little rostral to this (Fig. 23.20) shows the gracile and cuneate nuclei in which the fibres of the posterior columns of the white matter of the cord terminate. From these nuclei new fibres arise and, passing across the midline as the internal arcuate fibres, form the medial lemniscus (or medial fillet) which runs to the thalamus. This crossing can be called in physiological terms the *sensory decussation*. The spinothalamic fibres continue to occupy a ventrolateral position as in the cord but, as they travel rostrally, first the touch fibres in the medulla, and then the pain and temperature fibres in the pons pass medially on each side and join the medial lemniscus. In the upper part of the medulla the central canal is displaced towards the dorsal surface of the medulla and opens out.

In the pons the pyramidal fibres are separated into small bundles by the fibres of the middle peduncle of the cerebellum which, running at right angles to them, pass across the pons to the opposite cerebellar cortex. The superior cerebellar peduncles (Fig. 23.17) are composed chiefly of fibres coming from the dentate nuclei of the cerebellum which cross in the midline before entering the thalamus or the red nucleus.

The mid-brain (Fig. 23.17), only about 2 cm long, has a mass of grey matter centrally around the cerebral aqueduct which is the continuation of the fourth ventricle. In the ventral part of this grey matter lie the motoneurones of the third and fourth cranial nerves. Dorsal to the aqueduct are the nuclei of the superior and inferior colliculi. A large part of the mid-brain is occupied by the cerebral peduncles in which are embedded the deeply pigmented cells of the substantia nigra separating the peduncles into two parts, the base ventrally and the tegmentum dorsally. The base carries fibres from the cerebral cortex to the pons and spinal cord.

In the tegmentum three decussations occur. The most caudal is the decussation of the superior peduncles of the cerebellum;

the rubrospinal tracts and the tectospinal tracts cross more rostrally at the level of the third nerve nucleus. The red nucleus is part of the so-called *extrapyramidal system*. Fibres from this nucleus cross in the decussation of the rubrospinal tracts and pass down in the reticular formation of the pons and medulla oblongata to lie in front of the corticospinal tract in the cord.

Reticular formation of the brain stem. The reticular formation of the brain stem consists of scattered nerve cells lying in the central core of the brain stem which influences all parts of the central nervous system both rostrally and caudally. When the reticular formation is stimulated electrically motor activities, either phasic or postural, may be facilitated or inhibited according to the site of stimulation. An excess of the facilitating action of the reticular formation may be responsible for the exaggerated stretch reflexes which are expressed as spasticity.

The 'classical' afferent (lemniscal) pathways send lateral branches to the reticular core and this in turn influences the hypothalamus which affects the anterior pituitary (Chap. 29). Impulses passing up from the reticular area to the cerebral cortex are concerned with modifying wakefulness and arousal. This extralemniscal pathway seems also to conduct impulses subserving pain at about half the rate of conduction in the lemniscal pathway. This ascending pain pathway probably has many synapses on the way to the cortex. Adrenaline and noradrenaline are present in the central core of the brain stem and it may be that adrenergic transmission is important in the reticular formation. Good evidence has also been obtained for cholinergic transmission in the reticular activating system. The activity of the reticular activating system is reduced by anaesthetics and tranquillizing agents.

Decerebrate Rigidity

The modifying and integrating influence of the brain stem on the spinal reflexes has been investigated by making sections through it at various levels to cut off the higher parts of the brain. If a cut is made between the medulla and the spinal cord of a cat the *spinal preparation* shows, after an initial period of flaccidity, a certain amount of muscular tone not sufficient to bear the weight of the animal; respiration does not occur spontaneously and must be kept up by a pump if the preparation is to 'survive'. A more cranial cut through the medulla produces much the same condition as regards muscle tone but the animal may be able to breathe spontaneously. After a section made still further forward through the pons between the superior and inferior colliculi, the cerebral cortex and basal nuclei may be removed. This produces a *decerebrate preparation*. In spite of the removal of so large a portion of the brain, respiration, swallowing and other medullary reflexes are present. Temperature control is lost and voluntary control of movements is abolished; pain cannot be appreciated. When the effects of the anaesthetic have worn off, the cat shows decerebrate rigidity. The limbs are extended, the tail is raised and the head elevated. Stretch reflexes are hyperactive. Flexor and extensor muscles pull strongly against one another to hold the skeleton rigid so that the animal, if placed in the standing position, is able to support its weight. The standing position is maintained only if the rigid animal is placed with its four feet

on the ground in a stable position. After a moment or two, the animal usually slews round and collapses because, in the absence of the basal ganglia, stabilization of the joints between the limbs and the trunk is defective. The exaggerated muscle tone is reflex in origin and depends on impulses passing in the dorsal roots from the muscles themselves. The muscles relax if the tendons are cut. Section of the appropriate dorsal roots abolishes the reflex rigidity in the deafferented limbs. Subsequent removal of the anterior lobe of the cerebellum restores the rigidity, but this is now of a different kind (alpha rigidity, see below) because it is no longer dependent on stretch reflex activity.

For rigidity to appear it is necessary for the section to pass caudal to the red nucleus but cranial to the lateral vestibular nucleus which lies under the floor of the fourth ventricle. A section through the brain stem rostral to the red nucleus, that is well in front of the superior colliculi, leaves the muscle tone virtually normal. The vestibular nucleus and the vestibulo-spinal fibres arising from it are essential for decerebrate rigidity, since section of the brain stem caudal to the nucleus or section of the anterolateral columns of the spinal cord, which carry the vestibulospinal fibres, abolishes it. Unilateral destruction of the vestibular nucleus abolishes rigidity on the same side (Fig. 23.21). The cerebral cortex seems not to be deeply involved in the production of decerebrate rigidity since removal of the cerebral hemispheres alone does not produce rigidity. Further, the cerebral cortex controls the muscles on the contralateral side of the body, whereas unilateral section between the red nucleus and the vestibular nucleus is followed by rigidity on the same side. The rigidity must depend, therefore, on pathways that go straight down from the pons to the cord, without any decussation, that is to say on tracts which have already decussated above the level of the section.

We are thus led to conclude that decerebrate rigidity occurs in the cat when the vestibular nuclei no longer receive impulses from higher parts of the brain that exercise an

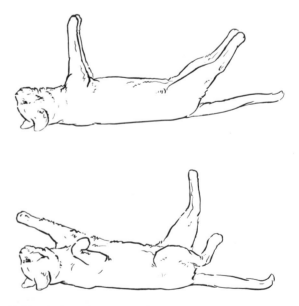

Fig. 23.21 A, decerebrate cat in the supine position to show rigidity of limbs. B, the same after destruction of the vestibular nucleus on the right side. (L. M. N. Back & H. W. Magoun (1947) *Journal of Neurophysiology*, 5, 331.)

inhibitory influence on these nuclei. Since destruction of the red nuclei alone does not produce rigidity, the inhibitory impulses cannot be derived from this source. The source of the inhibitory impulses is probably the suppressor reticular formation. When this is put out of action by decerebration the facilitatory reticular system is left unopposed, the stretch reflexes are facilitated and decerebrate rigidity occurs. Although a cat deprived of its cerebral cortex (decorticate preparation) has a normal attitude and normal distribution of muscle tone when standing or walking, it shows rigidity when lifted off the ground. Thus the cortex may play a small part in inhibiting the vestibular nucleus although the impulses cannot be conveyed in the pyramidal tracts. Since the decorticate animal does not show rigidity when sitting or standing it is probable that the vestibular nuclei receive inhibitory impulses mainly from parts of the brain other than the cerebral cortex.

The γ efferents (p. 374) are specially active in decerebrate rigidity. The spindles discharge rapidly; the stretch reflexes are, therefore, very active and they are in fact responsible for the rigidity. If the dorsal roots of such a preparation are cut, the γ efferents still discharge at the same rate but, since the discharge from the muscle spindles cannot reach the cord, the rigidity in the limbs disappears. Another type of decerebrate rigidity can be produced by tying off the arterial supply to the anterior part of the cerebellum. In this case deafferentation (by cutting the dorsal roots) does not abolish the rigidity. This second type of rigidity, therefore, cannot be brought about by excitation of the γ efferents and must depend on direct activation of the α motoneurones; in fact the muscle spindles are discharging quite slowly.

Decerebrate rigidity persists, or even increases, after cerebellectomy and furthermore a decerebrate preparation rendered flaccid by deafferentation is made rigid again by removal of the anterior cerebellum. It is now known that the cerebellum receives an afferent influx from muscle spindles and Golgi tendon organs and that spindle activity declines after cerebellectomy. The rigidity must be caused by increased direct excitation of the α pathway; in other words, the operation has caused a switch-over from γ excitation to the α mode of excitation.

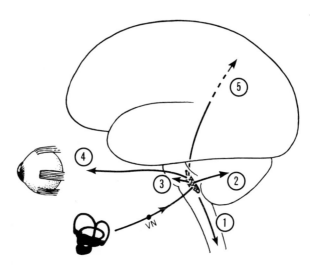

Fig. 23.23   Diagram to show the connexions of the vestibular fibres. 1, vestibulospinal tract; 2, to cerebellum via inferior cerebellar peduncle; 3, to reticular formation; 4, medial longitudinal bundle to the external eye muscles via the oculomotor nuclei; 5, to cerebral cortex. Shaded area, vestibular nuclei. VN, vestibular nerve.

Decerebrate rigidity is occasionally seen in man. Mid-brain lesions usually produce extension and pronation of the arms but higher lesions usually result in flexion (as in Fig. 23.22). The legs are always rigidly extended.

Tonic neck reflexes. The decerebrate cat has been used to study postural reflexes which arise in the neck. To investigate the tonic neck reflexes it is necessary to exclude impulses from the labyrinths by performing a double labyrinthectomy.

When the head of the decerebrate cat is turned to the right the right limb is extended and the left limb becomes relaxed. The limb responses are the same both for lateral flexion (ear to shoulder) and for torsion about the longitudinal axis (chin to shoulder). If the head is tilted so that the nose is raised the fore-limbs extend and the hind-limbs relax. The opposite effect is seen when the nose is directed downwards. Pressure with the hand over the cervical vertebrae causes a relaxation of all four limbs. These alterations in the position of the neck give rise to afferent impulses that enter the central nervous system by the first three cervical dorsal roots to initiate reflex alterations of tone in distant parts of the body and produce attitudes often observed in the normal dog and cat (Fig. 23.34). Similar reflexes may be seen in decerebrate or decorticate man (Fig. 23.22).

THE LABYRINTHS

The bony labyrinth (Fig. 23.24) consists of three communicating cavities, the vestibule, the semicircular canals and the cochlea, hollowed out of the petrous part of the temporal bone, all containing clear fluid of high sodium content, the perilymph. The membranous labyrinth (Fig. 23.25) lying within the bony labyrinth consists of the duct of the cochlea, the utricle and saccule (two small sacs lying in the vestibule) and the three semicircular ducts. The membranous labyrinth is a closed system containing endolymph, a fluid of high potassium content. The superior and posterior canals lie in vertical planes at right angles to one another while the lateral

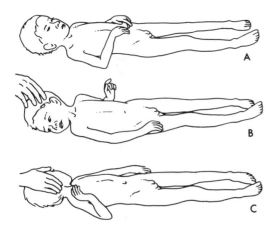

Fig. 23.22   Tonic neck reflexes shown in a decerebrate child. A, the characteristic position, flexion of the arms with extension of the legs. B and C, the position of the neck affects the tone of the muscles of the arms. (L. E. Davis (1925) *Archives of Neurology and Psychiatry (Chicago)*, 13, 572.)

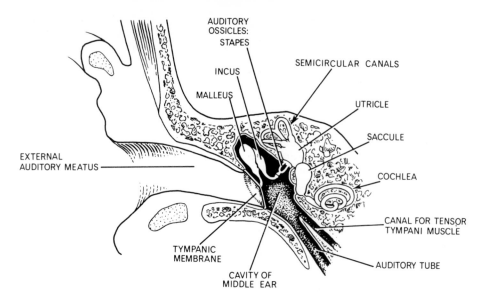

Fig. 23.24 The bony and membranous labyrinths. The utricle and saccule lie in the vestibule. The foot plate of the stapes is attached to the margins of the oval window. The round window lies below the oval window in the diagram. Compare with Figure 27.26

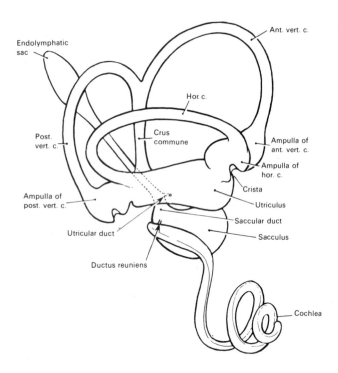

Fig. 23.25 The membranous labyrinth of the right ear of the guineapig. The viewpoint is from below and slightly behind the transverse axis. Nerve trunks and supporting connective tissue have been omitted. The whole of this membranous structure is suspended by connective tissue trabeculae within the slightly larger, bony labyrinth, a cavity in the petrous temporal bone. The macula in each ampulla is formed into a crest of jelly-like material, the cupula, which reaches across to the opposite wall. The macula of the saccule is approximately vertical and the macula of the utricle is approximately horizontal; the hairs of the hair cells pass into canals in a jelly-like material containing particles of calcium carbonate (otoconia). (T. D. M. Roberts, (1975) Vestibular physiology. In *Scientific Foundations of Otolaryngology*, ed. D. Harrison & R. Hinchcliffe. London: Heinemann.)

or horizontal canal is in a plane that is horizontal in the 'characteristic attitude' of the animal's head. In man this corresponds to the attitude used to look at something held in the hand, or at the ground two or three paces ahead. The superior canal of one side is in a plane approximately parallel to the plane containing the posterior canal of the other side. The semicircular ducts, each about 15 mm long in man, are one-fourth of the diameter of the bony semicircular canals which enclose them; each duct has a wider portion or ampulla containing the ampullary crests (cristae) which possess hair cells covered with a mass of gelatinous material, the cupula. The cupula is composed of a network of fibres 10 nm in diameter embedded in a protein matrix. The saccule and utricle each consist of a rounded membranous bag in the wall of which is a patch, 2 to 3 mm in diameter, of hair cells forming a sensory *macula*. The hairs of the hair cells of the utricular and saccular maculae pass into a mass of gelatinous material (otolith membrane) which is loaded with crystals of calcite (otoliths or otoconia).

The fine nerve filaments from the hair cells in the cristae and maculae become myelinated as they pass centrally in the vestibular nerve, to the vestibular ganglion and then to the vestibular nuclei (Fig. 23.23). From these nuclei, fibres pass to at least five destinations. Some fibres run in the medial longitudinal bundle to the oculomotor nuclei through which changes in position of the eyes are effected. This is the pathway for vestibular eye-deviations and counter-rolling. Fibres also pass in the medial lemniscus to the thalamus; others go in the inferior cerebellar peduncle to the cerebellar cortex, chiefly to the flocculonodular lobe. Some fibres pass into the reticular formation while others go in the vestibulospinal tract. In addition to these afferent impulses, efferent impulses from the lateral vestibular nuclei reach the hair cells. The function of these efferent fibres is related to habituation to vestibular stimuli. Vestibular impulses also end in the temporal lobes but the pathway is not yet known. Dizziness occurs when certain parts of the cortical area are stimulated in man but removal of the cortex does not produce any disturbance of equilibrium.

Receptors in the labyrinth. The operation of the receptors in the labyrinth is best understood in terms of the forces operating between the wall of the labyrinth and the contained endolymph. When the head is moved, contact forces are transmitted throughout the tissues of the head from one part to another so that the inertia of each part receives the appropriate acceleration to keep it in its proper place relative to the other parts. Contact forces are also needed for support to avoid accelerating toward the centre of the earth under the action of gravity. The transmission of a contact force involves deformation of each part according to its compliance and to its contribution to load bearing, just as a spring balance is deflected when it supports a weight.

The presence of the otoconia confers on the otolith organs (utricle and saccule) the properties of differential-density accelerometers, the density gradient tending to align itself along the direction of the vector of the contact force, as in a centrifuge tube. The loaded jelly mass in the endolymph is restrained from free movement over the macula by fine filaments tethering it to the wall of the organ. Small sliding movements occur as these retaining filaments stretch under the imposed forces. The amount of the resulting shearing movement is signalled by the hair cells (Fig. 23.26) which

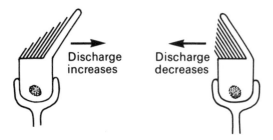

Fig. 23.26 Electron miscoscope studies have shown that vestibular sensory cells have one thick kinocilium and many thin stereocilia. When movement of lymph occurs towards a kinocilium the discharge increases, and when it occurs in the opposite direction the discharge decreases.

generate trains of impulses in their afferent nerve fibres (Fig. 23.27). The receptors in the cristae of the semicircular ducts also depend for their stimulation on deformations produced by contact forces, but there is normally no system of differential densities in the ampullae and consequently very little sensitivity to linear accelerations. An angular acceleration in the plane of a particular canal calls for a force to act on the endolymph in a direction parallel to the lumen of that canal. Such a force can only be provided by the cupula which becomes correspondingly deformed. The shearing motion of the jelly over the hair cells of the crista during this deflexion of the cupula alters the firing frequency in the afferent nerve fibres and thus generates a signal related to the angular acceleration of the skull.

The nerve fibres from the receptors in the semicircular canals and in the otolith organs for the most part fire continuously when the skull is at rest. Because the firing frequency can be either increased or decreased, these afferent nerves can signal changes in either direction in the corresponding stimuli. For the anterior vertical (superior) and posterior vertical (inferior) canals an angular acceleration in the ampulla-leading direction (towards 'side-down') produces

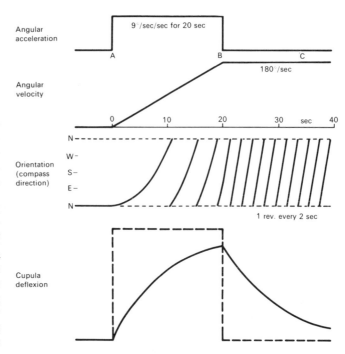

Fig. 23.27 Time courses of the changes in angular velocity, orientation of the skull in space, and cupula-deflexion arising from the application of a constant angular acceleration during the period from A to B. (T. D. M. Roberts (1978) *Neurophysiology of Postural Mechanisms*. London: Butterworth.)

an increase in afferent discharge. For the horizontal (lateral) canals an increase in firing frequency is produced by 'ampulla-trailing' acceleration, that is, towards the right for the horizontal canal of the right side.

Because any deflexion of the cupula implies a displacement of the endolymph within the canal, and because such a displacement is resisted by viscous forces, the time course of the change in the afferent signal does not closely follow the time course of the imposed angular acceleration. A step change in angular acceleration leads to a slower change in firing frequency. This increases or decreases exponentially towards a value appropriate to the new angular acceleration (Fig. 23.27). Consequently for rapidly fluctuating accelerations, such as those to which the skull is subjected in normal conditions, the time course of the change in firing frequency follows the time course of the angular velocity of the skull, rather than that of its angular acceleration (Fig. 23.28). At constant speed, however, the angular acceleration is zero and the cupula moves with an exponential time course towards its rest position and the nerve discharge fails to indicate continued rotation.

This effect can be used to study the reflexes generated by the signals from the semicircular canals. The subject sits in a chair (Bárány chair) that can be rotated about a vertical axis. Starting with a moderate acceleration, the chair is set to rotate at a constant speed of about 2 seconds for each full turn. The initial acceleration produces various effects but these are difficult for a stationary observer to see while the subject is rotating. After about 30 seconds of constant speed rotation, the chair is brought to a fairly sudden stop. The associated angular deceleration deflects the cupulae, which then gradually return to their resting positions during the ensuing seconds (Fig.

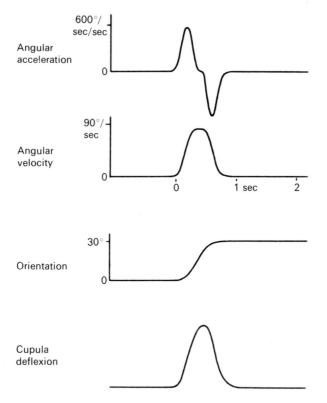

Fig. 23.28 Angular acceleration, angular velocity and cupula-deflexion to be expected during a naturally occurring movement. The curve for acceleration (generated electronically) was chosen to give (by double integration) a time course of displacement which closely matched an experimental record from a human subject. The cupula-deflexion (y) is computed from the angular acceleration (x) of the skull, by using the equation $\ddot{y}+10\dot{y}+y=kx$, and an analogue computer. (T. D. M. Roberts (1978) *Neurophysiology of Postural Mechanisms.* London: Butterworth.)

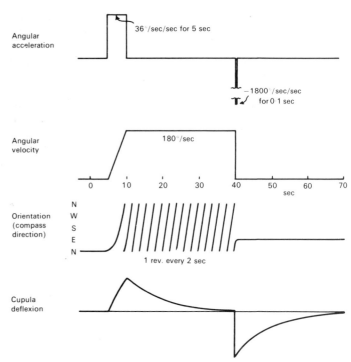

Fig. 23.29 Sequence of changes in angular velocity, orientation, and cupula-deflexion, during the procedure for imposing an impulsive deceleration on the Bárány chair. Note that the cupula-deflexion persists after the skull has been brought to rest. Note also that, if the deceleration were spread over 1 sec, instead of occupying only 0·1 sec, the force needed would be reduced to one-tenth, yet the cupula-deflexion reached in the rest position would have the same value as that shown here. (T. D. M. Roberts (1978) *Neurophysiology of Postural Mechanisms.* London: Butterworth.)

23.29). So long as the cupulae remain deflected, corresponding neural signals pass to the central nervous system and produce their usual reflex effects, even though these may not now be appropriate. Because the subject is at rest, the effects may now be easily seen by an observer. The eyes rotate in the subject's head, moving in the direction of the rotation to which the subject was previously exposed. This eye rotation is interrupted before the eyeball reaches the limit of its available travel by jerks back toward the 'straight ahead' position. The alternation of slow deviation with fast return is called *nystagmus*, named according to the direction of the quick phase, although it is the slow phase that is physiologically relevant. In normal head movements, the slow phase deviations of the eyeballs generated reflexly from the semicircular canals serve to keep the eyeballs pointing in roughly the same direction in spite of head movements.

Fine adjustment of the fixation of gaze depends on the visual system and involves processes of recognition of details in the visual field. When the eyeballs are moved voluntarily, the image of the visual field moves over the retina but the subject does not consider that the external world is moving. On the other hand, if the retinal image moves in the absence of a voluntary command to the eye muscles, the subject receives the impression that it is the outside world that is moving. When

the eyeballs move in reflex response to cupula deflexion after sudden deceleration on the Bárány chair, the consequent movement of the retinal image, because it is unaccompanied by voluntary commands to move the eyeball, is interpreted as movement in the external world. The subject 'sees' his surroundings turning round him and at the same time experiences a sensation of turning.

In addition to the reflex effects upon the eye muscles, the neural signal from the semicircular canals also produces reflex effects upon the musculature of the neck, trunk and limbs. The effects are such as to counteract the forces producing angular acceleration of the skull. Thus the skull tends to be maintained by reflex muscular action in its state of rest or of uniform motion in spite of externally applied forces. In the postrotatory phase after sudden deceleration on the Bárány chair, these reflex muscular actions are inappropriate and may have the effect of throwing the subject to the ground. This is because the neural signal from the canals, in these special conditions, indicates an angular acceleration when the skull is, in fact, at rest.

The otolith organs, utricle and saccule, give an indication related to the magnitude and direction of the resultant contact force acting on the skull. If the skull is at rest, this supporting contact force balances the action of gravity and the direction indicated may be taken as that of the inclination of the 'vertical' with respect to the skull. This information is combined with signals from the intervertebral joints in the neck to provide an indication of the vertical with respect to the trunk. Supporting forces in the limbs and in the trunk musculature can then be adjusted so that the body is held upright even if the ground under the feet is tilted. The separate roles of the reflexes from labyrinth and from the neck may be analysed by studying the limb dispositions in selected postures (Fig. 23.34), for example labyrinth reflexes are seen alone when the head is tilted with the neck straight, and neck reflex effects may be seen alone when the head is in the normal position with the neck bent. In the positional reflexes from the labyrinth, the downhill limbs extend. In the neck reflexes the effect of the limbs is such as to push the body round to straighten the neck.

Nystagmus. At rest the whole vestibular system is in a state of tonic activity manifested by a steady discharge of action potentials. The vestibular tone of the two sides has equal and opposite actions on the eyes and skeletal muscles.

In the normal state the right vestibule tends to deviate the eyes to the left and the left vestibule deviates the eyes to the right. With normal tone the two effects cancel and the eyes remain in the straight ahead position (Fig. 23.30). If the right vestibule is destroyed the normal tone exerted by the left side pushes the eyes to the right; this is corrected to the central position with a quick movement and so there is a nystagmus to the left. If the right side is hyperactive then the eyes are pushed

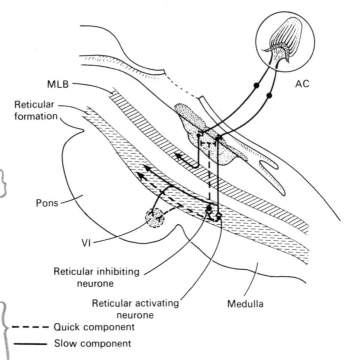

Fig. 23.31 The mechanism of nystagmus. VI, abducent nerve; MLB, medial longitudinal bundle, AC, ampullary crest. (A. G. D. Maran (1966) *Scottish Medical Journal,* 11, 379.)

to the left side, and corrected to the central position so that a nystagmus to the right occurs. The pathway followed by the nerve impulses involved in vestibular nystagmus is from the vestibular nerve to the vestibular nuclei in the brain stem; the slow component is produced by fibres passing in the medial longitudinal bundle (Fig. 23.31) and in the reticular formation which go to the nuclei of the eye muscles. Slow component fibres send impulses to high threshold reticular neurones; when their threshold is reached they fire off to produce the quick component and at the same time they fire inhibitory neurones in the reticular formation which cut off a slow component discharge. The high threshold neurones then rest until their threshold is reached again and the cycle is repeated. If the inhibitor neurone is destroyed impulses in the median longitudinal bundle, which by-pass the reticular formation, are unopposed and both eyes are deviated towards the same side (conjugate deviation).

The vestibular centres are not the sole sources of nystagmus. If a region, medial to the lateral geniculate body is stimulated, horizontal nystagmus with a quick component to the opposite side occurs. Direct stimulation of the vestibular nuclei results in a horizontal nystagmus to the same side. If both the vestibular and diencephalic nystagmogenic areas are stimulated at the same time the effects cancel each other; if the stimulations are crossed, the effects are additive. The diencephalic area moderates the nystagmogenic action of the ipsilateral vestibular nucleus and increases the action of the contralateral vestibular nucleus.

Motion sickness. Excessive stimulation of the semicircular canals, especially if the rotational movement is about a horizontal axis, may produce the drowsiness, pallor, vertigo, salivation, nausea and vomiting characteristic of sea-sickness.

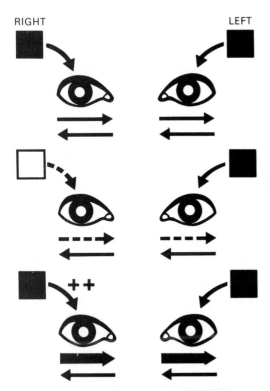

Fig. 23.30 Illustrating the concept of vestibular tone. The horizontal arrows indicate the directions of the vestibular eye-deviations (slow phase of nystagmus). The upper arrow in each pair shows the influence from the right labyrinth; the lower, that from the left. Upper diagram shows normal state. Middle diagram shows how hypofunction of the right labyrinth causes nystagmus to the left. The lower diagram shows how hyperfunction of the right labyrinth causes nystagmus to the right. (A. G. D. Maran (1966) *Scottish Medical Journal,* 11, 382.)

The unpleasant sensations arise from a conflict of sensory information; the deck of the ship is accepted as horizontal and stationary because the eyes are fixed on it but the labyrinths in stormy weather signal rotational and unsteady movements. More than half of those subjected to these stimuli suffer from motion sickness. Some people suffer similarly if they travel on trains, buses or aircraft or if they go on a swing. There may be a large psychological element in the production of their discomfort but this is not necessarily the whole explanation; the removal of the posterior lobe of the cerebellum in dogs gives them complete protection from motion sickness. Healthy subjects on swings become sick most often if the vertical canals are subjected to acceleration, but people who suffer from swing-sickness are not necessarily subject to sea-sickness. An intact vestibular system is necessary to produce motion sickness; deaf mutes and labyrinthectomized animals never experience it.

In certain circumstances, however, people have been sick without motion. For example, instructors on helicopter simulators are occasionally sick since they see the impression of motion but they know they are not moving; this leads to a conflict of information reaching the central nervous system. The central nervous system is used to a certain amount of 'normal acceleration and velocity'; for example, head movements, lying down quickly or standing up suddenly, motor car or bus motion, are particular movements which the central nervous system accepts as a normal part of life. In other words, habituation has occurred and the vestibular efferents prevent too much information leaving the vestibular system.

The headache, pallor, perspiration, nausea and vomiting of motion sickness are due to vagal stimulation. The dorsal vagal nucleus is very near the medial vestibular nucleus and the two are interconnected. When the inhibitory influence is lifted from the vestibular system the increased neural activity overflows to some of the cells in the dorsal vagal nucleus and causes motion sickness.

With practice and training it is possible to habituate to vestibular stimuli produced by aerobatics and space flight so that motion sickness is overcome. Head movement during motion amplifies the input to the vestibular nucleus. The reason the American astronauts suffered less from sickness than their Russian counterparts was that the American craft were much smaller and less movement was possible.

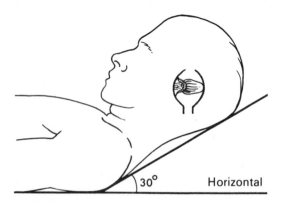

Fig. 23.32 When a caloric test is performed the patient lies supine with the head raised to bring the lateral canal into an approximately vertical position so that convection in the endolymph deflects the cupula in the ampulla of this canal.

Induced nystagmus. The canals may be stimulated in man by pouring either warm (44°C) or cold (30°C) water through a tube into the external meatus of the ear (caloric tests) while the subject lies on his back with his head tilted forward. In this attitude the lateral canal is in the vertical plane (Fig. 23.32). The convection currents produced in the canal cause nystagmus, a twisting of the trunk and a feeling of giddiness. Syringing the ear with water at 44°C causes a flow of endolymph towards the ampulla of the lateral canal and a deflexion of the cupula with nystagmus to the same side. These observations show that it is unwise to syringe out the external auditory meatus with water unless it is at 37°C otherwise the patient may become dizzy and may vomit. The eye movements can be recorded from electrodes placed on the skin at the outer canthi of the eyes; this is called electronystagmography and a typical record is shown in Figure 23.33.

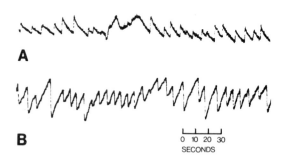

Fig. 23.33 Nystagmus as recorded by electronystagmography. When the eyes move to the right the pen moves upwards and when the eyes move to the left the pen moves downwards. Nystagmus to the right (named after the quick component) is represented as ∿⋀⋀ and nystagmus to the left is represented as ⋀⋁⋁. Figure A shows nystagmus to the right in response to a caloric stimulus with water at 30°C run into the left ear for 30 sec. Figure B represents a similar response with water at 30°C run into the right ear. If the patient fixes his eyes on a point during such a test nystagmus tends to be inhibited; with electronystagmography it is possible to record nystagmus with the eyes closed thus abolishing such inhibition. (*By courtesy of A. G. D. Maran.*)

Hallpike has shown that tests based on recording the duration of nystagmus after a standard caloric stimulus are valuable for the diagnosis of lesions of the vestibular apparatus and its nervous connexions.

The Coriolis effect. The Coriolis effect occurs when one set of semicircular canals has equilibrated to a constant angular velocity (for example, a constantly rotating platform) and a head motion is made in a different plane (standing on a rotating platform and nodding). When a second set of canals is rotated into the plane of constant angular velocity an angular acceleration is imposed on them, and as the first set are rotated out of the plane of constant velocity an angular deceleration is applied to them.

The motion felt by the subject during the manoeuvre is a rotation about an axis at right angles to both of the axes of actual rotation. For example, if a subject is rotating about his vertical axis in a clockwise direction and the head is nodded forwards so that the chin touches the chest, he will feel that he is rolling clockwise to his right about an anteroposterior horizontal axis.

The magnitude of the Coriolis effect is proportional to $\omega_1\omega_2 t$, where ω_1 and ω_2 are the angular velocities about two different axes and t is the time over which the two rotations occur together. The Coriolis effect can take place even if the value of ω_1 is very small. If ω_1 is as high as 40 rev/min the slight head motions accompanying breathing can result in a Coriolis effect. Because Coriolis effects on the canals are not accompanied by corresponding movements of the visual field they can give rise to pronounced disorientation and severe motion sickness. People who man space stations would be constantly subjected to this very intense stimulation.

Habituation. Habituation is the process whereby normal individuals adapt to complex new stimuli or situations. With repeated exposure to vestibular stimulation many people develop relative insensitivity. For example, the figure-skater ending her performance with a spin of about 7 rev/s comes to a full stop in about 0·1 sec, a deceleration of some 2000 degrees/s²—enough to pole-axe the untrained individual. Ballet dancers, pilots and seamen show a similar decreased response to stimuli that would be very uncomfortable to persons not habituated to the motion. Despite the apparent hypofunction of the vestibular system these people have quite normal inner ears and can pass vestibular tests requiring very sensitive monitoring by the end organs and central nervous system.

To develop habituation and a depression of sickness and giddiness astronauts have to spend long periods of training on centrifuges and other disorienting devices.

Labyrinthine Reflexes

Roberts eliminated the neck reflexes of a cat by denervating the first three intervertebral joints in the neck and by holding the axis vertebra in a clamp. When the head was tilted towards the nose-down position the forelimbs extended and the hind limbs flexed; that is, the responses in the four limbs were in opposite directions. If the head were tilted towards the right-side-down position the right foreleg extended. Lateral rotations of the head were without effect because rotation of the head about a vertical axis did not affect the otolith organs.

Movements of the head produce alteration in posture through the neck reflexes (p. 375) which may be in the opposite direction to those produced by the labyrinthine reflexes. Thus if the head is tilted nose-up the neck reflexes produce extension of the forelimbs and the labyrinthine reflexes a flexion of the forelimbs. In the intact animal the effects cancel one another and tilting the head nose-up extends all four limbs equally. The normal posture of an animal depends on the interaction of the labyrinthine and neck reflexes (Fig. 23.34). The conflict between the labyrinthine and neck reflexes when both are active seems to be resolved centrally so that the animal is able to move its head without reflex restraint.

Righting reflexes. The decerebrate animal cannot right itself if it is pushed over. However, the animal with the thalamus and brain stem intact but with the cerebral cortex and cerebellum removed, the *thalamic animal*, possesses more adequate postural reflexes. The thalamic cat or dog shows normal posture and can carry out walking movements. The muscle tone is normal when sitting or walking but if the animal is supported with the feet off the ground hyperextension of all four limbs occurs.

The thalamic animal shows positive supporting reactions which convert the limbs into pillars by simultaneous contraction of the flexors and extensors so that the body weight is taken on four columns. The actual contact of the feet with the ground produces an extensor response and at the same time the flexor muscles in the distal joints of the feet are stretched. This causes reflexly a contraction of all the muscles, extensors, flexors, abductors and adductors, which allows the limbs to carry the weight of the body. At the same time the vertebral column is made rigid by a contraction of the long muscles which run dorsally and ventrally along it. This supporting reaction is a static reflex and necessarily disappears when movements are carried out; the limbs loosen (negative supporting reaction) when the extensor muscles of the distal joints are stretched. These supporting reactions, although shown quite well by the thalamic animal, are best seen in the intact animal.

In contradistinction to the animal with decerebrate rigidity, the thalamic animal possesses righting reflexes which ensure that the animal brings itself back to the upright position if it is made to deviate from it. The righting reflexes arise in the labyrinths and in the muscles of the neck and trunk. To study the righting mechanism it is necessary to employ one or more of the following procedures—labyrinthectomy, denervation of the neck, blindfolding. When the results of such experiments are put together it is possible to explain how an animal rights itself when put in an abnormal position.

If a cat is held upside down above the ground and released, it turns over in mid air and lands on all four feet. In this manoeuvre probably the eye righting reflexes are the most important; they depend on the integrity of the visual area of the cortex in the occipital lobe. The animal, when it sees its surroundings, quickly brings its head to the normal position relative to the ground. The labyrinthine reflexes are also of some importance in correcting the position of the head since the otolith organs inform the animal of the position of its head in space before it is released, but a cat with congenital absence of the labyrinths (provided it was not blindfolded) could turn over without delay quite nimbly in mid air. A normal cat blindfolded and then released turns over after a delay of about 100 ms but makes a poor landing as it has no information about the position of the floor. McDonald investigated this old problem by high-speed (1500 frames per s) cinephotography and showed that the rotation after release occurs in two principal stages: (1) the righting of the head and forepart of the body together; and (2) the rotation of the lumbar region, pelvic girdle and hind-limbs all in one, the whole turn taking less than 150 ms.

A further source of righting is displayed by a blindfolded labyrinthectomized animal laid on its side on a table. When the animal is released the head immediately rotates into the normal position relative to the ground and the position of the remainder of the body is corrected as before. If the animal is laid on its side again under a weighted board, so that the pressure on the body is the same on both sides, this righting reflex does not occur.

When the chin of an intact blindfolded cat is laid on a table, or when the fore-legs are brought into contact with the edge of

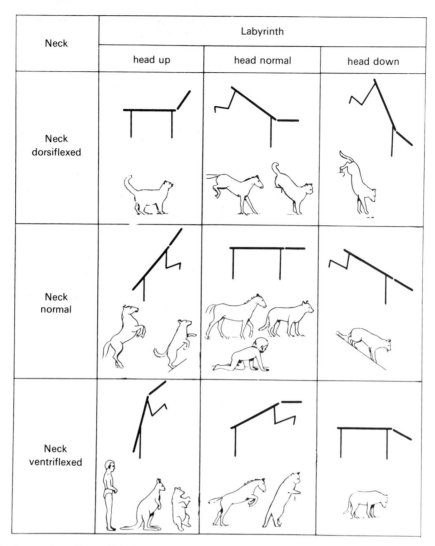

Neck	Labyrinth		
	head up	head normal	head down
Neck dorsiflexed			
Neck normal			
Neck ventriflexed			

Fig. 23.34   Scheme of the interacting effects of labyrinthine and neck reflexes on the limbs of various animals. The middle column shows the neck reflexes acting alone. The middle row shows the labyrinthine positional reflexes acting alone. In the top left and bottom right corners, the neck and labyrinthine reflexes are in opposition; in the top right and bottom left corners they reinforce one another. (T. D. M. Roberts (1968) Labyrinthine control of the postural muscles. *Third Symposium on the Role of the Vestibular Organs in Space Exploration.* P. 163. N.A.S.A.)

the table, the feet are immediately placed on the table in a position ready to support the weight of the body. These are called *placing reactions*. When an intact animal is disturbed by being pushed sideways the normal position is regained by a series of hops (*hopping reaction*). The hopping and placing reactions depend on the integrity of the motor cortex.

The maintenance of the standing posture in man is necessarily a very complex affair. His centre of gravity is somewhere in the pelvis high above the very small base provided by the feet. It therefore takes the infant a long time to acquire the ability to stand upright. Little swaying movements occur continuously due to wandering away of the centre of gravity and its restoration to a stable position. The sensory information which governs these corrections comes from the eyes, the vestibular apparatus, the muscles and the joints. If muscle-joint sense is diminished as in tabes dorsalis the patient becomes very unsteady if the eyes are closed. Electromyography shows that when the erect posture is being maintained easily and comfortably the antigravity muscles show surprisingly little activity. This economical maintenance must depend on early signalling of small deviations and their prompt reflex correction.

REFERENCES

Boyd I A, Eyzaguirre C, Matthews P B C, Rushworth G 1964 The role of the gamma system in movement and posture. Association for the Aid of Crippled Children, New York

Brodal A 1957 The reticular formation of the brain stem: anatomical aspects and functional correlations. Oliver & Boyd, Edinburgh

Brodal A, Pompeiano O, Walberg F 1962 The vestibular nuclei and their connections, anatomy and functional correlations. Oliver & Boyd, Edinburgh

REFERENCES

de Reuck A V S, Knight J 1968 Myotatic, kinesthetic and vestibular mechanisms. Ciba Foundation Volume 1967. Churchill, London

Eccles J C 1969 Inhibitory pathways of the central nervous system. University Press, Liverpool

Guttman L 1973 Spinal cord injuries. Blackwell, Oxford

Hallpike C S 1967 Some types of ocular nystagmus and their neurological mechanisms. Proceedings of the Royal Society of Medicine 60: 1043–1054

Henneman E 1967 Relation between size of neurones and their susceptibility to discharge. Science 126: 1345–1347

Hunt C C, Perl E R 1960 Spinal reflex mechanisms concerned with skeletal muscle. Physiological Reviews 40: 538–579

Iurato S 1969 Submicroscopic structures of the inner ear. Pergamon, Oxford

Joseph J 1960 Man's posture: electromyographic studies. Thomas, Springfield

Kornhuber H H 1974 Vestibular system. Handbook of sensory physiology, vol VI, pt 1, Basic mechanisms; pt 2 Psychophysics, applied aspects and general interpretations. Springer-Verlag, Berlin

Liddell E G T 1960 The discovery of reflexes. Oxford University Press

Magoun H W 1958 The waking brain. Thomas, Springfield

Marsden C D, Merton P A, Morton H B 1973 Is the human stretch reflex cortical rather than spinal? Lancet i: 759–761

Martin J P 1967 The basal ganglia and posture. Pitman Medical, London

NASA 1968 Third symposium on the role of the vestibular organs in space exploration. National Aeronautics and Space Administration, Washington DC

Reason J T, Brand J J 1975 Motion sickness. Academic Press, New York

Roberts T D M 1978 Neurophysiology of postural mechanisms, 2nd edn. Butterworth, London

Sherrington C S 1947 The integrative action of the nervous system. Cambridge University Press

Stable J (ed) 1971 Vestibular function on earth and in space. Pergamon, Oxford

Wall P D 1970 Sensory and motor role of impulses travelling in the dorsal columns towards cerebral cortex. Brain 93: 505–524

Walsh E G 1964 Physiology of the nervous system. 2nd edn. Longmans, London

24 Sensorimotor Cortex, the Cerebellum and the Control of Movement

The important role of the cerebral cortex in voluntary movement is discussed in this chapter. The cerebellum and basal nuclei are also of importance in the control and co-ordination of movement. All these structures require accurate information to enable them to bring about normal movements. In other words a very complex train of events in the central nervous system determines the output from the motor neurones, the anterior horn cells, which bring about the actual movements of the skeletal muscles.

The superficial layer or cortex of the hemispheres consists of grey matter containing numerous nerve cells, while the deeper part or white matter is made up of fibres connecting the various parts of the hemispheres with one another and with lower parts of the central nervous system such as the brain stem and spinal cord.

The surface of the cerebral cortex is marked by furrows called sulci, the areas between sulci being called gyri or convolutions. The two major sulci are the lateral sulcus and the central sulcus (Fig. 24.1). The area in front of the central sulcus is the frontal lobe; the area immediately behind the central sulcus is the parietal lobe. The posterior part of the cerebral hemisphere is the occipital lobe. The area below the posterior ramus of the lateral sulcus is the temporal lobe. Smaller sulci divide up each lobe into numerous gyri, which are named in Figures 24.1 and 24.2. The term limbic lobe is applied to the region of the cerebral cortex which lies on the medial side of the hemisphere adjacent to the corpus callosum and the attachment of the brain stem; this includes the cingulate lobe, isthmus, hippocampal gyrus, hippocampus and uncus. The hippocampus is important in laying down or retrieving long term memories.

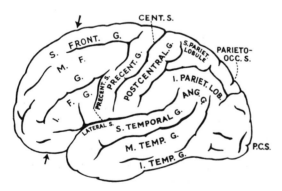

Fig. 24.1 The lateral aspect of the left cerebral hemispheres. S. FRONT. G. = superior frontal gyrus. M. F. G. = middle frontal gyrus. I. F. G. = inferior frontal gyrus. PRECENT. S. = precentral sulcus. PRECENT. G. = precentral gyrus. POSTCENTRAL G. = postcentral gyrus. S. TEMPORAL G. = superior temporal gyrus. M. TEMP. G. = middle temporal gyrus. I. TEMP. G. = inferior temporal gyrus. S. PARIET. LOBULE = superior parietal lobule. I. PARIET. LOB. = inferior parietal lobule. CENT. S. = central sulcus. PARIETO-OCC. S. = parieto-occipital sulcus. P.C.S. = postcalcarine sulcus. LATERAL S. = lateral sulcus (posterior ramus). ANG. G. = angular gyrus. A line joining the arrows gives the approximate plane of section in the operation of prefrontal leucotomy.

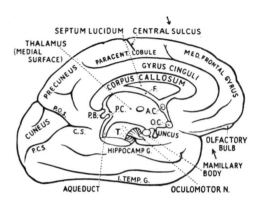

Fig. 24.2 The medial aspect of the left cerebral hemisphere. A. C. = anterior commissure. O. C. = optic chiasma. P.-O. S. = parieto-occipital sulcus. C. S. = calcarine sulcus. MED. FRONTAL GYRUS = medial frontal gyrus. P. C. S. = postcalcarine sulcus. F. = fornix. PARACENT. LOBULE = paracentral lobule. HIPPOCAMP. G. = hippocampal gyrus. P. B. = pineal body. P. C. = posterior commissure. T. = tegmentum. I. TEMP. G. = inferior temporal gyrus. AQUEDUCT = cerebral aqueduct. A line joining the arrows gives the approximate plane of section in the operation of prefrontal leucotomy.

The brain and its coverings, the dura and pia mater, may be cauterized or stimulated without the patient feeling pain but dilatation of the large arteries or veins or traction on them gives rise to pain. For this reason removal of cerebrospinal fluid is sometimes followed by headache.

Most of the cerebral cortex (the *neocortex*) consists of six layers of cells but a small area in the medial part of each hemisphere including the hippocampus, the allocortex, has a less complex structure with only three layers of cells. Many years ago Brodmann numbered various areas of the cortex on the basis of their histological appearances (Fig. 24.4). The numbering has no physiological significance but it is useful.

The white matter of the cerebral hemispheres consists of myelinated fibres which may run (1) as *association fibres* from one part to another part of the same hemisphere, or (2) as *commissural fibres* from one hemisphere to the other in the corpus callosum, or (3) as afferent or efferent *projection fibres* which carry impulses from or to the lower parts of the brain and the spinal cord. The main efferent fibres pass from all parts of the cortex to run in the *internal capsule* which lies medial to the lentiform nucleus (Fig. 24.3).

Nerve impulses have been shown by electrical methods to pass in the corpus callosum from one hemisphere to the corresponding area of the other. If a conditioned reflex is established in an animal in response to a stimulus applied to one side of the body it can generally be evoked by a contralateral stimulus. After section of the corpus callosum this is no longer possible but conditioned reflexes can still be established independently for each side. Monkeys can learn to perform tasks with one hand and this learning is immediately transferred to the other hand. If the corpus callosum has been cut it is necessary for the animal to learn the task with each hand separately. If the corpus callosum is sectioned after the task has been learned the untrained hand shows a slight drop in performance indicating that the trained hemisphere in the intact animal normally makes some contribution to the performance of the untrained side.

Similar phenomena have been observed in patients who have had the corpus callosum surgically divided for the relief of severe epilepsy. After section of the corpus callosum learned and volitional activities persist independently in each hemisphere and learning takes place in each hemisphere separately and without the awareness of the other. The patient can describe what occurs in the right field of vision and stimulates the left, major or speaking, hemisphere. He is unable, however, to talk about the things which stimulate his right or minor hemisphere. While it is possible to communicate without difficulty with the dominant hemisphere the minor hemisphere has very little language capacity either for speech or writing. It is possible, however, to present the non-dominant hemisphere with test material and while it has little verbal capacity it appears to be able to match objects presented to it visually or by touch.

The process of myelination of the fibres of the central nervous system begins at the sixth month of intrauterine life in the spinal cord and is seen at the eighth month in the sensory pathways going to the post-central gyrus. Soon after this the afferent fibres of the visuosensory and auditosensory areas receive their myelin sheaths but the corticospinal (pyramidal) fibres are not completely myelinated until the child is three months old; the process continues in the so-called association areas until the eighteenth year. Since it has been shown that a nerve fibre can conduct impulses only relatively slowly until it is myelinated, we have a physical basis for the continuous process of mental development up to adolescence. Because they are not yet myelinated it is unlikely that in the new-born child the cerebrospinal motor fibres are functioning normally and it may be that motor activities are carried out chiefly through the brain stem and spinal cord.

Motor Areas of the Cerebral Cortex

In 1870 Fritsch and Hitzig found that electrical stimulation of the frontal cortex of the dog caused movements of the limbs on the opposite side of the body. Ferrier confirmed this a few years later in the monkey and showed further that removal of the area which on stimulation gave rise to movements of the hand resulted in paralysis of the hand. The area with the lowest threshold for electrical stimulation is area 4 of Brodmann (Fig. 24.4) and this area is called, therefore, the *motor area* although there are, in fact, several other cortical areas concerned with motor function. This most easily excited region of the cortex contains the giant Betz cells which are its most important constituents.

The path of the axons of the Betz cells is shown by the degeneration which follows removal of area 4. The fibres pass down in the genu and in the anterior two-thirds of the posterior limb of the internal capsule in such a way that the fibres to the head are in front and those to the legs are posterior (Fig. 24.3). These fibres then pass through the centre of the basis pedunculi and through the pons to the pyramids, where about 80 per cent of the fibres cross to the opposite side in the decussation of the pyramids and pass down in the lateral

column of the spinal cord as the lateral cerebrospinal tract (p. 363). There are about a million fibres in each pyramid but only about 34 000 Betz cells in each hemisphere, sufficient to account for only three per cent of all the pyramidal fibres; 30 per cent or so of the fibres arise from small or medium-sized pyramidal cells in the precentral gyrus. The origin of the remainder is unknown. To produce total degeneration of all the fibres in the pyramidal tracts it is necessary to destroy the whole hemisphere.

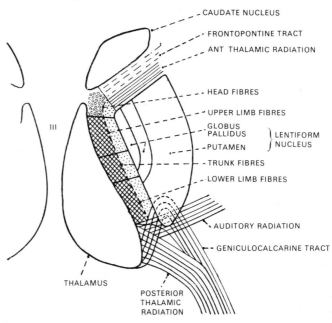

Fig. 24.3 The internal capsule. The sensory fibres of any part of the body emerging from the thalamus (cross-hatched) are medial to the motor fibres (dotted) of the same part. There is, however, a considerable admixture of motor and sensory fibres. The bend in the internal capsule (containing the head fibres) is called the genu. (*After* S. W. Ranson & S. L. Clark (1951) *The Anatomy of the Nervous System.* 9th edition. p. 295. London: Saunders.)

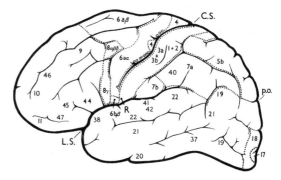

Fig. 24.4 Architectonic fields of the lateral aspects of the human cortex numbered according to Brodmann. C.S. = central sulcus; L.S. = lateral sulcus; p.o. = parieto-occipital fissure; R = respiration; 4 = true pyramidal cortex. Stimulation of areas 5, 6, 7, and 8, produces adversive movements if the stimulation is strong enough. Stimulation of 8, 18 and 19 produces adversive eye movements. Stimulation of 22 produces eye and ear adversive movements. Stimulation of 6b produces mastication. Some of these fields extend on to the medial aspect. The gyrus cinguli (not shown here) is numbered 24 rostrally and 23 caudad. The names of the main gyri are given in Figures 24.1 and 24.2. (*After* W. Penfield & E. Boldrey (1937) *Brain,* 60, 393.)

The majority of the fibres in the pyramidal tract, about one-third of which are non-myelinated, are quite small in diameter; only 1·7 per cent are in the range 10 to 22 μm and these may arise from the Betz cells. The vast majority of the fibres conduct impulses relatively slowly. After removal of the motor area examination of the spinal cord shows degenerated synaptic knobs on the interneurones (p. 364) and not on the anterior horn cells. The corticospinal fibres, therefore, end at a position where the impulses carried by them may interact with impulses arriving by other descending tracts or through the posterior roots; the result of this interaction probably determines the nature of the signal transmitted by the interneurones to the motor cells of the anterior horns. Efferent fibres also pass to the reticular formation and to many of the nuclei in the brain, including the basal nuclei.

The part of the motor area nearest the vertex of the skull is concerned with movements of the leg, the middle part with those of the arm, while the lowest part of area 4, near the lateral sulcus, is concerned with movements of the face. The area of the cortical representation of any part is in proportion to the complexity of movements and not to the size of the part. Thus cortical representation of trunk movements is quite small, but that of the thumb, fingers, lips and tongue which are involved in skilled movements is large. In Figure 24.5, an attempt is made to illustrate this diagrammatically. Area 4 should not be regarded as a fixed mosaic of excitable cells with definite and circumscribed connexions with the periphery but as something with wide connexions, a certain lability and a reserve of function as the following findings prove. Removal of or damage to a *small* part of the motor cortex does not result

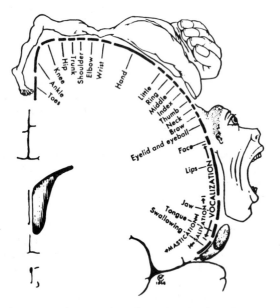

Fig. 24.5 Motor homunculus. The right side of the figurine is laid upon a cross-section of the hemisphere. This diagram gives the results of many experiments carried out at operation under local anaesthesia of the scalp. The exposed cerebral cortex was stimulated directly, usually by laying bipolar electrodes on it, the points of the electrodes being 3 mm apart. The stimulator provided 60 pulses of current per second. Stimulation of the cortex over the areas marked in thick lines produced movements of the muscles in the parts labelled. (W. Penfield & T. Rasmussen (1950) *The Cerebral Cortex of Man*. P. 57. New York: Macmillan.)

in permanent paralysis; the adjacent unharmed cortex eventually takes over the function of the portion removed. The connexions of any one area of the motor cortex are much wider than would be expected from the fixed mosaic idea. Thus after excision of a small part corresponding to the hand degenerated fibres can be traced to all parts of the spinal cord as far down as the lumbar region. Repeated stimulation of a single point on the cortex does not invariably lead to the same muscular movement. Finally, as described below, the actual map obtained varies with the method of stimulation.

Most investigators believe that area 4 deals with movements, not with individual muscles. The effect of cortical stimulation on limb muscles depends on the position of the limb and also on the position of the head. This is not surprising since voluntary movements are always being modified by afferent sensory information. In the words of Penfield and Rasmussen, 'The movements produced by cortical stimulation are never skilled acquired movements but instead consist of either flexion or extension of one or more joints, movements which are not more complicated than those the new-born infant is able to perform.' Area 6, the premotor area, immediately anterior to area 4, contains no Betz cells and is not so easily stimulated. Electrical stimulation of area 6 produces movements of small groups of muscles or more widespread movements involving perhaps a whole limb or a large part of the opposite side of the body. If currents above threshold strength are applied to area 4, groups of muscles having the same action (synergic muscles) are activated but, if the current is made still stronger, movements begin in the same part of the body as before and spread to other parts of the body as adjacent motor cells are excited. The order of spread depends upon the anatomical arrangement of the excitable areas of the cortex; a movement starting in the thumb may spread to the fingers, forearm and shoulder, involving larger and larger groups of muscles, so that eventually the entire musculature on the opposite side of the body may be called into action. This is the sequence of events in a typical Jacksonian fit which may arise from irritation of the cortex as the result of damage to the skull or meninges. After such an epileptic fit, as after strong electrical stimulation, the excitability of the cortex declines for a time, and the subject is inclined to fall asleep.

In 1873 Hughlings Jackson described the initial signs of an epileptic fit due to a discharging focus in the cortex in the following words. 'There are three parts where fits ... mostly begin, (1) in the hand, (2) in the face or tongue or both, (3) in the foot. ... When the fit begins in the hand the index finger and thumb are usually the digits first seized: when in the face the side of the cheek is first in spasm: when in the foot almost invariably the great toe.' It is difficult to believe that the cortical area for the thumb, angle of the mouth and great toe (as shown on a classical map such as Figure 24.5) have a specially high incidence of discharging foci. In fact such foci may occur at any part of the motor cortex.

An explanation of this apparent anomaly is afforded by the experiments of Liddell and Phillips illustrated in Figure 24.6. They used single pulses of current to stimulate the exposed motor cortex of the baboon. The area representing the movements of the opposite thumb and index varied according to the strength of the pulses (Fig. 24.6a); the threshold was always lowest for the thumb complex. The areas for the thumb, hallux and mouth overlapped as shown in Figure 24.6c and

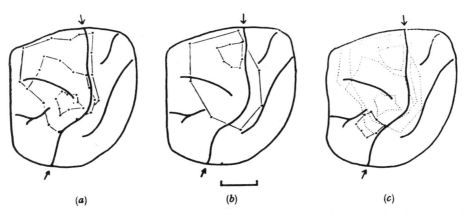

Fig. 24.6 Female baboon. Left sensorimotor area of the cerebral cortex, stimulated with single pulses 4·5 msec in duration. Scale 10 mm. Arrows mark the central sulcus. (Traced from photograph.) (a) Extent of thumb-index-minimus area at strengths 1·2 mA, 1·6 mA and 2·7 mA. (b) Extent of hallux-middle toe area at strengths 2·05 mA and 4·7 mA. (c) Area for angle of mouth (solid line) at strength 2·35 mA. Thumb and toe areas indicated by dotted lines. (E. G. T. Liddell & C. G. Phillips (1950) *Brain*, 73, 130; also (1952). *Brain*, 75, 510–525.)

when the strength of the pulse was sufficient movements of all three parts were obtained. If instead of single pulses a series of pulses at the rate of 50 per second was used, the simple large scale map (Fig. 24.6) of distal parts changed into the traditional map of finer grain in which movements of all parts of the body are represented (Fig. 24.5 was obtained in this way). The presence of these fields of low threshold explains adequately the common sites of onset of 'Jacksonian epilepsy'.

Effects of removal of the motor cortex. Removal of the whole cerebral cortex in dogs and cats has little effect on walking or running but the hopping and placing reactions (p. 382) are lost. In the monkey, ablation of area 4 produces a *hemiplegia*, that is a paralysis or loss of voluntary movements on the opposite side of the body; immediately after this operation the muscles are hypotonic and the condition is described as a *flaccid paralysis*. Voluntary movement begins to return in a few days; first at the proximal joints and somewhat later in the fingers and toes. Although a remarkable degree of recovery occurs eventually, it is usually possible to detect a slight residual clumsiness in the fingers, for example in picking up small objects. In man recovery after destruction of the motor cortex is much slower and dexterity of movements, especially the rapid and highly complex movements made with the fingers, is rarely regained. A mild degree of spasticity may eventually appear. The amount of the final disability is greater the greater the amount of motor cortex removed.

If numerous intersecting cuts are made into the grey matter of the sensorimotor cortex of the monkey very little upset of motor function ensues. Horizontal, that is tangential, intra-cortical transmission cannot, therefore, be of any great importance. If the superficial layer of the motor cortex is cooled fine movements become jerky and inaccurate.

When both pyramidal tracts are divided at the level of the medulla (Fig. 23.18) in the monkey, the muscles become hypotonic so that the head sags and the abdomen protrudes. After some time, sitting and, later, walking become possible but the animal is unwilling to move and the ability to carry out accurate and delicate movements is lost. This experiment shows that some voluntary movement can be carried out by extra-pyramidal fibres since the loss of movement on section of the pyramidal tracts is very much less than that seen when area 4 and area 6 of the cortex are both removed.

Extrapyramidal fibres are clearly important for locomotion.

As already mentioned, removal of area 4 in the primate causes a flaccid paralysis. If a *spastic paralysis* follows, as is seen in man after haemorrhage into the internal capsule, it is probably due to damage to area 6 lying in front of area 4. In man and other primates a spastic paralysis is characterized by an increase of flexor tone in the arms and of extensor tone in the legs. The hemiplegic patient, therefore, carries his paralysed arm flexed across his chest and his paralysed leg extended at the knee; there is loss of voluntary movement of the limb, but the limb is rigid and an attempt to flex it meets with resistance like that seen in decerebrate rigidity; the tendon reflexes are exaggerated and clonus can readily be demonstrated. Apart from the paralysis all these abnormalities are due to over-activity of the spinal stretch reflexes (p. 367). In most patients with an increase in muscle tone (due either to hemiplegia or Parkinsonism) injection of dilute procaine solution into the area where the motor nerve enters a muscle causes a reduction of spasticity before it causes loss of motor power. Since procaine blocks γ motor fibres long before it blocks α fibres it seems that spasticity depends on overactivity of γ fibres. Since lesions restricted to the pyramidal tract in primates produce a hypotonic paralysis, the spastic paralysis seen after extensive cortical ablation or cerebral haemorrhage in man must be due to simultaneous interruption of pyramidal and extrapyramidal pathways.

Increase in tone and activity of reflexes has also been observed when the medial surface of the hemisphere just in front of the leg area has been damaged. Stimulation of this *supplementary motor area* in man has produced movements on the opposite side; removal does not cause paralysis but an increase in muscle tone.

Normally firm stroking of the sole of the foot from behind forwards produces plantar flexion of the great toe. However, when the corticospinal tract is interrupted by injury or disease stroking of the sole of the foot produces dorsiflexion of the great toe (extensor plantar response). In addition, if the stimulus is strong enough, there may be flexion of the ankle, knee and hip; this suggests that the plantar reflex is actually part of a general flexor withdrawal reflex. However, dorsi-flexion of the great toe occurs after destruction of the precentral motor cortex but in this case it may be accompanied by hypotonia and diminished tendon reflexes. If the sole of a healthy subject's foot is stimulated electrically the effect is local withdrawal from the stimulus. Thus if the heel is stimulated the effect is to raise it from the ground and this is assisted by plantar flexion of the toes. The same effect occurs with stimuli applied elsewhere on the sole but if the stimulus is applied to the great toe the reaction is one of generalized flexion with dorsiflexion of the toe. In the presence of a suprasegmental lesion this effect can be seen with stimulation anywhere on the sole and the pathological extensor plantar response (Babinski's sign) can be seen as a generalized flexor response to a nocuous stimulus, the field of excitation having become much larger so as to override the local withdrawal responses. An extensor plantar response is normally found in infancy. The change to a flexor response occurs between the ninth and twenty-fourth month, the time at which myelination of the pyramidal tract becomes complete.

Stimulation of the premotor area usually causes movements of a small group of muscles—the same group that is activated by stimulation of the adjacent area 4. The effect depends on fibres running from area 6 to area 4 since after a cut has been made between the two areas, or after area 4 is removed, the character of the response is altered and stimulation of area 6 yields only adversive movements consisting of rotation of the head and of the eyes to the opposite side with movements of the contralateral limbs. The impulses from area 6 must in these circumstances reach the spinal cord (probably by relaying in the reticular formation) by an extrapyramidal route. This is illustrated further by the finding that stimulation of area 6 produces movements of muscles even when the pyramids have been sectioned.

If in a chimpanzee a part of the premotor cortex (area 6) is removed there is a slight weakness of the muscles of the opposite side but, although this soon disappears, skilled movements are permanently disturbed. These findings also apply to man after removal of the premotor cortex. A destructive lesion of the upper part of area 6 produces on the opposite side of the body a phenomenon called *forced grasping*. If the palmar surface of the hand or fingers is touched reflex flexion of the hand occurs to grasp the stimulating object and any attempt to withdraw the object is followed by a firmer grasp. Since this reflex is normally present in infants its appearance in the adult is considered to be a regression to the infantile stage of the function of grasping. The grasp reflex is not seen after section of the pyramids alone, hence area 6 normally inhibits flexor activity through extrapyramidal pathways.

In addition to the main motor and premotor areas there are, as mentioned before, other areas of the cortex concerned in muscular movements. For example areas 44 and 45 together comprise the premotor area of the face (Broca's area); in right-handed persons lesions of this area on the left side produce motor aphasia, that is an inability to speak although the muscles of articulation are themselves not paralysed. This may be the basis for the well known association of right hemiplegia and aphasia; the left is usually the dominant hemisphere. Injection of barbiturate into one carotid artery produces a temporary loss of function of the parts of the brain supplied by the artery. If aphasia occurs it indicates that the hemisphere under the influence of barbiturate is the dominant one for speech. Stimulation of the frontal eye fields in the posterior

part of the second frontal convolution (area 8) in man produces conjugate deviation of the eyes to the opposite side without head movements and without visual hallucinations. Stimulation of the occipital eye fields (areas 18, 19) causes visual hallucinations and movements of the eyes to the opposite side. From area 17 visual hallucinations are obtained but not eye movements.

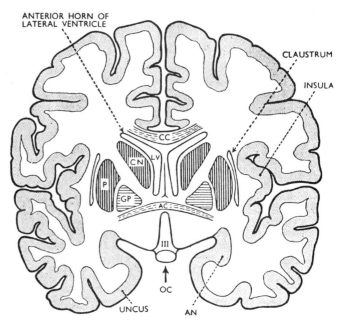

Fig. 24.7 Coronal section through the adult human brain just behind the optic chiasma. Vertical shading, neostriatum (lentiform and caudate nuclei). Horizontal shading, globus pallidus. LV = lateral ventricle. CN = caudate nucleus. P = putamen. GP = globus pallidus. CC = corpus callosum. OC = optic chiasma. AN = amygdaloid nucleus. F = anterior column of fornix. III = third ventricle. AC = anterior commissure. The caudate nucleus, the putamen and the globus pallidus together form the corpus striatum.

BASAL NUCLEI

The basal nuclei (basal ganglia) include the corpus striatum, the amygdaloid nucleus and the claustrum. (Figs. 24.3 and 24.7). The caudate nucleus and putamen contain small cells and together receive many afferent fibres from areas 4 and 6 of the cortex and also from the thalamus. The globus pallidus possesses large cells and from it efferent fibres make up a large part of the descending *extrapyramidal system*; they go to the thalamus, hypothalamus, subthalamic nucleus, red nucleus, substantia nigra and reticular substance of the mid-brain. Relay fibres pass from these nuclei down the spinal cord to influence the motor cells of the anterior horn of grey matter.

The role of the basal nuclei is poorly understood but they appear principally to have motor functions. When its caudate nucleus is stimulated a monkey becomes inactive and destruction of this nucleus makes the animal hyperactive. Destruction of the globus pallidus leads to loss of the postural reflexes.

Disorders of the basal nuclei in man. The most common clinical disorder associated with damage to the globus pallidus and substantia nigra is *paralysis agitans* (Parkinson's disease).

The damage seems to interfere with the central connexions, concerned especially with visual and proprioceptive information, needed for normal postural reactions; postural fixation, righting, locomotion and phonation are all disturbed. The patient has a tremor of which the principal component is present when the limb is at rest; in some subjects, however, the tremor is also present during voluntary movement. The affected muscles are rigid but, unlike the spasticity of upper motor neurone lesions, the rigidity generally affects flexor and extensor muscles equally. It probably depends on the gamma efferents since blockage of them by procaine results in its disappearance. The face has an expressionless or mask-like appearance. The muscles may offer an intermittent (cog wheel) resistance when moved passively. The tremor disappears if such a patient develops a hemiplegia or if the motor cortex is destroyed. The tremor is not simply the result of release of the basal nuclei from cortical control since it is also abolished by destruction of the globus pallidus or of the ventrolateral nucleus of the thalamus. The site of origin of the tremor is unknown but it is clearly the result of disturbance of a complex neuronal circuit which includes the basal ganglia, thalamus and motor cortex. Paralysis agitans may be relieved surgically by the production of small lesions within the globus pallidus or the thalamus.

The substantia nigra of a patient with Parkinson's disease is depigmented and the dopamine content of the corpus striatum and the substantia nigra, where it is normally present in high concentration, is markedly reduced. This finding led to the treatment of the disease by L-dopa given by mouth. Most of this is converted by a decarboxylase to dopamine both outside and inside the brain; only a small amount reaches the deficient neurones. However, many patients show clinical improvement particularly as regards the slowness of movement (bradykinesia); tremor and rigidity may also be relieved. Parkinson's disease is probably the result of degeneration of a dopaminergic nigrostriatal pathway with a consequent imbalance between excitatory acetylcholine and inhibitory dopamine in the striatum.

Disease of the corpus striatum in man, and injuries placed experimentally in this region in chimpanzees, may produce involuntary movements called *athetosis*. The lips, jaw and tongue may be affected but more frequently the hands show alternating movements of extension of the fingers with pronation at the wrist to full flexion with supination. Although these are associated with disease of the globus pallidus they may be due to compensatory extrapyramidal activity, since they are abolished by removal of the premotor area of the cortex (area 6). Damage to the caudate nucleus may result in quick, short, jerking movements, especially of the fingers, arm or face called *chorea*. Small lesions destroying the subthalamic body of Luys cause *hemiballismus*, rhythmic, powerful, involuntary movements of the limbs on the opposite side; destruction of the neighbouring globus pallidus abolishes the movements.

THE CEREBELLUM

The cerebellum, one-tenth of the mass of the brain, consists of a superficial layer of grey matter, the cortex, overlying a mass of white matter. It has a large number of fine parallel

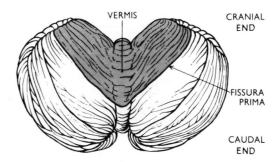

Fig. 24.8 The superior aspect of the cerebellum. The anterior lobe is stippled. The remainder belongs to the middle lobe. (*After Gray's Anatomy* (1954) 31st edition. P. 961. London: Longmans.)

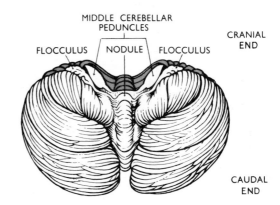

Fig. 24.9 Inferior aspect of the human cerebellum. The flocculus and nodule form the posterior lobe. The anterior lobe is stippled. The remainder belongs to the middle lobe. (*After Gray's Anatomy* (1954) 31st edition. p. 964. London: Longmans.)

furrows on its surface (Figs. 24.8 and 24.9) which give it a surface area about one-third that of the cerebral hemispheres.

The cerebellum is developed from the cephalic portion of the hind-brain and can be divided into anterior, middle and posterior lobes. The middle lobe, or neocerebellum, is very much larger than the anterior and posterior lobes. The three cerebellar peduncles, superior, middle and inferior, carry fibres connecting the cerebellum with other parts of the central nervous system.

The grey matter on the surface of the cerebellum has a characteristic histological appearance owing to the presence of the large Purkinje cells but there are no local differences, such as exist in the cerebrum, to distinguish one part of the cerebellar cortex from another. Each Purkinje cell has an arborescent arrangement of dendrites and a single axon which passes down to one of the deep nuclei of the cerebellum. The *climbing fibres* may be the terminations of fibres from the vestibular and pontine nuclei. The Purkinje dendrites are also associated with dendrites from *basket cells* and *granular cells*. The granular cells receive the terminations of *moss-fibres* which may be the main afferent fibres of the cerebellum. Practically all the afferent fibres of the cerebellum terminate in the cortex.

Independent centres of grey matter, four on each side, lying in the white matter of the cerebellum receive the axons of the cells of Purkinje and are the source of nearly all the efferent fibres of the cerebellum. The dentate nucleus is connected with

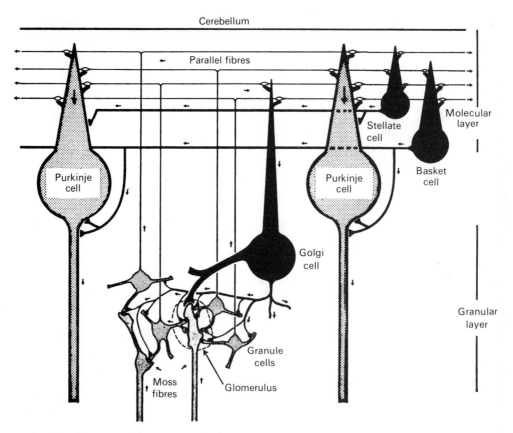

Fig. 24.10 Diagram showing the principal features that have been postulated for the moss-fibre input and the cerebellar glomerulus. The Golgi, stellate and basket cells, shown in black, are all inhibitory in action. The broken line represents the glial lamella that ensheathes a glomerulus. The diagram is drawn as for a section along the folium and the main distribution of the basket and stellate cells would be perpendicular to the plane of the diagram, but they are also distributed as shown to a band of several Purkinje cells along the folium. The arrows indicate the direction of impulse propagation. (J. C. Eccles (1969) *The Inhibitory Pathways of the Central Nervous System.* P. 89. Liverpool University Press.)

the neocerebellum and through the superior cerebellar peduncles with the thalamus and cerebral cortex (areas 4 and 6) of the opposite side. The dentate nucleus also sends fibres across the mid-line to the red nucleus from which new fibres cross the mid-line and descend as the rubrospinal tract.

A great deal has been learned about the function of the cerebellar cortex from experimental work with intracellular electrodes (Fig. 24.10). It is clear that the output from the Purkinje cells to the cerebellar nuclei is exclusively inhibitory. The afferent fibres to the cerebellar cortex, namely the climbing fibres which connect directly with the Purkinje cells, and the moss-fibres which connect through a relay arising from the granule cells, all may exert an excitatory effect on the Purkinje cells. The Golgi cells provide an inhibitory feedback loop on moss-fibre input; their dendrites are excited by the parallel fibres formed by branching of the axons of the granule cells, and their axons have an inhibitory action on the granule cells. The cerebellum thus contains an immensely complex and largely inhibitory system which receives its input from the higher centres and from the periphery. It delivers an inhibitory output to the cerebellar nuclei and the vestibular nuclei through which it exerts its action in the control and adjustment of movement.

Adrian inserted a fine wire about 1·5 mm deep into the cerebellum of a monkey under barbiturate anaesthesia and

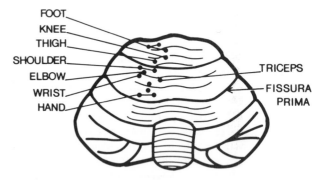

Fig. 24.11 Localization of discharges in the dorsal surface of the cerebellum from different parts of the fore- and hind-limb in a monkey. (E. D. Adrian (1943) *Brain, 66*, 298.)

recorded afferent impulses when the limbs on the same side were pressed or moved (Fig. 24.11). A movement of the whiskers on the face produced a discharge in the anterior part of the middle lobe. Dorsiflexion of the wrist or pressure on the hand produced discharges just anterior to the fissura prima, while pressure on the foot of the hand-limbs gave discharges well forward. Some afferent impulses to the cerebellum arose from the surface of the body but the majority came from the muscles, tendons and fasciae of hand and foot. These

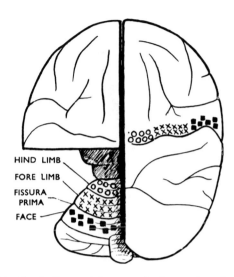

HIND LIMB
FORE LIMB
FISSURA PRIMA
FACE

Fig. 24.12 Cerebellar receiving areas in the monkey, showing their connexion with different parts of the motor cortex. Stimulation of the area of the motor cortex marked ○ (leg area) produced potentials in the cerebellum in the area marked○; a similar relationship held for the areas marked × and ■. (E. D. Adrian (1943) *Brain*, 66, 301.)

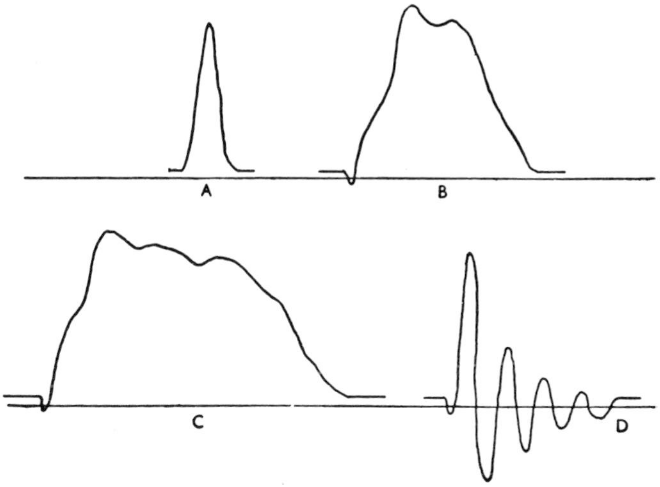

Fig. 24.13 Drawings A of a simple muscle twitch, B— of a normal knee jerk, C— of a knee jerk in a spastic limb, D— of a pendular knee jerk from a patient with an acute cerebellar lesion. (Gordon Holmes. (1968) *Introduction to Clinical Neurology*. 3rd edition. Revised by B. Matthews. p. 87. Edinburgh: Livingstone.)

experiments show that spinocerebellar afferents end chiefly in the anterior lobe. Afferents from the skin and the viscera project to both sides of the anterior cerebellum. The flow of impulses in this pathway to the cerebellum can be inhibited by painful stimulation; descending pathways from the cerebral cortex have some control over the ascending pathway.

When the cerebral cortex is stimulated, either electrically or by application of a solution of strychnine, discharges are obtained in the cerebellum in the contralateral areas shown in Figure 24.12. Thus the cerebropontine impulses reach cerebellar areas in which the foot is represented craniad and the hand caudad. This is the same order of distribution as in the case of the afferent spinocerebellar fibres but the cerebro-pontine afferents reach more caudad into the middle lobe. Visual and auditory receiving areas occur mainly in the middle lobe, the visual and auditory areas being almost coextensive; there is a second proprioceptive receiving area on the posterior part of the cerebellum. Impulse traffic also passes in the opposite direction, namely from the cerebellum to the sensorimotor area, the visual area and the auditory area of the cerebral cortex. There is thus two-way traffic between corresponding areas of the cerebral cortex and the cerebellar cortex.

Removal of parts of the central nervous system, although a useful method for investigating function, has given results which must be interpreted with care in the case of the cerebellum because it is difficult to ablate this part of the brain without damaging the adjacent brain stem. Since the cerebellum possesses a modifying rather than an initiating function its removal does not destroy any reflexes but it usually alters their character (Fig. 24.13). There is never any loss or disturbance of sensation after removal of the cerebellum but the gait is abnormal not because there is any disorder of the sensory pathways but because the muscles are not under normal control.

Removal of the cerebellum in dogs is followed by an increase in extensor tone and by clonic spasms. About 10 days later the decerebellate dog shows *asthenia* (weakness), *hypotonia* (reduction of the tone of the muscles) and irregular contractions of muscles instead of the normal smooth, well-regulated muscle movements. The staggering gait is described as *cerebellar ataxia.* This phase is followed by a certain amount of compensation in which standing and walking are much improved but recovery is never complete. The improvement is due largely to the use of the eyes for, if the eyes of an animal which has recovered from the initial effects of decerebellation are covered, the gait at once deteriorates. Complete removal of one side of the cerebellum is followed by weakness and defects of muscular control on the same side of the body.

The cerebellum possesses localization of function to a limited extent and partial removal shows that different parts vary in their regulatory functions. Each side of the cerebellum modifies the tone and movements of the muscles on the same side of the body. If only the flocculonodular lobe is removed in monkeys there is an oscillation of the head, a tendency to fall, and the animal walks with a staggering gait with the limbs abducted. This is due to overactivity of the vestibular apparatus since it does not occur if the labyrinths are previously destroyed. There is, however, no tremor and no change in reflexes. If the inferior peduncles are cut the results are similar. Lesions of the posterior lobe, which result from midline cerebellar tumours occurring particularly in children, lead to great difficulty in maintaining balance; the feet are kept wide apart and there is a tendency to fall backwards but there is no tremor.

The cortex of the cerebellar hemispheres is the part most often damaged in man and, therefore, more is known of the effect of lesions in it than of lesions in the more deeply placed parts. In gunshot wounds of the cerebellum, in which the vestibular nuclei do not appear to be involved, hypotonia with weakness and disturbances of voluntary movement are the main effects (Figs. 24.14 and 24.15). In unilateral lesions these effects are confined to the same side of the body as the lesion. Unilateral cerebellar injury in man always causes disturbances

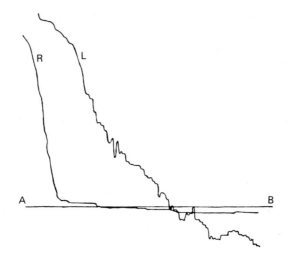

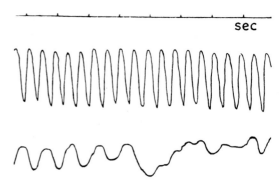

Fig. 24.16 Tracings of rapid pronation-supination. The movements of the affected arm (below) were for a time regular though slower and of smaller amplitude than the normal, but later they became irregular and the arm became more or less fixed in supination. (Gordon Holmes (1939) *Brain, 62*, 22.)

Fig. 24.14 A patient, who had a wound of the left side of his cerebellum, was asked to extend springs of equal strength with his two arms at a given signal and to maintain the stretch at a level indicated by the line AB. Note the slowness of the left arm in exerting power, the irregular tremulous character of the movement and the failure to maintain the final posture. The record was made on a slowly revolving kymograph. Read from left to right. (Gordon Holmes (1939) *Brain, 62*, 13.)

tremor which may be very severe. On attempting to touch the nose with the finger the face may be struck violently for not only is the force of the movement excessive but it is so badly directed that the nose may not be touched at the end of the movement (*dysmetria*, Fig. 24.15). On the other hand, willed movements may be carried out with an undue slowness and deliberation, a complex movement being *decomposed* into its several parts. Rapid movements of the limbs, such as rapid pronation and supination of the forearms, are faulty, the movements in the affected side being slower, irregular and jerky (*dysdiadochokinesia*, Fig. 24.16). If a patient suffering from loss of cerebellar function is asked to look to the right, the eyes are moved to the right quickly enough but they return slowly to the mid-position only to be deviated quickly to the right once more. This *nystagmus*, like the defects of voluntary movement just described, is a defect of postural fixation and is particularly likely to occur with lesions of the cerebellum and of its connexions with the vestibular system. Speech in cerebellar lesions is slow and 'scanning', each syllable in a word being pronounced separately as if it were a separate word.

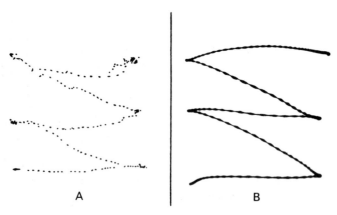

Fig. 24.15 Records obtained by photographing points of light attached to the tips of the forefingers as a patient with a lesion of the right side of the cerebellum attempted to move each finger slowly and accurately between series of luminous red points (not visible in the photographs) in a dark room. Each flash of light corresponds to 0·04 second. The range of each movement was about 75 cm. B is the record obtained from the left hand, A, that from the right. The irregularity in the rate and in the directions of movements of the affected hand, and the failure to arrest this finger accurately at the points, are well shown in A. (Gordon Holmes (1939) *Brain, 62*, 12.)

METHODS FOR STUDYING CORTICAL FUNCTION

The methods for exploration of the function of the cerebral cortex given earlier nearly all involve surgical procedures. The methods to be discussed here, conditioned reflexes and electroencephalography, provide different approaches to the problem because they permit the behaviour of the conscious intact animal or person to be studied.

Conditioned Reflexes

At the end of the nineteenth century the Russian physiologist Pavlov was engaged in studying problems of digestion and in particular the control of salivation. He soon found that this was not a simple physiological matter since a large variety of factors, for example the sight, as well as the presentation, of food, would cause an animal to salivate; also the experimental results were considerably influenced by the presence and behaviour of the observer. Pavlov, realizing the

in both ipsilateral limbs and thus both the arm and the leg on the affected side show the same kind of abnormal behaviour. Hypotonia in man is shown by an alteration in the knee-jerk (Fig. 24.13); the knee-jerk may be diminished in extent because of the hypotonia but the leg, if hanging free, tends to swing to and fro before coming to a stop (Fig. 24.13D). The reflex remains since the alpha system is normal but is undamped because the gamma system is underactive (see also p. 345). The most prominent disturbance of movement is *intention tremor*—any voluntary effort is accompanied by importance of these factors, gave up his work on the digestive glands and began a long investigation of 'conditioned reflexes'.

Classical conditioned reflexes. Pavlov used dogs in his experiments and, to avoid disturbing influences, carried out the work in specially built quiet rooms. The animals were trained to stand still on a table, restrained only by loops passing loosely round the legs. The experimenter observed the animal's behaviour unseen in another room from which by remotely controlled apparatus he could present food to the animal or apply various stimuli. The parotid duct was exteriorized and the production of saliva measured. In these experiments food in the mouth is the unconditioned stimulus for salivation. The response to be conditioned may be one of a number of glandular or muscular activities provided that they are, at the outset of the experiment, reliably evoked by a specific stimulus (the *unconditioned stimulus*). The experiment begins with the presentation of a new stimulus (the *conditioned stimulus*), such as a sound, which is shown initially to have little effect upon salivary secretion.

The conditioned and unconditioned stimuli are now presented either simultaneously or with a short time interval between them on a number of occasions. This procedure is called *reinforcement*. As a result the conditioned stimulus given alone now evokes a response resembling that originally produced only by the unconditioned stimulus. Thus, in the experiment summarized in Table 24.17, after nine repetitions of the combined stimuli the conditioned stimulus (the sound) was presented alone and the amount of salivation recorded; the strength of the conditioned response was tested in the same way after 15, 31, 41 and 51 repetitions of the combined stimuli. It can be seen that the response had become fully established when sound and food had been presented together 31 times.

Table 24.17 Development of a conditioned reflex to a sound of 637·5 Hz

Number of times combination of sound with feeding had been performed	Extent of reflex in drops of saliva per 30 seconds	Latent period of conditioned reflex in seconds
1	0	—
9	18	15
15	30	4
31	65	2
41	69	1
51	64	2

(*From* G. V. Anrep (1920) *Journal of Physiology*, 53, 367.)

If a conditioned stimulus is repeatedly presented without the unconditioned stimulus, the strength of the conditioned reflex progressively decreases (*experimental extinction*) until it ultimately disappears. Extinction is usually more rapid than reinforcement; in the case quoted above, it would be complete in about twenty trials.

The study of conditioned reflexes has provided physiologists with a useful method for examining the sensory abilities of animals. For example a dog can be conditioned to respond to one tone but not to another. Tone A is always accompanied by food whereas tone B, of a different frequency, is not. Tone A when given alone always produces salivation. Tone B alone

may at first produce salivation but when training has continued for some time tone B alone ceases to cause salivation. In other words the animal is able to distinguish between the two tones A and B.

The limits of differentiation may then be discovered by bringing the frequency of tone B nearer and nearer to that of tone A. In this way it has been found that the dog can distinguish very small intervals of pitch (an eighth of a tone) and that it can hear frequences up to 60 000 Hz. The dog can readily distinguish between different shapes and varying degrees of luminosity, although he is unable to distinguish colours if great care is taken to make their luminosities equal.

Higher order conditioning. Conditioned reflexes once established may themselves be used as a basis for further conditioning (*higher-order conditioning*). A striking illustration of this has been provided by Hudgins, who trained human subjects to develop voluntary control over a normally involuntary response, namely the pupillary reflex. When a strong light is shone into the eye the pupil becomes smaller. If a bell is sounded whenever the light is shone into the eye then the bell becomes a conditioned stimulus and the sound of the bell alone ultimately produces contraction of the pupil. The subject is now given a hand dynamometer (two bars kept apart by springs) with electrical switches so arranged that when he grasps it firmly and squeezes the bars together he closes the light and bell circuits; when he relaxes the circuits are broken. At first the subject squeezes at the command of the experimenter but later the bell and dynamometer are removed so that eventually the experimenter's commands to contract and relax are the conditioned stimuli which produce contraction and relaxation of the pupil. In the next stage of training, the subject is asked to speak the words 'contract' and 'relax', then to whisper them, and finally to say them to himself. In this way the subject acquires voluntary control over his pupillary reflexes. Such an experiment suggests that there is less difference than is usually supposed between voluntary and involuntary reflex activity. A similar technique has been used to establish voluntary control of relaxation in patients suffering from chronic anxiety.

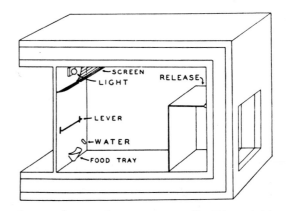

Fig. 24.18 A diagram of the apparatus used by Skinner in his studies of instrumental conditioning. One side has been cut away to show the chamber into which the animal is released through the door at the right. When the animal depresses the lever, apparatus behind the panel at the left automatically releases a pellet of food into the tray, or delivers a drop of water. (B. F. Skinner (1938) *The Behaviour of Organisms*. New York: Appleton-Century-Crofts.)

Instrumental conditioned reflexes. This procedure is most simply demonstrated in an apparatus, such as the Skinner box (Fig. 24.18), which is just big enough to permit free movement of a rat. From one wall projects a lever which can be arranged to release a pellet of food into a tray. A hungry animal placed in this box at first demonstrates a great variety of movements. Eventually some movement results in pressing the lever. If no food is delivered, the rate of lever-pressing is low and steady over a number of experimental sessions; but if pressing the lever is then made to produce a pellet of food, the rate of pressing soon rises sharply. The change of rate serves as a measure of the reinforcing effect of giving food.

As in classical conditioning, the procedure which strengthens a response is referred to as reinforcement; the procedure of omitting reinforcement is likewise referred to as experimental extinction, and similarly leads to a decline in the strength of the conditioned reflex. It was once hoped that the study of conditioned reflexes in animals and man would provide clues about the nature of learning; but the complex phenomena of learning cannot yet be explained satisfactorily.

The Electroencephalogram

Electrical potentials developed in the human brain can be detected on the surface of the head. Electrodes are placed at various positions on the scalp and simultaneous recordings from different sites are made through amplifiers each connected to a direct-writing oscillograph. The tracing is called an electroencephalogram or EEG. Alterations in electrical potential occur rhythmically, the dominant frequency being the alpha (α) rhythm at about 10 Hz and an amplitude of about 50 microvolts. This α rhythm has the highest amplitude postcentrally and may arise from the occipital cortex around the visual association area. It is found in some blind people; in normal subjects it is best seen when the person is relaxed with eyes closed. When the eyes are opened and attention is paid to objects in the visual field, or when a mental task like mental arithmetic is undertaken, the α rhythm disappears and is replaced by small rapid waves (Fig. 24.19). The α rhythm is, therefore, as Adrian put it, a 'rhythm of inattention'. Its origin and that of other cortical rhythms remains imperfectly understood. The changes recorded are too slow to be readily attributed to the action potentials of discharging nerve cells and it is likely that the potential changes on the cortex are due to changes in the postsynaptic potentials which occur particularly in the dendrites of cortical neurones. Many of these neurones are aligned vertically in the cortex with dendrites lying parallel so that if many neurones are activated synchronously quite large changes in potential may be recorded.

More rapid oscillations are recorded further forward in the precentral region. These beta (β) waves which have a frequency of 16 to 25 Hz probably originate in the motor

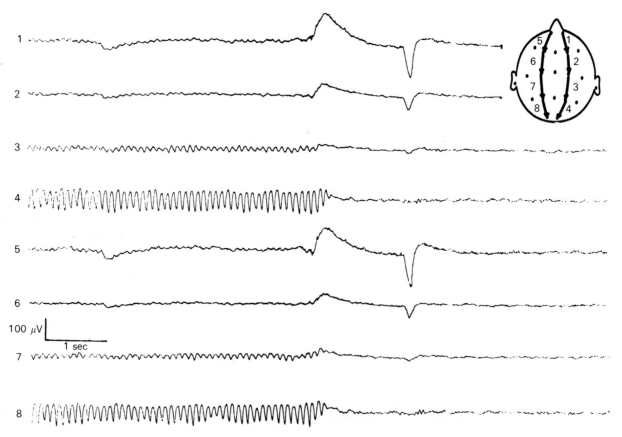

Fig. 24.19 The normal human electroencephalogram (EEG). The dominant (alpha) rhythm spreads forward from the occipital regions and is blocked by eye opening. Vertical calibration 100 μV. Horizontal calibration 1 sec. High frequency filters off. Time constant 0·3 sec. (*By courtesy of Alison M. Fleming.*)

cortex; they may be blocked by movement of the part of the body represented in the cortex underlying the electrodes. Theta (θ) rhythm with a frequency of 4 to 7 Hz is inconspicuous in healthy adults but may be the dominant rhythm of children in whom it may be blocked by visual attention and augmented by emotion. Delta (δ) waves of less than 4 Hz are not seen in the healthy walking adult, but occur in sleep and may be the dominant rhythm of infants. They also occur in hypoglycaemia (Fig. 24.20). Spindles, bursts of waves about 14 Hz, are characteristic of moderately deep sleep.

Young children below 18 months show electroencephalograms of low amplitude with little rhythmic activity. The α rhythm may not be fully established until the thirteenth year; before that the dominant rhythm is slower.

When the eyes are exposed to a uniform field lit with a flickering light the potentials recorded from the occipital region vary at the same rate as the flicker up to 30 Hz as if the cells of the visual cortex were discharging synchronously in response to each flash of light (Fig. 24.21). This 'photic stimulation' can cause changes in the emotional state and may even induce an epileptic attack.

In disease of the brain normal rhythms are often absent from affected areas and may be replaced by slow activity. In epilepsy the synchronous discharge of large numbers of cortical neurones give rise to high voltage waves which stand out against the background as spikes or slow waves. Paroxysmal discharges of this kind, however, occasionally occur in healthy individuals, particularly children; epileptic patients not uncommonly have a normal electroencephalogram.

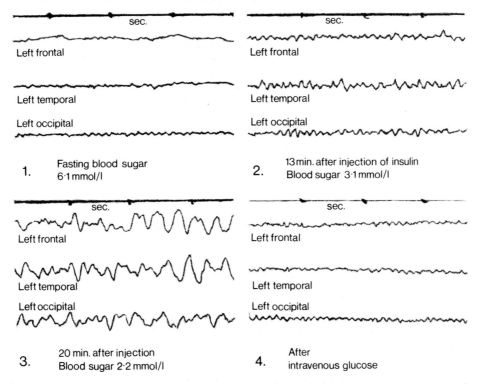

Fig. 24.20 Sequence of changes in the human electroencephalogram during hypoglycaemia after the intravenous infusion of insulin (0·5 unit per kg of body weight). Note that the appearance of slow activity in record 2 occurs first in the frontal regions and spreads to involve the whole cortex as the blood sugar falls (record 3). Complete and immediate recovery occurs after the intravenous infusion of glucose. Time in minutes after insulin injection. All records are from the left frontal, temporal and occipital regions, the electrodes being in pairs along the head (bipolar recording). (*By courtesy of D. A. Pond.*)

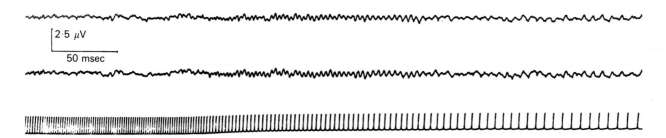

Fig. 24.21 Electroencephalogram (EEG) from occipital cortex of man (upper traces) (Montage P4 to O2, P3 to O1 left) showing change in frequency of response following visual stimuli from light source flashing at a changing frequency (lowest trace). (*By courtesy of Alison M. Fleming.*)

The electroencephalogram has proved of value in the study of epilepsy and intracranial disease, particularly in defining the area affected by a pathological process.

Cerebral evoked responses. A sudden noise evokes a widespread discharge from the cortex of a drowsy subject. This is a non-specific evoked response. On the other hand the response of the visual cortex to flicker is a specific evoked response. Specific responses evoked from the sensory cortex following a sensory stimulus to the skin are known as somatosensory responses. Visual evoked responses obtained by observing a changing visual pattern such as a reversing chequer board are of particular interest (Fig. 24.22) because the latency of the main positive deflexion is normally relatively constant but may be delayed in disease of the optic nerve as in multiple sclerosis.

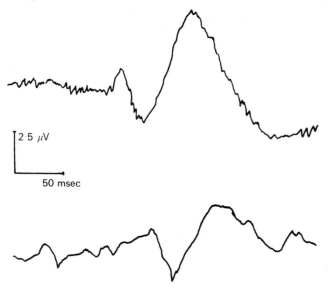

Fig. 24.22 Visual evoked responses to reversing chequer board pattern. Upper trace from a healthy subject shows the response of the visual cortex to a visual stimulus to both eyes. Latency of the main positive deflexion 100 msec. Lower trace from patient with optic atrophy (neurofibromatosis). Latency of main positive deflexion 130 msec. Time constant 1 sec. H. F. off. Horizontal calibration 50 msec. Vertical calibration $2.5 \mu V$; positive deflexion downwards. Montage 5 cm above inion to vertex (Cz). (*By courtesy of Alison M. Fleming.*)

CONSCIOUSNESS

Consciousness can scarcely be defined but it involves a state of alertness in which the subject can react appropriately to the situation existing at the moment and which allows him to remember the events in the situation. Consciousness allows him to think and to be aware of his own personal identity. It was at one time assumed that, since the cerebral cortex carries out the intellectual functions, consciousness depends on that part of the brain. In anencephaly very little cerebral cortex is present and the mental status may be described as idiocy but the 'person' is not unconscious; he sleeps and wakes, sees and hears, utters crude sounds indicating pleasure or displeasure. It seems paradoxical that stimulation of an afferent nerve of an anaesthetized unconscious animal produces cortical activity; the cortex has received impulses from the periphery.

However, anaesthetics have been shown to block the impulses passing to the cortex via the reticular system (p. 999). Accidental or surgical damage to the cortex alone does not produce unconsciousness but lesions of the upper brain stem and diencephalon, for example by haemorrhage, are often followed by unconsciousness. Injection into the cerebral ventricles of a variety of substances, such as adrenaline, noradrenaline, calcium chloride and also of some anaesthetics in doses which are quite ineffective intravenously produce a sleep-like state by acting on the nuclei in the wall of the third ventricle.

SLEEP

The human nervous system cannot long continue to function without sleep. Sleep is distinguished from other forms of unconsciousness by the relative ease with which the waking conscious state is reached. Sleep is no doubt a cerebral phenomenon but no physical changes in, for example, cerebral blood-flow have been demonstrated. The heart rate, blood pressure (Fig. 11.9) and metabolic rate are reduced in sleep. In deep sleep the respiration rate is reduced, the alveolar Po_2 falls and the arterial oxygen saturation may fall from 96 to 87 per cent; at the same time the alveolar Pco_2 is raised to 46 mm Hg or more. Short periods of apnoea (sleep apnoea) lasting more than ten seconds may occur several times a night during REM sleep even in normal subjects. Salivary and lacrimal secretions are reduced. The tendon reflexes are diminished. The volume of urine formed during sleep is small; this permits a long period of unbroken sleep. During sleep plasma levels of growth hormone, prolactin and luteinizing hormone are raised; plasma levels of cortisol decrease quickly in the morning and more slowly towards midnight but increase sharply about 2 a.m.

Sleep cannot be entirely a cortical phenomenon since decorticate animals, as well as very young animals and human infants, show rhythmic waking and sleeping which, however, bear no relationship to day and night but are repeated several times during the twenty-four hours. The ability to sleep during the night and remain awake during the day probably depends on the development of conditioned reflexes.

According to Bremer, a cat with its mid-brain sectioned immediately behind the third nerve nucleus, the basilar artery remaining intact, sleeps and the electroencephalogram shows a rhythmic waxing and waning of the α-rhythm. A cut made between the medulla oblongata and the spinal cord leaves the brain 'awake'. These findings led Bremer to the conclusion that afferent impulses reaching the fore-brain maintain wakefulness.

Magoun believes that the cortex is kept awake, not by impulses travelling in the classical sensory paths of the lemnisci to the thalamus and cortex but by impulses travelling up the central brain stem reticular formation to the posterior hypothalamus and the medial nuclei of the thalamus and then to the cortex. He showed that stimulation of the reticular formation and the diencephalic region gave the EEG picture of arousal with fast low amplitude waves but that lesions in the same area produced a state of sleep associated with a characteristic EEG record. However, this does not mean that the cortex does not receive impulses during sleep; EEG records show that impulses reach the sensory areas of the cortex from the peripheral nerves. This is described as 'cerebral vigilance'. Even in deep sleep discrimination can be made between meaningful and meaningless auditory stimuli. Sleep appears to be a passive state from which we are aroused.

Prolonged sleep (hypersomnia) is associated with lesions of the posterior hypothalamus such as are encountered in encephalitis lethargica, and injection of fluid into this area, if it produces mechanical injury, also causes sleep. Hess found that stimulation of the posterior hypothalamus caused arousal, and increased motor activity and excitability, dilatation of the pupils and a rise in blood pressure and heart rate. Such observations support the conception of a 'waking centre' in the posterior hypothalamus. Hess produced 'sleep' by low frequency stimulation of the thalamus in the region of the interthalamic connexion.

The difficulty in all such experiments is that it is not possible to say when an animal is truly asleep. The experimenter is always unable to say whether an animal is exhibiting true sleep or whether it is merely showing a great decrease of activity.

It is often said that sleep occurs most readily after muscular exertion but there is no good evidence to support this statement. It has been suggested that a soporific substance produced during wakefulness is responsible for the onset of sleep but this is unlikely since conjoined twins have each his own sleep rhythm. The best method of inducing sleep is to cut off afferent stimulation as much as possible by darkening the room and excluding noise. Warmth and a comfortable bed, by promoting muscular relaxation, reduce proprioceptive afferent impulses and facilitate sleep.

It was found many years ago that cerebrospinal fluid from sleep-deprived dogs injected into the fourth ventricle of a wakeful dog caused sleep in the recipient. Some workers have suggested that the sleep-producing substance is a peptide— TrpAlaGlyAspAlaSerGlyGlu. Others think it is a tetrapeptide. But the sleep factor may be arginine vasotocin (AVT), a nonapeptide from the pineal gland.

Sleep in man, as judged by EEG records, shows several cycles of alternation between the two categories illustrated in Figure 24.23. The REM (rapid eye movement) phase occupies about

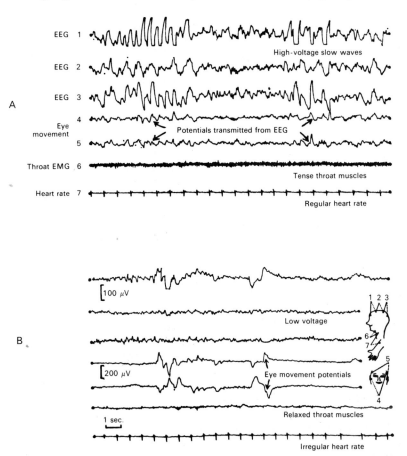

Fig. 24.23 The tracings show simultaneous records of electroencephalogram (EEG) (channels 1–3), eye movements (channels 4–5), electromyogram (EMG) from throat (channel 6) and heart rate (channel 7). The key on the extreme right in (b) shows the positions of electrodes and their connexions. The two excerpts are from the same tracing and are separated by two minutes. Excerpt (a), above, shows the orthodox or slow wave or NREM (non rapid eye movement) phase of sleep and excerpt (b), below, shows the paradoxical or REM (rapid eye movement) phase of sleep in a normal adult. In excerpt (a) there are large slow waves and fast spindle activity in the EEG, the eyes are quiescent, the throat muscles tense, though not as tense as in wakefulness, and the heart rate regular. In excerpt (b) the EEG is of low voltage; but there is a short run of 'saw-toothed', 3-per-sec, waves in channels 1 and 3 just before the burst of eye-movement potentials in channels 4 and 5. The eye-movement potentials have also been picked up by the frontal electrode and appear in channel 1, and one or two small muscle-spike potentials from accompanying facial twitches are visible in this trace as well. The throat muscles have relaxed and there are occasional irregularities in the heart rate. (I. Oswald (1964) *British Medical Bulletin,* **20,** 60–64.)

20 per cent of sleeping time and the orthodox (or slow wave) occupies 80 per cent. The REM phase is especially related to dreaming and the rapid eye movements could perhaps be described as scanning movements made in response to the visual imagery of the dream. Normally REM sleep does not develop until an hour or longer after sleep develops. In patients with narcolepsy who have an abnormal tendency to fall asleep REM sleep may develop almost immediately.

People vary greatly in the amount of sleep they 'need'. Young babies sleep about 14 to 18 hours, about half being in the REM phase, but young adults may sleep any time between 5 and 9 hours. Old people have an even wider range. It is difficult to detect a loss of efficiency in carrying out mental tasks if sleeping time in young adults is reduced to 5 hours but efficiency is greatly impaired if it is reduced to 3 hours. It is not at all clear why sleep is necessary but a human being deprived of sleep for long periods, for example 100 hours, becomes irritable and has hallucinations and delusions. After prolonged sleep deprivation restoration to normal health is remarkably rapid.

Sleep occurs most readily at the time of day that we are accustomed to go to sleep. The biological clock is of overwhelming importance.

REFERENCES

Adrian E D 1943 Afferent areas in the cerebellum connected with the limbs. Brain 66: 289–315

Brain Lord 1966 Speech disorders. Aphasia, apraxia and agnosia, 2nd edn. Butterworth, London

Brazier M A B 1978 (ed) Brain mechanisms in memory and learning. International Brain Research Organization vol 4. Raven Press, New York

Butler S R 1971 Organization of cerebral cortex for perception. British Medical Journal ii: 544–547

Calne D B 1973 Clinical neuropharmacology of levodopa. The Scientific Basis of Medicine Annual Reviews. Athlone Press, London

Crisp A H, Stonehill E 1976 Sleep nutrition and mood. John Wiley, London

Denny-Brown D 1962 The basal ganglia and their relation to disorders of movement. Oxford University Press

Denny-Brown D 1966 The cerebral control of movement. Liverpool University Press

Drucker-Colin R R, McGauch J L (eds) 1977 Neurobiology of sleep and memory. Academic Press, New York

Dimond S J, Beaumont J G 1974 Hemisphere function in the human brain. Elek Science, London

Eccles J C 1969 Inhibitory pathways of the central nervous system. Liverpool University Press

Eccles J C, Ito M, Szentágothai J 1967 The cerebellum as a neuronal machine. Springer, Berlin

Edelman G M, Mountcastle V B 1979 The mindful brain: cortical organisation and the group-selective theory of higher brain function. MIT Press

Franks C M (ed) 1964 Conditioning techniques in clinical practice and research. Springer, New York

Fulton J F 1949 Functional localization in the frontal lobes and cerebellum. Oxford University Press

Gazzaniga M S, Sperry R W 1967 Language after section of the cerebral commisures. Brain 90: 131–148

Geschwind N 1970 The organization of language and the brain. Science 170: 940

Harris A J 1974 Inductive functions of the nervous system. Annual Review of Physiology 36: 251–306

Holmes G, Revised by Matthews B 1968 Introduction to clinical neurology, 3rd edn. Livingstone, Edinburgh

Jansen J, Brodal A 1954 Aspects of cerebellar atatomy. Johan Grundt Tanum, Oslo

Jouvet M 1967 Neurophysiology of the states of sleep. Physiological Reviews 47: 117–177

Lance J W, McLeod J 1975 A physiological approach to clinical neurology 4, 2nd edn. Butterworth, London

Libassi P T 1974 Where the past is present: how does memory reside in the brain? The Sciences 14: No. 8, 17–23

Magoun H W, Rhines Ruth 1947 Spasticity. The stretch reflex and extra-pyramidal systems. Thomas, Springfield, Illinois

Mark R 1974 Memory and nerve cell connections. Oxford University Press, London

Martin I, Levey A B 1969 The genesis of the classical conditioned response. Pergamon, Oxford

Meddis R 1977 The sleep instinct. Routledge and Kegan Paul, London

Moruzzi G 1950 Problems in cerebellar physiology. Blackwell, Oxford

Oswald I 1964 The experimental study of sleep. British Medical Bulletin 20: 60–64

Penfield W 1958 The excitable cortex in conscious man. Liverpool University Press

Penfield W, Roberts L 1959 Speech and brain mechanisms. Oxford University Press, London

Phillips C G, Porter R 1977 Corticospinal Neurones. Their role in movement. Monograph of the Physiological Society No. 34. Academic Press, London

Refsum S, Lossius H M, Dietrichson P (eds) 1962 The so-called extrapyramidal system. Scandinavian University Books

Regan D 1972 Evoked potentials in psychology, sensory physiology and clinical medicine. Chapman and Hall, London

Ritchie Russell W 1975 Explaining the brain. Oxford University Press, London

Skinner B F 1938 The behaviour of organisms. An experimental analysis. Appleton-Century, London

25 Autonomic Nervous System and Smooth Muscle

The autonomic nervous system has central connexions which are still under investigation. The frontal lobe of the cerebral cortex has an influence on the cardiovascular system and the intestinal tract by virtue of its connexions with the hypothalamus but the main regulation of the autonomic system seems to be located in the hypothalamus itself. Important reflex centres, including the vagal centres, are located in the brain stem and much autonomic activity is initiated there under the controlling influences of the hypothalamus and higher centres.

The autonomic fibres leave the cord in two great 'outflows' the thoracolumbar (sympathetic) and the craniosacral (parasympathetic).

The autonomic fibres to the viscera, unlike the somatic fibres to skeletal muscles, are interrupted by synapses. A fibre emerging from the central nervous system as a *preganglionic* fibre synapses in a ganglion with *postganglionic* neurones supplying glands or smooth muscle cells. One preganglionic fibre may synapse with twenty or more postganglionic fibres.

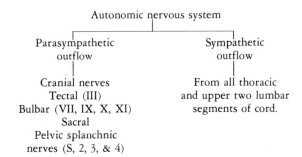

Autonomic nervous system

Parasympathetic outflow	Sympathetic outflow
Cranial nerves Tectal (III) Bulbar (VII, IX, X, XI) Sacral Pelvic splanchnic nerves (S, 2, 3, & 4)	From all thoracic and upper two lumbar segments of cord.

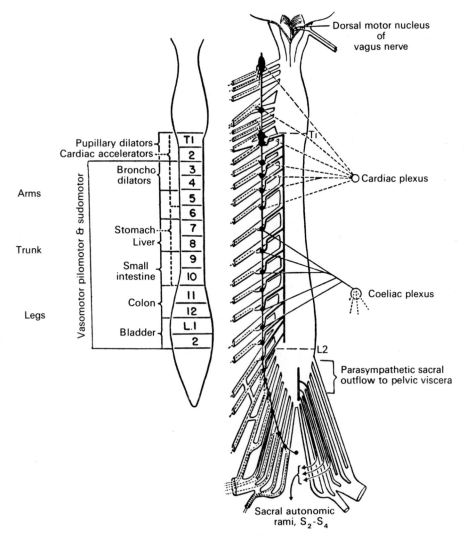

Fig. 25.1 The autonomic outflow. ——— Preganglionic axon. - - - Postganglionic axon. T, thoracic segment. L, lumbar segment. S, sacral segment. (J. C. White, R. H. Smithwick & F. A. Simeone (1952) *The Autonomic Nervous System.* 3rd edition, p. 24. London: Henry Kimpton.)

In the case of the sympathetic system the synapses occur in the ganglia of the sympathetic trunk or in the more peripheral ganglia lying along the anterior surface of the abdominal aorta. Most of the sympathetic postganglionic fibres are distributed with the spinal nerves but some enter visceral branches. The parasympathetic ganglia, on the other hand, commonly lie on or in the organ supplied.

Sympathetic outflow. The thoracolumbar outflow in man arises from all the thoracic segments of the spinal cord and from the upper two lumbar segments (Fig. 25.1); each fibre begins in a cell of the lateral horn (the intermediolateral column) of the grey matter of the spinal cord and emerges in an anterior root, leaving the spinal nerve in a *white ramus communicans* (WR) which passes to a sympathetic ganglion (Fig. 25.2). Here the fibre may either synapse or turn aside to run up and down in the sympathetic trunk to a neighbouring, or sometimes a distant, ganglion where there is a synapse. From the sympathetic trunk, postganglionic fibres, chiefly non-myelinated, pass in the *grey rami communicantes* (GR) to every spinal nerve. They are distributed in the peripheral nerves to blood vessels, skin, sweat glands and pilomotor muscles and in the splanchnic nerves to the abdominal organs. Postganglionic

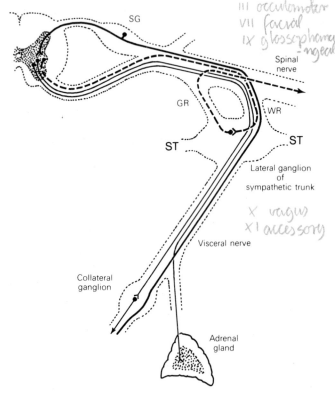

Fig. 25.2 Pathways of the sympathetic fibres from the lateral horn of the grey matter of the spinal cord. The fibres arising in the lateral horn, preganglionic fibres, pass to a lateral ganglion (dashed line) or a collateral ganglion (thin line) or to the adrenal medulla (thin line). The preganglionic fibres may synapse in these ganglia with cells which give rise to postganglionic fibres. The coeliac and hypogastric ganglia are examples of collateral ganglia. The thick continuous line represents afferent fibres from the viscera. The spinal nerve contains, in addition to the postganglionic sympathetic fibres represented in the diagram, afferent and efferent somatic fibres and is therefore known as a mixed nerve. GR, grey ramus; WR, white ramus; SG, spinal ganglion; ST, sympathetic trunk.

fibres also reach the viscera by running in the nerve plexus surrounding the arteries that supply them. The adrenal medulla is exceptional in that it receives only preganglionic sympathetic fibres from the spinal cord directly, that is without an intervening synapse. The chromaffin cells of the adrenal medulla which produce adrenaline and noradrenaline have differentiated from a cell type similar to the cells of the peripheral sympathetic ganglia. Fluorescence histochemical methods have shown that the sympathetic ganglia and also the adrenal medulla possess 'small intensely fluorescent' cells (SIF cells) which may be either interneurones between pre-ganglionic and postganglionic fibres or may play a regulatory role in controlling the release of a transmitter. The SIF cells seem to be dopaminergic or noradrenergic depending on the species and the ganglion studied.

Parasympathetic (craniosacral) outflow. The cranial section of the parasympathetic outflow is described in other chapters which deal with the organs it supplies. Myelinated preganglionic fibres are found in the third nerve going to the ciliary ganglion, in the seventh going to the submandibular and sphenopalatine ganglia, in the ninth to the otic ganglion, and in the tenth and eleventh cranial nerves to small ganglia and plexuses in the walls of the viscera. The postganglionic fibres are not myelinated and pass to the intraocular muscles, salivary and lacrimal glands, heart, lungs, and abdominal viscera. The sacral outflow comes from cells situated laterally in the grey matter and leaves the cord by the anterior roots of the second, third and fourth sacral nerves as the pelvic splanchnic nerves (nervi erigentes). Their ganglia are usually in the walls of the viscera to which they run. The sacral parasympathetic supplies the colon, rectum, generative organs and urinary bladder. Parasympathetic nerves have not been proved to go to the limbs or the surface of the body.

Autonomic reflexes. Just as in the somatic nervous system, there are in the autonomic nervous system reflexes, both sympathetic and parasympathetic, and these are described elsewhere. Most afferent impulses enter the cord from the viscera but some come from the muscles and skin. Through such reflex arcs diseases in the viscera can produce areas of hyperaesthesia and other effects on the skin and, on the other hand, the application of heat to the skin can produce effects on the motility of the viscera. Most of these reflexes depend upon pathways involving the brain stem where interactions of afferent impulses from different sensory structures can occur (for example baroreceptors, chemoreceptors and volume receptors) or the hypothalamus (for example thermo-regulatory reflexes and a number of vasodilator reflexes). Some autonomic reflexes exist solely at a spinal level (p. 364) or both spinal and central pathways can be involved (for example somato-sympathetic reflexes). In addition to auto-nomic reflexes through the spinal cord there are others that operate through the peripheral ganglia. Thus the reflex activity responsible for the controlled motility of the small intestine is under local control, the ganglion cells being in the myenteric and submucosal plexuses in the walls of the gut. The inferior mesenteric ganglion likewise contains ganglion cells through which local autonomic reflexes of the bladder and rectum occur. Axonal reflexes may exist in the autonomic nervous system. In this kind of reflex it is assumed that impulses from a receptor pass up its axon to a branch where they turn down to affect neighbouring muscles or blood vessels. For example piloerection may occur in response to repetitive electrical stimulation of the skin.

CHEMICAL THEORY OF NEUROTRANSMISSION

The pioneering work of Dale, Feldberg and Gaddum in the 1930s provided irrefutable evidence that transmission across synapses involves the release of a chemical neurotransmitter. In the control of the viscera the two major neural types are *adrenergic* which release noradrenaline and *cholinergic*, where acetylcholine is the transmitter. Most postganglionic sympathetic fibres are adrenergic with the exception of sympathetic cholinergic vasodilator fibres innervating the blood vessels of the skeletal muscles and sweat glands. All parasympathetic and all autonomic ganglia are cholinergic (Fig. 25.3).

Adrenergic Nerves

In contrast to a large proportion of the adrenomedullary chromaffin cells, sympathetic nerve endings do not contain the methylating enzyme phenylethanolamine N-methyl trans-

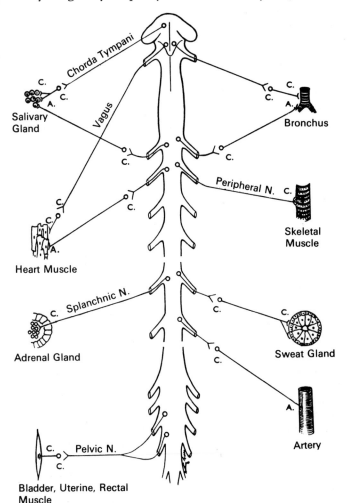

Fig. 25.3 Some examples of adrenergic and cholinergic nerve-endings. A, adrenergic nerve-ending. C, cholinergic nerve-ending. (*From* J. C. White, R. H. Smithwick & F. A. Simeone (1952) *The Autonomic Nervous System.* 3rd edition, p. 96. London: Henry Kimpton.)

ferase (PNMT) and so do not convert noradrenaline to adrenaline. The finding that the neurotransmitter is noradrenaline accounted for previously observed discrepancies between the effects of adrenaline and sympathetic stimulation. Fluorescence histochemistry involving the condensation of noradrenaline with formaldehyde has been used to locate adrenergic neurones both centrally and in the periphery.

General sympathetic stimulation initiates an adrenomedullary catecholamine release which in most species adrenaline accounts for approximately 80 per cent of the released catecholamine, the remainder being noradrenaline. The adrenaline within the adrenal medulla is present in chromaffin cells containing PNMT which are thus able to methylate noradrenaline to form adrenaline (see p. 481). Noradrenaline is a powerful vasoconstrictor. If given to man by intravenous infusion, in doses of about 20 μg per min, both the systolic and diastolic blood pressures are raised, the heart is reflexly slowed and the cardiac output is reduced probably because of the increased cardiac after-load. Adrenaline on the other hand, in small doses (say 3 μg/min), augments the cardiac output directly with little alteration in blood pressure. If larger doses are administered, of the order of 20 μg per min, the heart accelerates and the systolic blood pressure increases with little change in the diastolic pressure. This is accounted for by a dilatation of the skeletal muscle resistance vessels which reduces the peripheral resistance. Even higher doses of adrenaline cause marked vasoconstriction in a manner similar to noradrenaline, with a rise in total peripheral resistance. The actions of the two substances are compared in Table 25.4.

Table 25.4 Table to compare the effects of L-adrenaline and L-noradrenaline in man

	Effect of	
	L-Adrenaline	L-Noradrenaline
Heart rate	Increase	Decrease*
Cardiac output	Increase	Variable
Total peripheral resistance	Decrease	Increase
Blood pressure	Rise	Greater rise
Respiration	Stimulates	Stimulates
Skin vessels	Constriction	Constriction
Muscle vessels	Dilatation	Constriction
Bronchus	Dilatation	Less dilatation
Eosinophil count	Increase	No effect
Metabolism	Increase	Slight increase
Oxygen consumption	Increase	No effect
Blood sugar	Increase	Slight increase
Central nervous system	Anxiety	No effect
Uterus *in vivo* in late pregnancy	Inhibits	Stimulates
Kidney	Vasoconstriction	Vasoconstriction

*On the *isolated* heart, where vagal reflexes are absent, noradrenaline increases heart-rate though to a smaller extent than adrenaline.

α and β receptors. The action of adrenaline on smooth muscle has for long been known to be complex. For example in an anaesthetized cat with the vagi cut the blood pressure is high; adrenaline lowers the pressure. In a spinal cat the blood pressure is usually low; adrenaline produces a rise in pressure. Ahlquist suggested in 1948 that this double action of adrenaline can be accounted for by supposing that it can

Table 25.5 α and β adrenergic effects

	α Effects	β Effects
	Vasoconstriction Intestinal muscle relaxation Pupillary dilatation	Vasodilatation (especially muscle (β_2) Heart: increased force and rate; arrhythmias (β_1) Bronchial relaxation (β_2)
Noradrenaline	+ + +	+
Adrenaline	+	+ + +
Blocking drugs Propanolol } Practolol }	– no blockade	+ + + blockade
Ergotamine Piperoxan Phentolamine Phenoxybenzamine	+ + + active blockade	– no blockade

(Slightly modified from R. H. Johnson & J. M. K. Spalding (1972) *Clinical Physiology of the Autonomic Nervous System.* Oxford: Blackwell.)

combine with two receptor types. When adrenaline produces vasoconstriction it acts on α receptors and when it causes a vasodilatation it is by an action on β receptors (Table 25.5). Noradrenaline acts predominantly on α receptors, producing cutaneous and splanchnic vasoconstriction, a rise in blood pressure, pupillary dilatation and relaxation of intestinal muscle. The agonist isoprenaline acts almost entirely on β receptors since it increases the rate and force of the heart beat, causes skeletal muscle vasodilatation and relaxation of the bronchi and of the uterus. In parallel with the selective actions of agonists the subdivision of adrenergic receptors has been predominantly based on the action of antagonists. For example if the α receptors are blocked by ergotamine, phentolamine or phenoxybenzamine, the action of adrenaline on the spinal cat is reversed and the vasodilatation mediated by the action of adrenaline on β receptors predominates. The β receptors can be blocked by a number of drugs notably oxprenolol, propranolol, atenolol and practolol. The discovery of practolol which blocks the β receptors in the heart but not those in the bronchi, and of salbutamol which stimulates bronchial but not cardiac β receptors, has indicated that there are two populations of adrenergic β receptors. These are designated β_1 in the heart, β_2 in the bronchi and vascular smooth muscle.

Recently, as the result of work by Langer a subdivision of α receptors has been made. The α_1 receptors are the 'traditional' postsynaptic type mediating vasoconstriction whereas α_2 receptors are presynaptic and act to control the release of noradrenaline from adrenergic nerve endings. These receptors act in a negative feedback mechanism by which the neurotransmitter partially controls its own release. Selective α_2 agonists have been found, for example, clonidine; yohimbine is an α_2 antagonist. The antihypertensive agent prazosin seems to block postsynaptic α_1 receptors selectively.

The cellular response following the activation of β receptors by agonists has been closely investigated. The action on the receptor leads to an increase in adenylate cyclase activity with an enhanced production of cyclic 3'5' adenosine monophosphate (cAMP) from adenosine triphosphate (ATP). The increased cAMP level within the cell is believed to alter either the ion conductance or the Ca^{2+} ion levels within the cell, or

both. On the other hand most actions on α receptors seem to lead to depolarization and contraction of muscle.

Noradrenaline is stored in presynaptic vesicles along with ATP and protein in sympathetic nerve endings from which they are all released on the arrival of nerve impulses, provided that Ca^{2+} ions are present. Noradrenaline thus released together with adrenaline derived from the adrenal medulla are removed from the circulation by two uptake processes. 'Uptake$_1$' involves the re-uptake into sympathetic neurones where degradation occurs through the action of monoamine oxidase located in the mitochondria of the presynaptic nerve ending. A second uptake 'Uptake$_2$' is observed into smooth muscle: degradation of the transmitter thus depends on both monoamine oxidase and the methylating enzyme *catecholomethyltransferase* (COMT) which is located extraneurally.

Denervation makes tissues supplied by sympathetic nerves more sensitive to adrenaline and particularly to noradrenaline. Noradrenaline disappears from denervated organs which suggests that the nerve fibres are the only important source of noradrenaline. Resynthesis appears to keep pace with loss of neurotransmitter following stimulation but this is controlled by re-uptake, α_2 regulation of the release of transmitter and by changes in the rate of synthesis in response to increased neural activity.

Sympathectomy. Postganglionic fibres reach blood vessels by two routes. Fibres from the sympathetic chain pass directly to plexuses around the aorta, which extend on to the abdomen, thorax and skull and to the proximal parts of the limbs. The fibres to the vessels in more distal parts of the limbs reach them through the peripheral nerves. Preganglionic sympathectomy or removal of the ganglia of the sympathetic chain (ganglionectomy) leads to widespread and lasting dilatation of arteries and arterioles in the limbs which is greatest in the skin and least in the skeletal muscles. The reduction in vascular tone is not maximal after sympathetic denervation for local changes in inherent myogenic tone can compensate. Further dilatation can be produced by local heating, by histamine, by exercise and by reactive hyperaemia. The vasodilatation after sympathectomy of the legs is greatest on the day after the operation. By the fifth day the blood flow has fallen considerably to remain for many years two or three times greater than that of the normal limb. This persistent vasodilatation is confined to the skin; there is no lasting effect on muscle flow which compensates by autoregulation. It should be emphasized that the influence of sympathectomy on vascular tone is far from uniform throughout the body.

Cholinergic Nerves

In 1921 Loewi showed that during stimulation of the vagus, Ringer's solution perfusing a frog's heart acquired a substance which could inhibit another frog's heart. This 'Vagusstoff' was later shown to be acetylcholine (ACh) and nerves acting in this way were described by Dale as *cholinergic*. Acetylcholine is the neurotransmitter at the neuroeffector junction of all postganglionic parasympathetic fibres but a number of other synaptic sites in the autonomic nervous system also involve ACh as the neurotransmitter.

Sympathetic vasodilator fibres to the blood vessels of skeletal muscle are cholinergic and they play an important role in the anticipatory response to exercise. The preganglionic sympathetic fibres to the adrenal medulla liberate ACh which in turn evokes a secretion of adrenaline and noradrenaline. This directly parallels the action of ACh as the neurotransmitter at all sympathetic and parasympathetic ganglia where it initiates postganglionic firing. Postganglionic sympathetic fibres running to sweat glands act in most animals, including man, to release ACh, that is they are cholinergic. The release of ACh at the endings of preganglionic nerve fibres in the sympathetic ganglia (p. 325) and at myoneural junctions (p. 401) is referred to elsewhere.

Cholinergic receptors have been shown to be present on postganglionic sympathetic nerve endings where they may play a role in the regulation of transmitter output. In addition, the 'cholinergic link' hypothesis of Burn and Rand postulates a role for acetylcholine in the initiation of noradrenaline release from adrenergic neurones during normal neurotransmission. This hypothesis is still highly controversial and has been neither proved nor disproved.

Unlike what happens in adrenergic neurones ACh is metabolized, without re-uptake, by an enzyme, *cholinesterase*, on the postsynaptic membrane and in the blood. Normally after ACh is released from cholinergic nerve endings it is quickly hydrolysed by the esterase to choline and acetic acid and its action is local and transient; because of its rapid destruction it has no action as a circulating hormone. A number of compounds with a powerful anticholinesterase action are known; some actions are reversible, for example those of physostigmine, neostigmine, pancuronium; other actions are irreversible, for example those of di-isopropylfluorophosphonate (Dyflos).

Minute amounts of ACh are still detected by bioassay. The eserinized frog rectus abdominis muscle, for example, can detect 1 part in 10^9 of ACh. Acetylcholine is synthesized in the presynaptic nerve endings following the active uptake of choline which is acetylated by choline acetyltransferase (CHAT) with acetyl CoA as a co-factor. The ACh may be stored and released from vesicles though this is not certain. Certainly the ACh in the nerve ending is in a form which is protected from the action of cholinesterase. When acetyl-

choline is released it acts on the effector tissue by depolarizing its cells and the distance across the synaptic cleft is so small that the usual synaptic delay is of the order of a few milliseconds. Denervation of tissues supplied by cholinergic nerves sensitizes them to ACh and this appears to be associated with changes in the number of postsynaptic receptors and alterations in cholinesterase activity. Cholinergic nerves cannot synthesize choline: choline seems to be taken up by cholinergic nerve terminals from the interstitial fluid.

A diagram of the distribution of adrenergic and cholinergic nerves is given in Fig. 25.3. Where a tissue receives both sympathetic and parasympathetic fibres they may act antagonistically. For example, vagal impulses (parasympathetic) slow the heart whereas sympathetic impulses cause tachycardia. Both neurotransmitters, noradrenaline and acetylcholine, act on the pace-maker cells of the sinu-atrial node, the former increasing their rate of firing and the latter slowing them.

Such inhibitory and excitatory influences displayed by the autonomic nervous system make it of prime importance in homeostasis. For example in man this balance becomes particularly apparent after transverse lesions of the spinal cord. Consideration of Figure 25.1 shows that a lesion above the first thoracic segment (T1) cuts off the whole of the thoracolumbar autonomic outflow from higher control. Tilting such a patient suddenly from the supine to the upright position causes a fall of blood pressure, a rise in pulse rate and a loss of consciousness as there is no compensatory vasoconstriction. Neither is such a patient, since he has no control of skin vessels, able to produce vasodilatation or sweating to keep the body temperature steady; if he becomes cold the muscles below the lesion cannot shiver as they are paralysed. These disabilities obviously become smaller the lower the lesion lies in the spinal cord.

Dopamine. It has been accepted for many years that *dopamine* is an important neurotransmitter in the central nervous system, but it was formerly regarded merely as the percursor of adrenaline and noradrenaline in the periphery (see p. 481). Dopamine has been found in significant amounts in a number of tissues and it seems to be released from the adrenal medulla. Specific dopamine receptors, characterized by selective dopamine agonists and antagonists, are present in many tissues, for example, kidney, mesentery, cerebrum, and skeletal muscle blood vessels. Dopamine-mediated vasodilatation is of prime importance in the renal vascular bed and may form the basis of a number of vasodilator reflexes in other vascular beds. More and more evidence indicates that dopamine may be an important neurotransmitter in the peripheral as well as the central nervous system.

THE HYPOTHALAMUS

Visceral functions are to a major extent controlled and integrated in the hypothalamus. Anatomically this occupies the ventral and inferior parts of the lateral walls and floor of the third ventricle and together with the thalamus forms that part of the forebrain known as the diencephalon. The thalamus, estimated to weigh about 4 g, consists of the posterior perforated substance, the mamillary bodies, the tuber

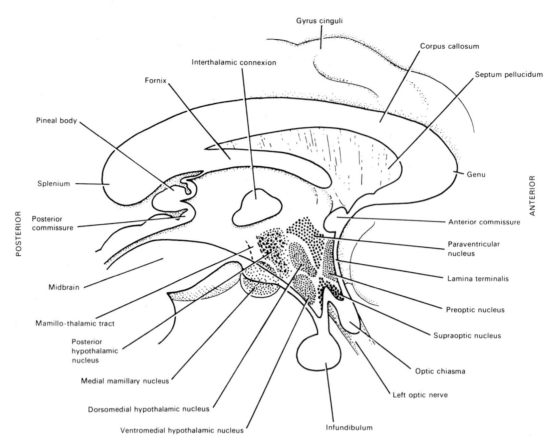

Fig. 25.6 A diagrammatic sagittal plane to show the hypothalamic area and adjacent structures. The hypothalamic nuclei have been projected on to the lateral wall of the third ventricle. ×2½. (*Partly after* W. E. Le Gros Clark (1936) *Journal of Anatomy*, 70, 204.)

cinereum, the infundibulum and the neurohypophysis; the other nuclei are found in the wall of the third ventricle below the hypothalamic sulcus and are shown in Figure 25.6. For physiological purposes the nuclei of the hypothalamus can be divided into four groups: anterior (including the paraventricular and supraoptic nuclei), middle (including the tuberal, dorsomedial, and ventromedial hypothalamic nuclei), posterior (including the posterior hypothalamic nuclei and the mamillary nuclei) and the lateral. The nuclei are well supplied with blood. For example, the supraoptic nucleus contains 2500 capillaries per mm³.

The hypothalamus receives impulses from the main brain areas. The median forebrain bundle brings fibres from the cortex, the periventricular fibres come from the thalamus and the fornix brings fibres from the hippocampus. From the cerebral cortex fibres pass to the medial nucleus of the thalamus and then to the hypothalamus. Fibres which ascend from the reticular formation of the brain stem to enter the hypothalamus seem to be concerned in maintaining alertness. The mamillary peduncles contain fibres from spinal nerves and probably from the ninth and tenth cranial nerves.

The hypothalamus sends fibres to many destinations. The mamillothalamic tract passes from the mamillary nucleus to the anterior thalamic nuclei. The dorsomedial thalamic nuclei are reached by periventricular fibres and projected thence to the frontal cortex. Important descending fibres from the lateral and posterior hypothalamic areas pass to the reticular formation and hence to the brain stem and spinal cord. Each side of

the hypothalamus sends fibres to both right and left halves of the sympathetic system. The neurohypophysis (posterior pituitary) receives a large number of hypothalamic fibres from the paraventricular and supraoptic nuclei. The anterior pituitary is controlled by releasing and inhibitory hormones which pass from the hypothalamus down the portal system to the capillaries supplying it (p. 464).

The hypothalamus has a great influence on many activities of the body. It affects all kinds of metabolic activities; it regulates body temperature, it influences the cardiovascular and alimentary systems, it controls the anterior and posterior lobes of the pituitary (Chap. 28) and it is concerned with appetite and thirst.

The hypothalamus can be stimulated in the conscious animal through electrodes implanted under general anaesthesia. Mild stimulation through these electrodes produces an 'alerting reaction' or 'preparatory reflex' in which the ears are erected and the pupils dilated. Stronger stimulation produces 'sham rage' and at the same time vasodilatation in the skeletal muscles. The latter effect forms part of an anticipatory reaction to exercise known as a 'defence reaction' and is mediated predominantly by atropine-sensitive sympathetic cholinergic fibres supplying the arterioles of muscles. These nerves do not appear to take part in the ordinary homeostatic circulatory reflexes. The muscular vasodilatation is accompanied by skin and splanchnic vasoconstriction, by venoconstriction and by tachycardia. The blood pressure and heart rate increase because of an inhibition of the normal baroreceptor reflex. The fact that the hypothalamus can alter the sensitivity, that is 'reset', the response to baroreceptor and other vascular reflexes indicates its over-riding control. Electrical stimulation of the hypothalamus and the amygdala in man can produce similar circulatory changes in muscle and skin, and similar changes occur during stressful situations such as cardiac catheterization. Stimulation of the posterior hypothalamic areas produces sympathetic effects and an increase in adrenomedullary secretion which can be adrenaline or noradrenaline depending on the area stimulated. On the other hand destructive lesions of the hypothalamus tend to reduce sympathetic activity. There may be a number of special cardiovascular changes initiated by the hypothalamus which have proved hard to define in anaesthetized preparations because of the depressant actions of most commonly used general anaesthetics on hypothalamic activity.

The hypothalamus is not essential for sympathetic or parasympathetic effects since the cardiovascular reflexes function normally in a decerebrate animal, but it may be much more closely involved in cardiovascular homeostatic reflexes than was previously believed and is essential in mediating the response to stress. The hypothalamus may also play a regulatory role in the long term control of sympathetic activity which may be influenced by changes in the levels of catecholamine synthetic enzymes in the periphery, under the control of one or more hypothalamic pathways.

Stimulation of a region in the anterior part of the hypothalamus causes contraction of the urinary bladder, a parasympathetic effect. Since the effect persists after degeneration of fibres from the cerebral cortex, this region seems to be a true parasympathetic centre as far as the bladder is concerned. Although stimulation of the anterior part has produced other parasympathetic actions, such as increased gastrointestinal activity and bradycardia, it may be that this is due to stimulation of fibres passing through the hypothalamic area from other brain areas.

The superficial nuclei of the hypothalamus are affected by drugs placed in the third ventricle (see also p. 404). Feldberg has found that in the unanaesthetized cat intraventricular injection of anticholinesterases produces a catatonic state in which the animal can maintain fixed postures for long periods. The level of neurotransmitters and metabolites within the third ventricle can to some extent reflect the activity in adjacent areas of the hypothalamus.

Pituitary tumours in man may be accompanied by obesity due to damage to the middle group of hypothalamic nuclei. If hypophysectomy in animals involves damage to the hypothalamus, there is genital atrophy and obesity because of increased appetite. The control of appetite is more fully discussed on page 18. The genital atrophy can be attributed to the loss of the adenohypophysis. The relationship of the hypothalamus to pituitary and endocrine functions is discussed in Chapter 28. In addition to the role of the hypothalamus in neuroendocrine function there is some evidence that releasing factors may have additional actions as neurotransmitters. We cannot yet state unequivocally that hypothalamic peptide hormones (for example, luteinizing hormone releasing hormone, thyrotropin releasing hormone) comprise a class of chemical transmitters but the evidence is at least consistent with this view. Similarly both types of opiate peptides, endorphins and enkephalins (p. 358) have been identified in

the hypothalamus where they may play an important functional role.

Injury to the hypothalamus, during surgical operations for example, may result in erosions or ulcers of the gastric mucosa, and is commonly followed by a persistent rise in body temperature. The key position of the hypothalamus in temperature regulation is described in Chapter 26. Tumours of the posterior region may be associated with a fall of body temperature, a reduction in bodily activity (hypokinesia) and a tendency to fall asleep (hypersomnia). Disease of the mamillary bodies produces a remarkable state in which the events of ordinary daily life are forgotten as quickly as they occur but events of childhood are well remembered.

Cortical Representation of Autonomic Activities

The visceral or autonomic activities of the body seem to be controlled by the hypothalamus but there is a certain amount of cortical representation of autonomic activities, both sympathetic and parasympathetic. Stimulation of some points in areas 4 and 6 on the frontal lobe of the chimpanzee gives a rise of blood pressure and an increase in heart rate, but if the stimulating electrodes are moved only a short distance along the cortex, the reverse effects may be obtained. Some of these effects may be independent of the hypothalamus.

Injury to the cortex may produce vasomotor effects in man. Soon after a cerebral haemorrhage which gives rise to a hemiplegia there is a cutaneous vasodilatation and an increase in sweating on the affected side; at the same time the surface temperature of the paralysed limbs is increased, though later it usually falls to subnormal levels. Autonomic effects are especially pronounced on stimulation of the orbital gyrus and ungulate gyrus. In dogs stimulation of the cingulate gyrus arrests the movements of the pyloric antrum. Since destruction of the hypothalamus or vagal section abolishes this effect, but section of the splanchnic nerves does not, the chain of connexions must be cerebral cortex, hypothalamus, medulla and vagus nerves to the stomach. Removal of the frontal lobes in monkeys increases the movements of the gastrointestinal tract and the animals become increasingly hungry; stimulation of area 6 may inhibit peristaltic activity. Salivary secretion in response to a conditioned stimulus involves area 6a. Stimulation of area 8 produces dilatation of the pupil while stimulation of area 19 causes constriction. Certain areas of the cortex can influence adrenomedullary release of catecholamines by an inhibitory action on the hypothalamus; modification of cardiovascular reflexes has also been observed following cortical stimulation. These are illustrations of the ability of the cortex to modify the activity of the hypothalamus and hence the autonomic nervous system, but the pathways for these autonomic effects are known with certainty in only a few instances.

SMOOTH MUSCLE

The muscles that serve the motor functions of the autonomic nervous system are different in many respects from skeletal muscles. They lack the characteristic cross-striations of skeletal muscles and are therefore described as 'smooth muscles'. Smooth muscle is found in the intestinal tract, bladder, uterus, and other viscera, in the walls of blood vessels, and in the intra-ocular and pilo-erector muscles.

Structure. Smooth muscles are made up of narrow cells, 4 to 10 μm wide and about 400 μm long, tapering toward their ends. Each cell has a single centrally placed nucleus. These cells are arranged in bundles in which the longitudinal axes of the different cells lie in the same direction. Although the cells are distinct from each other, in that there is no protoplasmic continuity between them, electronmicrographs show regions where the membranes of adjacent cells are fused together into what are known as 'tight junctions'. These regions of close contact between the cells offer little resistance to the passage of electric current. Although smooth muscles are made up of anatomically distinct cells, electrically they may behave as a syncytium.

Smooth muscle cells contain actin filaments and myosin molecules normally lying parallel to the long axis of the cell but not so regularly arranged as in skeletal muscle. It is generally believed that smooth muscle, like skeletal muscle, operates on the sliding filament principle with cross bridges. The force developed per unit cross sectional area is about the same in both kinds (about 350 mN per mm²) but of course smooth muscle is much slower in action.

Spontaneous activity. Smooth muscles, like skeletal muscles, contract in response to depolarization of their cell membranes. This depolarization may follow activity in the motor nerve fibres, as it does in skeletal muscles, but it may also occur without neural activity. Some muscle cells undergo repeated spontaneous depolarization and contraction but, although the rate and extent of this may be modified by activity in the nerve fibres, it does not necessarily depend on neural activity; in this respect it resembles the more rapid and more regular spontaneous activity of heart muscle. In some smooth muscles, spontaneous depolarization and contraction follows extension of the muscle cells; this too may occur independently of activity in the motor nerve fibres. In some large organs activity may be driven from one or more pace-maker regions. Waves of depolarization spread along the organ via the tight junctions between cells.

The spontaneous activity of smooth muscle may be influenced by the levels of circulating hormones; for example, oestrogens, progesterone and oxytocin have powerful effects on uterine muscle, and angiotensin has an effect on vascular smooth muscles. Gastrointestinal hormones affect gut mobility, the best documented being cholecystokinin.

Innervation. The nerve fibres supplying smooth muscle run for long distances (up to 10 cm) among the muscle cells; they have a number of swellings or 'varicosities' along their length which contain the transmitter substance. The motor nerve fibres do not have the same close relation to the muscle cells seen in the motor end-plates of skeletal muscles and the site of transmitter release is much further from the muscle cell membrane (20 to 100 nm). The muscle cells are sensitive to the action of the transmitter along much if not all of their length.

A smooth muscle cell may be supplied by more than one nerve fibre, but in some tissues (such as the uterus) there are many cells which are not directly supplied by any nerve fibre at all. The motor nerve fibres may be 'first order' postsynaptic fibres that have their cell bodies in the autonomic ganglia, or they may be derived from local nerve plexuses, and thus smooth muscle may be remotely controlled by the central nervous system through a number of peripheral neurones and synapses.

Two different chemical transmitters are certainly involved in the neural control of smooth muscle, acetylcholine, and noradrenaline. A number of other substances have also been thought to function as transmitters at particular sites (5-hydroxytryptamine, ATP, prostaglandin E), but their roles are as yet uncertain.

Noradrenaline and acetylcholine function in a way that is broadly similar to the action of ACh in skeletal muscle fibres, diffusing across the gap between the nerve endings and the muscle cell to act at receptor sites on the cell membrane, but whereas the ACh is destroyed by the enzyme acetyl choline esterase, much of the noradrenaline is transported back into the nerve terminals for subsequent re-use. Each of these substances may depolarize the muscle cell membrane to produce an excitatory effect, but may also, at other sites, have an opposite inhibitory effect on the muscle cell. Most smooth muscle is innervated by more than one type of fibre; its activity is often the result of opposing excitatory and inhibitory effects. (See p. 403.) Endorphins influence smooth muscle activity by presynaptic action on the transmitter release of ACh in the myenteric plexus of many parts of the intestinal tract. The physiological role of this is uncertain but it may explain the inhibitory action of opiates.

Neural excitation. In a normal skeletal muscle, each action potential in the motor nerve fibre releases sufficient transmitter (ACh) close enough to the muscle membrane to achieve a threshold depolarization and generate a conducted action potential. In smooth muscle, however, this is not necessarily the case; the amount of transmitter released from a nerve terminal may only be sufficient to produce a subthreshold depolarization which fails to initiate an action potential. This 'excitatory junction potential' may, however, be due to the depolarization of a large area of the cell membrane, and it may be associated with a muscular contraction; further, the presence of tight junctions allows some electrotonic spread of this (subthreshold) depolarization to surrounding cells which also contract. This form of excitation is essentially local, in that it does not give rise to propagated action potentials but, since a single nerve terminal often supplies many different smooth muscle cells, it may still result in quite a widespread contraction.

If a sufficient quantity of transmitter is released close enough to a muscle cell to depolarize it beyond its threshold and initiate an action potential, this may spread to neighbouring cells by current flow through the tight junctions and the action potential together with an associated muscle contraction may spread for some distance through a whole muscle bundle. Such a contraction is, however, much slower than the twitch contraction seen in skeletal muscles.

Smooth muscle may be excited in two ways by its nerve supply. In some tissues (such as the intra-ocular muscles), most of the cells are probably accessible to nerve terminals, and propagation from cell to cell is relatively unimportant; whereas in other tissues (such as the uterus), only a few of the cells are directly innervated and much of the activity is due to propagation of action potentials through tight junctions. Other tissues have properties intermediate between these and use both mechanisms to a greater or lesser extent.

Neural inhibition. In some tissues, such as the intestinal wall, stimulation of noradrenergic fibres leads to inhibition of smooth muscle activity; in other tissues, such as the arterioles of skeletal muscle, cholinergic fibres may have an inhibitory effect. These inhibitory effects are associated with hyper- polarization of the muscle cell membrane in the region of the nerve terminals (an inhibitory junction potential) which inhibits spontaneous activity in the muscle and also tends to oppose the excitatory action of other nerve fibres.

REFERENCES

Antonaccio M J 1977 Cardiovascular pharmacology. Raven Press, New York

Bannister R 1971 Degeneration of the autonomic nervous system. Lancet ii: 175–179

Bennet M R 1972 Autonomic neuromuscular transmission. Monograph of the Physiological Society, no 30. Cambridge University Press

Blaschko H, Sayers G, Smith A D 1975 In: Handbook of physiology, section 7 (Endocrinology), vol VI, The adrenal gland. The American Physiological Society

Bülbring E, Bolton T B (eds) 1979 Smooth muscle. British Medical Bulletin 35: no 3

Bülbring E, Brading A, Jokes A, Tomita (eds) 1970 Smooth muscle. Arnold, London

Burn J H 1971 The autonomic nervous system, 4th edn. Blackwell, Oxford

Day M D 1979 Autonomic pharmacology. Churchill Livingstone, Edinburgh

Ferry C B 1966 Cholinergic link hypothesis in adrenergic neuroeffector transmission. Physiological Reviews 40: 420–456

Gabella G 1976 Structure and function of the autonomic nervous system. Chapman & Hall, London

Gadon G (ed) 1977 Somatic and visceral sensory mechanisms. British Medical Bulletin 33: no 2

Greene N M 1962 Physiology of sympathetic denervation. Annual Reviews of Medicine 13: 87–104

Hughes J (ed) 1978 Centrally acting peptides. Biological Council Symposium on drug action. Macmillan, London

Iverson L L (ed) 1973 Catecholamines. British Medical Bulletin 22: 92–96

Johnson R H, Spalding J M K 1974 Disorders of the Autonomic nervous system. Blackwell, Oxford

Koizumi K, Brooks C M 1972 The integration of autonomic reactions; a discussion of autonomic reflexes, their control and their association with somatic reactions. Ergebnisse der Physiologie 67: 1–68

Newman P P 1974 Visceral afferent functions of the nervous system. Monographs of the Physiological Society, no 25. Arnold, Maidenhead

Prosser C L 1974 Smooth muscle. Annual Reviews of Physiology 36: 503

Reichlen S, Baldessarini R J, Martin J B 1978 The hypothalamus. Raven Press, New York

Sato A, Schmidt R F 1973 Somatosympathetic reflexes: afferent fibres, central pathways, discharge characteristics. Physiological Reviews 53: 916–947

Thorner M O 1975 Dopamine is an important neurotransmitter in the autonomic nervous system. Lancet i: 662–665

26   The Control of Body Temperature

Chemical reactions in the body catalysed by enzymes are dependent upon temperature. The optimal temperature for enzyme-catalysed reactions is the one at which the chemical change is maximal. In addition, thermal inactivation by denaturation is important.

Animal species are commonly described as either 'cold-blooded' or 'warm-blooded'. These widely used but inaccurate terms recognize the fact that fish, amphibia, reptiles and invertebrates are *temperature conformers* whose internal temperature is nearly the same as that of their environment: the rate of their enzyme activity is also largely determined by the ambient temperature which varies not only seasonally but throughout the day and night. The activities of these *poikilothermic* animals are dependent on the environmental temperature. Because the temperature of large masses of water has little diurnal and seasonal variation, aquatic poikilotherms are less dependent on their environmental temperature than terrestrial poikilotherms which must find methods of avoiding the worst stresses by behavioural responses: some desert lizards, for example, bury themselves in sand during the cool night and during the day periodically shelter beneath rocks. A fast-moving, dangerous alligator is made helpless by cooling and the lives of the huge reptiles that once populated the world must have been at the mercy of changes in the climatic temperature. Many enzymes in poikilotherms have been found to have optimal temperatures appropriate to the usual environmental temperature of the animal.

Birds and mammals, on the other hand, have evolved means of maintaining a deep body temperature that is relatively constant even in the face of considerable environmental temperature stress: they are *temperature regulators* and are called *homeothermic* (Fig. 26.1). At the cost of a high metabolic heat production from oxidation and a complicated and rather vulnerable mechanism of temperature regulation they have largely become freed from the constraints of their environmental temperature so that the tiniest mammal, still able to be active in the cold, can compete against much larger poikilothermic predators. The optimal temperatures of the enzymes of homeotherms generally range between 30° and 40°C.

BODY TEMPERATURE

Man is a homeotherm. The range of deep body temperature in a group of healthy persons is quite small. Indeed the coefficient of variation of body temperature in man is one of the smallest for which quantitative data are available (Fig. 26.2).

Since the metabolic rates and the heat conductances of the different tissues and organs of the body differ, so do their temperatures, though in any one region the range of variation may be small. The range of temperatures measured in a number of regions well below the body surface is also small, so it is useful to talk of a relatively stable 'core' or deep body temperature. In contrast the temperature gradients of the superficial 'shell', the thickness of which varies considerably, depend on the site of measurement, the blood flow in muscle and skin and the environmental conditions.

Core Temperature

Since most of the heat produced in the body is the result of oxidations, the main sources of heat are the most active tissues—the liver, secreting glands, and the muscles—which together make up more than half the body weight. The temperature of a single organ, then, varies to some extent according to its metabolic activity, to the rate of blood flow through it, and to the heat gradient between it and surrounding parts. The temperature of the surface of the liver in dogs can be as much as 1·0°C higher than the temperature of the arterial blood, and blood in the right side of the heart has been shown to be some 0·2°C warmer than blood in the left. The temperatures of man in warm conditions taken simultaneously in the mouth, axilla, and rectum usually differ by less than 1°C. Because the temperature recorded in the rectum is usually the

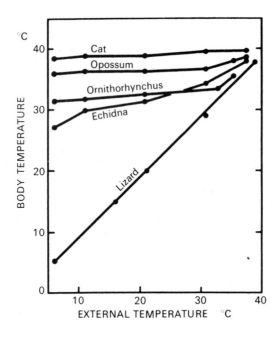

Fig. 26.1 Variation of body temperature of different species of animals after 2 hours in environmental temperatures of from 5°C to 35°C. This figure shows that there is a difference between the behaviour of homeothermic animals (like the cat), which can maintain a constant body temperature in spite of large changes in the external (ambient) temperature, and poikilothermic animals (like the lizard) where body temperature varies with that of the environment. Ornithorhynchus (platypus) and echidna are Australian monotremes, phylogenetically primitive mammals. (C. J. Martin (1930) *Lancet*, ii, 565.)

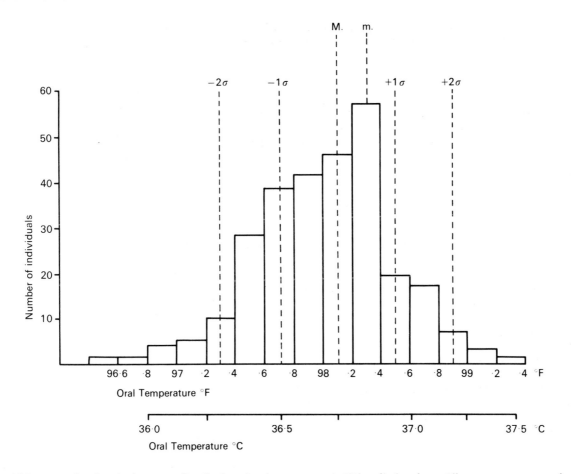

Fig. 26.2   A histogram showing the frequency distribution of oral temperature in 276 medical students. All temperatures were taken between 8 a.m. and 9 a.m. with the subjects seated in a warm classroom. M (arithmetic mean) = 36·7°C; m (mode of the series) = 36·8°C; δ (standard deviation) = 0·22°C. The range was from 35·8°C to 37·3°C. (*Data from* A. C. Ivy (1944) *Quarterly Bulletin of the Northwest University Medical School*, 18, 22; taken with modifications from Du Bois (1949) *Fever and the Regulation of Body Temperature*. Springfield, Ill.: Thomas.)

highest it has generally been assumed to be the best index of the core or central body temperature, say the temperature of the blood in the aorta. However, the rectal temperature may exceed the aortic by as much as 0·3°C; this suggests that heat may actually be produced in the rectum by bacterial action. On the other hand the temperature in the rectum may be lower than arterial temperatures as the result of the arrival of cool blood from the legs. The temperature in the axilla is almost invariably somewhat lower (usually 0·6°C) than that in the mouth but it is difficult to measure accurately with a clinical thermometer. It has been shown that the rectal temperature may vary only very little as the blood is rapidly warmed or cooled, and the same is true of the temperature recorded in the axilla. Mouth temperature, on the other hand, may show rapid alterations as a result of mouth breathing or of drinking warm or cold fluids (Fig. 26.3). Benzinger has shown that the temperature of the tympanic membrane gives the most meaningful correlations with heat losing activities such as vasodilatation and sweating. The ear drum and the hypothalamus are both supplied by blood from the internal carotid artery. When a man is exposed to cold, temperatures recorded from the mouth, ear and other 'deep temperature' sites can differ considerably.

The temperature in the mouth of a healthy man at intervals during the day varies from say, 35·8°C to 37·3°C, being highest in the evening and lowest in the early morning; this pattern, largely unrelated to environmental conditions (Fig. 26.4), is an example of a circadian rhythm. Exercise, because it increases heat production may raise the oral temperature 1° or 2°C and violent exercise can produce temperatures of 39°C. In the female the body temperature varies during the menstrual cycle (p. 492); injections of certain β-steroids (pregnenolone and pregnanediol) cause a rise of body temperature. Temperatures in general tend to be higher in children and lower in the elderly and in neonates.

Shell Temperatures

In temperate climates the body temperature is nearly always higher than the environmental temperature so there is a continuous loss of heat through the skin, the temperature of which may fall as low as 17°C if the air is cold. There is thus a considerable temperature gradient in the superficial half-inch or so of tissue made up chiefly of subcutaneous fat and skin (Table 26.5). In other words the human body is insulated to a

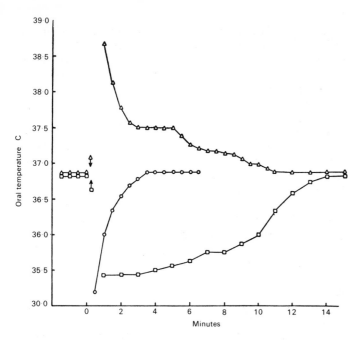

Fig. 26.3 Oral temperatures of the same subject taken with a standard 'half minute' mercury-in-glass clinical thermometer every 30 seconds in 'normal' conditons (O), showing that 3 to 4 minutes are required to obtain an accurate reading. Also shown are the effects on oral temperature of drinking 350 ml of hot tea (△) at 50°C and 350 ml cool water (□) at 10°C; in both cases oral temperature took at least 10 minutes to approach the original level. (C. S. Leithead & A. R. Lind (1964) *Heat Stress and Heat Disorders*. London: Cassells.)

certain extent from its environment. Many animals, especially aquatic animals living in cold regions, are insulated by a thick layer of fat in addition to a coat of fur. The layer of insulation provided by the superficial fat in obese persons may so limit heat loss that on a hot day they may suffer much more discomfort than thin persons.

The temperature of the skin of the body is by no means uniform. The temperature on the surface of a limb exposed to an environmental temperature of 18°C is higher in the proximal part of the limb than in the distal (Fig. 26.6). However, the pattern of this *acral temperature gradient* depends very much on circumstances since the surface temperature of the distal regions is much influenced by the temperature of the environment and by the degree of vasodilatation.

Table 26.5 Temperatures of different tissues of the forearm determined electrically as rapidly as possible after removing clothes. The room temperature was 18·5°C and the oral temperature was 36·9°C.

	Average temperature (°C)
Skin	33·0
Subcutaneous tissue	33·6
Deep muscle	36·2

(H. Barcroft & O. Edholm (1946) *Journal of Physiology*, 104, 366.)

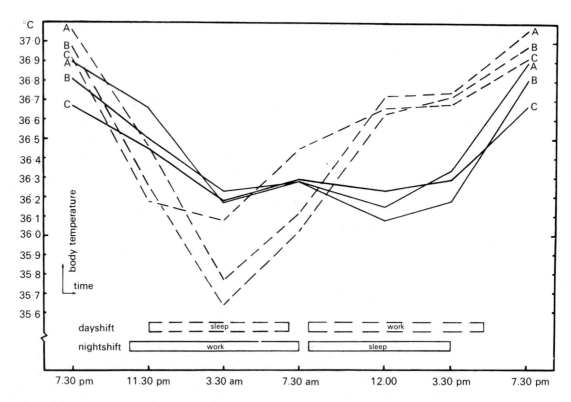

Fig. 26.4 Average body temperature curves of three subjects (A, B and C) in day shift (----) and night shift (———). (*From* J. H. van Loon (1963) *Ergonomics*, 6, 267–273.) The flattening of the circadian rhythm during night shifts tends to increase over successive nights.

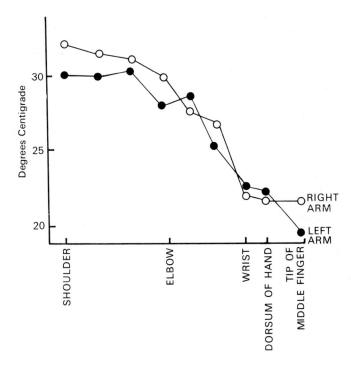

Fig. 26.6 Readings of skin temperature on the two arms of a healthy subject 30 minutes after the limbs had been exposed to an ambient temperature of 18°C, showing an acral (axial) gradient.

THE HEAT BALANCE OF THE BODY

Man evolved as a tropical animal, but most men now live in environmental temperatures much lower than 37°C. The relatively accurate control of body temperature is achieved by balancing heat lost from the body against heat gained either by production within the body or by absorption from outside.

Table 26.7   Heat balance in man

Heat Gains	Heat Losses
Metabolic:	Convection:
Basal metabolism	Ambient temperature
Specific dynamic action (food)	Air currents
Physical exercise	Radiation (long wave)
Shivering	To surroundings and sky
Non-shivering thermogenesis	Skin vasodilatation
Radiation:	Evaporation:
Short-wave from sun	Insensible perspiration
Long-wave from surroundings	Thermoregulatory sweating
Ingestion: hot foods	Ventilation (panting)
Ventilation: hot climates	Conduction:
	Immersion in water.

Reduction of Heat Loss	Reduction of Heat Gain
Vasoconstriction of skin	Behaviour:
(Pilo-erection)	Reduction of clothing
Behaviour:	Increased radiative body
Clothing	surface
Artificial heating	Cooler environment

When calculated over a period of 24 hours the mechanical efficiency of the human body (see p. 16) is relatively low and at least 95 per cent of the 13 MJ produced per day appears as heat which must be lost if the body temperature is not to rise.

Heat produced in the body is lost mainly from the skin and respiratory tract. To preserve a balance any surplus heat must be brought to the surface for dissipation. This is achieved by conductance in the tissues and their fluids, but above all by the circulating blood which has a high heat capacity because of its large water content. At the body surface heat can be shed by radiation, convection and conduction so long as there is a favourable temperature gradient from within outwards. Convection currents set up in the atmosphere aid the spread of heat from the body surface to some extent, but most (60 to 65 per cent) is lost by radiation to surfaces at a lower temperature. More heat is lost by the evaporation of water (20 to 30 per cent) so long as the ambient air is not saturated and the water-saturated layer of air next the body is steadily removed by air currents.

Because air is a poor conductor of heat the amount trapped in clothing near the skin provides some insulation, particularly when air humidity remains low. The fibres of most types of clothing are also poor conductors so the effective shedding of heat by the body in a temperate climate depends largely on temperature gradients and radiation. When the environmental temperature prevents an outward flow of heat the evaporation of water from the surfaces of the respiratory tract and the wetted skin becomes the only effective method of losing heat and restraining a rise in body temperature.

Body heat balance equation. A mathematical expression that describes the net rate at which a body generates and exchanges heat with its environment according to the first law of thermodynamics has its physiological expression in the *body heat balance equation*:

$$S = M \pm E - (\pm W) \pm R \pm C \pm K$$

in which all the terms represent a transfer of energy expressed in watts or watts/m². S is the rate of storage of body heat, M that of the metabolic production of free energy, E that of heat transfer by evaporation, W that of work (+ for positive work against external forces), R that of radiant heat exchange, C that of convective heat transfer, K that of conductive heat transfer. It should be noted that in this equation 'positive work' $(+W)$ in terms of body heat balance is the transfer of energy from the body to an external system and is therefore a loss of energy, represented in the equation by $-(+W)$ or a loss, W; 'negative work' is the converse.

Table 26.7 shows the ways in which the human body gains or loses heat.

Heat Gains

Non-shivering thermogenesis. A proportion of the heat produced in the body may be regarded as inevitable or *obligatory* since it arises from vital activities such as respiration, heart-beat and circulation, maintenance of muscle tone, secretion and metabolism. Heat produced by such means, though not of course constant, does not change in response to the demands of temperature control.

The amount of heat produced by a man in a temperate climate depends on the kind and amount of food eaten and metabolized, variations in heat loss compensating for variations in the amount of heat produced at different levels of food intake. In very hot or very cold environments, however, there is a notable alteration in the appetite and in the amount of food consumed, the increased appetite during a cold day in winter being a familiar experience. Observations made during the Second World War showed that the amount of food eaten by troops with access to as much food as they wanted varied with the local ambient temperature (Fig. 26.8) but the percentage of the total energy provided by protein, fat and carbohydrate varied very little with the climatic conditions; that derived from protein was surprisingly constant, about 12 per cent.

The pituitary, thyroid and adrenal medulla, controlled by the hypothalamus, each play a part in endogenous thermogenesis (Fig. 26.9).

The source of most non-shivering thermogenesis in infants is the brown adipose tissue (Fig. 26.18).

Shivering. A large amount of heat can be produced by the muscular effort of exercise voluntarily performed when the subject feels cold. Heat can also be produced by involuntary muscular activity when a subject is cold. This activity may be of two kinds. There is first an irregular but imperceptible activity of muscle units contracting out of phase with one another known as *thermal muscular tone*. Later the activity becomes regular and phasic and *shivering* occurs. Heat produced in these three ways may be regarded as *adjustable*. The onset of shivering is not closely related to rectal temperature, but can be initiated by afferent impulses from the surface of the body, since, in a cold person, painful stimuli or a stream of cold air or water playing on the skin produces shivering within a few seconds. However, shivering has been produced in the intact fore-limbs of a dog, whose spinal cord had been transected, by

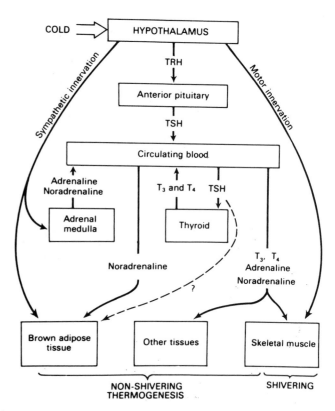

Fig. 26.9   The main mechanisms of endogenous thermogenesis in response to exposure to cold. Maclean, D. & Emslie-Smith, D. (1977). *Accidental Hypothermia*. Oxford: Blackwell.

the immersion of the paralysed and anaesthetic hind limbs in cold water. This experiment shows that, at any rate in the dog, there must be a central mechanism sensitive to a fall in temperature of the blood flowing through it. However, in a rabbit whose spinal cord is cut across either cooling of the isolated part of the cord or cooling of the limbs supplied by it causes shivering identical in rhythm with that seen when the central nervous system is intact. The rhythm of cold shivering seems to originate within the areas of the motoneurone pool. A healthy young male athlete when shivering produces heat at a maximum rate of about 38 kJ per kg per minute.

Heat cannot be produced by muscles paralysed by disease (Fig. 26.10), or by a relaxant drug, like curare, or by an anaesthetic. The temperature of an anaesthetized patient thus tends to fall to that of the environment. For this reason surgical operating theatres are kept warm.

Radiation. Man often gains some heat from direct solar radiation in the form of short-wave (0·3 to 3·0 μm) electromagnetic radiation and also gains heat as long-wave (3·0 to 100 μm) radiation from his warmer surroundings.

Heat Loss

Although the amount of heat produced in the body can be varied to some extent, it is mainly by variations in heat loss that the accurate control of body temperature is achieved. During ordinary life in a temperate climate our activities are such that it is more likely that the body becomes overheated than overcooled. During the winter, however, the aged and

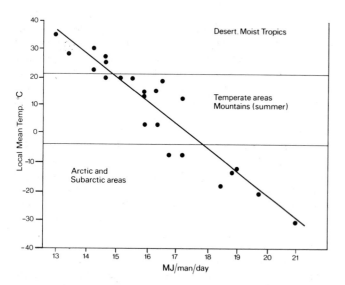

Fig. 26.8   Voluntary caloric intake, North American troops (averages for groups of 50 or more men). The diagram shows the relation between caloric intake and climatic conditions. The increased requirements in arctic conditions are partly caused by the impeding effect of heavy clothing (R. E. Johnston & R. M. Kark (1947) *Science*, 105, 378.)

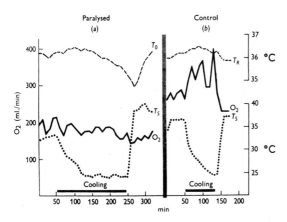

Fig. 26.10 Changes in total oxygen consumption (O_2) during cooling; in oesophageal temperature (T_o); in rectal temperature (T_R); and skin temperature (T_s). (a) Paralysed patient. (b) Control subject. In the paralysed subject, virtually deprived of skeletal muscle, the oxygen consumption did not rise when he was cooled because he had no means of increasing his heat production. The skin temperature fell to a minimum of 17·6°C and the oesophageal temperature by as much as 1·8°C. (R. H. Johnson & J. M. K. Spalding (1963) *Journal of Physiology*, **166**, 24P.)

infirm may suffer from overcooling (p. 421), and may die with hypothermia.

Some 500 kJ are lost per day in warming the food and air taken into the body and another 1·5 MJ are consumed in evaporating water to saturate the air expired from the lungs. These 2 MJ represent, however, only about 16 per cent of the total of 12·5 MJ of heat which must be lost each day, leaving some 84 per cent to be lost through the skin.

Cutaneous blood flow. Heat loss from the skin by convection, radiation and conduction is much influenced by environmental conditions such as ambient temperature, relative humidity and the movement of air: it is greatest, for example, when the weather is cool and windy. It also depends on the state of the blood vessels in the subcutaneous tissues.

Vasoconstriction can reduce the conductance of the superficial tissues to about that of cork: the transfer of heat from the core to the surface is lessened and less heat is lost by convection and radiation. On the other hand vasodilatation may increase the superficial blood flow to as much as 100 times the minimum, virtually abolishing the gradient between the core and the surface and allowing greater heat loss by radiation and convection. When a man is not sweating the greater part of the heat produced by the body is lost in this way, convection accounting for 15 per cent, and radiation for 60 per cent, of the heat loss. Heat loss by conduction is important only during immersion in cold water; this applies particularly to shipwrecked persons and even to fit but thin young people in swimming baths.

Sweating. In the basal state there is a loss of body weight, due to evaporation from the lungs and to *insensible perspiration* of about 30 g per hour. This water passes through the skin by diffusion and osmosis, and not as the result of the activity of the sweat glands. Since the latent heat of vaporization of water at body temperature is 2·4 kJ/g this water loss represents

$$30 \times 2\cdot4\,kJ/h = 72\,kJ/h = 1\cdot73\,MJ/day$$

For an average man (see p. 16) the basal metabolism is 300 kJ/h (7·2 MJ/day). Thus about one-quarter of the heat is lost by the skin and lungs even when no sweating occurs. It is usually reckoned that one-quarter of the heat loss occurs in this way whatever the level of activity. Insensible perspiration is not controlled by the hypothalamus.

For over 30 years it has been taught that there are two distinct kinds of sweating, *thermoregulatory sweating* occurring all over the body and *emotional sweating* largely confined to the palms of the hands, soles of the feet and axillae. Roddie and his colleagues recently measured the emotional sweat loss provoked by mental arithmetic from various areas of the body. They found that the contribution of sweat from each region was a substantial fraction of the total body sweat and appeared to be roughly proportional to the calculated number of sweat glands in each region; the sweat glands of the hands and feet behaved no differently from those of the rest of the body.

If the circulation to a limb is cut off by a tourniquet sweating is unaffected for several minutes before it decreases gradually to zero in half an hour or so. Sweat must therefore be produced by the activity of the cells and not by filtration.

Although the sweat glands are supplied by post-ganglionic sympathetic fibres the humoral effector substance is acetylcholine. After an injection of atropine sweating is much reduced. This can be seen in a hot operating theatre if the patient has had an injection of atropine before the operation to diminish bronchial secretion. The intravenous injection of adrenaline in man has no effect on sweating but the intra-arterial injection of adrenaline in relatively high dosage does produce sweating blocked by phentolamine but not by atropine. Fox and Hilton have found a bradykinin-forming enzyme in sweat just as in saliva (p. 37). Presumably the enzyme released from the sweat glands acts on tissue-space proteins to produce bradykinin which is responsible for the accompanying vasodilatation.

About 50 per cent of the total sweat produced on a hot day comes from the skin of the trunk, about 25 per cent from the lower limbs, and the remaining 25 per cent from the head and upper limbs. When sweating becomes profuse, so as to give rise to visible drops, it usually does so quite suddenly and at about the same time all over the body. Thermal sweating is reduced if the person is short of fluid (dehydrated) and this may be the cause of 'dehydration fever'.

In hot climates, when atmospheric temperatures exceed body temperature, heat loss must continue, although now radiation and convection actually supply heat to the body. The mere production of sweat, even in large quantities, does not get rid of heat; indeed, the presence of sweat on the skin tends to inhibit further sweating. To accomplish this the sweat must evaporate; every gram of water evaporated requires the expenditure of 2·42 kJ. The removal of 12·6 MJ per day, for example, requires the evaporation of $12\cdot6 \div 2\cdot42 = 5\cdot2$ kg of water per day. Evaporation of sweat occurs readily in a dry atmosphere and efficiently prevents a rise in body temperature. The fluid loss from the skin and respiratory tract of men living in summer by the Persian Gulf or in the Sudan is about 2 to 4 litres per day. In a warm atmosphere a hot drink, by promoting sweating, cools the body better than a cold drink. Evaporation of sweat is impeded by a humid atmosphere; thus very hot humid environments are incompatible with life.

Heat Storage

Homeotherms, apart from the dehydrated camel and a few other equatorial animals, normally only store heat for brief periods during and just after physical exertion. A ready means of estimating whether heat is being stored or lost by the body would be available if the change in *mean body temperature* ($\overline{T}_b$) could be found and the average body specific heat calculated:

Heat stored = change in mean body temperature
$\times$ specific heat of body $\times$ mass of body.

The specific heat of the body is usually taken to be 3·48 kJ per kg per °C. If it is assumed that the rectal temperature—which can easily be measured—is that of two-thirds of the body, and the mean skin temperature is that of the other third:

Mean body temperature $(\overline{T}_b) = (0 \cdot 67 T_{re} + 0 \cdot 33 \overline{T}_{sk})$ where T_{re} is rectal temperature, $\overline{T}_{sk}$ the mean skin temperature.

If we suppose that each area of the skin contributes to the mean skin temperature in proportion to its fraction of the total body surface, we can construct an equation for the mean skin temperature:

Mean skin temperature $= (0 \cdot 7 T_{he} + 0 \cdot 14 T_a + 0 \cdot 05 T_{ha}$
$+ 0 \cdot 07 T_f + 0 \cdot 13 T_l + 0 \cdot 19 T_{th} + 0 \cdot 35 T_t)$

where T_{he} is the temperature of the skin of the head, T_a of the arms, T_{ha} of the hands, T_f of the feet, T_l of the legs, T_{th} of the thighs and T_t of the trunk.

The last equation allows us also to calculate the approximate *thermal conductance* (C) within the body. This is the 'coefficient of heat transfer from the core to the surface of the body':

Heat conductance

$$= \frac{\text{rate of heat transfer}}{\text{rectal temperature} - \text{mean skin temperature}}$$

The conductance is measured in J/hr/°C, or, when related to unit area body surface, in W per square metre per °C. When the body is in thermal equilibrium, that is, not changing its net heat content, the rate of total body heat transfer must equal the metabolic rate and that can be measured.

THERMOREGULATION

Thermoregulation is a good example of homeostasis maintained through a feedback mechanism. The control system is more complicated than some others in the body because it includes two different afferent channels, changes in the temperature of arterial blood and nervous impulses from temperature receptors.

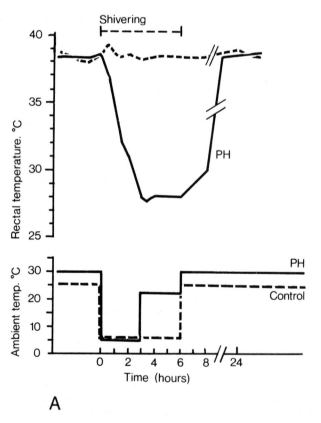

A

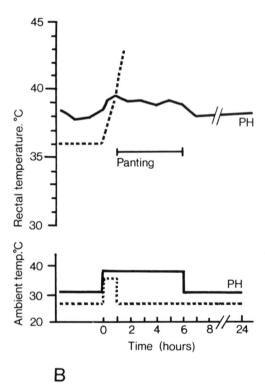

B

Fig. 26.11 The effect of experimentally induced lesions of the hypothalamus on three dogs, whose rectal temperatures and corresponding ambient temperatures are represented by solid, dashed and dotted lines. A shows the response of a normal control dog (dashed line) and an experimental dog (solid line) to a cold environment: by shivering the normal dog maintained his rectal temperature, but the dog with the hypothalamic lesion (PH) became hypothermic. B shows that the same dog (PH) could maintain a normal temperature by panting when exposed to a hot environment, while another dog with a different hypothalamic lesion (dotted line) rapidly became hyperpyrexic. (*Modified from* A. D. Keller (1950) *Physical Therapy Review*, 30, 511–519.)

The balance between heat gain and heat loss is controlled by the nervous system. Heat production can be increased by voluntary muscular effort or by shivering; both activities are effected through motor nerves. In man shivering is mediated through the anterior motoneurones, activated not by the pyramidal tract but by the lateral tectospinal or rubrospinal tracts. Heat loss can be altered by varying the amount of blood flowing through the vessels of the skin or it can be increased by sweating. These activities are controlled through the sympathetic nervous system. Small adjustments of body temperature are made by altering the skin blood-flow, larger adjustments by shivering or sweating. In homeothermic animals other than man panting is a method of increasing heat loss and piloerection a method of conserving heat.

Temperature Receptors

Central thermoreceptors. It is generally agreed that the main temperature regulating region lies in the hypothalamus. There is less agreement about the details of the nervous control. The experimental destruction of small areas in the hypothalamus has shown that lesions in the anterior hypothalamus render the animal unable to regulate its temperature in a warm environment although thermoregulation remains normal in the cold. Lesions of the posterior hypothalamus, however, impair the animal's ability to conserve heat in a cold environment without altering thermoregulation in warm conditions (Fig. 26.11). Such experiments led to the classical view that a group of cells in the anterior hypothalamus acted as a 'heat loss centre' while another group in the posterior hypothalamus acted as a 'heat conservation centre'. This view was supported by the results of experimental electrical stimulation of these areas: stimulation of the anterior site causes skin vasodilatation, panting and the inhibition of shivering even in the cold, while stimulation of the posterior site produces shivering, vasoconstriction and piloerection. The anterior centre is extremely sensitive to heating by an implanted electrode ('thermode') and the animal with an implanted thermode increases its heat loss in the usual ways. If the hypothalamus is continuously heated the animal continues to lose heat even though the increased heat loss has caused a fall in the core temperature. There is no agreement about the presence or absence of cold receptors in the posterior hypothalamus. Central thermoreceptors, at any rate in the experimental animal, are not confined to the hypothalamus but can be demonstrated in the spinal cord.

Peripheral thermoreceptors. Heat and cold can be felt on the skin and in the upper part of the gastrointestinal tract because of the existence of *peripheral thermoreceptors*. Peripheral receptors to cold begin to fire when the skin temperature falls below about 35°C: a cold receptor investigated by Hensel by studying a single fibre of his own radial nerve had a maximum firing rate at 20°C. Thermoreceptors in skin are possibly connected to two different effector systems, one pathway conveying impulses to the cortex, producing conscious sensation, the other running to the posterior hypothalamic centre.

The usual class experiments on temperature regulation suggest that its control is complex and dependent partly upon reflexes originating in the cutaneous receptors and partly on

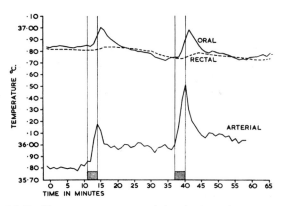

Fig. 26.12 Temperature measured in the mouth, rectum and contralateral subclavian artery in a normal subject during immersion of one forearm in a bath of warm water (shaded areas indicate duration of immersion). (*From* W. I. Cranston (1966) *British Medical Journal*, ii, 69–75.)

the central receptors, sensitive to the temperature of blood from the periphery. If one hand is immersed in cold water the temperature of the other soon begins to drop, even if the circulation to the hand immersed had first been occluded by a cuff. The effect must be due to reflex vasoconstriction. Extensive vasoconstriction may cut down the total heat loss to such an extent that the oral temperature may actually rise a little. The afferent pathways for this reflex are in the cutaneous nerves and the efferent pathways are in the sympathetic nervous system; the central connexions are in the spinal cord but whether they communicate with the brain is uncertain. But if one hand is immersed in warm water (40°C) there is, after some delay, vasodilatation and increase in skin temperature in the opposite hand. This does not occur if the circulation to the hand immersed in water is occluded before immersion. Blood warmed in the immersed hand raises the arterial and oral temperatures, but not the rectal, (Fig. 26.12) and stimulates central control receptors in the hypothalamus to release cutaneous vasomotor tone.

When the skin of the trunk is exposed to radiant heat the hand blood flow increases in about 15 seconds although the central temperature falls rather than rises. The reflex arc for this response runs at a level higher than C5 in the spinal cord and the reflex is inhibited if the central temperature is below 36·5 to 36·8°C; it is also progressively inhibited if the initial skin temperature of the trunk is less than 33°C.

Integrated Control of Thermoregulation

Using whole-body gradient calorimetry (p. 13) and measuring temperatures at the tympanic membrane Benzinger has shown how accurately the interactions between the peripheral and central thermoreceptors are adjusted. Figure 26.13 shows that when a warm subject swallows ice the cool blood lowers the intracranial temperature and sweating is inhibited. Because evaporation from the skin is reduced the skin temperature rises, only to fall as sweating begins to increase. The relationship between the intracranial temperature and the sweating rate at different ambient temperatures is shown in Figure 26.14. At ambient temperatures above 33°C sweating starts promptly when the intracranial temperature

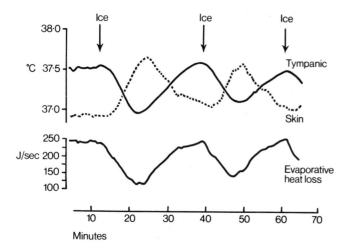

Fig. 26.13 Records of the evaporative heat loss and the temperatures of the skin (dotted line) and the tympanic membrane (solid line) of a human subject in an ambient temperature of 45°C. Three times, on the ingestion of 450 g iced sherbet ('Ice'), the tympanic temperature (equivalent to the intracranial temperature) and the heat loss from sweating declined in parallel, while the consequent reduction in sweating allowed the skin temperature to rise. The rate of sweating follows the intracranial, not the skin, temperature. (*Adapted from* T. H. Benzinger (1959) *Proceedings of the National Academy of Sciences, U.S.A.*, 45, 645–659.)

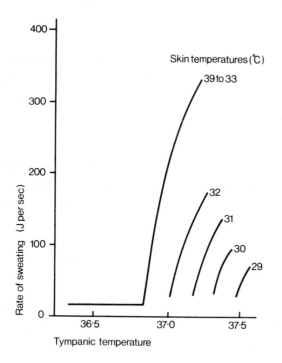

Fig. 26.14 Rates of evaporative heat loss (sweating) from a healthy naked man at varying tympanic membrane temperatures. At skin temperatures between 39° and 33°C sweating began at a sharply defined 'internal' temperature (about 36·9°C). At any given 'internal' temperature evaporative heat loss diminished progressively with skin temperatures falling below 33°C. The experiment demonstrates the 'set-point for sweating' and the inhibition of sweating by cutaneous cold receptors. (*Modified from* T. H. Benzinger (1959) *Physiological Reviews*, 49, 671–759.)

rises a little above 36.8°C; when the ambient temperature is only 29°C sweating does not occur until the intracranial temperature is about 37·5°C; its onset seems to be inhibited by peripheral cold receptors. The intracranial threshold ('set-point') for sweating, normally about 36·8°C, is raised when the skin temperature is less than 33°C.

Similar interactions between peripheral and central receptors are involved in the control of heat production. In a cold environment shivering begins at a higher intracranial temperature than in a warm environment and as the ambient temperature increases shivering is delayed until the intracranial temperature falls further (Fig. 26.15).

Such experiments suggest the existence of a set-point in the human 'thermostat'. Benzinger considers that the thermostat is situated in the anterior hypothalamic centre which he regards as a sensory organ sensitive to temperature, normally the temperature of the perfusing blood. He considers that the posterior hypothalamic centre is insensitive to temperature but is excited by impulses from the cold receptors of skin and inhibited by impulses from the anterior centre that arise when the temperature of the blood perfusing the anterior hypothalamus reaches a level about 1°C below the set-point for sweating.

Benzinger maintains that the hypothalamic cold receptor centre in man is too weak to play a major role under ordinary circumstances. It must, however, be important in fur-covered animals in which the cutaneous receptors are well sheltered.

The central cold receptors in man can undoubtedly be brought into play in special circumstances. Downey, Chiodi and Darling studied patients with section of the cervical cord. They showed that in these patients central cold receptors could bring about effects independently of impulses from cutaneous receptors, though the effects are comparatively small and slow compared with the rapid and powerful responses demonstrated in intact man (Fig. 26.15).

Hemingway showed that shivering induced by cooling the skin in dogs could not be abolished by warming the anterior hypothalamus with a thermode whereas warming the posterior hypothalamus did. He seems to ascribe a stronger role to the central cold receptors than Benzinger would allow. Others believe that the posterior hypothalamus controls the set-point for body temperature regulation and it is possible that there are thermosensitive areas in other parts of the mid-brain and spinal cord.

Chemical Control of Central Thermoregulation

According to Myers, the set-point seems to depend on the ionic concentration in the blood perfusing the hypothalamus. When the $[Na^+]$ in the posterior hypothalamus of the cat or monkey is raised above the normal level the temperature rises and when the $[Ca^{2+}]$ is raised the body temperature falls. K^+ and Mg^+ have no effect. Further increasing the $[Ca^{2+}]$ lowers the set-point of the hypothalamic thermostat. When warm water is put in its stomach the animal's temperature rises only slightly and soon returns to its previously low value; when ice-cold water is used instead the body temperature falls for a short time but soon rises to the experimentally induced, but low, set-point. Conversely if the set-point is raised by increasing the $[Na^+]$, thermoregulation occurs around this higher set-point.

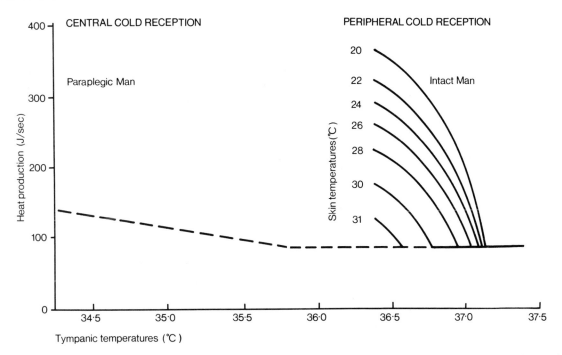

Fig. 26.15 Right-hand side (solid lines): oxygen consumption (heat production) of a healthy man at various tympanic membrane and skin temperatures. After the 'internal' temperature fell below a set-point of about 37·1°C the metabolic heat production rose to remarkably high levels, driven by impulses from cutaneous cold-receptors and released from inhibition by central warm-receptors. Increasing skin temperatures inhibited heat production even at lower 'internal' temperatures. Left-hand side (dashed line): the much smaller and slower metabolic response to cooling of a paraplegic patient, mediated by the central cold receptors. (*Adapted from* T. H. Benzinger (1959) *Physiological Reviews*, 49, 671–759.)

Perfusion of the cat's cerebral ventricles with artificial cerebrospinal fluid containing excess calcium lowers body temperature and counteracts the hyperthermic effect of leucocyte pyrogen (p. 421).

The hypothalamus contains relatively high concentrations of 5-hydroxytryptamine (5HT) and noradrenaline. When injected into the anterior hypothalamus or into the ventral half of the third ventricle of the unanaesthetized cat 5HT causes a rise of body temperature and shivering, whereas adrenaline and noradrenaline cause a fall in body temperature and abolish shivering. It may therefore be that these substances act as transmitters. However, not all laboratory animals react in this way; perhaps they use different monoamines. The effect of injection of the catecholamines is observable within 2 minutes; injection of bacterial pyrogens (Fig. 26.19) into the anterior hypothalamus produces a rise of temperature only after quarter of an hour.

Myers using the conscious rhesus monkey employed an ingenious crossed circulation technique to transfer CSF or hypothalamic perfusate from a donor which could be heated or cooled to a recipient. On cooling the donor the recipient shivered; on heating the donor the recipient either showed little change or else a sharp drop in temperature. Clearly something had been transferred, but the transmitter need not have been 5-HT or noradrenaline; these substances on infusion might simply mimic its action.

The role of 5-HT as a transmitter in the temperature regulating region has not been completely established but there is considerable evidence in favour of the idea that it is involved. The enzymes necessary for synthesis and decompo-

sition are present and 5-HT can be stored in the neurones of the regulatory regions. The latest candidate for the role of transmitter is prostaglandin E_1; it produces an obvious rise of temperature when injected in doses of 100 ng or less into the lateral ventricle of both cats and rabbits. The amount of prostaglandin in the CSF is increased when fever is induced by pyrogens.

Removal of the cerebral cortex in the dog does not seriously impair temperature regulation and in man, too, control of body temperature is believed to be independent of the cortex. However, in both dog and man emotional stress can cause a rise of body temperature.

THERMONEUTRALITY AND THERMAL COMFORT

When faced with an unfavourably cold environment homeothermic animals increase their metabolic rate to produce more heat. In an unduly hot environment the increased sweat rate is also associated with a rise in the metabolic rate. The *thermoneutral zone* (*TNZ*) is defined as the range of ambient temperature within which metabolic rate is at a minimum and within which temperature regulation is achieved by nonevaporative physical processes alone. The *critical temperature* is defined as the ambient temperature below which the metabolic heat production of a resting thermoregulating animal increases to maintain thermal balance. The 'metabolic rate' used in these definitions is not synonymous with the basal metabolic rate (BMR). Figure

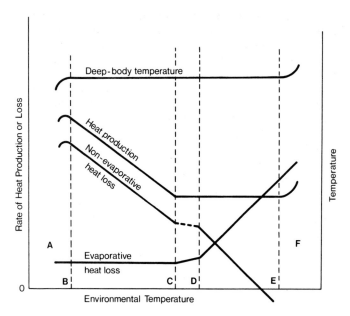

Fig. 26.16 Diagrammatic representation of the relationships between heat production, evaporative and non-evaporative heat loss and deep-body temperature in a homeothermic animal resting but free to move in a metabolic chamber. A, zone of hypothermia; B, temperature of peak metabolism and incipient hypothermia; C, critical temperature; D, temperature of marked increase in evaporative loss; E, temperature of incipient hyperthermal rise; F, zone of hyperthermia; CD, zone of least thermoregulatory effort; CE, zone of minimal metabolism; BE, thermoregulatory range. 'Environmental temperature' assumes air and mean radiant temperatures equal to one another, free convection and relative humidity 50 per cent. (Mount, L. E. (1974) The concept of thermal neutrality. In *Heat Loss from Animals and Man*, ed. Monteith, J. L. & Mount, L. E., pp. 425–439. London: Butterworth.)

26.16 shows some relationships between heat production, heat loss and deep body temperature in a homeotherm. This scheme illustrates principles and does not claim to be accurate in detail: for example, it would be rare to find the core temperature of an animal staying constant over the full range of thermoregulation. The range CD may sometimes be very small indeed.

The zone of thermoneutrality, or least thermoregulatory effort, should not be confused with the *preferred ambient temperature* which is the range of ambient temperature associated with specified radiation intensity, humidity and air movement from which an unrestrained animal does not seek to move to a warmer or colder environment. This temperature is associated with *thermal comfort*. Man produces it by intelligent behaviour, using appropriate clothing, shelter from heat and cold and the help of fire.

Clothing

We are all accustomed to choosing our clothing according to the prevailing climatic and weather conditions. We can cope reasonably well with hot conditions by wearing light clothes, by remaining inactive and taking cooling drinks but we are quite unable to produce enough heat to keep warm in severe cold. Certain combinations of central and cutaneous tempera-

tures may also prevent an adequate rise in metabolic rate to maintain normal body temperature, since we cannot reflexly raise our metabolic rate by more than three or four times the basal value.

When the air is still, the layer of warm air round the body acts as an insulator because air is a poor conductor of heat. If air currents disturb this layer of air it is continuously replaced and heat is lost by convection. In cold weather we diminish this loss by putting on clothes, the amount being adjusted by experience so that the regulation of body temperature is brought within the range of our physiological mechanisms.

The thermal insulation provided by clothes depends on the air imprisoned in the meshes; the thermal insulation of an air space increases with its thickness up to a maximum at about 1 centimetre but, if the space is loosely filled with textile material to prevent convection currents, the insulation continues to be proportional to the thickness. For textiles of low bulk-density the insulation provided is the same whether the fabric is wool, cotton, kapok, or any other material. The essential insulator, then, is the air, the particular textile employed to imprison the air making little difference to its efficiency as an insulator. Clothes are warm when they entangle dry air in their fibres since dry air is a poor conductor of heat but they lose much of the insulating value if they become damp since damp air is a relatively good conductor. Clothing therefore should assist in maintaining a layer of warm still air close to the body but it must not hinder the escape of moisture. Mountaineers have also to contend with both cold and wind; the strength of the wind may be the dominating factor. Protective clothing is now made of material that is almost windproof and waterproof but not so tightly woven that it prevents the evaporation of sweat.

It is convenient to have a rating of the insulating value of clothing. The unit chosen is such that the business man's ordinary indoor suit has a value of 1 Clo. This allows maintenance of a comfortable skin temperature of about 33°C in a room at 21°C with air movement not over 30 cm/min and relative humidity not over 50 per cent when the subject's metabolic rate is 210 kJ/m²/h, designated 1 Met. The best ordinary clothing has a value of about 4 Clo per inch of thickness.

Comfort depends largely on skin temperature, the optimum being about 33°C. This temperature can be maintained in a cold environment only if the clothing is properly chosen in relation to the activity of the subject.

People about to leave a sinking ship should of course wear approved life jackets but, almost as important, if they have time, they should put on as much clothing as possible or wear approved survival suits. It is important to start with dry clothes and to try to keep them dry. Wet clothing may contain, say 3 kg of water, the evaporation of which at body temperature requires $3 \times 2.42 = 7.3$ MJ which is the equivalent of a good emergency food ration for a day. The same principles apply to endurance walks on mountain and moor. Inner clothing must be kept dry by windproof outer clothing. Water-repellent exposure suits have been specially designed so that they can be continuously worn over the clothing. They prevent spray from soaking the clothing but at the same time allow water vapour derived by evaporation from the body to escape.

In hot conditions, especially in strong sunlight, lightweight cotton or linen clothing or some of the modern substitutes is usually worn. White garments reflect the heating rays of the sun. Black clothing may absorb over 90 per cent of the sun's infra-red radiation whereas white clothing absorbs only about 30 per cent. The radiant energy met indoors has a longer wave length and white clothing is no protection. Low resistance to the transference of water vapour is a useful property of clothing used in hot climates. Cotton clothing is preferable to nylon since cotton threads act better as capillaries to carry water through the garment.

Environmental Conditions

The reactions of a human being to different climatic conditions depend on individual, subjective ideas of comfort and discomfort. It is therefore not surprising to find that no simple yet satisfactory method of estimating the suitability or otherwise of an environment either indoors or out-of-doors has been devised. Apart from the individual's preferences the physical factors involved are air temperature, air flow, humidity and incident radiant heat. Though air movement does increase markedly the cooling power of an atmosphere a certain amount is refreshing as it dissipates odours and removes the layer of damp air from the body surface.

Indoors the conditions should be such as to assist body temperature regulation and allow maintenance of a comfortable skin temperature without engaging too strongly the heat regulating mechanisms. Adjustment of the 'microclimate' where the individual actually sits or works may be difficult because of the incidence of radiant heat from the walls, the shape of the room, and the fact that air currents tend to circulate close to the walls. It is obviously important to find the factors which determine comfort so as to assist the heating and ventilating engineer to produce the optimum conditions.

The best test object is of course the individual himself and a number of individuals can be used to assess the comfort of a series of rooms on a suitably graded scale ranging from 'much too warm' through 'comfortable' to 'much too cool'. These judgments may be given numerical values in a seven point scale and various instruments may be used at the same time to measure the physical properties of the environment. Since the removal of the layer of moist air next the skin is essential for continuous heat loss and heat should be transferable from subject to surroundings rather than in the reverse direction the factors to be measured are fairly obvious. The instruments generally employed are:

1. Wet and dry bulb thermometers to indicate air temperature and humidity.

2. The whirling psychrometer (sling hygrometer) or the Assmann psychrometer, where air is dragged over the thermometer bulbs at speeds in excess of 3 m/sec, are preferable to (1) since the effect of random air currents is eliminated.

3. A silvered katathermometer or a vane anemometer to measure the rate of air movement.

4. A mat black globe thermometer to measure the radiation.

Bedford prepared tables and nomograms from which a single temperature indicative of the comfortableness of the atmosphere may be obtained, namely the 'effective temperature'. This is based on the temperature, humidity and rate of movement of the air. The effective temperature gives in fact the temperature of a room with still, saturated air which would give the same sensation of warmth as the room being measured. Where considerable radiant heat is present the 'corrected effective temperature' based on globe thermometer, humidity and air velocity is more suitable.

Thermal comfort is, of course, the chief concern of engineers interested in artificial ventilation and many complicated nomograms have been devised by them, and by physiologists such as Fanger, to determine satisfactory environmental conditions for people clad in different ways and engaged in different activities.

In the United Kingdom a room temperature of 16°C is laid down by law as the minimum for workers in offices and shops, and a living-room temperature not less than 18·3°C is officially recommended for elderly people when the outside temperature is –4°C.

TEMPERATURE REGULATION IN THE NEWBORN

The ability of mammals of any age to regulate body temperature is limited by their thermal insulation and by the surface area exposed to cold. The exposed surface of a small mammal is much greater relative to its body weight than that of a large animal of similar shape. For this reason alone one might expect differences between an infant and an adult, but the amount of motor development at birth also affects the activity, behaviour and maximum rate of endogenous heat production of infants.

The deep temperature of the normal fetus is about 37·6 to 37·8°C, not only higher than that of its mother but above the threshold for sweating of the newly born. At birth the baby is delivered wet into an ambient atmosphere often over 10°C lower than its critical temperature. It therefore loses heat rapidly at a rate of about 0·8 kJ/kg/minute. A healthy baby can produce about 0·34 kJ/kg/minute, less than half its heat loss. It is thus not surprising that immediately after birth a baby rapidly becomes cold. The newborn infant has all the

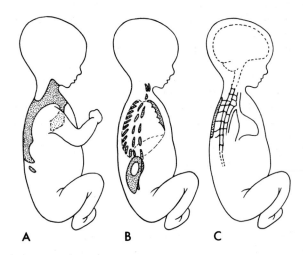

Fig. 26.17 A and B, distribution of brown adipose tissue in the baby. C, diagrammatic representation of the venous drainage from the interscapular pad. (*From* W. Aherne & D. Hull (1964) *Proceedings of the Royal Society of Medicine*, 57, 1172–1173.)

thermoregulatory mechanisms of the adult but they are less efficient and there is a considerable difference between the relative importance of the different mechanisms.

The baby is incapable of avoiding cold by intelligent behaviour. It responds first by vasoconstriction until the tissue insulation is maximal but this maximal insulation is low compared with that of an adult. After vasoconstriction the metabolic rate increases during the first 36 hours of life and becomes maximal at about two and a half times the resting rate of heat production. This increase in metabolic rate is the result of non-shivering thermogenesis, mostly in the thermogenic *brown adipose tissue* that lies deep to the insulative white subcutaneous fat (Fig. 26.18).

Brown adipose tissue looks brown only when the iron-containing cytochrome becomes visible because of lipid depletion. A brown-fat cell contains many small fat vacuoles and many large mitochondria; this arrangement permits such rapid oxidation of fat that the oxidative capacity may exceed that of heart muscle. The hypothalamic thermoreceptors, stimulated by impulses from cold-receptors in the skin, send impulses along sympathetic nerves which release noradrenaline in the brown adipose tissue. Noradrenaline stimulates the production of cAMP which activates a lipase that splits molecules of triglyceride into glycerol and fatty acids. Unlike white fat, brown fat does not release from the cell the fatty acids produced by lipolysis: most of it is either resynthesized to triglyceride or oxidized inside the cell. This cycle turns the chemical energy of fatty acid into heat, and is responsible for over 80 per cent of the increased body heat produced when a newborn rabbit is exposed to cold. During this exposure as much as a third of the total cardiac output of blood may be diverted through the brown fat. A similar mechanism is largely responsible for the tremendous heat production in hibernating mammals that accompanies arousal from hibernation. Although brown fat plays a very important part in the thermoregulation of the newborn human infant it is not important in later life. Cold babies are restless and cry but they shiver only if the stress is severe.

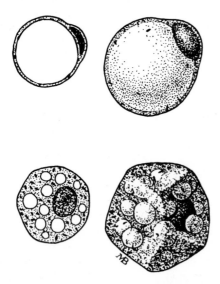

Fig. 26.18 Comparison between cells of white adipose tissue (top) and brown adipose tissue (bottom). On the left each cell is seen in section.

A normal infant responds to heat by vasodilatation, sweating and panting. Some of the heat is lost by radiation or convection and the loss may be increased by vasodilatation, particularly in the hands and feet, until the tissue conductance increases threefold, comparable to the increase found in an adult. When the rectal temperature rises above about 37·2°C the baby sweats. Sweating is the infant's most powerful protection against heat stress but few babies are able to increase their evaporative heat loss more than four-fold before their rectal temperature increases to 38°C.

Central thermoregulation in infants may differ from that in adults. The newborn does not possess a circadian temperature rhythm. Shivering, initiated by cutaneous thermoreceptors, is probably inhibited by receptors in the spinal cord sensitive to heat from the interscapular and cervical brown adipose tissue. Non-shivering thermogenesis is inhibited by hypothalamic receptors sensitive to warmth.

Because the temperature regulation of premature infants is even less efficient than that of full-term babies they must be nursed in an incubator for some time.

STATES OF DISORDERED THERMOREGULATION

Fever (pyrexia). Fever is produced if heat is applied to the body, or if heat is generated in the body, at greater rates than can be balanced by heat loss; hard exercise and hyperthyroidism (Chap. 29) are examples of the latter. Certain steroids (especially aetiocholanolone) formed during the metabolism of adrenocortical and sex hormones are pyrogenic. Infection is a familiar cause of pyrexia but the thermo-regulatory system is readily upset by disease and many non-infective disorders run a febrile course.

Even a small rise of temperature produces an increase in heart rate, and often a feeling of discomfort and fatigue (malaise). In hot environments the efficiency of mental activity is reduced. Body temperatures above 41·2°C (106°F) (*hyperprexia*) are accompanied by tachycardia, raised respiratory rate, weakness, headache, mental confusion, abnormal behaviour and finally loss of consciousness. A persistent temperature of over 43°C (109°F) is not compatible with life.

Fever can be produced experimentally by the injection of a *pyrogen*, such as a vaccine of killed typhoid bacilli (bacterial pyrogen) (Fig. 26.19). About an hour after the injection the patient begins to feel uncomfortable; the skin becomes pale and cold due to constriction of the superficial blood vessels. There is 'goose-flesh' due to pilomotor activity (p. 274). Both effects are the result of sympathetic stimulation. The subject feels cold, shivers and may actually have severe clonic movements (rigor); the body temperature rises. About an hour later the subject begins to feel more comfortable, the skin is warm and dry and the subject a little flushed; heat production and heat loss are both increased so that the body temperature remains high. This stage is not well displayed in experimental pyrexia. When this phase is prolonged in disease circadian variations in body temperature are often similar to, but often larger than, those seen in healthy persons. During fever, in fact, temperature regulation is quite precise; apparently the 'thermostat' is working efficiently, but it is set at a higher level. In the third stage of pyrexia, the patient again feels discomfort.

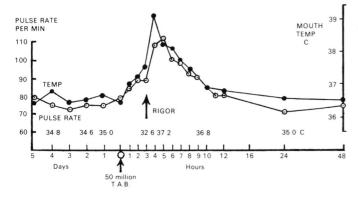

Fig. 26.19 Chart of mouth temperature and pulse rate in a male patient aged 37 who received an intravenous injection of typhoid vaccine (T.A.B.) containing 50 million organisms. An acute febrile reaction developed three hours later. The figures in the lower part of the chart indicate the temperature of the skin of the forearm measured electrically. At three hours after the injection the patient vomited and complained of pain in the back and legs and headache. He was pale and cold (skin temperature 32·6°C). Fifteen minutes later he developed a rigor. His mouth temperature increased rapidly and his skin became flushed and hot (37·2°C). Nine hours after the injection the patient felt much better. He was sweating profusely, his mouth temperature had fallen, but his skin temperature remained high.

He is hot, flushed and sweating; his body temperature falls because the heat loss is greatly increased.

The evidence now seems strong that during the hour or so between the injection of bacterial pyrogen and the subsequent fever, a reaction takes place between a lipopolysaccharide from the bacteria and the leucocytes of the host as the result of which a polypeptide *endogenous (leucocyte) pyrogen*, is released. It produces fever rapidly, probably by a direct action on the anterior hypothalamus and preoptic areas; it causes fever when injected into the lateral cerebral ventricle of rabbits. Pyrogens increase the synthesis and release of prostaglandin E in the anterior hypothalamus. Antipyretics, such as aspirin, act by inhibiting this synthesis. Leucocyte pyrogen cannot be detected in the blood of persons with fever possibly because the concentration is too small.

Heatstroke (heat hyperpyrexia). Sometimes after exposure to extreme temperatures as in hot, humid mines or in strong sunlight in the tropics, men may suddenly and quite unexpectedly collapse, become unconscious and die within a short time with body temperatures of over 41°C. Exposure to heat increases cardiac output and cutaneous circulation with often a rise of venous pressure. It seems likely, but by no means proved, that cessation of sweating and circulatory failure are the causes of the fatal hyperpyrexia. The symptoms are apparently due to a combination of salt loss, dehydration and hyperpyrexia with breakdown of the heat regulating mechanism and circulatory failure.

Heat exhaustion. In very hot climates the body is heated by the solar radiation which in a tropical desert near noon may amount to 54kJ/m²/min. After allowing for the area exposed and for reflexion, the heat absorbed by the body in these circumstances is about 17kJ/min or 1MJ/hr, which is more than twice the resting metabolism. A man marching in the

desert at 4·8km/h (3 m.p.h.) produces, say 1·13 MJ/h. The total heat to be lost is therefore 2·13 MJ per hour which requires the evaporation of 880g of water per hour. In such extreme circumstances a man may lose up to 10 litres per day of sweat containing as much as 30g of salt. If water and salt are not taken at frequent intervals the blood becomes concentrated and the circulation may fail. During acclimatization to a hot climate the sweat glands produce sweat with a comparatively low sodium content, and salt loss is reduced.

Heat cramps. Cramping pains in the muscles, often those muscles in most active use, sometimes occur in men, for example stokers, who work in hot places. 'Stokers' cramp' occurs when the loss of large amounts of sodium-containing fluid in the sweat is made up by the drinking of quantities of water, or other fluid containing little or no sodium. The pains are probably due in some way to lowered sodium concentration; they are found in acute sodium depletion from other causes such as diabetic coma (p. 93) or Addison's disease (p. 478). They may be rapidly relieved by taking salt and can be prevented by drinking weak salt solution (0·25 per cent sodium chloride) instead of water. In Great Britain 8 to 12 g of salt are normally consumed each day and this is many times the minimum quantity needed to maintain metabolic balance. No extra salt is required unless the subject is working hard in a tropical climate with a fluid intake of more than 5 litres. An excessive salt intake increases the urinary loss of fluid and may increase the risk of dehydration. The kidney conserves salt very efficiently so that almost all the intake is available to compensate for salt lost in the sweat.

Spontaneous and accidental hypothermia. Normal persons exposed to cold without adequate protection begin to shiver as the body temperature falls; the heart rate increases, the skin vessels constrict and the blood pressure rises. These compensating reactions fail if the body temperature falls below 32°C and shivering is replaced by muscular rigidity, consciousness is impaired and reflexes are sluggish. Death usually occurs below about 25°C though some patients have survived core temperatures as low as 18°C. Immersion in cold water or the chilling effects of cold wind blowing through wet clothing accounts for many such deaths in young people in temperate climates. The temperature-regulating mechanism of old people is often defective so many elderly people die each winter with hypothermia.

Shipwrecked men immersed in very cold water lose heat rapidly even when fully clothed. Survival from immersion in sea water at 15·5°C is usually not more than 5 hours, at 0°C it is only 15 minutes, death being due to hypothermia. Death can, of course, come earlier because of drowning caused by the reflex respiratory distress initiated by stimulation of cutaneous cold receptors. Although exercise produces heat it is rapidly lost to cold water, and chilling is increased. Vigorous swimming cannot be maintained for very long except by people like channel swimmers. Experiments with subjects in cold water tanks have led to the conclusion that body temperature is best maintained by clinging to wreckage and that no attempt should be made to swim.

Artificially induced hypothermia. If shivering is abolished either by a general anaesthetic, or by a drug that paralyses the muscles, the body temperature can be reduced to 27°C by deliberate cooling. At this temperature the oxidation of glucose ceases and metabolism is reduced by some 30 to 40 per cent. The cardiac and respiratory rates are reduced, arterial pressure is low and the patient passes into a state of suspended animation from which he can completely recover if he is allowed to warm up slowly. In such a state the circulation can be interrupted for 10 to 15 minutes so that surgical operations on the heart and large blood vessels become practicable. If an extracorporeal pump and oxygenator with a heat exchanger are employed lower temperatures can be reached—even as low as 9°C in man. At temperatures below 27°C ventricular fibrillation occurs fairly often but normal rhythm can be restored on rewarming by injecting potassium citrate or by applying an electric shock to the ventricle. At low temperatures there is a metabolic acidosis which can be overcome by giving sodium bicarbonate.

Poikilothermia. In cases of haemorrhage into the midbrain or pons the balance between heat production and heat loss is seriously disturbed and the body temperature may rise as high as 40·6°C. On the other hand it may become very low and the patient may react like a poikilothermic animal. If he is covered with blankets and surrounded by hot-water bottles his body temperature quickly rises and may reach a dangerous

level (Fig. 26.20). Such disturbances are probably the result of interruption of the pathway from the hypothalamus to the spinal cord. Poikilothermia is sometimes the result of severe damage to the hypothalamus.

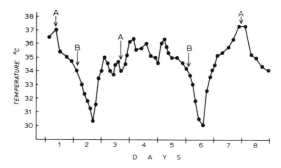

Fig. 26.20 Record of axillary temperatures from a female patient aged 68 unconscious for 3 months as the results of thrombosis of blood vessels at the base of the brain. At the arrows marked B extra blankets were applied; at A they were removed. The body temperature depended on external influences because the central thermo-regulatory mechanism had been destroyed.

REFERENCES

Aherne W, Hull D 1966 Brown adipose tissue and heat production in the newborn infant. Journal of Pathology and Bacteriology 91: 223–225
Benzinger T H 1969 Heat regulation: homeostasis of central temperature in man. Physiological Reviews 49: 671–749
Bligh J 1973 Temperature regulation in mammals and other vertebrates. North-Holland, Amsterdam
Bligh J, Johnson K G 1973 Glossary of terms for thermal physiology. Journal of Applied Physiology 35: 941–961
Burton A C, Edholm O 1954 Man in a cold environment. Physiological Society Monograph No. 2. Arnold, London
Cabanac M 1975 Temperature regulation. Annual Review of Physiology 37: 415–439
Cooper K E 1966 Temperature regulation and the hypothalamus. British Medical Bulletin 22: 238–242
Cooper K E 1972 The body temperature 'set-point' in fever. In: Bligh J, Moore R (eds) Essays in temperature regulation. North Holland, Amsterdam, pp 149–162
Cranston W I 1973 Fever. The Scientific Basis of Medicine Annual Reviews
Crowdy J P 1968 Water requirements in hot countries. Journal of the Royal Army Medical Corps 114: 116–122
Dyson J 1979 The hot arctic. Heineman, London
Edholm O G, Bacharach A L (eds) 1965 Exploration medicine: being a practical guide for those going on expeditions. Wright, Bristol
Edholm O G, Bacharach A L (eds) 1965 The physiology of human survival. Academic Press, London
Edholm O G 1978 Man – hot and cold. Studies in Biology No 97. Edward Arnold, London
Fanger P O 1973 Thermal comfort. McGraw-Hill, New York
Fanger P O 1973 Assessment of man's thermal comfort in practice. British Journal of Industrial Medicine 30: 313–324
Folk G E 1974 Textbook of environmental physiology, 2nd edn. Kimpton, London
Fox R H 1974 Temperature regulation with special reference to man. Recent Advances in Physiology 9: 340–405
Gale C C 1973 Neuroendocrine aspects of thermoregulation. Annual Review of Physiology 35: 391–430
Gates D M 1972 Man and his environment: climate. Harper & Row, New York
Handbook of fundamentals 1972 American Society of Heating, Refrigerating and Air-Conditioning Engineers, New York
Hardy J D, Gagge A P, Stolwijk J A J (eds) 1970 Physiological and behavioural temperature regulation. Thomas, Springfield, Illinois
Hardy R N 1972 Temperature and animal life. Arnold, London
Hellon R F 1975 Monoamines, pyrogens and cations: their actions on central control of fever. Advances in Pharmacology 6A: 307–317
Hemingway A 1963 Shivering. Physiological Reviews 43: 397–422
Hensel H 1973 Neural processes in thermoregulation. Physiological Reviews 53: 948–1017
Hensel H 1974 Thermoreceptors. Annual Review of Physiology 36: 233–249
Hey E N 1972 Thermal regulation in the newborn. British Journal of Hospital Medicine 8: 51–64
Hey E N 1975 Thermal neutrality. British Medical Journal 31: 69–74
Hull D 1966 Brown adipose tissue. British Medical Bulletin 22: 92–96
Itoh S, Ogata K, Yoshimura H 1972 Advances in climatic physiology. Igaku Shoin, Tokyo
Keatinge W R 1969 Survival in cold water: the physiology and treatment of immersion hypothermia and of drowning. Blackwell, Oxford
Kerslake D McK 1972 The stress of hot environments. Monographs of the Physiological Society No. 29: Cambridge University Press
Leithead C S, Lind A R 1964 Heat stress and heat disorders. Cassell, London
Lewis H E, Foster A R, Mullan B J, Cox R N, Clark R P 1969 Aerodynamics of the human environment. Lancet ii: 1273–1277
Lindberg O (ed) 1970 Brown adipose tissue. Elsevier, Amsterdam
Maclean D, Emslie-Smith D 1977 Accidental hypothermia. Blackwell, Oxford
Macpherson R H (ed) 1960 Physiological responses to hot environments. HMSO, London
Monteith J L, Mount L E (eds) 1974 Heat loss from animals and man. Assessment and control. Butterworth, London

REFERENCES

Precht H, Christophersen J, Hensel H, Larcher W 1973 Temperature and life. Springer-Verlag, Berlin

Robertshaw D (ed) 1974 Environmental physiology. Butterworth, London

Smith A V 1961 Biological effects of freezing and supercooling. Arnold, London

Smith R E, Horwitz Barbara A 1969 Brown fat and thermogenesis. Physiological Reviews 49: 330–425

Snell E S, Atkins E 1968 The mechanisms of fever. In: Bittar E E, Bittar N (eds) The biological basis of medicine. Academic Press, London, vol 2, pp. 397–419

Wolstenholme G E W, Birch J (ed) 1971 Pyrogens and fever. Churchill Livingstone, Edinburgh

Yousef M K, Horvath S M, Bullard R W (eds) 1972 Physiological adaptations. Desert and mountain. Academic Press, New York

27 Special Senses

VISION

A horizontal cross section of the eye is shown in Figure 27.1. The eyeball, which is approximately spherical and about 24 mm in diameter, has a tough fibrous coat whose opaque posterior part, the sclera, becomes continuous at the limbus with the more strongly curved transparent cornea.

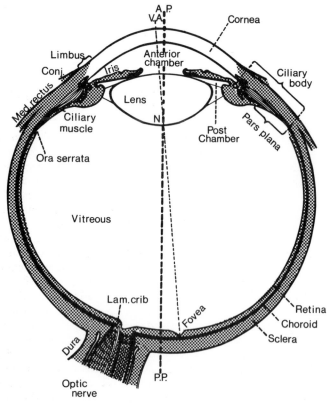

Fig. 27.1 Horizontal section of the eye. P.P., posterior pole; A.P., anterior pole; V. A., visual axis; N, nodal point; Lam. crib., lamina cribrosa; Conj., conjunctiva. (Modified from Salzmann.) (Wolff's *Anatomy of the Eye and Orbit.*)

Light entering the eye through the cornea passes through the aqueous humour in the anterior chamber, the pupillary aperture of the iris, the lens and the vitreous body before striking the photosensitive retina that lines the posterior two-thirds of the eyeball. The retina is separated from the sclera by a vascular pigmented layer, the choroid, which is continued forward into the ciliary body and the iris.

The eye is normally directed so that the image of an object being fixated falls upon the fovea, a depression in the retina situated a short distance to the lateral side of the posterior pole of the eye. Nerve fibres arising in the retina run across the retinal surface to pass out of the eyeball through perforations in the sclera (lamina cribrosa) a short distance to the medial side of the posterior pole. The point of exit of the nerve fibres is seen as the optic disc.

External protection of the eye. The human eye is protected by the strong bony orbit and by the eyelids which are lined by conjunctiva on their inner surfaces. A number of sensitive hairs (eye-lashes) project from the margins of the lids. In addition to the sweat and sebaceous glands associated with the hair follicles, the lids contain tarsal glands that secrete an oily fluid that covers the edge of the lids and prevents tear fluid from flowing over.

The eyelids are closed by the orbicularis oculi innervated by the seventh (facial) nerve. The upper lid is raised by the levator palpebrae superioris supplied by a branch of the third (oculomotor) nerve. Deep within this muscle are some smooth muscle fibres supplied by nerve fibres from the sympathetic plexus on the carotid artery (see Fig. 27.21).

The lids close reflexly when the cornea, conjunctiva or eye-lashes are touched, when a very bright light is shone into the eye or when an object suddenly approaches close to the eye. Blinking also occurs spontaneously about 20 times a minute and serves to renew the fluid film over the cornea. Since a blink lasts about 300 milliseconds we are normally blacked out for about one-tenth of our waking time, but we are quite unaware of it. The eyelids can of course be closed voluntarily although many people have difficulty in closing just one eye. The eyelids normally close during sneezing and sleep.

The fluid that moistens the conjunctiva and cornea is secreted partly by the lacrimal glands which lie in the upper and outer part of the orbit and partly by accessory lacrimal glands on the inner surfaces of the lids. Since tear fluid does not normally accumulate, its rate of secretion is presumably adjusted to compensate exactly for the rate of loss by evaporation. When foreign bodies or other irritants get into the eye, the discharge of tear fluid from the lacrimal glands into the upper conjunctival sac is greatly accelerated by reflex activation of the parasympathetically innervated glands. Adrenergic fibres innervate the blood vessels and may innervate the secreting cells. If the rate of discharge is so great that drainage of the fluid into the nasolacrimal duct through the small orifices, puncta lacrimalia, at the medial margin of each lid cannot remove the fluid fast enough, then tears spill over on to the cheek (lacrimation). Weeping may also occur in emotional circumstances.

The tear fluid produced during lacrimation is an isotonic solution of sodium chloride and bicarbonate having a pH of about 7·4 and a low protein content. The fluid, which contains a bactericidal enzyme, lysozyme, serves to wash foreign bodies or irritant materials out of the conjunctival sac. The fluid that normally fills the conjunctival sac and is spread by blinking to form a film over the cornea is rather more viscous, because of evaporation, and has an oily surface layer.

Cornea. The cornea is composed mainly of collagen fibrils with the same refractive index as that of the mucopolysaccharide matrix in which they lie. The fibrils are arranged in lamellae between which lie the fixed cells. Anteriorly the

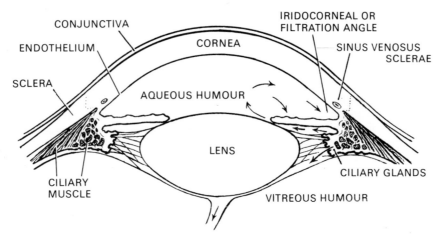

Fig. 27.2   To illustrate the probable source of aqueous humour in the ciliary glands and the routes of absorption into the circulation. The ciliary glands lie in the ciliary body which is an annular or ring-like structure. The suspensory ligaments of the lens are shown.

cornea is bounded by a condensed stromal layer that is covered by a stratified epithelium of remarkable regularity. The cornea obtains nearly all the oxygen required for its metabolism directly from the atmosphere through its anterior epithelium. The anterior surface of the cornea forms the major optical focusing component of the eye; its good optical properties rapidly disappear if it is not continuously moistened with tear fluid. At the edge of the cornea the epithelium continues as the conjunctiva; this covers the anterior part of the sclera and is reflected forwards to line the eyelids. Posteriorly the cornea is bounded by an elastic membrane and an endothelium. The transparency of the cornea depends critically on its state of hydration which appears to be regulated by the stratified corneal epithelium which actively transports sodium from the tear fluid to the stroma and chloride in the opposite direction. The cornea is richly supplied with free nerve endings; even slight damage to the corneal epithelium is intensely painful.

Anterior chamber and aqueous humour. The anterior chamber of the eye is filled with aqueous humour, a fluid whose composition is rather like that of plasma without the proteins. The aqueous humour is continuously being formed by the ciliary glands (Fig. 27.2). It flows forwards past the lens into the anterior chamber; from there it drains into the sinus venosus sclerae and the venous plexus which lies within the sclera at the corneoscleral junction. By introducing inulin into the anterior chamber of the eye of an animal and measuring the rate at which its concentration subsequently falls, it has been estimated that about 1 per cent of the aqueous humour drains away each minute to be replaced by freshly formed fluid. The cells of the endothelial membrane of the trabecular meshwork separating the anterior chamber from the sinus venosus sclerae possess large vacuoles which begin as indentations on the inner surface of the cells and gradually enlarge and eventually rupture and discharge on the outer surface of the cell and then reseal. This mechanism provides the channel through which aqueous fluid escapes and keeps the intraocular pressure at a normal level.

The continuous production of aqueous humour keeps the intraocular pressure about 1·3 to 2·6 kPa (10 to 20 mm Hg). This pressure keeps the eyeball rigid but if it rises unduly, for example by blockage of the drainage channels, the flow of

blood in the retinal and choroidal circulations may be impeded with consequent retinal damage. This not uncommon condition is called glaucoma.

Although the composition of aqueous humour is like that of an ultrafiltrate of plasma it is doubtful whether the aqueous humour is formed by simple filtration. The glucose and urea concentrations in the aqueous humour are substantially lower than those in the plasma; the low glucose concentration is probably due to its utilization by the lens whose metabolic requirements are provided by the aqueous humour.

The aqueous and vitreous humours, as well as the lens and cornea, all contain quite high concentrations of ascorbic acid (vitamin C). Although this is assumed to have a local function no ocular changes are seen even in severe scurvy (p. 29).

The lens. The lens is composed of ribbon-like fibres arranged in concentric laminae. The cortex of the lens is softer than the central nucleus. The substance of the lens has a very high protein content (about 35 per cent) and is enclosed by a strong, elastic, membranous capsule which is attached to the ciliary body by suspensory ligaments (Fig. 27.2). The thickness of the lens capsule is not uniform; the part covering the posterior surface of the lens is uniformly thin, while the part covering the anterior surface is mostly thicker with a thin central portion. The anterior surface of the lens is much less curved than the posterior surface.

The suspensory ligaments of the lens are kept tense by the intraocular pressure which tends to increase the diameter of the annular ciliary body. When the tension is released by contraction of the ciliary muscle, the anterior surface of the lens bulges forward. The increased convexity of the central portion of the anterior surface increases the optical power of the lens. The change in shape of the lens is restricted to its anterior surface by the non-uniform thickness of its capsule.

The ciliary muscle is responsible for the accommodative changes (alterations in optical power) of the lens. It has several different groups of fibres, circular and longitudinal, which form a meshwork so that it may be regarded as a single muscle. The main nerve supply to the ciliary muscle is by parasympathetic fibres which run from a mid-brain nucleus together with the third nerve to the ciliary ganglion where they relay to pass in the short ciliary nerves to the eye. Parasympathetic stimulation causes the ciliary muscle to contract so that the eye is accommodated for near vision. There is probably also antagonistic sympathetic control of accommodation although the mechanism of this action is not clear (Fig. 27.21).

Although the lens has no blood supply it is a metabolically active tissue which continues to grow throughout life. The lens uses glucose as its source of energy but since the Po_2 of aqueous humour is low most of its metabolism is by anaerobic glycolysis. Oxygen is relatively unimportant in lens metabolism; a lens can be kept anaerobically without affecting its transparency provided that the medium contains glucose. The interior of the lens is 75 mV negative to the aqueous humour.

It has long been assumed that the chief cause of presbyopia was increasing hardening of the lens associated with dehydration. However, the water content of both the nucleus (63 per cent) and the cortex (67 per cent) does not change significantly as age increases. The hardening is best explained by an increased adhesion of the fibres (cells) of the nucleus. The ciliary muscle does not become weaker as age advances but because of the increasing stiffness of the lens it is unable to produce so much accommodation. In children the lens is pale yellow having a pigment that absorbs strongly in the near ultraviolet; the senile lens is even more yellow and may be somewhat cloudy. The senile lens is very liable to become opaque (cataract).

The vitreous body is a transparent jelly-like substance that fills the posterior cavity of the eye. In fact the vitreous body is not simply a structureless protein gel but a tissue with an extensive, though delicate, skeleton of collagen-like fibres.

The iris. The iris is a heavily pigmented screen containing muscle fibres lying in front of the lens. The outer edge of the iris is hidden behind the corneoscleral junction while the inner edge forms the margin of the normally circular pupil. The iris has a well differentiated sphincter muscle which can constrict the pupil to as little as 1 mm in diameter. The iris also contains some radially arranged myoepithelial cells which lie posterior to the sphincter muscle and help to dilate the pupil.

The sphincter muscle of the iris is innervated by parasympathetic nerves and the dilator muscle by sympathetic fibres. Variations in the tonic level of activity in the parasympathetic system provide the major control of pupil diameter. The origin and pathway of these fibres is illustrated in Figure 27.21.

Although the dilator muscle normally plays only a small part in controlling pupil diameter, injuries of the cervical cord which interrupt the sympathetic pathway give rise to an obviously small pupil (miosis). Such a lesion, which also paralyses the smooth muscle of the levator palpebrae superioris, causes the upper eyelid to droop (ptosis) and the eyeball to retract (enophthalmos). These signs constitute Horner's syndrome.

Effect of Drugs on the Intraocular Muscles

Accommodation of the lens and constriction of the pupil can be produced by placing parasympathomimetic substances such as eserine into the conjunctival sac from which they reach the intraocular muscles by diffusion. Conversely parasympatholytic substances such as atropine cause accommodation to be relaxed and the pupil to dilate. Pupillary dilatation can also be produced by activating the sympathetic system or simulating its action with drugs such as amphetamine or phenylephrine.

Morphine causes intense pupillary constriction while intoxication by alcohol causes dilatation.

Image Formation in the Eye

In a lens system, light is refracted or bent out of its original direction when it passes from one medium into another with a different refractive index. The refractive indices of the cornea, aqueous humour and vitreous body are all very nearly the same as water (1·33) while the material of the lens has an effective refractive index of 1·42. Thus light is refracted when it passes into the eye through the air–cornea interface and again on entering and leaving the lens (Fig. 27.3).

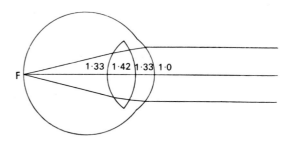

Fig. 27.3   The normal (emmetropic) eye. This diagram shows how the rays of light are refracted where there is a difference of refractive index between any two media. The figures give the approximate refractive indices of the media.

The power of the whole eye when unaccommodated for near vision is about 60 dioptres (the power of a lens in dioptres is the reciprocal of its focal length in metres). Some 20 dioptres of this power are contributed by the lens and 40 dioptres by the anterior corneal surface. If refraction at the corneal surface is eliminated, as when swimming under water, the eye becomes very long-sighted and clear vision is impossible. Normal vision can, of course, be achieved underwater by wearing goggles which exclude water and allow the refractive power of the air–cornea surface to remain intact. If the lens of the eye has to be removed because it becomes opaque a spectacle lens of approximately 10 dioptres must be supplied. The power of the spectacle lens that is needed is less than that of the lens that has been removed because it is placed further away from the retina.

Accommodation. When the gaze is suddenly transferred from a distant object to one nearer at hand the retinal images in the two eyes are at first both blurred and also disparate, that is they do not fall on corresponding points of the two retinae. After a latent period of about 160 milliseconds, however, the axes of the eyes begin to converge so as to move the images of the nearer object on to corresponding parts of the two retinae. After a longer latent period (about 360 milliseconds) the power of the lenses starts to increase so as to bring the images of the nearer object into focus. Although these corrections may take about a second to complete, the subject is usually unaware of their occurrence.

An object that is as close to the eye as it can be without appearing blurred is said to be at the near point. The near point is normally about 7 cm from the eye at 10 years of age. By the age of 40 the near point has receded to about 20 cm and tasks such as threading a needle may become difficult. When presbyopia is fully established the near point may be 40 cm

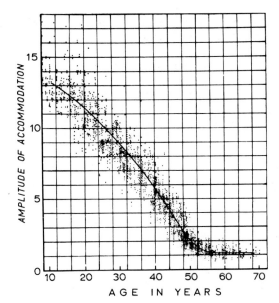

Fig. 27.4 One thousand and fifty observations on the amplitude of accommodation to show how it varies with age. The amplitude is expressed on the ordinate in dioptres. (*After* A. Duane (1912) Studies of the accommodation. *Ophthalmoscope,* 10, 489.)

from the eye and reading fine print without spectacles becomes difficult.

The range of accommodation can be simply measured by finding the range of convex and concave (plus and minus) lenses that can be placed in front of the eye without causing a distant object to appear blurred. The range of accommodation diminishes steadily throughout life (Fig. 27.4) until the condition of presbyopia is fully established at the age of 50 or 60 years.

Errors of refraction. If a subject has normal vision parallel rays of light entering the eye are brought to a focus on the retina when his accommodation is relaxed naturally or when his ciliary muscle is paralysed with atropine. Such a subject is said to be an emmetrope. On the other hand if the subject is myopic (short-sighted), parallel rays are brought to a focus in front of the retina, while if he is hypermetropic (long-sighted or, in U.S.A., hyperopic) parallel rays are focused behind the retina (Fig. 27.5).

The refractive error of a myope can be corrected if he wears a minus (or diverging) lens in front of the eyes (Fig. 27.5E) of the appropriate power to bring distant objects to a sharp focus. About 6 per cent of school children aged 15 in the U.K. are found to be short-sighted. A short-sighted child is not likely to be good at games because he cannot see well at a distance but often his intelligence is slightly better than average. The middle-aged myope at the onset of presbyopia has the advantage that he can read if he removes his glasses.

The refractive error of a hypermetrope can be corrected by placing converging lenses in front of the eyes (Fig. 27.5B, C), but he can see distant objects clearly without spectacles by using his accommodation and he may for this reason be less hampered than his short-sighted neighbour. However, uncorrected hypermetropia may lead to fatigue and headaches from the continuous effort of accommodation and a convergent squint may develop because of the close link between accommodation and convergence.

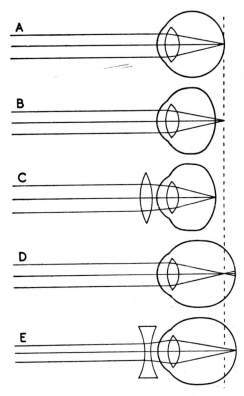

Fig. 27.5 Diagram illustrating the common refractive errors of the eye and the methods of correction. A, emmetropic eye. B and C, hypermetropic eye. D and E, myopic eye.

A refractive error arises when the refractive power of the eye is not well matched to its axial length. Although the powers of the cornea and lens, as well as the length of the eye, show quite wide variations from person to person a surprisingly large proportion of the population have an insignificantly small overall refractive error (Fig. 27.6). This suggests that the three variables are not randomly associated but must be partially correlated.

Another type of defect, known as *astigmatism*, occurs when the curvatures of the refracting surfaces of the eye are different along different meridians. This results in the focal length of the eye being different in different meridional planes (that is in different planes passing through the visual axis of the eye). If the shortest and longest focal lengths occur in meridional planes at right angles to each other and if the focal length changes smoothly between these values, the subject is said to have a regular astigmatism. When a subject with a regular astigmatism views a fan of radiating lines some appear sharply focused while those at right angles are blurred. The error can be corrected by providing a cylindrical spectacle lens of the correct power with its axis set at such an angle as to equalize the focal lengths in the different meridional planes. If a spherical correction is also required it is usually formed on one side of the spectacle lens while the cylindrical surface is formed on the other.

If the corneal surface becomes irregularly distorted, due for example to healed ulceration, irregular astigmatism is present. In this case the only means of correction is a 'contact lens' which effectively replaces the irregular corneal surface by an optically regular one.

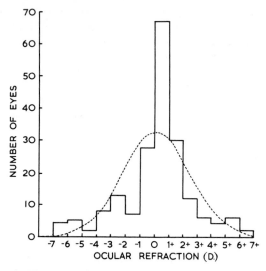

Fig. 27.6 The curve of distribution for ocular refraction in 194 eyes. The continuous lines indicate the actual observations while the dotted lines indicate the fitted normal curve. The fact that the former is more peaked than the latter suggests that, while the optical components vary over a wide range, in an individual eye these components are usually so correlated as to produce emmetropia. (A. Sorsby, B. Benjamin, J. B. Davey, M. Sheridan & J. M. Tanner (1957) *Special Report Series. Medical Research Council. No. 293*, Fig. 8.) (*By kind permission of the Controller of H.M. Stationery Office.*)

The magnitude of a subject's refractive error can be measured by placing lenses of different power in front of his eyes until the best visual acuity (p. 429) is obtained. Where difficulties of age or language prevent the co-operation of the patient, the refractive error can be estimated by retinoscopy. In this technique the examiner shines a light into the subject's eye and then checks whether the light reflected back from the fundus leaves the eye in a parallel beam.

The pupil. If the image produced by an optical system is not correctly focused it is blurred. The extent of the blurring depends upon the magnitude of the focusing error and the diameter of the entrance pupil. As the pupil becomes smaller the effect of defocusing becomes less, the optical system having a greater depth of focus. However, even when it is in best focus, the image formed by any optical system is usually somewhat degraded by spherical and chromatic aberrations and the effects of diffraction at the pupil.

Spherical aberration is due to the central and peripheral parts of the lens system having different focal lengths while chromatic aberration arises because the focal length is different for light of different wavelengths. The amount of blurring produced by these defects can be reduced by having a small pupil so that only the central portion of the lens is used. Reducing the pupil size, however, reduces the amount of light reaching the retina and increases the blurring caused by diffraction. Since the resolving power of the nervous part of the visual system diminishes as the retinal light intensity is reduced there is, for every external light intensity, an optimum pupil size at which these various factors most nearly balance each other. It is found that over a wide range of light levels the natural diameter of the pupil of the eye corresponds closely to the optimum size.

The diameters of both pupils are normally the same and

depend upon the amount of light falling on both retinae. Thus shining a light into one eye not only causes contraction of the pupil in that eye (direct light reflex) but also an equal contraction of the pupil of the other eye (consensual reflex). The pupillary light reflex has a latent period of about 250 milliseconds and the contraction may not be complete for several seconds. Dilatation of the pupil in response to reduction of the light entering the eye may be even slower. The pathways of these reflexes are described on page 439.

Contraction of the pupils also occurs when a subject looks at a near object (the near reflex). The increase in the depth of focus produced in this way probably helps to minimize the blurring resulting from the slight under-accommodation usual in near vision.

The pupils contract during sleep, although they normally dilate if the eyes are closed. Dilatation of the pupils occurs in conditions such as fear, pain or asphyxia, presumably as part of the generalized sympathetic response.

Visual Acuity

Visual acuity is measured by the appreciation of fine detail in a visual image. If a subject with normal vision looks at a well-lit pattern of parallel light and dark bars of equal width he can distinguish the individual bars only if they subtend an angle at his eye of at least half a minute of arc. A visual acuity as high as this is achieved only over a small region of the subject's visual field around his fixation point and only when the level of illumination is high. Only a short way away from the fixation point the acuity is very much less, and even in the centre of the visual field visual acuity is reduced if the light is dimmed. Visual acuity is also much reduced if the contrast of the pattern is reduced, that is if the luminances of the light and dark regions of the pattern are made more nearly equal.

It is not surprising that the ultimate limit of 'grating' acuity should be reached with bars about half a minute of arc wide because this is approximately the angle subtended by the central foveal cones which are 2 μm in diameter. However, the effect of diffraction and aberrations in the lens system is to reduce the contrast of the detail of the retinal image below that of the object and it has been shown that this reduction in image contrast plays some part in determining the ultimate acuity. Optical factors (and these include the size of the elements of the receptor mosaic) are not alone in determining visual acuity. The reduction in acuity associated with lower contrast and lower levels of illumination, as well as that associated with peripheral vision, depend upon the nervous mechanisms involved.

Resolution of the separate elements of a pattern is not the only kind of task that taxes to the limit the ability of the visual system to detect spatial differences. The ability of a subject to detect the lateral displacement of one half of a line with respect to the other half (Vernier acuity) has been much studied. The minimum displacement, rather less than 10 seconds of arc, that can be detected when the lines are long presumably depends upon the organization of the visual nervous system at quite a high level.

For clinical purposes a subject's visual acuity is usually measured by asking him to read a specially constructed chart of test types. (Snellens' types, Fig. 27.7). Each line of letters is

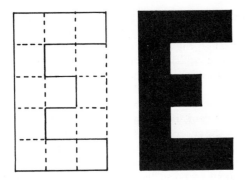

Fig. 27.7 The method of construction of Snellen's types.

marked with the distance in metres at which the small squares subtend one minute of arc. A normal subject standing 6 metres from a well-lit chart should easily be able to distinguish the letters of the 6 metre line. If this is so his acuity is reported as 6/6. A subject with defective vision might only be able to read the 60 metre line; his acuity would be reported as 6/60. If the low acuity is due to a refractive error it will be raised by making the subject look through a small aperture which increases the depth of focus and reduces the amount of blurring produced by any error in focusing or by aberrations.

The Visual Fields

The visual field is that area of the inner surface of a sphere around the subject within which a luminous object can be seen. The extent of the field of vision is measured with a perimeter. The subject covers one eye and looks with the other at a fixation point at the centre of the apparatus. A small white disc is brought from the periphery towards the fixation point until the subject indicates that he can see it. The angular distance of the disc from the visual axis is recorded and the measurement is repeated for another meridian. The shape of the field is dependent to some extent upon the shape of the face since it is restricted on the medial side by the nose and above by the supra-orbital margin (Fig. 27.8). Laterally there is no obstruction; with the eyes looking straight ahead objects can be

seen up to about 100° away from the visual axis on each side. If the eyes are moved left and right the total field of vision around the head becomes quite considerable with a blind zone behind the head of as little as 130°.

Although an object may be detected when it is far from the centre of the visual field, especially if it is moving or flashing, visual acuity and colour recognition may be so poor that the object cannot be recognized. A subject's inability to recognize an object, although he is aware of its position, is in normal circumstances overcome by turning the eyes so that the image of the object falls upon the fovea. Flashing lights, or moving objects appearing in the periphery of the visual field, have a strong tendency to cause the appropriate involuntary changes of fixation. In retinitis pigmentosa central vision may remain but peripheral vision is lost. The patient is greatly handicapped because he has difficulty in finding objects in his environment.

The blind spot. If a small object is moved within the visual field until its image falls upon the optic nerve head, where there are no photo-receptors, it is no longer visible. Thus the normal visual field of each eye has a 'blind spot' or scotoma about 5 or 6° in diameter situated some 15° lateral to the fixation point. We are usually quite unaware of the existence of this blind area as we may also be unaware of other scotomata resulting, for example, from local retinal damage.

The Retina

The retina is formed from the optic vesicle which grows out from the fore-brain of the embryo and is thus a part of the central nervous system. The outer wall of the optic vesicle forms the pigmented layer of the retina while the photo-receptors and nervous layers of the retina are formed from the inner wall. In the adult eye (Fig. 27.1) the retina lines the posterior part of the eyeball extending as far forward as the ora serrata, about 5 mm in front of the equator of the eyeball. Near the centre of the retina, a millimetre or so from the posterior pole of the eye, there is a depression in the retina, the fovea centralis, formed by lateral displacement of the cells of the inner retinal layers. About 3 mm to the nasal side of the fovea the sclera is pierced by the optic nerve.

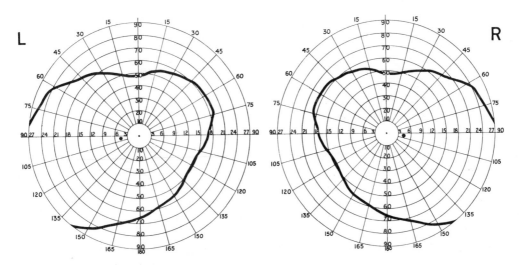

Fig. 27.8 The fields of vision. The black spot 15° lateral to the centre of the field is the blind spot.

The retinal blood supply. The retina has two blood supplies. The central retinal artery enters the eye with the optic nerve and spreads its branches out over the inner surface of the retina to nourish its inner layers. The tributaries of the retinal vein run alongside the arteries, the retinal vein passing out of the eye in the optic nerve. A separate choroidal system of vessels lies between the pigment epithelium and the sclera and supplies the outer layers of the retina. Damage to either vascular system can cause blindness. The retinal circulation does not appear to be under nervous control. High arterial CO_2 concentrations and low oxygen concentrations produce some degree of vasodilatation. High arterial oxygen tension causes vasoconstriction. Light pressure on the globe of the eye increases the intraocular pressure and decreases the pressure gradient across the walls of the retinal arteries which dilate in a minute or so. This is presumably a local myogenic response responsible for autoregulation of blood flow.

Ophthalmoscopy. The structures inside the eye can be examined by the use of an opththalmoscope. A beam of light is directed through the subject's pupil to illuminate the back of the eye (fundus oculi). The examiner looks along the beam of light into the subject's eye and if both his eye and the subject's eye are focused for infinity the retinal vessels and optic nerve head (optic disc) can be clearly seen but the retina itself, being nearly transparent, is not visible. The pigment layer of the retina hides the choroidal vessels so that the background of the fundus is a fairly uniform orange colour. The yellow colour of the macula lutea cannot usually be distinguished although its position, about two disc diameters to the temporal side of the optic disc, can be inferred from the absence of large blood vessels. The nerve fibres leaving the eye become myelinated, and therefore visible, only as they reach the optic disc.

Fine structure of the retina. The photosensitive cells, the rods and cones (Fig. 27.9) lie in the outermost layer of the

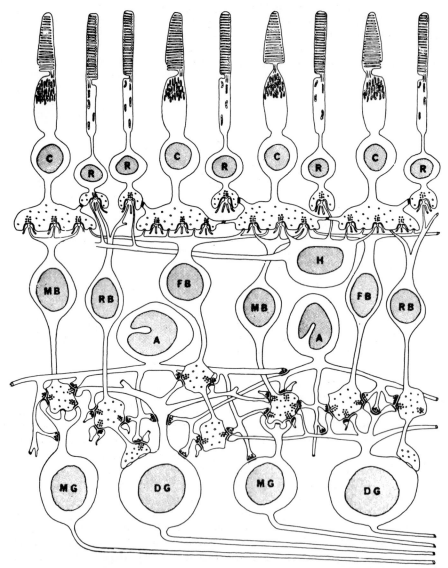

Fig. 27.9 A summary diagram of the contacts in the retina. R, rod; C, cone; MB, midget bipolar; RB, rod bipolar; FB, flat bipolar; H, horizontal cell; A, amacrine cell; MG, midget ganglion; DG, diffuse ganglion. (J. E. Dowling & B. B. Boycott (1966) *Proceedings of the Royal Society* B, **166**, 80–111.) The outer segments of the rods and cones have closely packed lamellae in which the visual pigment is located. The inner segments contain large mitochondria. Light passes upwards in the figure and traverses the nervous elements before reaching the rods and cones.

retina next to the pigment epithelium. Except in the foveal region, light reaching the photoreceptors must first pass through the other layers of the retina. Over most of the retina, rods and cones are found side by side, but in the central fovea only very closely packed (rod-shaped) cones are found. The most peripheral parts of the retina, where the receptors are widely separated, have very few cones.

The rods and cones make synaptic connexions with bipolar cells and these in turn connect with the ganglion cells. The ganglion cells give rise to the optic nerve fibres which run towards the optic nerve head as the innermost layer of the retina. Ganglion cells, and to a lesser extent bipolar cells, can have quite extensively spreading dendrites so that each ganglion cell may be influenced by the activity of a large number of rods and cones. Further lateral interactions are mediated by the horizontal and amacrine cells (see Fig. 27.9). In all regions of the retina, except the central fovea, the ganglion cells can be seen to be connected, through intermediate bipolar cells, to rods as well as cones. Over most of the retina there are many more photoreceptors than ganglion cells although in the fovea the ratio of ganglion cells to cones may be more nearly one; however, this does not necessarily mean that even in the fovea each nerve fibre is connected to only a single cone.

Photopigments and Vision

Rhodopsin and scotopic vision. In order that light falling upon the retina should generate signals that can be transmitted to the nervous system, the light must first be absorbed by the photosensitive pigments of the rods and cones. The first photopigment to be isolated from the retina was rhodopsin which was extracted from the outer segments of the rods.

Rhodopsin (called visual purple, although its colour is mauve) is a conjugated protein which has as its prosthetic group a molecule of retinal (vitamin A aldehyde) present in the form of its 11-*cis* stereoisomer. It has been found that when a molecule of rhodopsin absorbs a quantum of light the retinal moiety undergoes a stereo-isomeric change to the all-*trans* form (Fig. 27.10). It is believed that it is this change that somehow results in the generation of a nervous signal. Subsequently the retinal splits from the opsin; the free retinal and opsin no longer absorb visible light and the rhodopsin is said to be bleached. In the presence of the appropriate enzyme systems the retinal and opsin are reconjugated to regenerate rhodopsin. In cases of chronic vitamin A deficiency rhodopsin synthesis is impaired, dark-adaptation (p. 434) may be slow and incomplete and in extreme cases overt retinal degeneration may occur (p. 24).

The relative ease with which solutions of extracted rhodopsin can be bleached by lights of different wavelengths can easily be measured to provide the 'action spectrum' of rhodopsin. It is important to distinguish this 'action spectrum', which relates to the effect of light upon the pigment, from the 'absorption spectrum' which simply relates to the amount of light that is absorbed without consideration of any change that it produces. Although the absorption and action spectra of rhodopsin come from quite different kinds of measurement, they are, in fact, very similar in shape because each quantum of light that is absorbed has the same chance of causing a pigment molecule to be bleached.

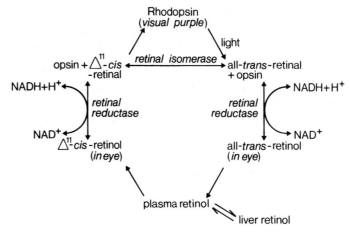

Fig. 27.10 The visual cycle. The *trans*- form of vitamin A (retinol), which predominates in the liver reserves and the blood, is the most active isomer in all physiological roles of the vitamin other than that of vision. For vitamin A to give rise to a visual pigment, it must be converted in the eye to a *cis*- isomer of retinal by the enzymes retinal reductase and retinal isomerase. The *cis*-retinal combines with the protein opsin to form rhodopsin. Light falling on the retina splits retinal from the protein opsin by isomerizing it to the *trans*-configuration. The liberated *trans*-retinal may then be either changed back to the *cis*- form by retinal isomerase to regenerate rhodopsin, completing an isomerization cycle in the eye, or reduced to vitamin A by retinal reductase.

Rhodopsin in solution is bleached by lights with a range of wavelengths (λ) corresponding to the orange-to-violet part of the visible spectrum (Fig. 27.11) with an optimum in the green ($\lambda = 502$ nm). Rhodopsin also absorbs and can be bleached by ultraviolet radiation.

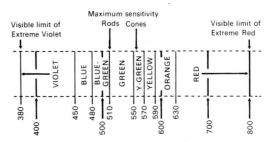

Fig. 27.11 The colour names given to the various parts of the spectrum. Wavelengths are in nm.

The bleaching of photopigments in the living eye can be demonstrated by an ophthalmoscopic technique. A weak monochromatic light is shone on the retina through one half of the pupil. A fraction of this light, after passing through the retina, is reflected back from the pigment epithelium and choroid, passes back through the retina and leaves the eye through the other half of the pupil. The emerging light is allowed to fall on a sensitive photocell so that its intensity can be measured. If measurements of the intensity of the reflected light are made before and after the retinal photopigments are bleached by exposing them to a very bright light, then the fraction of the weak measuring light that returns through the pupil is found to be greater after bleaching, since less is absorbed. This technique shows that the absorption spectrum of the photopigment in the peripheral retina is the same as that of rhodopsin in solution.

When measurements are made of the relative abilities of low intensity lights of different wavelengths to produce visual sensation, it is found that the curve obtained (the equal energy scotopic luminosity curve, Figure 27.12a) is very similar to the action spectrum of rhodopsin. This, and the fact that those parts of the retina where the rhodopsin-filled rods are most closely packed function best at low light levels, has led to the conclusion that rhodopsin is the photosensitive pigment responsible for vision at low luminance levels (scotopic vision).

Photopic vision. When a subject views a scene illuminated by white light of low intensity his visual acuity is low and he is unaware of any sensation of colour. However, when the illumination level is sufficiently raised objects can be seen in much greater detail and in their natural colours (Fig. 27.13). Vision at high luminance levels (phototopic vision) appears to be mediated by retinal cones (high acuity being achieved by using the densely packed mosaic of cones in the fovea) while scotopic vision is mediated by peripherally sited rods.

Measurements of the absorption spectra of the outer segments of cones from primate and human retinae show that cones do not all contain the same pigment. The measured absorption spectra fall into three separate groups probably corresponding to the presence of three different photo-pigments . None of the cones has an absorption spectrum like that of the rod pigment rhodopsin (with a maximum absorption at about 500 nm).

The absorption spectra of two photopigments present in the human foveal cones have been measured in the living eye by the ophthalmoscopic technique described earlier (p. 431). The two foveal cone pigments detected in this way by Rushton have been called 'erythrolabe' (the more red sensitive pigment) and 'chlorolabe' (the more green sensitive one). The absorption spectra of these two pigments correspond to the two commoner types found in isolated cones. Cones containing the blue-sensitive 'cyanolabe' seem to be relatively scarce and probably completely absent from the central fovea. The chemical nature of these pigments is unknown but it is probable that, like rhodopsin, the cone pigments are conjugated proteins.

When the relative energies of high intensity lights of different wavelengths needed to give a particular sensation of brightness are measured (Fig. 27.12b), it is found that a yellow-green light of wavelength 560 nm is the most effective. This wavelength lies between the absorption maxima of the cone pigments erythrolabe and chlorolabe (540 and 570 nm) which are probably largely responsible for determining the brightness of lights at the photopic level. If the equal energy luminosity curves of photopic and scotopic vision are compared (Fig. 27.12) it is evident that the whole scotopic sensitivity curve is displaced towards shorter wavelengths. The displacement of the peak scotopic sensitivity towards the blue is known as the 'Purkinje shift'.

Ultraviolet (u.v.) radiation is normally invisible not because the retinal photopigments are insensitive to u.v. but because the lens contains a yellow pigment which prevents the u.v. from reaching the retina. People who have had their lenses removed (because they have become opaque) can see u.v. quite well. Normal people may be aware of ultraviolet radiation as a vague haze because the lens pigment fluoresces strongly.

Colour Vision

Trichromacy. The quality of the sensation produced by a light of moderate or high intensity depends upon its spectral composition. However, the spectral composition does not uniquely determine the sensation because different mixtures of monochromatic lights may appear identical. For two light stimuli to be indistinguishable it is only necessary for them to be alike in the values of three suitably chosen independent quantities. This three-fold nature of colour vision is known as trichromacy.

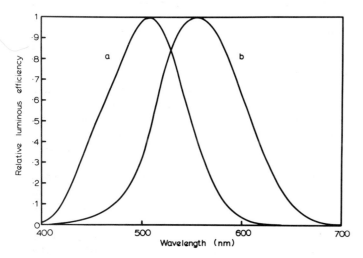

Fig. 27.12 The equal energy luminosity curve, a, for rod vision, as measured at low intensities in the extrafoveal area of the retina; b, for cone vision, as measured at high intensities at the fovea.

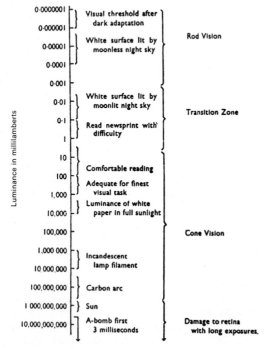

Fig. 27.13 Range of luminance to which the eye may be subjected with indications of the receptive mechanisms involved. (*By courtesy of F. W. Campbell.*)

The trichromacy of colour vision may be illustrated by the familiar fact that the stage lighting engineer, provided with red, green and blue lights, can, by mixing them in suitable proportions, reproduce almost any other colour. In fact, although any pale or unsaturated colour can be reproduced exactly, it is only possible to match approximately some pure spectral, that is 'saturated', colours. ('Saturation' is the technical term for freedom of a colour from admixed white.) An exact match can always be obtained, however, if one of the three primary colours is added not to the other two, but to the test colour which it is required to match. For example, spectral yellow can nearly be matched with a mixture of red and green but, to perfect the match, a little blue must be added to the yellow to make it slightly paler. If the addition of a light to one of the two fields on which the matching is being carried out is by convention represented as equivalent to its subtraction from the other, then the amounts, positive or negative, of three specified primaries required to match a given light provide a set of three quantities which define uniquely the sensation which it produces. Figure 27.14 shows the result of measuring these quantities for monochromatic lights of all spectral wavelengths, when red, green and blue primaries are used. The primaries need not necessarily be red, green and blue, but these have the advantage as primaries that the quantities of them required to match other colours are mostly positive, and when negative, are small.

Basis of trichromatic vision. It is now accepted that the trichromatic nature of normal colour vision is determined by the existence in the retina of three kinds of photosensitive pigment molecules segregated in three different groups of cones. If there are just three different pigments, and if the nature of the effect on a pigment molecule of absorbing a quantum of light is independent of its wavelength, which it is,

then the trichromacy of normal colour vision is an inevitable consequence. Since the degrees of excitation of the three kinds of cone are the only independent variables, the sensation produced by a visual stimulus must be capable of description in terms of three quantities.

This is not to say that the perceived colour of a visual stimulus is entirely determined by its spectral composition. It is well known that the appearance of a coloured object is dependent upon the visual environment in which it is seen and the recent visual experience of the subject. If a subject places a coloured filter in front of one eye for a few minutes and then, after removing it, looks around first through one eye and then the other, he will see that the apparent colours of things around him are very different according to which eye he uses. Again, the colour of a small object may appear quite markedly different if viewed against different, large, strongly coloured backgrounds. These effects do not disturb colour matches however much they change the subjective appearance.

It should be noted that objects which seem to have the same colour when lit by one source of light may well not match when lit by a light of different spectral composition. The spectral composition of the light reflected from an object depends, of course, upon both the illumination and the spectral variation in reflectivity of the object.

Colour-blindness. Abnormalities of colour vision known as colour-blindness, are common in men (about 8 per cent) but much less common in women (0·4 per cent). The common abnormalities are inherited as X-linked recessive characters.

Colour-blind subjects fall into a number of fairly sharply defined categories. Monochromats are quite unable to distinguish colours at all: a monochromat can match any two lights simply by adjusting their intensities. Monochromats are of two kinds. Rod monochromats have a luminosity curve like that of normal dark-adapted subjects; they see very poorly in bright surroundings and are presumed to lack functional cone mechanisms. Cone monochromats, on the other hand, appear to lack the rod mechanism: although their vision is more or less normal in bright surroundings, they see very badly when the illumination is reduced to scotopic levels. Monochromatism is rare, cone monochromatism exceptionally so.

Dichromats, who can match all colours with suitable mixtures of two primaries, are of three kinds. Protanopes and deuteranopes (each about 1 per cent of males) are often grouped together with the anomalous trichromats as 'red–green' blind. They have very little ability to discriminate colours at the red end of the spectrum, and thus confuse red, brown and green objects, though they can usually distinguish yellow objects by their higher reflecting power. Protanopes and deuteranopes differ from each other in the form of their photopic luminosity curves. Protanopes are relatively insensitive to red light and appear to lack the more red-sensitive pigment erythrolabe. Deuteranopes have luminosity curves similar to normal subjects and appear to have none of the green-sensitive pigment. The third kind of dichromatic vision is tritanopia. Tritanopes, who are as often female as male, are rare. They have normal colour discrimination at the red end of the spectrum, but they have little ability to distinguish blue from green. Tritanopes, sometimes called 'blue-blind', appear to lack the blue-sensitive pigment cyanolabe.

Anomalous trichromats, comprising nearly 6 per cent of the male population, resemble normal subjects in that they require

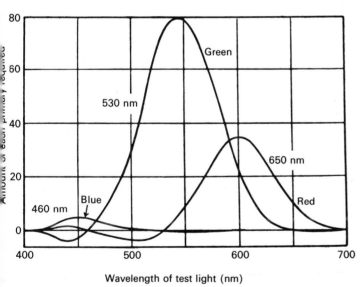

Fig. 27.14 The amounts of red (wavelength 650 nm), green (530 nm) and blue (460 nm) primaries required to match a constant quantity of a test light of variable wavelength. Where the ordinate of any curve is negative, this means that the corresponding primary must be added to the test light in order to match a mixture of the other two primaries. (*After* W. D. Wright (1928) *Transactions of the Optical Society*, 30, 141. *From* A. F. Rawdon-Smith (1938) *Theories of Sensation.* Cambridge University Press.)

three primaries to match all colours by colour mixture, but they require them in abnormal proportions. The cause of anomalous trichromacy is unknown: anomalous trichromats may have abnormal pigments.

Colour-blind subjects, even when their colour-discrimination is very poor, are often unaware of their defect. In familiar situations they compensate for their defective colour-discrimination by an increased use of alternative clues based upon prior knowledge of the usual colours of objects which they recognize by their shape. It may only be on rare occasions, when these clues are absent, that the defect becomes apparent.

The detection of colour-blindness is important in selecting people for jobs in which it is necessary to be able to distinguish coloured markings or coloured light signals. A convenient quick test consists of a set of 'pseudoisochromatic plates', of which Ishihara's are probably most widely used. Each plate has an array of multi-coloured dots so that a letter or figure is formed by dots of one colour, other colours forming the background. Some plates are designed to be read easily by the normal, but not by the colour-blind subject, while others can be read only by the colour-blind subject; some plates are interpreted differently by normal and colour-blind. This test is very efficient at separating the normal from the abnormal, but it does not distinguish well between different types of abnormality. To decide whether a subject with a mild abnormality can safely be employed in a particular occupation, a special test designed to imitate the task that has to be performed is often used.

Though hereditary colour-blindness is very much commoner, defects of colour vision can also be acquired as a result of diabetes mellitus or disease of the retina, optic nerve or visual cortex. These acquired defects are usually accompanied by severe defects of visual acuity or of visual fields.

Dark-Adaptation

It is a familiar fact that on leaving a brightly lit house on a dark night one sees badly but, after some time in darkness, one can see many objects which were at first invisible. The increase in visual sensitivity (fall in threshold) which occurs while the eyes are in darkness or near-darkness is called dark-adaptation, and the decrease in sensitivity caused by exposure to bright light is called light-adaptation. In subjects with vitamin A deficiency dark-adaptation occurs more slowly and the ultimate sensitivity is less.

The following simple experiments indicate that light-and dark-adaptation are probably properties of the retina and not of the central nervous pathway: previous exposure of one eye to light or to darkness has no effect upon the threshold for stimuli presented to the other eye; if an eye is made temporarily blind by pressing it sufficiently firmly to stop its blood supply, light which falls on it while it is blind raises the threshold for stimuli which are presented after it has recovered from the pressure-blindness. In any case the phenomena of light- and dark-adaptation have been shown to be characteristic of retinal ganglion cells.

The course of dark-adaptation after the eye has been adapted to a bright white light is shown in Figure 27.15. Thresholds were tested with 1° circular fields of various colours placed 5° away from the fixation point. It is clear that the curve for orange test stimuli falls into two phases separated by a sudden

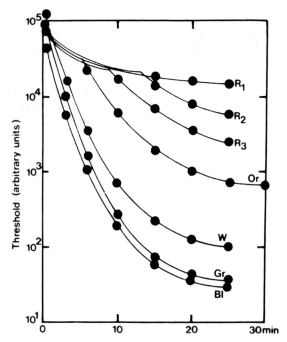

Fig. 27.15 Course of dark-adaptation for 1° circular fields of various colours, placed 5° from the fixation point. Wavebands were isolated by means of filters. Bl = blue, Gr = green, W = white, Or = orange; R_3, R_2 and R_1 are reds of successively longer wavelength. (*From* G. S. Brindley (1970) *Physiology of the Retina and Visual Pathway.* London: Arnold.)

change in gradient. With slightly different conditions of pre-adaptation a similar two-phase dark-adaptation curve can be obtained with white, yellow, green or blue test stimuli but, if the test stimulus is either deep red (to which the rods are very insensitive), or falls upon the fovea (where there are no rods), the second phase is absent. Orange, yellow, green or blue test stimuli look coloured, however dim they seem, during the first phase but look white at threshold during the second phase. Deep red and foveal stimuli always appear coloured if they are visible at all. Vision during the first phase of dark-adaptation is attributed to cones and during the second phase to rods.

It appears, then, that both the rod and cone mechanisms are rendered less sensitive by light-adaptation, but that the sensitivity of the rod mechanism is lowered by a much larger factor, so that for the first few minutes of dark-adaptation the threshold is determined by cones. At the end of this time the sensitivity of the cone mechanism is increasing only slowly but the sensitivity of the rod mechanism (which is inherently greater) is increasing rapidly. Thus, when the rods overtake the cones, there is a sudden increase in the rate at which the threshold falls.

When dark-adaptation is complete, the sensitivity of the retina is such that a flash of blue-green light from a field whose diameter subtends 10 seconds of arc at the eye may be seen if as few as 50 quanta of light enter the eye. Probably no more than 5 of these quanta are absorbed by rhodopsin molecules, and these absorptions must in general occur in different photoreceptors, since a 10 seconds of arc field illuminates about 350 rods. Thus each rod must be capable of being stimulated by a single quantum, though only if several such stimulations occur within a small time and area is any sensation produced.

There is strong circumstantial evidence that the decrease in sensitivity which accompanies light-adaptation depends upon the bleaching of the retinal photopigments and that dark-adaptation depends upon their regeneration. During dark-adaptation the logarithm of the threshold of both the cone and rod mechanisms can be shown to be inversely related to the concentration of the appropriate photopigment present. This relation rules out the simple idea that the sensitivity at any time is determined by the amount of photopigment available for catching quanta. The mechanism by which sensitivity and photopigment concentration are related is still unknown.

NEUROPHYSIOLOGY OF VISION

Electrical activity in the retina. When light is absorbed by the photopigment in a retinal rod or cone it causes the cell membrane to become hyperpolarized. It seems likely that the action of light is to decrease the permeability of the cell membrane to sodium ions. It is possible that this change in permeability could be directly related to the light-induced change in the photopigment structure since it is now generally supposed that the photopigment is a constituent of the membrane of the outer segment of the photoreceptor cells (rods and cones) (Fig. 27.9).

The potential change generated in the outer segment is transmitted electrotonically to synapses on both bipolar and horizontal cells (Fig. 27.9). The bipolar cells in turn transmit a graded electrical signal to the ganglion and amacrine cells with which they are in contact, while the horizontal cells seem to be responsible for spreading an inhibitory effect to surrounding photoreceptors. The action potentials generated in the ganglion cells pass along the fibres of the optic nerve and tract to the lateral geniculate nucleus and the superior colliculus.

Electroretinogram. If the potential difference that exists between an electrode placed on the cornea and another on a remote part of the body is amplified and recorded it is found to change when the eye is illuminated. This response is the electroretinogram (ERG). Recorded in this way the ERG probably represents the summation over the whole eye of the electrical activity of bipolar cells. The human ERG is of some diagnostic use; for example, in certain hereditary disorders of the retina (retinitis pigmentosa) which ultimately cause blindness, the ERG disappears before there is much visual impairment.

Retinal ganglion cells. As a result of the extensive interconnexions between the cells of the retina, every ganglion cell responds to the pattern of illumination falling on a considerable area of the retina. In the cat and monkey (and probably in man) retinal ganglion cells have roughly circular receptive fields which are divided into functionally distinct concentric 'centre' and 'surround' regions. Light falling in one of these regions excites the ganglion cell, causing the frequency of its discharge to increase, while light falling in the other region has an inhibitory effect, causing the discharge frequency to decrease. As a consequence of this antagonism, light falling uniformly over the whole receptive field has little effect upon the activity of the ganglion cell. This is demonstrated in Figure 27.16 which shows the responses of an 'off-centre' ganglion cell, that is a cell whose discharge is inhibited by light falling on the centre of its receptive field. It is also clear from Figure

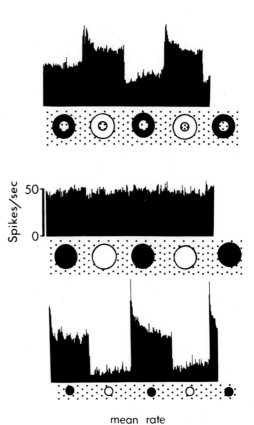

Fig. 27.16   Responses of an off-centre ganglion cell in a cat retina to switching off and on either an annulus (top record), a large spot (middle record) or a small spot (bottom record). The small spot illuminated only the centre of the receptive field, the annulus only the surround, while the large spot stimulated both centre and surround. (P. O. Bishop & R. W. Rodieck (1965) *Symposium on Information Processing in Sight Sensory Systems*. California Institute of Technology.)

27.16 that the response to a patterned stimulus can be very well maintained for many minutes, despite the initial adaptation which occurs. Some ganglion cells, particularly those in the peripheral retina, have much lower discharge frequencies when they are uniformly illuminated, respond with a transient increase in discharge frequency whenever the illumination is changed and adapt much more quickly and completely to patterned stimuli. Such ganglion cells probably serve to send information to the brain about the occurrence of changes in the visual environment which require attention, rather than about the exact nature of the stimulating pattern.

When the retinal illumination is reduced to scotopic levels the behaviour of retinal ganglion cells usually changes, the surround mechanism becoming less effective in antagonizing the action of the central region. This effect may be accompanied by an increase in the diameter of the central region of the receptive field and a change in the spectral sensitivity of the central mechanism. A ganglion cell which at high light levels has a spectral sensitivity typical of cones may, at low light levels, change to having one typical of rods. This is not surprising since ganglion cells are connected to both rods and cones (Fig. 27.9).

As well as differing from each other in the ways already described, retinal ganglion cells have receptive fields of widely differing sizes. The receptor fields are in general smaller in the central area of the retina than in the periphery. Also, in each area of the retina, the ganglion cells have overlapping receptive fields with a range of sizes. Since the dimensions of the stimulus pattern to which a ganglion cell is most sensitive are related to the size of its receptive field, the existence of receptive fields of different sizes means that information about spatial details of different dimensions is transmitted by different ganglion cells.

Lateral geniculate nucleus. Retinal ganglion cells send their axons to both the lateral geniculate nucleus and the superior colliculus (Fig. 27.20). Simultaneous records from single cells in the retina and lateral geniculate nucleus have shown that although the cells of the nucleus are influenced by the impulses in many optic tract fibres, they are often very strongly influenced by the discharges from one particular ganglion cell. It is thus not surprising that the behaviour of cells of the lateral geniculate nucleus is similar to that of the retinal ganglion cells

that drive them, though they usually adapt more rapidly and completely. Like ganglion cells they have concentrically organized receptive fields of various sizes many of which have colour-specific centre and surround regions. The antagonistic surround regions of the receptive fields of geniculate neurons are rather more diffuse than those of retinal ganglion cells though the significance of this difference is obscure. Cells in the primate lateral geniculate nucleus respond briskly to moving visual stimuli but they do not show any directional effects nor indeed any specific response to moving, as compared to flashing, stimuli.

The lateral geniculate nucleus receives afferent fibres from both eyes but individual cells can usually only be excited by stimulation of one eye. Most cells can be inhibited by stimuli falling on corresponding regions of the retina of the other eye. It has also been found that the activity of cells in the geniculate nucleus can be influenced by stimulation of the vestibular and other sensory systems. The functional significance of these influences is not yet known.

Occipital cortex. Removal of the cerebral cortex produces

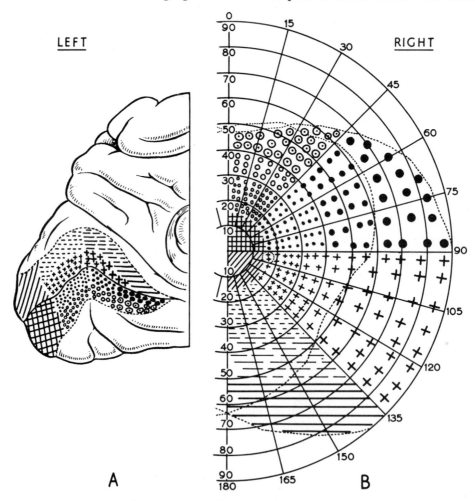

Fig. 27.17 The cortical retina. A diagram of the probable representation of the different portions of the visual fields in the calcarine. cortex. No great accuracy is claimed for this scheme. A. The postcalcarine fissure on the medial surface of the left occipital lobe is represented as widely opened. The macular area is relatively large, the peripheral area relatively small. B. The right halves of the field of vision are superimposed. Note that the centre of the field (macula) is represented at the tip of the occipital lobe and that the lower half of the field of vision (upper half of the retinae) is represented in the cortex above the postcalcarine sulcus. The peripheral parts of the field of vision tend to be represented in the anterior portion of the calcarine area. (*After* diagrams by Sir Gordon Holmes (1918) *British Journal of Ophthalmology*, 2, 383; also (1945) *Proceedings of the Royal Society* B, 132, 348.) More recent information is given by Teuber *et al.* (1960) (see references p. 461).

blindness without interfering with the reaction of the pupils to light. The area of the human occipital cortex involved in vision lies on the walls of the postcalcarine sulcus on the medial surface of the occipital lobe (Brodmann's area 17), occasionally extending a short distance on to its lateral surface.

The path of the fibres after the optic nerve has been found by studying the degeneration occurring after removal of different parts of the retina. The fibres from the nasal half of each retina in man cross over at the optic chiasma (Figs. 27.18 and 27.20) so that the fibres from the right halves of the two retinae pass into the right optic tract to the right lateral geniculate body from which new fibres go as the *optic radiations* to the calcarine cortex. The macular fibres concerned in central vision lie nearly centrally in the optic tracts and end on the posterior part of the lateral geniculate body, the macular relay fibres then going to the tip of the occipital lobe. Removal of the occipital cortex in man has often left some macular vision but this is likely to depend on incomplete removal of the area of cortex concerned rather than on bilateral cortical representation of the macula for which there is no anatomical basis. After damage to the visual cortex a patient may be able to localize large objects in his blind field even though he has no awareness of 'seeing' them. It may

be that the residual ability depends on the superior colliculus or other structures in the visual pathway.

The results of correlation of the position of lesions with the shape of the visual field obtained by perimetry show that the centre of the field is represented in the tip of the occipital lobe at the posterior end of the postcalcarine sulcus, and that the upper half of each retina (lower half of the field of vision) is represented on the upper part of the visual area of the cortex. Conversely the lower half of the retina is represented on the lower half. The area of the cortex connected with the macula and devoted to central vision is, as might be expected from the power of the macula to appreciate colour and fine detail, large compared with that subserving peripheral vision (Fig. 27.17).

The pathway from retina to cortex can be thought of in simple terms as six nerve cells, three in the retina, one in the lateral geniculate body and two in the cortex.

The areas adjacent to the occipital cortex, Brodmann's areas 18 and 19, are association areas in which co-ordination of eye reflexes with other reflexes occurs. The interpretation of what is seen, for example a printed word, requires the presence of these association regions; their destruction causes visual agnosia.

The responses of single neurones in the visual cortex were

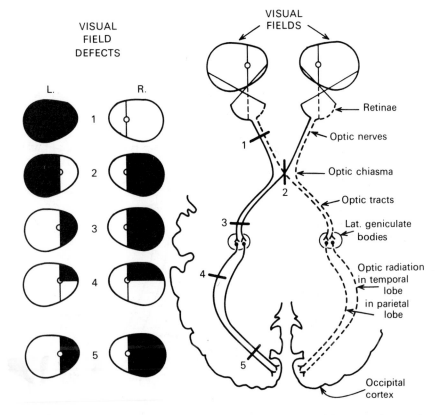

VISUAL
FIELD
DEFECTS

VISUAL
FIELDS

L.   R.

1

2

3

4

5

— Retinae

— Optic nerves

— Optic chiasma

— Optic tracts

— Lat. geniculate
   bodies

Optic radiation
in temporal
   lobe
in parietal
   lobe

Occipital
cortex

Fig. 27.18 The course of the fibres involved in vision from the right and left halves of the two retinae to the occipital cortex. The small diagrams on the left indicate the blind parts of the field of vision (in black) produced by the lesions 1 to 5 described below. There is a relay in the lateral geniculate body. A lesion at 1 cutting through the left optic nerve results in complete blindness of the left eye with loss of light reflexes. A lesion at 2 involving the central part of the optic chiasma interrupts the fibres from the nasal halves of the retinae and produces bitemporal hemianopia. A lesion at 3 divides the optic tract containing fibres from the left halves of both retinae and produces blindness in the right halves of the visual fields (homonymous hemianopia); the pupil does not contract when a light is thrown on the left halves of the retinae. A lesion at 4 cutting through the optic radiations also produces blindness in the left halves of the retinae (homonymous defect), but the light reflex is normal. A lesion at 5 at the posterior pole of the occipital cortex causes blindness in the right side of the macular field of vision. (J. Macleod (Ed.) (1974) *Davidson's Principles and Practice of Medicine.* 11th edition. Edinburgh: Churchill Livingstone.)

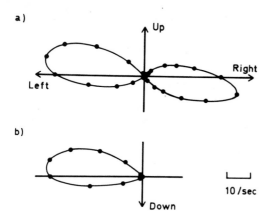

a)

b)

10 /sec

Fig. 27.19 The orientation specificity of two cells in the visual cortex of a cat. The cells (which had very low resting discharge frequencies in the absence of stimulation) were stimulated by a grating pattern moving continuously in one direction across their receptive fields. The frequency of discharge of the cells is plotted vectorially for different directions of movement. The distance of each point from the centre of the diagram shows the magnitude of the response when the grating was moved in a direction parallel to the line joining the point to the centre. (a) This cell responded equally well if the pattern moved to the left or right; it also responded well to patterns flashed on and off. (b) This cell did not respond at all to patterns moving to the right; it responded very much better to moving than to flashing stimuli. (*By courtesy of G. F. Cooper and J. G. Robson.*)

first extensively studied by Hubel and Wiesel. They found, initially in cats and later in monkeys, that the behaviour of cortical cells was very different from that of retinal ganglion cells or the cells of the lateral geniculate nucleus. Cortical cells were found to respond best not to small spots or patches of light but to straight lines or edges adjusted to have a particular optimum orientation. The orientation specificity of most cortical cells has been found to be quite high, the response typically falling to one half of the maximum when the stimulus is rotated about 15° to 20° in either direction from its optimum orientation (Fig. 27.19a). Kittens reared in a visually abnormal environment do not develop cortical cells with normal orientation specificities.

Very few cortical cells show any response at all to stationary patterns; they usually discharge at low frequencies unless they are being stimulated by patterns that are being moved or flashed on and off. Some cortical cells respond equally well to both flashing and moving stimulus patterns but others respond much better to a moving stimulus. The cells that seem to be specifically sensitive to moving patterns (Fig. 27.19a) often respond only when the pattern moves in one direction, movement in the opposite direction producing little or no effect upon the cell.

If grating patterns made up of parallel light and dark bars are used as visual stimuli some cortical cells are found to respond selectively to patterns with a particular spacing between the bars.

The ability of cortical cells to respond selectively to particular spatial stimulus patterns is presumably determined by the interplay of excitatory and inhibitory influences from different regions of their receptive fields. In this respect it is significant that the receptive fields of visual cortical cells are

linearly, rather than circularly, organized, the excitatory and inhibitory influences coming from adjacent strip-like regions of the field. Some receptive fields are made up of several such antagonistic strips side by side. In general terms the strip-like form of the receptive-field subdivisions can be assumed to account for the orientation specificity while the existence of multiple antagonistic subdivisions could provide the selectivity for patterns with particular periodicities.

Some cortical cells, called 'hypercomplex' by Hubel and Wiesel, do not respond well to lines or edges, even when they are set at their optimum orientation, unless they are of limited length. Such cells are probably driven by the outputs of the simpler cortical cells already described.

Most cells in the visual cortex can be excited by stimuli applied to either eye although one eye is usually dominant. If the stimulus pattern is presented simultaneously to both eyes then the response of the cell may be much greater than when

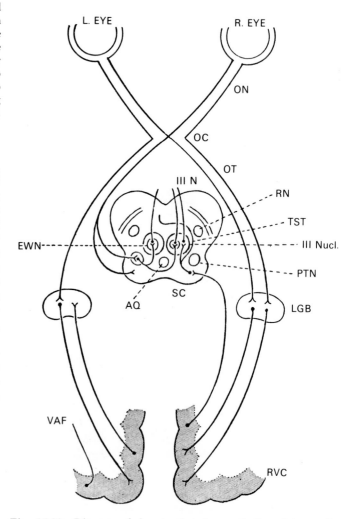

Fig. 27.20 Diagram of the visual pathways. L. Eye = left eye. R. Eye = right eye. ON = optic nerve. OC = optic chiasma. OT = optic tract. III N = third nerve. TST = tectospinal tract. III Nucl. = third nerve nucleus. AQ = aqueduct of mid-brain. RN = red nucleus. EWN = Edinger-Westphal nucleus. PTN = pretectal nucleus. SC = superior colliculus. LGB = lateral geniculate body. VAF = visual association fibre. RVC = right visual cortex. (*By courtesy of G. W. Pearce.*)

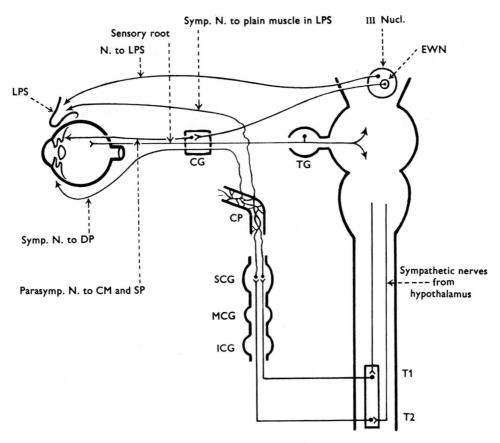

Fig. 27.21   Diagram of the course of the autonomic fibres to the eye. III Nucl. = oculomotor nucleus. EWN = Edinger-Westphal nucleus. LPS = levator palpebrae superioris. CG = ciliary ganglion. T1, T2 = first and second thoracic segments of spinal cord. SCG, MCG and ICG = superior, middle and inferior cervical sympathetic ganglia. TG = trigeminal ganglion. DP = dilatator pupillae. SP = sphincter pupillae. CM = ciliaris muscle. CP = plexus on internal carotid artery. (*By courtesy of G. W. Pearce.*)

either eye is stimulated alone. To obtain the maximum response, however, the stimulus pattern must be appropriately positioned on both retinae. With the eyes in their normal positions the optimal positioning of both retinal images of a real object can only be achieved if the object is at a certain distance from the eyes. It is probable that different cortical cells respond best to objects at different distances, thus providing a basis for stereoscopic vision.

Perhaps surprisingly very few cortical cells respond in any discriminatory manner to coloured stimuli.

In a person who is blind because of lesions of the retina or peripheral visual pathways electrical stimulation of area 17 produces *phosphenes*, subjective sensations of lights whose brightness depends on the strength of the stimulation. They appear and disappear with the beginning and end of stimulation but may fade in 10 or 15 seconds if the stimulation is prolonged. As might be expected from Figure 27.17 the apparent position of a phosphene depends on the part of the visual cortex stimulated. Electrodes nearer than 3 mm cannot usually be distinguished. It has therefore been suggested that an array of electrodes, each producing its own phosphene, could act as a visual prosthesis.

Visual reflexes. When the superior colliculi are stimulated electrically dilatation of the pupil occurs along with conjugate movements of the eyes towards the opposite side, that is lateral movements of both eyes simultaneously through equal angles.

It is possible, however, that these results are due simply to spread of current to neighbouring structures. When the superior colliculi are destroyed the pupillary contraction on exposure to light remains but, if the pretectal area just rostral to them is destroyed at the same time, the light reflex can no longer be obtained. This is explained in Figure 27.20; some fibres from the retina travel in the optic nerve and optic tract but pass medial to the lateral geniculate bodies to end in the pretectal area where the first synapse occurs. Second order relay neurones cross in the posterior commissure and reach the Edinger-Westphal part of the third nerve nucleus on both sides from which nerve fibres pass via the ciliary ganglion to the sphincter pupillae. The phenomenon of contraction of the pupil on accommodation but not on exposure to light, a common finding in certain diseases of the nervous system, is probably due to interruption of the pathways in the pretectal region. The light reflexes remain after cortical ablation since they do not require a cortical pathway. The very much longer sympathetic pathway to the eye is illustrated in Figure 27.21.

MOVEMENTS OF THE EYES

The eyeball is supported by the fatty tissues of the orbit which form a sort of socket for it. Within this socket the eyeball is free to rotate and also, since the socket is not rigid, to move a little from side to side and up and down. The eyeball is made to rotate by the action of three pairs of muscles. The lateral and medial recti rotate the eyeballs outwards or inwards about a vertical axis, but the other four muscles cause rotation around oblique axes so that they produce movements with both vertical and horizontal components. The extraocular muscles are supplied by the cranial nerves III, IV (superior oblique) and VI (lateral rectus) which originate from nuclei in the mid-

brain. The actions of the extraocular and intraocular muscles (which are controlled from associated midbrain nuclei) are very closely linked so that both eyes act together and conjugate movements, convergence and accommodation all occur together in a harmonious fashion. This prevents double vision (diplopia) by ensuring that the two retinal images always fall on corresponding points on the retinae in the two eyes. Corresponding points are distributed around the two foveae so

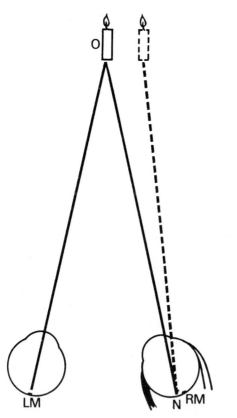

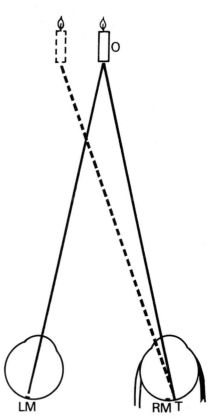

Fig. 27.22a Paralysis of the right lateral rectus. Rays reach both eyes from an object O the image of which falls on the left macula LM. The right eye is deviated inwards by the unopposed medial rectus, the image of O falling on an area N to the nasal side of the retina. This area possesses innate directional value (local sign) to the right. Since the eccentric area is less sensitive than the macula the image belonging to it is less clear (the false or 'ghost' image). The false image is to the same side as the paretic eye—homonymous diplopia.

Fig. 27.22b Paralysis of the right medial rectus. Rays reach both eyes from an object O the image of which falls on the left macula. The right eye is deviated outwards by the unopposed lateral rectus the image of O falling on an area T to the temporal side of the retina. This area possesses innate directional value (local sign) to the left. Since the eccentric area is less sensitive than the macula the image belonging to it is less clear (the false or 'ghost' image). The false image is to the side opposite the paretic eye—crossed diplopia.

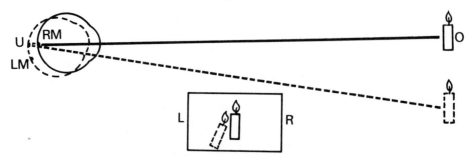

Fig. 27.22c Paralysis of the left superior oblique. The action of the superior oblique comprises depression, abduction and intorsion. In paralysis the eye is elevated and extorted by the inferior oblique and deviated inwards (adducted) by the superior and inferior recti. The image of O will fall on the macula of the right eye but, in the left eye, on the area U above and to the nasal side of the macula. The false image is therefore below and homonymous. It is the vertical element of the diplopia that is noticed by the patient. The inset shows the position of the images in detail. RM, right macula; LM, left macula. (*By courtesy of A. A. Douglas.*)

that those in the right half of one retina correspond with those in the right half of the other; those in the upper half of one retina with those in the upper half of the other, and so on.

If the two eyes do not move sufficiently precisely together double vision may occur. However, when the two retinal images do not correspond with each other there may be a tendency for one of the retinal images to be suppressed so that it gives rise to no conscious perception. In children with refractive errors who squint, the image from the squinting eye is often suppressed to such an extent that vision in that eye progressively deteriorates unless use of the squinting eye is deliberately forced by frequent occlusion (that is covering up) of the other eye. When paralytic squint occurs diplopia is quite obvious to the patient. The false image seen by the squinting eye is projected as indicated in Figure 27.22.

Fixation movements. When a subject looks around him his gaze is continually being shifted from one point to another in discrete jumps called 'saccades'. The nature of saccadic eye movements can readily be seen if the eyes of a subject are observed while he is reading. A normal subject makes four or five separate saccadic fixation movements in scanning along each line of text (Fig. 27.23a). Saccadic movements may involve rotation of the eyeballs through many degrees or through only a few minutes of arc. The saccadic rotation always occurs very quickly, its time course not being under voluntary control.

Even if a subject attempts to fixate a target as steadily as he can, his eyes do not stay perfectly still but continue to make small drifting and saccadic movements of which he is unaware (Fig. 27.23b). This microtremor, about 100 Hz, is so small that to an unaided observer the eyes appear to be quite still. In the

absence of such small movements of the eyes, and hence of the image on the retina, vision of the outside world rapidly fades. A simple way of experiencing this fading can be achieved by looking at a large, uniformly illuminated field (such as the blue sky) through a small pin-hole in a piece of card held very close to the eye. If the pin-hole is moved from side to side about two or three times a second, then a fine network of lines will be seen superimposed upon the uniform background. These lines are the shadows of the small blood vessels which lie in front of the receptor layer of the retina. As soon as the movement of the pin-hole is stopped the shadows disappear. Experiments in which the retinal images of objects in the outside world are stabilized instrumentally have shown that the fading is most rapid and complete if the objects are small, but that it always occurs to an appreciable extent. It has been suggested that the fading is a result of sensory adaptation in the retina, but in view of the fact that many retinal ganglion cells have very well maintained discharges (p. 435), while adaptation is much more rapid and complete at higher levels in the visual pathway, it seems more likely that the fading is a result of adaptation at these higher levels.

If the object being fixated is moving the subject's eyes make the appropriate smooth following movements (Fig. 27.23c) upon which saccadic fixation movements may be superimposed. Smooth following movements of the eyes are produced reflexly whenever the gaze is transferred to a moving target; they cannot be produced voluntarily in the absence of such a target. The only kind of eye movement that can be made voluntarily is the saccade. If a subject in a moving vehicle looks out at the passing landscape then his eyes alternately make smooth following movements and saccadic jumps in the opposite direction (Fig. 27.23d). The resulting oscillation is known as 'optico-kinetic nystagmus'. During the slow phase of the nystagmus the image of the passing scene remains more or less stationary on the retina, while in the fast phase the eyes are restored towards their undeviated position.

Smooth eye movements are also produced when a subject's head is rotated. If the head rotates through a small angle then an approximately compensating rotation of the eyes in the opposite direction is brought about by vestibular reflexes. A larger or more prolonged rotation of the head results in a nystagmoid movement. These movements occur even if the eyes are closed and may persist for some time after cessation of a prolonged rotation.

At birth the fixation reflex is present but weak, and eye movements are rather independent and unco-ordinated. By 5 to 6 weeks of age both eyes can simultaneously fixate an object, that is the conjugate fixation reflex is established, and a child can follow a moving target over a short range. By about 3 months objects of interest are voluntarily fixated and the beginning of co-ordinated eye and hand movements is seen. Fully co-ordinated movements of convergence and divergence do not usually appear before 6 months.

Although it has been found possible to elicit eye movements by electrical stimulation of many different nervous structures, the central mechanisms involved in the control of eye movements are not well understood.

Perception of depth and distance. A subject with one eye covered can still estimate, with a fair degree of accuracy, the relative distances from him of objects in his field of vision, as well as the actual distance from him of objects of known size.

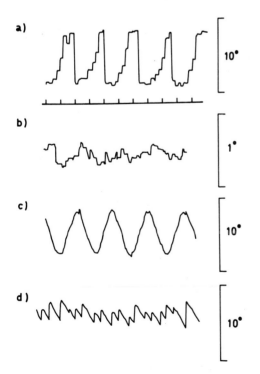

Fig. 27.23 Horizontal eye movements of a subject (a) reading, (b) steadily fixating a small object (note different vertical scale), (c) looking at a pendulum bob, (d) looking at a rotating drum. The time scale below record (a) shows seconds. (*By courtesy of J. G. Robson.*)

The relative distances of objects can be judged from such clues as the relative sizes of their retinal images (if the objects are of similar actual size), the occlusion of part of a distant object by a nearer one, the greater amount of detail visible in nearer objects and, if there is relative movement between the objects in the field and the subject, the paralactic changes which result. If the subject can use both eyes a further clue to the absolute distance of an object from him is given by the degree of convergence of his eyes necessary to make the two retinal images of the object fall on corresponding retinal areas.

As well as these effects, a subject who examines a near object with both eyes can make use of the fact that he gets somewhat different (that is disparate) views of the object with each eye. If the disparity of the retinal images is not too great the subject is unaware of it although he perceives the object extending in depth in a way which never occurs if he uses one eye only. Binocular vision of this kind is called stereoscopic vision. The existence of stereoscopic vision is believed to depend upon the presence in the visual cortex of cells which respond specifically to retinal images with particular degrees of disparity. In man the nasotemporal division at the decussation of the optic chiasma is complete. The cortical visual cells for central vision seem to be connected by fibres going across the corpus callosum from one hemisphere to the other. These inter-hemispheric fibres seem to be necessary for midline stereopsis. If kittens are brought up in such a way that they are not allowed to use both eyes at the same time during a short critical period of their development, they do not establish the required neural connexions and do not achieve stereoscopic vision.

HEARING

Hearing is one of the perceptual processes by which animals are continually being informed about their environment. In man the general information from the ears, such as the proximity of a source of sound, is augmented by the more specific information contained in speech. Speech and hearing must be regarded as two complementary activities which subserve the function of communication. If complete deafness is congenital or occurs in infancy before vocalization has reached the stage of speech the child fails to develop the ability to speak, although he may be taught to speak intelligibly by special methods.

The External Ear and Middle Ear

The external acoustic meatus, about 2·5 cm long in the adult, passes down from the auricle to the tympanic membrane. The skin of the outer one-third of the meatus possesses numerous ceruminous or wax-secreting glands which are modified sweat glands; numerous sebaceous glands open into the hair follicles. Wax, a mixture of the two kinds of secretion, contains lysozyme and immunoglobulins. Accumulation of wax in the external meatus is a common cause of impaired hearing.

The tympanic membrane, about 1 cm in diameter, is composed of radial and circular collagenous fibres covered externally by stratified squamous epithelium continuous with the skin and internally by a mucous membrane of ciliated columnar epithelium. The outer surface of the membrane is concave; the inner convex surface, as seen from the middle ear or tympanic cavity, has the manubrium of the malleus (handle of the hammer) attached to it. The malleus articulates with the incus (anvil) and the incus with the stapes (stirrup), the base of which is attached by fibrous tissue to the margins of the fenestra vestibuli (oval window). These very light ossicles in the air-filled tympanic cavity link the ear drum to the inner ear (Fig. 27.26). The tensor tympani muscle, by its attachment to the root of the manubrium of the malleus, draws the tympanic membrane in, and at the same time, through the articulations between the three ossicles, pushes the stapes into the internal ear. The small stapedius muscle tends to have the opposite effect, namely to pull the stapes out of the internal ear. In response to sound, or to mechanical stimulation of the external acoustic meatus, auricle or surrounding skin, these muscles contract reflexly, pulling in the tympanic membrane and tightening it and pushing the footplate of the stapes inwards, presumably because the tensor tympani is more powerful than the stapedius. The result is that sound transmission across the middle ear is impaired for tones of low frequency and the ear is partially protected from damage by loud sounds.

The ear drum and the ossicles act as a kind of transformer to convey vibrations of the light medium, air, to the denser, watery media in the internal ear. The area of the ear drum is about 90 mm², whereas the area of the base of the stapes is only 3·2 mm². The pressure on the fluid under the stapes is thus many times greater than the air pressure which makes the ear drum move. In the absence of this impedance-matching function only a very small proportion of the energy of the sound would reach the inner ear as happens if the conducting function of the middle ear is abolished and the sound reaches the internal ear fluids directly. In the course of the condition called otosclerosis, a familial and progressive deafness beginning in young people, the base of the stapes become joined by bone to the margins of the fenestra vestibuli. This condition causes severe deafness (Fig. 27.33D).

The auditory tube leads from the anterior part of the middle ear to the nasal part of the pharynx. The pharyngeal end is normally closed but during swallowing it opens and allows the air pressure in the middle ear to be equalized with the atmospheric. If the pressure is not equal on the two sides the drum is pushed in (as in the case of the descent of a diver) or drawn out (as on ascending in an aeroplane). Such abnormal displacement may produce pain and impaired hearing and damage to the ear drum but this discomfort can be avoided by frequent swallowing while the air pressure is altering. Reduced acuity of hearing may also result when the tube is blocked by the swelling of the mucous membrane which accompanies a 'cold'; in this case the oxygen in the middle ear is absorbed and the ear drum is pushed in by the external atmospheric pressure.

The Internal Ear

This section deals with cochlear function only. Other parts of the internal ear, the semi-circular canals and otolith organs, are concerned with the maintenance of balance and play no part in hearing; they are discussed in Chapter 24. The basic structure of the cochlea is given in Figure 27.24. If the three canals are wrapped two and threequarter times round the modiolus (the central pillar of the cochlea) and a cross section made the appearance seen in Figure 27.26 can be accounted for. More details can be seen in Figure 27.25. The *basilar membrane*, about 31 mm long, is composed of fibres which run radially from the osseous spiral lamina of the modiolus to the spiral ligament, or crista basilaris, which binds the basilar membrane to the external bony wall of the cochlea. The fibres

are short (0.04 mm) near the foramen vestibuli and increase gradually to the apex of the cochlea at the helicotrema, where they are about 0.5 mm long. The spiral organ of Corti is formed of about 4000 rods of Corti which make a spiral tunnel on top of the basilar membrane. On either side of this tunnel are hair cells whose bristle-like processes are attached to the underside of the tectorial membrane (Fig. 27.28). Filaments of the cochlear nerve lie on the exterior of the hair cells and pass to the spiral ganglion lying nearer the modiolus. The fluid in the scala vestibuli and the scala tympani (the perilymph) is very like cerebrospinal fluid in chemical composition except for a somewhat higher protein content; the perilymph, however, may not be continuous with the cerebrospinal fluid. The endolymph in the ductus cochlearis has a composition more like that of intracellular fluid with high potassium and low

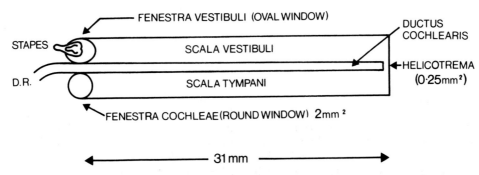

Fig. 27.24 Basic structure of the inner ear. If this system of three tubes (scala vestibuli, ductus cochlearis and scala tympani) could be wrapped two and three-quarter times round the modiolus (central pillar of the inner ear) the actual anatomical relationships would be reached. D.R. = ductus reuniens which communicates with the saccule.

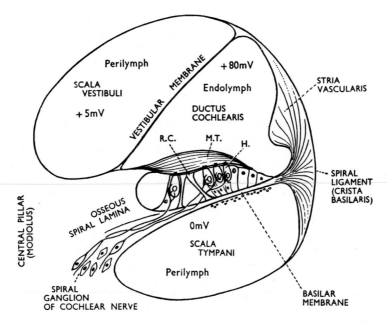

Fig. 27.25 A cross-section through the three canals of the cochlea to show the structures on the basilar membrane. H., hair cells; M.T., membrana tectoria; R.C., rods of Corti. The reticular lamina is a net-like membrane holding in its apertures the hairs of the hair cells (Fig. 27.28). The cochlear partition comprises the basilar membrane, the vestibular membrane (Reissner's membrane) and the structures contained in the ductus cochlearis. The endolymph in the ductus cochlearis (scala media) is 80 mV positive with respect to the perilymph in the scala tympani. The perilymph in the scala vestibuli is 5 mV positive to the perilymph in the scala tympani. The naked nerve fibres are about 0.15 μm in diameter as they arise from the hair cells. As they pass centrally they become myelinated (2 to 5 μm). The fine nerve fibres passing through the organ of Corti must be bathed in perilymph or fluid resembling it. All the sensory hair cells are richly innervated; the nerve endings are of two kinds, sparsely granular afferent and richly granular efferent.

sodium concentrations; however, the main anion is chloride as in extracellular fluid. It is probably secreted by the cells of the stria vascularis (Fig. 27.25).

Mechanical aspects of cochlear function. If the air pressure in the external auditory meatus is suddenly increased the tympanic membrane is pushed inwards and this movement is transferred by the chain of ossicles to the footplate of the stapes, which also moves inwards, increasing the pressure in the scala vestibuli. This increased pressure causes the cochlear partition to be displaced towards the scala tympani, raising in turn the pressure in the latter and causing the secondary tympanic membrane (the membrane of the round window) to bulge outwards into the middle ear. This displacement of the cochlear partition is not maintained because the partition is elastic and the scalae communicate via the helicotrema. The pressure difference between the scala vestibuli and scala

tympani is soon equalized by fluid transfer via the helicotrema and the partition returns to its rest position. However, if the tympanic membrane is being moved in and out fairly rapidly, as by the vibrations of a sound wave, there is not sufficient time for the fluid to move back and forth through the helicotrema and the cochlear partition accordingly vibrates in sympathy with the sound waves. The ability of perilymph to move through the helicotrema instead of displacing the cochlear partition is one of the factors which limit the low frequency range of hearing to about 30 Hz.

The characteristics of the vibration of the cochlear partition have been observed under the microscope with stroboscopic illumination. The response to a tonal stimulus is a travelling wave moving from base to apex (Fig. 27.27). An example of a travelling wave is that produced by moving one end of a slack horizontal rope rhythmically up and down. The waves in the

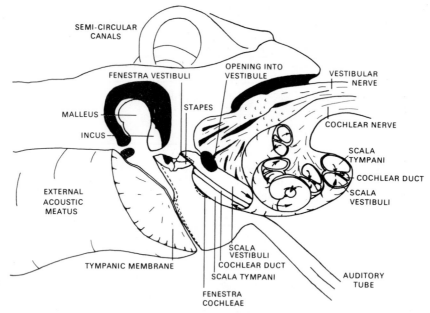

Fig. 27.26 A three-dimensional view of the ear. When the tympanic membrane is pushed inwards to the position indicated by the dotted lines the ossicles move to the positions shown by dotted lines. The stapes attached by the annular ligament to the margin of the fenestra vestibuli (oval window) is pushed into the scala vestibuli and the secondary tympanic membrane which closes the fenestra cochleae (round window) bulges. The arrows indicate the flow of lymph. It should be noted that the diagram has been slightly distorted to show the actions of the oval and round windows which do not as a result occupy their true anatomical relation. (*By courtesy of I. C. Whitfield.*)

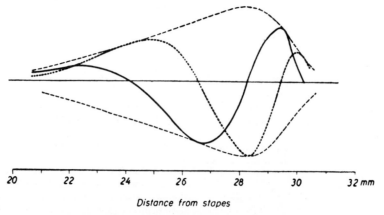

Distance from stapes

Fig. 27.27 The measured longitudinal bending of the cochlear partition for a tone of 200 Hz for two moments in time separated by a quarter period. (G. von Békésy (1947) *Journal of the Acoustic Society of America*, **19**, 455.)

rope appear to progress along it, whereas plucking a stretched string produces standing waves and the nodes and antinodes remain in the same positions. However, there are important differences between the travelling waves in a rope and those in the basilar membrane. Whereas the rope is uniform along its length, the membrane is certainly not so. Not only does it increase some twelve-fold in width between the base and the apex but it is very much stiffer at the basal than at the apical end. An important result of this gradation of properties is that the wave grows progressively in amplitude as it travels away from the base and then it rather suddenly dies out. Further, the point of maximum amplitude varies with the sound frequency, being in the basal turn for the highest frequencies and moving further and further towards the apex as the sound frequency is decreased.

Recently the use of coherent light has enabled the patterns in the 10 to 20 kHz region to be observed directly by a form of laser interferometry. Further confirmation has come by placing a very small (80 μm) radioactive source on the membrane. As the membrane vibrates the velocity of the source produces a corresponding change in the frequency of the emitted radiation which can be measured by suitable techniques.

The direction of movement of the travelling wave (base to apex) is entirely determined by the intrinsic properties of the basilar membrane and is in no way dependent on the vibration being 'introduced' into the cochlea at the basal end. If an artificial stapes is constructed near the apex it is found that the wave still travels from the (stiffer) basal region of the membrane to the less stiff apical end. Indeed our ability to hear by bone conduction depends on this property, since in this case the vibration is introduced into the cochlea rather diffusely via the bony wall itself.

The mechanics of the basilar membrane thus provide some separation of the frequency components of a sound but this separation is clearly quite insufficient to account for the observed pitch discrimination of the auditory system. It has indeed become obvious that neurological mechanisms must play a major role. It must be remembered that pitch discrimination is not the only, or even perhaps from an evolutionary point of view the most important, role of the cochlea. In the localization of sound, transients like those produced by snapping twigs are far more important than tones, and a good transient response is not readily compatible with a sharply tuned filter system. Some compromise has therefore been inevitable.

Endocochlear potential. By inserting microelectrodes into guinea-pig cochlea, Békésy found that the endolymph in the ductus cochlearis (scala media), even in the absence of any acoustic stimulation of the ear, was electrically positive by some 80 mV to the perilymph in the scala tympani and the scala vestibuli. This is called the endocochlear potential. When a microelectrode penetrated into the cellular structures on the basilar membrane (hair cells and supporting cells) negative potentials were found; such internal negativity in cells is to be expected and is, of course, well known in nerve and muscle cells. The total potential difference between the endolymph in the cochlear duct and the interior of the cells is about 140 mV.

Although the fluid in the cochlear duct has a high potassium content and the scala tympani contains perilymph whose sodium/potassium ratio is akin to extracellular fluid, it does not seem that the differences in ion concentrations are responsible for the endocochlear potential. However, the potential falls rapidly when the oxygen supply is cut off and is abolished when cyanide is injected into the endolymphatic space. The dependence of the potential on metabolism has suggested that the stria vascularis is closely implicated in its production. It is to be noted that the large potential difference (that is, 80 mV) between endolymph and perilymph is found only in the mammalian cochlea; the endocochlear potential in birds is very small. In spite of the anatomical continuity of the membranous labyrinth, the potential difference in the semicircular canals, utricle and saccule, is nearly zero (less than 2 mV).

The main barrier between the cochlear duct and the scala tympani appears to be the reticular lamina, the stiff membrane covering the hair-bearing ends of the hair cells. Thus the structures of the organ of Corti and indeed the basilar membrane itself lie within the perilymphatic space. There may be, nevertheless, slight local differences in the lymph in the vicinity of these structures. For example, the composition of the fluid in the space between the reticular lamina and the tectorial membrane probably differs from that in the rest of the cochlear duct, being rich in mucopolysaccharides.

Cochlear microphonic. The steady potential difference between the cochlear duct and the scala tympani is reduced by a displacement of the basilar membrane towards the scala vestibuli and increased by a displacement of the basilar membrane in the opposite direction, that is, towards the scala tympani. These alterations in potential are maintained so long as the deformation of the basilar membrane is maintained. Such displacements have been made experimentally by applying pressure to the fluids in the scalae or by gently touching the membrane itself with a needle. These potential changes are associated with the shearing forces between the tectorial membrane and the hair cells held in the reticular lamina (Fig. 27.28). The mechanism can be visualized by flexing a book and observing the relative motion between the two covers. The alternating potential produced in this way when the basilar membrane is set into vibration by a sound is known as the cochlear microphonic. It was first recorded from the fenestra cochleae and an 'indifferent' electrode in the neck, but with suitable filtering techniques it is possible to record it in man from more accessible points, for example the tympanic membrane.

The cochlear microphonic corresponds closely to the

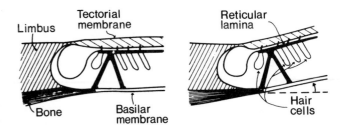

Fig. 27.28 The shearing action between the hair cells and the tectorial membrane, when the cochlear partition is deflected. This shearing action results in bending or deflexion of the hairs relative to the reticular lamina. (*From* H. Davis (1960) *Neural Mechanisms of the Auditory and Vestibular Systems.* Eds. G. L. Rasmussen & W. F. Windle. Springfield: Thomas.)

characteristics of the applied sound stimulus; it is virtually an electrical equivalent of the applied acoustic stimulus and is quite different from the action potentials in the auditory nerve. The potential changes of the microphonic follow the frequency of the applied sound stimulus at all audible frequencies; they resemble quite closely the waveform of the stimulus. They have virtually no latent period or threshold and increase progressively in amplitude with increase in sound energy up to quite high sound pressure levels (100 dB SPL). (SPL is defined on p. 456.) The fact that the potentials decline and eventually disappear when oxygen is cut off shows that they depend on the metabolism of the cells of this region.

Because of the conductivity of the fluids, recording from the electrode on the fenestra cochleae, as described above, reproduces the recombined microphonics from all points of the cochlea, albeit predominantly those from the basal turn. However, if a pair of electrodes is inserted through the cochlear wall so that they lie opposite to one another across the basilar membrane/hair cell complex, one in the cochlear duct and the other in the scala tympani, a record of cochlear microphonics from a much more localized region can be made. Tasaki, Davis and Legouix used this method to confirm the observations of Békésy on the mechanical disturbance of the basilar membrane. They found that tones of low frequency produced microphonics whose amplitude was greatest at the apical parts of the cochlea while microphonics from tones of high frequency could be recorded only near the base. By studying the phase relations of the microphonics at different distances from the stapes they were also able to confirm the existence of travelling waves.

In addition to the pure alternating component of the cochlear microphonic, which reproduces the sound stimulus frequency, there is often observed, at high stimulus intensities, a steady displacement of the baseline lasting as long as the stimulus. This so-called 'summating potential' may be ascribed to non-linear vibration of the basilar membrane/hair cell complex at large displacements.

Action Potential of Cochlear Nerve Fibres

The estimate of the threshold sensitivity of the ear given on page 455 shows that the amount of mechanical energy available for stimulating the nerve endings in the cochlea is, even for the every-day range of sounds, very small indeed. The tiny mechanical movements of the hair cells produced by such sounds must release a store of energy many times that of the original sound. Just how the nerve impulses are initiated is not understood. There has been considerable discussion about whether the cochlear microphonic corresponds to a receptor generator potential. It seems on the whole unlikely that the microphonic potential stimulates the nerve endings directly; electron microscope studies have revealed what appears to be a synaptic junction between the base of the hair cell and the afferent nerve fibre, but so far no transmitter has been identified.

The responses of individual fibres in the auditory nerve have been investigated by a number of workers; a comprehensive study in the cat has been made by Kiang. All these studies show that there is for each fibre some characteristic sound frequency

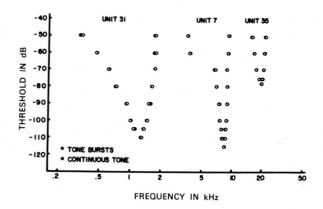

Fig. 27.29   Threshold response curves for three cat auditory nerve fibres. Each fibre responds best to some particular frequency, the 'characteristic frequency', but responds over a progressively wider band of frequencies as the sound intensity is raised. The response areas are similar whether the stimulus tone is short lasting (50 msec) or continues indefinitely. (*From* N. Kiang (1965) *Discharge Patterns of Single Fibers in the Cat's Auditory Nerve.* Cambridge, Mass.: M.I.T. Press.)

for which it is most sensitive (Fig. 27.29). As the stimulus intensity is raised, the fibre responds over a wider and wider frequency range which may reach as much as two or even three octaves at high intensities. It will be noted that the response curves are asymmetric triangles which qualitatively mirror the mechanical disturbance of the basilar membrane. Fibres arising from internal hair cells may have higher thresholds than those arising from external hair cells but clear evidence is lacking. The nerve fibres arise from the basilar membrane in an orderly manner, those with high characteristic frequencies arising from the basal end and those with lower characteristic frequencies arising progressively farther towards the apical end. Just as any single sound frequency sets in motion a considerable length of the basilar membrane, so too does the membrane in turn excite a large number of auditory nerve fibres. It can be inferred from curves like those of Figure 27.29 that a single tone at a moderate intensity (say 40 dB SPL) may cause some 20 per cent of all the fibres in the auditory nerve to discharge. There is thus no question of discrimination being carried out in terms of excitation of specific auditory nerve fibres by specific frequencies. It can also be seen that increasing the stimulus intensity increases the number of excited fibres, as well as increasing the rate of discharge in individual fibres.

Many, if not all, auditory nerve fibres show some 'spontaneous' activity in the absence of a sound stimulus—the mere presence of nerve impulses is not of itself capable of eliciting a sensation of sound. It appears to be the juxtaposition of groups of active fibres and groups of relatively inactive fibres which is necessary for this. It has been suggested that localized neural damage, by giving rise to spurious patterns of activity and inactivity, may be one basis of the distressing condition of tinnitus, in which persistent noises are heard in the head without any external stimulus. There is a tendency for nerve impulses to be discharged preferentially for one direction of shear of the hair cells rather than the other, as the basilar membrane moves back and forth. This means that at low frequencies (say up to 1000 Hz) the impulses in the auditory nerve tend to be synchronized with the waves of the stimulating tone. However, the nerve fibres are unable to 'follow' at very high rates, and for tones above 1000 Hz this synchrony is progressively lost.

There has been much argument as to whether or not the periodicity of the impulses in the auditory nerve is capable of providing information about the pitch of the note at low frequencies. At the present time there is little evidence in support of this hypothesis and a good deal against it. It is not possible to review this evidence here; suffice it to say that it has been shown that there is not a one-to-one correspondence between perceived pitch and nerve impulse periodicity.

Central Connexions of the Cochlear Nerve

The fibres of the auditory nerve leave the cochlea in an orderly manner so that they are arranged in order of their frequency sensitivity. As the nerve enters the brain stem, this orderliness is preserved and the individual fibres terminate in the cochlear nucleus in the same way. Second order fibres arising in the cochlear nucleus synapse in olivary and lemniscal nuclei and eventually reach the inferior colliculus. Throughout this pathway the same anatomical orderliness is preserved, so that the spatial relation of two given groups of active fibres remains the same in the colliculus as it was at the cochlea. However, owing to crossing over of some fibres in the medulla, inputs from both ears reach each colliculus. There is no sharpening of the response as we ascend the system, so that a single tone activates just as high a proportion of neurones at the collicular level as it did at the auditory nerve level. The identification of a musical note appears to depend on the pattern of distribution of activity in the total array of nerve fibres rather than the activation of some specific neurone. Indeed the patterns of distribution of activity in the auditory pathway seem to mimic closely the corresponding acoustic spectra (Fig. 27.40) and this may indeed be how we 'recognize' a particular sound such as a vowel or a note produced on a musical instrument.

Bilateral removal of the auditory cortex does not seriously interfere with the ability to discriminate the pitch and intensity of sounds. However, it does interfere with the ability to recognize temporal sound patterns. A cat without its auditory cortex can, for example, still distinguish tone A from tone B, but cannot distinguish the sequence ABA from the sequence BAB. Neurones have been found in the auditory cortex which respond to a rising frequency but not to a frequency falling through the same range (Fig. 27.30), while others respond only to falling and not to rising frequencies. Presumably such neurones play an important role in the discrimination of the patterns just referred to, and perhaps in responding to the complex frequency changes involved in speech.

The classical auditory pathway, as just described, from the ear to the cortex, is not the only one, since cats in which this pathway had been cut in the mid-brain could readily be aroused from sleep by loud sounds. The nerve impulses must be presumed to pass in a parallel pathway in the mid-brain reticular formation. There are also ascending pathways, which can be shown electrically, from the cochlea to the vermis of the cerebellum and from there to the cerebrum.

Descending paths. The ascending pathway is paralleled throughout its length by a system of descending fibres terminating in the various nuclei and even, in the form of the olivo-cochlear bundle, reaching the hair cells in the cochlea itself. It has been shown electrophysiologically that the olivo-cochlear bundle is capable of inhibiting auditory nerve activity, while the brainstem centrifugal pathway can alter the acoustic thresholds of the ascending neurones in which they terminate. Behaviourally, in cats, blocking of descending pathways has been shown to impair the resolving power of the ear—that is to say the ease with which two or more simultaneous sounds such as a set of harmonics can be separately heard, or the ease with which a signal may be detected against a noisy background. These pathways are quite as complex as the ascending ones and may well have a whole range of other functions not yet understood.

The right ear predominates in hearing; this is evidence for dominance in the brain's left hemisphere. If different sounds are presented in each ear at the same time the tendency is to hear only one sound—that fed to the right ear.

Localization of the Apparent Source of a Sound

The position of the source of a sound may be detected in either of two ways. If the head is kept still the observer can point to the source of the sound right or left of the saggital plane. Alternatively the head may be turned from side to side until the sound seems to be directly ahead. The second is the more accurate method. In practice the eyes as well as the ears are used in localization. If the source cannot be seen, for example, a bird singing in a tree, localization by hearing alone is sometimes quite difficult.

The ability to localize the source of a sound depends partly on the difference in loudness at the two ears and partly on the difference in time of arrival at the two ears. If the wavelength much exceeds the width of the head the sound waves readily pass round the head and reach the further ear with only a small

Fig. 27.30 Response of a neurone in the auditory cortex of the cat to a rising frequency. The signal bar represents a steady tone which rose in pitch at the point shown by about 10 per cent (1½ semi-tones) to a new steady value. The time taken to make the change was 50 msec. The neurone responded to the change but not to either of the steady tones. Note that it did *not* respond when the frequency *fell* through exactly the same range. (*After* I. C. Whitfield & E. F. Evans (1965) *Journal of Neurophysiology,* **28,** 655.)

and undetectable reduction in intensity; with such tones the difference in time of arrival is the clue to localization. (Fig. 27.31A). Some subjects can detect time differences as small as 0·01 msec which corresponds to a path difference in air of 3·5 mm. When the frequency is such that the wavelength is nearly the same as the width of the head (about 1500 Hz) the phase difference gives ambiguous clues about localization as shown in Figure 27.31B. Above 1500 Hz the head casts a 'sound shadow'; these short waves cannot get round the head, just as the waves of the sea cannot get round a long breakwater. Consequently if the source of a high-frequency note is to one side of the median plane the difference of intensity at the two ears allows of localization. The superior olive is the first level at which binaural interaction occurs, and the lateral division of this nucleus is thought to play a role in localization. It has been shown that the probability of firing of a neurone in this nucleus depends on the relative time of arrival of a click stimulus at the two ears (Fig. 27.32).

These two clues, difference in time of arrival and difference in intensity, are not enough to decide whether the source is in front of or behind the observer. Small rotational movements of the head may enable more information to be obtained. A familiar sound, such as the human voice, may be easily recognized as coming from behind the observer because the

auricle shades the ear from high frequencies and so alters slightly the quality of the voice. This differential filtering effect of the auricle indeed varies continuously as the position of the sound source changes in azimuth and elevation. The resultant change of timbre is probably one factor which enables persons totally deaf in one ear to locate the source of a sound.

Inside a room, reflexions cause the sound to arrive from many directions. However, if the reflected sound is delayed by not more than a few milliseconds, we hear only the primary source, without any echoes (the 'precedence effect'). Although the secondary sources are not heard as such, they are not entirely suppressed, since they reinforce the apparent loudness of the direct sound. If two sound sources in a room are quite different, as for example two different speakers at a cocktail party, then it is usually possible by switching attention to suppress either source at will.

The Temporal Lobes

The route taken by impulses from the cochlea to the medial geniculate body and to a relatively small area of auditory cortex in the superior temporal convolution has already been described (p. 447). The auditory cortex when in its normal state and free from anaesthesia, shows little of the tonotopic arrangement which is a feature of lower neural levels. The cortex does not appear to be essential for pitch discrimination, but is concerned with the processing of more elaborate sound patterns and the way they change with time. It thus plays an essential role in the recognition of such things as speech and music.

Although destruction of both temporal lobes in the cat does not render the animal deaf and does not deprive it of the ability to discriminate pitch and intensity, nevertheless there is some effect on the appreciation of tones. Removal of one temporal lobe results in a hearing loss of up to 5 decibels. Destruction of either the ipsilateral or contralateral cochlea in addition to removal of one temporal lobe increases the loss to some 15 dB, an increase greater than the sum of the losses produced by destruction of the cochlea or the cortex alone.

However ablation of both temporal lobes has a very severe effect on the localization of a single sound source, although as long as one lobe remains intact localization of such sources is virtually unimpaired. In the presence of more than one sound source localization is affected even when only one lobe is destroyed. Thus, for example, the 'precedence effect' (above) is disrupted for sounds originating on the side opposite to the lesion. Thus we may expect that with damage to a single temporal lobe localization will be more difficult in a room than in the open air, because of the presence of reflected sound in the room.

Electrical stimulation of the superior temporal convolution in man gives subjective buzzing, clicking or booming sounds but it has not so far been possible to produce any 'organized' response by such stimulation.

The effect of lesions in the temporal lobes in man is extremely variable. A circumscribed lesion of the superior temporal gyrus on the left side may give rise to pure word deafness in which the subject is unable to understand spoken words with no deficit in reading or verbal expression. Aphasia

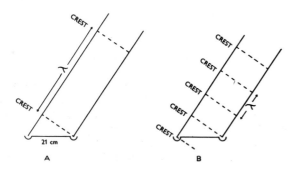

Fig. 27.31   (A) shows how a sound source is located by the crest of a wave (or some other distinctive part) reaching one ear before the other. The semicircles at the ends of the 21 cm horizontal line represent the ears. (B) shows how this method breaks down when the wavelength is short compared with the distance between the ears, that is 21 cm. In this case one crest arrives at the left ear as the following crest reaches the right ear. The velocity of sound in air is approximately 330 metres per second at 0° C and varies directly as the square root of the absolute temperature of the air.

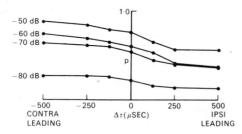

Fig. 27.32   The relative probability of firing (p) of cells in the lateral nucleus of the cat's superior olive as a function of the time difference ($\Delta \tau$) between the arrival of a click at the two ears. Curves are given for various intensity levels of the stimulus. (Note: sound travels about 15 cm in 500 μsec.) (*From* J. L. Hall (1965) *Journal of the Acoustical Society of America*, 37, 814–823.)

in one or other form is a common result of damage to the temporal cortex.

The temporal lobe has a function in relation to memory and recall for, although damage to one temporal lobe has little effect on the memory, removal of both lobes may reduce the memory span to a few minutes.

Methods of Measuring Acuity of Hearing

Quantitative measurements of hearing are made with a *pure-tone audiometer*. The test must be made in a sufficiently quiet room since extraneous sounds cause masking (p. 452) which raises the threshold of hearing. The pure-tone audiometer consists of an oscillator producing pure sine waves which are fed to a telephone earpiece through an attenuator network to control the intensity of the sound. When the intensity of a given note is made very small it is inaudible but if the intensity is increased slowly then at a certain value the note is heard. This is the *threshold of audibility*. If the test is performed separately for each ear at a selected number of frequencies the threshold can be established and specified in terms of a standard set of values corresponding to the hearing of normal young persons. There are national and international standards for the normal threshold of hearing for pure tones. The current British Standard is BS2479: Part 1: 1968; and Part 2: 1969.

The threshold of audibility is lowest, that is the auditory acuity is greatest, in the region 1000 to 4000 Hz; at lower and higher frequences the sound intensity must be greater to produce an auditory sensation. The lowest and highest audible frequencies thus depend on the intensity of the tone used, but the average limits are 30 and 20000 Hz in young persons. In old people the threshold in the higher frequencies is raised so that in practice their upper limit may be much lower, say 5000 Hz (see Fig. 27.33C).

By varying the intensity of the note produced by a pure-tone audiometer in a rhythmic fashion the minimum perceptible difference in intensity can be measured. Except near the threshold of audibility it is of the order of 1 dB. By varying the frequency of a note rhythmically the minimum fractional difference in frequency which is perceptible can be found; in the range 500 to 4000 Hz it is 0·3 per cent, but outside this range it is greater. A tone must persist for 10 to 15 msec before a pitch can be assigned to it but most people require the tone, especially if it is of low frequency, to last upwards of 100 msec before it supplies an experience of pitch.

The method of measuring intelligibility, first used by telephone engineers, is also useful for investigating deafness and the efficiency of deaf aids. A list of disconnected words containing a wide variety of speech sounds but without context is read out to a listener who writes down what he hears. The script is then checked with the original list and the percentage of sounds heard correctly—spelling errors are of course neglected—is usually referred to as the 'intelligibility'. Suitable word lists have been constructed by Fry (see References, p. 460).

When this test is made in the simplest possible conditions—that is, with the reader speaking directly to the listener in the same room—the intelligibility is high, but the vowel *e* as in 'ten' and the consonants *th*, *f* and *v* often give rise to errors. If now the listener hears the voice of the reader through a loudspeaker system which transmits all the speech frequencies up to 1000 Hz but cuts out all the higher frequencies the intelligibility may be only 40 per cent although almost all the energy (85 per cent) of the original speech sounds is present. Sounds like *s*, *th* and *f* are particularly difficult to distinguish. This is an artificial *high-frequency deafness*. If, on the other hand, the loudspeaker transmits only the speech frequencies above 1000 Hz the intelligibility is now 86 per cent although only a small fraction of the original speech energy (17 per cent) is transmitted. In spite of this severe frequency distortion, ordinary speech with its context is easily understood but it does not, of course, sound natural.

The pure-tone audiometer can be used to investigate the hearing of persons with impaired hearing. Useful diagnostic information is obtained by measuring the amount by which the threshold is raised over the range of frequencies. Audiometers intended for clinical use are calibrated so that the zero mark on the intensity control at each frequency corresponds to the average threshold found in young people with normal hearing. This statistical concept of normal hearing is shown on the graph paper used to record the results as a straight line marked 0 dB hearing level (Fig. 27.33). If a person has impaired hearing of a particular tone its intensity must be increased x dB above the average threshold before it is heard; this is plotted as a point *below* the normal threshold in Figure 27.33, and is known as a hearing loss of x dB at the frequency tested. If a number of tones is used the results fall into a curve called the *audiogram*. A few characteristic audiograms are shown in Figure 27.33.

Important prognostic information can be gained from the audiogram since a definite relationship has been found between the degree of deafness in the important speech frequencies, say 500 to 2500 Hz, and the quality of the speech. Deaf children learn to speak normally provided the loss is less than 30 dB; a greater degree of impairment prevents an infant from learning to speak naturally but may permit him to acquire speech with careful training. In the presence of a loss of 90 dB, however, even acquired speech is poor. Good hearing in the lower frequencies (up to 500 Hz, say) does not compensate for deafness in the high frequencies, since it is the latter which allows us to distinguish the different speech sounds.

Deafness due to middle-ear disease is so common that it is important to be able to test large numbers quickly. The pure-tone audiometer is not suitable because it is a rather uninteresting artificial test requiring a special room and considerable time; it can be applied only to one person at a time. The gramophone audiometer provides a somewhat empirical but yet practical test which can quickly pick out persons with defective hearing. Specially made records are played with an electrical pick-up which is connected to twenty or more single earphones to allow a whole class of children to be tested simultaneously. The children apply the earpiece to one ear at a time and hear a voice calling out numbers which they copy down. As the record proceeds the voice becomes fainter and fainter in steps of 3 dB. When the speech is too faint to be understood the children either make mistakes or stop writing. When the performance of normal children has been found with this apparatus, it is easy to detect children who have even minor defects of hearing.

Von Békésy test. A useful modification of the pure tone test

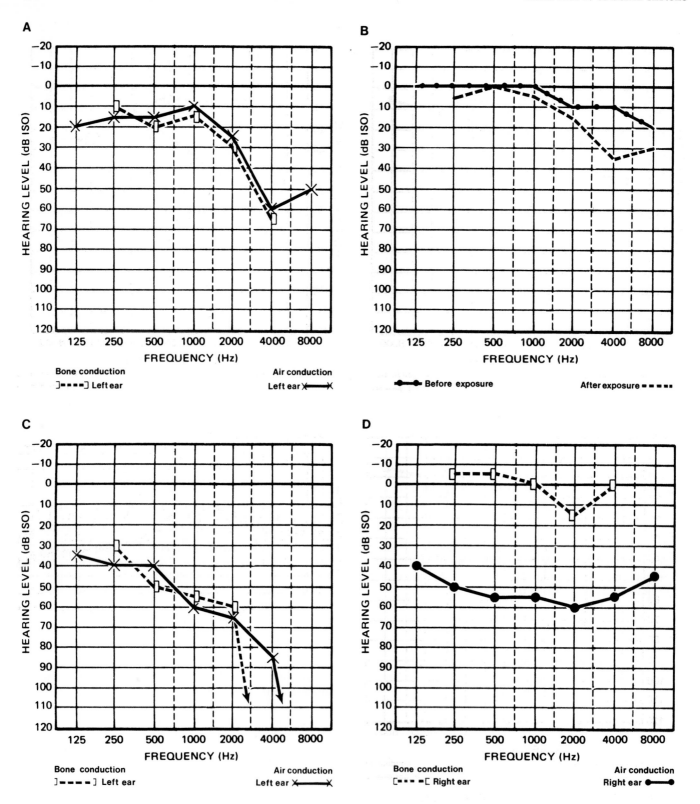

Fig. 27.33 Audiograms. Air conduction was tested by an earphone placed over the external auditory meatus. Bone conduction was tested by a vibrator on the mastoid process. The hearing level in dB is shown on the ordinate, zero indicating the threshold of hearing in young healthy people. The abscissa is scaled (in octaves) in Hz. A, industrial deafness of moderate degree at age 59; B, one hour's exposure to noise in a jute mill, continuous line before and dotted line after; C, well marked presbycusis; D, otosclerosis at age 36; E, early Ménière's disease; F, perforation of tympanic membrane; G, secretory otitis media; H, Békésy test. (A to G by courtesy of A. G. Gibb; H is adapted from a diagram in *Clinical Symposia*, copyright by CIBA Pharmaceutical Company, Division of CIBA-GEIGY Corporation. All rights reserved.)

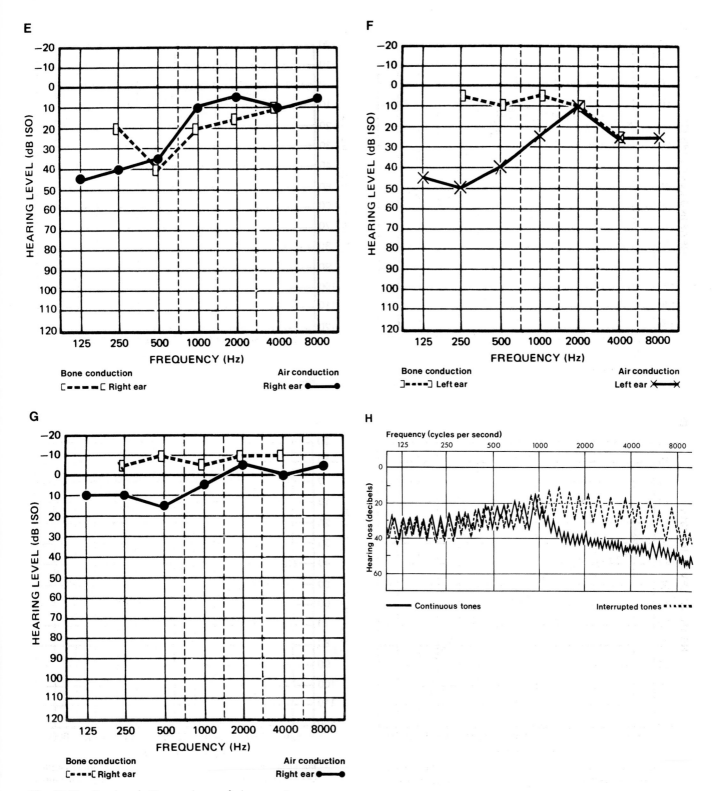

Fig. 27.33 Continued. (See caption on facing page.)

has been described by von Békésy. As before, the patient listens to a tone in an earphone. A low tone just below threshold is gradually increased in intensity until the sound becomes audible; at this point the patient presses down a switch, which results in a gradual reduction in intensity; when the tone becomes inaudible the patient releases the switch. The process

is repeated throughout the complete frequency range. The tone is presented initially as a continuous tone and then as an interrupted note every 2·5 sec to give a series of short 'beeps'.

In subjects with normal hearing the audiograms for continuous and interrupted tones are superimposed (Type I). In cochlear deafness (as in Ménière's disease) the two curves are superimposed up to 1000 Hz and then the continuous tone tracing falls below that given by the interrupted tone (Type II) (Fig. 27.33H). In retrocochlear deafness, two types of tracing may be obtained. The continuous tone falls sharply away from the interrupted tone at low frequencies (Type III). The continuous tone is below and parallel to the interrupted tone at all frequencies (Type IV). In non-organic deafness, the tracing of the continuous tone may be above that of the interrupted tone (Type V).

Rinne's and Weber's tests. Sound vibrations can be conducted to the inner ear through the bones of the skull, but normally air conduction is much more effective. This can be shown by applying a vibrating tuning-fork (500 Hz) firmly to the mastoid process just behind the ear. When the sound dies away the prongs of the fork are brought near the external auditory meatus and the sound is heard once more, provided that the meatus is not blocked and that the ear drum and ossicles are intact. Rinne's test is then said to be positive.

Weber's test is carried out by placing a vibrating 500 Hz fork on the mid-sagittal line of the head (the vertex). If one ear is plugged by the finger to exclude room noise the sound produced by the fork appears to be louder in that ear. Thus in unilateral disease affecting the conducting system (middle-ear disease) Weber's test is referred to the diseased ear. When the organ of Corti or the cochlear nerve is damaged unilaterally Weber's test is referred to the normal ear.

Rinne's and Weber's tests are used in clinical practice to distinguish middle-ear (conduction) deafness from inner-ear (perceptive) deafness. In conduction deafness Rinne's test is usually negative and Weber's test indicates the diseased ear. In perceptive deafness Rinne's test is positive and Weber's test indicates the normal ear.

Noise

Noise is not only to be defined in physical terms but also in psychological terms such as a sound which is disturbing or annoying. The loudness of sounds can be measured either subjectively or objectively. In the subjective method the loudness of a sound is compared with the loudness of a note of 1000 Hz which can be adjusted until the listener judges that it has the same loudness as the sound being investigated. When this equality has been achieved the intensity of the 1000 Hz note can be read from the instrument in dB above an arbitrary zero which has been internationally agreed as 2×10^{-5} N/m². If the reading is n dB the sound is said to have an intensity of n phons. It is more usual to employ objective sound level meters which have a microphone and a calibrated amplifier with a number of alternative frequency response characteristics based on those of the ear at different sound levels. Such instruments give a reading of the sound level in dB above the same reference level. This objective method does not necessarily give a true index of loudness. A range of phon values is given in Figure 27.34.

Masking. Whenever there is a noise (as in a railway train) conversation becomes difficult and the speech power must be raised. This effect begins when the noise level reaches 20 phons and the loudness of speech is increased up to noise levels of 90 phons beyond which the intensity of the speech cannot compete with the noise. The increase in the loudness of the

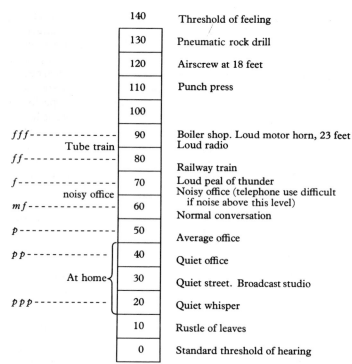

Fig. 27.34 A range of phon values. The phon is defined on this page. On the left are given the values of the musical p (piano) and f (forte) markings as used by the orchestral conductor Leopold Stokowski.

voice is often revealed if the noise suddenly ceases. The nature of this masking effect has been investigated with the pure-tone audiometer. First, in a quiet room the threshold of audibility is measured, than a masking tone is continuously sounded and the threshold is measured again. Masking tones of moderate intensity make it difficult to hear notes of neighbouring frequency but if the masking tone is very loud there is masking not only of neighbouring tones but also of all tones of higher frequency. For this reason loud tones of low frequency impair the intelligibility of speech.

SPEECH

The importance of the left cerebral hemisphere for speech was clearly demonstrated by Broca in 1861 when he showed that in adults loss of speech could be associated with disease of the left frontal lobe. In children cerebral dominance is less well established so that before the age of four unilateral injury to the brain may result in little impairment of speech and in later childhood speech disorders due to localized brain damage may recover relatively well. The non-dominant cerebral hemisphere in adults may aid comprehension of words but it is not clear if it contributes to the production of speech. Although Broca's area on the third frontal convolution is particularly important for the expressive side of speech, the temporal lobe and particularly Wernicke's area on the first temporal gyrus and the adjacent portion of the parietal lobe are the main regions concerned with the understanding of speech and the process of word-finding.

Children vary greatly in the rate and manner of acquiring speech. The baby's first cries usually express hunger or discomfort, but if they always have the effect of attracting attention he may learn to cry for this reason alone. By three months he has acquired several vowels and has learned to smile. By six months he can vocalize consonants and he is learning how to laugh. By nine to ten months he speaks his first word, usually Dada or Mama and by one year of age he has acquired another word, for example Ta. The time at which this is accomplished depends on many factors, such as the state of health and level of intelligence, and it may be accelerated or delayed by learning to walk. At 18 months the vocabulary is about 12 words. In the second year the child may have a vocabulary of 80 words and he often uses one-word sentences, such as 'Up', meaning 'Lift me up'. At the end of the second year two-word phrases are uttered and by the age of five years sentences of five words are being used. From two years onwards the vocabulary increases rapidly.

Disorders of language function. The importance of Broca's area (areas 44 and 45) for the expression of speech and the temporal lobe for comprehension and word finding has been referred to above. Hughlings Jackson in his analysis of expressive aphasia drew attention to the fact that although propositional speech is lost when this area is damaged simple emotional utterance may be preserved. At the same time as the ability to talk out loud is lost, there is also loss of internal speech, so that the patient cannot put his thoughts into words. In *jargon aphasia*, which occurs in disease affecting the temporal lobe, there is failure to understand both written and spoken language but speech remains fluent; however because the patient can no longer adequately monitor his own speech he makes many errors and the speech may amount to jargon. If the pathway between Wernicke's and Broca's area is interrupted the patient is able to understand spoken and written speech but talks fluently with many errors—*conduction aphasia.* In extensive lesions of the dominant hemisphere involving both frontal and temporal lobes both language production and comprehension are lost—*global aphasia.* In *nominal aphasia* there is inability to name objects; this may be due to impairment of the connexions between Wernicke's area and the surrounding brain and is often the earliest manifestation of dysphasia.

The organs of speech. The lungs and chest wall act as bellows which drive air through the larynx between the two sharp folds, the *vocal folds* or vocal cords, and set them into vibration, much in the way that air blown through the lips makes them vibrate. Normally speech is produced on expiration but an abnormal type of speech can be produced on inspiration. The vocal folds stretch from the thyroid cartilage in front to the mobile arytenoid cartilages at the back of the larynx; the triangular space between them is called the *glottis* or *rima glottidis*. The muscles controlling the arytenoids (Fig. 27.35) open or close the glottis, while the tension of the folds is regulated by the vocalis muscle lying in each fold and by the cricothyroid muscle which tilts the thyroid cartilage and so elongates the vocal folds (Fig. 27.36). When the interior of a normal larynx is inspected through a mirror placed obliquely against the soft palate, the vocal folds are midway between full adduction and full abduction in quiet breathing. During vigorous breathing the folds open farther in inspiration. When the subject is asked to say 'ah' or 'ee' (that is, to phonate) the

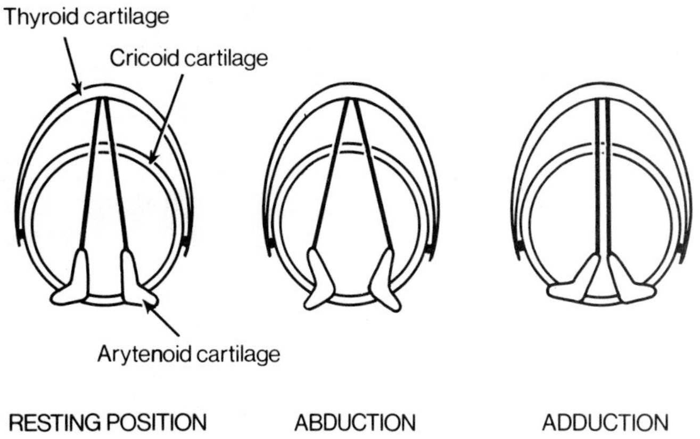

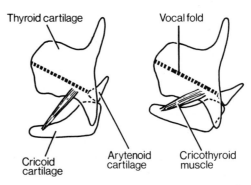

Thyroid cartilage
Cricoid cartilage
Arytenoid cartilage

RESTING POSITION   ABDUCTION   ADDUCTION

Fig. 27.35 A diagrammatic cross-section of the larynx to show the movement of the arytenoid cartilage and the vocal folds.

Thyroid cartilage   Vocal fold
Cricoid cartilage   Arytenoid cartilage   Cricothyroid muscle

Fig. 27.36 A side view of the cartilages of the larynx to show the manner in which the cricothyroid muscle approximates the cricoid and thyroid cartilages and so stretches the vocal folds.

folds approximate. The frequency of a note can be regulated by the tension in the vocal folds. If the tension increases, the frequency rises and there may be considerable increase, up to 50 per cent, in the length of the folds. The vocal folds are lubricated by thin mucus secreted mainly in the ventricles which are spaces formed by folds of the laryngeal mucosa immediately above the vocal folds. In whispering the anterior two-thirds of the vocal folds are approximated, free escape of air occurring in the space between the two arytenoid cartilages posteriorly.

Small needle electrodes have been placed in the intrinsic laryngeal muscles in man to record action potentials. Even in quiet respiration there is some electrical activity which increases on inspiration in the adductors (vocalis and cricothyroid mainly) whereas it is diminished in the abductor (the posterior crico-arytenoid). The process of phonation begins with an increase in the electrical activity in the adductor muscles which reaches a maximum just before the onset of the sound (Fig. 27.37). The time between the beginning of the electrical activity and the onset of the sound—0·35 to 0·55 sec—is necessary to allow the pressure to build up to the value needed to produce the sound. On the other hand the activity of the posterior crico-arytenoid muscle is inhibited just before sound is produced. An increase in the volume of the sound causes no change in electrical activity in the adductors but with a rise in pitch there is an increase in activity which indicates

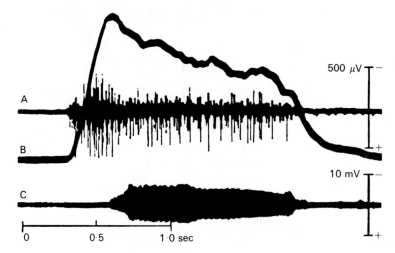

Fig. 27.37   Electrical activity in the left vocalis muscle during phonation. *A.* The action potential pattern. *B.* A trace electronically derived from *A* which gives the mean action potential amplitude. *C.* Microphone recording of sound ee, frequency 285 Hz. The subject was a 64-year-old women with the right vocal cord immovable but with the left vocal cord moving normally. (K. Faaborg-Anderson (1957) *Acta physiologica scandinavica,* 41, Suppl. 140, 54.)

that the tension in the vocal folds is adjusted to a given pitch before the sound is actually produced. No change in the pattern of electrical activity is seen when different vowels are produced. When the subject is asked to think about production of a vowel without actually emitting any audible sound, the electrical activity of the adductor muscles increases.

The sound produced in the larynx is greatly modified by the acoustic properties of the mouth, throat and nasal cavities. The tongue, by alterations in its shape and position, has the main control over the resonant characteristics of the oral cavity (Fig. 27.38) but the positions of the lips and jaws are also of importance in the production of speech sounds. The vowel sounds are produced by vibrations of the vocal folds (that is, are voiced), the air stream passing freely through the mouth. In the production of a consonant the air stream is either partially or completely obstructed so that it cannot issue freely from the mouth. Some of the consonants are very short, for example *t* and *p* and *k,* and may be regarded as particular ways of

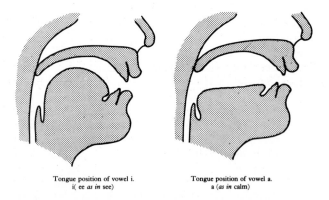

Tongue position of vowel i.
i(ee *as in* see)

Tongue position of vowel a.
a (*as in* calm)

Fig. 27.38   The positions of the tongue used in the formation of two vowels to show how the shape of the cavity of the mouth is altered. In this way the resonant properties of the cavity can be made to vary over a wide range. (*After* I. C. Ward (1948) *The Phonetics of English.* Cambridge: Heffer. Other examples are given by A. Ewing & E. C. Ewing (1964) *Teaching Deaf Children to Talk.* Manchester University Press.)

beginning or ending vowel sounds, but some consonants, such as *m,* can be spoken without a vowel. The larynx does not appear to be involved in the production of many consonants, that is the majority are unvoiced. A laryngeal component can, however, be added to some consonants to make them voiced; in this way *f* becomes *v,* and *s* becomes *z.*

The vagus nerve carries motor and sensory fibres to and from the larynx. The superior laryngeal branch after receiving a twig from the sympathetic divides into the internal laryngeal nerve which is sensory to the upper larynx and the external laryngeal nerve which supplies the cricothyroid muscle. All the other intrinsic muscles are supplied by the recurrent laryngeal nerve which also gives sensory fibres to the larynx below the vocal folds. After section of one recurrent nerve the vocal fold on the denervated side lies in or close to the midline. The cricothyroid muscle (which is, of course, unaffected) stretches the paralysed vocal fold by tilting the thyroid cartilage. Full adduction or overadduction of the opposite vocal fold brings the folds together and in many cases speech is normal. In bilateral recurrent nerve paralysis the folds lie motionless near the midline producing hoarseness. If the superior laryngeal nerves are cut, the upper part of the larynx is anaesthetic and voice is hoarse because the vocal folds cannot be made tense.

There are good reasons for regarding the upper resonators (mouth, throat and nose) and not the larynx as the main organs of speech, but the most dramatic evidence is furnished by the phenomenon of oesophageal speech. After complete surgical removal of the larynx the trachea is made to open on the surface of the neck while the oesophagus retains its relation with the mouth. If the patient acquires the trick of swallowing air he can bring it up in a belch which sets the lower edge of the inferior constrictor of the pharynx (cricopharyngeus muscle) into irregular vibrations which are conveyed to the mouth cavity. The patient uses the same mouth positions as he did before his operation to modify this oesophageal sound and although the vibrations of this pseudolarynx are extremely irregular compared with those of the true larynx, yet he can with practice produce oesophageal speech which, although rather hoarse, is readily intelligible.

For natural and normal speech the larynx of course produces the sound and determines the fundamental pitch of the voice. But the variable resonances of the mouth and throat determine the quality of the sound which conveys the information from speaker to listener; this is also shown by the fact that the intelligibility of words is only slightly affected by singing them at different pitches. The mouth and throat are put into the proper position for the formation of speech with the help of the kinaesthetic sense which gives information to the brain of the position of the tongue, lips and jaws. In addition the ear, in both normal and oesophageal speech, is used to monitor the muscular adjustments so that the desired speech sounds are produced. We hear our own words by air conduction about 1 msec after they are spoken; if this auditory feed-back is delayed by electromechanical methods for say 0·2 sec the subject is apt to stutter and his speech is slowed. If a speaker is deaf the ear cannot function as a proprioceptor and his speech is defective; if a normal subject is asked to sing a simple musical scale when a strong masking noise smothers the sound of his own voice he sings badly out of tune. When a steady note is sung there is a periodic fluctuation in frequency of 5 or 6 Hz. These fluctuations are produced by the auditory feed-back mechanism because, if the sound of the voice is delayed electrically before reaching the subject's ears, the fluctuations are larger and occur more slowly.

Analysis of Speech Sounds

The energy involved in speech is very small (10 to 25 microwatts in ordinary conversation) but the complexities of speech and musical sounds can be easily shown by using a microphone and amplifier connected to a cathode-ray oscillograph (Fig. 27.39). The vowels have waveforms which recur regularly throughout their duration at the frequency of vibration of the vocal folds. The pattern is usually very complicated showing, in addition to the fundamental laryngeal tone, a considerable number of harmonics of much higher frequency, some of which may even be of greater amplitude than the fundamental. Consonants like *p, b, t, d* are so short—electrical engineers refer to them as 'transients'—that no sensation of pitch is given by them; sibilants, *s* and *z*, may last as long as vowels and are characterized by small waves of

very high frequency. Transitional consonants like *m, n, ng* also last for some time. Voiced consonants such as *z* and *v* have a waveform which recurs at the fundamental laryngeal frequency. A study of oscillograms of vowels suggests that each puff of air that comes up from the larynx sets the cavities of the mouth and throat into vibration. This vibration gradually diminishes until the next puff of air comes up from the larynx. This is well illustrated by the oscillogram of the vowel 'ah' as in 'father', when spoken by a man (Fig. 27.39A). When the same vowel is spoken by a woman (Fig. 27.39B) the time between the laryngeal puffs is reduced to about half with the result that the vibrations of the air in the mouth diminish very little before the next puff comes along. Although the two waveforms of 'ah' in Figure 27.39, are quite different, the listener has no difficulty in recognizing that both speakers are pronouncing the same vowel. It is thus unlikely that the ear recognizes vowels by their waveforms and this is confirmed by the following considerations. When one listens to speech in a room, part of the sound arrives directly from the speaker to the ear and part indirectly after reflexion from the walls; the reflected waves are out of phase with the direct wave. In many gramophone or microphone amplifiers the higher frequencies are not emitted from the loudspeaker in their original phase relationship to the low frequencies. In both examples, although the original waveform is considerably changed, the sound does not appear to be altered.

An acoustic spectrum is obtained by analysing a speech waveform to obtain the amplitude and frequency of its various components and some examples are given in Figure 27.40. If spectra of the same vowel spoken at different pitches (or, to express it objectively, at different laryngeal frequencies) are compared it is found that, in spite of the alteration in the frequency of the fundamental as the pitch of the voice is raised, the overtones are relatively unchanged and a characteristic grouping of the higher frequency components can be recognized in all the spectra. Presumably it is this grouping or 'formant' which is recognized by the ear and clearly it is the higher frequencies produced in the mouth and throat which are important for differentiating and recognizing the vowels.

The rate of vibration of the vocal folds, which can be easily found from oscillograms, gives a clue to the sex of the speaker. A deep-voiced man may have a laryngeal tone of 90 Hz, but in the average man it is usually between 125 and 145 Hz. The average woman's laryngeal tone is from 230 to 256 Hz, but in a shrill-voiced woman it may be as high as 300 Hz. The deepest bass note that can be sung is about 66 Hz, while the highest soprano note is about 1056 Hz. This is a range of 2^4 or four octaves.

The decibel notation. The energy involved in speech ranges from 0·0001 microwatts in a very soft whisper up to 1000 microwatts in very loud talking. The ear, like the other sense organs, follows approximately the Weber-Fechner law (p. 348), which implies that equal steps on a logarithmic scale of intensity are equal steps on a loudness scale, and it has been found convenient to describe differences in power-level in the decibel notation:

Difference in power-level in decibels =

$$10 \log_{10} \text{(ratio of the two powers).}$$

For example, if we use the figures quoted above the difference

A. Male voice. Laryngeal frequency 110 Hz

B. Female voice. Laryngeal frequency 229 Hz

Fig. 27.39 Oscillograms of the vowel sound 'ah' as in 'father'. (A) Spoken by a man and (B) spoken by a woman. The vertical white lines are 0·01 sec apart. The ordinate gives a measure of air pressure at the speaker's mouth. (Harvey Fletcher (1929) *Speech and Hearing,* Fig. 37, p. 49. London: Macmillan.) (Bell Telephone Laboratories.)

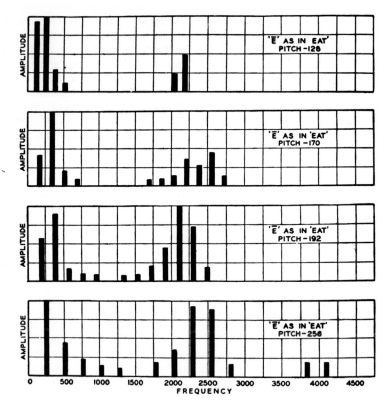

Fig. 27.40 Acoustic spectra of vowel sound 'EE' at different frequencies of the fundamental laryngeal tone (128, 170, 192 and 256 Hz) to show the general similarity of the spectra. (Harvey Fletcher (1929) *Speech and Hearing*, Fig. 41, p. 54. London: Macmillan.) (Bell Telephone Laboratories.)

in power-level between a soft whisper and loud talking is

$$10 \log_{10} \frac{1\,000}{0\cdot001} \quad = 10 \log_{10} \frac{10^3}{10^{-3}} \quad = 10 \log_{10} 10^6 = 10 \times 6$$

$$= 60 \text{ decibels, or } 60 \text{ dB.}$$

This formula shows that 1 dB is equivalent to a 26 per cent

increase in power; 10 dB to a ten times increase in power; 20 dB to one hundred times increase in power.

The magnitudes of sounds may be stated in absolute values of intensity or sound pressure by the use of an agreed reference zero, namely $0\cdot00002$ Newton per square metre (N/m^2), which can be denoted by p ref. The 'Sound Pressure Level' (SPL) in decibels is given by $20 \log p/p$ ref where p is sound pressure.

THE CHEMICAL SENSES

Taste and smell are referred to as the chemical senses because the receptor organs are remarkably sensitive to a wide variety of chemical substances. However the nose, the mouth and the genital apertures, and many mucous membranes are sensitive to irritants such as ammonia. This third form of chemical sense is referred to as 'common chemical sensibility'. A sensation described as a taste may in fact arise from the simultaneous stimulation of the taste and smell receptors; this is the case with onions and with wine. The close association between the two senses is shown by the lack of flavour of many food substances when the sense of smell is lost during a cold in the head. It is convenient to use the word flavour for the sensation aroused by the simultaneous stimulation of these receptors.

The senses of taste and smell are not as well developed in man as they are in other mammals. Man can detect quite minute amounts of certain substances but he has come to depend so much on his visual equipment that it is not

surprising that the olfactory part of his brain is relatively small. The sense of smell is, like the sense of vision, normally projected on to the environment but the sense of taste is not so projected. Although an odorous substance stimulates end-organs in the nose the sensation is referred to or projected on to the source of the odour. Thus we say that the rose has a sweet perfume, not 'there is a sweet perfume in the nose'.

SENSE OF SMELL (OLFACTION)

The greater part (or respiratory region) of the nasal cavities is lined by columnar ciliated epithelium interspersed with goblet cells which are capable of producing large quantities of mucus. In man the olfactory area, about 3 cm² in area on each side, is situated in a narrow cleft in the highest part of each nasal cavity above the superior concha. Each area possesses 50 million olfactory cells which lie among supporting cells (Fig.

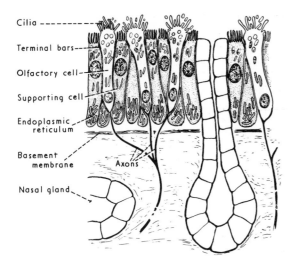

Cilia - - - - - - - - -
Terminal bars - - -
Olfactory cell - -
Supporting cell -
Endoplasmic
reticulum
Basement
membrane
Axons
Nasal gland

Fig. 27.41 Olfactory epithelium and component cells. The nasal glands keep the epithelium moist. Each olfactory cell has about a dozen cilia each up to 200 μm long on its free surface. The microvilli of the supporting cells project into the layer of mucus which covers the olfactory epithelium (*After* H. S. D. Garven & A. J. D. de Lorenzo.)

27.41). Non-medullated nerve fibres arise from the olfactory cells and form a plexus in the deeper parts of the mucosa and then pass through the cribriform plate of the ethmoid bone to the olfactory bulb where contact is made with second order neurones in complicated synapses (glomeruli). These second order neurones are mainly mitral cells going to the prepiriform cortex and tufted cells sending axons to the opposite bulb. To establish conditioned reflexes to odours, the olfactory receptors, the olfactory bulbs and tracts and the piriform cortex are necessary but no other parts of the rhinencephalon.

Direct inspection of the nasal cavities after inhalation of light magnesia powder shows that the air-stream does not rise above the superior concha on inspiration and is at an even lower level on expiration. Thus in ordinary quiet breathing the air does not impinge on the olfactory area directly but only as eddies coming off the main stream. When we attempt to smell a substance by sniffing, the air-stream reaches the olfactory area directly either because it is travelling more rapidly or because it is directed there by a change in the shape of the nostrils. If air cannot reach the olfactory areas, for example because of swelling of the mucosa during a cold in the head, the sense of smell is lost. To give rise to a sensation of smell an odorous substance must be soluble in the mucus covering the olfactory area. Odorous substances must of course be volatile and must be soluble in lipids.

Many substances lose their odour within a very few minutes of presentation. This may be a result of either a rapid adaptation of the end-organs or a washing away of the odoriferous molecules by mucus. Adaptation is at least part of the explanation since loss of odour tends to be specific, that is, any other odour, if quite different from the first, is easily perceived. The term adaptation seems appropriate in the case where the occupants of a stuffy room are quite unaware of their odour whereas a newcomer is at once unpleasantly conscious of it. Neutralization of one odour by another occurs to some extent but usually disagreeable odours, for example that of

faeces, are disguised by overwhelming them with powerful, but more pleasant, odorous substances.

There is much speculation about the physical or chemical nature of the stimulus which gives rise to an olfactory sensation. The old classification of odours into four main groups, (1) fragrant, (2) acid or sour, (3) burnt and (4) caprylic (disagreeable or putrid) is not satisfactory. There is no simple relationship between chemical constitution and odour. Atomic bromine and chlorine have no odour but Br_2 and Cl_2 have. Similar odours may be given by substances with very different chemical constitution, for example hydrocyanic acid and nitrobenzene both smell of bitter almonds. Some sulphur containing compounds have a smell like bad eggs. If, however, the sulphur is replaced by oxygen the compound is odourless. In the case of optically active substances it frequently happens that one stereoisomer has a more intense smell than its mirror image.

Substances having similar odours are adsorbed to a similar extent on adsorbents such as active carbon even if they have quite different chemical constitutions; conversely substances having different odours behave differently towards the adsorbents used. Some sort of selective adsorption may occur in the nose. Molecules with a similar odour have a similar shape and size even if they differ considerably in chemical formula. The odour of substances may depend on their molecules fitting into specifically shaped receptor sites.

The minimum stimulus required to arouse a sensation of smell varies with different substances. Some substances, like mercaptan, chlorophenol and skatole, can be detected in the air at very high dilutions. The nose is a very sensitive chemical detector. It is possible to detect 0·01 mg of mercaptan in a room of 230 cubic metres (say 28 ft by 22 ft by 13 ft high). Since 0·01 mg of mercaptan contains 1×10^{17} molecules each sniff of 20 ml contains 1×10^{10} molecules, about enough to cover the receptive area with a layer one molecule thick. However, in the absence of some selective action by the olfactory epithelium it is difficult to understand how one molecule of mercaptan in 50 thousand molecules of air can produce an olfactory sensation or indeed how the adsorption of a small number of molecules can set up a nerve impulse. A clue to the olfactory code may be furnished by cases of specific anosmia just as clues to the mechanism of colour vision are supplied by cases of colour-blindness. Examples of specific anosmia are: 10 per cent of people cannot detect the odour of HCN; 3 per cent cannot detect isobutyric acid; 0·1 per cent cannot detect butyl mercaptan.

Records of the electrical activity of the mitral cells in the olfactory bulb of the rabbit when air containing an odoriferous substance is drawn through its nose show that the anterior part of the olfactory area is easily excited by esters (fruity smell) which are slightly soluble in water. Oil-soluble substances on the other hand excite the posterior area more easily.

Potentials have been recorded from microelectrodes placed in the olfactory epithelium of both man and animals. The frequency response is different for different odours but similar for similar odours. In animals experiments with microelectrodes have shown that an individual olfactory cell (primary receptor) responds to some odours and not to others. The possession of a relatively small number of primary receptors of this yes-or-no character could account for the ability to detect a very large number of odours. For example, if an animal possessed only one such receptor it would be able to detect two classes of substances, odorous and non-odorous; if it possessed two different types of receptors it could discriminate four classes; if it possessed 20 different receptors over a million different patterns are possible.

The perception of nearly all odours depends on simultaneous stimulation of the olfactory end-organs and the nerve endings of the trigeminal nerve in the nasal cavity. The proportion of the trigeminal element varies from odour to odour. Pinching recommends that, instead of the traditional camphor and peppermint which have large trigeminal components, musks and floral odours which are relatively 'pure' olfactory stimulants should be used clinically to test the olfactory apparatus.

Many mammals react to odours (pheromones) emitted by members of the same or other species. For example the introduction of a strange male into a group of female rats may cause fetal reabsorption. The steroid hormones have an odour like that of musk and women but not men are said to be able to detect steroid odours. It is difficult to assess the influence of pheromones in man because of the complexity of his behaviour but these external chemical messengers may act at the subconscious level.

SENSE OF TASTE (GUSTATION)

The taste receptors or *taste buds*, about 9000 in the adult, are placed mainly on the peripheral parts of the dorsum of the tongue, being most easily found in the groove surrounding the vallate papillae: some buds occur on the soft palate and a few on the epiglottis. In children they are much more numerous and much more widely distributed over the tongue and on the insides of the cheeks. The oval taste buds embedded in the stratified epithelium covering the tongue are usually described as containing thin fusiform taste cells surrounded by supporting cells like the staves of a barrel. Electron microscope pictures suggest that the different appearances of the cells in the taste bud are due to their being at different stages of development. The taste cells have microvilli on their free surfaces. Experiments with tritiated thymidine have shown that taste cells are produced by mitotic division of cells at the edge of the bud which migrate to the centre of the bud where they disintegrate and disappear after a week. Since the afferent nerve fibres do not degenerate the nature of the receptor-nerve contact is rather difficult to imagine. Radiotherapy of the mouth region may damage the taste buds; all foods then may taste alike (mouth blindness).

The *main nerves of taste* (Fig. 27.42) are the lingual branch of the glossopharyngeal (IX) for the posterior third of the tongue, including the vallate papillae, while the anterior two-thirds are served by the chorda tympani branch of the facial (VII). All the nerve fibres pass centrally to the tractus solitarius, a long column of grey matter in the medulla oblongata. From here fibres cross the midline and pass to the posterior ventral nucleus of the thalamus and then on to the lower part of the postcentral gyrus and probably other areas nearby. After destruction of the postero-medial ventral nucleus, goats drink strong solutions of quinine, acid or salt which they had repeatedly refused before the operation. Stimulation of this area of the thalamus in intact unanaesthetized animals produces 'rejecting' movements of the jaw and tongue exactly as seen when a solution of quinine is squirted into the mouth. The lingual branch of the fifth nerve is the nerve of common sensibility for the anterior two-thirds of the tongue; the lingual branch of the glossopharyngeal (IX) carries both taste and common sensibility fibres for the posterior third.

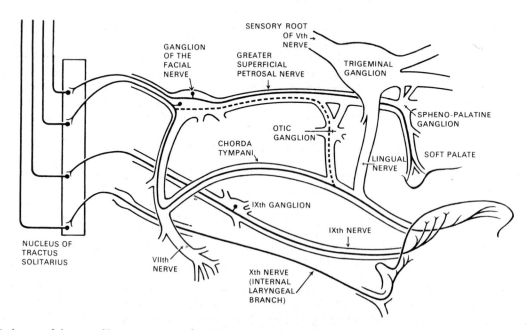

Fig. 27.42 Pathways of the taste fibres are given by bold lines. The interrupted line is an alternative route for taste from the anterior two-thirds of the tongue which appears to be present in some persons. Although these pathways are accepted by most neurologists there is still some doubt as to details. (Diagram modified and simplified from A. Brodal (1948) *Neurological Anatomy in relation to Clinical Medicine.* Oxford: Clarendon Press.)

Probably no true taste fibres pass into the brain stem by the fifth nerve but tactile, pain and thermal sensations conveyed by this nerve play an important part in the recognition of taste sensations. When the fifth nerve in man is cut or destroyed the sense of taste is immediately lost in the front of the tongue but it returns in some cases after a few hours, in others after years. If the facial nerve is divided above its ganglion the sensation of taste is lost permanently on both the palate and the anterior part of the tongue; although the fifth nerve is intact, it is unable to provide a sensation of taste.

The sensibility of the tongue can be investigated by placing small drops of the test substances in solution in water on the protruded tongue while the subject holds his nose. Such experiments seem to show that there are four basic tastes, namely *sweet, sour, salt* and *bitter*. It is, however, difficult to get good evidence to support this simple classical description. For example many people confuse sourness and bitterness and most people say that the sweetness of lactose differs from that of glucose. Further it has been shown that individual receptor cells are sensitive to many stimuli, that is they are not rigidly specific but an individual cell may be more sensitive to one kind of chemical stimulus than another. Sweet tastes are most easily perceived at the tip of the tongue, bitter at the back, sour at the edge and salt both on the tip and the edge. Sour and bitter tastes can also be appreciated at the posterior margin of the hard palate. The speed of recognition of the particular variety of taste, especially when the tongue is protruded, is relatively slow. The full sensation which allows the taste to be correctly recognized may not appear for several seconds. Tastes in everyday life, that is apart from laboratory experiments, are a mixture of gustatory, olfactory, tactile, thermal, and kinaesthetic sensations. By kinaesthetic sensation is meant the notion of hardness or toughness or elasticity obtained from the impulses arising in the end-organs of the muscles and joints used in chewing. If the nose is held and chewing is forbidden it is exceedingly difficult to distinguish between turnips, apples and onions.

A microelectrode placed in a taste cell of the rat usually detects a depolarization in response to a taste stimulus. Electrodes have been placed on the exposed chorda tympani of man during operations on the middle ear. Action potentials were recorded when salt, sweet and bitter substances were placed on the tongue but the application of water reduced the spontaneous activity in the nerve. It thus appears that man, unlike the cat, dog and rhesus monkey, does not possess a specific water taste.

Sour-tasting materials all contain acids—vinegar contains acetic acid, citrous fruit citric acid, sour milk lactic acid. Whereas very weak acids do not have a sour taste, strong acids like hydrochloric acid, which dissociates almost completely in aqueous solution, have a sour taste at very high dilution. The sour taste of hydrochloric acid must be due to H^+ ions and not to Cl^- ions because 0·00125 N-NaCl is tasteless whereas 0·00125 N-HCl is sour. Organic acids like citric acid are, however, sourer than would be expected if hydrogen-ion concentration were the only factor determining sourness. It seems reasonable therefore to assume that both the anion and the undissociated molecule as well as the hydrogen ion play a part in determining the degree of sourness of an acid.

The typical salt substance is sodium chloride; calcium chloride and potassium chloride also have a salt taste but, since all chlorides do not have exactly the same taste, the cations must have a modifying influence. The salt taste is not, however, a specific property of the chloride ion since sodium bromide, sodium iodide, sodium sulphate and sodium nitrate all have salt tastes.

The factors determining sweetness are more puzzling and are not clearly related to chemical constitution. A number of organic substances, certain proteins, sucrose, glycerine, sodium cyclamate and saccharine, and a few inorganic substances, such as the salts of lead and beryllium, all have a sweet taste. The α-amino acids are sweet but polypeptides are often bitter. L-tryptophan is bitter, D-tryptophan is sweet and the racemic mixture is bitter-sweet. The sweetest sugar is fructose, then come sucrose and glucose, with lactose a long way behind. If a 2 per cent solution of sucrose is used as the standard of comparison then saccharine is apparently 350 times sweeter than sucrose. Cyclamate is less sweet than saccharine but more stable at cooking temperatures: in weak solutions it is 10 to 20 times sweeter than sucrose. Cyclamates have been used in 'soft' drinks without any apparent bad effect for many years. Some experiments on rats on a very high intake of saccharine or cyclamate have suggested that they may be carcinogenic and their use as sweeteners has been banned in some countries. Numerous sweetening agents, some many thousand times sweeter than sucrose, have recently been prepared and are of great interest to food manufacturers and to diabetics whose sugar intake must be small. Obviously these substances cannot be made available for incorporation in foodstuffs until extensive tests of carcinogenicity have been completed.

A bitter taste is given by a variety of substances, for example caesium chloride, potassium iodide, magnesium sulphate, picric acid, and alkaloids such as quinine, strychnine and aloin.

Some tastes are not easily included in the above four-fold classification, for example alkaline and metallic tastes. It may be that in these cases the common chemical sensibility is stimulated. Freshly distilled water has an alkaline taste owing to the absence of carbon dioxide. Electrical stimulation of certain parts of the tongue with a.c. or d.c. gives rise to an 'electric taste'. Anodal stimulation of the tip of the tongue gives a sour or metallic taste which is at least partly dependent on an intact chorda tympani. Some substances give rise to a persistent taste sensation, for example, saccharine and iodides. This is presumably due to their excretion in the saliva.

No instance has been reported in which one of the four taste sensations has been absent or impaired by disease. It has, however, been found that phenylthiocarbamide and allied substances are bitter to about 60 per cent of persons and tasteless (unless very high concentrations are used) to 40 per cent, and that the ability to taste these substances is inherited according to Mendelian laws. Most people cannot taste sodium benzoate; a few describe it as either sweet or bitter.

The threshold concentration needed to arouse a sensation of taste, varies widely with different individuals and depends somewhat on the method of testing but the following are average values: sour, 0·0045 per cent HCl; salt 0·055 per cent NaCl; sweet, 0·45 per cent fructose, 0·7 per cent sucrose, 0·01 per cent cyclamate, 0·001 per cent saccharine; bitter, 0·001 per cent brucine. The smallest difference in the strength of a test solution which can be distinguished is about 30 per cent.

McCance lowered the salt content of the blood of a number

of subjects on a low-salt diet by making them sweat in a radiant heat bath. The subjects found that nearly all food stuffs had lost their flavour but the sense of taste returned within half an hour of taking salt by mouth.

Patients with adrenal cortical insufficiency have a very much lower threshold for the four modalities of taste. Treatment with mineralocorticoids does not alter the threshold but treatment with glucocorticoids brings it back to the normal level. D-Penicillamine used in the treatment of a number of conditions lowers the serum caeruloplasmin and serum copper and decreases the taste-sensitivity in all four modalities. Administration of copper by mouth restores taste-sensitivity. Diabetics have a slight hyposensitivity to glucose not correlated with the level of blood glucose. In old age the taste threshold is raised partly because of a reduction in the number of taste buds and possibly because of a loss of cerebral neurones.

The sense of taste shows adaptation. After cane sugar has been held in the mouth for 2 minutes the threshold for cane sugar may be raised 10 times. At the same time the threshold for salt may be lowered a little. It is a matter of ordinary experience that successive draughts of a sweet drink become noticeably less sweet. After a sour stimulus, distilled water may arouse a sweet sensation. Many examples of interaction between substances with easily recognized tastes could be given. Caffeine increases the sourness of citric acid and, as every coffee drinker knows, sucrose reduces the bitterness of caffeine. The temperature of the food affects gustation. Food has often more flavour when it is hot; iced food needs much more flavouring. Such a loss of flavour on cooling is not, however, universal; for example, the threshold for quinine is lower when the temperature of the solution is low. The flavour of food can be accentuated by adding flavour potentiators such as monosodium glutamate and certain 5'-nucleotides (disodium inosinate and disodium guanylate). These substances are effective in concentrations of the order of 100 parts per million but how they enhance flavour is quite unknown.

Symmetrical gustatory sweating is the name given to the sweating occurring on the head and face when irritants, such as chillies, are chewed; in a few persons it is aroused by eating chocolate. It is seldom felt in a cool climate or when the body is cooled but is experienced by nearly everyone in a tropical climate. This form of sweating has usually been described as a reflex phenomenon initiated by excitation of pain receptors in the mouth but recent experiments indicate that the response is not related to the spicy nature or temperature of the food. The physical or mental effort associated with eating may be enough to account for the phenomenon.

REFERENCES

Bacy-y-Rita P, Collins C C, Hyde J E 1971 The control of eye movements. Academic Press, New York

Beidler C M 1961 Mechanism of gustatory and olfactory receptor stimulation. In: Rosenbluth W A (ed) Symposium of sensory communication. M.I.T. Press, Cambridge, Massachusetts; John Wiley, New York

Békésy G von 1960 Experiments in hearing. McGraw-Hill, New York

Békésy G von, Rosenbluth W A 1951 In: Stevens S S (ed) Handbook of experimental psychology. John Wiley, Chichester p 1075–1115

Birch G G 1974 Sweetness and sweeteners. British Nutrition Foundation Bulletin, 12: 23–30

Bito L Z, Davson H, Fenstermacher J D (eds) 1978 The ocular and cerebrospinal fluids. Academic Press, London

Brindley G S 1970 Physiology of the retina and visual pathway, 2nd edn. Arnold, London

Brindley G S 1973 Sensory effects of electrical stimulation of the visual and paravisual cortex in man. Handbook of Sensory Physiology 7: 582–594

Burns W 1965 Noise as an environmental factor in industry. Transactions of the Association of Industrial Medical Officers 15: 2–11

Burns W 1973 Noise and man, 2nd edn. John Murray, London

Burns W, Robinson D W 1970 Hearing and noise in industry. HMSO, London

Campbell F W, Maffei L 1970 Electrophysiological evidence for the existence of orientation and size detectors in the human visual system. Journal of Physiology 207: 635–652

Cornsweet T N 1970 Visual perception. Academic Press, New York

Critchley MacDonald, Henson R A (eds) 1977 Studies in the neurology of music. Heinemann, London

Dallos P 1973 The auditory periphery: Biophysics and physiology. Academic Press, London

Davson H 1072 The physiology of the eye, 3rd edn. Academic Press, London

Douek E 1974 The sense of smell and its abnormalities. Churchill Livingstone, Edinburgh

Edmonds C, Freeman P, Thomas R, Tonkin J, Blackwood F A 1973 Otological aspects of diving. Australiasian Medical Publishing

Eldredge D H, Miller J D 1971 Physiology of hearing. Annual Review of Physiology 33: 281–310

Evans E F, Wilson J P (eds) 1977 Psychophysics and physiology of hearing. Academic Press, London

Fletcher H 1929 Speech and hearing. Macmillan, London. See also 2nd edn 1953. Macmillan, London

Fry D B 1961 Word and sentence tests for use in speech audiometry. Lancet ii: 197–199

Gilbert J H (ed) 1973 Speech and cortical functioning. Academic Press, London

Hardcastle W J 1976 Physiology of speech production. An introduction for speech scientists. Academic Press, London

Helmholtz H von 1909 Handbuch der physiologischen Optik 3rd edn. Translated for the Optical Society of America 1924 as Treatise on physiological optics. English translation republished 1962. Dover, New York

Hope A 1975 Does loud music make you deaf? New Scientist 65: 254–256

Jerger J F 1973 Modern developments in audiology. Academic Press, London and New York

Jones J 1977 The wonders of the stereoscope. Cape, London

Keidel W D, Neff W D 1974 Auditory system. In: Handbook of sensory physiology vol V, pt 1 Anatomy-Physiology (Ear). Springer-Verlag, Berlin

Kiang H 1965 Discharge patterns of single fibres in the cat's auditory nerve. MIT Press, Cambridge, Massachusetts

Kling J W, Riggs L A (eds) 1971 Woodworth and Schlosberg's experimental psychology. Holt, Rinehart & Winston, New York; Methuen, London

Kryter K D 1970 The effects of noise on man. Academic Press, London and New York

McGinty, L 1977 Noise: a standard error. New Scientist 73: 452–454

Møller A R (ed) 1973 Basic mechanisms in hearing. Academic Press, London

Moncrieff R W 1967 The chemical senses, 3rd edn. Leonard Hill, London

Moses R A 1970 Adler's physiology of the eye: Clinical applications, 5th edn. Mosby, St Louis

Motokawa K 1970 Physiology of color and pattern vision. Lange & Springer, Berlin

Moulton D G, Beidler L M 1967 Structure and function in the peripheral olfactory system. Physiological Reviews 47: 1–52

Oakley B, Benjamin R M 1966 Neural mechanisms of taste. Physiological Reviews 46: 173–211

Ohloff G, Thomas A F 1971 Gustation and olfaction. Academic Press, New York

Perkins E S (ed) 1970 Recent research on the retina. British Medical Bulletin 26: 99–184

Pinching A J 1977 Clinical testing of olfaction reassessed. Brain 100: 377–388

Pirenne M H 1967 Vision and the eye, 2nd edn. Science Paperbacks, London

Plomp R 1977 Aspects of tone sensation. Academic Press, London

Rice C E 1967 Human echo perception. Science 155: 656–664

Rushton W A H 1971 Colour vision: an approach through the cone pigments. Investigative Ophthalmology 10: 311–322

Shaw J H, Roussos G G 1978 Sweeteners and dental caries. Information Retrieval, London

Shepherd G M 1972 Synaptic organization of the mammalian olfactory bulb. Physiological Reviews 52: 864–917

Sterling T D, Bering E A, Pollack S V, Vaughan H (eds) 1971 Visual prostheses. Academic Press, London

Stevenson S D G (ed) 1976 Disorders of auditory function II. Academic Press, London

Stiles N S 1978 Mechanisms of colour vision. Academic Press, London

Teuber H L, Battersby W S, Bender M B 1960 Visual field defects after penetrating missile wounds of the brain. Harvard Univerity Press, Cambridge, Massachusetts

Toates F M 1972 Accommodation function of the human eye. Physiological Reviews 52: 828–863

Weale R A 1963 The aging eye. Lewis, London

Wever E G 1966 Electrical potentials of the cochlea. Physiological Reviews 46: 102–107

Whitfield I C 1967 The auditory pathway. Arnold, London

Zotterman Y (ed) 1963 Olfaction and taste. Pergamon, Oxford

Zotterman Y (ed) 1967 Sensory mechanisms. Progress in Brain Research 23: 1–154

28 The Hypothalamus and Endocrine Glands

The term *hormone* is applied to a substance which, produced in one part of the body, enters the circulation and is carried to distant organs and tissues to modify their structure and function.

A gland such as the thyroid is described as an *endocrine gland* or ductless gland since its secretion is not conveyed along a duct but passes directly into the blood or into the lymphatics. The production of hormones is not confined to the endocrine glands, for secretin and cholecystokinin (p. 67) produced in the intestine are hormones; hormones are produced by the kidney (p. 258) and noradrenaline and acetylcholine liberated at nerve-endings by nerve impulses (p. 325) may enter the circulation in sufficient amounts to produce effects in distant parts.

This chapter deals with the pituitary gland and the endocrine function of the hypothalamus, the thyroid and adrenal glands together with a number of 'local hormones'. Insulin and glucagon are dealt with in Chapter 6, parathyroid hormone, calcitonin and the metabolites of vitamin D in Chapter 18 and the endocrine functions of the gonads in Chapter 29.

The physiological actions of the various hormones have been explored in a number of ways; first by studying the effects of complete removal of an endocrine gland from the body and secondly by grafting experiments or injections of active extracts of the gland to attempt to restore the animal to normal; thirdly by observing the effects of the administration of large amounts of the hormone to normal animals. Conclusions based upon such experiments are often amplified by the study of disease in man since disorders due to overactivity, or to destruction, of the various endocrine glands are well recognized. The effects of over-secretion by an endocrine gland may be relieved or cured by the surgical removal of part of the overactive tissue. On the other hand the operative removal of too much tissue or the destruction of all or part of an endocrine gland by disease gives rise to a 'deficiency syndrome' which is controlled, but not cured, by replacement therapy, that is by supplying the deficient hormone or another substance with a similar action.

Mode of Action of Hormones

Our knowledge of hormonal mechanisms is still incomplete but it is becoming clear that for most, if not all, hormones the first requisite for hormonal action is the binding of the hormone to a specific receptor (Fig. 28.1). In the case of protein, peptide and amine hormones the receptor appears to be on the cell membrane, while steroid and sterol hormones enter cells and bind to specific proteins in the cytosol.

The cell membrane. A hormone may act by altering the permeability or the active transport mechanisms for particular molecules. Such effects may be seen in the increase in glucose uptake by many tissues in the presence of insulin, in increases in amino acid transport into muscle cells by growth hormone

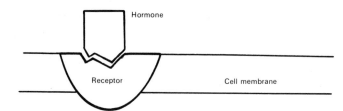

Fig. 28.1 A hormone receptor on a cell membrane to show the 'lock and key' interaction with a hormone.

and in the effects of aldosterone on the movement of Na^+ through the kidney. Such actions could have an effect on the metabolic activity in the cells if, for example, the transported substance had previously been present in rate-limiting quantities.

While it is possible that the effects of hormones on membranes could be direct this would not explain all the effects of hormones on metabolic processes. It seems likely that both membrane effects and metabolic effects are mediated by a 'second messenger' produced or released within the cell as a result of the binding of hormone to receptor. Among the second messengers which have been proposed are prostaglandins, calcium, cyclic AMP (cyclic adenosine 3':5'-monophosphate) and cyclic GMP (cyclic guanosine 3':5'-monophosphate). Of these cyclic AMP has been the most fully investigated and hormones whose action involves cyclic AMP include adrenaline, vasopressin, ACTH, LH, TSH, glucagon and parathyroid hormone.

These hormones activate adenyl cyclase, a membrane-bound enzyme found in all mammalian tissues with the exception of the mature erythrocyte. In the cell membrane adenylate cyclase catalyses the conversion of ATP to cyclic 3':5'-adenosine monophosphate (*cyclic AMP*) and inorganic pyrophosphate. Cyclic AMP produced within the hormonally stimulated cell alters the metabolism in a manner characteristic of the particular tissue, by activating certain protein phosphokinases (enzymes which can phosphorylate serine and threonine residues in protein molecules at the expense of ATP); the activated phosphokinase can then phosphorylate and change the activity of certain rate controlling enzymes. The various effects shown in different tissues depend upon the specificity of the particular phosphokinase. Equally the characteristics of the cell membrane may be altered in the same way. An example is shown in Figure 28.2.

The effects of cyclic AMP are largely limited to the tissue in which it is produced because it does not readily penetrate membranes and because it is rapidly destroyed by a specific enzyme, cyclic AMP phosphodiesterase.

Insulin and some prostaglandins have the ability to decrease cyclic AMP formation in some tissues such as adipose tissue. Insulin can decrease the activation of adenyl cyclase caused by adrenaline, and may increase the activity of phosphodiesterase. The effects of the prostaglandins depend

462

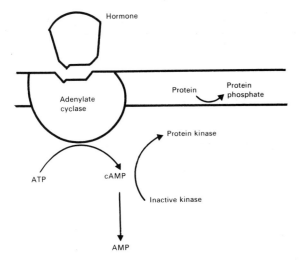

Fig. 28.2 The role of adenylate cyclase and cyclic AMP in mediating the action of a hormone. In this case the hormonal action results in an alteration in the cell membrane but a similar mechanism could lead to an alteration in the activity of an intracellular enzyme.

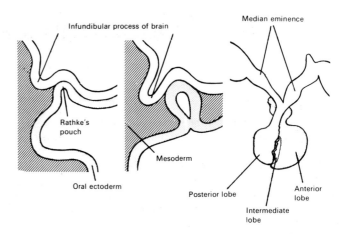

Fig. 28.3 Embryological origin of the two parts of the pituitary gland. (*After* F. Netter and W. C. Bloom.)

on the type of prostaglandin and the particular tissue. For example, in the ovary PGE_2 increases cyclic AMP production.

Actions on protein synthesis. Steroid and sterol hormones act mainly by entering the cell and binding to receptor proteins within the cytosol. The hormone-receptor complex then enters the nucleus where it influences the synthesis of particular proteins. For example 1,25 DHCC (p. 31) specifically stimulates the production in intestinal mucosa of a protein required for the active transport of calcium.

The precise action of the hormone-receptor complex within the nucleus is still unknown. One possibility is that it binds to the repressor gene in a particular part of the chromosome. The operator gene can then promote the synthesis (transcription) of messenger RNA. The effects of many steroid hormones can be blocked by the drug actinomycin D which binds to DNA and prevents transcription.

Other hormones also have actions on protein synthesis but the precise mechanism is not yet clear. The thyroid hormones, thyroxine and tri-iodothyronine probably act, at least in part, at the transcription stage in the synthesis of proteins involved in oxidative phosphorylation. Somatomedin probably acts on protein synthesis by affecting translation, possibly by controlling the uptake of amino acids by transfer RNA.

THE HYPOTHALAMUS AND THE PITUITARY GLAND

In the control of the endocrine system the hypothalamus and pituitary gland function as an integrated unit. The pituitary gland is attached by a stalk to the hypothalamus in the base of the brain. The pituitary gland (hypophysis) is composed of two morphologically and functionally distinct components:

1. The adenohypophysis or anterior pituitary.
2. The neurohypophysis or posterior pituitary.

The two parts of the pituitary gland develop embryologically from distinct anatomical sites. The neurohypophysis

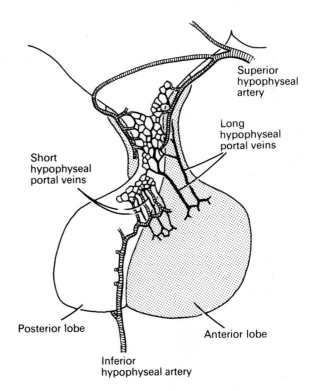

Fig. 28.4 The blood supply of the pituitary gland. Note that the anterior lobe is largely supplied by portal vessels which arise from a capillary plexus in the pituitary stalk. The posterior lobe is supplied directly from the inferior hypophyseal artery. The venous drainage of the anterior pituitary (not shown) carries with it the hormones produced by the gland.

is derived from neural cells in the floor of the developing third ventricle in a region from which the hypothalamus is also formed. The thinner upper portion of the developing neurohypophysis which connects the neural lobe with the hypothalamus is the neural stalk or infundibulum, and the wall of the upper portion of the stalk expands to form the median eminence.

The adenohypophysis originates as an out-pocketing of ectodermal cells (Rathke's pouch) in the roof of the primitive oral cavity. This group of cells containing an inner cavity migrates upward and is separated from the oral cavity by the proliferation of surrounding mesoderm. Rathke's pouch assumes a position anterior to the neurohypophysis (Fig. 28.3). A superior extension of Rathke's pouch develops into the pars tuberalis which in man is a thin sheet of cells on the anterior and lateral surfaces of the neural stalk and median eminence.

The pituitary gland in the adult male weighs approximately 500 mg, the weight is slightly greater in the female and increases during pregnancy. The pituitary fossa (*sella turcica*) is covered by an extension of the dura mater (the diaphragma sellae) through which passes the pituitary stalk connecting the gland to the hypothalamus. The optic chiasma lies just anterior to this connexion. Enlargement of the gland, for example by tumour, results in upward growth towards the base of the brain and may result in pressure on the optic chiasma and defects in the field of vision (Fig. 27.18).

The blood supply to the pituitary gland is derived from the internal carotid artery. The posterior lobe is supplied directly from an arterial ring formed by branches of the two inferior hypophysial arteries. The branches of the superior hypophysial arteries supply the median eminence and the neural stalk to form a capillary plexus at these sites. A system of portal veins arising from this plexus delivers blood to the anterior lobe which receives little direct arterial blood supply (Fig. 28.4). Within the anterior lobe the blood enters sinusoids in which it is separated from the hormone-producing cells only by sinusoidal epithelium and the perisinusoidal space. This 'pituitary portal system' has great physiological significance since the blood not only provides nutrition for the anterior lobe but also delivers to it humoral substances from the neural centres of the hypothalamus and median eminence.

The anatomical basis for the control of the anterior pituitary gland by the hypothalamus was established by the work of Harris and his co-workers. Hypothalamic neurones of different types liberate hormonal substances from their nerve endings into the primary capillary plexus of the hypophyseal portal system in the median eminence and then these substances are carried by the portal vessels to the anterior pituitary gland (Fig. 28.5) where they stimulate or inhibit the release of the various anterior pituitary hormones (Table 28.6). It has been suggested that the neurosecretory granules detected in the neurones of the median eminence may be related to hypothalamic releasing hormones.

As early as 1924 it was realized that the hormones secreted by the posterior lobe of the pituitary gland are also found in the hypothalamus. It was later shown that the two hormones of the posterior pituitary, oxytocin and vasopressin, are manufactured in specialized nerve cells in the hypothalamus—the paraventricular and supraoptic nuclei (Fig. 28.7). The two hormones combine with specific binding proteins called neurophysins and flow down the axons of the nerve fibres of the hypothalamic tract to the storage cells in the posterior pituitary (Fig. 28.8).

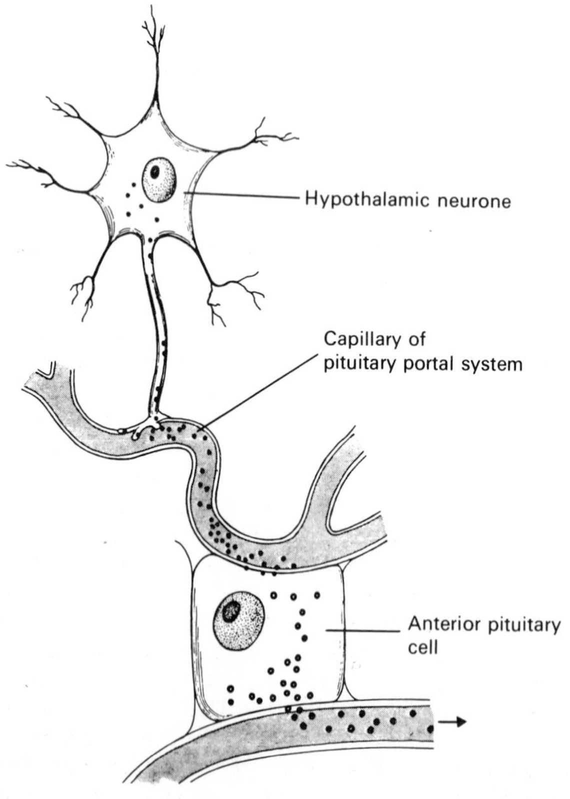

Fig. 28.5 Relationship between hypothalamic neurones and anterior pituitary cells. (*From* R. Guillemin & R. Burgus (1972) *Scientific American* **227** (5) 24–33.)

Table 28.6 The anterior pituitary hormones and the appropriate hypothalamic releasing hormones or release-inhibiting hormones. In general the hypothalamic hormones are known as *factors* until their structure has been determined.

Hormone	Structure	Hypothalamic control
Thyroid stimulating hormone (TSH)	Glycoprotein	Thyrotrophin releasing hormone (TRH)
Luteinizing hormone (LH)	Glycoprotein	Luteinizing hormone releasing hormone (LHRH)
Follicle stimulating hormone (FSH)	Glycoprotein	Luteinizing hormone releasing hormone (LHRH)
Growth hormone (GH)	Protein	Growth hormone releasing factor (GHRF) Growth hormone release inhibitory hormone (somatostatin, GHRIH)
Adreno-cortico-trophic hormone (ACTH)	Polypeptide	Corticotrophin releasing factor (CRF)
Prolactin	Protein	Prolactin release inhibitory factor (PIF)

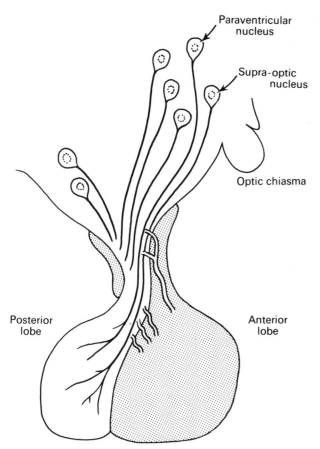

Fig. 28.7 The tracts from the hypothalamus to the pituitary. The paraventricular nucleus and the supra-optic nucleus are thought to be responsible for the elaboration of oxytocin and ADH respectively. The other tracts terminate in the capillary plexus shown in Figure 28.4 and carry the hypothalamic hormones which control the release of the hormones of the anterior pituitary.

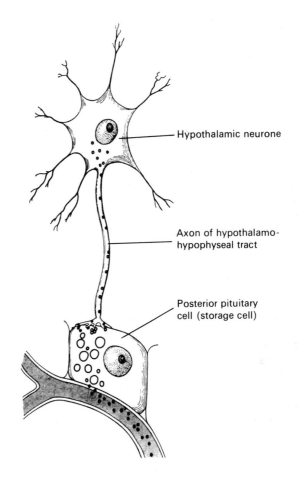

Fig. 28.8 Role of the posterior pituitary cells in the storage of the hormones oxytocin and ADH elaborated by hypothalamic neurones (*From* R. Guillemin & R. Burgus (1972) *Scientific American* 227 (5) 24–33).

The Hypothalamic Hormones

The hypothalamus has a major influence on the release and synthesis of the anterior pituitary hormones. Cutting the pituitary stalk leads to a reduction in the secretion of adrenocorticotrophic hormone (ACTH), thyroid stimulating hormone (TSH), luteinizing hormone (LH), follicle stimulating hormone (FSH) and growth hormone. As a consequence atrophy of the adrenal cortex, thyroid gland and gonads occurs.Regeneration of the portal blood vessels reverses the action. Prolactin production increases following section of the pituitary stalk.

Evidence from experimental stimulation or from localized lesions indicates that corticotrophin releasing factor (CRF) is produced in the posterior hypothalamus while thyrotrophin releasing hormone (TRH) is formed in the anterior region. The mid-hypothalamic region appears to be the site of luteinizing hormone releasing hormone (LH-RH) release. The ventral hypothalamus appears to control the secretion of growth hormone and prolactin, but the control centres have not yet been precisely located. The neurosecretory cells are probably scattered throughout the hypothalamus rather than clustered in specific areas since extensive hypothalamic

destruction is needed to produce a significant alteration in anterior pituitary function.

The hypothalamus contains only a few nanograms of releasing hormones. Much smaller quantities are secreted into the portal vessels but sufficient to cause the cells of the anterior pituitary to synthesize and release a thousand or more times the weight of trophic hormone. The trophic hormones in turn cause the target glands to secrete at least a thousand times as much hormone. Just as in electronic amplifiers this 'cascade amplifier' is controlled by feed-back mechanisms.

It is now generally accepted that neurohormones act by combining with specific receptors on the surface of the pituitary cell. Adenylate cyclase is activated leading to changes in membrane composition as shown in Figure 28.2. As a consequence calcium is taken up and exocytosis, in which the secretory granule fuses with the cell membrane and the granular core is extruded, occurs (fig. 28.9). As well as stimulating this release of hormone the releasing hormones probably also influence synthesis. Synthesis takes place on the endoplasmic reticulum and the packaging into secretory granules occurs in the Golgi apparatus. Increased release of hormone occurs immediately after the arrival of the releasing hormone; increased synthesis occurs later.

Corticotrophin Releasing Factor (CRF). Although CRF was the first hypothalamic hormone to be described it has not yet been isolated in pure form. It is probably a small polypeptide.

CRF is a potent stimulator of ACTH release, and ACTH in turn releases cortisol from the adrenal cortex. The secretion of CRF is influenced by neural impulses from higher centres as well as by circulating levels of ACTH and cortisol. The existence of periodic variations in the secretion of cortisol and ACTH is well established in the human from the age of three years and persists throughout life (p. 478). It is thought that the periodicity of ACTH secretion reflects cyclical changes in CRF secretion, and that these cyclical changes are determined by the pattern of sleep. Clinical studies have shown abnormalities of circadian rhythm of plasma cortisol in patients with psychiatric disorders, especially depression and altered states of consciousness, as well as in those with diseases of the hypothalamus or limbic system. At present there is much speculation concerning the role of neurotransmitter substances in the control of CRF release. Serotonin and acetyl choline appear to have stimulatory actions but the existence of inhibitory adrenergic control is more controversial.

Thyrotrophin Releasing Hormone (TRH). The isolation, elucidation of structure and synthesis of TRH eliminated the scepticism concerning the existence of the elusive hypothalamic hormones. TRH is a tripeptide (Table 28.10) which promotes the release of thyroid stimulating hormone (thyrotrophin, TSH) by the anterior pituitary when given orally or intravenously. TRH acts rapidly to release preformed TSH by acting on specific receptors on the plasma membranes of the appropriate cells of the anterior pituitary. Cyclic AMP is the likely intermediate messenger, both Ca^+ and Na^+ are required for the reaction. TSH in turn stimulates the thyroid gland to produce thyroxine and tri-iodothyronine. High circulating levels of these two hormones block the stimulatory action of

Table 28.10 The structures of some of the hypothalamic hormones which control the release of hormones by the anterior pituitary. pGlu is pyroglutamate.

TRH
pGlu-His-Pro(NH₂)

LHRH
pGlu-His-Trp-Ser-Tyr-Gly-Leu-Arg-Pro-Gly-(NH₂).

GHRIH (Somatostatin)
H-Ala-Gly-Cys-Lys-Asn-Phe-Phe-Trp
| |
HO-Cys-Ser-Thr-Phe-Thr-Lys

TRH on the TSH-producing cells of the anterior pituitary. After destruction of the thyroid gland circulating levels of thyroxine and tri-iodothyronine fall to low levels. If TRH is given to patients with primary thyroid failure there is an augmented TSH response. Oestrogens also augment the response and females respond with a greater TSH response than do males (Fig. 28.11). Dopamine and somatostatin block the action of TRH on the pituitary.

Significant concentrations of TRH are found in the CNS outwith the hypothalamus and a possible role as a neurotransmitter has been suggested. It has also been shown to have an antidepressant action.

Luteinizing hormone and follicle stimulating hormone releasing hormone (LH-RH). It is now clear that only one hypothalamic releasing hormone is involved in the regulation of the release and synthesis of both luteinizing hormone (LH) and follicle stimulating hormone (FSH). It is a decapeptide (Table 28.10) and is produced in specific areas of the hypothalamus, namely the median eminence, and the arcuate and ventromedial nuclei.

The response of the anterior pituitary to LH-RH is modulated by the circulating levels of the gonadal hormones which are produced in response to LH and FSH. In the female the ovarian steroids, in particular oestradiol-17β, exert a negative feedback on the pituitary to inhibit gonadotrophin

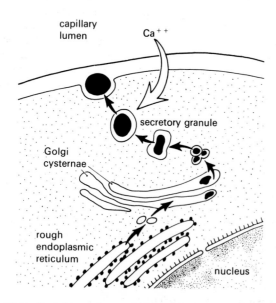

Fig. 28.9 Probable pathway of LH synthesis and release from the anterior pituitary cell. LH-RH is thought to increase cell permeability to calcium which in turn induces exocytosis (*From* S. J. McCann (1977) *New England Journal of Medicine,* **296,** 797–802.)

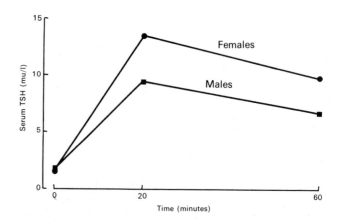

Fig. 28.11 Response in serum TSH levels to the administration of 200 μg TRH intravenously in 25 normal females and 20 normal males. (*After* B. J. Ormston, R. Garry, R. J. Cryer, G. M. Besser and R. Hall (1971) *Lancet,* **ii** 10–14.)

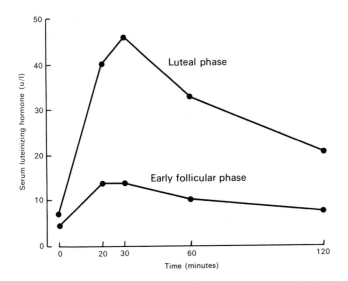

Fig. 28.12 Response in serum LH to an intravenous injection of 100 μg LH-RH. Mean values in ten normal women in whom the study was carried out in the follicular phase and in the luteal phase of the same menstrual cycle. (*After* R. W. Shaw, W. R. Butt, D. R. London & J. C. Marshall (1974) *Journal of Obstetrics and Gynaecology of the British Commonwealth*, 81, 632–639

production during most of the menstrual cycle but the pre-ovulatory discharge of FSH and LH is brought about by a stimulatory or positive feed-back of oestrogen at mid-cycle. These feed-back effects are accompanied by marked changes in responsiveness of the pituitary gland to LH-RH. Figure 28.12 compares the response to LH-RH in the early or follicular phase of the menstrual cycle when oestradiol-17β levels are low with the response in the luteal phase when oestradiol-17β levels are greater. There are two major sites within the hypothalamus that take up and concentrate oestradiol-17β, the arcuate nucleus and the pre-optic region; both also contain LH-RH neurones. Noradrenaline appears to be involved in mediating the stimulatory effect of gonadal steroids localized in the pre-optic region, as well as the negative feed-back thought to be localized in the arcuate nucleus. There is also evidence for the participation of other transmitters in the control of LH-RH release; acetyl choline may be a stimulatory transmitter and serotonin may inhibit. In addition prostaglandins, particularly PGE$_2$, appear to be involved in the releasing mechanism.

In the adult male gonadotrophin production, particularly LH, is controlled by negative feedback by testosterone. There is also evidence of production of an additional hormone *inhibin* by the seminiferous tubules; this mainly regulates FSH production.

Somatostatin and growth hormone releasing factor. The studies of Krulich and co-workers in 1968 established the concept that growth hormone secretion by the anterior pituitary gland is regulated by two hypothalamic factors, growth hormone releasing factor, the structure of which is unknown, and growth hormone-release inhibiting factor or somatostatin (Table 28.10). It is now known that somatostatin is present in many tissues other than the hypothalamus. It is found elsewhere in the central nervous system, in peripheral ganglia and in such extraneural tissues such as stomach, small intestine, pancreas and thyroid gland; the highest concen-

trations are found in hypothalamic tissue and in pancreatic islets. Morever it is now appreciated that somatostatin has many actions in addition to inhibiting the secretion of growth hormone (Table 28.13). Somatostatin is a potent inhibitor of TRH-stimulated TSH release but does not block the release of prolactin in response to TRH.

The exact mechanism by which somatostatin inhibits secretion is still under investigation. Somatostatin has been reported to lower cyclic AMP levels in the pituitary gland, to block elevation of cyclic AMP during glucose-stimulated release from pancreatic islets and to increase cyclic GMP levels in pituitary tissue. Somatostatin does not appear to be bound to specific receptors on the external surface of target cells but an intracellular cytosolic somatostatin binding protein has been identified in a number of tissues.

Since somatostatin is found in nerve endings throughout the brain, spinal cord and peripheral ganglia and since it has been reported to alter neuroral function and to cause behaviour changes in some species, it is possible that it may also function as a neurotransmitter. It seems unlikely that somatostatin acts as a conventional systemic hormone because it has diverse actions and a very short half life, and because its presence cannot be demonstrated in plasma. Accordingly it has been suggested that somatostatin may be the prototype of a new class of local chemical messengers called *cybernins*.

The release of both somatostatin and GHRF appears to be regulated by monoaminergic neurones. Noradrenaline, dopamine and serotonin have stimulatory effects on growth hormone production although it is not known whether the effect is a consequence of decreased somatostatin or increased GHRF.

Prolactin release inhibiting factor and prolactin releasing factor. The control of prolactin secretion is by two hypothalamic factors, prolactin release inhibiting factor (PIF) and prolactin releasing factor (PRF). Prolactin is unique among the anterior pituitary hormones in that its secretion is under tonic inhibitory control by the hypothalamus and PIF is thus dominant in regulating secretion. It is now clear that the main prolactin inhibitory factor is dopamine (Fig. 28.36, p. 481).

TRH releases prolactin from anterior pituitary cells both *in vivo* and *in vitro*. However it seems unlikely that TRH acts as the physiological prolactin releasing factor as prolactin can be released without thyrotrophin for example during suckling. In addition prolactin and thryotrophin have different circadian rhythms.

Table 28.13 Some reported biological actions of somatostatin. *After* J. E. Gerich and G. S. Patton (1978) *Medical Clinics of North America*, 62, 375

Endocrine actions
Inhibits secretion of: growth hormone, TSH, ACTH, gastrin, CCK-PZ, secretin, human pancreatic polypeptide, vasoactive intestinal polypeptide, gastric inhibitory polypeptide, motilin, glucagon, insulin, renin

Non-endocrine actions
Inhibits gastric secretion and emptying
Decreases xylose absorption
Decreases splanchnic blood flow
Diminishes electrical activity in CNS neurones
Inhibits platelet aggregation

The Hormones of the Anterior Pituitary

The hormones of the anterior pituitary gland are listed in Table 28.6.

Adrenocorticotrophic Hormone (ACTH) This is a single chain peptide comprising 39 amino acids (Fig. 28.14). In all species the 24 amino acids at the N-terminal (the end of the molecule with the free amino group) are identical and are needed for biological activity. There are minor differences between the ACTH molecules in different species.

NH_2-**Ser-Tyr-Ser-Met-Glu-His-Phe-Arg-Trp-Gly-Lys-
-Pro-Val-Gly-Lys-Lys-Arg-Arg-Pro-Val-Lys-Val-Tyr-
-Pro**-Asp-Ala-Gly-Glu-Asp-Gln-Ser-Ala-Glu-Ala-Phe-
-Pro-Leu-Glu-Phe-COOH.

Fig. 28.14 Amino acid sequence of human ACTH. The first 24 residues, shown in bold type, are those essential for biological activity.

ACTH has a number of biological effects and is the only hormone known to control the secretion of cortisol by the adrenal cortex. In addition ACTH causes increased adrenal blood flow, a rapid fall in adrenal ascorbate and an increased adrenal cortical cholesterol concentration. This is associated with an increase in the steroid content, especially cortisol, which is then secreted into the circulation. ACTH also stimulates protein synthesis in the adrenal cortex and prolonged ACTH stimulation causes hypertropy of the adrenal cortex.

ACTH secretion is believed to be controlled mainly from the hypothalamus by corticotrophin releasing factor. In the absence of CRF, due either to hypothalamic destruction or to interruption of the portal circulation between hypothalamus and pituitary, ACTH and consequently cortisol secretion is severely impaired. Three major mechanisms appear to control ACTH release and thus cortisol secretion: circadian rhythm, 'negative feed-back', and stress (Table 28.15).

Cortisol and ACTH levels are lowest at around midnight and increase to maximum levels at about 8 a.m.; levels then fall throughout the day with peaks sometimes occurring around mid-day and 18.00 hours. This periodicity of ACTH secretion is well established from the age of three years and persists throughout life, even in patients without adrenal function. The rhythm is controlled by the pattern of sleep, but several days are needed for the rhythm to adapt to a change, for example to a different time-zone ('jet-lag').

Table 28.15 Factors controlling the release of ACTH

Increased ACTH production:
Increased CRF production due to
    Physical stress (particularly exercise)
    Emotional stress
    Hypoglycaemia
    As part of the circadian rhythm

Decreased ACTH production
Decreased CRF production
    Increased ACTH levels ('short feed-back loop')
    Increased cortisol levels ('long feed-back loop')
    As part of circadian rhythm
Increased cortisol levels (direct effect)

The reciprocal relationship between circulating ACTH and cortisol levels constitutes a major homeostatic mechanism; as cortisol levels rise so ACTH levels fall, ACTH secretion decreases within two minutes of the rise in plasma cortisol. This is the 'fast feed-back' and appears to be directly related to the rate of rise in plasma corticosteroids, for example after intravenous administration, while the second phase ('delayed feed-back') is related to the actual dose of steroid administered. The first phase of inhibition occurs immediately after steroid administration whereas the second phase does not occur until some hours later. There is also some evidence for the existence of a 'short loop' negative feed-back system in experimental animals whereby the ACTH level itself exerts an influence over CRF secretion.

The neuroendocrine system regulating ACTH secretion can respond to stress with great rapidity; for example ACTH secretion in response to surgical stress occurs within a few minutes of the beginning of surgery. Many different forms of stress can cause ACTH release including fever, noise, pain, fear and hypoglycaemia. Such stress factors override both circadian rhythm and feed-back control.

Thyroid Stimulating Hormone (TSH). Thyroid stimulating hormone, a glycoprotein of molecular weight 28 000 consists of two dissimilar sub-units α and β. The structure of the α sub-unit closely resembles that of the α sub-units of the other glycoprotein hormones: follicle stimulating hormone (FSH), luteinizing hormone (LH) and human chorionic gonadotrophin (HCG). The β sub-unit confers on the hormone its biological specificity and most of its immunological specificity.

After hypophysectomy the thyroid gland atrophies and ceases to produce thyroid hormones. The administration of TSH reverses these abnormalities; it increases the weight and size of the thyroid, stimulates glucose oxidation and the synthesis of RNA and protein. TSH administration causes an increase in the uptake of iodine by the thyroid gland as well as stimulating the synthesis and release of tri-iodothyronine and thyroxine. The action of TSH is mediated by cyclic AMP; it is rapidly bound to a receptor on the plasma membrane of thyroid cells.

Plasma levels of TSH normally range from less than 0·5 mu/l (the limit of detection with current analytical methods) to 4·5 mu/l.

There is a circadian rhythm in TSH secretion with peak values between 9 p.m. and 6 a.m. and minimum values between 4 p.m. and 7 p.m. Superimposed upon this are fluctuations which are presumed to reflect the episodic secretion of TRH. The circadian rhythm of TSH is also thought to reflect the rhythmic secretion of TRH.

The production of TSH is controlled by a negative feed-back mechanism. After destruction of the thyroid gland either by disease or by a surgical operation, the level of thyroid hormones in plasma falls and TSH production is stimulated. It is only very rarely that over-activity of the thyroid gland is caused by over-production of TSH.

The Gonadotrophins (LH and FSH). Like TSH, luteinizing hormone (LH) and follicle stimulating hormone (FSH) are glycoproteins composed of two different sub-units—the α and β sub-units.

The secretion of the gonadotrophins by the anterior pituitary determines testicular and ovarian function. The activity of the anterior pituitary gland is regulated both by the hypothalamus and by feed-back mechanisms from the testis and ovary. The administration of FSH to the female results in growth and maturation of the ovarian follicle. LH is also needed for normal follicular development and function but the major action of LH in the female is to promote the development and endocrine function of the corpus luteum (p. 489).

In the male FSH increases the growth of the seminiferous tubules and stimulates spermatogenesis. In this action the LH also appears to be necessary for full effect. LH increases the production of testosterone by the interstitial cells of the testes and was at one time also known as *interstitial cell stimulating hormone* (ICSH). The secretion of the gonadotrophins at different stages in the development of gonadal function— infancy, puberty, adult life and old age—is qualitatively and quantitatively different. As a person ages, the germinal and endocrine functions of the ovary, and to a lesser extent the testis, diminish and this in turn leads to changes in pituitary function. The plasma concentrations of LH and FSH fluctuate markedly during a 24 hour cycle. In the adult male there are between 9 and 14 secretory episodes when LH levels rise sharply two-or three-fold at irregular intervals during each 24 hour period (Fig. 28.16). The variations of FSH are much smaller.

In the adult female, in ovulatory cycles, there is a peak of LH and FSH at mid-cycle. FSH levels are also moderately elevated during the first few days of the follicular phase and decrease during the days preceding ovulation (Fig. 29.11 p. 491). In menopausal women basal gonadotrophin levels are not maintained at a steady level but consist of a series of abrupt peaks and troughs. The plasma levels of FSH are higher than in the course of a normal menstrual cycle and persist at this high level for many years, whilst plasma levels of LH are similar to those found in mid-cycle in younger women.

Regulation of gonadotrophin secretion. The administration of testosterone to males is followed by a rapid fall in plasma LH levels, and a smaller fall in plasma FSH levels. The ability of the pituitary gland to respond to LH-RH is not affected by the administration of testosterone suggesting that the decrease in normal gonadotrophin levels is not related to a diminished pituitary responsiveness to LH-RH but rather to insufficient stimulation of the anterior pituitary by LH-RH.

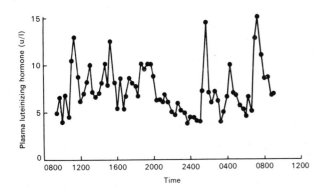

Fig. 28.16 Plasma concentrations of LH sampled every 20 minutes for 24 hours in a normal male adult. (*After* R. Boyar, M. Perlow, L. Hellman, S. Kapen & E. Weitzman (1972) *Journal of Clinical Endocrinology and Metabolism*, 35, 73–81

The evidence therefore suggests that testosterone acts at the hypothalamic level but whether this action is due to testosterone itself or one of its metabolites is not yet clear. Oestradiol-17β also suppresses LH production but by a different mechanism: testosterone decreases the number of pulsatile episodes of LH secretion per day whereas oestradiol-17β decreases the amplitude of the pulses of LH and has a more marked effect on the secretion of FSH. In addition oestradiol-17β blunts the response of the anterior pituitary to LH-RH. Recent studies suggest that there is a nonsteroidal hormone (*inhibin*) which is important in the control of FSH secretion. A peptide fraction (MW 10 000 – 20 000) has been isolated from human seminal fluid which selectively inhibits FSH secretion. It is probable that this peptide is produced by the germinal epithelium since high FSH levels occur most commonly in association with severe damage to the germinal epithelium.

In females oestrogens inhibit FSH secretion whereas they exert a biphasic action on LH: first a negative (or inhibitory) effect followed by a positive (or stimulatory) effect. During the menstrual cycle the oestradiol-17β peak in plasma precedes the rise in LH by between one and three days. This chronological sequence makes it likely that oestrogens stimulate the release of LH at mid-cycle.

Before the onset of puberty gonadotrophin levels are fairly stable with FSH levels usually greater than LH levels. The administration of LH-RH in prepubertal children results in a greater rise in FSH than in LH and the response is usually more pronounced in female children. During puberty the levels of gonadotrophins increase greatly. In boys FSH levels increase rapidly during the early phases of puberty and stabilize in the later stages, whereas LH levels rise steadily throughout all stages. In girls also FSH levels increase during the early stages of puberty then level off; LH levels rise steadily until the later stages just prior to menstruation when a rapid increase in LH levels occurs.

Growth hormone. Human growth hormone (GH) is a single chain polypeptide composed of 190 amino acids containing two intra-chain disulphide bridges. It is structurally similar to prolactin and human placental lactogen. GH promotes skeletal growth, as well as increasing growth of muscles, connective tissue and viscera such as liver, kidney, intestines, pancreas and adrenals. GH modifies the level of various constituents in plasma and elevated levels of glucose, phosphorus and fatty acids are found when growth hormone is present in excess. An increase in the urinary excretion of calcium and a decrease in urinary nitrogen excretion also occur.

Growth hormone does not stimulate anabolic processes in cartilage *in vitro*, although the growth of cartilage is readily stimulated *in vivo* in response to GH administration. This finding led to the hypothesis that GH exerts its anabolic effects on cartilage and possibly also on other tissues by stimulating the release of a second hormonal mediator, *somatomedin*, which acts directly on the target tissues. Somatomedin was first noted to stimulate the incorporation of sulphate into cartilage chondroitin sulphate and was originally known as *sulphation factor*. It is now known to stimulate many other anabolic processes. Somatomedin has a half-life of several hours whilst GH has a half-life of approximately 20 minutes. The slow disappearance of endogenous somatomedin from plasma can be attributed to the fact that it circulates bound to a

Table 28.17 Factors controlling the production of growth hormone (GH) by the anterior pituitary

---

Increased GH production
Increased GHRF secretion by the hypothalamus
    Exercise
    Anxiety
    Hypoglycaemia
    Amino acids
    Sleep

Decreased GH production
Increased somatostatin secretion by the hypothalamus
    Hyperglycaemia

---

plasma protein, which is also dependent on GH.

Growth hormone secretion is regulated by two hypothalamic factors: growth hormone releasing factor (GHRF) and somatostatin. An increase in circulating GH levels occurs in response to various stimuli including exercise, anxiety, hypoglycaemia and the administration of certain amino acids such as arginine (Fig. 6.10 & Table 28.17). Hyperglycaemia inhibits growth hormone release. Growth hormone is released in a pulsatile manner with the largest surges occurring during the first two hours of sleep at night. The number and magnitude of spontaneous growth hormone pulses depend on age, increasing during the growth spurt of adolescence and declining thereafter. Sleep-associated release of growth hormone is commonly absent in adults over 50 years of age. The release of both of the hypothalamic factors controlling growth hormone secretion appears to be regulated by monoaminergic neurones; drugs which modify the levels of these compounds have a marked effect on growth hormone production.

Excess production of growth hormone in children results in gigantism, whilst inadequate production causes dwarfism p. 512). In adults, the epiphyses have fused so that further linear growth of the long bones is not possible in response to growth hormone excess; however there is enlargement of the jaw, hands and feet, as well as of the viscera. This condition is called *acromegaly*. Inadequate production of growth hormone in adults produces no recognizable clinical disorder.

Prolactin. It was not until 1970 that clear evidence was obtained from bioassay studies that prolactin existed as a distinct hormone in man, separate from growth hormone. Although it is possible that prolactin is important in a variety of metabolic processes its only established roles in the human are concerned with the control of lactation and gonadal function.

Prolactin is unique amongst the anterior pituitary hormones in that its secretion is under tonic inhibitory control by the hypothalamus. If the connection between the hypothalamus and the pituitary gland is damaged the secretion of all the anterior pituitary hormones is reduced with the exception of prolactin which is secreted in excess. Studies in the rat have shown that after transplantation of the pituitary gland the only anterior pituitary hormone to be secreted is prolactin. Such studies confirm the inhibitory effect exerted by the hypothalamus over prolactin secretion.

There is evidence that prolactin is inhibited by increased plasma prolactin levels (short-loop feed-back); this effect is mediated through the hypothalamus. Oestrogens also affect prolactin secretion, and high oestrogen levels, as for example are found during pregnancy, stimulate prolactin production. *In vitro* studies have shown that oestrogens increase the rate of mitosis of prolactin secreting cells; this probably accounts for the pituitary hypertrophy seen during pregnancy. Prolactin levels are higher in females during the reproductive years than in either males or in post-menopausal females.

It is thought that prolactin production is controlled by two hypothalamic factors, prolactin release inhibiting factor (PIF) and prolactin releasing factor. Although it is now recognized that dopamine is the major PIF there is some evidence that there may be other inhibitory factors. Although TRH has been shown to release prolactin it is unlikely that it is the physiological releasing factor.

Prolactin is secreted in a pulsatile fashion and plasma levels may fluctuate markedly over a short period. There is a circadian rhythm in secretion related to sleep. Prolactin levels increase shortly after falling asleep, and fall again in the morning. Prolactin levels also increase during day-time naps. Both physical and emotional stress have been found to elevate prolactin levels. The magnitude of the stress-induced increase is higher in females than in males.

The best known function of prolactin is in the control of lactation and gonadal function. Prolactin is one of several hormones including oestrogens, corticosteroids, insulin and thyroxine involved in the initiation and maintenance of lactation. At parturition there is an immediate decrease in the levels of placental hormones in maternal blood. The withdrawal of these hormones, which during pregnancy have been responsible for the full development of the breast, allows the prolactin (the concentration of which also rises during pregnancy) to initiate the secretion of milk into the duct system (p. 506). Milk does not flow out of the ducts to the nipple unless suckling takes place. If this occurs the tactile stimulation of the nipple results in a reflex release of oxytocin (p. 471) which acts by stimulating contraction of the myoepithelial cells and the ducts. Suckling stimulates the production of prolactin as well as oxytocin so that plasma levels of prolactin remain high throughout lactation, particularly in societies in which no supplementary feeding is used. These high prolactin levels play a part as a contraceptive (p. 506).

Prolactin appears to exert a direct inhibitory effect on the ovaries reducing the production of both oestradiol and progesterone. Conversely gonadal dysfunction in both males and females is frequently associated with high blood levels of prolactin. In the male hyperprolactinaemia is an uncommon finding associated with impotence and galactorrhoea (milk production).

Many drugs affect the production or action of amines in the central nervous system so that the production of prolactin is frequently affected by centrally acting drugs. Elevated prolactin levels, with the consequent effect on breast tissue and gonadal function, are a side-effect commonly seen with these drugs. Conversely any drug that mimics the action of dopamine lowers prolactin levels; *bromocriptine*, derivative of ergot, is widely used for this purpose.

The Posterior Pituitary

The posterior pituitary gland is a prolongation of the floor of the third ventricle. Approximately 100 000 nerve fibres connect the posterior pituitary with the hypothalamus particularly the supra-optic and paraventricular nuclei (Fig. 28.7). The two hormones *oxytocin* and *antidiuretic hormone* (ADH) are synthesized in the hypothalamus, oxytocin mainly in the paraventricular nuclei and ADH largely in the supra-optic nuclei (Fig. 28.18). After elaboration in the hypothalamus they are incorporated into granules with a binding protein, *neurophysin*, of which two forms, specific for oxytocin and vasopressin, are recognized. The granules are approximately 100 nm in diameter and consist of a dense core surrounded by a membrane (Fig. 28.19). Differential ultracentifugation suggests that the hormones are stored in separate granules. The granules pass down the axons of the neurohypophyseal tract to dilated nerve endings in the posterior pituitary from which they enter the blood (Fig. 28.8).

Oxytocin. This peptide hormone has a molecular weight of 1025. It causes uterine contractions; lesions in the neurohypophyseal tract may interfere with parturition. Other results of oxytocin administration include increased uterine mobility during coitus and stimulation of the myoepithelial cells of the ducts of the mammary gland to induce milk ejection. Whether it has a physiological role other than in lactation is uncertain; women with destruction of the neurohypophyseal tract sufficient to produce diabetes insipidus are able to have a normal labour (p. 501). Blood oxytocin levels are high in the fetal cord suggesting that the fetus itself may have a role to play in its own delivery. The function of oxytocin in the male is not known.

The half-life of oxytocin is 1 to 4 minutes. It is metabolized in the liver and kidneys. During pregnancy, increasing levels of a placental enzyme, oxytocinase, can be detected in the blood but its function is unknown.

The release of oxytocin results from depolarization of the neurosecretory cells and is mediated through neural pathways whose afferent components begin in the uterine cervix and the nipple. Oxytocin and ADH are usually secreted together although the relative amounts secreted are related to the nature of the stimulus.

Oxytocin or a synthetic analogue is used to induce labour or to strengthen uterine contractions in a prolonged labour. Care must be given to the rate of administration since even synthetic analogues of oxytocin have some ADH-like properties (Table 28.20). Overdosage may therefore cause water retention.

Antidiuretic hormone (ADH, vasopressin). This is also a peptide (Fig. 28.18) and has a molecular weight of 1102. Its principal function is the control of water reabsorption in the distal convoluted tubule and the collecting ducts of the kidney (p. 252). The mode of action of ADH involves activation of adenyl cyclase and the production of cyclic AMP; cyclic AMP can mimic the action of ADH in the toad bladder and theophylline, which inhibits cyclic AMP breakdown, has an antidiuretic effect. Patients with diabetes insipidus have low urinary levels of cyclic AMP.

In large doses ADH causes contraction of smooth muscle particularly in the blood vessels of the skin and in the splanchnic bed; this leads to a rise in blood pressure. The effects of ADH on smooth muscle are probably not important in physiological concentrations.

Secretion of ADH provides a homeostatic mechanism to maintain the osmolarity of body fluids within a relatively

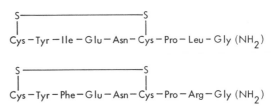

Fig. 28.18 The structures of human oxytocin (above) and antidiuretic hormone (below). Vertebrates all have the same oxytocin but the structure of ADH varies from species to species; in pig ADH for example, the arginine residue is replaced by lysine.

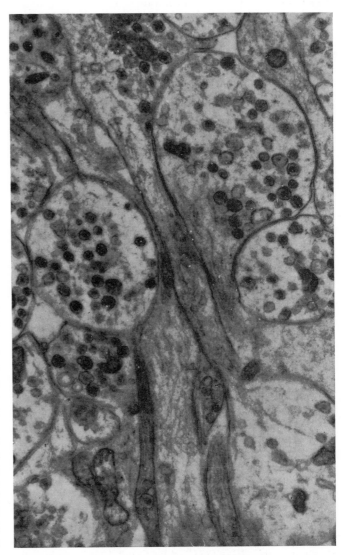

Fig. 28.19 Electron microscopic view of the posterior pituitary of the rabbit to show unmyelinated nerve fibres in longitudinal section and a number of neural swellings. Most of the swellings contain granules about 130 nm in diameter with an electron-dense centre; these are known as neurosecretory granules. Fixed OsO_4, strained $Pb(OH)_2$, × 24 000. (R. Barer, H. Heller & K. Lederis (1963) *Proceedings of the Royal Society B*, **158**, 338–416.)

Table 28.20   Relative potencies of oxytocin and vasopressin

	Oxytocin	Vasopressin
Antidiuretic potency	1	200
Milk ejection activity	100	1

narrow range. Two main types of receptor have been postulated: hypothalamic receptors sensitive to changes in osmolarity (*osmoreceptors*) and baroreceptors, sensitive to changes in blood volume, which are situated in the large thoracic blood vessels. The latter are linked to the hypothalamus by the vagus nerve. ADH is secreted continuously, basal plasma levels being 1 to 5 ng/l. When there is an increase in plasma osmolarity due to dehydration or a fall in blood volume due to haemorrhage, the secretion of ADH increases and the resulting water retention restores the osmolarity or blood volume to normal. ADH cannot be detected in the plasma in patients with diabetes insipidus or in normal subjects after a water load.

The steps involved in the release of ADH from the posterior pituitary are still not clear but the following sequence of events is likely. Reception of an appropriate stimulus produces depolarization of cells in the supra-optic nucleus. The depolarization propagated down the axons in the neurohypophyseal stalk allows an influx of calcium ions into the neurosecretory cell. The neurosecretory granules are extruded through the cell membrane of the axon terminals and enter the capillary blood. Presumably ADH and neurophysin dissociate before the effects on the renal tubules can be produced but the site of dissociation is not known.

ADH has a half-life in the plasma of approximately 5 minutes and is metabolized in the liver and kidneys. ADH lack causes *diabetes insipidus* while a syndrome of excessive ADH secretion is also recognized. These disorders are described in Chapter 15.

Other Hypothalamic and Pituitary Polypeptides

In addition to the releasing and inhibiting factors produced by the hypothalamus and the hormones produced by the anterior and posterior pituitary, a number of other polypeptides are produced in this area. Of particular interest is β-lipotrophin, a single-chain peptide containing 91 amino acids. Various fragments of the β-lipotrophin molecule and of the ACTH molecule (Fig. 28.21) including α-melanocyte stimulating hormone (α-MSH) which is identical to the first 13 amino acids of ACTH and *corticotrophin-like intermediate lobe peptide* (CLIP), which is the C-terminal portion of the ACTH molecule. These two compounds are only found in the human pituitary gland during fetal life and during pregnancy, when a distinct *intermediate lobe* can be found. γ-lipotrophin, the first 58 amino acids of β-lipotrophin, is also secreted by the human pituitary but β-MSH (amino acids 41–58 of β-lipotrophin) has never been found in man; material previously reported as human β-MSH is an artefact of the extraction procedure.

Pharmacological studies into the effects of opiates revealed that the brain itself contained a morphine-like factor. This was isolated and its structure elucidated; it was found to be a

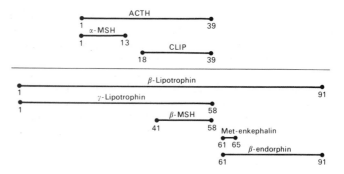

Fig. 28.21   *Above:* relationship between the amino acid sequences of ACTH and related peptides. Sequences are numbered from the amino-terminal (N-terminal). Below: relationship between β-lipotrophin and related peptides.

mixture of two pentapeptides, *met-enkephalin and leu-enkephalin* (Fig. 28.22). The structure of met-enkephalin is contained in β-lipotrophin, forming the first part of the molecule remaining after cleavage to give γ-lipotrophin. The opiate action of the entire 31 amino acid fragment was then studied and found to be more potent than met-enkephalin. The peptides with opiate properties related to β-lipotrophin are generally known as *endorphins* and this 31 amino acid fragment is called β-endorphin. High concentrations of β-endorphin are found in the pituitary gland of those species

Met-enkephalin

H$_2$N-Tyr-Gly-Gly-Phe-Met-COOH

Leu-enkephalin

H$_2$N-Tyr-Gly-Gly-Phe-Leu-COOH

Fig. 28.22   Structures of the enkephalins

with an intermediate lobe. The release of β-endorphin from the pituitary has been shown to be regulated in parallel with ACTH but the function of β-endorphin is still not known; it is possible that these peptides may be involved in the control of mood.

THE THYROID GLAND

The thyroid gland, weighing about 25 g in the healthy adult, consists of an enormous number of closed spherical follicles, the walls of which, in the resting phase of the gland, are composed of a single layer of flattened epithelium. The follicles, which vary in diameter from 0·05 to 0·1 mm, are filled by a structureless semifluid protein material, the 'colloid'. The gland has a very rich blood supply.

The thyroid gland is not essential to life but it is essential for growth and for physical and mental well-being. The gland begins to synthesize thyroxine about the third month of fetal life. At birth it contains large amounts of colloid which diminish during the first few weeks of extra-uterine life. The secretion of thyroid hormones appears to be fairly constant throughout life but hyperplasia with increased secretion occurs at puberty and during pregnancy.

The activity of the thyroid gland is regulated by variations in the plasma levels of thyroid-stimulating hormone (TSH). The immediate action of this hormone is to release thyroid hormone from the gland. Subsequently it increases the uptake of iodine from the blood and promotes hyperplasia of the gland. The output of TSH from the anterior pituitary is itself governed by the plasma levels of the thyroid hormones, a fall in the latter increasing the output and a rise diminishing it. This negative feed-back mechanism is mediated through the production of thyrotrophin releasing hormone (TRH) by the hypothalamus (p. 466).

The thyroid gland contains a large amount of iodine (0·06 per cent), almost all of which is firmly bound to protein either in the cells lining the follicles or in the colloid material within them. The characteristic protein of the colloid, *thyroglobulin*, though mainly found in the thyroid itself, has been found in the neighbouring lymphatic glands and in small amounts in blood. On hydrolysis it yields several iodine-containing derivatives of tyrosine including mono- and di-iodotyrosine, and tetra-iodothyronine (thyroxine). The structures of these compounds are shown in Figure 28.23 in which it can be seen that thyroxine has one asymmetrical carbon atom (**C**). The L-isomer is always more active than the D-isomer.

The thyroid hormones are thyroxine and tri-iodothyronine.

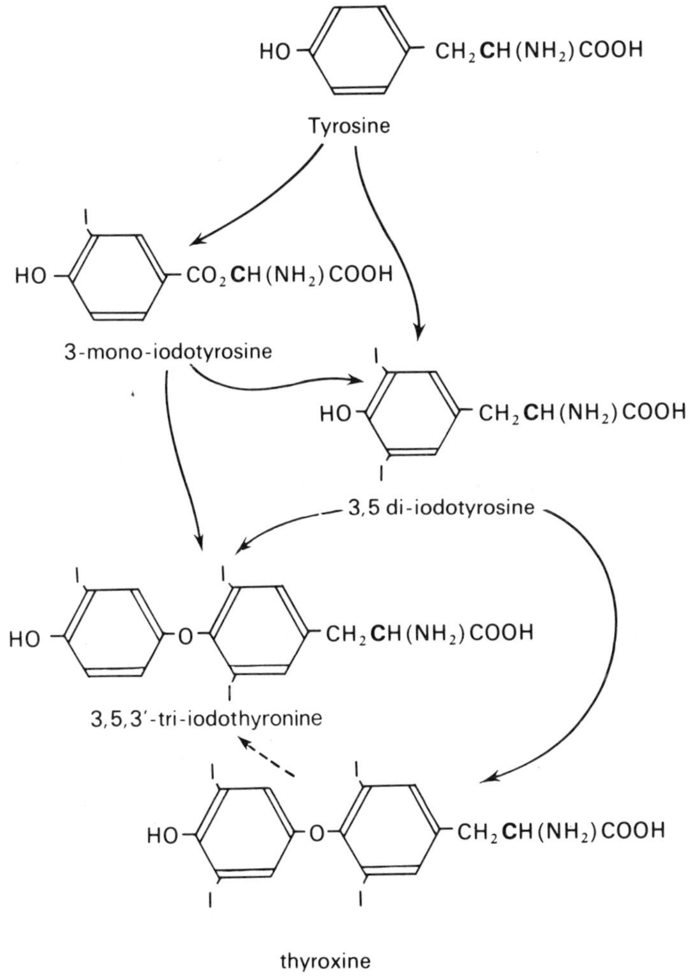

Fig. 28.23 Pathways leading to the synthesis of the thyroid hormones.

Thyroxine was the first to be discovered but tri-iodothyronine is the more potent. For example, it is three to five times more active than thyroxine in raising the oxygen consumption of patients with hypothyroidism and this action occurs much sooner, usually within 4 hours. When administration ceases, its effects rapidly disappear. Approximately one-third of the thyroxine secreted by the thyroid is metabolized in the tissues to tri-iodothyronine which appears to be the active hormone at the cellular level.

In the blood more than 99 per cent of both hormones are bound to proteins: thyroxine to thyroxine binding globulin (TBG), prealbumin and albumin, while tri-iodothyronine is bound to TBG and to albumin. Only about one-third of the total thyroxine binding capacity is taken up in a normal person. In hyperthyroidism more of the binding capacity is taken up while in hypothyroidism less hormone is bound. Many factors, particularly drugs, affect this binding capacity; oestrogens increase it while corticosteroids and androgens decrease it.

The active components of both thyroxine and tri-iodothyronine in the plasma are the very small fractions which are not bound to proteins: approximately 0·03 per cent of thyroxine and 0·5 per cent of the total tri-iodothyronine.

Synthesis of thyroid hormones. In the first stage in the formation of the hormones, inorganic iodide from the plasma is concentrated in the acinar cells of the thyroid. The gland's remarkable powers of accumulating iodide can readily be demonstrated with the aid of ^{131}I. This accumulation is controlled by TSH and reduced by perchlorate or thiocyanate. Normally the iodide becomes organically bound as fast as it is taken up but, after administration of certain anti-thyroid drugs (imidazoles such as carbimazole), the organic combination is blocked and a large amount of iodide remains in inorganic form in the gland (Fig. 28.24).

As iodide is absorbed by the acinar cells it is oxidized to iodine ($2I^- \rightarrow I_2 + 2e$) by an enzyme system requiring the participation of a cytochrome. The iodine never appears as such in the free state but is immediately taken up by the tyrosine of the glandular protein to form mono-iodotyrosine and di-iodotyrosine as residues still incorporated in the protein molecule. These residues then undergo oxidative coupling with removal of one side chain so as to form thyroxine and tri-iodothyronine.

Tri-iodothyronine is also produced by removal of one atom of iodine from thyroxine (Fig. 28.23). The enzyme *iodotyrosine deiodinase* which brings about this reaction is present in most body tissues as well as in the thyroid. It has been estimated that some 80 per cent of the plasma tri-iodothyronine is produced in peripheral tissues and only 20 per cent by the thyroid. Thyroxine is also de-iodinated in the tissues to 3,3′,5′-tri-iodothyronine (reverse T_3) which is physiologically inactive. In normal adults the plasma level of thyroxine (T_4) is 75 to 140 nmol/l, of tri-iodothyronine (T_3) 1·1 to 2·3 nmol/l and of reverse T_3 0·3 to 0·9 nmol/l. High levels of reverse T_3 are found in the blood in the neonatal period.

The thyroxine and tri-iodothyronine produced in the gland itself are still in peptide linkage in the thyrogobulin molecule and are stored in the colloid. Under stimulation by TSH the thyroglobulin of colloid is engulfed by the follicular cells and broken down by lysosomal enzymes to yield thyroxine, tri-iodothyronine and mono- and di-iodotyrosines. The thyroxine and tri-iodothyronine pass into the blood while the iodotyrosines are broken down within the cell to yield iodide which can be used again.

Mode of action of thyroid hormones. The wide range of effects of the thyroid hormones suggests that they may operate by regulating enzymes which control energy metabolism. However, little is yet known of the detailed mode of action of thyroid hormones on tissues beyond the fact that they are taken up by receptors within the nuclei and stimulate protein synthesis probably by enhancing transcription. How such an action leads to the tissue changes associated with the thyroid hormones is quite unknown.

Thyroid hormones are essential for normal protein synthesis; deficiency leads to impaired physical growth while excessive plasma levels of thyroid hormones are associated with excessive protein breakdown.

Thyroid hormones operate in part by enhancing the effects of other hormones. For example breakdown of lipids in adipose tissue is stimulated partly by a direct effect and partly by increasing the tissue's sensitivity to other hormones, notably catecholamines and glucagon.

Diseases of the Thyroid Gland

The isotopes ^{131}I and [132]I are of value in the diagnosis of thyroid disease in man. Forty-eight hours after a single dose (microcuries) is given by mouth in the form of sodium iodide about 80 per cent of the dose has either been taken up by the thyroid or excreted in the urine. A larger proportion is taken up by an overactive than by a normal gland, and this difference can be detected by a suitable counter placed over the gland (Fig. 28.25).

[131]I in much larger doses (millicuries) may be used to treat hyperthyroidism. The high local concentration of radioactive material destroys some secreting cells and also reduces the reproductive capacity of others.

The development of radioimmunoassay has made possible the measurements of concentrations of TSH, thyroxine and tri-iodothyronine in plasma both in subjects with normal thyroid function as well as in patients with thyroid disease. Thyroid releasing hormone (TRH) has also become available and the response of the pituitary to the administration of this substance, as reflected by changes in plasma TSH, is used as a sensitive test of the integrity of the pituitary-thyroid axis (p. 468).

The availability of assays for plasma tri-iodothyronine levels has also allowed the diagnosis of conditions in which excessive amounts of this hormone as distinct from thyroxine are being produced.

Hypothyroidism. Thyroidectomy produces a marked fall in the metabolic rate, with subnormal temperature, slow pulse and respiration and mental apathy. Hypothyroidism in the human infant is described as *cretinism* (Fig. 28.26). Unless treated from an early age the child is small, mentally defective, with coarse, scanty hair and a thick, yellowish scaly skin. A rarer type of cretinism is known which tends to be familial and is associated with an enlarged thyroid gland. In such patients

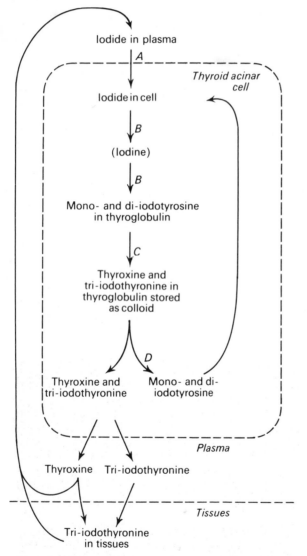

Fig. 28.24 The metabolism of iodine in the thyroid cell to show the actions of TSH and of the antithyroid drugs. Iodine uptake (*A*) is accelerated by TSH and inhibited by thiocyanate or perchlorate. Both steps involved in the iodination of tyrosine (*B*) are inhibited by thiouracil or carbimazole. The oxidative coupling of mono- and diiodotyrosine (*C*) is acclerated by TSH, as is the breakdown of thyroglobulin, to give thyroxine and triiodothyronine(*D*).

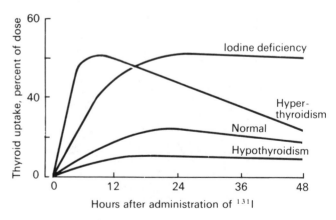

Fig. 28.25 Patterns of uptake of radioactive iodine (^{131}I) by the thyroid in various disorders. (*After* R. Hoffenburg (1970) *Annals of Clinical Biochemistry*, 7, 126.)

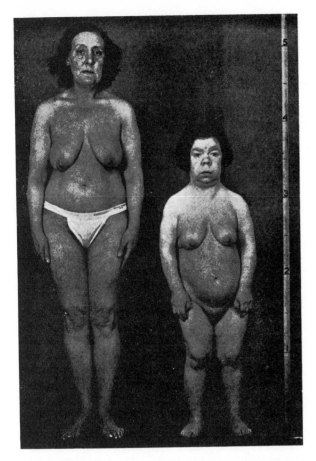

Fig. 28.26 On the right a cretin, aged 38 years, and on the left her normal sister, aged 48. The mental age of the cretin is about 4 years. She has a deep, croaking voice, coarse dry skin and hair. (*By courtesy of A. C. Crooke.*)

there is a defect in one of the enzymes responsible for the synthesis of thyroxine.

Severe hypothyroidism occurring in the adult is called *myxoedema* (Fig. 28.27) because of the puffiness of the hands and face. This is due to a thickening of the skin by the deposit in it of a proteoglycan. Hypothyroidism occurs most commonly in middle-aged women. It is frequently associated with an auto-immune thyroiditis in which antibodies to constituents of thyroid cells can be demonstrated in the blood.

A patient with myxoedema feels cold and has a low metabolic rate. Body temperature and pulse rate are reduced and the weight is increased. All bodily and mental processes are retarded. In primary thyroid failure the plasma TSH is usually raised.

Hyperthyroidism. Administration of an excessive amount of thyroid hormone leads to an increase of the metabolic rate but the body temperature is not usually raised since the extra heat is lost by vasodilatation and sweating. Weight is lost as the result of increased catabolism of tissue protein and oxidation of the stored fat. Similar effects are produced by hyperthyroidism (thyrotoxicosis), an increase in the secretory activity of the thyroid gland often accompanied by enlargement of the gland (a *goitre*). The patient may have nervous excitability, a tremor (Fig. 28.28), breathlessness on exertion, a rapid heart rate and a warm flushed skin. Protrusion of the eyeballs (*exophthalmos*) may also be present and may persist long after the other features have been abolished by treatment. The cause of the exophthalmos is not known.

Some patients with hyperthyroidism have in their blood *thyroid stimulating immunoglobulin* (TSI), an antibody produced by plasma cells and lymphocytes. Iodotyrosines are often present in the plasma of hyperthyroid patients but not in normal subjects.

Goitrogens or antithyroid substances. The action of a goitrogen is due to its ability to diminish the synthesis of thyroid hormone by interference with its production at a number of points. For example, thiocyanates and perchlorates interfere with the uptake of iodine by the gland, while the thiourea and imidazole compounds block the synthesis of

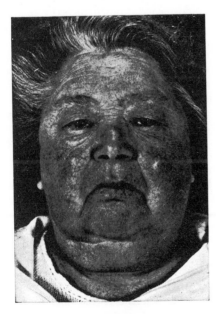

Fig. 28.27 The face of a woman, aged 69, suffering from myxoedema. Note the puffiness, dull expression, scanty eyebrows and dilated vessels on the cheeks. (*By courtesy of W. T. Cooke.*)

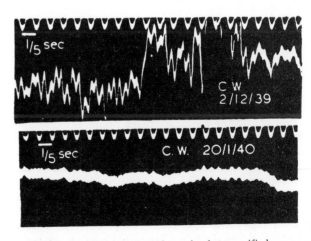

Fig. 28.28 Muscular tremor as shown by the magnified movements of the tip of the extended index finger of a patient, aged 20, with hyperthyroidism before operation (upper tracing), and 45 days after partial removal of the thyroid gland (lower tracing). (S. Lazarus & G. H. Bell (1943) *Glasgow Medical Journal*, 140, 77.)

Fig. 28.29 Endemic goitre in the Western Sudan. Note the massive enlargement of the thyroid gland. (*By courtesy of Dean A. Smith.*)

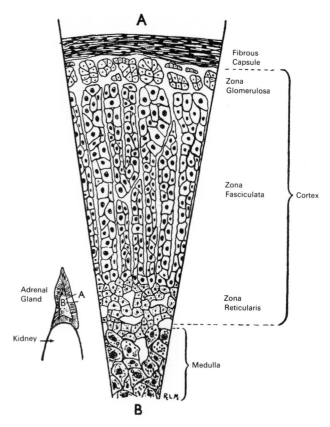

Fig. 28.30 Diagram of adrenal gland showing differentiation into medulla and cortex, the latter being divided into three zones not clearly demarcated from one another. The part of the gland from which the secretion was taken is shown alongside (AB).

organic iodine compounds in the gland. The latter group is useful for the treatment of hyperthyroidism (see Fig. 28.24). One group of drugs, the β-adrenergic blocking drugs (for example propranolol) is not goitrogenic but reduces those symptoms of hyperthyroidism caused by the increased sensitivity to catecholamines.

Endemic goitre. Iodine is essential for the synthesis of the thyroid hormones and a diet severely deficient in iodine leads to an enlargement of the thyroid gland ('goitre') (Fig. 28.29). In districts where the supply of iodine in the diet is deficient a large part of the population may be goitrous, hence the name endemic goitre. Exceptionally, in regions such as the Congo where the deficiency is very severe, hypothyroidism may occur. In many such areas the incidence of goitre has been greatly reduced by the provision of iodine supplements by adding potassium iodide to table salt in the proportion of 1 part KI to 100 000 parts of NaCl.

THE ADRENAL CORTEX

The adrenal (suprarenal) glands contain two different kinds of tissue, *cortex* and *medulla*, which have quite different embryological origins. Removal of both glands is fatal within a few days but all the medullary tissue can be extirpated with little apparent effect; the adrenal cortex is therefore essential to life, while the medulla is not.

The adrenal cortex is made up of three zones (Fig. 28.30) which in most animals are fairly distinct. In man the outermost or glomerular zone is usually irregular and ill-defined, forming islands of cells. The zona fasciculata is of variable width, and is filled with cells rich in lipid. During the preparation of sections for histological examination this lipid may be washed out leaving empty spaces in the cells which are accordingly described as 'clear cells'. The more 'compact' cells of the zona reticularis contain little lipid and form the innermost zone of the cortex.

In patients with pituitary insufficiency the fascicular and reticular zones atrophy and the secretion of cortisol and corticosterone ceases. By contrast, the glomerular zone and the secretion of aldosterone, known to occur in this zone, are unaffected. The fascicular zone stores lipids (principally cholesterol esters) which may be precursors of steroid hormones.

Administration of corticotrophin (ACTH) or exposure to stress increases the production of cortisol and certain other steroids. This increase is accompanied by a fall in the amount of lipid and of ascorbic acid in the cortex and an increase in the size of the gland. In man lipid depletion of the fascicular cells is most pronounced and these cells are transformed into 'compact' reticular zone cells, so that this zone appears to occupy more space in the cortex.

ACTH has little or no effect on the glomerular cells or on aldosterone secretion, which is controlled by the renin-angiotensin system (p. 256).

More than 40 steroids have been isolated from extracts of animal adrenal glands. Many of these compounds are precursors or metabolites of the active hormones. The principal steroid hormones produced by the adrenal cortex contain either 21 or 19 carbon atoms. Those containing 21 carbon atoms are known as corticoids and are further divided into *glucocorticoids* and *mineralocorticoids*. Glucocorticoids influence primarily carbohydrate and protein metabolism, *cortisol* being in man the most active steroid in this group.

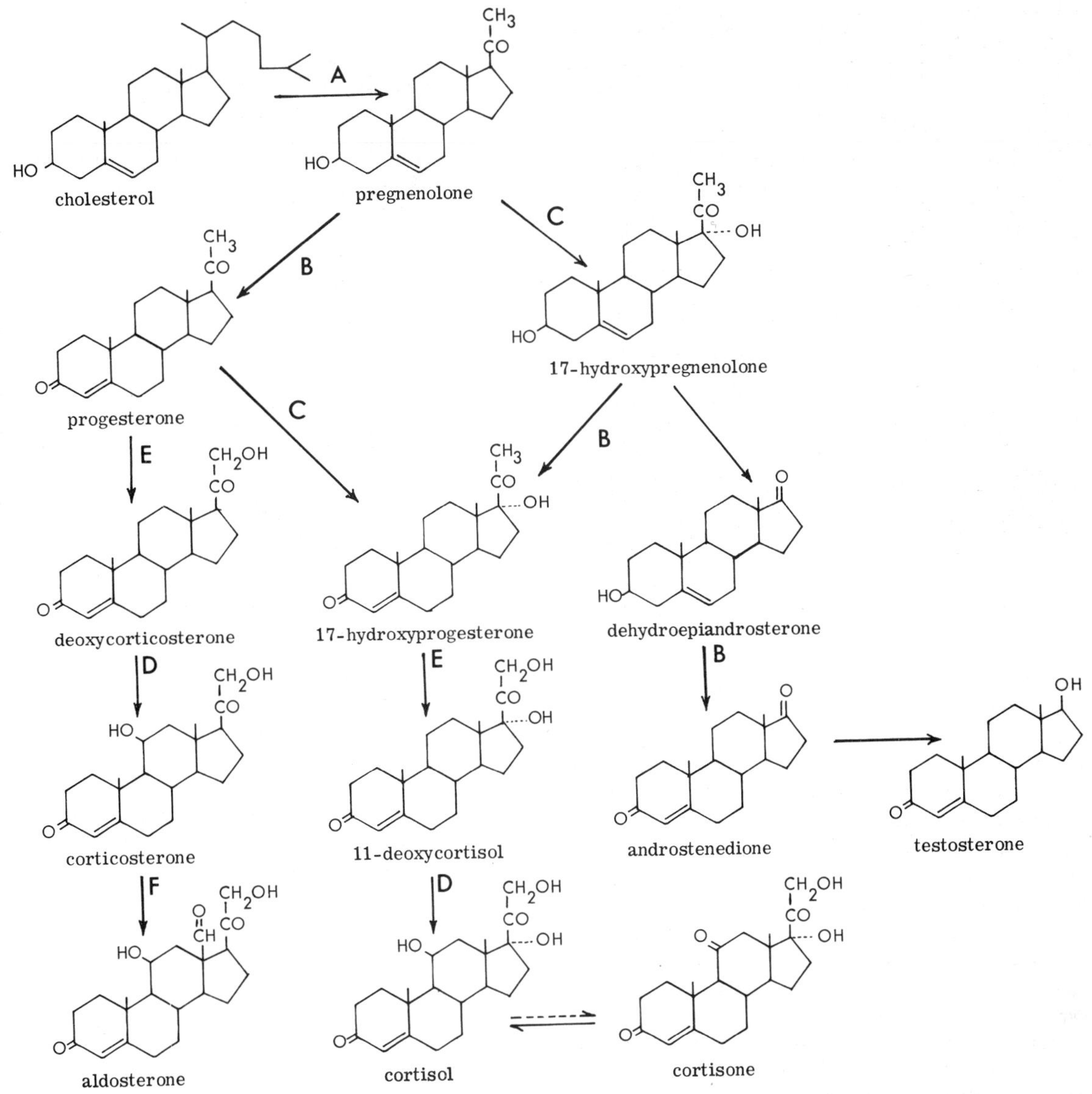

Fig. 28.31 Pathways for the synthesis of adrenal steroids. The enzymes involved are as follows: A, desmolase; B, △5-isomerase 3β-hydroxydehydrogenase; C, 17α-hydroxylase; D, 11β-hydroxylase; E, 21-hydroxylase; F, 18-oxidase. (*After V. H. T. James and J. Landon.*)

Table 28.32 The defects in congenital adrenal hyperplasia

Enzyme defect	Hormone deficiency	Urine excess	Clinical features
3ß-Hydroxydehydrogenase	Cortisol, aldosterone	△5,3ß-ol steroids particularly DHA	Salt loss; male—hypospadias; female—mild virilism
17-Hydroxylase	Cortisol, androgens	Tetrahydrocorticosterone Tetrahydrodeoxycorticosterone	Immature female, hypertension, hypokalaemic alkalosis
21-Hydroxylase	Cortisol, aldosterone	Pregnanetriol	Masculinization, ±salt loss
11-Hydroxylase	Cortisol, aldosterone	Tetrahydro-11-deoxycortisol	Masculinization, hypertension
18-Hydroxylase	Aldosterone	Tetrahydrocorticosterone	Salt loss

Mineralocorticoids are compounds which specifically affect electrolyte metabolism; *aldosterone* is the most active compound in this group. Glucocorticoids such as cortisol also have some mineralocorticoid activity. The adrenal steroid hormones containing only 19 carbon atoms may have androgenic activity and are collectively known as the 'adrenal androgens'. In females the adrenal cortex is the principal source of androgens.

The synthesis of adrenal steroids. Within the adrenal gland cholesterol is the precursor of all adrenal steroids. It may be synthesized there from acetate or derived from the plasma. The metabolic pathways for the synthesis of the adrenal steroids is shown in Figure 28.31. Cholesterol sulphate has also been shown to be converted to various steroid sulphates. Indeed in the adrenal venous blood the concentration of dehydroepiandrosterone sulphate is higher than that of all other steroids but the reason is not known.

Rarely a deficiency of one of the enzymes may occur due probably to a genetic defect. As a result, there is an accumulation of steroid precursors with a deficiency in the formation of cortisol or of aldosterone. The resulting low plasma cortisol level activates the negative feedback mechanism with consequent increased output of ACTH. In turn this causes adrenal hyperplasia and, in some cases, depending on the site of the enzyme defect, increased production of adrenal androgens. This condition is known as *congenital adrenal hyperplasia*.

The commonest defect, 21-hydroxylase deficiency, accounts for about 90 per cent of all cases of congenital adrenal hyperplasia. The site of the enzyme defect may be identified by the detection of metabolites of the cortisol precursors in the urine or the detection of the precursors themselves in the plasma. Table 28.32 illustrates the clinical consequences of some of these uncommon enzyme defects. The condition is treated by administration of replacement doses of glucocorticoids which suppress the excessive output of ACTH, and subsequently reduce androgen production where this occurs. If aldosterone synthesis is impaired as a result of the enzyme deficiency replacement therapy with a synthetic mineralocorticoid such as fludrocortisone is needed.

Glucocorticoids

The most important of these substances, cortisol, secreted in normal adults at a rate of 30 to 90 μmol (10 to 30 mg) per day, but the cortisol secretion rate may be considerably higher during times of 'stress'. The plasma levels of cortisol show a marked circadian variation, being highest before awakening in the morning (4 a.m. to 8 a.m.) and lowest during the early hours of sleep. The peak level lies between 270 and 700 nmol/l falling, between midnight and 3 a.m., to a level of less than half the morning value (and less than 270 nmol/l) (Fig. 28.33). The variation in cortisol secretion is secondary to a variation in ACTH secretion. In turn this is probably the result of a circadian variation in the release of CRF by the hypothalamus. The variation in glucocorticoid level is not influenced by light since it persists in completely blind subjects, but may be altered by changes in the pattern of sleeping and waking as long as these changes are maintained for several days. It may be absent during times of stress and certain abnormalities of the

hypothalamo-pituitary-adrenocortical system such as Cushing's syndrome (see below).

Most of the cortisol secreted by the adrenal cortex is reversibly bound to protein in the blood and is biologically inert, since only free cortisol is physiologically active. At concentrations up to 600 nmol/l about 95 per cent of cortisol is bound to an α-globulin (*transcortin*). Transcortin provides highly specific binding but its capacity is low. When plasma levels of cortisol exceed 600 nmol/l the steroid is bound to albumin; the binding is less specific but the capacity is much greater. Protein binding provides a buffer mechanism which mops up cortisol when the plasma free cortisol levels are high and releases the hormone when the plasma free cortisol level is low. Corticosterone with qualitatively similar activity is secreted in about one tenth the amount of cortisol.

The glucocorticoids are important in the regulation of carbohydrate metabolism. They promote the synthesis of glycogen in the liver and encourage gluconeogenesis from protein by accelerating protein catabolism. These actions are accompanied by a rise in the concentration of glucose in the blood. Cortisol also has anti-inflammatory and anti-allergic properties, although these effects are more obvious when excess cortisol is produced or when synthetic steroids are administered therapeutically. The glucocorticoids also possess some mineralocorticoid properties; they probably act on the distal tubule of the kidney to promote sodium and water retention.

When the adrenals are damaged as a result, for example, of tuberculosis or autoimmune adrenalitis, the output of both cortisol and aldosterone is impaired; the patients have hypoglycaemia and excessive sodium loss in urine. The administration of replacement doses of synthetic glucocorticoids and mineralocorticoids corrects the metabolic abnormalities. Excessive production of cortisol (Cushing's syndrome) or the administration of large amounts of synthetic

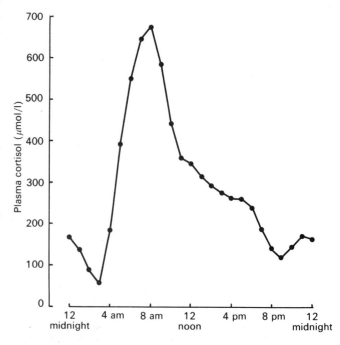

Fig. 28.33 Circadian variation in plasma levels of cortisol.

glucocorticoids may cause hyperglycaemia (or even diabetes mellitus) and excessive sodium and water retention.

In addition to a circadian rhythm of ACTH secretion glucocorticoid secretion is also controlled by the circulating level of cortisol itself. The median eminence of the hypothalamus contains receptors sensitive to the level of plasma cortisol (or synthetic glucocorticoids). A negative feedback mechanism operates by which a plasma glucocorticoid level lower than normal for the time of day induces the release of *corticotrophin releasing factor* (CRF) which is carried to the anterior lobe of the pituitary gland and induces the release of ACTH. The resulting increase in plasma glucocorticoid levels is in turn monitored by the hypothalamic receptors with subsequent reduction in CRF, ACTH and cortisol secretion.

Stress and the hypothalamo-pituitary-adrenal axis. The hypothalamo-pituitary-adrenal axis is involved in maintaining homeostasis during times of 'stress'. The adaptation to 'stress' is a complex and ill-understood phenomenon. One of the responses to stress in a normal subject is an increased output of glucocorticoids which, in an ill-defined manner, allows adjustment to the stress which might be caused by infection, emotion or trauma (including surgery). This response to stress overrides the normal feedback mechanism and also the circadian variation in steroid secretion. Patients with untreated adrenocortical insufficiency are unduly sensitive to the effects of stress; they often have a low blood pressure and gastro-intestinal disturbances. Unless such persons are treated with glucocorticoids and mineralocorticoids, they may die. The stress response is therefore another mechanism controlling steroid release and is thought to originate in the cerebral cortex.

Mineralocorticoids

Aldosterone (Fig. 28.34) is the powerful salt-retaining steroid of the adrenal cortex. Its secretion by the cells of the zona glomerulosa is independent of ACTH and patients with pituitary insufficiency excrete normal amounts of aldosterone. The secretion of aldosterone is governed by changes in extracellular fluid volume or by alterations in the blood volume. A fall in plasma sodium or a rise in plasma potassium also causes an increase in aldosterone production. An enzyme, *renin*, secreted by cells of the juxtaglomerular apparatus in the kidney, catalyses the transformation of a plasma protein angiotensinogen into angiotensin I which, in turn, is converted to angiotensin II. This stimulates the production of aldosterone by the adrenal cortex (p. 478).

Aldosterone secretion is markedly affected by the sodium content of the diet. The secretion rate is usually measured first with the subject on a high and then on a low sodium intake in order to suppress and to stimulate aldosterone production respectively. Normal aldosterone secretion rates are 0·9 to 3·0 μmol/24 hours with salt restriction and 0 to 0·4 μmol/24 hours on a high salt diet.

The production of aldosterone is increased in many oedematous states such as chronic cardiac, hepatic or renal disease (secondary aldosteronism) and in patients with certain uncommon tumours of the adrenal cortex (primary aldosteronism or Conn's syndrome).

The synthetic steroid spironolactone has an anti-aldosterone action; it apparently competes with aldosterone at the renal tubule by blocking sodium retention and potassium excretion.

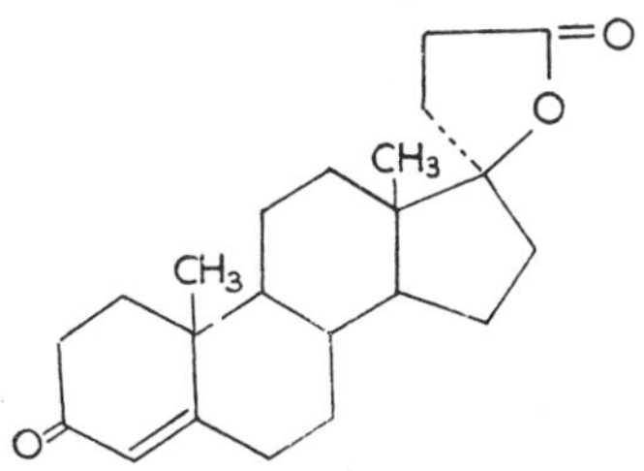

Spironolactone

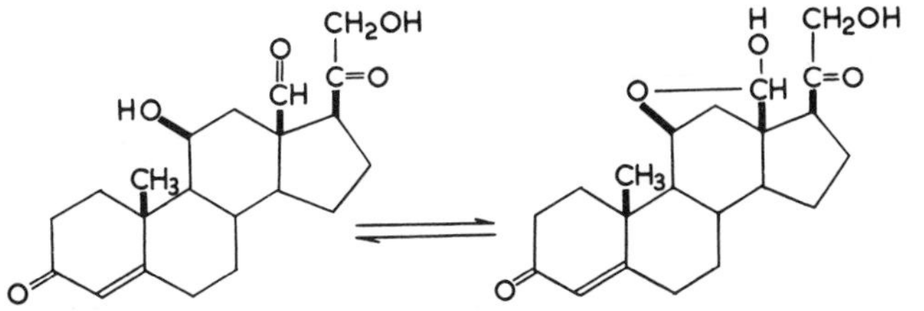

Androgens

The adrenal androgens have only weak masculinizing properties. Although a small amount of testosterone is elaborated by the adrenal, this is relatively unimportant compared with that produced in males by the testes. However, raised circulating testosterone and androstenedione levels may be found in virilized women (Fig. 28.35). In general the importance of the adrenal androgens is not known but they have anabolic properties and may be involved in nitrogen retention.

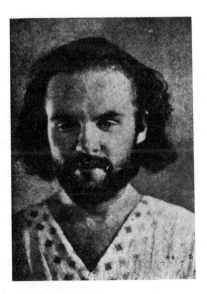

Fig. 28.34 The structure of aldosterone. In solution the aldehyde form (*left*) appears to be in equilibrium with the hemiacetal form (*right*).

Fig. 28.35 Adrenogenital syndrome in a female aged 17 with an adrenal cortical tumour. (F. D. W. Lukens & H. D. Palmer (1940) *Endocrinology*, **26**, 941.)

Disorders of the Adrenal Cortex

When both adrenal glands are destroyed, generally by an autoimmune process or by tuberculous infection, the resulting disorder is known as Addison's disease. The symptoms include weakness and lassitude and the patient may also have a low blood pressure, loss of weight, hypoglycaemia, extreme sensitivity to insulin, excessive loss of sodium and chloride in the urine and an impaired elimination of water by the kidneys. Patients with Addison's disease can usually be kept in good health provided they take some 20 to 30 mg of cortisol ('hydrocortisone') daily by mouth. In many patients the synthetic salt-retaining compound fludrocortisone must also be given (0·05 mg to 0·2 mg daily by mouth).

Fludrocortisone (9α-fluorocortisol)

When the adrenal cortex is overactive the production of any or all of its hormones may be increased. Overactivity may be caused by excess stimulation of the adrenal by increased output of ACTH or by a tumour of the adrenal cortex itself. Tumours of the adrenal cortex may secrete predominantly cortisol, androgens or, more rarely, aldosterone. For example, Cushing's syndrome is the result of overproduction of cortisol and many of its characteristics can also be produced by administration of large doses of cortisol or its analogues; obesity, glycosuria, hirsutism and osteoporosis are its main features.

THE ADRENAL MEDULLA

The adrenal medulla, which has a common origin with the ganglion cells of the sympathetic nervous system from the primitive neuro-ectoderm, consists of masses of polyhedral cells separated by large blood sinuses.

The cells contain granules which are stained blue by ferric chloride or brown by salts of chromic acid (*chromaffin tissue*). Chromaffin tissue is also present, especially in infants, along the aorta near the origin of the inferior mesenteric artery (organ of Zuckerkandl) and chromaffin cells are present in human skin, scattered around nerves and blood vessels, and throughout the alimentary canal (enterochromaffin cells). The adrenal medulla is richly supplied by sympathetic nerve filaments derived mainly from the greater splanchnic nerve. The efferent fibres are myelinated preganglionic fibres; the cells of the medulla correspond to the sympathetic ganglion cells and their post-ganglionic fibres. Afferent impulses can be detected in small filaments of the adrenal nerve; their frequency decreases after intravenous injection of adrenaline, noradrenaline or acetylcholine or stimulation of the splanchnic nerve.

The hormones of the medulla are easily extracted and when injected into animals they produce a sharp rise of blood

pressure. This was one of the first hormonal effects to be discovered. In 1894 Schäfer and Oliver injected a watery extract of the adrenal into a dog and obtained an immediate but transient rise of blood pressure. It was later found that this property belonged to the medulla only and in 1900 adrenaline (epinephrine) was isolated. Much later it was found that normal adrenal tissue from man and many other animals also contains *noradrenaline* (norepinephrine). These hormones are often referred to together as *catecholamines*. The ratio of adrenaline to noradrenaline in human adrenals is 4:1.

adrenaline

noradrenaline

Adrenaline in solution is readily oxidized and inactivated but blood and tissue fluids contain reducing agents, such as glutathione and ascorbic acid, which can protect it from rapid oxidation.

Adrenaline and noradrenaline are metabolized in the tissues in two stages: methylation to the inactive 3-methoxy derivatives and oxidative deamination by monoamine oxidase (Fig. 28.36). The second step is inhibited by the monoamine oxidase inhibitor iproniazid, an antidepressant drug.

The steps by which adrenaline is synthesized by the chromaffin tissue are outlined in Figure 28.36. The rate-limiting step is that catalysed by tyrosine hydroxylase; this enzyme is induced by the stimulation of the preganglionic nerves. Catecholamines are stored within the cell in granules which also contain ATP and a specific protein. Both in sympathetic nerves and in the adrenal medulla, the hormone is released by the extrusion of granules from the cells (*exocytosis*).

The medullary secretion is under the control of the splanchnic nerves which are cholinergic, that is they act by liberating acetylcholine (ACh) from their endings in the medulla. ACh depolarizes the chromaffin cells and increases their uptake of calcium which in some way causes the release of the granules containing adrenaline and noradrenaline. Some, but not all, of the adrenal medulla receives its blood supply from a capillary plexus which has already passed through the adrenal cortex. In this way adrenal cortical steroids influence medullary activity particularly in promoting the conversion of noradrenaline to adrenaline.

Neither complete removal of all medullary tissue nor denervation of the adrenals, which reduces the output of adrenaline and noradrenaline, handicaps the animal seriously if it is not exposed to stress. In other words the adrenal medulla, though important in an emergency and in adverse environmental conditions, is not essential to life.

The effects of injection of adrenaline or noradrenaline are dealt with in Chapter 25.

Plasma levels of noradrenaline and adrenaline can be determined either by chemical techniques or with a bioassay using organs which respond differently to the two substances. For example, the cat's blood pressure is more easily raised by noradrenaline, while adrenaline produces a greater relaxation of the rat's uterus. It should be emphasized here that the vascular system of man is more sensitive to both adrenaline and noradrenaline than that of other species and this should be borne in mind whenever an attempt is made to apply to man conclusions drawn from animal experiments.

The adrenal vein of the cat usually contains more noradrenaline than adrenaline. When the carotid arteries are clamped there is reflex vasoconstriction and the adrenal effluent contains mostly noradrenaline. If, however, a painful stimulus is applied more adrenaline is secreted. In hypoglycaemia, adrenaline is secreted; in hyperglycaemia there is a reduction of the adrenaline output with no change in the noradrenaline output. Denervation of the cat's adrenal reduces the noradrenaline output to one-third. Folkow and von Euler found that stimulation of one area of the hypothalamus caused mainly adrenaline to appear in the effluent whereas stimulation of another area released mainly noradrenaline. These findings imply that adrenaline and noradrenaline are released separately and histochemical tests suggest that there may be two sets of cells in the adrenal medulla, one responsible for secreting adrenaline and the other for secreting noradrenaline.

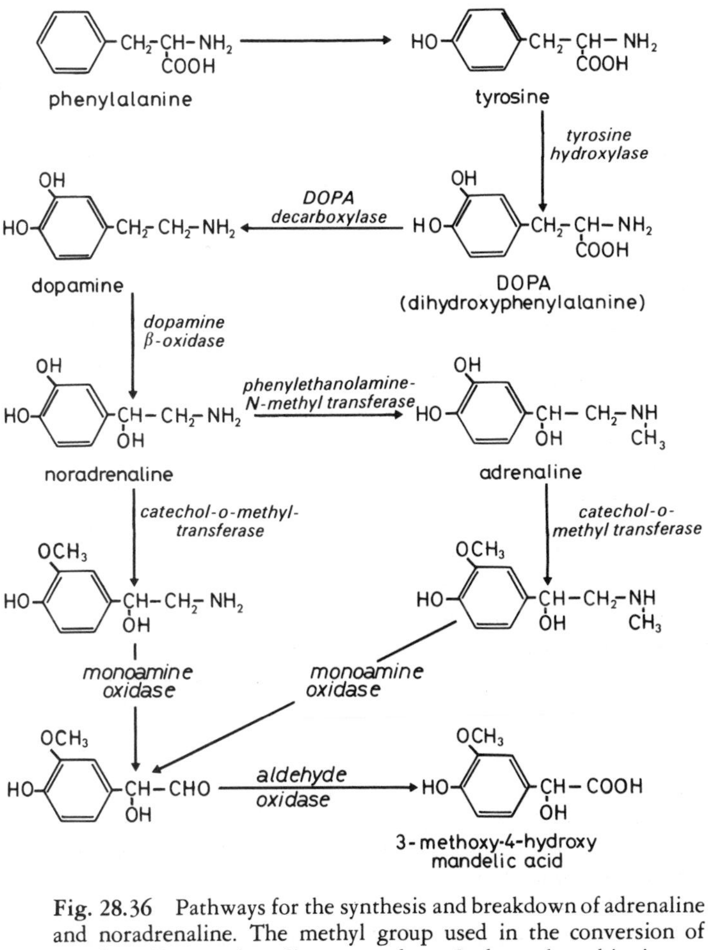

Table 28.37 Urinary excretion of catecholamines in man

Condition	Urinary excretion in pmol/min	
	Adrenaline	Noradrenaline
Rest	11–35	95–160
Mild excercise	2 times	2 times
Strenuous excercise	10 times	10 times
Mental stress	Increased	No effect
Insulin hypoglycaemia	10 times	No effect
Tilt, recumbent to head up	Little change	Increased
After adrenalectomy	0	40–80
Chromaffin cell tumours	Up to 910	Up to 36000
Myocardial infarction	Up to 1200	Up to 1200

In man at rest plasma contains about 1·5 nmol/l noradrenaline and about 0·3 nmol/l adrenaline. The urinary excretion of free catecholamines (Table 28.37) provides further information on the activity of the adrenal medulla.

The absence of adrenaline from the urine after adrenalectomy suggests that the urinary adrenaline comes from the medulla; the urinary noradrenaline output continues and must therefore, come from other sources such as the adrenergic nerves. In strenuous exercise the increase in output is correlated with fatigue rather than with the amount of work.

On the basis of these findings it seems likely that the two hormones have different roles. Adrenaline, by producing vasoconstriction in the skin and vasodilatation in the muscles, moves blood from the skin to the muscles; it stimulates metabolism and mobilizes glycogen as glucose. These reactions are valuable for 'fight or flight', the emergency function suggested by Cannon. Noradrenaline on the other hand produces a general vasoconstriction (except in the coronary arteries) but it has little effect on metabolism. Noradrenaline may be regarded as a hormone for maintenance of blood pressure.

Disorders of the adrenal medulla. Hypofunction of the adrenal medulla has not been recognized as producing any clear-cut clinical syndrome. Actively secreting tumours (*phaeochromocytomata*) of the chromaffin cells of the adrenal medulla or of the organs of Zuckerkandl produce large quantities of noradrenaline with a small amount of adrenaline, and their discharge at intervals into the blood may produce elevations of arterial pressure.

THE PINEAL GLAND

The pineal gland, often visible in X-rays of the skull because of its tendency to calcify, is a small structure about 8 mm long and 4 mm wide on the dorsal aspect of the superior colliculi. The gland contains much serotonin (5-HT) which is converted to melatonin (*N*-acetyl-5-methoxytryptamine). Melatonin is the most potent substance yet found to constrict the melanocytes of the frog's skin.

In mammals melatonin secretion is increased by exposure to darkness and inhibited by light; melatonin seems to have a role in the control of seasonal behaviour such as mating and hibernation. This effect does not seem to involve a direct connexion with the optic tracts but is mediated by

Fig. 28.36 Pathways for the synthesis and breakdown of adrenaline and noradrenaline. The methyl group used in the conversion of noradrenaline to adrenaline comes from *S*-adenosyl methionine.

β-adrenergic fibres in the sympathetic nervous system. There are also nervous connexions to and from the hypothalamus. In man the function of melatonin is unknown but plasma levels are higher at midnight than at noon and this is related to sleep, particularly REM sleep (p. 397), rather than to darkness. Plasma melatonin levels also vary with the menstrual cycle; high values are found during menstruation and low values at the time of ovulation. Tumours which destroy the pineal in boys may cause precocious puberty, while pineal tumours that secrete melatonin are associated with a diminution of gonadal function.

'LOCAL HORMONES'

Great interest is being shown at present by physiologists and pharmacologists in substances which are released locally and have local effects, such as vasodilatation or vasoconstriction, in the surrounding tissue. The local hormones include the prostaglandins, histamine, 5-hydroxytryptamine, bradykinin, adrenaline, noradrenaline and acetylcholine.

Histamine. Histamine is synthesized by the decarboxylation of histidine in the mast cells of the tissues or the basophils of the blood. Like noradrenaline it is stored within the cell in granules which are released from the cell surface.

histamine

Histamine causes an increase in capillary permeability, constriction of postcapillary venules, dilatation of arterioles, contraction of smooth muscle in bronchi or intestine and stimulation of mucous gland secretion. All these actions of histamine can be blocked by antihistamine drugs; the stimulatory action of histamine on gastric acid secretion cannot be blocked in this way but drugs such as cimetidine, which specifically block histamine receptors in the gastric mucosa, have been discovered (p. 59). While there is increasing evidence that histamine plays a part in the normal control of gastric secretion, the physiological function of histamine at other sites is uncertain. Histamine plays a part in a number of diseases such as asthma and urticaria.

5-Hydroxytryptamine. The serum obtained after blood clots has vasoconstrictor properties due to 5-hydroxytryptamine (5-HT, serotonin) which is released from damaged platelets and may contribute to haemostasis. Human blood normally contains 90 to 180 μg 5-HT per litre; almost all of this is in the platelets.

5-Hydroxytryptamine is also found in brain (0·2 μg/g). Its function in the brain is not understood but in experimental animals, 5-HT depletion is associated with retardation of learning, suppression of the rapid eye movements seen in sleep and an increase in sexual activity.

Much of the 5-HT in blood seems to be derived from the argentaffin cells of the gastrointestinal tract since the concentration is much lower after large parts of the intestine have been removed at operation. The intestinal mucosa contains about 6 μg per g of 5-HT.

5-HT is derived from dietary tryptophan by preliminary hydroxylation to 5-hydroxytryptophan which is then decarboxylated. It is oxidized in the tissues to 5-hydroxyindoleacetic acid (5-HIAA) under the influence of monoamine oxidase. Some 5 to 10 mg of 5-HIAA are normally excreted in the urine every 24 hours but when there is a tumour of the argentaffin cells of the small intestine (carcinoid tumour) very much larger amounts of 5-HIAA are excreted in the urine and the concentration of 5-HT in the blood may also be raised.

A large number of antagonists of 5-HT are known, one of the most important being lysergic acid diethylamide (LSD). If 30 μg of LSD are taken by mouth, mental disturbances and hallucinations may result. Monoamine oxidase inhibitors increase the amount of 5-HT in the brain; they are used in the treatment of depression.

Prostaglandins. The prostaglandins are fatty acid derivatives containing 20 carbon atoms. They were originally identified in prostatic secretions but are now known to be present in all tissues. Prostaglandins are synthesized from certain 20-carbon essential fatty acids such as arachidonic acid and have a structure which includes a five-membered ring and at least two oxygen atoms (Fig. 28.38).

Almost all prostaglandins are synthesized at their site of action and are rapidly inactivated by enzymes found in all tissues. The lung and liver are particularly active in removing prostaglandins from the plasma.

Although minute amounts of prostaglandins have been shown to have striking actions on tissues, their physiological roles are still uncertain. The pharmacological actions include effects on intestinal, uterine and bladder motility, on acid secretion by the stomach, on sperm motility, on renal blood flow (p. 258), on the heart, on capillaries, on bronchi and on spinal reflexes. In many cases different prostaglandins have opposing actions. For example PGE- and PGA- series prostaglandins reduce blood pressure while PGF prostaglandins increase it. Prostaglandins are also concerned in inflammatory reactions. Prostaglandins modify the response of tissues to hormones probably by altering the cyclic AMP response.

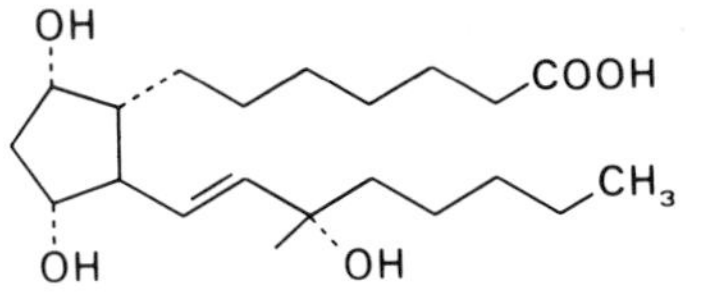

Fig. 28.38 Structures of two typical prostaglandins.

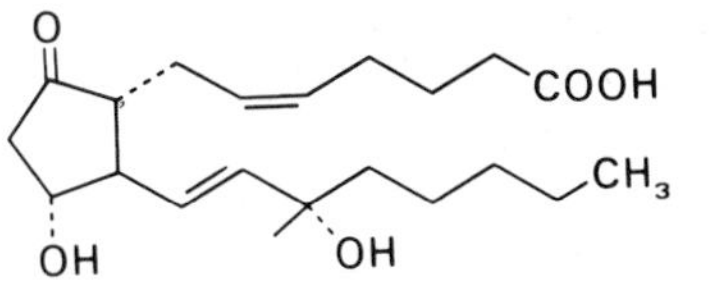

Two derivatives of prostaglandin, prostacyclin and thromboxane play an important part in normal haemostasis. (p. 120).

The kinins. The kinins are a group of peptides liberated from plasma proteins ('kininogens') by endogenous enzymes ('kininogenases' or 'kallikreins'). The principal kinin in plasma is *bradykinin* with the sequence:

Arg-Pro-Pro-Gly-Phe-Ser-Pro-Phe-Arg.

The kinins cause vasodilatation and hypotension when administered systemically. While they may have a role in some antigen-antibody reactions and in haemostasis, their physiological function is still unknown.

REFERENCES

Besser G M 1977 The hypothalamus and pituitary. Clinics in Endocrinology and Metabolism 6: 1–281
Bomboy J D, Salmon W D 1975 Somatomedin. Clinical Orthopaedics 108: 228–240
British Medical Journal 1977 Iodine and the thyroid. BMJ 2: 1566
Chard T 1975 The posterior pituitary gland. Clinical Endocrinology 4: 89–106
De Groot L J, Niepomniszcze H 1977 Biosynthesis of thyroid hormones. Metabolism 26: 665–718
De Groot L J, Stanbury J B 1975 The thyroid and its diseases, 4th edn. Wiley, New York
Edwards C R W 1975 Diabetes insipidus. In: Lant A F (ed) Advanced medicine symposium II. Pitman, London, p 276–288
Evered D C 1976 Diseases of the thyroid. Pitman, London
Ezrin C, Godden J O, Volpé R, Wilson R (eds) 1973 Systematic endocrinology. Harper & Row, Hagerstown, Md. and London
Hall R, Anderson J, Smart G A, Besser M 1974 Fundamentals of clinical endocrinology, 2nd edn. Pitman, London
Harland W A, Orr J S 1975 Thyroid hormone metabolism. Academic Press, London
Harris G W 1955 Neural control of the pituitary gland. Arnold, London
Kahlson G, Rosengren E 1972 Histamine: entering physiology. Experientia 28: 993–1002
Landsberg L 1977 Catecholamines. Clinics in Endocrinology and Metabolism 6: 3
Malkinson A 1975 Hormone action. Chapman & Hall, London
Martin J B, Reichlin S, Brown G M 1977 Clinical neuroendocrinology. Davis, Philadelphia
Martini L, Besser G M 1977 Clinical neuroendocrinology. Academic Press, New York
Montgomery D A D, Welbourn R B 1975 Medical and surgical endocrinology. Arnold, London
Page I H 1969 Serotonin. Wiley, Chichester
Randle P J, Denton R M 1974 Hormones and cell metabolism. Oxford University Press
Relkin R 1976 The pineal. Lunesdale House, Lancaster
Rickenberg H V (ed) 1974 Biochemistry of hormones. Butterworth, London
Ross E J 1975 Aldosterone and aldosteronism. Lloyd Luke, London
Sachs B A (ed) 1978 The brain and the endocrine system. Medical Clinics of North America 62: 2
Sterling R, Lazarus J H 1977 The thyroid and its control. Annual Review of Physiology 39: 349–371
Thompson E B, Lippman M E 1974 Mechanism of action of glucocorticoids. Metabolism 23: 159–202
Thomson J A 1974 Clinical tests of thyroid function. Crosby Lockwood Staples, St Albans
Tixier-Vidal A, Farquhar M G (eds) 1975 The anterior pituitary. Academic Press, New York
Vale W, Rivier C, Brown M 1977 Regulatory peptides of hypothalamus. Annual Review of Physiology 39: 473–527
Williams R H 1974 Textbook of endocrinology, 5th edn. Saunders, Philadelphia

29 Reproduction

Reproduction involves transmission to the next generation of genetic material that results in the offspring having the characteristics of the species and of an individual within the species. The genetic material is carried on *chromosomes* in highly specialized cells called *gametes*. Male gametes, spermatozoa, are produced in the testes, female gametes, ova, are produced in the ovaries. The fusion of a spermatozoon with an ovum combines the genetic material from the mother and from the father and begins the process of development which results in the formation of a new individual.

In order that fusion of a spermatozoon and an ovum can take place, a complex series of events has to occur. In the male this involves the continuous production of vast numbers of spermatozoa and their storage and transport, as well as the sequence of events that culminates in the delivery of the sperms in a suitable medium to the correct site (the posterior vaginal vault) often enough to make conception likely. This sequence requires normal libido (which depends on endocrine and psychogenic factors), the erection of the penis (dependent on vascular, nervous and psychogenic factors), penetration, orgasm (dependent on psychogenic and neurogenic processes), and ejaculation, which involves neuromuscular co-ordination and the mixing of spermatozoa with the other components of semen. These other components depend upon the correct functioning of the accessory sex organs, especially the prostate and seminal vesicles.

In the female ova must be produced regularly enough to allow conception and the secretions of the genital tract must permit the passage of spermatozoa and their access to the ovum. The lining of the uterus must be in a suitable condition to allow the newly fertilized ovum to embed and then the embryo has to be sustained until it is ready for independent existence.

SPERMATOGENESIS

The testes have two main functions: the production of spermatozoa and the production of the male steroid hormones.

The testes develop during embryonic life in the abdominal cavity. The gubernaculum testis (a mesenchymal structure not containing muscle) connects each to the area of the skin which later forms the scrotum. As development proceeds the testes travel to the scrotum which they normally reach about the eighth month of intrauterine life. Sometimes this process is delayed and the testes are retained in the abdominal cavity after birth (*cryptorchidism*). The incidence of undescended testis at birth is about 10 per cent and at one year about 2 per cent. Most of those whose testes have not descended by one year need surgical treatment. The cutaneous muscle of the scrotum, the *dartos muscle*, by contracting when the environment is cold and relaxing when it is warm so regulates the distance between the testes and the groin that they are kept 2 to 4°C below the temperature of the abdominal cavity. At this temperature

spermatogenesis proceeds normally. Spermatozoa are not formed when the testes remain in the abdominal cavity.

Each adult testis is an oval body weighing about 25 g covered by the tunica albuginea, a membrane of fibrous tissue, containing about 750 convoluted *seminiferous tubules*. On cross-section these tubules, each of which is about 70 cm long and 200 μm in diameter, show a basement membrane on which three irregular layers of epithelial cells can be distinguished (Fig. 29.1). The outermost layer of cubical cells or *spermatogonia* give rise by cell division to the second layer, the *spermatocytes*, which are large cells with large nuclei. Two types of spermatocyte are found in this layer, namely the primary spermatocytes containing the somatic or diploid number of chromosomes and the secondary spermatocytes formed from them by meiosis (Fig. 29.2). The nucleus of the spermatid forms the head of the spermatozoon; the Golgi complex forms the cap or acrosome which contains proteases. During this transformation the spermatids cluster around the *supporting cells of Sertoli* which produce an androgen-binding protein and are a major site of hormone action. The spermatozoa (Fig. 29.3) leave the Sertoli cells and lie around the inner margin of the germinal epithelium where they can easily be recognized by their densely staining heads and long curved tails pointing into the lumen of the tubule. At this stage they are immature, being not yet capable of fertilizing an ovum. About 10^7 spermatozoa are produced per gram of testis per day. The time required for spermatogenesis is about 70 days.

Spermatozoa are first produced at puberty and spermatogenic activity is maintained into old age so that there is no definite end to reproductive life in the male. Both FSH and testosterone are necessary for spermatogenesis. The germinal cells are easily damaged by ischaemia. Obstruction of the blood supply for more than four hours leads to irreversible damage to spermatogenic tissue.

From the seminiferous tubules (Fig. 29.4) the spermatozoa pass into the *rete testis*, a series of channels in the fibrous stroma of the posterior part of the testis. About a dozen efferent ductules pass from the upper part of the rete testis into a single canal some six metres long which by its convolutions make up the *epididymis* in which the spermatozoa mature and are stored until ejaculation takes place. Spermatozoa are also stored in the ampulla of the vas deferens. Production continues whether or not ejaculation occurs; spermatozoa not ejaculated are reabsorbed in the vas deferens.

Bilateral vasectomy (removal of a short portion of each vas deferens with ligature of the open ends) is frequently used as a means of sterilization. It causes no loss of weight of the testis nor change in its histology; spermatogenesis continues and spermatozoa collect in the epididymis where they are taken up by phagocytosis. The prostate and seminal vesicles are unaffected. If, even many years later, the vasa are reunited, in many cases sperms reappear in the semen and fertility is restored.

The vas deferens rises up over the brim of the pelvis and passes down to the *prostate gland* at the base of the urinary

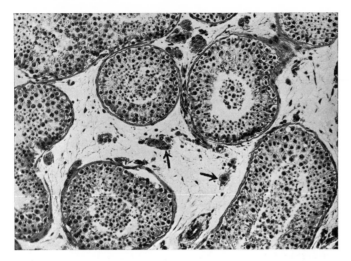

Fig. 29.1 Normal adult male testis. Note especially the intensive proliferative activity in every tubule, the thin basement membranes, and the relatively scanty interstitial (Leydig) cells (examples are arrowed) in the interstitial tissue. This is surgical biopsy and most of the loose cells in the centre of each tubule are the result of pressure during removal: however, the minute dots of spermatozoon heads can be recognized among them. ×105. (*By courtesy of B. Lennox.*)

bladder. Here it is joined by the duct of the *seminal vesicle* to form the ampulla and the ejaculatory duct which passes through the prostate and enters the prostatic urethra. The seminal vesicles do not normally store spermatozoa. The prostate, surrounding the first part of the urethra, is a glandular organ containing much muscle tissue and numerous acini which communicate with the prostatic urethra by about a dozen small ducts. About 2·5 cm distally in the penile part of the urethra are the openings of the ducts of the two bulbo-urethral glands.

Semen

The composition of semen varies greatly between individuals and from time to time in one individual, a fact which is not surprising when one considers its several sources—the testis, the prostate and the seminal vesicles. At an average ejaculation 2 to 5 ml of semen containing 40 to 100 million spermatozoa per ml are emitted. A figure of 20 million spermatozoa per ml is often quoted as the dividing line between fertility and infertility. However many fertile men have counts below this and many infertile men have higher counts. The principal measurable parameters of semen are volume, pH, sperm count, sperm motility and morphology. It may be that these are not the most important factors for the achievement of fertility.

From 60 to 80 per cent of the sperms are of normal shape and, after incubation for one hour at 37°, 50 per cent are motile. The sperms from the testis collect in the dilated end of the vas deferens until they are swept out by fluid from the seminal vesicles. Less than 10 per of the ejaculate is spermatozoa, the remainder being seminal fluid and prostatic secretions. The volume of the semen is unaffected by bilateral

vasectomy. Semen clots soon after ejaculation but it is liquefied shortly after by fibrinolysis; then the spermatozoa become fully motile.

About 70 per cent of the semen is *seminal fluid* produced by the seminal vesicles. This has a pH of about 7.4 and contains fructose, citrate, ascorbic acid, prostaglandins and various enzymes. The fructose is a source of energy for the spermatozoa. The function of the prostaglandins in semen is not yet understood. The seminal fluid acts as an activator and as a diluent for the spermatozoa which are tightly packed in the epididymis. Seminal fluid contains hyaluronidase which acts on hyaluronic acid found in mucus and so allows the sperms to pass more readily through the cervix to the uterus and uterine tubes.

The thin prostatic secretion forms about 20 per cent of the volume of semen. It is colourless and slightly acid (pH 6·5) due to the presence of citric acid; it contains substances important for sperm mobility, notably albumin and the proteolytic enzymes fibrinolysin and fibrinogenase. It also contains acid phosphatase and an antibacterial substance of low molecular weight.

Spermatozoa after ejaculation obtain energy from the seminal fluid and vaginal secretions by the anaerobic breakdown of fructose to lactate. Spermatozoa are also able to

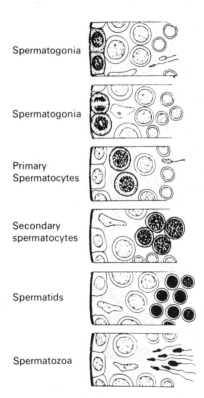

Spermatogonia

Spermatogonia

Primary Spermatocytes

Secondary spermatocytes

Spermatids

Spermatozoa

Fig. 29.2 A wave of spermatogenesis in seminiferous tubules, shown diagrammatically. Cells in a single sequence are shown darkly. (*From* D. L. Gardner and T. C. Dodds (1976) *Human Histology* 3rd edition. Edinburgh: Churchill Livingstone.)

oxidize fructose to CO_2 and water if oxygen is available. The spermatozoa within the epididymis are, because of the lack of oxygen and glycolysable sugar, metabolically inactive; they can survive in this situation for perhaps a month. Outside the body, spermatozoa survive only a short time at body temperature, a few days at 4°C and a few years at −79°C.

Hormones of the Testis

The testis grows a little during the first two years of life and remains about 1 g in weight till about 11 years of age when there is a rapid spurt to 15 g reached at 17 years. The prostate and the other accessory glands increase in size at the same time. The first external sign of puberty is rapid growth of the penis and the development of pubic hair (p. 511), but active spermatozoa may be detected in the urine many months earlier. About the middle of pubescence the larynx enlarges and the pitch of the voice falls about an octave. The vocal folds lengthen by 10 mm, that is by almost half their original length. At this time the muscles develop rapidly and the pattern of behaviour alters. There is considerable variation in the age of onset of puberty; for most boys it is between 10 and 14.

These changes depend on the testes since they do not occur if these organs are removed before puberty. The patient, known as a eunuch, usually becomes a tall man because of the prolonged period of growth of the long bones. Often rather fat, he retains the treble voice of the boy, the penis remains small and hair does not grow over the face and abdomen in the typical masculine fashion; the common masculine form of baldness does not develop and sebaceous secretion is diminished. Such a person is sterile and seldom has any sexual desire (libido).

Castration after puberty produces muscular weakness and atrophy of the prostate and seminal vesicles. Although psychological changes are common, sexual desire may be retained, but the individual is sterile although he is potent, so that is he is able to copulate.

Testosterone and other androgens. Testosterone, a potent androgen, is usually regarded as the hormone responsible for transforming the boy into a man. It is produced by the

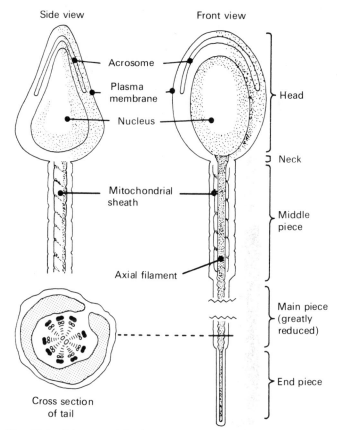

Fig. 29.3   Diagram of the fine structure of a spermatozoon. (*From* D. L. Gardner and T. C. Dodds (1976) *Human Histology* 3rd edition. Edinburgh: Churchill Livingstone.)

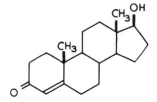

Testosterone

interstitial cells or Leydig cells which contain yellow pigment granules and possess a rich supply of nerves. They lie scattered between the seminiferous tubules (Fig. 29.1). Exposure to X-rays destroys the seminiferous tubules without affecting the interstitial cells which, by producing testosterone, maintain the secondary sex characteristics. The metabolic pathways for the synthesis of testosterone are described in Figure 29.5. Testosterone has been found in the spermatic vein blood in amounts ranging from 1·3 to 5·5 μmol/l. The total production is about 50 μmol per day. The average concentrations of testosterone in peripheral blood plasma in young men are 9 to

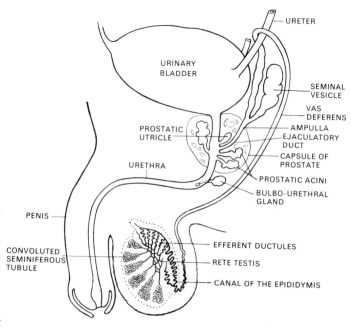

Fig. 29.4   Diagram of the male sex organs.

40 nmol/l, falling to about half after the age of 50, and for women 0·7 to 2·8 nmol/l. Both follicle stimulating hormone (FSH, p. 468) and luteinizing hormone (LH, p. 468) together with testosterone are necessary for spermatogenesis. In other words spermatogenesis depends on interstitial cell function. At puberty LH stimulates the interstitial cells and the plasma testosterone is increased ten times. The output of LH is in turn inhibited by the feed-back action of testosterone, while the output of FSH is inhibited by a peptide hormone *inhibin* produced by the Sertoli cells. When the testes are removed these inhibitory influences are lost. Malnutrition causes a fall in the production of testosterone by inhibiting the production of FSH and LH by the anterior pituitary.

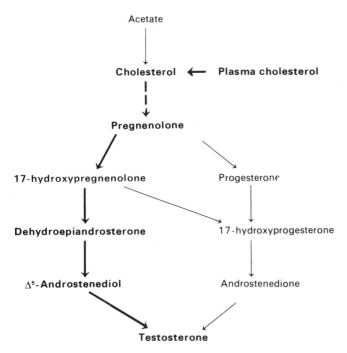

Fig. 29.5 Principal pathways for the synthesis of testosterone in the testis. The pathway shown with heavy lettering and arrows is probably the most important.

Both in males and females the adrenal cortex produces small amounts of androgens: testosterone, androsterone and dehydroepiandrosterone. The 17-oxosteroids found in the urine after castration come from this source.

Oestrogens. Feminization has been seen in association with tumours of the interstitial cells and of the cells of Sertoli; these are therefore possible sites of oestrogen production in the testes. The adrenal cortex also contributes to the oestrogen found in the urine of men. The functional significance of the oestrogen produced in males is not known.

Biological action of androgens. Testosterone and other androgens have actions on most tissues. In the fetus they are responsible for the differentiation of the Wolffian ducts, external genitalia and brain. In the adolescent they are responsible for the physical changes of puberty (p. 510). They stimulate growth, muscular development, normal libido and aggressive behaviour.

At the molecular level testosterone enters a cell and in most tissues is converted by the membrane-bound enzyme, 5 α-reductase, to dihydrotestosterone, a steroid which is a more potent androgen in some assays. This is then bound to a specific binding protein and the protein-hormone complex enters the nucleus where it stimulates protein synthesis. In some tissues, notably the brain, pituitary, and kidney, testosterone itself is the main intracellular androgen.

Clinical use of androgens. In cases of delayed puberty in boys administration of testosterone produces hair in the typical male distribution and also growth of the larynx. Testosterone is of no value in the treatment of psychogenic impotence but is of clinical value in the rare cases of impotence due to testicular insufficiency.

In undernourished and emaciated persons injection of testosterone has an anabolic effect, nitrogen and other tissue-forming materials such as potassium, calcium and phosphorus being retained. The value of this form of treatment is limited by virilization particularly in females. Various derivatives of testosterone, such as methandienone, have a much higher ratio of anabolic to androgenic potency than testosterone and these so-called 'non-virilizing androgens' are used clinically.

OVULATION

The internal genital organs in the female consist of the ovaries, the uterine tubes, the uterus and the vagina (Figs. 29.6 and 29.7). The *uterus* is a pear-shaped muscular organ about 7·5 cm long with a flattened triangular lumen, the upper part of which communicates through the *uterine tubes* with the peritoneal cavity, while the lower part is continuous through the narrow canal of the *cervix* with the *vagina* (7 to 11 cm long) which passes to the exterior. The walls of the uterus, about 1 cm thick, are composed of smooth muscle fibres (the *myometrium*) among which is a considerable amount of fibrous tissue. The body of the uterus has very little elastic tissue but it is abundant in the cervical region. The mucous membrane or *endometrium* lining the interior is covered by a columnar epithelium which dips down into the stroma of the endometrium to form simple tubular glands. The epithelium covering the interior of the tubes and uterus, with the exception of the lower part of the cervix, is provided with cilia which tend to move ova or secreted material towards the exterior. Mucus is secreted by the glands within the cervix and plays a part in the transport of spermatozoa (p. 495). The columnar cells of the cervix give place abruptly, close to its external orifice, to the stratified squamous epithelium covering the vaginal portion of the cervix. The vagina is lined by a stratified squamous epithelium 0·2 mm thick without any glands. During reproductive life the vagina contains *Lactobacillus acidophilus* which keeps the vaginal pH between 4·9 and 3·5 by producing lactic acid from glycogen. The acid inhibits the growth of pathogenic bacteria which otherwise might invade the vagina.

The uterine tubes (Fallopian tubes) emerge laterally from the uterine cornua within the upper aspect of the broad ligament and pass laterally and downwards towards the ovaries to which they are loosely attached by an *ovarian fimbria* on each side. Each tube is lined by ciliated epithelium whose cilia beat towards the uterus. Smooth muscle, which can

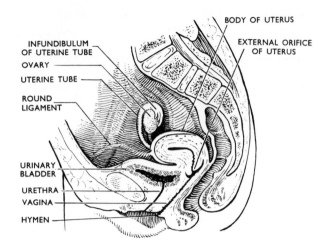

Fig. 29.6 Sagittal section through the female pelvis to show the main features of the female genital organs.

show characteristic peristalsis, lies between the mucosa and the serosa. The serosal layer is formed of parietal peritoneum. The tube is more than an anatomical conduit—it is within the tube that the ovum is fertilized and where the embryo develops into a blastocyst ready for implantation. The secretory activity of the mucosa of the tubes ensures optimal conditions for fertilization and for the transport of ova and spermatozoa.

The Ovaries

The ovaries in the adult are oval bodies weighing 2 to 8 g, covered by a cubical epithelium called the *germinal epithelium*. The stroma or framework is particularly dense below the epithelium where it forms the tunica albuginea. Immediately below this are numerous *vesicular ovarian (Graafian) follicles* in various stages of development or degeneration (Fig. 29.8).

The primordial sex cells in man arise either from the endoderm or the overlying mesoderm of a small area of the yolk sac and migrate to the wall of the hind gut and then along its mesentery to the genital ridge where they are found under the germinal epithelium. Near the end of intrauterine life groups of cells from the germinal epithelium form themselves around the sex cells (oogonia) to give the primordial ovarian

follicles. No oogonia seem to be formed after fetal life. At birth the ovary weighs about 0·3 g; it contains some 750 000 follicles but most eventually disintegrate and disappear; about 70 000 follicles are found in the ovaries from 25 to 40 years, but after 40 years less than 10 000 are present.

From puberty onwards a limited number of follicles mature in succession so that various stages of their development may be seen in one adult ovary. In each follicle the primitive ovum or oocyte can be recognized by its larger size. As the follicle begins to mature (Fig. 29.8) the cells investing the ovum multiply rapidly and a cavity filled with *liquor folliculi* appears among them giving the follicle the naked eye appearance of a clear vesicle on the surface of the ovary. The outer layer of investing cells is called the *stratum granulosum*

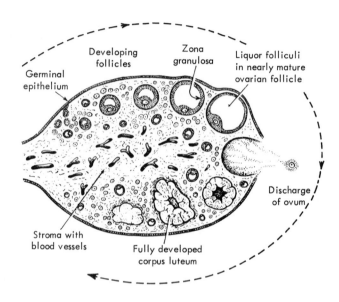

Fig. 29.8 A diagrammatic representation of a section made obliquely through an adult human ovary to show the stages in the development of the vesicular ovarian or Graafian follicle, the process of ovulation and the formation of a corpus luteum. The processes occur in the sequence indicated by the arrows.

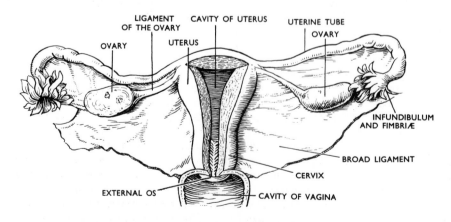

Fig. 29.7 Posterior aspect of the female genital organs.

and the layer around the ovum is the *cumulus ovaricus*. The ripe follicle is surrounded by a *tunica interna* consisting of spindle cells with numerous capillaries and a more compact *tunica externa*. The follicle begins to enlarge about the ninth day of the menstrual cycle and in four days grows from 2 to 15 mm in diameter. A digestive enzyme appears in the liquor folliculi and weakens both tunicae. At *ovulation* the follicle ruptures and the ovum, surrounded by a mass of some 3000 oestrogen-producing granulosa cells, is set free into the abdominal cavity, the first polar body having already been formed. The ovum then passes into a uterine tube where it becomes free of cumulus cells. The empty space in the ruptured follicle is filled with serous exudate and a varying amount of blood that is gradually replaced by large cells containing yellow pigment (*lutein cells*) which are mainly hypertrophied cells of the stratum granulosum although a few (*paralutein cells*) may be derived from the tunica interna. The resulting structure, known as a *corpus luteum*, persists till shortly before the next menstrual period if the ovum is not fertilized. If the woman becomes pregnant the corpus luteum continues to grow up to the third month of pregnancy, when it may be as large as 2·5 cm in diameter. Later it diminishes in size so that at the end of pregnancy it is only 1 cm across.

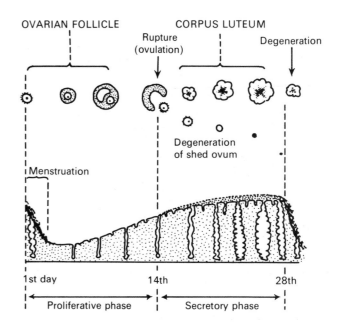

Fig. 29.9 Changes in the endometrium, the follicle and corpus luteum during a normal menstrual cycle.

The Menstrual Cycle

From the time of puberty the endometrium undergoes cyclical changes which result in bleeding from the uterus. This bleeding or *menstruation* lasts 4 to 6 days and recurs every 28 days approximately. In describing the menstrual cycle it is usual to date events from the first day on which bleeding occurs. However because of the variations in the length of cycles it is sometimes preferable to relate events to the time of ovulation (see Fig. 29.11).

During the first half, the *follicular* or *proliferative phase* of the cycle, an ovarian follicle enlarges and comes to the surface of the ovary, ovulation occurring about the fourteenth day. The subsequent 14 days in which the corpus luteum is active are referred to as the *luteal* or *secretory phase*. The corpus luteum degenerates just before the next menstruation (Fig. 29.9) probably as a result of local actions of prostaglandins.

Some days before menstruation many women experience abdominal pain, irritability, headache and even emotional disorders. The cause of these premenstrual symptoms is not clear but since they are relieved in some cases by the administration of synthetic analogues of progesterone, they may be due to the fall in progesterone output from the corpus luteum.

On the first three days or so of the menstrual cycle (Fig. 29.9) the more superficial layers of the endometrium degenerate and are cast off with some bleeding leaving the endometrium about 1 mm thick. The bleeding process has been studied by transplanting small fragments of endometrium into the anterior chamber of the eye of a monkey where they can easily be observed microscopically through the transparent cornea. In the follicular and luteal phases of the cycle the circulation through the spiral arteries supplying the endometrium is continuous. When the time of menstruation approaches, the circulation in the spiral arteries supplying the superficial parts of the endometrium slows down and then stops for some hours so that the endometrium blanches and then degenerates. After a time these arteries open again and blood escapes through the walls of capillaries, venules and arterioles with the formation of subepithelial haematomata. The cause of the vasoconstriction is not clear.

The menstrual flow consists of blood mixed with mucus and at first contains numerous leucocytes. The blood clots and is simultaneously broken down by plasmin formed by the activation of the fibrinolytic system. The fibrinolytic activity of the endometrium and the concentration of fibrin degradation products in the plasma are greatest at the time of menstruation. The volume of the blood lost varies greatly from woman to woman but in 80 per cent is in the range 6 to 60 ml, a loss of 3 to 30 mg of iron and 1 to 12 g of protein. Losses greater than 60 ml are often associated with iron-deficiency anaemia (p. 111).

Histological changes. At the end of menstruation the endometrium is regenerated from the deeper parts of the glands next to the myometrium. During the *phase of proliferation*, occupying from the fifth to the fourteenth day, new capillaries grow out from the spiral arterioles, the endometrial glands progressively increase in length and tortuosity and the cells of the stroma hypertrophy so that at the end of this phase the endometrium is some 3 to 4 mm thick.

During the next 14 days the glands continue to grow, becoming more dilated and convoluted and showing secretory activity. The cells of the stroma enlarge and the content of glycogen increases. These premenstrual changes may be regarded as preparation for a fertilized ovum and when they are complete the endometrium is about 6 or 7 mm thick. If the ovum is not fertilized small collections of blood appear in the endometrium and the degenerative changes which result in menstruation begin again.

The endometrium is a major site of prostaglandin synthesis. The level of prostaglandin in the human endometrium is low in the proliferative phase and rises significantly during the luteal phase. This may be the source of the prostaglandin responsible for the breakdown of the corpus luteum.

Bleeding normally takes place, as just described, from endometrium in the secretory phase but periodic bleeding can occur even if the secretory stage is not reached and the endometrium, just before bleeding, is histologically still in the proliferative phase. Since the secretory phase of the endometrium is dependent on an active corpus luteum (p. 489) it can be assumed that in these cases ovulation has not occurred and that the corpus luteum has not developed; bleeding of this kind is described as *anovular menstruation.*

In healthy women menstruation occurs at intervals of about 28 days but there is considerable variation. In any one woman successive cycles may vary in length by 1 to 2 days. At the onset of menstruation, and also when the menopause is nearly reached, the cycles may be irregular and anovulatory. The process is absent during pregnancy, may be suppressed during lactation and ceases finally at the *menopause,* usually between 45 and 55 years (p. 518).

Ovarian Hormones

Oestrogens. Oestrogens were originally identified in the liquor folliculi when it was found that extracts could cause the histological changes of oestrus in the vaginal epithelium of spayed mice. In women the principal oestrogen produced by the ovary in reproductive life is oestradiol-17β. It is the most potent of the oestrogens. Some oestrone arises from peripheral conversion of oestradiol or androstenedione in adipose tissue and liver.

The theca interna seems to be the main site of oestrogen production. Oestradiol-17β is only slightly active when taken by mouth and is therefore given parenterally. Oestrogenic effects are, however, simply and cheaply achieved by the oral admistration of a synthetic oestrogen such as ethinyl oestradiol, mestranol or stilboestrol. The mode of action of oestrogens at the cellular level is still not known.

All the plasma oestrogens circulate in the plasma bound to protein and are excreted in the bile and in the urine after being made more soluble in the liver by conjugation with glucuronides or sulphates.

Progesterone. This hormone is secreted by the corpus luteum and, in pregnancy, by the placenta. Its main action during the menstrual cycle is on the oestrogen-stimulated endometrium which develops further with increased tortuosity of the glands which begin to secrete. Progesterone prevents bleeding from the endometrium and a fall in progesterone secretion is probably the signal for the start of menstruation. The slightly higher body temperature in the second half of the cycle is probably due to progesterone. If fertilization takes place the progesterone-prepared endometrium is loose and oedematous so that it is readily entered by the trophoblast.

In the liver progesterone is reduced to *pregnanediol* and conjugated with glucuronic acid to be excreted in the urine as a biologically inactive glucuronide. About 10 to 40 per cent of injected progesterone can be recovered in the urine and about 5 per cent in the bile as conjugated pregnanediol. The granulosa cells convert pregnenolone to progesterone and, in smaller quantities, to oestrogens; the theca cells produce mainly oestrogens.

Ovarian androgens. The ovarian stroma produces androgens, particularly androstenedione. Their significance is not fully understood but they may play a part in the pubertal growth spurt. Androgens are probably the principal hormones responsible for sexual desire in both men and women.

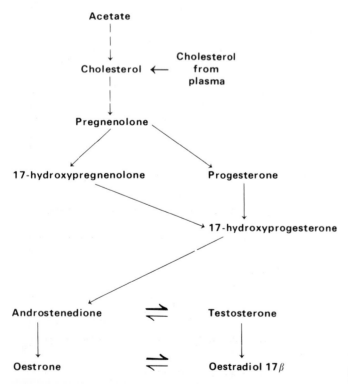

Fig. 29.10 Pathways for the synthesis of oestrogens in the human ovary.

Synthetic 'hormones'. Large numbers of oestrogenic compounds having little or no chemical resemblance to the naturally occurring steroid hormones have been synthesized. Stilboestrol was one of the first nonsteroidal oestrogens to be synthesized. Ethinyl oestradiol is closely related to the natural oestrogen oestradiol-17β. It is about 25 times as potent as stilboestrol; its 3-methyl ether derivative, mestranol, is used in oral contraceptive preparations. These compounds have the great advantage that they are cheap to make and active by mouth. Oestrogens, both synthetic and natural, have proved of value in the treatment of cancer of the prostate, some cases of cancer of the breast and for the relief of post-menopausal symptoms.

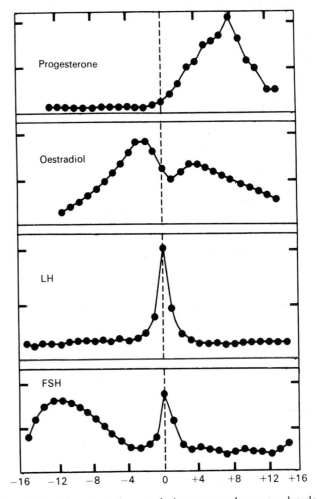

Stilboestrol   Ethinyloestradiol

For a long time progesterone was the only available compound with progestational activity but a number of compounds is now available which are not only more active than progesterone itself but are effective by mouth. The most widely used compounds are norethisterone and norethynodrel.

The Hormonal Control of the Menstrual Cycle

After removal of the ovaries the menstrual cycle is abolished, the vagina atrophies and the vaginal smear consists almost entirely of leucocytes; at the same time the uterus atrophies and the endometrium becomes thin. Treatment with oestrogens causes the walls of the vagina to become cornified (so that the smear contains squamous cells), the vaginal secretion returns to its normal acid pH; the uterine muscle hypertrophies, the endometrium proliferates and the glands of the cervix uteri begin to secrete again. If oestrogen treatment is stopped or if the dosage is suddenly reduced the uterine mucosa becomes oedematous and about 5 days later there is bleeding from the endometrium. This is called *withdrawal bleeding*. If, however, treatment is continued when the endometrium is showing proliferative changes and progesterone as well as oestrogen is given in suitable dosage a typical premenstrual endometrium can be produced. Cessation of hormonal treatment is followed as before by bleeding but in this case it takes place in a premenstrual endometrium just as in a normal menstrual cycle. This cycle of hormone administration forms the basis of the action of oral contraceptives.

Since the endometrial changes of the menstrual cycle can be imitated by injection of oestradiol and progesterone, it is a fair assumption that these hormones are responsible for the changes in the normal menstrual cycle; indeed many studies have made it clear that the plasma levels of oestrogens and progesterone (and the urinary excretion of their metabolites) correspond with this view (Fig. 29.11). The peak level of oestradiol, 3·5 nmol/l, is found in the day before ovulation. The highest values of progesterone are found in the mid-luteal

phase of the cycle—500 pmol/l—and a secondary rise in the plasma oestradiol occurs at the same time. The first rise of oestrogen 'production' parallels the maturation of the ovarian follicle and the second rise after the transient fall corresponds to the growth and regression of the corpus luteum.

Gonadotrophic hormones. If the pituitary gland is removed from an immature female animal the gonads remain infantile and, since the development of the secondary sex organs, the clitoris, uterus and vagina, is dependent on the hormones of the gonads, these organs also remain immature. The secondary sex organs atrophy after removal of the ovaries in spite of the presence of the pituitary gland; it is clear therefore that the gonadotrophins produced by the adenohypophysis have no direct influence on the secondary sex organs but only an indirect one through the gonads. In both male and female two gonadotrophins FSH and LH are produced by the anterior pituitary and another gonadotrophin is produced by the placenta in pregnancy (*human chorionic gonadotrophin*, HCG). The release of the pituitary gonadotrophins is controlled by the hypothalamic peptide hormone *luteinizing hormone releasing hormone* (LHRH) (p. 466).

FSH controls the development and maturation of the ovarian follicle in the female. In the follicular phase of the

Fig. 29.11 Hormonal changes during a normal menstrual cycle. Events are timed before and after the time of ovulation since cycle length varies from person to person. (*After* C. Faiman, J. D. Winter & F. I. Reyes (1976) *Clinics in Obstetrics and Gynaecology*, 3, 467–483.)

menstrual cycle, oestrogen production increases under FSH control. In the adult female, plasma levels of FSH rise gradually during the follicular phase of the menstrual cycle and fall just before ovulation (Fig. 29.11). A further brief increase occurs at the time of ovulation, and then the levels fall in the luteal phase of the cycle to values lower than those found in the follicular phase. High values are found in postmenopausal women and patients with primary gonadal failure (gonadal dysgenesis, castrates); low levels are found in hypopituitarism.

LH controls the development of the corpus luteum and its secretion of progesterone during the luteal phase of the menstrual cycle. The pattern of changes in plasma LH levels in menstruating women is similar to that for FSH but at ovulation the LH peak is much higher than the FSH peak. It is likely that the peak in LH level is the signal for ovulation. The release of LH at this time is thought to be triggered off by the rise in plasma oestradiol—an example of positive feed-back. The plasma level of LH is raised in patients with primary gonadal failure; in pituitary insufficiency LH levels are low.

In some cases of infertility due to failure of ovulation, ovulation can be induced by accurately timed administration of gonadotrophins. Patients are given human FSH for several days and if an adequate rise in plasma oestradiol is obtained a single dose of HCG (similar in action to LH) is then given in an attempt to trigger ovulation. Excessive stimulation of the ovary can cause multiple ovulation and in consequence multiple births.

The hypothalamus therefore appears to control the menstrual cycle. If the woman has a period every 28 days then this periodicity exists in the hypothalamus or its associated nuclei. The cycle of release of these factors can be modified by signals coming back from the gonads, and also by signals coming from the higher centres of the brain, so that stresses of various kinds can affect the menstrual cycle by way of the higher centres and the hypothalamus. It is not uncommon for girls under stress such as leaving home, sitting examinations, or losing a relative to have a disturbance of menstruation even to the point of amenorrhoea (absence of menstruation). This is probably the result of an increased level of *prolactin* which results from a failure to utilize dopamine in the hypothalamus.

The pituitary gonadotrophins are affected by the gonadal hormones in a negative feed-back system and in general it can be said that the production of FSH and LH is reduced by a rise in the secretion of oestrogens and progesterone by the ovary. The main effect of the synthetic oestrogens and progestogens contained in the contraceptive pill is to interfere with the pituitary gonadotrophin secretion and thus with ovulation.

In young children the secretion of gonadotrophic hormones is very low; it rises slowly throughout childhood until with approaching puberty the secretion of both hormones increases rapidly to the adult levels. These levels are maintained in the male; in the female there are cyclic changes during reproductive life and then a further increase after the menopause when the inhibitory influence of the ovarian steroids is much reduced.

Time of Ovulation

It is almost certain that ovulation in woman always occurs spontaneously, that is it is not induced by coitus.

The finding of an actual ovum is, of course, the best proof that ovulation has recently occurred and human ova can be obtained by washing out the uterine tubes and collecting the fluid which emerges from the fimbriated end; ova are found only at the middle of the cycle (about the fifteenth day) and not at other times. Inspection of human ovaries during abdominal operations shows that ovulation usually occurs between the twelfth and fifteenth day of the menstrual cycle. The change from the proliferative to the secretory phase of the endometrium, which depends on the presence of a corpus luteum, also occurs about the middle of the cycle. It is difficult to obtain information about mating in the human subject but analysis of cases in which conception resulted from a single insemination on a known day of the cycle shows that ovulation can occur at any time between the sixth and twentieth day of the cycle.

It has been claimed that the slight fall of body temperature followed by a slight rise, usually less than 0·5°C, which occurs about the middle of the menstrual cycle indicates the time of ovulation. This slight elevation of body temperature in the second half of the cycle has been attributed to progesterone; it can be imitated by giving progesterone after a preparatory course of oestrogens in women with amenorrhoea. A peak in plasma oestrogen levels (and in urinary oestrogen excretion) provides another guide to the time of ovulation. This occurs about 24 hours before the rise in LH. In turn the rise in LH is followed by ovulation some 24 to 36 hours later, as early as 4 days before or as late as 6 days after mid-cycle.

Administration of progesterone to a rabbit inhibits ovulation by reducing the output of pituitary gonadotrophin. Presumably this mechanism prevents superfetation (additional conceptions) in pregnancy. On the basis of this information Pincus in 1956 gave a group of normal women 300 mg of progesterone by mouth from the fifth to the twenty-fifth day of the menstrual cycle. Examination of endometrial biopsies and vaginal smears, as well as records of basal temperature, suggested that ovulation had not occurred and indeed there were no pregnancies in the group. A number of synthetic steroid compounds have progestogen (progesterone-like) effects when given orally; they act on the pituitary suppressing the formation of FSH and LH and they reduce the amount of glandular epithelium in the endometrium. Contraceptive 'pills' containing both oestrogens and progestogens also alter the chemical and physical composition of cervical mucus so that spermatozoa may fail to penetrate into the uterine cavity.

In postmenopausal women dithiocarbamylhydrazine derivatives inhibit the pituitary and reduce the urinary output of gonadotrophin. In normally menstruating women these nonsteroid compounds, like the progestogens, suppress ovarian activity. Clomiphene, an anti-oestrogen, binds to the oestrogen receptor sites in the hypothalamus. In so doing it prevents the negative feed-back of oestradiol and thus increases the production of pituitary gonadotrophin and therefore stimulates the human ovary as judged by the increase in output of steroid hormones. It is used therefore to stimulate ovulation in infertile women with ovarian failure.

Changes in the genital tract at ovulation. Under the influence of oestrogen the mucus secreted by the glands within the cervix becomes thin and watery; this allows the passage of spermatozoa. After ovulation the mucus become viscid and cellular and sperm penetration is impossible. In this way spermatozoa are unlikely to reach the uterine tubes except at the time of ovulation when the oestrogen effect is maximal.

The cilia of the fimbriae are adapted to pick up the viscous contents of the ovarian follicle and pass this, with the ovum, into the tubal ostium. The tubal mucosa secretes bicarbonate which is responsible for the dispersal of the cumulus cells of the ovum prior to sperm penetration. Tubal secretions, maximal at the time of ovulation, are the result both of transudation from plasma and of epithelial secretion. The oxygen uptake of spermatozoa increases with exposure to tubal fluids; this increased uptake correlates with tubal bicarbonate ion secretion. The process of sperm capacitation which occurs within the uterine tube before penetration of the ovum is discussed on page 494.

FERTILIZATION

The determination of the time of ovulation in woman is important in the study and treatment of infertility. An ovum can be fertilized at a mating which precedes ovulation only if the spermatozoa placed in the genital tract survive until ovulation occurs; fertilization can occur after ovulation only so long as the ovum remains capable of being fertilized. If, as is likely, the period of viability of both spermatozoa and ova is short the time of ovulation determines to a large extent the time during which mating is fertile.

Viability of spermatozoa and ova. Microscopic examination of spermatozoa gives little information as to their fertilizing power; at most it can be said that semen containing a large number of abnormally shaped spermatozoa is unlikely to bring about a pregnancy. Normal spermatozoa retain their motility long after they have lost the power to fertilize; motile sperms have been found in human cervical mucus 3 days after coitus and in the uterine tubes 7 days after coitus. The results of artificial insemination by donors (A.I.D.) indicate that the period during which human sperms are able to fertilize an ovum is not more than 24 hours.

The ovum has an even shorter life than the spermatozoon. Histological examination shows that the unfertilized ovum quickly degenerates in the uterine tubes. It is unlikely that the fertilizable life of the human ovum is more than 8 hours.

Coitus

Conception occurs after a fertile mating in which the spermatozoa deposited in the vagina reach an ovum shortly after ovulation. In response to psychological and sensory stimuli the penis becomes erect, increasing in length from about 9·5 to 17 cm by engorgement of the erectile tissue of the corpora cavernosa and spongiosa. Their arterioles dilate and the venous outflow in some way, not satisfactorily explained, is obstructed. The dartos and cremaster muscles contract and elevate the testes. The testes themselves become congested while the skin flushes. The penis is inserted into the vagina and stimulation of the penis, clitoris and vagina is increased by rhythmic voluntary movements.

The nipples of the woman become erect by contraction of their smooth muscle, the areolae and breasts become engorged. The passage of the penis into the vagina is facilitated by the mucus secreted by the cervix and by the glands of Bartholin in the vulva. Later the clitoral glans becomes engorged and the clitoris is retracted against the anterior border of the symphysis pubis. The vagina becomes lengthened and distended. The outer third becomes congested and is described as the orgasmic platform. The uterus is raised.

As physical and psychological stimulation increases the heart rate rises, breathing becomes deeper and the blood pressure increases. Semen is moved from the vas deferens, prostate and seminal vesicles into the urethra by contraction of smooth muscle. Coitus culminates both physiologically and psychologically in the *orgasm*, in which semen is ejaculated from the urethra into the upper part of the vagina by rhythmic contractions of bulbocavernosus and ischiocavernosus muscles. The internal sphincter of the bladder prevents retrograde ejaculation. Orgasm in the woman, which may occur simultaneously with the male orgasm, consists of rhythmical contractions of vaginal and uterine muscle and dilatation of the cervix.

After ejaculation of the highly buffered semen the vaginal pH increases to 7 and may not return to pH 4 for 10 hours or so. Sperm motility is favoured by a neutral pH and inhibited by a low pH. While the unaided random movements of spermatozoa (about 100 μm/sec) are insufficient to explain their transport to the uterine tubes, it is possible that coitus causes uterine contractions which aid the transport of sperm.

Coitus must be regarded primarily as a cerebral event although the reflex changes in the genitalia are governed by lumbar and sacral spinal centres. Stimulation of the sacral (parasympathetic) outflow in the pelvic splanchnic nerves (p. 80) causes erection of the penis or clitoris by dilatation of their blood vessels. Somatic nerves arising in the sacral region of the cord pass out in the pudendal nerves to the ischiocavernosus and bulbocavernosus muscles in both sexes and, therefore, both somatic and autonomic nerves are involved in coitus.

The internal organs of reproduction in both sexes are supplied by sympathetic fibres from the lumbar outflow travelling in the hypogastric nerves. Stimulation of these nerves in non-pregnant women produces a contraction, followed by an inhibition, of the body and cervix of the uterus. After section of the hypogastric nerves in man the power of ejaculation but not of erection is lost. Failure of ejaculation is common in patients with high blood pressure who are being treated with adrenergic neurone-blocking drugs that prevent the internal sphincter of the bladder from closing. Failure of erection is called impotence.

Fertilization

Although only one spermatozoon is necessary for the fertilization of an ovum, pregnancy does not occur unless many millions are deposited in the vagina. The male ejaculate (p. 485) usually contains 100×10^6 to 200×10^6 spermatozoa per ml. Only a tiny fraction of this number reaches the site of fertilization.

Freshly ejaculated spermatozoa are unable to enter the

ovum; they acquire this capacity after a few hours' stay in the reproductive tract of the female. This essential change is known as *capacitation*. It involves an alteration in the membrane potential of the acrosome and occurs over a period of a few hours if the sperms are exposed to genital tract fluid of the mid-cycle female (tubal, uterine or cervical secretions). This phenomenon occurs *in vitro* and is an essential step in the process of *in vitro* fertilization.

Fertilization involves the mixing of genetic material from the chromosomes of the ovum and the spermatozoon. To do this both germ cells reduce their chromosomes from the normal diploid state (46) to the haploid (23) stage by meiotic division (p. 521). In the ovum the second meiotic division is triggered by the penetration of the fertilizing spermatozoon into the zona pellucida.

The cumulus cells surrounding the ovum are dispersed partly by the bicarbonate secreted by the tubal mucosa and partly by hyaluronidase produced by the accumulated spermatozoa. The events of fertilization are shown in Figure 29.12. The fertilizing spermatozoon penetrates the zona pellucida by digesting it with an enzyme produced in the acrosome; this

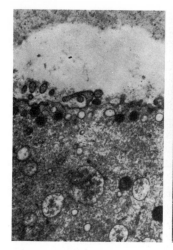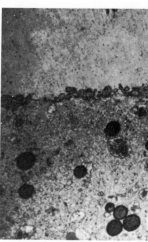

Fig. 29.13   Electron microscope view of the surface of an unfertilized human ovum (left) to show the electron-dense cortical granules. A similar view of an ovum which has been penetrated by a spermatozoon is shown on the right. *(Courtesy of J. A. Mills and Y. K. Oh.)*

enzyme has been called acrosomal proteinase. When the fertilizing spermatozoon passes through the zona pellucida into the ovum the zona becomes impenetrable to further spermatozoa. This is achieved by the release of a substance from many cortical granules round the periphery of the ovum itself into the space between the ovum and the zona pellucida (Fig. 29.13). Some animals are polyspermic in their fertilization but woman is not. If an ovum is fertilized by more than one sperm then excess of genetic material may be passed on to the embryo and this may be a cause of abortion.

Once it has entered the ovum the sperm head enlarges to form the male pronucleus and the chromatin left in the ovum, after the second polar body has been extruded, condenses to form the smaller female pronucleus. These two condensations of genetic material migrate together and fuse to form the nucleus of the fertilized embryo. Further mitotic division of this cell results in orderly cleavage of the embryo towards the blastocyst stage.

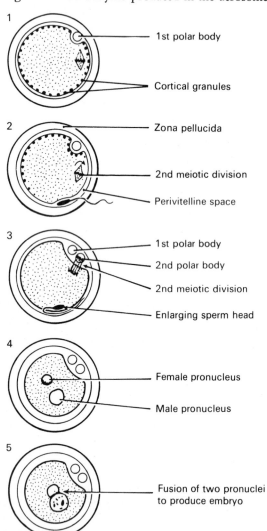

Fig. 29.12   The steps in the fertilization of an ovum by a spermatozoon. *(After* C. Thibault (1972) *International Journal of Fertility*, 17, 1–13.)

PREGNANCY

Fertilization usually occurs in the uterine tubes, probably within 12 hours of coitus in man, and the ovum then passes along the tube into the uterine cavity, undergoing cleavage as it goes (Fig. 29.14) so that, as far as can be estimated, it is implanted in the endometrium at the blastocyst stage 5 days after fertilization. The transport may be facilitated by peristaltic or ciliary activity or by the secretion of the uterine tube which is greatly increased at ovulation.

When an ovum is fertilized the corpus luteum persists instead of degenerating at the end of the menstrual cycle and menstruation does not occur. The hormonal or nervous mechanism responsible for this is not known with certainty but it is likely that chorionic gonadotrophin is produced very early by the embedding blastocyst and has an LH-like effect which maintains the corpus luteum. This ensures a continuous production of progesterone to maintain the secretory changes

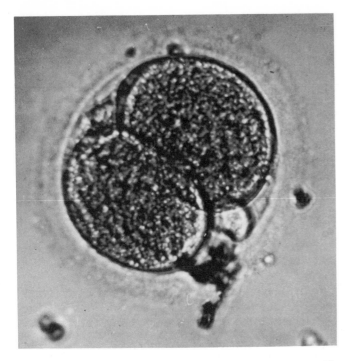

Fig. 29.14 Human embryo, fertilized *in vitro*, at two cell stage. The embryo has been stripped of cumulus cells and is surrounded by the translucent zona pellucida. The two polar bodies can also be seen. *(Courtesy of M. Seitz, L. Mastroiani & B. Bracket.)*

in the endometrium and prevent it from breaking down in menstruation. Failure to menstruate at the expected date is thus one of the first presumptive signs of pregnancy in women.

Little is known of the factors which control the process of implantation (Fig. 29.15) but HCG produced by the implanting embryo is probably important.

The endometrium continues to grow during pregnancy since there is no menstrual degeneration, and it may eventually reach 10 mm or more in thickness. The three layers seen in the premenstrual endometrium become more obvious (Fig. 29.16). The superficial layer of the stroma becomes compact and the greatly enlarged stromal cells are known as *decidual cells*. The value of this decidual reaction is not clear since it occurs a considerable time after implantation. It may protect the uterus against invasion by trophoblast.

In the decidua basalis under the developing embryo there is from an early stage a great dilatation of the maternal blood vessels and small finger-like outgrowths of the outer layer of the blastocyst, the *chorionic villi*, grow into them by erosion of the decidua. This penetration by the villi is aided by obliteration of small arteries of the decidua causing necrosis and the formation of large spaces in the decidua which fill with maternal blood. As the villi are soon invaded by mesoderm carrying fetal blood vessels, the fetal and maternal circulations are brought very close to one another and in this way the placenta is formed. There is, however, no direct connexion between the two vascular systems and blood does not normally pass from the mother to the fetus or vice versa. Intervening between the fetal and maternal circulations are only three thin layers, namely the fetal vascular endothelium, the connective

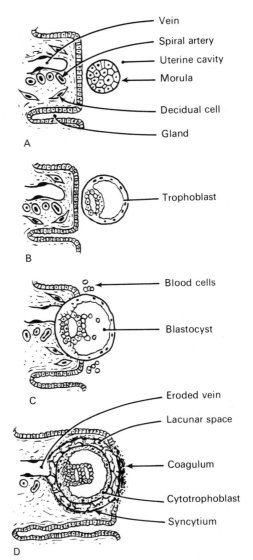

Fig. 29.15 Steps in the implantation of the embryo into the uterine wall.

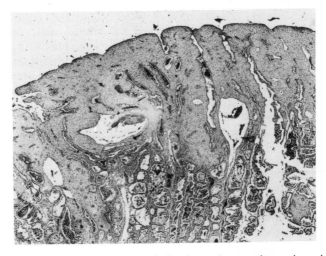

Fig. 29.16 Decidua (the modified endometrium) at the tenth week of pregnancy. The thickened uterine lining is divided into a deep *stratum spongiosum* and a superficial *stratum compactum*. Haemotoxylin and eosin (×13). *(By courtesy of W. W. Park.)*

tissue of the villi and the trophoblast, across which the transfer of nutrient materials readily occurs.

The fetus, because it possesses genes derived from its father, must have antigens foreign to its mother and, since the gestation period is longer than the homograft rejection period, by all the 'laws' it should be rejected. The placental barrier no doubt plays a part in the protection of the fetus but it is not a complete immunological barrier since fetal red and white cells can pass into the mother's circulation and Rh antibody (p. 131) can pass into the fetus. Fetuses removed from the uterus of pregnant rats and rabbits and transplanted in the abdominal muscles are rejected like any other homografts. Grafts placed in the pregnant uterus of animals survive for a considerable time if surrounded by decidual cells. Another possible factor in the remarkable immunological privilege of the fetus is suggested by the finding of immuno-suppressive substances in maternal plasma in pregnancy.

In view of the increased blood flow to the uterus and other tissues it is not surprising to find that the cardiac output increases in pregnancy up to 40 per cent; the blood volume is also increased. In early pregnancy most of the increase goes to the kidneys—the GFR is markedly increased; later the uterus receives a larger share.

Amniotic Fluid

As pregnancy advances the products of conception increase in size and eventually occupy the whole of the uterine cavity. The growing fetus attached by its umbilical cord to the placenta is bathed by the amniotic fluid which is contained within the 'bag of membranes' consisting of the amnion and chorion. The volume of the amniotic fluid can be estimated by the dye-dilution technique.

The volume of the amniotic fluid is variable: it is present at 8 weeks' gestation, is a little over 30 ml at 10 weeks' gestation and is about 400 ml at 19 weeks. The highest value, between 37 and 38 weeks' gestation, is between 500 ml and 1100 ml, thereafter there is a steady decrease. The amniotic fluid maintains the fetus in a shock-proof and weightless condition in a constant temperature environment. Amniotic fluid is fairly freely exchanged with the maternal fluids and its protein and amino acid content approaches that of blood plasma; it is mainly a secretory product of the amniotic epithelium.

The fetus swallows amniotic fluid and also voids urine into it. Excess of amniotic fluid (hydramnios) may be associated with anencephaly and oesophageal atresia in which the fetus cannot swallow; lack of amniotic fluid is sometimes associated with renal agenesis so that the fetus cannot produce urine. There are, however, many conditions in which the fetus is unable to swallow or to pass urine where the volume of fluid is within normal limits. Hydramnios is also associated with maternal diabetes mellitus, hydrops fetalis and multiple pregnancies.

Complex changes occur throughout pregnancy in the amniotic fluid. The bilirubin content of the fluid may be raised in a fetus whose mother has antibodies to its red cells so that haemolysis occurs in the fetus. The phospholipids lecithin and sphyngomyelin are present in varying ratio and the rise in lecithin level to at least 35 mg/l, usually occurring quite suddenly at 35 weeks' gestation, is an indication that the baby's lungs are producing surfactant and that the baby on delivery is unlikely to die from the respiratory distress syndrome. In babies with a neural tube defect (anencephaly or spina bifida) alpha fetoprotein (AFP), synthesized by the fetal liver and yolk sac, escapes in excessive amounts into the amniotic fluid; the concentration may be 350 mg/l instead of the normal 16 mg/l. A high concentration at 16 weeks allows a diagnosis of fetal abnormality. More sensitive tests now permit the estimation of AFP in maternal serum.

Amniotic fluid always contains a number of fetal cells and the sex of the fetus can be discovered by examination of their chromatin content (p. 521). After culture of the cells the chromosome picture may reveal abnormalities such as Down's syndrome (mongolism) (Chap. 32). Biochemical tests may be applied to cultures of cells in the diagnosis of inborn errors of metabolism.

The Hormonal Control of Pregnancy

The ovary is necessary in the early stages of pregnancy since progesterone from the corpus luteum is responsible for preparing the endometrium for the reception of a fertilized ovum but after this preliminary stage the ovaries can be removed without disturbing the pregnancy. The placenta apparently provides all the hormones needed for the continuation of pregnancy.

The endocrine function of the conceptus begins early in pregnancy about the time of implantation when the primitive trophoblast secretes HCG which increases the life span of the corpus luteum which supplies oestrogen and progesterone necessary for the growth and development of the uterus and fetus. The main precursor of steroids in the fetus is pregnenolone (Fig. 29.10) which is synthesized in the placenta from maternal cholesterol. The main oestrogen produced by placental tissue is oestriol. Progesterone is also produced by the placenta; the total amount increases as pregnancy advances. At term the placenta produces about 800 μmol progesterone per 24 hours. The human placenta also makes a number of polypeptide hormones including HCG (p. 491). HCG probably maintains the secretion of progesterone by the corpus luteum until this function is assumed by the placenta. In agreement with this idea is the finding that injection of chorionic gonadotrophin into non-pregnant women increases the progesterone production and delays the onset of the next menstrual period. The corpus luteum may therefore be maintained by gonadotrophins.

Oestrogens. Figure 29.17 shows the urinary excretion of oestriol, the main oestrogen metabolite, throughout pregnancy. The high output (about 1000 times that in the non-pregnant state) reached at the end of gestation is maintained up to parturition after which the excretion declines rapidly to the non-pregnant level. The plasma level of oestrogens in the mother also rises steadily during pregnancy (Fig. 29.18).

The oestrogens produced by the placenta are formed from precursors synthesized by the fetal adrenal glands (Fig. 29.19). Since the placenta cannot synthesize oestrogens from simple precursors, the production of oestrogens depends on there being a live fetus with functional adrenal glands. After fetal death the urinary excretion of oestriol falls; in the presence of an anencephalic fetus with poorly developed adrenals the oestriol excretion is low. The placenta possesses enzymes lacking in the fetus but the fetus has enzymes lacking in the

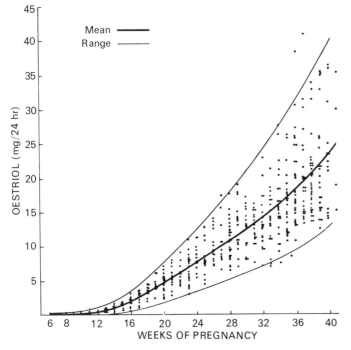

Fig. 29.17 Urinary oestriol excretion during 36 normal pregnancies (baby weight over 3 kg) showing fitted mean, maximum and minimum ($P = 0.05$) values. Oestriol is exreted as conjugates with sulphate or glucuronic acid. (M. G. Coyle & J. B. Brown (1963) *Journal of Obstetrics and Gynaecology of the British Commonwealth*, 70, 225.)

placenta; the two together, the feto-placental unit, form a complete system for steroid synthesis.

Progesterone. The maternal plasma contains progesterone at levels between 30 and 150 nmol/l in early pregnancy, and as

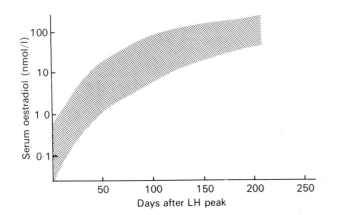

Fig. 29.18 Plasma levels of oestradiol during pregnancy plotted on a logarithmic scale. (*After* S. L. Kaplan and M. M. Grumbach (1978). *Clinics in Endocrinology and Metabolism*, 7, 487–511.)

pregnancy advances the level rises to about 500 nmol/l (Fig. 29.20). The plasma progesterone level remains high during labour and falls after parturition. The plasma progesterone levels are higher in the maternal uterine vein, which is nearer the site of production, than in the peripheral blood and are even higher in the fetal umbilical vessels. The fetus uses the progesterone produced in the maternal placenta for the production of corticosteroids.

Gonadotrophic substances. The presence of gonadotrophins in the urine of pregnant women was first demonstrated by Aschheim and Zondek in 1928, and the detection of these substances forms the basis of pregnancy diagnosis tests. Quantitative measurement shows that HCG excretion begins

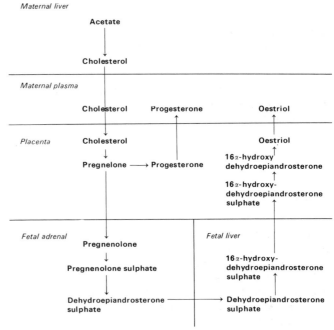

Fig. 29.19 Metabolic pathways for the production of progesterone and oestriol in the 'feto-placental unit'.

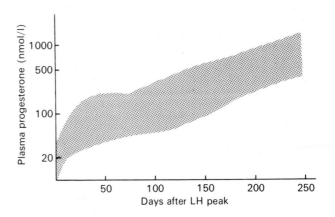

Fig. 29.20 Plasma levels of progesterone in the maternal circulation during pregnancy plotted on a logarithmic scale. The urinary excretion of pregnanediol increases in a similar way. (*After* W. Hobson, F. Coulston, C. Faiman, J. S. D. Winter & F. Reyes. *Journal of Toxicology and Environmental Health*, 1, 657–668.)

about the time of the expected, but missed, menstrual period, rises to a peak about 10 weeks later and then falls to a lower value, around which it fluctuates until the end of pregnancy. The amount of HCG in the serum shows similar changes (Fig. 29.21). HCG production seems to depend on the number of cells of the cytotrophoblast in the placenta; the number of these cells increases rapidly in early pregnancy and then declines until they can scarcely be seen at term. Within a few days after parturition the excretion falls to non-pregnancy levels when the test, in fact, measures LH.

Pregnancy diagnosis tests. The rapid rise in HCG excretion early in pregnancy is the basis of these tests. The principle is as follows. HCG is prepared from the urine of pregnant women and injected into a rabbit; the rabbit produces anti-HCG antibodies in its serum. When a suspension of latex particles is coated with HCG and mixed with the anti-HCG serum agglutination of the particles occurs. If urine containing HCG (that is urine from a pregnant woman) is added to anti-HCG serum the reaction between the HCG and anti-HCG leaves no free anti-HCG. On subsequent addition of latex particles coated with HCG no agglutination occurs. The absence of agglutination indicates that the urine contained HCG and constitutes a positive pregnancy test.

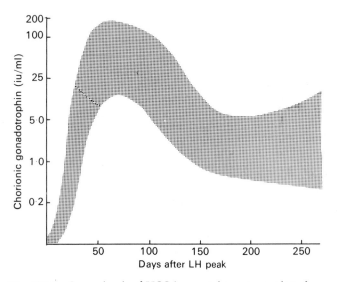

Fig. 29.21 Serum levels of HCG in normal pregnancy plotted on a logarithmic scale. (*After* W. Hobson, F. Coulston, C. Faiman, J. S. D. Winter & F. Reyes *Journal of Toxicology and Environmental Health*, 1, 657–668.)

Water Retention in Pregnancy

The total body water in pregnant women has been measured with deuterium oxide and the results are summarized in Table 29.22. There is a good agreement between the estimates and measured increases in water for women with little or no oedema at 20 and 30 weeks. The discrepancy at term of 1 to 2 litres must be due to additional water storage.

In pregnancy the blood volume increases so that at term it is 20 to 100 per cent (average 30 per cent) higher than the non-pregnant level. Since the average increase in total red cells is about 20 per cent the haemoglobin concentration in the

peripheral blood falls but this is not a true anaemia. After delivery the blood volume returns to the non-pregnant level in a few hours.

Table 29.22 The water component of weight gain in pregnancy compared with the measured increase in body water

Component	Water content (g)		
	20 weeks	30 weeks	40 weeks
Fetus	264	1185	2343
Placenta	153	366	540
Amniotic fluid	247	594	792
Added uterine muscle	483	668	743
Added mammary gland	135	270	304
Plasma	506	1058	920
Red cells	32	98	163
Total	1820	4239	5805
Measured increase			
No oedema	1740	4300	7500*
Leg oedema	1810	4290	7880*
Generalized oedema	2230	5740	10830*

* Extrapolated from 30–38 week gain.
From F. E. Hytten, A. M. Thomson & Nan Taggart (1966) *Journal of Obstetrics and Gynaecology of the British Commonwealth*, 73, 553–561.

The retention of water and sodium may be related to the increased production of oestrogens in pregnancy, since oestrogen therapy in women also produces an increase in blood volume. The sodium retention of pregnancy may be due to aldosterone; the urinary excretion of aldosterone is some 10 times greater in pregnancy than in the non-pregnant state. The high production of aldosterone is related to increased renin production.

The total gain in weight during pregnancy, about 12·5 kg, is greater than would be expected from the gain in water. The difference can be accounted for by an increase in depot fat of about 3·5 kg and in protein (mainly in the uterus and its contents) of 0·8 kg. Even greater increases in weight have been reported but many obstetricians advise that the gain in weight during the whole of pregnancy should not exceed 12·5 kg. A sudden gain of weight, say 0·5 kg or more in a week in the later stages of pregnancy, is often a sign of developing pre-eclampsia. Failure to gain weight may be evidence of placental insufficiency and poor fetal growth.

It is difficult to determine the energy requirements in pregnancy. The increased tissue stores amount to about 170 MJ and the cumulative extra need for the metabolism of the fetus and uterus may be about 150 MJ. However, the mother tends to reduce her activity and may consume only half of this extra amount. The increase in maternal stores (about 3 kg) which the mother possesses after parturition may be used up in breast feeding. In pregnancy the β cells of the pancreas increase in number and the plasma insulin rises. This suggests that pregnancy puts a strain on carbohydrate homeostasis and indeed pregnancy is occasionally followed by diabetes mellitus.

During pregnancy the respiratory centre is more sensitive to CO_2 and hyperventilation occurs. The arterial P_{CO_2} in pregnancy is about 30 mm Hg, in labour it may be 16 mm Hg. Progesterone may be responsible for the changes since injection of progesterone into men and women produces a decrease in alveolar P_{CO_2}.

Functions of the Placenta

The early stages in the formation of the placenta have already been described. The organ increases in weight steadily throughout pregnancy and at term its weight is about 500 g, one-sixth of that of the child. The human placenta can be localized by ultrasonic techniques. The circulation through the placenta is illustrated in Figure 29.23. Occlusion of a spiral artery causes an area of infarction (necrosis); such lesions are seen in 25 per cent of normal pregnancies.

The placenta has two main functions: as an endocrine gland and in the transfer of substances between mother and fetus (Fig. 29.24). The role of the placenta in the production of oestrogens and progesterone has already been described. At least three peptide hormones are produced by the placenta: human chorionic gonadotrophin (HCG), human chorionic thyrotrophin (HCT) and human placental lactogen (HPL). HCG has been mentioned earlier (p. 491). HCT has an action similar to TSH (p. 468) but is not structurally identical. HPL is a substance in human placental tissue which promotes lactation in some animals. There is as yet no evidence that HPL is concerned with lactation in man but it may have a role in controlling the volume and osmolarity of the amniotic fluid, in which it is present in high concentration. The production of HPL increases throughout pregnancy and measurements of HPL levels in the maternal plasma gives some indication of placental function.

A wide variety of substances is able to cross the placenta —among the most important are oxygen, CO_2 and the waste products of fetal metabolism. In general substances of small molecular weight cross more readily than larger molecules and lipid-soluble substances cross more readily than water soluble substances. Some substances such as glucose are transported actively. Certain proteins, notably immunoglobulins and some enzymes are able to cross the placenta unchanged, possibly in pinocytotic vesicles. Many drugs given in pregnancy cross the placenta; in particular anaesthetics used to relieve pain in labour may affect the fetus.

A full term human fetus requires 15 to 25 ml oxygen per minute. If the arterio-venous oxygen difference of the blood supplying the uterus is 7 ml per 100 ml the fetal requirement could be met with a blood flow of 200 to 350 ml per min. In fact the uterine blood flow is between 500 and 750 ml/minute but this supplies the needs of the uterus and placenta as well as the

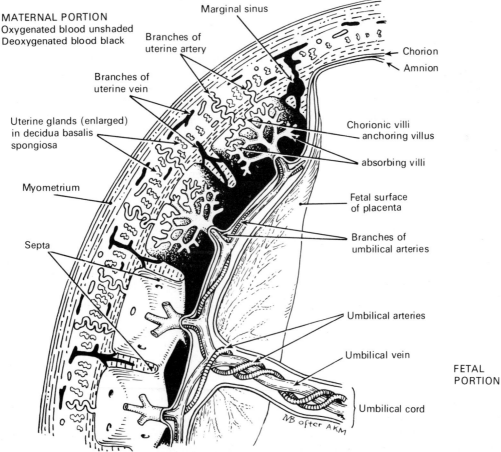

Fig. 29.23 The essential features of placental structure after the 60 mm stage. Four cotyledons, including a marginal one, are illustrated; the cotyledons are separated from each other on the maternal side by the septa. They each contain the group of villi which constitute the associated 'fetal' cotyledon. The villi branch freely and there are many adhesions between adjacent ones so giving a partially labyrinthine nature to the intervillous space. The openings of the endometrial arteries and veins into the intervillous space through the basal plate are indicated. About 70 uterine (spiral) arteries supply the mature placenta which has about 200 cotyledons of various sizes. (*After* W. J. Hamilton & J. D. Boyd (1960) *Journal of Anatomy, London,* 94, 297–328.)

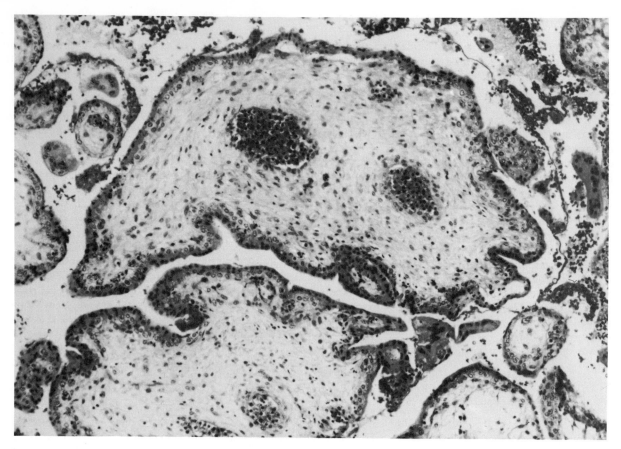

Fig. 29.24 Chorionic villi at the 3rd month of pregnancy. The stroma of the whole villus (central, in cross-section) contains two relatively large, and, near its upper edge, one small fetal blood vessel recognizable by the content of nucleated red blood corpuscles (normoblasts). Two additional vessels can be seen in the stroma of the villus occupying the lower left part of the field. The villi have a covering of chorionic epithelium or *trophoblast*. In places this epithelium is recognizable as having two layers: an outer layer consisting of small dark nuclei in a background of uniform cytoplasm, the *syncytiotrophoblast*; an inner layer of larger paler cells and nuclei, the *cytotrophoblast*. The intervillous space, normally filled with maternal blood, also contains several free-lying islands of syncytiotrophoblast. Haematoxylin and eosin ×165. (*By courtesy of W. W. Park.*)

fetus. The blood flow is reduced by uterine contractions and by exercise.

The umbilical vein taking fetal blood from the placenta has a Po_2 up to 40 mm Hg and the umbilical artery has a Po_2 of 8 to 16 mm Hg immediately after delivery but probably 20 to 30 mm Hg *in utero*. The Po_2 gradient across the placenta, that is between the intervillous space (containing maternal arterial blood) and the umbilical vein, is therefore considerable; since the area of the placental exchange membrane at full term is about 14 m² and the amount of tissue between the fetal vessels is quite small oxygen can easily cross the placental membrane by diffusion. The Pco_2 difference between the umbilical artery and the intervillous space is said to be about 7 mm Hg.

The Po_2 of the blood going to the fetus is low when compared with the adult value of 100 mm Hg for arterial blood. Three factors contribute to the efficiency with which oxygen is transported to the fetal tissues. One is that fetal haemoglobin has a higher oxygen affinity than adult haemoglobin; in other words the oxygen saturation curve is shifted to the left (p. 224). The second is that fetal blood has a higher haemoglobin content and the third is the *Bohr effect* (p. 224). The oxygen saturation curve is affected by the pH of the blood and this effect is greater for fetal haemoglobin than for adult

haemoglobin. In the placenta the pH is low because of the combined effects of the metabolism of the fetus and placenta. As a result of this low pH the oxygen affinity of fetal blood is increased to a much greater extent than that of the maternal blood so enhancing oxygen uptake. In the fetal tissues which are less acid, oxygen is more readily released from haemoglobin.

The fetuses of mothers who smoke heavily are smaller than normal and have a greater risk of perinatal death. These effects have been attributed to the high concentration of carboxyhaemoglobin in the maternal and fetal blood; the consequent shift of the oxygen dissociation curve to the left leads to hypoxia in the fetus.

The fetal blood sugar is lower than the maternal and a rise in blood sugar in the maternal circulation is followed by an increase in that of the fetus. Since the latter returns quickly to the resting value, the sugar must be utilized or stored in the fetal tissues. Glucose passes through the placenta from a zone of high concentration to a zone of lower concentration but the amount transferred is more than would be expected in simple diffusion. The glycogen content of the fetal liver varies more rapidly than the glycogen stored in the decidual tissue of the placenta; the former fluctuates with the fetal blood sugar while the latter is relatively constant. Insulin does not appear to pass across the placenta.

The fat in the fetal stores is produced from maternal free fatty acids which are continually exchanging across the placenta.

The concentration of free amino acids in the fetal blood is higher than in the maternal blood; the concentration ratio for different amino acids varies between 1·2 and 4. Injection of amino acids into the mother increases their concentration in the fetal blood. As might be expected from the rate of increase in fetal weight, protein synthesis in the fetus is at its highest at the end of pregnancy and must depend on active transfer of amino acids across the placenta.

Even if the mother is anaemic the child is usually born with a normal haemoglobin concentration. It may, however, quickly develop anaemia since even in the most favourable circumstances the fetal stores of iron are low. Studies with ^{51}Fe have shown that a pregnant woman absorbs a much larger proportion of ingested iron than a non-pregnant woman and that the iron may pass very quickly to the fetus. The iron concentration in the fetus at term is higher than that in the mother; it is likely therefore that there is an active transfer of iron across the placenta.

The haemoglobin content of the mother's blood is often low but it is doubtful whether this should be regarded as a true anaemia since it is largely the result of the increased plasma volume. While it is usual to give iron supplements in pregnancy it is doubtful whether these are of value unless the mother is iron-deficient at the start of the pregnancy. Folic acid deficiency seldom causes anaemia except in multiple pregnancies.

Many official bodies recommend that supplementary calcium should be given in pregnancy but it now seems clear that with calcium, as with iron, the intestine adapts to increase calcium absorption to meet the needs of the fetus (p. 282).

The placenta acts as a heat exchanger between fetus and mother; the fetal temperature is about 0·5°C above the deep body temperature of the mother.

The placenta functions adequately for about 40 weeks. If parturition is delayed the gaseous and other needs of the fetus may not be adequately met. The child born after a prolonged pregnancy has a reduced chance of survival.

Parturition

Labour occurs in some 55 per cent of all women at approximately 280±7 days from the first day of the last menstrual period; in 25 per cent it occurs before the 273rd day and in 20 per cent after the 287th day. There is no evidence that the length of the menstrual cycle has an influence on the duration of pregnancy. Since the non-pregnant uterus shows spontaneous activity it is not surprising to find that contractions occur early in pregnancy; they are small and usually separated by periods of an hour or so in which the uterus is quiescent. From the twentieth week the contractions are greater in amplitude and much more frequent, although they remain irregular until the last few weeks of pregnancy when rhythmic contractions begin. The interval between the contraction waves in late pregnancy is usually from 5 to 10 minutes.

It is not easy to account for the onset of labour in hormonal terms. The oestrogen and progesterone blood levels continue to rise (p. 497) until parturition has occurred and the final decline in the production of these hormones is the result rather than the cause of parturition. Some workers have claimed that there is a late fall in progesterone levels which allows the combined effect of oestrogens and prostaglandins to initiate uterine contractions.

Oxytocin may play a part in the onset of labour. Certainly infusions of oxytocin may bring on labour; also the sensitivity of the uterus to oxytocin increases steadily throughout pregnancy. However this does not prove that oxytocin is responsible for parturition. If it were, one would expect that hypophysectomy would delay parturition but this is not necessarily the case. Further the plasma concentration of oxytocin is low in pregnancy and does not increase in labour. Its concentration in the amniotic fluid, however, increases at term because of increased production by the fetus. It is possible that parturition is brought about by the increase in the sensitivity of the uterus to oxytocin. Synthetic oxytocin is used near term to induce labour.

The plasma of pregnant but not of non-pregnant women contains oxytocinase, produced by the syncytiotrophoblast, which destroys oxytocin. The half-life of injected oxytocin in pregnancy is only 2 to 4 minutes. The oxytocinase activity increases with gestational age up to a maximum at term but there is no decline before or during labour; it disappears after parturition. The presence of this enzyme makes accurate assay of plasma oxytocin difficult.

Prostaglandin E given by mouth can produce uterine contractions and induce labour, even in early pregnancy, but its effect is even greater when it is delivered directly to the uterus by intrauterine injection. Prostaglandin is detectable in the plasma during labour with peaks associated with each uterine contraction.

It was shown by Sir James Simpson in 1856 that the nervous system is not responsible for the uterine contractions of labour. In his experiments on pigs, destruction of the thoracic and lumbar cord did not interfere greatly with delivery although the contractions of the abdominal muscles were abolished. Near full term the onset of labour may be hastened by emotional factors but it is not affected by section of the sympathetic and parasympathetic nerves.

Since the ovaries can be removed early in pregnancy in women without causing abortion and since the corpus luteum begins to degenerate in the third month of pregnancy, the hormones produced in the ovary can have little influence in determining the onset of labour. The placenta certainly produces gonadotrophic hormones as well as oestrogens and progesterone, all of which are apparently necessary for the maintenance of pregnancy.

Distension of the uterus is unlikely to be an important factor in the onset of labour. The duration of pregnancy remains constant in spite of great variations in size of the fetus and in spite of the presence of excessive amounts of amniotic fluid (hydramnios); even in extrauterine pregnancies in which the embryo is in the uterine tube or abdominal cavity and the uterus is empty the patient may experience labour pains at full term. Furthermore single pregnancies come to an end at a distension which is much less than that obtaining in a multiple pregnancy long before parturition. If distension of the uterus were the only exciting factor in parturition it would be expected that it would occur when a certain total litter weight was reached. This is not so since the total litter weights in singletons, twins, triplets and quadruplets at birth are 3·38, 4·79, 5·45 and 5·58 kg respectively. It is likely however that the uterus becomes less tolerant of distension as pregnancy advances since the mean period of gestation decreases in the four categories just given in the order 280·5, 261·6, 246·8 and 236·8 days.

On two occasions twin pregnancies have been reported in which one twin was present in each horn of a bicornuate uterus. There was an interval of several weeks between the births of the children. It is difficult to see how conditions at the same time in one woman can be suitable for the maintenance, as well as the termination, of pregnancy unless there is some local factor which triggers off the mechanism of parturition. It has long been suspected that the fetus itself has some influence on the length of gestation. If it has a poorly developed pituitary gland with hypoplasia of the adrenal cortex, gestation is often prolonged. Although the evidence for a fetal triggering of parturition in women is rather slender there is no doubt of fetal influence in the sheep. Electrocoagulation of pituitary glands of fetal lambs prolongs gestation for many days. This of course causes adrenal hypoplasia and, in conformity with this, fetal adrenalectomy results in prolongation of pregnancy. Conversely infusion of ACTH into fetal lambs is followed by parturition in a few days. Cortisol given to the ewe has no effect but given to the fetuses causes labour. In this way it seems clear that the fetus, probably through its hypothalamic and adrenal hormones, plays a part in determining the time of its own birth.

Labour. The muscular activity of the human uterus can be studied by passing a catheter through the cervix, or through the abdominal wall and through the uterine wall, into the amniotic cavity and by connecting it to a manometer which records the variations in pressure. The slight contractions of the uterus which occur throughout pregnancy increase the pressure in the uterine veins and assist the movement of blood through the intervillous placental spaces and so aid the oxygenation of the fetal blood. Towards the end of pregnancy, but long before labour begins, the basal amniotic pressure is about 5 mm Hg with slow oscillations of 1 to 5 mm Hg above this value. At the onset of labour these rhythmic contractions increase and the basal intrauterine pressure rises to 8 or 12 mm Hg.

In the *first stage* of normal labour the intrauterine pressure rises slowly with each contraction to a peak of 30 to 50 mm Hg above the basal value and then falls more slowly to the basal level. These contractions, which occur at intervals of two to five minutes, can be felt by the hand placed on the abdominal wall. When the pressure is above a certain value, which varies with different patients, but is in the region 25 to 35 mm Hg, the mother is conscious of a labour pain, that is a pain commencing in the lumbosacral region and radiating to the front and down the thighs. This pain is relieved by injecting a local anaesthetic alongside the cervix. By pressing on the amniotic fluid the uterine contractions dilate first the upper part of the cervical canal and later the os uteri. The membranes finally rupture and a small quantity of amniotic fluid escapes.

In the *second stage* of labour the intrauterine pressure at the height of a contraction may rise to 110 mm Hg and the pressure between contractions is usually about twice that recorded in the first stage. The head of the child is slowly forced through the pelvis and is born, the remainder of the body following almost at once. During this stage voluntary contraction of the abdominal muscles can double the intra-uterine pressure, so that the combined pressure caused by the contractions of the uterine and of the abdominal muscles may be as much as 260 mm Hg.

Uterine activity has been recorded by placing small balloons (0·02 ml) in the myometrium. When the muscle contracts the pressure rises in the balloons and is recorded. The contraction wave in labour starts at a pace-maker at the uterine end of one uterine tube, either right or left; the wave is propagated mainly downwards to the cervix at a speed of 1 or 2 cm per sec and reaches its peak in 50 sec or thereby. The contraction lasts longer in the parts near the pace-maker and diminishes in intensity as it passes down the uterus.

The pressure within the uterus at the height of a contraction may be sufficient to squeeze out the maternal blood from the uterine vessels into the vena cava and even occasionally into the aorta if the intrauterine pressure rises above the maternal arterial pressure. Thus at the height of each contraction the venous pressure is considerably raised, and this rise may be dangerous in patients with cardiac disease. The arterial pressure increases slightly during a labour contraction but quite considerably if the abdominal muscles contract at the same time. The fetal heart rate falls during a uterine contraction, the amount of the fall depending on the rise of intrauterine pressure.

After the birth of the child uterine contractions cease for a time, usually 5 to 15 minutes, and then in the *third stage* of labour they begin again and the placenta and membranes are expelled. With the detachment and delivery of the placenta a raw bleeding surface is left but the average loss of blood is only 300 ml. The mechanisms which limit blood loss are not clearly understood. The contraction of the uterus no doubt plays a part; when the child is allowed to suck, oxytocin is released and the uterus contracts firmly but does not go into a prolonged spasm. However, administration of oxytocin makes no apparent difference to the blood loss. During the *puerperium*, that is the period immediately following parturition, the uterus shrinks until, when involution is complete, it is only a little larger than in the virgin state.

The average maternal oxygen uptake in the last hour of labour ranges from 285 to 700 ml/min and this indicates that labour may be described as mild to moderately heavy work (see p. 18). The blood lactate rises from a resting value of 1·5 up to 2·8 mmol/l or more; this is higher than would be expected from exercise like cycling.

THE FETUS

The fertilized zygote at conception measures approximately 1 to 3 mm and an average baby at delivery is 50 cm in length and weighs 3·4 kg. There is a slowly accelerating pattern of growth which slows up towards term, and after delivery there is a drop and a rather slow growth immediately after delivery. Then the growth pattern of the middle trimester is regained. The fall-off in growth rate towards term is thought to be a reflexion of the decreasing ability of the placenta to nourish the fetus. The clinical estimation of growth of the fetus has become increasingly important since an attempt is made to prevent intrauterine deaths caused by placental insufficiency. This is associated with the so-called dysmature child which is light for dates and lacking in subcutaneous fat. Many tests have been devised to try and recognize this condition before birth but recently a more direct appreciation of fetal size has been possible by the use of ultrasound.

Nearly half of the weight of the fetus is acquired in the final 6 to 8 weeks and during this time, if the mother does not receive sufficient food, the fetus draws on the maternal tissues. The birth weight of the infant is not, therefore, governed by the mother's diet unless there is severe undernutrition. Individual birth weights of the children of a multiple pregnancy are on the average lower than those of children of single birth. The mean birth weights of singletons, twins, triplets and quadruplets born in Britain are respectively 3·38, 2·40, 1·82 and 1·40 kg. The rate of fetal growth in multiple pregnancies may be retarded in the last few weeks, perhaps because the smaller size of the placenta restricts fetal growth or because the maternal circulation cannot supply sufficient nutrients.

During the last months of pregnancy the glycogen content of the liver, skeletal muscles and heart rises to several times the adult level. These easily available carbohydrate reserves may help the child to survive the changes in food and oxygen supply as well as the drop in environmental temperature occurring after birth. Brown adipose tissue (p. 419) can be recognized in 28-week human fetuses.

At least two factors influencing birth weight are social class and prematurity. On average the infant's birth weight is lower, the lower the social group to which the mother belongs; the reason for this is undoubtedly complex and the differences are not likely to be attributable to dietary causes alone. Premature birth or birth at any age of an infant which is small for its gestational age is associated with a higher death rate during the first month of extrauterine life (neonatal mortality).

Fetal Circulation

The sheep is a convenient animal for investigating the fetal circulation because the uterus does not contract as soon as the lamb is delivered. Also catheters may be implanted into the fetal vessels and fluids *in utero*. When a lamb is delivered and the umbilical cord is tied, respiration begins and a number of circulatory adjustments takes place. The pathway taken by the circulating blood can be studied before and after respiration has begun by X-ray angiography of the fetus. The information afforded by this method has been supplemented by Dawes and his colleagues at Oxford who have measured the oxygen saturation of the blood at various points in the fetal circulation of the sheep.

The fetal circulation (Figs. 29.25 and 29.26A) is quite different from that in the adult, chiefly because the heart has to pump the blood through the placenta as well as through the fetal body. Of the blood passing down the descending aorta only a small part goes to the lower limbs, the major part passing by the two *umbilical arteries* to the fetal side of the placenta. After taking up oxygen there the blood is returned in the *umbilical vein* and flows either through the liver or by means of a by-pass, the *ductus venosus*, directly to the inferior vena cava which receives also the blood from the alimentary canal and from the lower extremities. At the cardiac end of the

inferior vena cava the blood is divided by the edge of the interatrial septum, the *crista dividens*, into two streams, a large stream which goes directly through the foramen ovale into the left atrium and a somewhat smaller stream which reaches the right atrium. In the left atrium the blood coming from the inferior vena cava is mixed with a small pulmonary bloodstream and then passes to the left ventricle which pumps it to the arch of the aorta. This blood, the most highly oxygenated blood available in the systemic arteries of the fetus, first supplies the heart by the coronary arteries and then the head and upper part of the body, the remainder reaching the descending aorta. The reduced blood returning from the head drains into the superior vena cava and right atrium where it is mixed with the reduced blood coming from the coronary sinus and with the right stream from the inferior vena cava which has a high oxygen content. The blood then passes to the right ventricle, the output of which is delivered partly into the lungs via the pulmonary artery but mainly to the aorta through the *ductus arteriosus*, a wide vessel about the same diameter as the aorta at the point where they meet. In this way the main stream of blood from the right ventricle by-passes the lungs

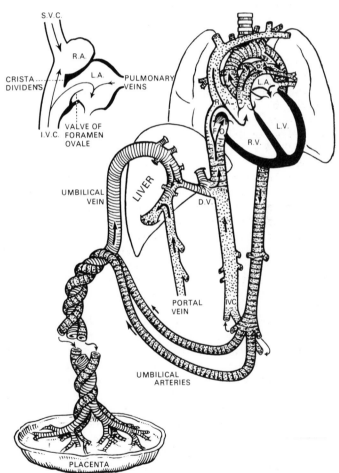

Fig. 29.25 A plan of the human fetal circulation. The upper end of the inferior vena cava opens directly into the left atrium through the foramen ovale (see inset) as well as into the right atrium. R.A. and R.V. = right atrium and ventricle. L.A. and L.V. = left atrium and ventricle. S.V.C. = superior vena cava. I.V.C. = inferior vena cava. D.A. = ductus arteriosus. D.V. = ductus venosus. F.O. = foramen ovale. *(By courtesy of G. S. Dawes.)*

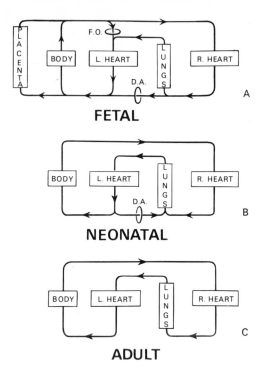

FETAL

NEONATAL

ADULT

Fig. 29.26 Diagrams to illustrate the changes in the circulation at birth as described in the text. In A the two ventricles are working in parallel to drive blood from the great veins to the arteries. B is the condition reached a few minutes after birth when the cord is tied and the foramen ovale, F.O., closes. When the ductus arteriosus, D.A., finally closes the adult circulation C is established with the two ventricles working in series. (G. V. Born, G. S. Dawes, J. C. Mott & J. G. Widdicombe (1954) *Cold Spring Harbor Symposia on Quantitative Biology,* 19, 106.)

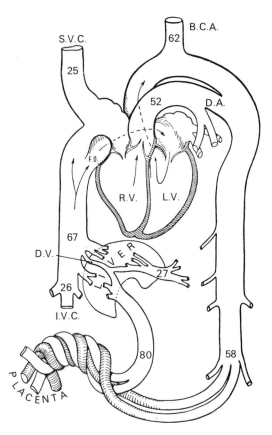

Fig. 29.27 Diagram of the fetal circulation in the lamb. The figures indicate the percentage oxygen saturation of blood withdrawn simultaneously from various vessels and averaged from determinations on six lambs. I.V.C., inferior vena cava; S.V.C., superior vena cava; D.V., ductus venosus; F.O., foramen ovale; D.A., ductus arteriosus; B.C.A., branchio-cephalic artery. (G. V. R. Born, G. S. Dawes, J. C. Mott & J. G. Widdicombe (1954) *Cold Spring Harbor Symposia on Quantitative Biology,* 19, 103.)

and is distributed to the thorax, abdomen and lower limbs as well as to the placenta through the umbilical arteries.

Figure 29.27 shows the oxygen saturation of blood in eight of the principal vessels of the mature lamb before respiration is allowed to take place. From these figures the distribution of the blood flow can be calculated. The right atrium receives blood with an oxygen saturation of 67 per cent from the inferior vena cava and of 25 per cent from the superior vena cava and these streams are mixed and ejected into the pulmonary artery at a saturation of 52 per cent. This means that nearly two parts of inferior caval blood are mixed with one part of superior caval blood. On the other hand the left atrium receives inferior caval blood and pulmonary vein blood in the ratio of 4·5 to 1. The greater proportion of blood flow from the inferior vena cava into the left side of the heart explains the observation that the oxygen content of the brachiocephalic artery supplying the head is larger than that of the umbilical artery. The fetal tissues receive oxygen at a pressure only one-third of that in the adult. Figure 29.26A shows that, since the two ventricles are not in series (as they are in the adult, Fig. 29.26C), there is no need for their outputs to be equal. There is little difference in the thicknesses of the walls of the two ventricles in the fetus and presumably little difference in the work done by them. The flow through the various tissues as a percentage of the combined output is, lungs, 10; other fetal

tissues, 35; placenta, 55; foramen ovale, ductus arteriosus and aortic isthmus, 40.

If a pregnant ewe is made to breathe air of varying Po_2 her blood Po_2 varies over a wide range but the fetal arterial and venous Po_2 vary very little. However, when the mother is made to breathe air containing a low percentage of oxygen the fetal oxygen saturation falls; fetal heart rate and blood pressure increase and umbilical blood flow also increases. Since the increased umbilical flow and rise of blood pressure can be produced by injecting adrenaline or noradrenaline into the lamb, it is possible that the mechanism compensating for maternal asphyxia is a reflex release of sympathetic amines originated by stimulation of the chemoreceptors of the aortic bodies. When the fetus is severely asphyxiated and the arterial oxygen saturation falls below 15 to 20 per cent the heart begins to slow down; this is an urgent signal to the obstetrician of fetal distress.

At a normal birth the umbilical cord is torn as the animal is delivered and the umbilical arteries constrict. The umbilical vessels are extremely sensitive to stretch and also contract firmly if, for example, an attempt is made to insert a needle into them to obtain blood. This is a local response of the smooth muscle and not a reflex adjustment since these vessels, which are outside the fetal body, have no nerves.

The fetal O_2 saturation falls at birth and signs of anoxia are present. Breathing is initiated and stimulated by anoxia and by sensory stimuli from the skin and from the carotid chemoreceptors and also by the clamping of the cord. At birth the sudden cessation of umbilical flow increases the peripheral resistance suddenly and causes a rise of fetal blood pressure; at the same time the arterial oxygen content falls. When breathing begins the expansion of the lungs is associated with a great decrease in pulmonary vascular resistance; hence the rate of blood flow through the lungs increases five- to ten-fold within a minute or so. Consequently the pressure in the left atrium rises; the pressure in the inferior vena cava falls as the blood flow from the placenta is cut off and the valve of the foramen ovale (Fig. 29.25) closes. Thus from within a minute of breathing all the venous blood enters the right atrium and passes through the lungs (Fig. 29.26B). About a week after birth the valve of the foramen ovale becomes fused to the atrial wall. The ductus venosus closes by collapse or contraction of its junction with the umbilical vein probably as a result of the decrease in transmural pressure when the umbilical flow is arrested.

Before the animal breathes the pulmonary arterial pressure exceeds the pressure in the descending aorta. The decrease in pulmonary vascular resistance results in a fall in pulmonary pressure and in a reversal of the direction of blood flow through the ductus arteriosus (Fig. 29.26B); that is to say within a few minutes of birth blood flows from the aorta to the pulmonary artery and may contribute half or more of the total pulmonary blood flow. This stream of blood flowing through the left heart, the ductus arteriosus and the lungs increases the pulmonary blood flow and leads to a substantial increase of carotid oxygen saturation. This increased flow is especially important at this stage for it must be remembered that at this time the lungs are not properly expanded, nor have they been cleared of the amniotic fluid with which they were filled before birth.

Closure of the ductus arteriosus begins within the first 10 minutes but it is not complete for many hours: the constriction is a response to the increased oxygen tension. The muscle of the ductus in immature fetuses is much less responsive to a rise in Po_2 than it it is in full term animals. In the lamb the external diameter is reduced from 10 mm to 5 mm in several minutes but since the aortic pressure is rising at this time and the pulmonary pressure is falling (Fig. 29.28), a large amount of blood continues to flow through producing vibrations which can be heard as a murmur. This is occasionally heard in new-born babies. At this time the left ventricular output is greater than the right. The circulation is now at the stage represented in Figure 29.26B. The flow of blood through the ductus ceases after 21 days or so and then the adult type of circulation is reached (Fig. 29.26C) in which the ventricular outputs are equal. The closure of the ductus arteriosus and ductus venosus is finally made permanent by a proliferation of the lining endothelium which takes several months to complete; eventually the obliterated vessels are represented only by fibrous cords. There is evidence that prostaglandins play a part in the closure of the foramen ovale and the ductus arteriosus.

There are good reasons for believing that the circulatory changes at birth in the human fetus are similar. Although the umbilical cord continues to pulsate for some time after the child is delivered it is customary to tie the cord as soon as the

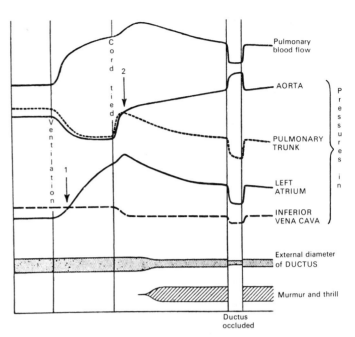

Fig. 29.28 Diagram to illustrate the changes which occur in the circulation of a lamb when ventilation is begun before the umbilical cord is tied. At 1 the mean pressure in the left atrium rises above that in the inferior vena cava and thereafter the valve of the foramen ovale is closed. At 2 the pressure in the pulmonary trunk falls below that in the descending aorta and the direction of blood flow through the ductus arteriosus is reversed. Temporary occlusion of the ductus arteriosus now reduces pulmonary blood flow and abolishes the murmur and thrill which have appeared in the pulmonary trunk. (G. V. Born, G. S. Dawes, J. C. Mott & J. G. Widdicombe (1954) *Cold Spring Harbor Symposia on Quantitative Biology*, 19, 104.)

child is born. This may not, however, be the best practice because, if drainage of blood from the placenta to the child is allowed by holding it below the level of the vulva until pulsation in the cord has ceased, it may gain up to 100 ml of blood and so increase its stores of iron. The blood volume of the new-born infant is about 275 ml. Before respiration begins the placenta contains 85 ml of blood but only 40 ml if the cord is clamped after the child has breathed; the difference, 45 ml, is presumably accommodated in the baby's pulmonary circulation.

The human umbilical cord varies in length from 30 to 129 cm (mean 61 cm). The blood flow in the human cord is 8·5 ml per minute in a 12 week fetus and 80 ml per minute in a 28 week fetus. The systolic blood pressure of the child at birth is about 70 mm Hg and rises to 90 mm Hg at 6 months.

LACTATION

The mammary gland consists of numerous lobules made up of clusters of rounded alveoli (Fig. 29.29). The secretion of the cells lining the alveoli passes into small ducts which unite with ducts from neighbouring alveoli to form the lactiferous tubules. These converge on the mammary papilla (usually called nipple or teat) and open on its summit. Beneath the areola, just before it reaches the nipple, each tubule has a dilatation, the ampulla, which acts as a milk reservoir. Smooth

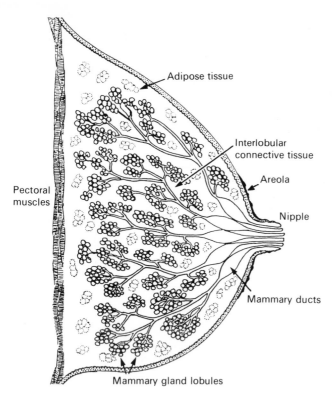

Fig. 29.29   Structure of lactating breast (*From* D. L. Gardner & T. C. Dodds (1976) *Human Histology* 3rd edition Edinburgh: Churchill Livingstone.)

muscle fibres are found in the nipple and around the ducts and the alveoli are surrounded by myoepithelial cells. In the non-pregnant woman the alveoli are small but during pregnancy they enlarge and the cells lining them increase in number.

Both sexes possess mammary glands but they remain rudimentary in the male. In the girl enlargement of the breasts is one of the signs of puberty; there may be a transient slight enlargement during the luteal phase of the menstrual cycle but full development is achieved only as a result of pregnancy. In a non-pregnant woman an increase in the size of the mammary gland can be produced by injection of oestrogen but a greater effect can be obtained by treatment with oestrogen plus progesterone. Experiments on rats show that oestrogen seems to be responsible chiefly for growth of the ducts, the combination of oestrogen and progesterone causing, in addition, alveolar growth. The full development of the lactating breast in these animals requires prolactin, growth hormone, oestrogen, progesterone, insulin, thyroid hormone and adrenal corticoids. In other words successful lactation

requires a normal hormonal environment. Although during pregnancy it is often possible by pressure to expel a few drops of milk from the breasts, a free flow of milk does not occur until the second or third day after the birth of the child. It seems that during pregnancy the mammary glands are kept in an unresponsive state by the direct action of the large amount of oestrogens and progesterone in the circulation but the lactogenic hormones cannot bring about milk secretion unless the mammary gland has been prepared by the ovarian hormones. The decline in the amount of these hormones in the blood after parturition allows the lactogenic hormone, *prolactin*, from the anterior pituitary to act directly on the alveolar epithelium. The plasma prolactin level in the last month of pregnancy is two or three times the non-pregnant level. The amount of prolactin in the blood and pituitary is not altered by the rise in oestrogens; it may be liberated from the pituitary by TRH or by withdrawal of the hypothalamic inhibitory factor, PIF (p. 467). Unfortunately prolactin administration does not increase output in women with inadequate milk production. During the puerperium adminis-tration of large amounts of oestrogen can stop the flow of milk probably by a direct action on the breast tissue and perhaps by inhibitory factor, PIF (p. 467). Unfortunately prolactin cryptine, a dopaminergic drug, inhibits prolactin secretion and diminishes milk secretion. The prolactin level falls soon after cessation of breast feeding.

Although the building up of secreting breast tissue and the initiation of lactation is mainly a hormonal affair there is no doubt that regular removal of milk from the breast is essential to maintain the flow. A woman with a strong, healthy, hungry child who sucks vigorously and empties the breasts, secretes more milk than one with a weak child. In dairy cattle more frequent milking produces more milk.

The fluid (colostrum) produced in the breasts during the first two or three days of the puerperium is small in amount and has a high protein and a low fat and sugar content. A healthy new-born baby put to the breast or given a bottle takes in so little fluid or nutrient that he may lose by catabolism and excretion of water up to one-tenth of his birth weight. Some regard this period of semi-starvation as physiological. Breast milk affords some protection against infection by virtue of its antibodies, principally IgA.

The level of prolactin remains high so long as a mother breast-feeds her child frequently. This hyperprolactinaemia results in a physiological amenorrhoea by inhibiting ovulation and a woman is therefore involuntarily infertile while lactating. Breast milk contains all the requirements for infant growth and it is free from contamination and subsequent infection. There is much evidence to show that it is superior to artificial milk unless lactation fails.

REFERENCES

Austin C R (ed) 1973 The mammalian fetus in vitro. Chapman & Hall, London
Barcroft J 1946 Researches on pre-natal life. Blackwell, Oxford
Beard R W 1975 The menopause. British Journal of Hospital Medicine 13: 631–637
Beard R W, Nathanielsz P W (eds) 1976 Fetal physiology and medicine. Saunders, London
Besser G M, Thorner M D 1975 Prolactin. In: Lant A F (ed) Advanced medicine symposium II. Pitman, London, p. 255–266
Boyd J D, Hamilton W J 1975 The human placenta. Macmillan, London
Campbell S 1974 Fetal growth. Clinics in Obstetrics and Gynaecology 1: 41–65
Chamberlain G V P, Wilkinson A W (eds) 1979 Placental transfer. Pitman, Tunbridge Wells

Cockburn F, Drillien C M (eds) 1974 Neonatal medicine. Blackwell, Oxford

Comline R S, Cross K W, Dawes G S, Nathanielsz P W (eds) 1973 Fetal and neonatal physiology. Cambridge University Press

Embrey M P 1975 The prostaglandins in human reproduction. Churchill Livingstone, Edinburgh

Fox H 1978 The pathology of the placenta. Saunders, London

Gomes W R, Van Demark N L 1974 The male reproductive system. Annual Review of Physiology 36: 307–330

Greep, R O (ed) 1974 Reproductive physiology. Butterworth, London

Hogarth P J 1978 Biology of reproduction. Butterworth, London

Hytten F E, Leitch I 1976 The physiology of human pregnancy, 3rd edn. Blackwell, Oxford.

Rudolph A M 1979 Fetal and neonatal pulmonary circulation. Annual Review of Physiology 41: 383–395

Scarpelli E M (ed) 1976 Pulmonary physiology of the fetus, newborn and child. Kimpton, London

Short R V (ed) 1979 Reproduction. British Medical Bulletin, 35: 97–208

Steven D 1975 Introduction to the placenta. Academic Press, London

Sutherland H W, Stowers J M 1975 Carbohydrate metabolism in pregnancy and the newborn. Churchill Livingstone, Edinburgh

Taylor R W 1975 The normal sexual response. British Medical Journal ii: 543–545

Tyson J E (ed) 1978 Neuroendocrinology of reproduction. Clinics in Obstetrics and Gynaecology 5: 249–502

Vorherr H 1974 The breast: Morphology, physiology and lactation. Academic Press, New York

Wilson E W, Rennie, P I C 1976 The menstrual cycle. Lloyd-Luke, London

Yen, S S C, Jaffe R B (eds) 1978 Reproductive endocrinology. Saunders, Philadelphia

30 Growth and Development

Accurate knowledge of the normal growth and development of children is essential for the recognition of the deleterious effects of any form of chronic disease. Body growth in boys and girls is a continuing process throughout childhood and adolescence. It is exceedingly rapid in the first 2 years of life and less so during the middle years of childhood. Later there is a growth spurt in relation to puberty followed by cessation of growth when the adult height is reached.

Charts of height plotted against age, known as *height charts*, and of height increment per year plotted against age, known as *height velocity charts*, have been constructed for normal British boys and girls by Tanner and his colleagues. The height chart for boys is shown in Figure 30.1. The centre line, or 50th centile, is the mean and represents the growth curve of the average boy; the 97th and 3rd centiles are ±1·881 standard deviations from the mean. A boy whose height lies above the 97th centile is taller than 97 per cent of the population whereas a boy whose height lies on the 3rd centile is taller than only 3 per cent of the normal population. Although 3 per cent of the heights fall above the 97th centile and 3 per cent below the 3rd

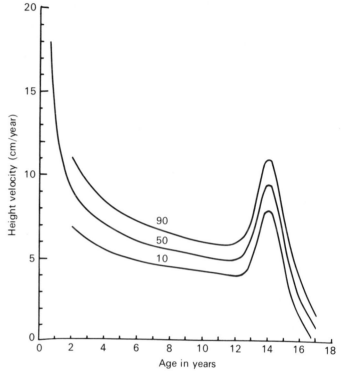

Fig. 30.2 Height velocity chart for boys. The centiles are appropriate to children who have their peak velocity at the average age. (*After* Tanner, J. M. & Whitehouse, R. H. (1976) *Archives of Disease in Childhood*, 51, 170–179.)

centile, boys with heights outside these limits are potentially abnormal and require investigation. The height velocity chart for boys, calculated over periods of 1 year, is shown in Figure 30.2. The height charts for girls are similar except that they show an earlier growth spurt. *Weight charts* for both boys and girls are also available.

The growth in head circumference for boys is shown in Figure 30.3. Girls have slightly smaller heads than boys but the growth pattern is similar. The head circumference velocity chart for both sexes is shown in Figure 30.4. A rapid increase in size occurs during the first year of life followed by a less rapid increase during the second year. Thereafter growth in head circumference is very gradual. The increase in head circumference during early life reflects the important postnatal growth spurt of the underlying brain (Fig. 30.5). The brain is particularly vulnerable during this period of rapid growth and adverse factors may damage the forebrain, brain stem or cerebellum and lead to mental subnormality, blindness, deafness or cerebral palsy. The cellularity of the cerebellum increases particularly rapidly during the first year of life and the cerebellum may suffer most from, for example, under-nutrition or deficiency of thyroid hormones at this time (Fig. 30.6).

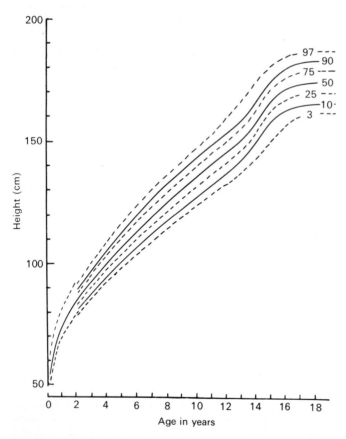

Fig. 30.1 Height chart for boys. The lines represent the centiles for children followed at successive ages. (*After* Tanner, J. M. & Whitehouse, R. H. (1976) *Archives of Disease in Childhood*, 51, 170–179.)

The weight of new-born boys in relation to gestational age is shown in Figure 30.7. A similar chart for girls shows that they are slightly lighter than boys from 34 weeks gestation onwards. By definition, infants of 'low birth weight' (formerly called 'premature') have a birth weight of 2 500 g or less. They are quite often of the expected weight for gestational age, for example, when born before term because of a sudden placental haemorrhage, the pregnancy having been clinically normal up to that point. Another group of infants is classified as 'light-for-dates' because their birth weights are below the normal standard for the gestational age. These infants have been subjected to adverse prenatal influences, such as inadequacy of maternal nutrition or of placental function, chronic intra-uterine infection or genetically determined congenital mal-formation. Both 'preterm' and 'light-for-dates' newborn infants, particularly the latter, are considered 'at risk' with regard to their future progress.

A further parameter of growth and development is the skeletal or bone age. Tanner and his colleagues have described a detailed method of assessment, based on an X-ray of the left wrist and hand, which may be used from the age of 1 year. Stages in the development of the lower end of the radius and ulna, the carpal bones and the metacarpal bones and phalanges of the first, third and fifth digits are used to compile a maturity score on which the bone age is based. In the United States, Greulich and Pyle have published an atlas of the stages of development seen in the X-ray of the left wrist and hand in boys and girls from which the bone age may be determined by visual comparison. Use of this atlas assesses the average normal British child's bone age as about 6 months retarded in

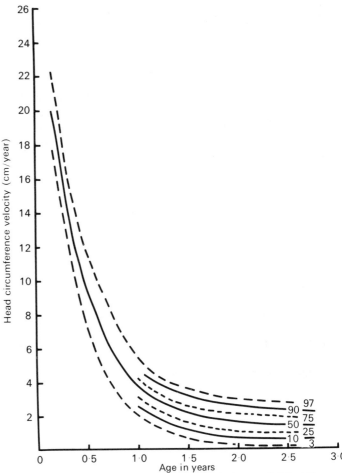

Fig. 30.4   Head circumference velocity chart for boys and girls. (*After* Tanner, J. M., 1973. *Physical growth and Development In:* Forfar, J. C. (ed) *Textbook of Paediatrics* Arneil, G. C. Churchill Livingstone, Edinburgh.)

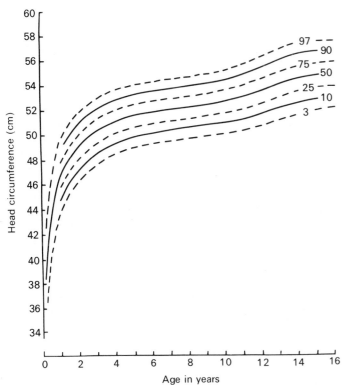

Fig. 30.3   Head circumference chart for boys. (*After* Tanner, J. M., 1973. *Physical growth and Development In:* Forfar, J. O., (ed) *Text-book of Paediatrics* Arneil, G. C. Churchill Livingstone, Edinburgh.)

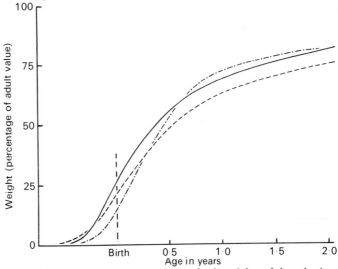

Fig. 30.5   Brain growth. Comparative fresh weights of three brain regions during growth. Weights for forebrain (———), brainstem (— — — —) and cerebellum (—.—.—) have been calculated as a percentage of the adult value, and smooth lines drawn through the points. (*After* Dobbing, J., Sands, J. C., 1973. Quantitative growth and development of human brain. Archives of Disease in Childhood 48: 757–767.)

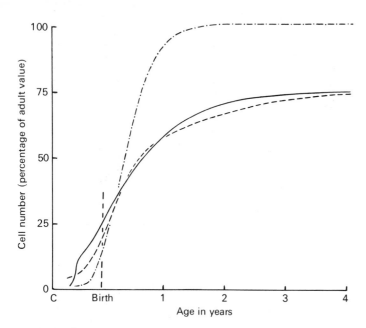

Fig. 30.6 Brain cellularity. Comparative values for cell number in three brain regions during growth. Values for forebrain (————), brainstem (— — —) and cerebellum (—·—·—) have been calculated as a percentage of the adult value, and smooth lines drawn through the points. (*After* Dobbing, J., Sands, J. C., 1973. *Quantitative growth and development of human brain. Archives of Disease in Childhood* 48: 757–767.)

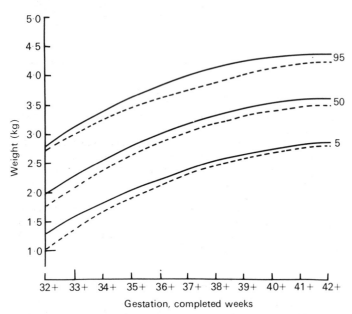

Fig. 30.7 Birth weight in relation to gestational age for boys. The channels marked by interrupted lines give the centiles of weight for first born infants; the channels marked by continuous lines give the centiles for later born infants. First born infants tend to have lower birth weights than their siblings. For greater accuracy, adjustments may be made for the mother's height and mid-pregnancy weight. (*After* Tanner, J. M., 1973. *Physical growth and Development In:* Forfar, J. O., (ed) *Textbook of Paediatrics* Arneil, G. C. Churchill Livingstone, Edinburgh.)

comparison with the Tanner method. There is considerable normal variation in bone age at a given chronological age, particularly during adolescence.

Puberty

During puberty there is a spurt in growth and the body undergoes functional and structural changes making it capable of procreation; the sexual organs mature and the secondary sexual characters develop. In females the pelvis grows rapidly in preparation for childbirth and the amount of fat increases over the shoulders, pelvis, buttocks and thighs. In males there is an increase in muscle mass, the shoulders become broader and the voice breaks. Transient gynaecomastia is common. Psychological changes occur in both sexes.

Tanner has described stages of puberty numbered 1 to 5, based on the growth of the genitalia and pubic hair in boys and the growth of the breasts and pubic hair in girls. Genital maturity ratings in boys are shown in Figure 30.8, breast development ratings in girls in Figure 30.9 and pubic hair ratings in boys and girls in Figure 30.10.

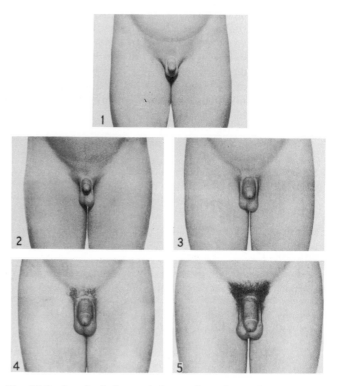

Fig. 30.8 Standards for genital maturity ratings. (*By courtesy of J. M. Tanner.*)

Stage 1 Pre-adolescent. The testes, scrotum and penis are about the same size and shape as in early childhood.

Stage 2 The testes and scrotum are enlarged slightly. The skin of the scrotum is reddened and changed in texture. There is little or no enlargement of the penis at this stage.

Stage 3 The penis is enlarged slightly, mainly in length. There is further growth of the testes and scrotum.

Stage 4 The penis is enlarged further in length and breadth and there is development of the glans. The testes and scrotum are further increased in size and the scrotal skin is darker.

Stage 5 The genitalia are of adult size and shape.

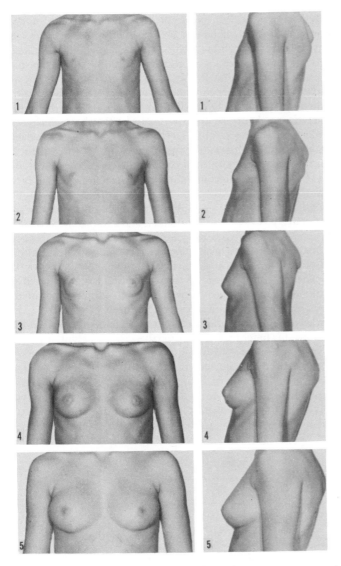

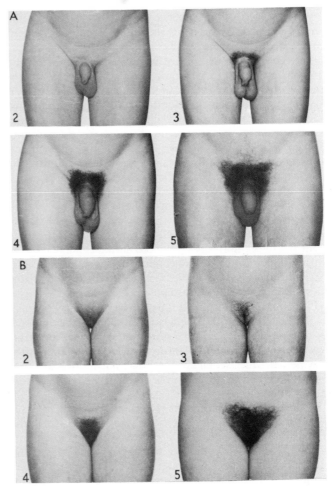

Fig. 30.9 Standards for breast development ratings. (*By courtesy of J. M. Tanner.*)

Stage 1 Pre-adolescent. There is elevation of the papilla only.

Stage 2 Breast bud stage: elevation of the breast and papilla as a small mound. There is enlargement of the areolar diameter.

Stage 3 There is further enlargement and elevation of the breast and areola, with no separation of their contours.

Stage 4 The areola and papilla form a secondary mound projecting above the contour of the breast.

Stage 5 Mature stage: there is projection of the papilla only, due to recession of the areola to the general contour of the breast.

Fig. 30.10 Standards for pubic hair ratings in boys (A) and girls (B). (*By courtesy of J. M. Tanner.*)

Stage 1 Pre-adolescent. No pubic hair is present.

Stage 2 There is a sparse growth of long, slightly pigmented, downy hair, straight or slightly curled, chiefly at the base of the penis or along the labia.

Stage 3 The hair is considerably darker, coarser and more curled. It spreads sparsely over the junction of the pubes.

Stage 4 The hair is now adult in type, but the area covered is still considerably smaller than in the adult. There is no spread to the medial surface of the thighs.

Stage 5 The hair is adult in quantity and type with a distribution of the horizontal (or classically 'feminine') pattern. Spread to the medial surface of the thighs is present. (In males, spread up the linea alba occurs late and is rated as stage 6.)

In both sexes the subcutaneous fat on the trunk and limbs increases in thickness rapidly during the first year of life and then decreases during the middle years of childhood. In girls an increase in trunk and limb fat begins from the age of about 8 years and continues during the years of puberty so that a girl who has tended to be obese during childhood may become markedly so as an adolescent. From the age of about 8 years trunk fat increases in boys but there is virtually no increase of fat in the limbs. Because of such variations in body fat distribution at different ages, weight charts give somewhat different information from that supplied by height charts.

In the average boy the penis begins to enlarge at the age of 12 years and pubic hair appears between the ages of 12 and 13 years. However, there is considerable normal variation in the time of onset of these pubertal signs and the penis may begin to enlarge at 10 years or as late as 14 years. If the scatter in 95 per cent of the normal British population is taken into account, a boy is showing precocious puberty if growth of the penis occurs before the age of 10 years or delayed puberty if growth of the penis does not begin until later than 14 years.

In the majority of girls breast enlargement begins at the age of 11 years and pubic hair appears between the ages of 11 and

12 years, the scatter for 95 per cent of the normal population being 9 years to 13 years for the commencement of breast development. The average age at the menarche is 13 years and 95 per cent of girls first menstruate between their 11th and 15th birthdays. A girl is showing precocious puberty if the breasts enlarge before the age of 9 years and delayed puberty if they show no enlargement after the age of 13 years. In normal individuals, as well as individual differences in the age of onset of puberty, there is variation in the time taken to advance through the various stages. Although the first breast development in girls is usually only 6 months earlier than the first genital development in boys, the growth spurt occurs about 2 years earlier in girls so that the adult height is reached at a correspondingly younger age.

It is thought that puberty begins when the hypothalamus becomes less sensitive to the feed-back mechanism of the small quantities of sex hormones produced during childhood by the gonads. Luteinising hormone releasing hormone (LHRH) therefore increases and the plasma levels of luteinizing hormone (LH) and follicle stimulating hormone (FSH) rise.

In the male FSH stimulates the production of spermatozoa by the testes while LH stimulates Leydig cell function and testosterone synthesis. When testosterone reaches the target organs it is converted into dihydrotestosterone (DHT) by the enzyme 5α-reductase. DHT is metabolically more active than testosterone and its formation is essential for full masculinization to take place.

In the female, FSH stimulates follicular development in the ovary and oestrogen synthesis by the follicles. LH also stimulates oestrogen synthesis, induces ovulation and hence the formation of corpora lutea which produce progesterone. The principal oestrogen is oestradiol-17β (p. 490). A small quantity of testosterone is formed in the female by the peripheral conversion of androstenedione to testosterone.

In both sexes, the plasma levels of androgens of adrenal origin rise sharply before those of LH and FSH. This may be in response to unidentified hypothalamic or pituitary hormones. Adrenal androgens stimulate the growth of pubic and axillary hair and may play a part in the anabolic processes associated with skeletal maturation and the growth spurt.

Disorders of Growth

Short stature during childhood and adolescence has many causes and, since an individual's height is related to the average of the father's and mother's height, parental height should always be taken into consideration. Racial differences also affect the rate of growth and the time of onset of puberty. Chromosomal defects of the autosomes or of the sex chromosomes may be associated with short stature. Hereditary defects of the skeleton lead to stunting; lack of growth hormone or of thyroid hormones causes failure of growth. Organic disorders of the central nervous system and the cardiovascular, respiratory, renal, haemopoietic or alimentary systems may interfere with growth. In addition, adverse psychological factors due to an unhappy home life are very important in this respect. In the developing countries undernutrition is a well recognized cause of short stature and delayed puberty. In Britain such undernutrition is rare but, in the condition known as coeliac disease (p. 10) in which the

small intestinal absorption of food is inadequate, undernutrition leads to failure of growth. Children whose growth has been slowed by illness show a greater than normal rate of growth upon correction of the disorder. This rapid phase of growth continues until the child has reached his normal growth centile before the illness and has therefore been called 'catch-up' growth. The mechanisms which control the return to the normal pattern of growth have still to be elucidated. A child whose congenital heart lesion is corrected by surgery may, after the operation, show catch-up growth when he grows faster than a normal child of the same age. Successful treatment of chronic pulmonary or renal disease leads to improved growth as does treatment of anaemia during childhood or the use of a gluten free diet in coeliac disease. Excessive growth during childhood and adolescence is a much rarer problem. It may be due to constitutional factors or to damage to the central nervous system and it is common in children who develop precocious puberty.

The following patients illustrate growth disturbances during childhood. A boy aged 14 years and 1 month with isolated growth hormone deficiency is shown in Figure 30.11. He showed no clinical abnormality other than short stature. At this age his height was 134·9 cm (the average height of a boy of 9 years 6 months), his weight was 28 kg and his bone age was 10·7 years. Although he was of normal intelligence, his face was more like that of a boy several years younger. He was treated with growth hormone. After one year his height was 142 cm and after two years it was 152 cm. Eight months later his height was 157 cm so that he had made excellent progress.

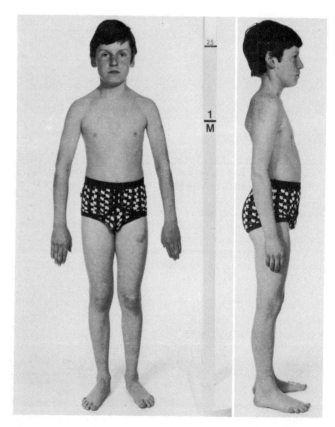

Fig. 30.11 Boy, aged 14 years 1 month, with deficiency of growth hormone. (*By courtesy of Constance C. Forsyth.*)

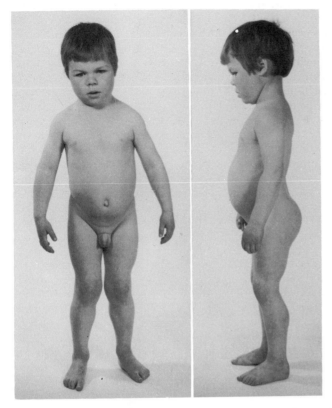

Fig. 30.12 Boy, aged 8 years 8 months, with deficiency of thyroid hormones. (*By courtesy of Constance C. Forsyth.*)

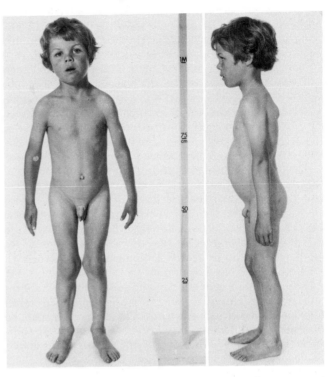

Fig. 30.14 The same boy as in Figure 30.12 after one year's treatment with thyroxine. (*By courtesy of Constance C. Forsyth.*)

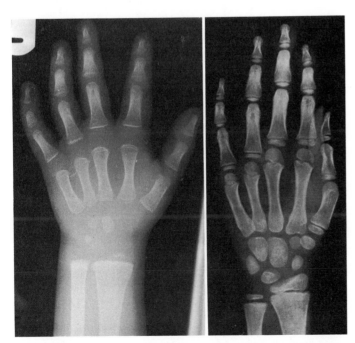

Fig. 30.13 Bone age of the boy (Fig. 30.12) with deficiency of thyroid hormones on the left compared with that of a normal boy of 8 years on the right. (*By courtesy of Constance C. Forsyth.*)

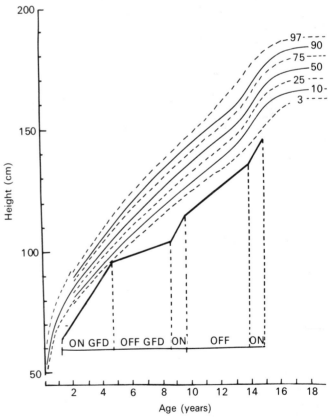

Fig. 30.15 Height chart of a boy with coeliac disease. GFD, gluten free diet. (*By courtesy of Constance C. Forsyth.*)

A second patient, a boy aged 8 years and 8 months with deficiency of thyroid hormones, is shown in Figure 30.12. His height was 104 cm, the average height of a boy of 4·4 years, his weight was 21 kg and his bone age was 1·8 years. He was very much overweight for his height; the distended abdomen typical of hypothyroidism is easily recognized in the photograph. His intelligence was in the low normal range. The bone age was considerably retarded compared with that of an average boy of 104 cm in height. This marked delay in bone age is characteristic of hypothyroidism and the X-ray of a normal boy of 8 years for comparison is shown in Figure 30.13. The cause of the hypothyroidism was dysgenesis of the thyroid gland which was situated at the back of the tongue. He was treated with thyroxine (maintenance dose 0·15 mg daily) and his appearance one year later is shown in Figure 30.14. By then he was 11 cm taller but his weight was unchanged. The bone age had advanced to 3·8 years. At 12 years and 6 months his height was 134 cm, on the 3rd centile. His bone age was still delayed and further catch-up growth could be expected.

The growth in height of a boy with coeliac disease is shown in Figure 30.15. He was the son of a rag-and-bone man and an illiterate mother; treatment with a gluten free diet could be maintained only under supervision in a hospital or convalescent home. Catch-up growth is shown during periods on the gluten free diet but his growth was abnormally slow when the diet was stopped at home. Eventually he learned to follow the proper diet himself and remained well.

Finally, the height chart of a boy who developed precocious

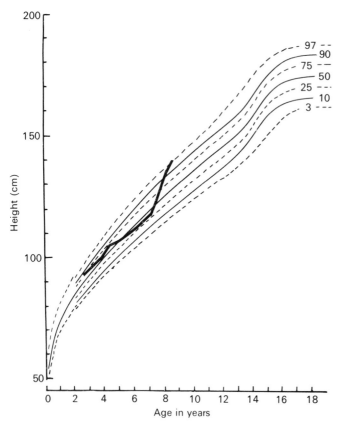

Fig. 30.16 Height chart of a boy with precocious puberty. (*By courtesy of Constance C. Forsyth.*)

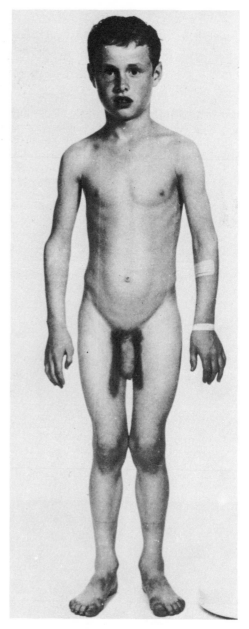

Fig. 30.17 Boy, aged 8 years, with precocious puberty. (*By courtesy of Constance C. Forsyth.*)

puberty at 7 years of age is shown in Figure 30.16. His height had been recorded for several years previously and had shown a normal growth pattern along the 50th centile line. When first seen at hospital with precocious puberty at the age of 8 years, his height, that of a normal boy of 10 years, was on the 97th centile and his bone age was 11·8 years. In this patient (Fig. 30.17) the control of the onset of puberty had been upset by the growth of a hypothalamic tumour.

Growth and development in childhood and adolescence show wide physiological variations and are affected by many pathological processes. As children who are too small or too tall or whose puberty is delayed or advanced may suffer from remediable disorders, accurate knowledge of the subject is of great clinical importance.

REFERENCES

Dobbing J, Sands J 1973 Quantitative growth and development of human brain. Archives of Disease in Childhood 48: 757–767
Dobbing J 1974 Later development of the brain and its vulnerability. In: Davis J A, Dobbing J (ed) Scientific foundations of paediatrics. Heinemann, London and Saunders, Philadelphia
Goss R J 1978 The physiology of growth. Academic Press, London
Greulich W W, Pyle S I 1959 Radiographic atlas of skeletal development of the hand and wrist, 2nd edn. Stanford University Press, Stanford and Oxford University Press, London
Lancet ii 1979 Adolescent sexuality and adolescent fertility
Marshall W A 1977 Human growth and its disorders. Academic Press, London
Savage D C L, Evans J 1978 Puberty and adolescence. In: Forfar J A, Arneil G C (ed) Textbook of paediatrics. Churchill Livingstone, Edinburgh
Sinclair D C 1973 Human growth after birth, 2nd edn. Oxford University Press
Smith D W 1977 Growth and its disorders. Saunders, Philadelphia
Tanner J M, Whitehouse R H, Marshall W A, Healy M J R, Goldstein H 1976 Assessment of skeletal maturity and prediction of adult height (TW2 Method). Academic Press, London
Tanner J M 1978 Foetus into Man: Physical growth from conception to maturity. Open Books, London

31 Senescence

Man reaches the zenith of his physical powers at the age of 20 years or so and sooner or later his bodily tissues, even if unaffected by disease processes, gradually begin to deteriorate. It is far from clear why this should be so, or what mechanisms are involved.

Theories of ageing may be divided into those that stress the importance of genetic factors, which have been demonstrated to operate in every species of animal examined, including, if to a relatively limited extent, man, and those which suppose that the principal factors are somatic. Among the latter are included errors in protein synthesis, with resulting malfunction of enzyme systems, increasing cross-linkage of structural macromolecules, alterations in immunological function and progressive intracellular accumulation of damaging waste products. All these theories have some factual support, but none is yet well enough developed to be capable of decisive experimental disproof, nor are they mutually exclusive. It seems reasonable at present to regard ageing as the result of a variety of processes operating at different rates in different organs and tissues. Thus the life span of red blood cells is 120 days, that of epidermal cells 6 months, and that of ova in the ovary many years. The cells most rapidly turned over are probably the white cells and the mucosal cells of the gastrointestinal tract.

Only the neurones of the central nervous system are incapable of reproduction.

The *average life span* of man is determined mainly by disease and accident and has increased dramatically over the last two thousand years. In the past 80 years the expectation of life at birth, that is to say the number of years a new-born baby may expect to live, has increased by 25 years (Fig. 31.1), because of the elimination of many causes of death in childhood and early adult life. The expectation of life in middle and late life has increased much less. The *maximum life span* of man is probably about 120 years but clearly the prevention of disease and the retardation of the ageing process, which together would result in a population free from disease and in peak physiological condition for an indefinite period, would present immense political and ethical problems.

Age-related alterations in structure and function are often extremely difficult to define and to distinguish from those due to disease. Thus the widespread occurrence of atherosclerotic disease of the coronary arteries makes it very hard to determine the effect of true age changes in the heart; similarly cigarette smoking makes it difficult to find the true effect of age on pulmonary function. Very few longitudinal studies have extended over a long enough time, and most investigations have been of cross-sectional type, with inevitable problems resulting from the possibility of differential loss from the population studied of individuals with time-related disease.

The *composition of the body* changes with age, with a reduction in fat-free mass (mainly the muscles and liver) and an increase in the proportion of fat. Basal oxygen consumption, being linked to fat-free mass, declines with age. So does maximum work output (Figs. 31.2 and 31.3). Although the total blood volume decreases the haematological indices change very little. There are no major changes in many biochemical measurements, such as serum sodium, potassium, chloride, bicarbonate and magnesium concentrations. The internal environment thus alters little.

Every centenarian is willing to offer advice on the diet needed to reach his venerable age. There is, however, little reliable evidence on the effect of diet on human longevity. Severe dietary restriction delays the maturation and prolongs the life of the rat but such a regimen cannot be recommended for man. Energy requirements decline with age, because both basal and exercise-related energy expenditure fails, but an adequate intake of protein and vitamins remains essential even for the very old. Indeed the protein intake needed to prevent a negative nitrogen balance may rise with age.

Changes in *cardiac function* include a reduction in the intrinsic heart rate, that is the heart rate after pharmacological denervation of the heart, and in the maximum rate that can be achieved on exercise. Cardiac output declines but intracardiac pressures at rest are little altered. Systolic blood pressure, and to a lesser extent diastolic pressure, rises with age, though there are populations in which this rise does not occur, and the phenomenon may be especially characteristic of Western man in so-called developed countries. Reduced elasticity of the

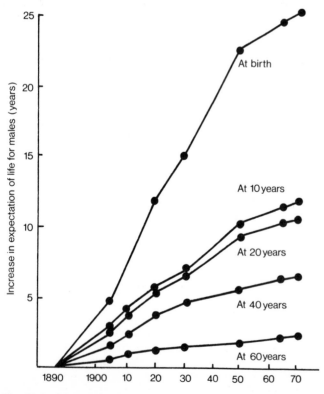

Fig. 31.1 Increase in expectation of life for males at different ages from 1881 to 1971. While more people are living to a greater age, the expectation of life at older ages is not increasing much. (Figures for England and Wales published by the Registrar General.)

lungs results in increased functional residual capacity and closing volume, reduced vital capacity and forced expiratory volume, and reduced transfer factor for carbon monoxide, however, arterial oxygen and carbon dioxide pressures are little if at all changed.

Kidney function declines after about 40 years of age, in parallel with the loss of nephrons. Glomerular filtration rate falls by about one per cent per year, with approximately proportionate reductions in tubular secretory and reabsorptive capacities, and in maximum rates of secretion of hydrogen ions and ammonia. However reduction in the rate of formation of urea and creatinine, presumably related to the lower fat-free mass, minimizes the increases in serum concentrations of these substances. A reduction in *liver function* has proved difficult to demonstrate, but serum albumin concentrations decline slightly. The ability to metabolize some drugs is also affected; this function of the liver is increasingly important.

The simplest everyday expression of ageing is seen in *the skin* which becomes wrinkled, thinner, and less elastic. These changes are most obvious on exposed surfaces such as the backs of the hands and forearms, and seem to be the expression of alterations in dermal collagen, the fibres of which become shorter, bent and frayed.

The total amount of bone in the body at maturity reflects the adequacy of nutrition and exercise during childhood. Bone loss is a universal feature of ageing (Fig. 31.4) but the amount of bone at any age is determined not just by the age but also by the amount the person had in early adult life. The rate of loss of bone with age is greater in females than in males and is probably related to the decline in the production of oestrogens after the menopause. Women who have an early menopause as a result of surgical removal of the ovaries lose bone more rapidly than other women of the same age. There is no evidence that dietary deficiency of calcium occurs or contributes to bone loss. Vitamin D deficiency (p. 31) is, however, not uncommon in elderly women who are inadequately exposed to sunlight.

Changes in the nervous system in old age have proved very difficult to define but they are obviously of extreme importance. Recent work suggests that the number of neurones in certain parts of the brain falls, mainly in the neocortex but not in other places such as brain stem nuclei. In some parts, such as the hippocampus, intracellular structure is altered in all cells; in others the changes are characteristic of diseases which cause diffuse brain disorder and severe impairment of intellectual function. Nerve conduction velocities decline in peripheral nerves but, since these changes cannot account for the prolongation of reaction times in psychological tests, central delays must be increased. Alterations in autonomic function, in particular in the co-ordination of responses to cold and heat, and in the reflex regulation of blood pressure, are common in old age and may represent true age changes.

The most important age-related alteration in the *endocrine*

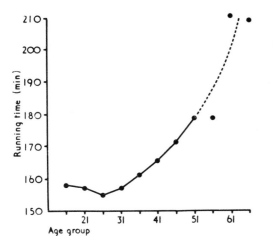

Fig. 31.2 Running times in relation to age. Mean times of each 5-year group of men. Lidingö cross-country race of 30 km. (L. E. Böttiger (1973) *British Medical Journal,* ii, 270).

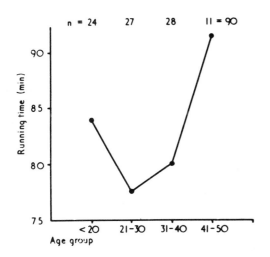

Fig. 31.3 Running times in relation to age. Mean times of each 10-year group of women. Lidingö cross-country race of 16 km. (L. E. Böttiger (1973) *British Medical Journal,* ii, 271.)

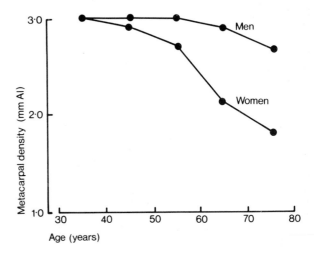

Fig. 31.4 The amount of bone in the metacarpal cortex at different ages. In this study the amount of bone was measured by comparing the X-ray image at the midpoint of the metacarpal with an aluminium step-wedge alongside. The results are expressed as millimetres of aluminium. Similar evidence of a fall in amount of bone with age, particularly in females, has been obtained on a number of skeletal sites, by a wide variety of methods and on several different populations. (*After* D. B. Morgan, F. W. Spiers, C. N. Pulvertaft & P. Fourman (1967) *Clinical Radiology,* **18,** 101–108.)

organs, apart from the cessation of ovarian function in women, is in pancreatic islet-cell function. The immediate release of insulin when blood glucose concentrations rise is unaffected, but delayed release, which reflects the new synthesis of the hormone, is impaired. Blood glucose levels thus rise further in

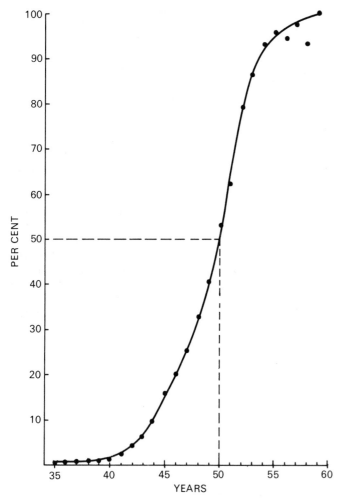

Fig. 31.5 Cumulative frequency for incidence for the natural menopause. (From data obtained from women in the London and Midland regions of the United Kingdom by Margot Jefferys.)

response to a glucose load in old age. The peripheral effectiveness of insulin seems to fall. The maximum secretion rate of cortisol is reduced, but its metabolism is also probably slower, so that basal levels are unaffected. The same is true of the thyroid hormones. Pituitary function is essentially unchanged.

In women menstruation ceases at the *menopause* which usually takes place between the ages of 45 and 55 (Fig. 31.5). In some women the cessation of menstruation is sudden but more commonly the periods become progressively more irregular. The term menopause refers to the end of menstruation but the associated endocrine changes may take place over a longer period. The oestrogen output from the ovaries declines and there is a corresponding rise in the output of gonadotrophins from the pituitary. Oestrogen production does not cease entirely since androgens from the adrenal cortex are still converted to oestrogens.

When cyclical uterine and ovarian changes cease the uterus, breats and external genitalia slowly atrophy. Because ovulation ceases corpora lutea are not formed and progesterone production fails. The endometrium does not show secretory changes and becomes atrophic. Pregnancy is very rare after the age of 50. This period of involutionary change, the *climacteric*, is often attended by vasomotor symptoms such as hot flushes and by giddiness, excessive sweating and temporary emotional disturbances. Similar changes occur after an artificial menopause induced for therapeutic purposes by surgical removal or destructive irradiation of the ovaries. The intensity of the symptoms varies greatly from woman to woman. In many women sexual desire and capacity continue for a number of years after the menopause.

There is no good evidence of a climacteric in men who may remain fertile to an advanced age.

This review of the various functional changes so far demonstrated to occur during ageing in man suggests that decline in the mass of metabolizing tissue may be regarded as the main phenomenon. Loss of reserve capabilities, rather than impairment of function when a system is not under stress, is also a common characteristic. Major alterations, for example in haematological or biochemical parameters, should always be considered as due to disease, and therefore as requiring investigation and treatment.

REFERENCES

Beard R W 1975 The menopause. British Journal of Hospital Medicine 13: 631–637
Brocklehurst J C 1978 Textbook of geriatric medicine and gerontology, 2nd edn. Churchill Livingstone, Edinburgh
Caird F I 1975 Biochemical normality in old age. In: Lant A F (ed) Advanced medicine symposium II. Pitman, London, p 306–316
Caird F I, Dall J L C, Kennedy R D (eds) 1976 Cardiology in old age. Plenum Press, London
Comfort A 1978 Biology of senescence, 3rd edn. Churchill Livingstone, Edinburgh
Finch C E, Hayflick L (eds) 1977 Handbook of the biology of ageing. Van Nostrand Reinhold, New York
Greenblatt R B (ed) 1978 Geriatric endocrinology. Raven Press, New York
Hall D A (ed) 1976 The ageing of connective tissue. Academic Press, London
Korenman S G, Sherman B M, Korenman J C 1978 Reproductive hormone function: the perimenopausal period and beyond. Clinics in Endocrinology and Metabolism 7: 625–643
Van Keep P A, Serr D M, Greenblatt R B (eds) 1979 Female and male climacteric. MTP, Lancaster

32 Chromosomes and Heredity

The nucleus of a cell contains heritable information in a code provided by the four bases of DNA (deoxyribonucleic acid). It is evident that this information must be passed unchanged from a cell to any cells derived from it. The information-bearing DNA is distributed between the nuclear structures, the chromosomes, and thus the orderly distribution of the DNA to new cells becomes a matter of the distribution of the chromosomes and the process by which this equable distribution is achieved is called *mitosis* (Fig. 32.1). In preparation for mitosis the DNA doubles itself during interphase by replication. At the outset of a division the nuclear material becomes condensed into discrete individual chromosomes which can be seen to have formed two identical halves called *chromatids* which remain joined at the centromere. The nuclear membrane then disappears, a spindle of hyaline fibres is formed between the two centrosomes and the 'split' chromosomes line up on the equator (*metaphase*). The chromatids then separate and travel towards the poles of the spindle so that each new nucleus has genetic information identical to that of the parent nucleus. The cytoplasm divides and two new daughter cells are formed, each containing the same DNA as the parent.

In man, the chromosome complement is derived equally from the two parents. The cells contain two numerically equal sets of chromosomes and the individual is said to be *diploid*. Each of the chromosomes of one set can be paired up with those of the other and these 'like' chromosomes of maternal and paternal origin are said to be *homologous*. In man the *diploid number* is 46 and this number of chromosomes is present in all somatic cells. These may be seen at mitosis (Fig. 32.2). The so called 'banding' techniques now permit each chromosome pair to be recognized (Fig. 32.3) and structural abnormalities can be identified. There are 44 *autosomes* and 2 *sex chromosomes*. The latter are designated XX in the female and are the same shape and size but in the male they are designated X and Y and are clearly distinguishable (Fig. 32.4).

The process of sexual reproduction involves the conjugation of two cells called *gametes* with union of their nuclei to form a *zygote* or fertilized ovum (Fig. 32.5). The gametes arise within the gonads from cells which remain in a relatively undifferentiated state until the onset of the reproductive period. These primordial germ cells contain the diploid number of chromosomes; if the gametes derived from them were to retain this full somatic number of chromosomes the number in the zygote

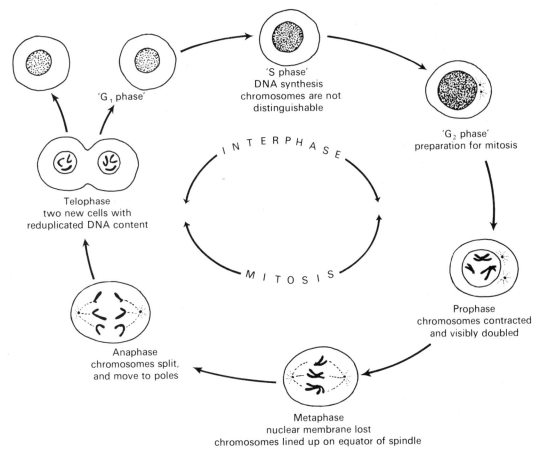

'G₁ phase'

'S phase'
DNA synthesis
chromosomes are not
distinguishable

'G₂ phase'
preparation for mitosis

INTERPHASE

MITOSIS

Telophase
two new cells with
reduplicated DNA content

Prophase
chromosomes contracted
and visibly doubled

Anaphase
chromosomes split,
and move to poles

Metaphase
nuclear membrane lost
chromosomes lined up on equator of spindle

Fig. 32.1 The cell cycle and the steps in cell division by mitosis.

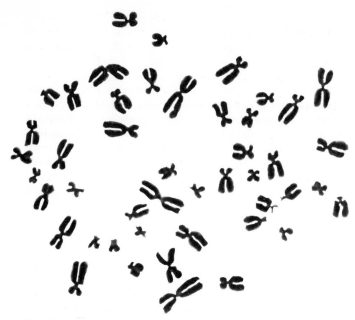

Fig. 32.2   Mitotic metaphase spread of a lymphocyte obtained from a culture of blood from a normal human male. ×1200. (*By courtesy of M. J. W. Faed.*)

would be doubled as would also the amount of DNA. Such an increase is avoided by the occurrence of *meiosis*. Before the onset of the first meiotic (reduction) division the nuclear material resolves itself into chromosomes and the homologous pairs come together to form *bivalents*. During this period of close apposition of the homologues one of the chromatids of one chromosome may exchange material with one of the chromatids of the other chromosome (Fig. 32.6). The cross-over points or *chiasmata*, which can be seen at the appropriate stage of meiosis, have an important role to play in the redistribution of the genetic material. The average number of chiasmata per cell is believed to be slightly more than 50 for man. Separation of the pairs of chromosomes accompanied by cell division then occurs resulting in two cells, each with a *haploid* chromosome constitution. The random distribution of the homologous chromosomes results in a shuffling of the chromosomes so that different combinations of maternal and paternal genetic material come to reside in the cells produced. A further, second division follows in which the chromosomes divide in a manner similar to that seen in mitosis but this time, because of the crossing over which took place earlier, the chromatids are not identical and therefore the resulting daughter cells carry different genetic information. Thus each female gamete or ovum and each male gamete or spermato-

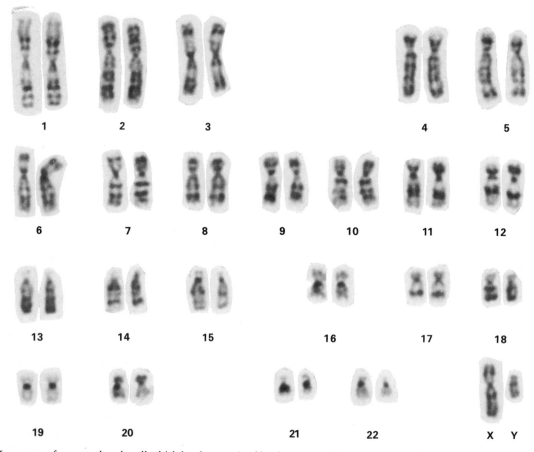

Fig. 32.3   Karyotype of a normal male cell which has been stained by the trypsin/Giemsa method. This treatment reveals a banded pattern which permits each chromosome pair to be identified. These bands are known as G-bands. Before the use of banding techniques became available chromosomes were classified by groups as follows: Group A, chromosomes 1–3; group B, chromosomes 4–5; group C, chromosomes 6–12; group D, chromosomes 13–15; group E, chromosomes 16–18; group F, chromosomes 19–20; group G, chromosomes 21–22. ×2400. (*By courtesy of M. J. W. Faed.*)

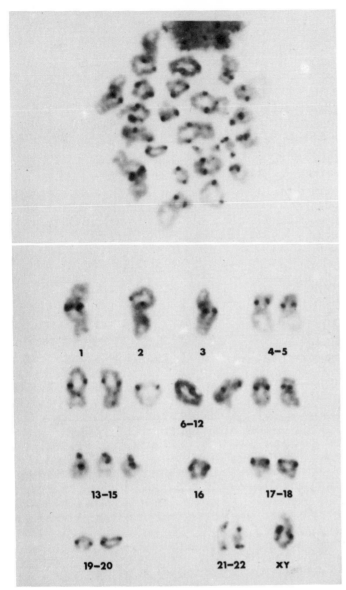

Fig. 32.4 Above, meiotic plate from a spermatocyte from a normal male. The homologous chromosomes are paired. This cell has been stained by a C-band technique which heavily stains the centromere region and makes it easier to identify the bivalents at this stage. Below, karyotype of cell above. ×1900. (*By courtesy of Ann Chandley.*)

zoon contains only the haploid number of chromosomes (in man, 23) and only half the amount of DNA.

In the seminiferous tubules (p. 484) each primary spermatocyte undergoes meiosis, the first reduction division giving two secondary spermatocytes; the second division gives four spermatids all of the same size (Fig. 32.5). In the transformation of a spermatid into a spermatozoon the nucleus is retained in the head and the centrosomes in the middle piece, and the much reduced cytoplasm forms a thin investing layer from which the axial filament of the tail projects (see Fig. 29.3 on p. 486).

During maturation of the ovum analogous changes occur, but the cytoplasm is not divided equally between the daughter cells (Fig. 32.6). The ovum (or primary oocyte) undergoes a reduction division so that each of the daughter cells has the haploid number of chromosomes; one of the two daughter cells, the secondary oocyte, retains most of the cytoplasm; the other smaller cell is cast off as the *first polar body*. The secondary oocyte now divides again and throws off another polar body; the first polar body may or may not divide again.

Fertilization occurs in the uterine tube by the entry of a spermatozoon into a mature ovum, the zygote formed by this union having the diploid number of chromosomes. Thus a new individual begins life with a chromosome complement derived equally from its parents and this complement is usually retained in all its somatic cells since all subsequent divisions are mitotic.

Sex Determination

It has been demonstrated that the Y chromosome is male-determining in man and that the X chromosome carries some, if not all, of the female-determining genes. As mentioned earlier the sex chromosomes are XX in the female and XY in the male. Since the X chromsomes pair and then separate at meiosis all the mature oocytes contain a single X chromosome. In males the X and Y chromosomes behave as a pair and at the reduction division X passes into one secondary spermatocyte and Y into the other. The second meiotic division results in two X-bearing and two Y-bearing spermatids which ultimately develop into two X-bearing and two Y-bearing spermatozoa. It follows that the sex chromosome pattern in the zygote is either XX or XY, according to whether the mature X-bearing ovum has been fertilized by an X-bearing or a Y-bearing spermatozoon. The XX zygote develops into a female and the XY zygote into a male (Fig. 32.7).

It is possible to diagnose the chromosomal sex of an individual by examination of cells from somatic tissues such as skin, buccal mucosa, nerve and many others. A small particle staining deeply with dyes like cresyl violet, the so called Barr body, sex chromatin body or X-chromatin body (Fig. 32.8) may be seen in contact with the nuclear membrane in the nuclei of 40 to 90 per cent of somatic cells in the normal female but not in the normal male. The sex chromatin body is derived from one X chromosome which has become inactive. This condensation presumably prevents an overdose of X-borne genes in the female (the male cell, it will be remembered, has only one X chromosome). The number of X-chromatin bodies seen within a nucleus is therefore one less than the number of X chromosomes in that nucleus. Thus a male with one X chromosome (XY) shows no X-chromatin body; a female with two X chromosomes (XX) shows one X-chromatin body. This pattern is maintained in abnormal individuals who have an XXX, XXXX or even XXXXX sex chromosome complement. Their cells shows two, three and four X-chromatin bodies respectively. Similarly males with XXY, XXXY or XXXXY sex chromosomes have one, two or three such bodies.

A similar morphological distinction can be made between polymorphonuclear leucocytes of the two sexes based on the recognition of a 'drumstick' mass of chromatin attached to one of the lobes of the nucleus (Fig. 32.9). This drumstick is not seen in males but is present in a small proportion (about 1 per cent) of the cells in all females.

It is also possible to recognize the presence of the Y

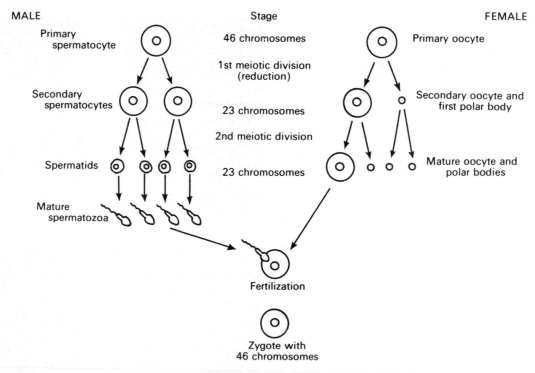

Fig. 32.5 The development of the cells involved in the reproductive process.

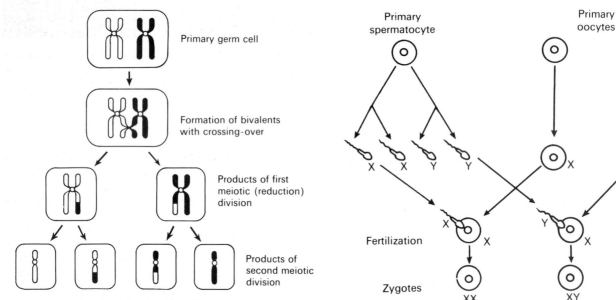

Fig. 32.6 Diagram to show the effect of a single crossover between a pair of homologous chromosomes at meiosis on the distribution of genetic material to the gametes.

Fig. 32.7 This diagram shows that the sex of the future individual is determined by the kind of spermatozoon which fertilizes the ovum.

chromosome in a cell. Cells containing a Y chromosome when stained with a fluorescent quinacrine dye and observed with blue light show a bright spot in interphase cells (Fig. 32.10) and similar staining of a cell in mitosis shows a highly fluorescent region on the long arm of the Y chromosome (Fig. 32.11). Cells with two Y chromosomes show two brightly fluorescent bodies.

Sex ratio. Since in the course of spermatogenesis X and Y spermatozoa are produced in equal numbers, a 1:1 sex ratio of

the zygotes would be expected. In other words, in a large group of offspring there should be an equal number of males and females. In fact, in England and Wales in 1962 for every 100 girls born alive there were 106 boys born alive; this gives a *secondary sex ratio* of 106 to 100. In addition there is a greater loss of male fetuses than female fetuses during intrauterine life. This suggests that the *primary sex ratio*, that is the ratio between males and females at conception, considerably exceeds unity; the reason for this is unknown. Attempts to

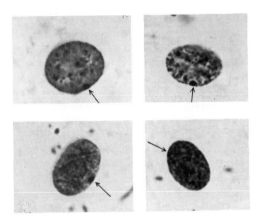

Fig. 32.8 Epithelial squames from the buccal mucosa of a female to show the sex chromatin particle. ×1400. (*By courtesy of B. Lennox and M. Ferguson-Smith.*)

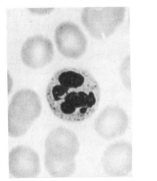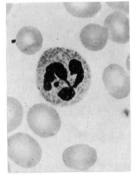

Fig. 32.9 Neutrophil polymorphonuclear leucocytes from a female to show the characteristic 'drumstick'. ×1100. (*By courtesy of W. M. Davidson.*)

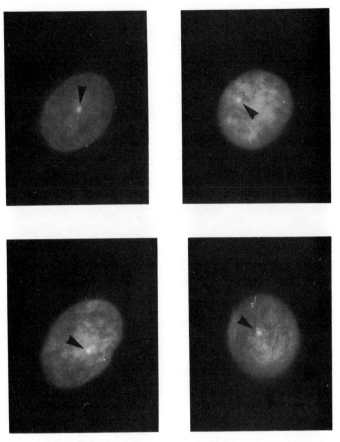

Fig. 32.10 Nuclei of cells obtained from the buccal mucosa of a male. The cells have been stained with a fluorescent quinacrine derivative and observed by blue light. The strongly fluorescent body characteristic of a cell with a Y chromosome is indicated. ×2400. (*By courtesy of M. J. W. Faed.*)

separate X and Y bearing sperm, or even to enrich samples with sperms of one or other type, have so far proved unsuccessful. The sex ratio in favour of the male gradually decreases in late adult life, and in old age there are substantially more females than males.

Twins

Identical twins result from the fertilization of a single ovum by a single sperm; at an early stage in development the egg divides to form two separate embryos. Such twins are also known as *monozygotic twins*. Non-identical twins arise from the fertilization of two separate ova by separate sperms; they are known as *dizygotic twins* and are genetically no more alike than other pairs of brothers and sisters. The frequency of dizygotic (DZ) twins varies in different ethnic groups and with maternal age; DZ twins show a tendency to recur in families. In contrast the frequency of monozygotic (MZ) twins, which occur in about 1 in 200 gestations, varies little with these factors. In Caucasian populations about 1 in 3 twin births are MZ.

Studies of twins have provided a valuable method for determining the extent to which genetic factors contribute to human characteristics or diseases. For example an inborn error of metabolism should occur together in both of a pair of identical twins if present in one. This is described as *concordance* of 100 per cent. Of special value are studies on identical twins which have been reared apart and have therefore been exposed to different postnatal environments. Even in situations in which genetic factors play a small role their contribution can be determined by the use of studies on twins. For example Verschuer demonstrated that for cancer of the stomach the concordance between identical twins was greater than that between non-identical twins.

MENDELIAN INHERITANCE IN MAN

For many inherited features each person has two factors or genes, occupying equivalent positions on a homologous pair of chromosomes. When the two genes are identical the person is said to be *homozygous* for that gene, but if the genes differ they are called *alleles* and the person is called a *heterozygote*. Thus if a homozygous person whose *genotype* is *aa* mates with another homozygous person who has a different pair of alleles *AA*, the children are all heterozygous with one *a* and one *A* allele.

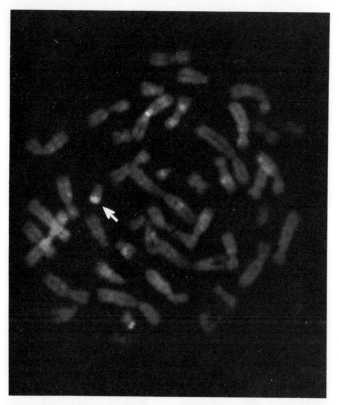

Fig. 32.11 Mitotic metaphase spread from a male stained by the same method as the nuclei in Figure 32.10. The chromosomes show regions of different intensity of fluorescence known as Q-bands. The end of the Y chromosome (arrowed) is particularly bright. ×2300. (*By courtesy of M. J. W. Faed.*)

Parent *aa*
↓
Gametes
⌢
a　*a*

	a	*a*
A	*Aa*	*Aa*
A	*Aa*	*Aa*

Parent *AA* → Gametes

When the heterozygous person (genotype *Aa*) has the features or *phenotype* of an individual with an *AA* genotype the allele *A* is said to be *dominant* while the allele *a* is called *recessive*. By convention when only two alleles are involved, a capital letter is used to denote a dominant gene.

A similar procedure can be used to predict the likely outcome of a mating between heterozygous people, *Aa*.

Parent *Aa*
↓
Gametes
⌢
a　*A*

	a	*A*
a	*aa*	*Aa*
A	*Aa*	*AA*

Parent *Aa* → Gametes

Such a mating would theoretically yield, for every four children, the following genotypes: one *aa*, two *aA* and one *AA*. If *A* is the dominant gene, there would be three children with the phenotype A (*AA* and *Aa* genotypes) and one with the aa phenotype (*aa* genotype). Human families are generally too small for such a pattern to be seen in a single family but a pattern can generally be demonstrated when the figures for large numbers of similar families are combined.

Genetic linkage. As a result of the segregation of homologous chromosomes at meiosis genes which are located near each other on the same chromosome tend to be inherited together, or be 'linked', while genes located on separate chromosomes associate in a random manner. Genes which lie on the same chromosome are known as *syntenic*. 'Crossing over' during meiosis, however, leads to an exchange of genetic material between homologous chromosomes. In this way genes originally located on the same chromosome of a particular pair may become separated while other genes, originally on different chromosomes of a pair, may be brought together. The further apart the genes are, the greater is the chance of a chiasma forming between them so that in family studies only genes that are close to each other appear to be linked. Such genes form *linkage groups* and the distances between the genes can be calculated by the frequency with which they become separated.

In man such studies are difficult because of the small size of families and the long generation time. Nevertheless genetic linkage can be studied in man by observing the segregation of a gene which is polymorphic. A polymorphic gene is one in which there are two or more different alleles present in the population. Polymorphisms which are useful for identifying linkage are those which are so common in the general population that they are likely to be found in the family under study. Polymorphic genes located on autosomal chromosomes include those controlling the ABO blood groups (p. 131), the varieties of certain plasma proteins such as transferrin and haptoglobin and the ability to taste phenylthiocarbamide. Genes on the X-chromosome include those for colour blindness and the Xg blood group.

Recently techniques involving the fusion of cultured cells from different species to give hybrid cells, with varying numbers of human chromosomes, have greatly increased the rate at which 'maps' of the position of genes on individual chromosomes have been constructed.

Patterns of Inheritance of Diseases

In determining the manner of inheritance of a particular disease in man reliance has to be placed mainly on observations of the distribution of the disease in particular families. Common familial diseases such as diabetes mellitus or high blood pressure have no simple pattern of inheritance but many less common diseases are known which have a manner of inheritance readily explained by Mendelian genetics. These disorders are divided into two main groups: dominantly and recessively inherited. They are further divided according to whether the abnormal gene is carried on the X-chromosome or on one of the autosomal chromosomes.

Autosomal dominant inheritance. The pattern of inheritance of an autosomal dominant trait is illustrated in

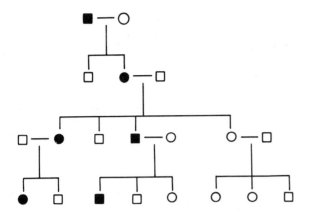

Fig. 32.12 Pattern of inheritance of an autosomal dominant trait. In this and in subsequent figures the following symbols are used: □ = normal male, ○ = normal female, ■ = affected male, ● = affected female.

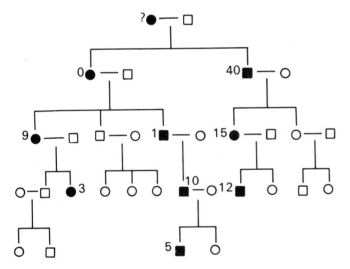

Fig. 32.13 Pedigree of an English family with osteogenesis imperfecta to show how the apparent severity of the disorder, indicated by the number of fractures each member sustained, varies from patient to patient. (*By courtesy of Claire Oldfield.*)

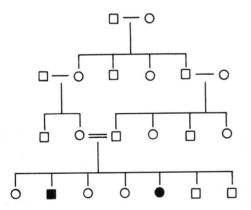

Fig. 32.14 Pattern of inheritance of a disorder inherited as an autosomal recessive. = represents a consanguineous marriage, in this case between first cousins.

Figure 32.12. It can be seen that both sexes are affected. Typically an affected person has one affected parent but this is not always the case. The abnormal gene may have arisen as a result of a new mutation. Apparently 'new' cases of the disease may also result from an undisclosed illegitimacy or because the affected parent is so mildly affected that the disease is difficult to detect. In *osteogenesis imperfecta*, characterized mainly by brittle bones, severely affected patients may not have offspring and the prevalence of the disorder in the population would diminish if new cases did not arise by mutations within previously unaffected families. The same is true of *achondroplasia*, a form of dwarfism. The rate at which new mutations occur can be calculated by examining the proportion of affected individuals who have affected parents.

Other dominantly inherited disorders have less serious manifestations. An example is brachydactyly (short fingers) a disorder which causes no inconvenience and can sometimes be traced back over many generations.

If a person with a disorder inherited as an autosomal dominant marries a normal person, each child has a 50 per cent chance of being affected:

Affected parent (Aa)
↓
gametes

	A	a
a	Aa affected	aa normal
a	Aa affected	aa normal

Normal parent aa → gametes

Since human families are small the parents might be lucky and have no affected children; equally they could be unlucky and all their children could be affected.

Disorders inherited as autosomal dominants tend to vary greatly in severity from one patient to another even within families. This is known as variation in the *expressivity* of the abnormal gene (Fig. 32.13). Sometimes a dominant gene is not expressed in a recognizable manner in all the individuals that carry it. A gene that behaves in this way is called a dominant gene with reduced *penetrance*. The penetrance of such a gene can be expressed as the percentage of those carrying the gene who show the characteristic features.

Autosomal recessive inheritance. Disorders inherited as an autosomal recessive affect both sexes, but the disorder is present only when the abnormal gene is present in a double dose, that is, when the patient is homozygous for that gene. Usually heterozygotes are perfectly healthy but in a few diseases, special tests can show up abnormalities in heterozygotes.

A typical pedigree for a disorder inherited as an autosomal recessive is shown in Figure 32.14. The parents of a patient with such a disorder being heterozygous are unaffected but the children of such a couple have a one in four chance of being affected:

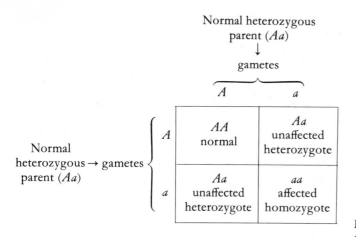

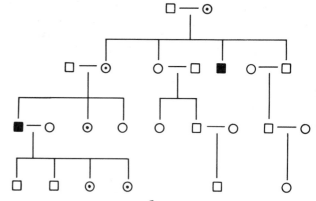

Fig. 32.15 Sex-linked recessive pattern of inheritance. ⊙ represents an unaffected female who is a carrier of the abnormal gene.

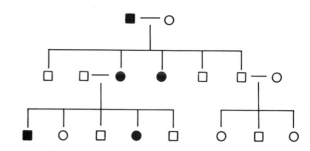

Fig. 32.16 Sex-linked dominant pattern of inheritance.

The parents of a patient with a rare recessive disorder are often related (*consanguineous marriage*). Since they have a common ancestor they are more likely to have some genes in common. Thus alcaptonuria has an incidence of 1 in 1 000 000 and a quarter or more of the patients have parents who are first cousins. In more common disorders such a preponderance of consanguineous marriages is not seen. For example the incidence of fibrocystic disease of the pancreas ('cystic fibrosis') is 1 in 2000 and about one person in 22 carries the abnormal gene; the chances of unrelated heterozygotes marrying is considerably greater than with rare disorders such as alcaptonuria.

It would be expected that, if two people affected with a clinically identical recessive condition married, all their children would be affected. This is usually the case but not invariably. In the exceptional cases in which the children are normal it can be assumed that the parents did not have the same abnormal gene but suffered from two genetically different disorders, with different abnormal genes which were responsible for similar clinical defects (phenotypes). Thus the two genes might cause defects in different parts of a metabolic pathway and patients heterozygous for both abnormal genes could carry out the metabolic process normally. This phenomenon is known as *complementation*. A probable example was provided by a family in which both parents were albinos (that is—had an inborn error of tyrosine metabolism which results in a failure to produce melanin) but all the children were normal. Careful examination of the parents revealed differences in the degree of their lack of pigment.

Intermediate inheritance. In certain disorders the heterozygote differs from both the homozygote and the normal subject. An example is provided by sickle-cell anaemia, a severe and often fatal disease in patients homozygous for the gene for haemoglobin S (p. 112). Patients heterozygous for this disorder usually have no symptoms unless they are exposed to a low oxygen pressure, for example when travelling by air; this condition is known as the sickle-cell *trait* and can readily be detected in the laboratory (Fig. 8.12). In a pedigree containing this abnormality sickle-cell anaemia would be seen to be inherited as a recessive while, if the sickle-cell trait were included, the disorder would then be regarded as dominant.

X-linked recessive inheritance. An X-linked recessive disorder is caused by an abnormal gene on the X-chromosome.

A female is therefore affected only if homozygous for the gene, but a male is affected if his only X chromosome carries the abnormal gene. The affected male is said to be *hemizygous* for the disorder. Diseases inherited in this way are transmitted either by an affected male or a heterozygous female carrier (denoted by ⊙ in Fig. 32.15).

Well-known disorders inherited as X-linked recessives include haemophilia (p. 118), red-green colour blindness (p. 433), glucose-6-phosphate dehydrogenase deficiency and one form of muscular dystrophy. In some of these disorders it is possible to identify the female carriers of the disorder by appropriate tests.

X-linked dominant disorders. In X-linked dominant inheritance (Fig. 32.16) both males and females are affected. An affected female passes the disorder to half of her sons and half of her daughters, while an affected male passes the disorder to all of his daughters and none of his sons. The best known disorder inherited in this way is familial hypophosphataemia, a disorder characterized by defective phosphate reabsorption in the renal tubule which results in phosphorus depletion and a bone disease resembling rickets.

Polymorphisms in the Population

Blood groups. Probably the best known human polymorphism is that of the ABO blood groups. It has long been known that when blood from two different individuals is mixed the red cells may agglutinate. This is due to the presence of an antigen on the red cells of one individual to which individuals who do not have that antigen have an antibody. This makes it possible to classify people into blood group *phenotypes* A, B, AB and O (p. 130). The antigens are glycolipids or glycoproteins, the differences between the antigens depending on the sugar component which can be either D-galactose (antigen B) or N-acetyl-galactosamine (antigen A). Which is present depends on whether the individual has the appropriate glycosyl transferring enzymes, transferases, which add the specific sugar moiety. There are thus three major alleles, one which codes for no enzyme and one coding for each of the two transferases. An individual receives one gene from each parent and must therefore belong to one of the following *genotypes*:

OO   AO   AA   BO   BB   AB

Since both the A and B antigens can be detected these genotypes give rise to the four phenotypes already mentioned.

Similar studies have given details of the inheritance of the other blood groups all of which, with the exception of Xg, are carried on autosomal chromosomes. The determination of several of the blood groups of a child and its alleged parents may be useful in the assessment of paternity.

HLA antigens. Polymorphisms which are proving to be of considerable interest are those for the genes of the HLA system (p. 132). These are closely linked genes, located on chromosome 6, responsible for cell surface antigens of importance in tissue histocompatibility. The four main loci, *HLA-A, B, C* and *D* are all highly polymorphic and as no single allele has a high frequency in the population most people are heterozygous. In Caucasian populations more than 75 per cent of people are heterozygous at both the *A* and *B* locus. On the other hand the close linkage of these loci means that whole *haplotypes*, consisting of particular *A, B, C* and *D* alleles, are usually inherited together. These attributes have proved very useful in studies on inherited diseases. Strong associations between certain diseases and the presence of specific HLA antigens have been established. For instance, 90 per cent of people with the condition ankylosing spondylitis have been found to have the *HLA-B27* allele which makes HLA determination of diagnostic importance. The functional significance of this is not yet altogether clear although it seems probable that a gene predisposing to the disease is closely linked to this allele.

Mutations

The significance of new mutations, apparently spontaneous changes affecting a single gene, in maintaining the prevalence in the population of some dominantly inherited disorders has already been mentioned. Mutations are more likely to occur after exposure to ionizing radiation, ultraviolet light or certain chemicals. While there is no lower limit to the radiation dose which may produce mutations, the chance of a mutation occurring increases as the dose of radiation increases. For this reason care should be taken to shield the gonads when radiographs are being taken.

Some new mutations are beneficial; animal and plant breeders are continually seeking new varieties with advantages in improved productivity or resistance to disease. However, most spontaneous mutations are harmful and in man harmful mutations are more likely to be detected than mutations which confer marginal advantages in survival or resistance to infection. Most mutations of importance to the population

take place in the gonads. A mutation may also occur in a somatic cell; only that cell and its progeny are affected but such a mutation may be the first event in neoplastic disease.

Mutation rate. In some diseases it is possible to estimate the frequency with which new mutations occur. For example in one study six cases of achondroplasia as a new mutant, that is with no evidence of the disorder in either parent, were found in 234 000 births. This is an incidence of 1 in 39 000 births. In each case the mutation could have occurred in either parent so the mutation rate is 1 in 78 000 genes (13 per million genes) per generation. Similar studies have indicated that in several other disorders the mutation rate is between 10 and 100 per million genes per generation.

MULTIFACTORIAL INHERITANCE

Up to this point it has been assumed that each inherited characteristic or disorder is controlled by a single gene. However, many common disorders, such as diabetes mellitus, hypertension and peptic ulceration, have a familial tendency but the proportion of affected relatives is much smaller than would be expected if the disorders were inherited in a simple Mendelian manner. It is likely that such conditions, together with normal characteristics such as skin colour, height and intelligence, depend on many genes as well as environmental factors such as climate and nutrition.

If a large population is studied it is found that these characteristics are distributed in an approximately Gaussian manner. If, for example, the height of the males in a large population is measured, a Gaussian distribution is obtained (Fig. 32.17a). If now the height of male relatives of all those more than 190 cm in height is measured, a similar distribution is obtained but shifted to the right (Fig. 32.17b).

For a characteristic like height, which is quantitatively and continuously variable, the position of an individual in a population distribution curve is clear. However, for many conditions of clinical importance, like cleft lip and cleft palate,

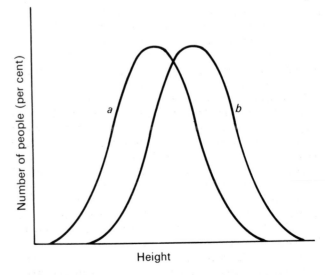

Fig. 32.17 Curve *a* shows the distribution of heights in a normal population of males. Curve *b* shows the distribution of heights of male relatives of men more than 190 cm in height.

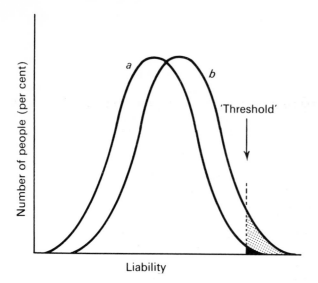

Fig. 32.18   Curve *a* shows the presumed distribution of 'liability' to malformation in the general population. Curve *b* shows the distribution of liability in the relatives of those already affected with the malformation.

Table 32.19   Risk of children being born with cleft lip, with or without cleft palate. (*After* C. O. Carter (1969) *British Medical Bulletin*, **25**, 52.)

Affected relatives	Risk of malformation (per cent)
Monozygotic twin	40
One first degree relative	4
Two first degree relatives	12
One second degree relative	0·7
One third degree relative	0·3
Incidence in general population	0·1

individuals either have the condition or they do not. Nevertheless, it is useful to consider these so called 'non-mendelian all or none' conditions in the same way, the distribution in this case being of *liability* for the condition (Fig. 32.18). The condition only occurs when a certain *threshold* of liability is reached. When an individual is affected the distribution of liability for his relatives, like the height distribution of relatives of tall individuals, is shifted to the right and the relatives therefore have a greater risk of exceeding the threshold. First degree relatives (parents, children, sibs) with whom, on average, the affected individual shares 50 per cent of his genes have their liability distribution shifted more to the right, and are therefore at higher risk, than second degree relatives (uncles, aunts, nephews, nieces) with whom only 25 per cent of genes are shared. If there is more than one affected relative the distribution curve shifts further to the right. For cleft lip (with or without cleft palate), for instance, the population incidence is about 1 in 1000 live births, the risk to relatives of affected patients is shown in Table 32.19. Factors which influence liability can sometimes be identified and taken into account in calculating risk. In the case of pyloric stenosis the incidence in females is much less than it is in males; this implies that the threshold is higher in females. It follows that the risk to relatives of affected females is considerably higher than it would be if the affected individual were a male. Similarly, severely affected individuals may reflect a higher liability among relatives.

It is of great interest to know how important inherited factors may be in producing a phenotype in which environmental factors also have a role. This *heritability* can be estimated by comparing relatives and seeing how far the correlation departs from that expected on the basis of the number of genes they have in common. Heritability for a character like the number of ridges on the patterns on the fingertips which, being determined at an early stage of intrauterine life is little affected by environmental factors, has been calculated to be about 92 per cent. Most other multifactorial characters have a much lower heritability than this.

REFERENCES

Beale, G, Knowles J 1978 Extranuclear genetics. Arnold, London
Bodmer W F, Cavalli-Sforza L L 1976 Genetics, evolution and man. Freeman, San Francisco
Carter C O 1977 Human heredity, 2nd edn. Penguin, London
Cavalli-Sforza L L 1977 Human genetics and heredity. Addison-Wesley, Reading, Mass
De Grouchy J, Turleau C 1972 Clinical atlas of human chromosomes. Wiley, New York
Edwards J H 1979 Human genetics. Chapman and Hall, London
Emery A E H 1975 Elements of medical genetics, 4th edn. Churchill Livingstone, Edinburgh
Fraser G R, Mayo O 1975 Textbook of human genetics. Blackwell, Oxford
Giblett E R 1969 Genetic markers in human blood. Blackwell, Oxford
Harris H 1975 The principles of human biochemical genetics, 2nd edn. North-Holland, Amsterdam
Kaback M M (ed) 1978 Symposium on medical genetics. Pediatric Clinics of North America 25: 391–653
Levitan M, Montagu A 1977 Textbook of human genetics, 2nd edn. University Press, Oxford
McDermott A 1975 Cytogenetics of man and other animals. Chapman and Hall, London
McKusick V A 1979 Mendelian inheritance in man, 5th edn. Johns Hopkins Press, Baltimore and London
McKusick V A, Claiborne R (eds) 1973 Medical genetics. HP Publishing Co, New York
Nora J J, Fraser F C 1974 Medical genetics: principles and practice. Lea & Febiger, Philadelphia; Kimpton, London
Race R R, Sanger R 1975 Blood groups in man, 6th edn. Blackwell, Oxford
Roberts J A F, Pembrey M E 1978 An introduction to medical genetics, 7th edn. Oxford University Press
Stern C 1973 Principles of human genetics, 3rd edn. Freeman, San Francisco
Woodward D O, Woodward V W 1977 Concepts of molecular genetics. McGraw Hill, New York

Appendix

UNITS AND MEASURES USED IN PHYSIOLOGY AND BIOCHEMISTRY

The set of metric rules known as *système internationale* or SI was proposed first in 1954 and was officially adopted in 1960 by nearly 30 countries. The SI has the following independent base units:

Physical quantity	Name of SI Unit	Symbol for SI Unit
length	metre	m
mass	kilogram	kg
amount of substance	mole	mol
time	second	s
electric current	ampere	A
thermodynamic temperature	kelvin	K
luminous intensity	candela	cd

There are also the supplementary units of radian [plane angle] and steradian [solid angle].

Decimal multiples and submultiples of the units are formed by the use of prefixes:

Multiple	Prefix	Symbol	Submultiple	Prefix	Symbol
10^{18}	exa	E	10^{-1}	deci	d
10^{15}	peta	P	10^{-2}	centi	c
10^{12}	tera	T	10^{-3}	milli	m
10^{9}	giga	G	10^{-6}	micro	μ
10^{6}	mega	M	10^{-9}	nano	n
10^{3}	kilo	k	10^{-12}	pico	p
10^{2}	hecto	h	10^{-15}	femto	f
10^{1}	deca	da	10^{-18}	atto	a

In the construction of derived units various rules apply (Baron *et al.*, 1974). The most important of these are as follows:

1. In general the prefix should be attached to one unit only, preferably the numerator. Thus mg/l is preferred to μg/ml. An exception is the kilogram since kg is a fundamental unit.

2. The solidus (/) or the word *per* should only be used once in a derived unit. Thus mg/l is as acceptable as mg l^{-1}. In more complex derived units the negative index should be used. Thus acceleration is expressed as m s^{-2} not m/s/s or metres per second per second.

3. Units which are multiplied by each other are separated by a space (and in some text books a point above the line); thus an 'Ampere $\times$ second' is represented as A s or A.s.

4. No space is allowed between a prefix and its unit; thus ms means millisecond while m s or m.s would mean a 'metre $\times$ second'. The units do not alter in the plural: two metres are 2 m not 2 ms.

Length

The SI unit of length is the metre (m).
1 Ångström unit (Å) (obsolete) $= 10^{-10}$ m $= 0.1$ nm
1 micron (μ) (obsolete) $= 10^{-6}$ m $= 1$ μm
1 millimicron (mμ)$= 10^{-9}$ m $= 1$ nm
1 inch (in) $= 2.54$ cm $= 0.0254$ m
1 foot (ft) $= 0.3048$ m
1 yard (yd) $= 0.9144$ m
1 mile $= 1760$ yd $= 1.609$ km
1 nautical mile $= 1.852$ km

Area

The SI unit of area is the square metre (m^2).
1 square inch $= 645.2$ mm^2
1 square foot $= 0.093$ m^2
1 square yard $= 0.836$ m^2
1 acre (4840 square yards) $= 4047$ m^2 $= 0.4047$ hectare
1 hectare $= 10^4$ m^2 $= 2.471$ acres
1 square mile $= 640$ acres $= 259$ hectares

Volume

The SI unit of volume is the cubic metre (m^3) but since this is inconveniently large for most applications in physiology and biochemistry, the litre (l) has been retained as an alternative to the cubic decimetre (dm^3).
1 dl $= 100$ ml
1 m^3 $= 1000$ l
1 fluid ounce (oz) $= 28.41$ ml
1 pint $= 20$ fluid oz $= 568$ ml
1 gallon $= 4.55$ l
1 cubic inch $= 16.39$ ml
1 cubic foot $= 28.32$ l

Mass

The SI unit of mass is the kilogram (kg).
1 kg $= 1000$ grams (g)
1 grain $= 64.8$ mg
1 ounce (oz) $= 28.35$ g
1 pound (lb) $= 16$ oz $= 453.6$ g
1 ton $= 2240$ lb $= 1016$ kg
1 tonne $= 1000$ kg $= 0.984$ ton $= 2204$ lb
1 microgram (μg) was formerly written γ
In prescriptions for drugs microgram should be written out in full or abbreviated to mcg.

Amount of Substance

Where the molecular weight of a substance is known, its amount should usually be expressed in terms of the mole (mol). One mole of a substance is that amount of the substance which contains the same number of particles (whether atoms, molecules, ions or radicals) as 12 g ^{12}C. In short 1 mole is the particle weight (such as atomic weight or molecular weight) expressed in grams.

The 'equivalent' is now obsolete. It was used to express the amount of an ionized substance; it is the number of moles multiplied by the valency. Thus $10\,mol\,Na^+ = 10$ equiv but $10\,mol\,Ca^{2+} = 20$ equiv.

Concentration and Osmotic Pressure

Concentrations of substances in biological fluids should be expressed in molar terms if the molecular weight is known and in terms of mass if not. Thus plasma glucose is expressed as mmol/l while plasma albumen is expressed as g/l. In each case the reference unit of volume is the litre. A special exception is haemoglobin whose concentration in blood is expressed as g/dl. The methods for expressing hydrogen ion concentration are given on page 269.

Osmotic pressure is expressed as osmolarity (moles per litre of solution) or osmolality (moles per kilogram of water) (p. 264). A very approximate estimate of the osmolality of a plasma sample can be obtained by doubling the sodium concentration (in mmol/l) and adding the molar concentrations of urea and glucose.

Force

The SI unit of force is the newton (N), the force which gives a mass of 1 kilogram an acceleration of 1 metre per second per second (1 m s^{-2}).
1 dyne (obsolete) $= 10^{-5}$ N
1 poundal $= 0.138$ N
Surface tension is expressed in SI units as newtons per metre (N/m).
1 N/m $= 10^3$ dyne/cm

Work, Energy and Power

The SI unit of work is the joule (J), the work done when a force of 1 N acts through 1 m in the direction of the force.
1 erg (obsolete) $= 10^{-7}$ J
1 kilocalorie (kcal or Cal) $= 4.184$ kJ
1 B.T.U. (British thermal unit) $= 1.055$ kJ
1 foot-pound (ft-lb) $= 1.356$ J
1 electron-volt (eV) $= 1.60 \times 10^{-19}$ J
1 kilowatt-hour (kWh) $= 3.6 \times 10^6$ J

Power is the rate of doing work; 1 watt (W) is 1 joule per second; 1 horse power (h.p.) $= 746$ W.

Pressure

The SI unit of pressure is the pascal (Pa); this is the pressure exerted by 1 newton acting on an area of a square metre (1 Pa $= 1$ N m^{-2}).
1 cm $H_2O = 98.1$ Pa
1 mm Hg $= 1$ torr $= 133.3$ Pa $= 0.1333$ kPa
1 kPa $= 7.50$ mm Hg $= 10.1$ cm H_2O
1 lb/in^2 $= 6.894$ kPa
1 normal atmosphere $= 1$ bar $= 760$ mm Hg $= 101.3$ kPa
1 millibar (mb) $= 0.1$ kPa
1 dyne/cm^2 $= 10^{-4}$ kPa

Temperature

The SI temperature scale is the kelvin scale (K) but this is inconvenient to use in medicine and the Celsius (formerly 'centigrade') scale (°C) has been retained.
Degree Celsius $=$ K-273.15
Conversion from the Fahrenheit scale to the Celsius scale can be carried out with either of these formulae:

$$\tfrac{9}{5}C = F-32 \qquad \qquad \tfrac{9}{5}(C+40) = F+40$$

where F is the temperature in degrees Fahrenheit and C is the temperature in degrees Celsius.

°C	-40	-10	0	10	20	30	35	37	40	45	100
°F	-40	14	32	50	68	86	95	98.6	104	113	212

Photometric Units

Candela (cd). The SI unit of luminous intensity. A full radiator (black body) at the melting point of platinum emits 60 candelas per square centimetre. The candela is approximately equal to the obsolete 'standard candle'.

Lumen (lm). The unit of luminous flux. It is the flux emitted into unit solid angle by a uniform point source of one candela.

Lux or metre-candle (lx). The unit of illumination, one lumen per square metre. It is approximately the illumination of a surface placed one metre from a standard candle.

Units of luminance (objective brightness). Two surfaces with the same *luminance* in a given direction look equally bright when viewed under similar conditions from this direction by a human observer. The internationally recognized unit of luminance is the candela per square metre (cd m^{-2}). The luminance of a surface in a given direction expressed in cd m^{-2} is the number of lumens per steradian emitted in this direction by any small element of it, divided by the area in square metres of the orthogonal projection of this element on a plane perpendicular to the given direction. Extensively used but no longer official units are the millilambert, equal to $10/\pi$ or 3.183 cd m^{-2}, and the foot-lambert, equal to 3.426 cd m^{-2}.

Electrical Units

Current: One ampere (A) is a flow of $6 = 10^{18}$ electrons per second past a given point.
Power: 1 watt (W) $= 1$ joule/second (J s^{-1})

Quantity of electricity: 1 coulomb (C) = 1 ampere second (A s)

Electric potential: 1 volt (V) = 1 watt/amp (W A^{-1})

Electric capacitance: 1 farad (F) = 1 coulomb/volt (C V^{-1} or A s V^{-1})

Electric resistance: 1 ohm (Ω) = 1 volt/amp (V A^{-1})

Radioactivity

The curie (Ci) is the unit of activity of radionuclides.

1 Ci = $3 \cdot 7 \times 10^{10}$ disintegrations per second

1 μCi = $3 \cdot 7 \times 10^4$ disintegrations per second

Time

1 hour (h) = 60 minutes (min) = 3600 seconds (s)

1 millisecond (ms) was formerly written σ.

Miscellaneous Units

Cycles per second (c/s) = Hertz (Hz)

Acceleration due to gravity (g) = $9 \cdot 807$ m s^{-2}

1 mile per hour = $1 \cdot 467$ feet/sec = $0 \cdot 447$ m s^{-1}

$\pi = 3 \cdot 14159$

$e = 2 \cdot 71828$

Approximate Atomic Weights

C	Ca	Cl	F	Fe	H	I
12	40	35·5	19	56	1	127

K	Mg	N	Na	O	P	S
39	24	14	23	16	31	32

ABBREVIATIONS FOR SUBSTANCES OF BIOCHEMICAL IMPORTANCE

Amino Acids

Alanine	Ala	Isoleucine	Ile
Arginine	Arg	Leucine	Leu
Asparagine	Asn	Lysine	Lys
Aspartic Acid	Asp	Methionine	Met
Cysteine	Cys	Phenylalanine	Phe
Cystine	Cys-S-S-Cys	Proline	Pro
Glutamic Acid	Glu	Serine	Ser
Glutamine	Gln	Threonine	Thr
Glycine	Gly	Tryptophan	Trp
Histidine	His	Tyrosine	Tyr
5-hydroxylysine	Hyl	Valine	Val
4-hydroxyproline	Hyp		

Other Substances

ATP	Adenosine triphosphate
ADP	Adenosine diphosphate
AMP	Adenosine monophosphate
cAMP	cyclic adenosine 3′, 5′ -monophosphate
DNA	Deoxyribose nucleic acid
FAD	Flavin-adenine dinucleotide
NAD	Nicotinamide-adenine dinucleotide
NADP	Nicotinamide-adenine dinucleotide phosphate
Pi	Inorganic phosphate
PPi	Inorganic pyrophosphate
RNA	Ribose nucleic acid
m-RNA	messenger RNA
t-RNA	transfer RNA

NORMAL VALUES

All reference ranges or 'normal ranges' are conventionally the range of values which includes 95 per cent of the members of a normal population. For measurements distributed in a statistically normal manner (Gaussian distribution) this is equivalent to the mean ± 2 standard deviations. It is important to recognize, too, that normal ranges vary with the method used for an assay, with sex, with age and with many other factors. The reference ranges given here are generally appropriate in adults.

Table A Normal values for the chemical composition of blood plasma in adults. (*After* Baron *et al.*, 1974.)

	Recommended convention	Obsolete convention	Multiplication factor for converting from old units to those currently recommended
Amino acid nitrogen	3 to 6 mmol/l	4 to 8 mg/100 ml	0·714
Ammonium	22 to 44 μmol/l	40 to 80 μg/100 ml	0·554
Ascorbate	11 to 40 μmol/l	0·2 to 0·7 mg/100 ml	57·0
Bicarbonate	24 to 32 mmol/l	24 to 32 m-equiv./l	1·0
Bilirubin (total)	5 to 17 μmol/l	0·3 to 1·0 mg/100 ml	17·1
Caeruloplasmin	300 to 600 mg/l	30 to 60 mg/100 ml	10
Calcium (total)	2·12 to 2·62 mmol/l	8·5 to 10·5 mg/100 ml	0·249
Carbon dioxide (P_{CO_2})	4·5 to 6·0 kPa	34 to 46 mmHg	0·133
Chloride	95 to 105 mmol/l	95 to 105 m-equiv./l	1·0
Cholesterol	3·6 to 6·7 mmol/l	140 to 260 mg/100 ml	0·0258
Copper	13 to 24 μmol/l	80 to 150 μg/100 ml	0·157
Cortisol	276 to 690 nmol/l	10 to 25 μg/100 ml	27·6
Creatinine	60 to 120 μmol/l	0·7 to 1·4 mg/100 ml	88·4
Glucose	2·5 to 4·7 mmol/l	45 to 85 mg/100 ml	0·0555
Haptoglobin (as haemoglobin (Fe) binding capacity)	19 to 112 mmol/l	30 to 180 mg/100 ml	0·621
Iron	14 to 28 μmol/l	80 to 160 μg/100 ml	0·179
Total iron binding capacity (as iron)	45 to 70 μmol/l	250 to 400 μg/100 ml	0·179
Ketones (as acetoacetate)	0·08 to 0·14 mmol/l	0·8 to 1·4 mg/100 ml	0·099
Lactate	0·4 to 1·5 mmol/l	3·6 to 13·0 mg/100 ml	0·112
Lipids (total)	4·0 to 10·0 g/l	400 to 1000 mg/100 ml	0·01
Magnesium	0·7 to 1·0 mmol/l	1·8 to 2·4 mg/100 ml	0·411
Non-protein nitrogen	14 to 21 mmol/l	20 to 30 mg/100 ml	0·714
Oxygen (P_{O_2})	12 to 15 kPa	90 to 110 mmHg	0·133
Phenylalanine	0·05 to 0·07 mmol/l	0·7 to 1·2 mg/100 ml	0·0605
Phosphorus (inorganic)	0·8 to 1·4 mmol/l	2·5 to 4·5 mg/100 ml	0·323
Phospholipid-phosphorus	1·6 to 3·2 mg/100 ml	5 to 10 mg/100 ml	0·323
Potassium	3·5 to 5·0 mmol/l	3·5 to 5·0 m-equiv./l	1·0
Proteins—total	62 to 82 g/l	6·2 to 8·2 g/100 ml	10
—albumin	36 to 52 g/l	3·6 to 5·2 g/100 ml	10
—globulins	24 to 37 g/l	2·4 to 3·7 g/100 ml	10
—fibrinogen	1·5 to 4·5 g/l	150 to 450 mg/100 ml	0·01
—IgG	5 to 16 g/l	500 to 1600 mg/100 ml	0·01
—IgA	1·25 to 4·25 g/l	125 to 425 mg/100 ml	0·01
—IgM	0·47 to 1·70 g/l	47 to 170 mg/100 ml	0·01
—IgD	0·01 to 0·14 g/l	1 to 14 mg/100 ml	0·01
Pyruvate	0·05 to 0·08 mmol/l	0·4 to 0·7 mg/100 ml	0·115
Sodium	136 to 148 mmol/l	136 to 148 m-equiv./l	1·0
Transferrin	16·2 to 27·0 μmol/l	120 to 200 mg/100 ml	0·135
Triglyceride	2·8 to 16·9 mmol/l	25 to 150 mg/100 ml	0·113
Urate	0·12 to 0·45 mmol/l	2 to 7 mg/100 ml	0·0595
Urea	2·5 to 6·0 mmol/l	15 to 40 mg/100 ml	0·166

Table B Normal values for the urinary excretion or chemical composition of urine in normal adults. (*After* Baron *et al.*, 1974.)

	Recommended convention	Obsolete convention	Multiplication factor for converting from old units to those currently recommended
Amino acid nitrogen	4 to 20 mmol/24 h	50 to 300 mg/24 h	0·0714
Ascorbate	114 to 285 μmol/24 h	20 to 50 mg/24 h	5·7
Calcium	2·5 to 7·5 mmol/24 h	100 to 300 mg/24 h	0·0249
Catecholamines (as adrenaline)	0·05 to 0·55 μmol/24 h	10 to 100 μg/24 h	0·00546
Copper	0·2 to 0·8 μmol/24 h	10 to 50 μg/24 h	0·0157
Coproporphyrins (I and III)	0·15 to 0·3 μmol/24 h	100 to 200 μg/24 h	0·00153
Creatine	0 to 0·4 mmol/24 h	0 to 50 mg/24 h	0·00763
Creatinine	9 to 17 mmol/24 h	1·0 to 2·0 g/24 h	8·84
Glucose	0 to 11 mmol/l	0 to 0·2 g/100 ml	55·5
5-Hydroxyindole acetate (5 HIAA)	16 to 73 μmol/24 h	3 to 14 mg/24 h	5·23
Magnesium	3·3 to 4·9 mmol/24 h	80 to 120 mg/24 h	0·0411
Nitrogen	0·7 to 1·5 mol/24 h	10 to 20 g/24 h	0·0714
Oxalate	0·23 to 0·46 mmol/24 h	20 to 40 mg/24 h	0·0114
Phosphorus	16 to 48 mmol/24 h	0·5 to 1·5 g/24 h	32·3
Porphobilinogen	0·9 to 8·8 μmol/24 h	0·2 to 2 mg/24 h	4·42
Potassium	40 to 120 mmol/l	40 to 120 m-equiv./l	1·0
Pregnanediol	0 to 3·1 μmol/24 h	0 to 1 mg/24 h	3·12
Protein	0 to 0·2 g/l	0 to 20 mg/100 ml	0·01
Sodium	100 to 250 mmol/l	100 to 250 m-equiv./l	1·0
Urate	30 to 120 mmol/24 h	0·5 to 2·0 g/24 h	59·5
Urea	250 to 500 mmol/l	1·5 to 3·0 g/100 ml	166
Urobilinogen	0·5 to 5 μmol/24 h	0·3 to 3·0 mg/24 h	1·69
Uroporphyrins (I and III)	0 to 0·03 μmol/24 h	0 to 25 μg/24 h	0·0012

DESIRABLE WEIGHTS FOR ADULTS

Figures for the United States based on the weights of insured persons, aged 25 and over, associated with the lowest mortality (*Metropolitan Life Insurance Company Statistical Bulletin*, 40, Nov.–Dec. 1959)

Height in shoes (cm)	Desirable weight (in kg) in indoor clothing Men			Women		
	Small frame	Medium frame	Large frame	Small frame	Medium frame	Large frame
147·5	—	—	—	41·8–44·6	43·6–48·6	47·3–54·1
150	—	—	—	42·6–45·8	44·5–49·9	48·1–55·3
152·5	—	—	—	43·5–47·2	45·8–51·3	49·4–56·7
155	—	—	—	44·9–48·5	47·2–52·6	50·8–58·1
157·5	50·8–54·4	53·5–58·5	57·2–64·0	46·3–49·9	48·5–54·0	52·2–59·4
160	52·2–55·8	54·9–60·3	58·5–65·3	47·6–51·3	49·9–55·3	53·5–60·8
162·5	53·5–57·2	56·2–61·7	59·9–67·1	49·0–52·6	51·3–57·2	54·9–62·6
165	54·8–58·4	57·5–62·9	62·1–68·8	50·2–53·9	52·8–58·9	56·5–64·3
167·5	56·1–60·2	58·9–64·8	62·5–70·7	51·6–55·7	54·3–61·2	58·4–66·1
170	57·9–61·9	60·6–66·5	64·2–72·8	53·3–57·4	56·0–62·8	60·1–67·8
172·5	59·7–63·8	62·4–68·7	66·5–75·1	55·1–59·2	57·9–64·7	61·9–69·9
175	61·5–65·6	64·2–70·8	68·5–77·1	57·0–61·0	59·7–66·5	63·8–71·5
177·5	63·3–67·8	66·0–72·4	70·1–78·7	58·8–63·3	61·5–68·3	65·6–73·7
180	65·1–69·7	67·8–74·6	71·9–81·0	60·6–65·1	63·3–70·1	67·4–76·0
182·5	66·8–71·4	69·6–76·8	74·1–83·2	62·3–66·8	65·0–71·8	69·1–78·2
185	68·6–73·2	71·4–79·1	75·9–85·4	—	—	—
187·5	70·4–75·3	73·1–81·4	78·1–87·6	—	—	—
190	72·2–77·2	75·3–83·1	80·3–89·9	—	—	—
192·5	74·0–79·0	77·7–85·8	82·3–92·1	—	—	—

THE GREEK ALPHABET AND GREEK AND LATIN PREFIXES USED IN PHYSIOLOGICAL AND BIOCHEMICAL TERMS

Greek Alphabet

Prefixes

Greek character		Greek name	English equivalent
A	α	alpha	A
B	β	beta	B
Γ	γ	gamma	G
Δ	δ	delta	D
E	ε, ϵ	epsilon	short E
Z	ζ	zeta	Z
H	η	eta	long E
Θ	θ	theta	Th
I	ι	iota	I
K	$\varkappa, \kappa$	kappa	K
Λ	λ	lambda	L
M	μ	mu	M
N	ν	nu	N
Ξ	ξ	xi	X
O	o	omicron	short O
Π	π	pi	P
P	ρ	rho	R
Σ	σ, ς	sigma	S
T	τ	tau	T
Υ	υ	upsilon	Y
Φ	φ, ϕ	phi	Ph
X	χ	chi	Ch (hard)
Ψ	ψ	psi	Ps
Ω	ω	omega	long O

Prefixes used to denote numbers

mono-	=one
di-	=two
tri-	=three
tetra-	=four
penta-	=five
hexa-	=six
hepta-	=seven
octo-	=eight
nono-	=nine
deka-	=ten
hendeka-	=eleven
dodeka	=twelve
icoso-	=twenty

Other prefixes

a-, an-	=not
contra-	=opposite
erythro-	=red
eu-	=normal
hyper-	=high
hypo-	=low
infra-	=below
inter-	=between
intra-	=within
ipsi-	=same (side)
iso-	=equal
juxta-	=near
leuco-	=white
macro-	=large
micro-	=small
normo-	=normal
oligo-	=few
peri-	=around
poly-	=many
pseudo-	=false, resembling
sub-	=under
supra-	=above

REFERENCES

Baron, D N, Broughton, P M G, Cohen, M, Lansley, T S, Lewis, S M, Shinton, N K 1974 The use of SI units in reporting results obtained in hospital laboratories. Journal of Clinical Pathology 27: 590–597

Diem, K 1970 Documenta Geigy scientific tables, 7th edn. Geigy Pharmaceutical, Manchester

Pennycuick, C J 1974 Handy matrices of unit conversion factors for biology and mechanics. Arnold, London

World Health Organization 1977 The SI for the health professions. WHO, Geneva

Young, D S 1974 Standardized reporting of laboratory data. The desirability of using SI units. New England Journal of Medicine, 290: 368–373

Index